Steric Effects
in Organic Chemistry

CONTRIBUTORS

Donald J. Cram
Professor
Department of Chemistry
University of California at Los Angeles

William G. Dauben
Associate Professor
Department of Chemistry
University of California, Berkeley

Ernest L. Eliel
Associate Professor
Department of Chemistry
University of Notre Dame

George S. Hammond
Associate Professor
Department of Chemistry
Iowa State College

M. Frederick Hawthorne
Research Chemist
Rohm and Haas Company
Huntsville, Alabama

Lloyd L. Ingraham
Western Utilization Research Branch
United States Department
of Agriculture

Melvin S. Newman
Professor
Department of Chemistry
The Ohio State University

Kenneth S. Pitzer
Professor
Department of Chemistry
University of California, Berkeley

Robert W. Taft, Jr.
Associate Professor
Department of Chemistry
Pennsylvania State University

Harry H. Wasserman
Assistant Professor
Department of Chemistry
Yale University

Frank H. Westheimer
Professor
Department of Chemistry
Harvard University

George F Wright
Professor
Department of Chemistry
University of Toronto

Steric Effects
in Organic Chemistry

Edited by

MELVIN S. NEWMAN

New York · John Wiley & Sons, Inc.

London · Chapman & Hall, Limited

**Copyright © 1956
by John Wiley & Sons, Inc.**

**Library of Congress Catalog Card Number: 56–7162
Printed in the United States of America**

Preface

In order to understand better the effect of structure on reactivity and properties of organic compounds, chemical knowledge is often subdivided into real or artificial areas. For example, inductive and resonance effects, ionic and homolytic type reactions, and polar and steric factors illustrate artificial categories in terms of which chemists carry on discussions. Although it is often possible to choose examples in which one or the other of the factors is clearly predominant, more often situations are encountered in which no clear-cut distinction can be made. The separation into polar and steric effects, however, is useful, just as the attempted separation of inductive and resonance effects has helped in an understanding of electronic aspects of organic chemistry.

During the last half century much progress has been made in quantitatively assessing the influence of polar groups. This information has been accumulated by studying systems in which the steric effect has been kept constant or relatively unimportant. The best example of this lore comprises the large number of studies of *meta-* and *para-*substituted benzene derivatives for which the Hammett $\rho\sigma$ treatment provides fairly accurate correlations and predictions. However, as soon as one deals with *ortho-*substituted benzene derivatives or with aliphatic compounds, quantitative treatment becomes difficult and even qualitative predictions must be made with considerable intuition. Accordingly it was felt that a book designed to focus attention on the steric aspects of organic chemistry could be quite useful in bringing to the attention of chemists much of the existing knowledge and ideas concerning steric effects. The writing of such a book seemed particularly urgent since so many of the advanced treatises already in print were rather incomplete with respect to treatment of steric factors.

In order to limit the size of this book no attempt has been made to include areas which are already well covered in existing treatises or to cover all of the reactions or phenomena in which steric effects have been noted. Rather, only enough data is presented in each chapter

v

to give the reader sufficient background so that he may interpret other reactions in that area for himself. It is hoped that by study of this book practicing chemists will be convinced that a proper appreciation for the role of steric factors in organic chemistry can be very useful in the laboratory, and theoretical chemists will be stimulated to expand and clarify this field.

The editor wishes to acknowledge the aid of many friends in the examination of the manuscripts. Valuable assistance was provided by Drs. E. Berliner, Herbert C. Brown, E. J. Corey, David Y. Curtin, R. C. Fuson, Milton Orchin, Ralph G. Pearson, John D. Roberts, W. M. Schubert, Harold Shechter, and Richard B. Turner.

MELVIN S. NEWMAN

Columbus, Ohio
June, 1956

Contents

Chapter

1   Conformational Analysis
   by William G. Dauben and Kenneth S. Pitzer   **1**

2   Substitution at Saturated Carbon Atoms
   by Ernest L. Eliel   **61**

3   Steric Effects in Aromatic Substitution
   by George S. Hammond and M. Frederick Hawthorne   **164**

4   Additions to Unsaturated Functions
   by Melvin S. Newman   **201**

5   Intramolecular Rearrangements
   by Donald J. Cram   **249**

6   Olefin Forming Elimination Reactions
   by Donald J. Cram   **304**

7   Cleavage Reactions of the Carbon-Carbon Bond
   by Harry H. Wasserman   **349**

8   Steric Effects among the Common Organometallic Compounds
   by George F Wright   **394**

9   Steric Effects on Equilibrated Systems
   by George S. Hammond   **425**

10   Molecular Complexes and Molecular Asymmetry
   by Melvin S. Newman   **471**

11   Steric Effects on Certain Physical Properties
   by Lloyd L. Ingraham   **479**

12   Calculation of the Magnitude of Steric Effects
   by Frank H. Westheimer   **523**

13   Separation of Polar, Steric, and Resonance Effects in Reactivity
   by Robert W. Taft, Jr.   **556**

Author Index   677

Subject Index   697

Chapter 1

by *William G. Dauben*
and *Kenneth S. Pitzer*

Conformational Analysis

INTRODUCTION

RESTRICTED ROTATION IN ACYCLIC HYDROCARBONS
     Ethane
     Butane
     Conformation and Reactivity in Acyclic Systems

NON-BONDED INTERACTIONS IN ALICYCLIC SYSTEMS
     Cyclohexanes
     Decalins
     Polycyclic Perhydroaromatic Systems
     Cyclopentanes
     Hydrindanes
     Cyclohexene and Cyclopentene
     Cyclohexanones
     Medium and Large Ring Compounds

1

GENERAL RULES OF REACTIVITY

General Application to Rate
Stability
Rate of Reaction
Ionic Eliminations
Pyrolytic Eliminations
Rearrangements
Miscellaneous

QUANTITATIVE ENERGY VALUES

Conformation Energies
Potential Barriers
Multiple Internal Rotations

Chapter 1

INTRODUCTION

The first explanation of the differences in ring stability was advanced by Baeyer [1] and was based upon the assumption that all rings must be planar. It was proposed that, in the various sized rings, the alteration of the usual tetrahedral C—C bond angle (109° 28′) would introduce varying degrees of strain. The strain was expressed in terms of a *valence deviation d* which was defined by

$$d = \tfrac{1}{2}(109° \, 28′ - \text{Bond angle of ring})$$

The values for such valence deviations d for a few alicyclic hydrocarbons are as follows: cyclopropane, 24° 44′; cyclobutane, 9° 44′; cyclopentane, 0° 44′; cyclohexane, −5° 16′; cycloheptane, −9° 33′. The positive values show that the bond angle is less than tetrahedral, whereas a negative value implies a larger angle.

Later it was recognized [2] that the basic assumption of Baeyer that all rings are planar needed to be true only for small rings and that a cyclic structure containing six or more carbon atoms could be puckered and could adopt non-planar, strainless isomeric forms or conformations. For example, in cyclohexane there are two conformations free from angle strain (I and II), called boat and chair, respectively. *By*

I   II

conformation is meant any arrangement in space of the atoms of a molecule that can arise by rotation about a single bond and that is capable of finite existence. Such arrangements would correspond to a potential minimum with respect to all types of small displacements in bond

[1] A. Baeyer, *Ber.*, *18*, 2269, 2277 (1885).
[2] H. Sachse, *Ber.*, *23*, 1363 (1890); E. Mohr, *J. prakt. Chem.*, [2], *98*, 315 (1918).

lengths, in bond angles, or in angles of rotation about single bonds (or double bonds).   Defined in this way conformations are rotational isomers entirely analogous to isomers related by rotation about a double bond.   However, since the potential barriers associated with rotation about single bonds are relatively low, isolation of such isomers is not likely to be feasible.   Nevertheless, each rotational isomer or conformation has definite and distinct physical properties, and the separate spectra of various conformations have been identified in a number of cases.

Work on the heats of combustion of alicyclic hydrocarbons has given additional evidence for the freedom from substantial Baeyer strain in rings of six or more carbon atoms.   Such strain when present should have a direct effect on the thermochemical stabilities of a molecule and be reflected in the heats of combustion.   For example, in acyclic n-alkanes, the heat of combustion per CH_2 group is 157.5 kcal./mole [3] while in the various cycloparaffins it is as follows: cyclopropane, 166.5; cyclobutane, 163.8; cyclopentane, 158.7; cyclohexane, 157.2; cycloheptane, 158.2; cyclooctane, 158.5; cyclononane, 158.7 kcal./mole.[4]   These data show the presence of strain in the three- and four-membered rings whereas all other sized rings are practically free from strain, the six-membered cycle being the least strained.

In adopting a puckered conformation for the various rings, however, consideration must be given to another type of strain, different from angle strain, which is caused by interaction of non-bonded atoms and which is similar in some respects to steric hindrance.   The evaluation of such steric interactions has received much attention since the early 1940's, and its development is best seen by an initial consideration of acyclic systems.

[3] Selected Values of Physical and Thermodynamic Properties of Hydrocarbons and Related Compounds, American Petroleum Institute Research Project 44, Carnegie Press, 1953.

[4] R. Spitzer and H. M. Huffman, *J. Am. Chem. Soc.*, *69*, 211 (1947); Sj. Kaarsemaker and J. Coops, *Rec. trav. chim.*, *71*, 261 (1952).

RESTRICTED ROTATION IN ACYCLIC HYDROCARBONS

Editor's note: The problem of a suitable notation for the presentation of three-dimensional structures on paper has always been a vexing one for the organic chemist.   Two types of notation are in use: perspective and projectional.   These notations are illustrated in the figure shown by application to *meso*-2,3-dibromobutane.

The perspective formulas have the advantage that all bonds are seen and the disadvantage that they do not give a good picture unless well drawn.   The well-known Fischer projections are excellent for purposes of designation of configuration

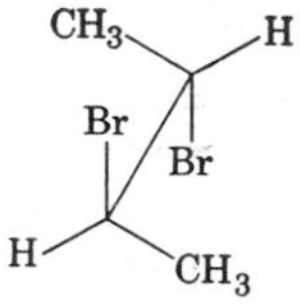

Perspective 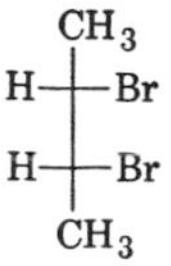   Projection (Fischer) 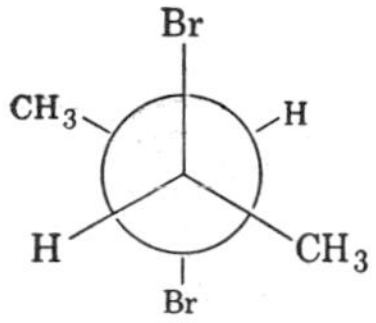   Projection (Newman)

(especially for molecules with multiple asymmetric centers) but, for conformational analysis, have the disadvantage that they show molecules only in eclipsed conformations. In the Newman projection formulas [see M. S. Newman, *Record Chem. Progr. Kresge-Hooker Sci. Lib.*, *13*, 111 (1952), and *J. Chem. Educ.*, *32*, 344 (1955), for complete descriptions of this notation] the view is that in which the eye is placed on the line of extension of the bond between carbons 2 and 3 for the dibromobutane in question. Carbon atom 2 (nearer the eye) is designated by the radii spaced at 120° angles. Carbon 3 (farther from the eye) is designated by the circle with equally spaced radial extensions. In such a projection formula, the bond between the two asymmetric carbons is not seen, but the relative angular geometry of the remaining bonds is readily seen and is not dependent upon careful drawing.

In the field of cyclohexane derivatives the perspective and Newman formulas are shown herewith.

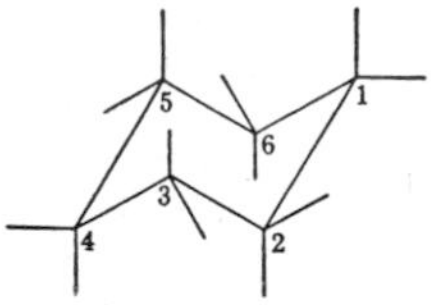

Perspective 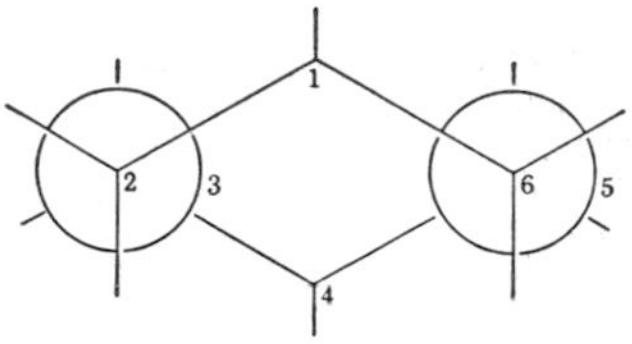   Projection (Newman)

In the perspective notation all bonds are seen, but, even when the formulas are skillfully drawn, some people have difficulty in visualizing the geometrical relationships. In the projection formula four bonds are not seen: the two bonds connecting carbon atoms 2 and 3, 5 and 6; the equatorial bond pointing toward the eye at carbon 1; and the equatorial bond pointing away from the eye at carbon 4. However, equatorial and axial bonds at carbons 2 and 3 and 5 and 6 are easily seen. When problems involving these centers are at hand these projection formulas may be preferred. In this book both notations are used. M. S. N.

Ethane

The calculation of thermodynamic properties utilizing statistical mechanics in which the contributions from translation, rotation, and ordinary vibrations were considered gave values in good agreement with experimental results when applied to molecules possessing a rigid structure. In the application of such methods to hydrocarbons it was first assumed that complete freedom of rotation about a single bond existed. However, the results obtained with such a model were in poor agreement with experimental values.

In 1936,[5] it was shown that the deviation of the calculated from the experimental values was due to the assumption of free rotation of an alkyl group, and a sinusoidal potential barrier restriction to such internal rotation was postulated. For example, in ethane three equivalent conformations (III, V, VII) are possible in which all the hydrogen atoms are equidistant from each other, that is, the hydrogen atoms

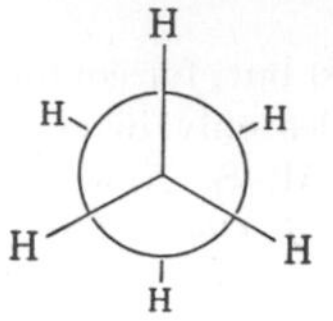

III
$\phi = 0°$

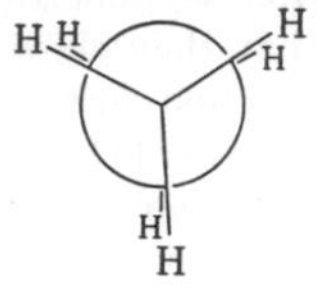

IV
$\phi = 60°$

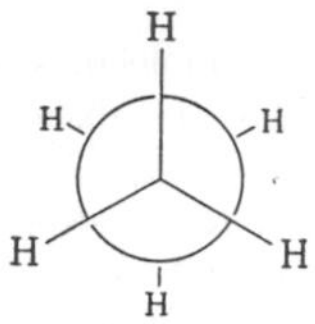

V
$\phi = 120°$

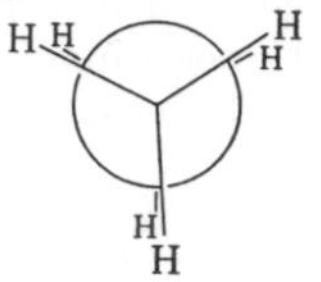

VI
$\phi = 180°$

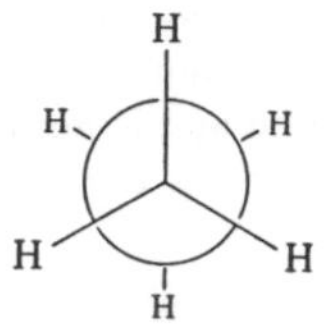

VII
$\phi = 240°$

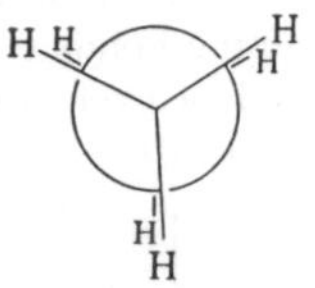

VIII
$\phi = 300°$

are staggered, and each conformation can be obtained by rotation of one methyl group 120° with respect to the other. Such forms are of equal energy. In a rotation of this type, however, orientations IV, VI, and VIII arise where all the hydrogen atoms are directly opposite one another, or eclipsed. Again, these orientations are of equivalent energy, but, owing to a repulsive interaction at this close distance, they are of higher energy than the staggered forms. Since, in going from conformation III to V, ethane must pass through the eclipsed higher-energy species, a barrier to free rotation exists, and, on account of the symmetry of the methyl group, this potential barrier will have three equal maxima and minima. Diagrammatically, the manner in which the energy E of a molecule would vary as one methyl group rotated with respect to the other is shown in Fig. 1.

With such a concept the height of this energy barrier could be evaluated, since, when the entropy contributions from translation, rotation, and ordinary vibrations were calculated, the difference between the calculated and the experimental values was taken as due to the internal rotation. Employing the sinusoidal potential barrier, as

[5] J. D. Kemp and K. S. Pitzer, *J. Chem. Phys.*, *4*, 749 (1936); *J. Am. Chem. Soc.*, *59*, 276 (1937); K. S. Pitzer, *J. Chem. Phys.*, *5*, 469, 473, 752 (1937).

above, the magnitude of the barrier in ethane was found to be about 3000 cal./mole.[6] It should be recalled that if the barrier, V_0, had been equal to or less than RT, i.e., about 600 cal./mole at room temperature, the rotation would be practically free because of thermal energy. However, to prevent rotation at room temperature a barrier of 20,000–30,000 cal./mole would be required, an activation energy which is observed for slow reactions. Since a value of 3000 cal./mole for ethane is intermediate, it means that rotation is neither completely free nor frozen out but only restricted.

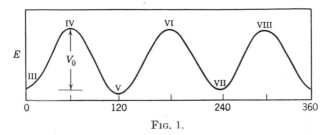

FIG. 1.

Although no quantitative theory has yet been devised that adequately accounts for these barriers to internal rotation, it seems reasonable to assume that they arise from the repulsion of the electron pairs forming the C—H bonds. The basic cause is presumably the same as that for the repulsive van der Waals forces between separate molecules.

Butane

Although the methyl group rotation in ethane has (owing to the symmetry of the molecule) a potential barrier with three equal maxima and minima, the internal rotation of a substituted ethane is not usually symmetrical and may have maxima and minima of different heights. Thus, in n-butane there are three conformations to consider, one in which the methyl groups are as far apart as possible in a zigzag *trans* planar structure (IX) and two equivalent conformations derived

[6] Present best values for numerical parameters are given on p. 57.

by a rotation of approximately 120° about the central bond in either direction (X and XI). In X and XI, the methyl groups are closer than allowed by the ordinary van der Waals or kinetic theory radii. Accordingly, these two conformations, called *gauche* or *skew*, are of somewhat higher energy than the *trans* form IX, and such energy differences again can be evaluated by consideration of experimental and calculated entropies.[7] For comparison with the ethane rotation-energy relationship, a diagram (Fig. 2) for *n*-butane is given. In

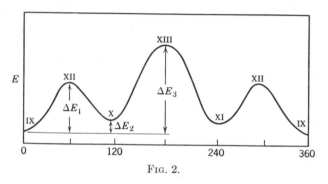

Fig. 2.

performing a 360° rotation two different eclipsed orientations result, one in which the H and the CH_3 are opposed (XII) and one in which the two CH_3 groups are opposed (XIII); the corresponding energy barriers are represented in Fig. 2 as ΔE_1 and ΔE_3, respectively. An orientation similar to XII but with only one H—CH_3 interaction is

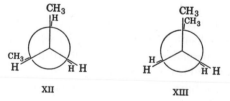

present in propane, and a value of 3300 cal./mole has been found for the barrier; thus ΔE_1 might be expected to be about 3300 cal./mole or a little greater. Since a CH_3—CH_3 interaction would be larger, a higher value is expected for ΔE_3. Values of 4400 and 6100 cal./mole have been estimated,[7,8] but no reliable calculation has been possible. Fortunately, the calculation of thermodynamic functions is not sensi-

[7] K. S. Pitzer, *Chem. Revs.*, *27*, 39 (1940). The potential curve (Fig. 2) assumed in this paper involves a discontinuity at position XIII. This discontinuity is, of course, spurious and was assumed only for mathematical convenience.

[8] K. Ito, *J. Am. Chem. Soc.*, *75*, 2430 (1953).

tive to ΔE_3; hence it is possible to obtain a reasonably reliable value of 800 cal./mole for ΔE_2, the energy difference between a skew and a *trans* conformation. Such a difference predicts a predominance of the *trans* conformation at normal temperatures, and the molecule can be viewed as existing as such in most reactions. These types of conformational isomers have never been separated since the energy barrier is still too small to allow a long-lived independence in such a non-rigid system.

It has been possible, nevertheless, to obtain evidence other than thermodynamic for the existence of internal rotational isomers. By means of electron or X-ray diffraction,[9] dipole moments,[10] and Raman spectra [11] studies on 1,2-dichloroethane and various 2,3-dihalobutanes, it has been shown that both *trans* and skew conformations are present, with a predominance of the former.

Conformation and reactivity in acyclic systems

The concept of the greater stability of certain conformations of a molecule as compared to others has been of great value in the prediction of the steric course of several reactions. This phase of conformational analysis will be discussed, in detail, in other chapters, but a brief reference to its utility can be given here in order to illustrate the reasoning employed.

First, in the debromination of a 1,2-dibromo compound to the corresponding olefin, conformational concepts allow one to predict the relative rates of reactions. In such a reaction it has been demonstrated that, for maximum ease of reaction, the four centers participating (the two carbon atoms and the two bromine atoms) should lie in one plane.[12] For 2,3-dibromobutane, the conformation of the *meso* and *dl* meeting such a requirement is shown in XIVa and XVb, respectively. It is seen that in XIVa the bromine atoms are resting in a valley between the small hydrogen atoms and the medium-sized methyl groups. This fact suggests the presence of only two skew types of steric interactions. In conformation XVa, for the *dl*, in addition to the methyl-bromine interactions, a methyl-methyl interaction is present. By analysis of the other possible conformations of these two isomers

[9] J. Y. Beach and K. Y. Palmer, *J. Chem. Phys.*, *6*, 639 (1938); D. P. Stevenson and V. Schomaker, *J. Am. Chem. Soc.*, *61*, 3173 (1939); J. D. McCullough, *ibid.*, *62*, 480 (1940).

[10] I. Watanabe, S. Mizushima, and Y. Morino, *Sci. Papers Inst. Phys. Chem. Research Tokyo*, *39*, 401 (1942).

[11] S. Mizushima, Y. Morino, and M. Takeda, *J. Chem. Phys.*, *9*, 826 (1941).

[12] D. H. R. Barton and E. Miller, *J. Am. Chem. Soc.*, *72*, 1066 (1950).

it is found that, whereas XIV*a* is the energetically preferred conformation for the *meso*, such is not the case for XV*a* in the *dl* series, and thus it should be of a higher free energy. In addition, in this elimination reaction, the transition state XIV*b* arising from the *meso* places the methyl group and the hydrogen atom in an opposed orientation while the transition state XV*b* from the *dl* has the two methyl groups

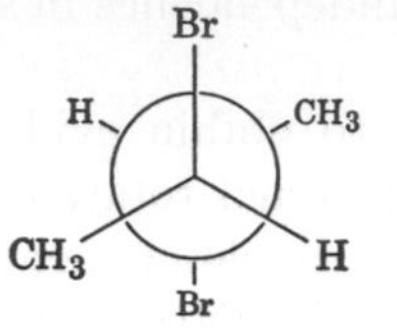

XIV*a. meso* 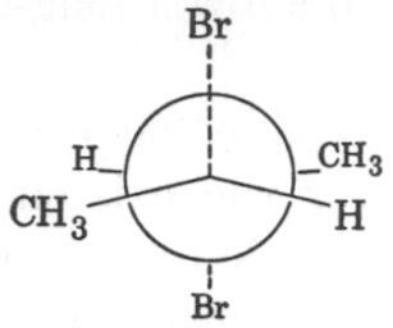   XIV*b*

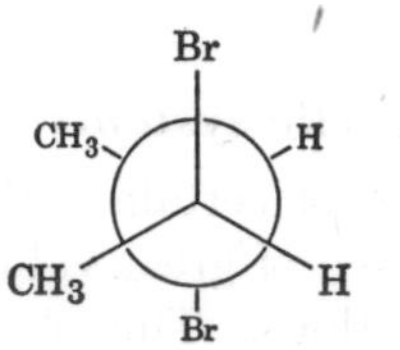

XV*a. dl* 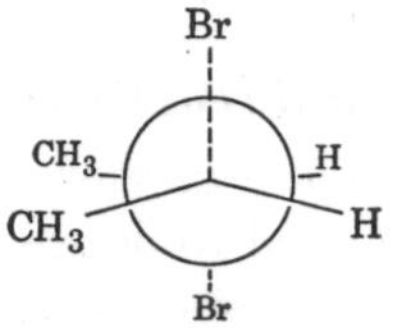   XV*b*

opposed. Accordingly, it would be expected that the latter transition state would be of a higher free energy. Since the free-energy difference between the starting conformations XIV*a* and XV*a* should be less than that of the transition states XIV*b* and XV*b*, the total free-energy difference between XIV*a* and *b* should be less than that for XV*a* and *b*. As a result the *meso* isomer XIV should react faster, and, indeed, it has been found [13] that it is favored by a factor of 2. The energetics of processes similar to the foregoing is examined in more detail on p. 44.

A second interesting application of the conformational ideas has been made in the study of the semipinacolic deamination of α-amino alcohols.[14, 15] It has been shown that the migratory aptitude depends more on the steric orientation than on electronic effects. For example, with 1,2-diphenyl-1-(*p*-chlorophenyl)-2-aminoethanol (XVI), the *threo* [16]

[13] W. G. Young, D. Pressman, and C. D. Coryell, *J. Am. Chem. Soc.*, *61*, 1640 (1939).

[14] S. Bernstein and F. C. Whitmore, *J. Am. Chem. Soc.*, *61*, 1324 (1939).

[15] D. Y. Curtin et al., *J. Am. Chem. Soc.*, *72*, 961 (1950); *73*, 3453 (1951); *77*, 354 (1955).

[16] The term *erythro* names that diastereomer whose configuration is such that in one of its eclipsed orientations at least two sets of substituents of identical or like composition are side by side. The term *threo* names the other diastereomer.

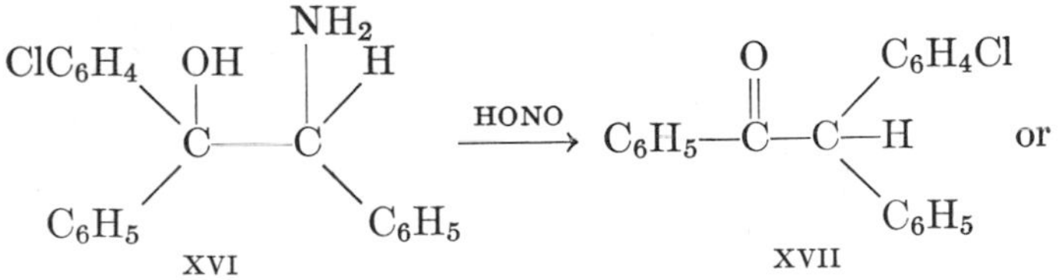

$$\underset{\text{XVI}}{\underset{\substack{C_6H_5}}{\overset{ClC_6H_4 \quad OH}{C}} \!-\! \underset{\substack{C_6H_5}}{\overset{\overset{NH_2}{|}\;H}{C}}} \xrightarrow{\text{HONO}} \underset{\text{XVII}}{\overset{O}{C_6H_5\!-\!\overset{\|}{C}\!-\!\underset{\substack{C_6H_5}}{\overset{C_6H_4Cl}{C}\!-\!H}}} \quad \text{or}$$

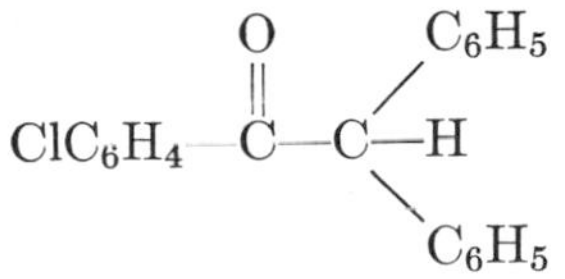

$$\underset{\text{XVIII}}{ClC_6H_4\!-\!\overset{\overset{O}{\|}}{C}\!-\!\underset{\substack{C_6H_5}}{\overset{C_6H_5}{C}\!-\!H}}$$

isomer gives rise to ketone XVII and the *erythro* yields ketone XVIII. From a conformational viewpoint, this reaction is more complex than the foregoing example, since two of the ground-state conformations (for example, XIX*a* and XIX*b* for the *threo*) satisfy the steric requirement of a planar four-centered transition state. In the reaction of

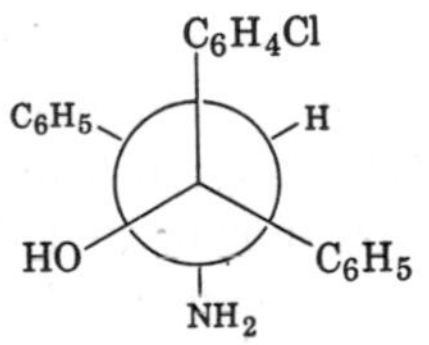

XIX*a*

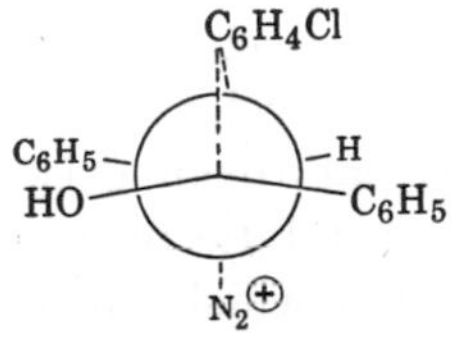

XIX*a*‡

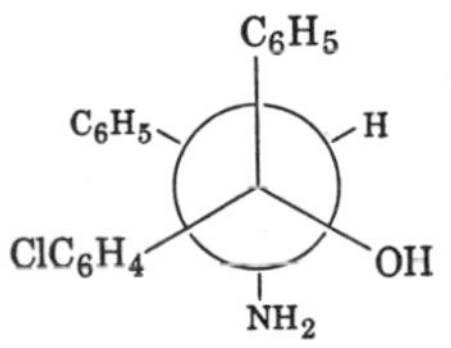

XIX*b*

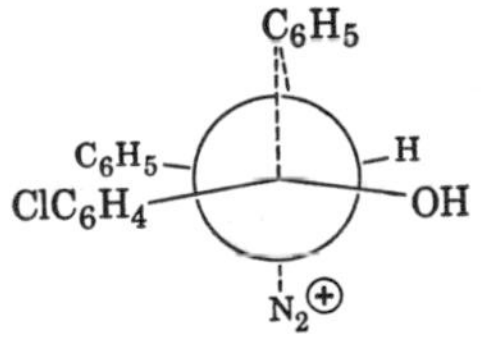

XIX*b*‡

two conformations of the same compound, the ratio of the rates of reaction of each individual conformation depends only upon the free-energy difference between the two transition states (i.e., XIX*a*‡ and XIX*b*‡ for the *threo*) and is independent of the relative population of the ground-state conformations (see p. 44 for a detailed development of this concept). Thus, viewing the transition states of the two *threo* conformations, it is seen that XIX*a*‡ places the two large aromatic groups on opposite sides of the central bond and resembles a *trans* transition state whereas XIXb‡ places these two large groups on the same side of the central bond and resembles a *cis* transition state. It would be expected that the free energy of XIXa‡ would be less than that of XIXb‡ and that *p*-chlorophenyl migration would be preferred, as is found. A similar examination of the *erythro* isomer would lead to the expectation that the transition state arising from the conformation XX would be of a lower free energy and accordingly phenyl migra-

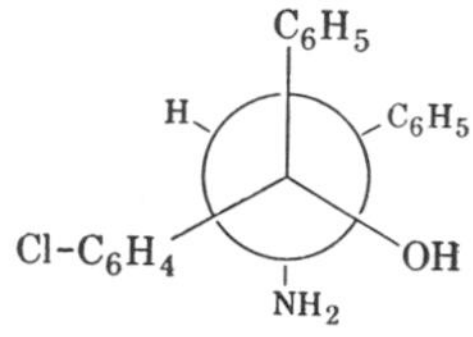

XX

tion would be preferred, as is also found. This sequence of reactions is discussed in detail in Chapter 5.

A third example of the usefulness of the conformational concept concerns the stereochemical direction of asymmetric induction in the reaction of an acyclic system in which a new asymmetric center is created adjacent to an existing one. Generally, it can be stated [17] that "in non-catalytic reactions of the type shown, that diastereomer will predominate which would be formed by the approach of the entering group from the least hindered side of the double bond when the rotational conformation of the carbon-carbon bond is such that the double bond is flanked by the two least bulky groups attached to the

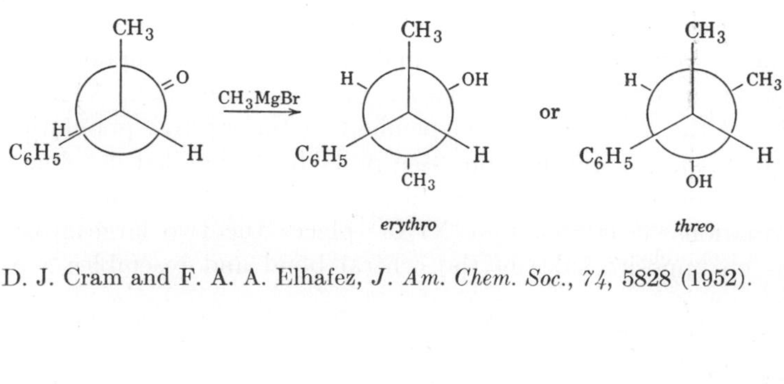

S = small group
M = medium group
L = large group

erythro   *threo*

[17] D. J. Cram and F. A. A. Elhafez, *J. Am. Chem. Soc.*, *74*, 5828 (1952).

adjacent asymmetric center." For example, in the reaction of 2-phenylpropionaldehyde with methylmagnesium bromide, either an *erythro* or a *threo* isomer is possible. By application of the above rule, it would be predicted that the *erythro* would predominate, and such actually is the case.

It should be noted that, when a ketone is employed, it is more difficult to assign a preferred conformation since alkyl and oxygen are of about the same size. In the studies to date, however, this difficulty has been obviated since all the reagents employed normally coordinate with the carbonyl group and thus the latter would be by far the more bulky grouping. Indeed, the fact that in all the cases studied the oxygen is coordinated with some reagent precludes any conclusion concerning the stable orientation for the uncoordinated oxygen.[18]

In much the same manner, Prelog [19] has advantageously employed a similar but more tenuous conformational analysis to predict the configuration of the α-hydroxy acids formed by the reaction of a Grignard reagent with the ester of benzoylformic acid and an optically active alcohol. By using his concept the absolute configuration (with

$$C_6H_5-\overset{\overset{O}{\|}}{C}-\overset{\overset{O}{\|}}{C}-O-\overset{\overset{H}{/}}{\underset{\underset{L}{\diagdown}}{C}}-M + R'MgX \rightarrow C_6H_5-\overset{\overset{OH}{|}}{\underset{\underset{R'}{|}}{C}}-\overset{\overset{O}{/\!/}}{C}-O-\overset{\overset{H}{/}}{\underset{\underset{L}{\diagdown}}{C}}-M$$

respect to glyceraldehyde) of the optically active alcohol employed can be determined, and the configuration of various terpenes and steroids has been assigned.[20]

NON-BONDED INTERACTIONS IN ALICYCLIC SYSTEMS *

Cyclohexanes

As discussed above, Sachse [2] and Mohr [2] postulated the existence of non-planar forms of rings with six or more carbon atoms and showed that in cyclohexane two conformations, the boat and the chair, were possible in which normal tetrahedral angles could be maintained and

---

[18] To appreciate the complexity of such a situation, see the discussion of *cis*-2-butene on p. 57.

[19] V. Prelog, *Helv. Chim. Acta*, *36*, 309 (1953).

[20] W. G. Dauben, D. F. Dickel, O. Jeger, and V. Prelog, *Helv. Chim. Acta*, *36*, 325 (1953), and later papers.

* For a comprehensive review see The Stereoisomerism of Cyclohexane Derivatives, by H. D. Orloff, *Chem. Revs.*, *54*, 347 (1954).

that consequently such rings would be free from *angle strain*. The first chemical data substantiating these concepts were furnished by Kohlrausch,[21] who reported that the Raman spectrum of cyclohexane was best explained by a chair structure (or D_{3d} in terms of group theory). A similar conclusion was reached on the basis of infrared spectroscopy.[22] In neither case were any lines observed which would require the presence of a significant amount of the boat conformation. More recently, an extensive study of cyclohexane by electron diffraction methods [23] also yielded the result that practically all the molecules were in the symmetrical chair form and that all C—C bond lengths were normal and all bond angles were approximately tetrahedral.

With attention focused on non-bonded interaction of the type discussed in ethane and *n*-butane, let us examine these two conformations.[24, 25] In the chair conformation (XXI) all C—H bonds on adjacent carbon atoms are staggered; in the boat form (XXII) two C—C bonds

XXI   XXII

are twisted by 60° and the C—H bonds on these carbon atoms in the major plane of the molecule are opposed. Since the staggered configuration is at the potential minimum, the chair should be favored over the boat. Estimates can be made of the energy difference between two such conformations by consideration of the types of non-bonded atom interactions present. The boat has twisted two C—C bonds into an opposed orientation similar to ethane, i.e., from the potential minimum to the maximum, and should have an energy difference approximately equal to twice the internal rotational barrier of ethane (~3 kcal.) or 6 kcal. Such a value is a *minimal* figure since no attempt has been made to evaluate the energies involved with the H—H interaction between the two hydrogen atoms on the carbons

[21] K. W. F. Kohlrausch and W. Stockmair, *Z. physik. Chem.*, *B31*, 382 (1936), and K. W. F. Kohlrausch and H. Wittek, *ibid.*, *B48*, 177 (1941).

[22] R. S. Rasmussen, *J. Chem. Phys.*, *11*, 249 (1943).

[23] O. Hassel and H. Viervoll, *Acta Chem. Scand.*, *1*, 149 (1947), and earlier papers.

[24] K. S. Pitzer, *Science*, *101*, 672 (1945).

[25] C. W. Beckett, K. S. Pitzer, and R. Spitzer, *J. Am. Chem. Soc.*, *69*, 977, 2488 (1947).

not in the major plane of the molecule. It is recognized that these hydrogen atoms in such a position in a boat conformation formally resemble the H—H interaction of an opposed, *cis*, *n*-butane structure.

Turner [26] has proposed an alternative approach to the evaluation of the energy difference between the boat and chair conformations. In his empirical methods, cyclohexane is viewed as consisting of six *n*-butane structures, i.e., C_1, C_2, C_3, C_4; C_2, C_3, C_4, C_5, etc., around the ring to C_1. Thus, the chair form (XXI) possesses six skew butane interactions, and the boat form involves four skew and two eclipsed (*cis*) interactions. Since a skew interaction has been evaluated [7] as 0.8 kcal. and an eclipsed as 4.4–6.1 kcal.,[7,8] the energy difference would be 7.2–10.6 kcal.[27] Although this method offers a simple way to evaluate energy differences between conformations, it must be pointed out that it lacks realism since the pair of hydrogen atoms whose interference presumably causes the energy, ΔE_2, in skew butane are no longer present in cyclohexane. These two hydrogen atoms are replaced by a pair of carbon atoms bonded to one another. Consequently the 0.8 kcal./mole value for a skew butane interaction should be employed only when the hydrogen atoms responsible for the interaction are present in the molecule. Actually most of Turner's calculated energy differences are correct because of a cancellation of these spurious skew interactions between the two molecules considered.

An entirely different approach to the calculation of the energy difference of these two conformations has been made by Barton.[28] The method employed was based on the semiempirical evaluation of steric hindrance in organic molecules as developed by Dostrovsky, Hughes, and Ingold [29] and Westheimer and Mayer,[30] and it involves a London type of calculation where the interaction energy between all pairs of non-bonded atoms is evaluated by means of the semiempirical potential energy curve of the type $E = ae^{-br}$. Depending upon the choice of parameters, Barton obtained values for the energy difference ranging from 1.31 to 6.85 kcal. All methods, nevertheless, arrive at the same conclusion as to the greater stability of the chair form of cyclohexane.

One of the chief features of the preferred chair conformation of this ring system is a six-fold axis of alternating symmetry. Geometrically,

[26] R. B. Turner, *J. Am. Chem. Soc.*, *74*, 2118 (1952).

[27] These values differ from those originally reported by Turner,[26] who employed the older value of 3.6 kcal. for the eclipsed butane barrier.

[28] D. H. R. Barton, *J. Chem. Soc.*, *1948*, 340.

[29] I. Dostrovsky, E. D. Hughes, and C. Ingold, *J. Chem. Soc.*, *1946*, 173.

[30] F. H. Westheimer and J. E. Mayer, *J. Chem. Phys.*, *14*, 733 (1946).

this symmetry divides the twelve carbon-hydrogen bonds into two classes (see Fig. 3). The six which parallel the axis as shown in XXIII

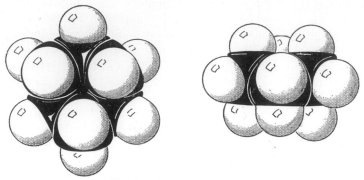

FIG. 3.   Cyclohexane views.

and Fig. 4 (three of which are on alternate carbons above the ring and three below) have been designated *axial* [31] (symbolized *a*); the

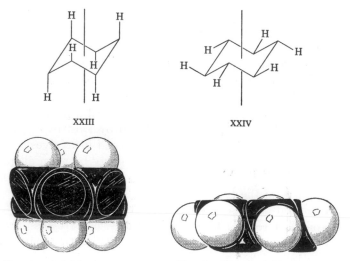

XXIII   XXIV

FIG. 4.   Axial hydrogens.   FIG. 5.   Equatorial hydrogens.

six which extend radially outward at angles of 109.5° to the axis and as shown in XXIV and Fig. 5 have been called *equatorial* (symbolized

[31] K. W. F. Kohlrausch, A. W. Reitz, and W. Stockmair [*Z. physik. Chem.*, *B32*, 229 (1936)] first called attention to such a division, and in 1943, O. Hassel [*Tidsskr. Kjemi Bergvesen Met.*, *3*, 32 (1943)] suggested that the six parallel bonds be called ϵ and the others κ. Subsequently, for the sake of convenience, C. W. Beckett, K. S. Pitzer, and R. Spitzer (see reference 25) introduced the names "polar"

e). Furthermore, in this chair form it is seen that the carbon atoms are in two planes, each plane containing three carbon atoms, and the distance between the planes is about 0.5 A. Owing to the flexibility of this cyclohexane conformation the two planes may interchange their positions, and the molecule will assume a second chair form in which all the bonds which were axial in the former will be equatorial in the latter, and vice versa.

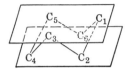 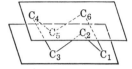

As long as all these bonds are to hydrogen atoms, nothing new has been obtained, but with the substitution of a group for one of the hydrogen atoms a form of isomerism becomes possible. In a mono-substituted cyclohexane, as methylcyclohexane, because of the flexibility of the ring system as shown above, the methyl group can be

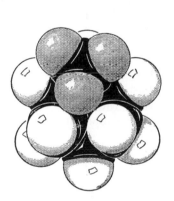 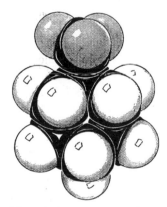

FIG. 6. Axial and equatorial methyl groups.

either equatorial or axial. By studying models of these two conformations, it is seen that non-bonded atom steric interactions of the skew *n*-butane type arise, and when the methyl group is in an axial conformation (**XXV**, see also Fig. 6) two such interactions are present as

and "equatorial" in analogy to the geographical terms. Because of the possible confusion between the use of the word "polar" for a stereochemical characteristic as well as an electropolar feature, D. H. R. Barton, O. Hassel, K. S. Pitzer, and V. Prelog [*Science*, *119*, 49 (1951)] have suggested that the term "axial" be used in place of "polar" since the bonds being referred to are parallel to the main cyclohexane axis, and the poles of the earth lie on its axis.

compared to none when the group is equatorial (XXVI, see also Fig. 6). Therefore, the energy of XXV is larger than that of XXVI by

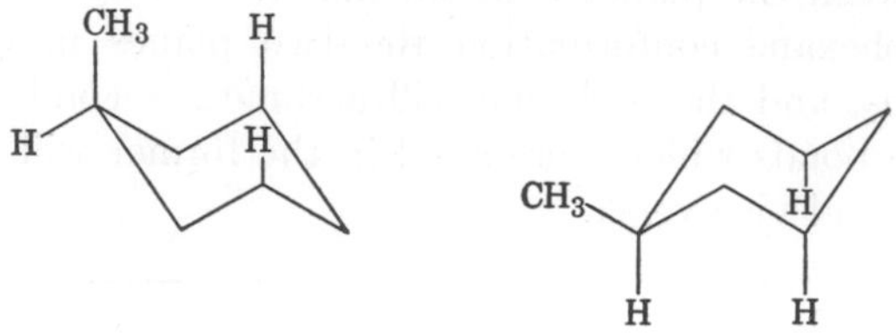

XXV   XXVI

approximately twice the skew (*trans*) *n*-butane energy difference ΔE_2, or 1.6 kcal./mole. A value of 1.8 kcal./mole has been assigned on the basis of thermodynamic data.[25] Thus, it can be concluded that an equatorial conformation is preferred by the alkyl group in methylcyclohexane. A similar conclusion has been reached [23, 32] on the basis of electron diffraction studies. Although the equatorial form is thermodynamically more stable, this does not mean that the molecule must react in this conformation since the energy barrier is less than the activation energy involved in most reactions.

When two hydrogen atoms are substituted by methyl groups as in the dimethylcyclohexanes, the additional stereochemical feature of *cis* and *trans* isomerism arises. In the *cis*-1,2 (XXVII), *trans*-1,3 (XXVIII), and *cis*-1,4 (XXIX) compounds, owing to the alternation of the *e* and *a* bonds on the same side of the ring, if one group is *e* the other is *a*, and hence the two possible chair conformations are equiva-

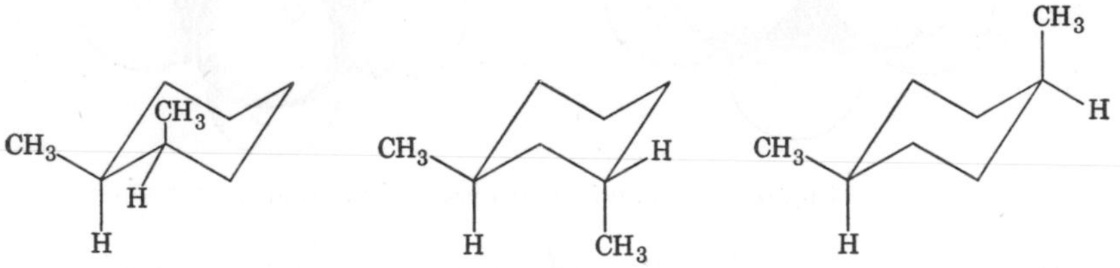

XXVII   XXVIII   XXIX

lent. On the other hand, with the *trans*-1,2 (XXX), *cis*-1,3 (XXXI), and *trans*-1,4 (XXXII) two conformations of different energy exist for each isomer, one with both methyl groups equatorial and one with both methyl groups axial. In the *trans*-1,4 compound, the energy difference between the diaxial (XXXII*b*) and diequatorial (XXXII*a*) is clearly twice that of methylcyclohexane, or 3.6 kcal./mole. In the

[32] O. Hassel, *Research* (*London*), *3*, 504 (1950).

trans-1,2 derivative, however, there is one skew interaction in the diequatorial form (**XXX***a*) as compared to four in the diaxial (**XXX***b*) conformation, thus giving an energy difference of 2.7 kcal./mole. For the *cis*-1,3-dimethylcyclohexane the diaxial (**XXXI***b*) encounters much more steric interference than the other axial forms because both groups are on the same side of the molecule, and the energy difference

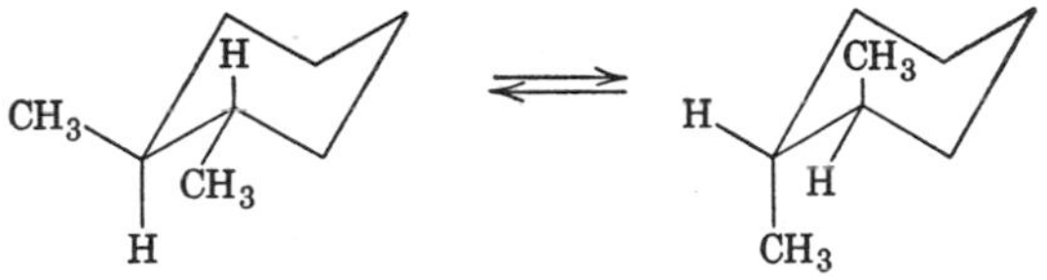

XXX*a*   XXX*b*

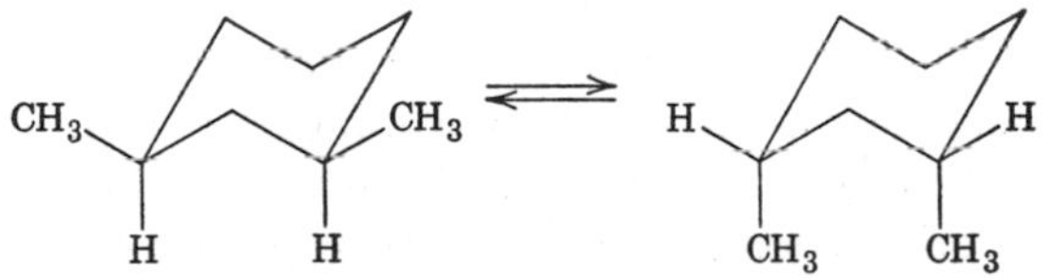

XXXI*a*   XXXI*b*

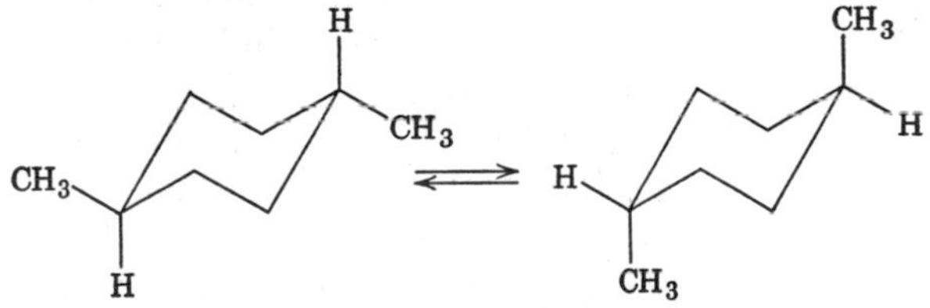

XXXII*a*   XXXII*b*

between (**XXXI***a*) and (**XXXI***b*) is larger than with the other two isomers and has arbitrarily been assigned a minimum value of 5.4 kcal./mole. Thus, in all the cases the diequatorial conformation would be the preferred form.

A preferred conformation having been assigned to each *cis* and *trans* isomer, it is possible to evaluate their relative energies and thus predict their stabilities. Since the placing of any group into an axial conformation introduces two skew *n*-butane energy values, the diequatorial conformation will be more stable than the equatorial-axial conformation. Accordingly, *trans*-1,2 and 1,4-disubstituted cyclohexanes should be the thermodynamically favored forms of the epimeric pairs. Just the reverse will be true for the 1,3 compounds, since here the *cis* is the diequatorial. This last conclusion is of interest since previously it was believed that all the *trans* compounds were more stable than *cis* derivatives. On the basis of the above conformational analysis, Beckett, Pitzer, and Spitzer [25] called attention to this abnormality. Direct chemical evidence was available for the 1,3-dimethylcyclohexanes since Mousseron and Granger [33] in 1938 prepared an optically active 1,3-dimethylcyclohexane which must have a *trans* configuration. Their compound was shown to be the less stable isomer. More recently, the 3-methylcyclohexanols [34] and 3-methylcyclohexylamines [35] have been investigated, and, as expected, here too the earlier assignments of configuration were inverted and the *cis* structure must be assigned to the more stable isomer.

When the two substituents on the cyclohexane ring are of a dipolar nature, such as halogen or carboxyl, it has been noted that the electrostatic repulsion between such groupings becomes important and the energy difference between a diequatorial and a diaxial conformation of an isomer is affected. For example, in various *trans*-1,2-disubstituted cyclohexanes containing dipolar groupings,[36-39] evidence is available which clearly shows that the diaxial conformation is preferred since in such an orientation the electrostatic repulsive forces are minimized.

In addition to the energy considerations, various physical properties such as boiling point, density, and refractive index have been utilized to assign configuration in cyclic systems.

The von Auwers-Skita rule,[39a] which is one example of such an empirical correlation, has suggested that the *cis* isomer will have the higher boiling point, density, and refractive index. As seen from examination of the properties of the isomeric dimethylcyclohexanes in Table I (using the configurations arrived at above on the basis of chemical evidence), the *cis*-1,3, *trans*-1,2, and *trans*-1,4 compounds have the lower values in these properties. Such is not unexpected when it is realized that in the actual geometry of the cyclohexane ring the equatorial-axial configurations are the significant ones.

[33] M. Mousseron and R. Granger, *Bull. soc. chim. France*, 5, 1618 (1938).

[34] H. L. Goering and C. Serres, Jr., *J. Am. Chem. Soc.*, 74, 5908 (1952); D. S. Noyce and D. B. Denney, *ibid.*, 74, 5912 (1952); S. Siegel, *ibid.*, 75, 1317 (1953).

[35] D. S. Noyce and R. J. Nagel, *J. Am. Chem. Soc.*, 75, 127 (1953).

[36] H. A. Smith and F. P. Byrne, *J. Am. Chem. Soc.*, 72, 4406 (1950).

[37] K. Kozima and T. Yoshima, *J. Am. Chem. Soc.*, 75, 166 (1953).

[38] M. Kilpatrick and J. G. Morse, *J. Am. Chem. Soc.*, 75, 1846 (1953).

[39] A. Tulinskie, A. D. Giacomo, and C. P. Smyth, *J. Am. Chem. Soc.*, 75, 3552 (1953).

[39a] K. von Auwers, *Ann.*, 420, 84 (1920); A. Skita, *Ber.*, 53, 1792 (1920); A. Skita and W. Faust, *ibid.*, 64, 2878 (1931).

The von Auwers-Skita rules should be restated to the effect that isomers having fully equatorial conformations have lower boiling point, density, and refractive index than isomers whose conformations are partially axial. It is to be understood, however, that empirical rules of this type are of limited reliability.

TABLE I

PROPERTIES OF ISOMERIC DIMETHYLCYCLOHEXANES [3]

Compound	B.P., °C.	n_D^{25}	d_4^{25}
1,2-cis	129.7	1.4336	0.7922
1,2-trans	123.4	1.4247	0.7720
1,3-cis	120.1	1.4206	0.7620
1,3-trans	124.5	1.4284	0.7806
1,4-cis	124.3	1.4273	0.7787
1,4-trans	119.4	1.4185	0.7584

Another peculiar characteristic of a chair conformation is the proximity, with respect to each other, of atoms attached to the ring. On account of the staggered nature of the bonds in this conformation and the preference of an equatorial over an axial configuration, the distances between adjacent atoms of trans-1,2-dimethylcyclohexane are the same as in the cis isomer, or 2.94 A. In the 1,3 series, the distance between groups in the trans is less than in the cis configuration. Such a fact might suggest that the formation of a cyclic system involving these two atoms would be favored in the trans compound; however, it must be recalled that the energy difference between a diequatorial and diaxial cis compound is less than typical activation energies, and if sterically favored the latter might be the reactive species. Consideration of the distance separating the cis-1,3 diaxial atoms shows that in this conformation the atoms are closer to each other than when on adjacent carbon atoms, or about 2.51 A if the substituents are carbon atoms. This relationship of the 1,3 system is not readily seen in a planar projection of a chair conformation.

It is also of interest to investigate the possibility of optical activity in the cyclohexane compounds when they are viewed as non-planar. First, consider a cyclohexane containing two identical substituents. In the cis-1,2 series, owing to the staggered nature of the bonds, the e:a conformation is asymmetric since the mirror images (XXXIIIa and XXXIIIb) are not superimposable. However, on account of the flexibility of the ring system the chair conformations of equal energy (XXXIII and XXXIV) are in rapid equilibrium and constantly changing the e:a relationship to the a:e system. It is seen that XXXIV with the *a:e* stereochemistry is superimposable with the mirror image XXXIIIb of the *e:a* conformation XXXIIIa, and consequently molecules are constantly changing from a *dextro* to a *levo*, and vice versa, and will not be capable of showing optical activity under normal conditions. Thus, it is a similar situation to a tertiary amine, which, on account of the internal vibrations, is incapable of resolution into stable

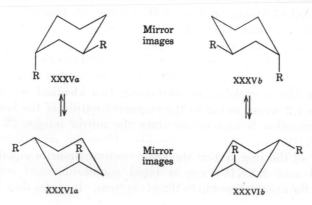

optical antipodes. In the *trans*-1,2 series, such internal motions change an *e:e* to an *a:a* conformation and obviously do not generate the mirror image of the original *e:e*, and hence the system is capable of resolution into a *dextro* and a *levo* form.

In contrast to the *e:a* form of a *cis*-1,2-disubstituted cyclohexane, the *trans*-1,3 compound by interconversion of *e:a* (XXXVa) to *a:e* (XXXVIa) does not transform the molecule into its mirror image (XXXVb) but only to a superimposable form, and accordingly the two interconvertible conformations represent only one optically active antipode and the enantiomorphs are true isomers interconvertible only by inversion of two carbon bonds. The other symmetrically disubstituted cyclohexanes, the *cis*-1,3, *trans*-1,4, and *cis*-1,4, are optically inactive because of a plane of symmetry in the molecule regardless of conformation. Finally, in a *cis*-1,2 compound where the two substituents are different, in contrast to where they are alike, the interconvertible conformations represent only one optical antipode, and optical isomerism is possible. Thus, in agreement with classical theory, only those forms which in a planar projection would suggest optical isomerism are capable of resolution.

Decalins

The application of conformational concepts to alicyclic systems has been of great utility in considering structure and reactivity in the decalin series. As with cyclohexane, Mohr [2] predicted that decalin should be composed of two fused, non-planar cyclohexane rings, and he further suggested that, whereas a planar model based upon Baeyer's concepts would not possess geometrical isomers, a non-planar system should be capable of existing with a *cis* and a *trans* ring fusion. In 1925, Hückel [40] confirmed the latter prediction by the isolation of the two isomeric decalins. In order to satisfy these geometrical requirements, Mohr [2] further predicted that the *trans* isomer would be formed by fusion of two chair forms of cyclohexane (XXXVII) whereas the *cis* compound would possess the boat forms (XXXVIII).

With the recognition of the importance of non-bonded atom interaction and the conclusion that the chair form of cyclohexane was at least 5.6 kcal. more stable than the boat, Hassel [41] reexamined the exact conformation of the decalins. In 1943, he pointed out that, whereas the chair-chair conformation of the *trans* isomer possessed all its bonds in a favorable steric position energetically, the boat-boat conformation of the *cis* compound had steric interference between the axial hydrogens on C_1, C_4 and C_5, C_8, and the bonds connecting carbons 2 and 3, 6 and 7, and 9 and 10 were in an eclipsed ethane orientation. Thus, it was suggested that a more favorable conformation for *cis*-decalin could exist in which each ring was a chair (XXXIX), and in 1946 Bastiansen and Hassel [42] presented electron diffraction data which substantiated their view.

The first quantitative evaluation of the energy differences between XXXVII, XXXVIII, and XXXIX was given by Barton,[28] the method employed being an extension of the calculations used for cyclohexane. The values obtained showed that the chair-chair conformation of

[40] W. Hückel, *Ann.*, *441*, 1 (1925).

[41] O. Hassel, *Tidsskr. Kjemi Bergvesen Met.*, *3*, 91 (1943).

[42] O. Bastiansen and O. Hassel, *Nature*, *157*, 765 (1946).

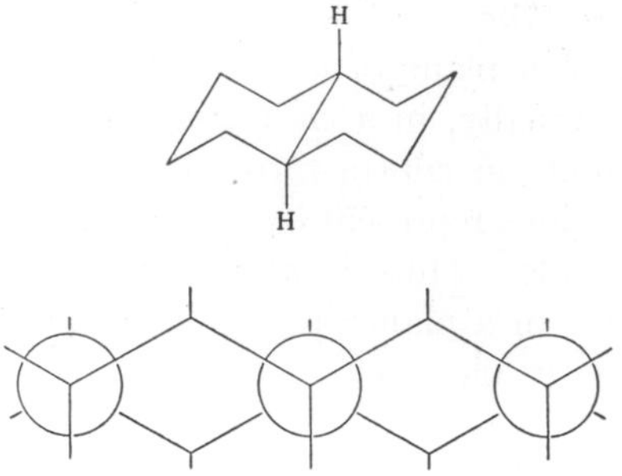

XXXVII

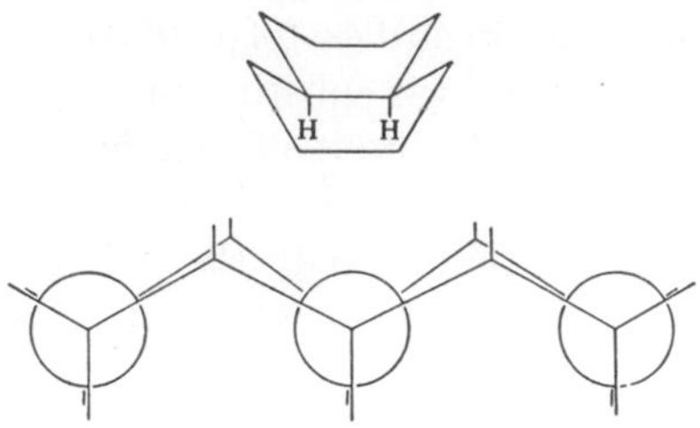

XXXVIII

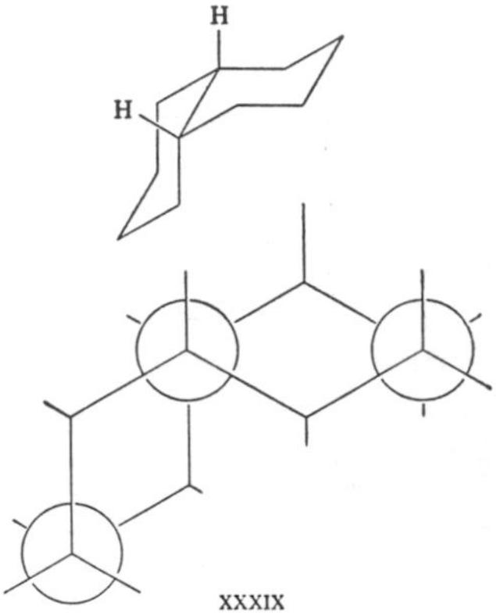

XXXIX

trans-decalin was 0.52–8.23 kcal. more stable than the chair-chair form of *cis*-decalin, which in turn was 2.87–7.28 kcal. more stable than the boat-boat conformation of this same isomer. These values fit well with the fact that the *trans* isomer is more stable than the *cis*. Turner [26] also has estimated the energy differences between these three forms of decalin utilizing his method of viewing the molecule to be composed of various conformations of *n*-butane. In the chair-chair conformations, it is seen that in *trans*-decalin there are six *trans* and twelve skew conformations, and in *cis*-decalin three *trans* and fifteen skew arrangements, or an energy difference equal to three skew butane interactions or 2.4 kcal. In comparing the chair-chair with the boat-boat *cis*-decalin, it can be estimated that the former is at least 8.8 kcal. more stable than the latter.

As mentioned in the discussion of cyclohexane, the method employed by Turner [26] lacks reality in that one of the major contributions to the 0.8 kcal. value allocated to skew butane is a hydrogen-hydrogen interaction, and such is not actually present in many of the skew con-

formations counted by him. However, a more direct evaluation can
be obtained by examination of decalin as a whole. In *trans*-decalin
(Figs. 7a and 7b) no non-bonded H—H interference is found, whereas

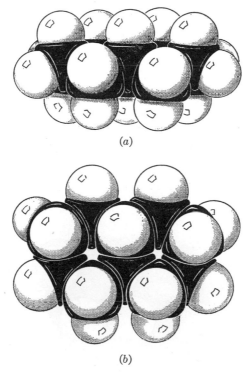

(a)

(b)

FIG. 7.   *Trans*-decalin.   (a) Side view; (b) top view.

in the *cis* isomer (Figs. 8a and 8b) there are three skew butane interactions, the hydrogens on carbons 1 and 5, on 3 and 5, and on 1 and 7
being closer than normal van der Waals radii allowances. Thus, the
difference between isomers is three skew interactions, or 2.4 kcal., a

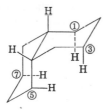

value identical to that given by Turner. These values are in agreement with the actual value of 2.12 kcal. as determined from heats of

isomerization.[43] From a value of 2.12 kcal. for the heat of isomerization at 25° for *cis*- to *trans*-decalin, if it is assumed for the sake of
simplicity that the entropy change is negligible, then the equilibrium
constant for this interconversion can be calculated, and the value
obtained is reasonable.[44] Thus, this relative stability is in harmony

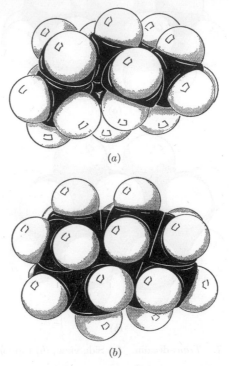

(a)

(b)

FIG. 8. *Cis*-decalin. (a) Side view; (b) bottom view.

with the concepts developed for cyclohexane that the isomer whose
conformation possesses the maximum number of equatorial substituents is the more stable. Looking upon the decalins as 1,2-disubsti-
tuted cyclohexanes, it is seen that the rings are joined by two equatorial bonds when in a *trans* configuration and one equatorial and one
axial when in a *cis* configuration.

[43] G. F. Davies and E. C. Gilbert, *J. Am. Chem. Soc.*, *63*, 1585 (1941).

[44] For example, since $\Delta S = 0$, $\Delta F = \Delta H = -RT \ln K$, or $\log K = -\Delta H/4.58T$,
$\log K = -(-2120)/4.58(298) = 1.56$, or $K = 36$. Hence, at equilibrium at 25°,
the mixture would contain 97.3% *trans* and 2.7% *cis*. Actually the *cis* isomer is a
racemic mixture of enantiomorphs (as in *cis*-1,2-dimethylcyclohexane) and might
be expected to have a larger entropy by $R \ln 2$, but this refinement is hardly significant.

The ring juncture of *trans*-decalin possessing two equatorial carbon substituents must of necessity place the two angular substituents, in this case hydrogens, in axial conformations. Such a ring fusion forces rigidity on the structure, since, although each chair can be distorted into a boat form, the conformation of the molecule cannot be inverted to interconvert all equatorial bonds to axial, and vice versa (as in cyclohexane), since it is impossible to have two rings fused through two adjacent axially directed bonds that are 180° apart. Such a rigidity allows a unique conformation to be allocated to a substituent on a *trans*-decalin ring since constant interconversion is no longer possible. For example, in *trans*-2-decalol, when the hydroxyl group is *cis* to the nearest ring juncture hydrogen atom (XL) it must be placed

H   OH   H   H

       H   OH

H   H

XL   XLI

in an axial conformation, and when the hydroxyl group is *trans* to the C$_9$-hydrogen atom (XLI) it must be equatorial. Hence, XLI would be expected to be the more stable isomer, thermodynamically.

The ring juncture of *cis*-decalin being of the equatorial-axial type allows for a great degree of flexibility in this isomer, and here again, as in cyclohexane, it is possible to completely invert the molecule by passing through intermediate boat forms. Such a change permits equatorial-axial interchanges of a group on any position, and hence it is possible for a substituent at any center and in any steric relationship to the ring juncture to be equatorial. Thus, conformational analysis as employed in rigid ring systems cannot be used in the *cis*-decalins to yield definite conclusions as to the stereochemistry of the molecule. However, let us consider the isomeric *cis*-2-decalols. In each isomer that conformation in which the hydroxyl substituent is equatorial (XLII*a* and XLIII*b*) has about the same free energy. When the hydroxyl group is *trans* to the ring juncture hydrogen atoms and axial (XLII*b*), it is placed in a position similar to a skew butane conformation (see Figs. 9 and 10) and should give rise to a steric interaction of a larger magnitude than the normal hydrogen-hydrogen interference. When the hydroxyl group is *cis* to the ring juncture hydrogens and axial (XLIII*a*), this additional steric interaction is absent and only the normal hydrogen-hydrogen interferences, characteristic of a *cis* structure, are present. Thus, the hydroxyl group in XLII should possess a greater equatorial character since at any time more molecules should have the substituent in the equatorial con-

XLIIa XLIIIa

XLIIb XLIIIb

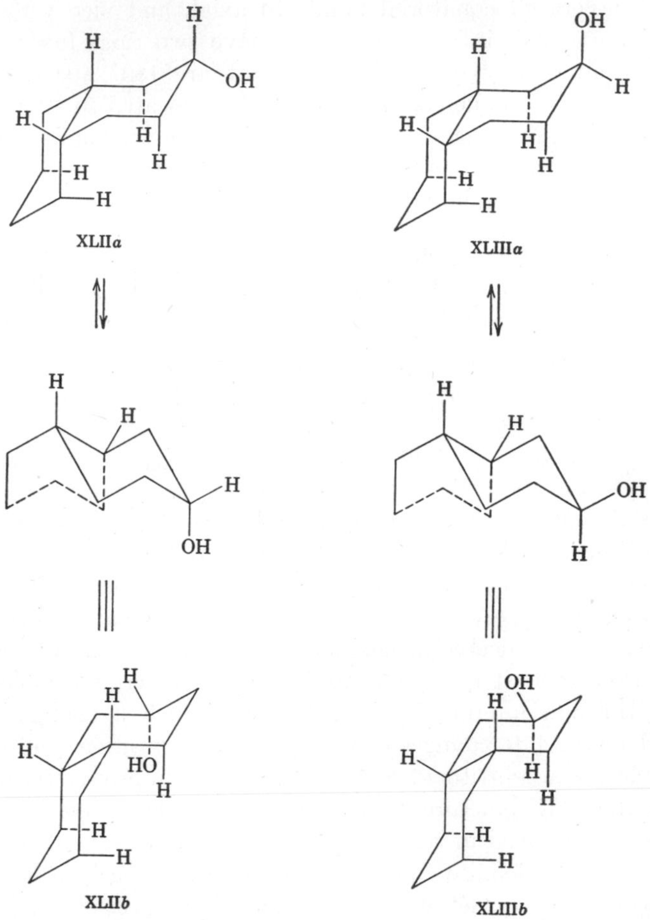

formation. To designate such an equatorial difference, a compound such as XLII has been referred to as *e* and XLIII as *ea*,[45] and a clear distinction as to the effect of this type of equatorial character on rate and on equilibrium must be maintained.

To illustrate the effect on rate, the saponification of the esters of

[45] W. G. Dauben, R. C. Tweit, and C. Mannerskanz, *J. Am. Chem. Soc.*, 76, 4420 (1954).

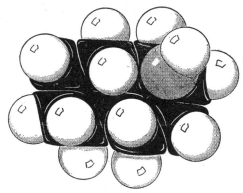

Fig. 9.   *Cis*-2-decalol, hydroxyl *trans* to ring juncture hydrogens, bottom view.

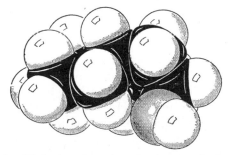

Fig. 10.   *Cis*-2-decalol, hydroxyl *trans* to ring juncture hydrogens, side view.

the two isomeric decalols XLII and XLIII [46] can be examined.   In such a reaction it is well known [46a] that the energy of activation is less for a compound possessing an ester group in an equatorial conformation than it is for a compound possessing an ester group in an axial conformation.   For the sake of simplicity, it can be assumed that the energy of activation for the equatorial conformations XLIIa and XLIIIb is about the same since in these two conformations the steric interactions are similar.   Such is not true for the corresponding axial conformations (reacting without conformational change); here it would be expected that, since the steric interactions of the axial conformation XLIIb are greater than those of the axial conformation XLIIIa, the energy of activation for reaction from XLIIb would be greater than that from XLIIIa.   Since the total rate of reaction of a compound is dependent upon the population of each ground state as

[46] For establishment of the configurations of these epimeric decalols, see W. G. Dauben and E. Hoerger, *J. Am. Chem. Soc.*, *73*, 1504 (1951).

[46a] D. H. R. Barton, *J. Chem. Soc.*, *1953*, 1027; S. J. Angyal and J. A. Mills, *Revs. Pure and Appl. Chem.*, *2*, 185 (1952).

well as the specific rate constant from each ground state (see p. 44), the distribution of the molecules in the ground state also must be considered. As discussed above, the population of the equatorial state in XLII is larger than the equatorial population of XLIII. As a result, the preferred equatorial pathway would be more favored in XLII than in XLIII. The contribution to the total rate of reaction from an axial pathway would be much less in XLII than in XLIII since not only is the axial concentration less but also the free energy of activation is greater. Accordingly, it would be expected that XLII would react faster than XLIII, and experimentally it has been found [47] that the p-nitrobenzoate ester of XLII is saponified 1.5 times more rapidly than that of XLIII.

On the other hand, in a reaction where the two epimers are in equilibrium, such as heating the decalols in decalin in the presence of potassium,[48] the ea epimer (XLIII) should predominate since conformations XLIIa and XLIIIb, being of the same energy, should be present in equal concentrations, whereas conformation XLIIIa, being of lower energy than XLIIb, should be present in greater concentration with regard to the axial conformations, and the sum of XLIIIa and b should exceed the sum of XLIIa and b. It has been reported,[48] however, that the equilibrium mixture contains 80% of XLII, in direct contrast to the prediction. These experimental results should be re-examined so that it can be determined whether the assignment of conformation on the above steric interaction type of reasoning has any utility.

A final point to consider in the decalins is the effect of substitution of a group for hydrogen at the ring junctures on the energy difference between cis- and trans-decalin. Using 9-methyldecalin as an example,[26] such an addition of a substituent at the 9 position in trans-decalin (XLIV) introduces four skew interactions whereas in cis-

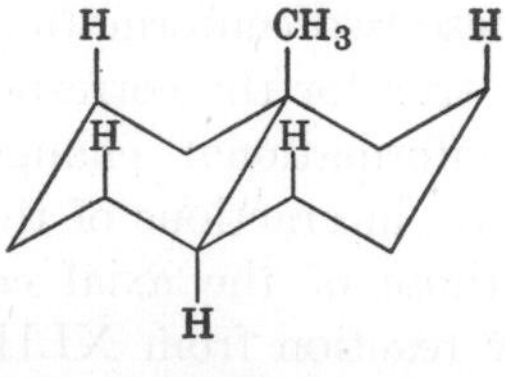

XLIV 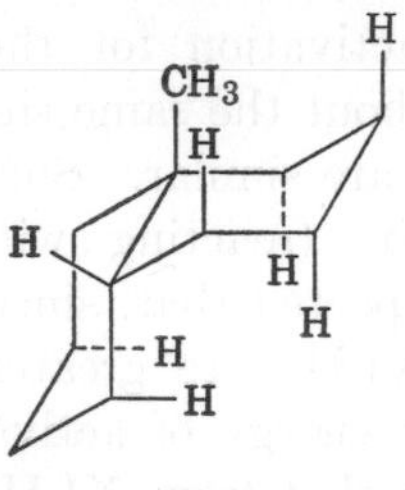   XLV

9-methyldecalin (XLV), in which the angular group is axial with respect to one ring and equatorial with respect to the other, only two additional skew interactions result. Since, by either method of con-

[47] W. Hückel, Ber., 67, 129 (1934).
[48] W. Hückel and H. Naab, Ber., 64, 2137 (1931).

formational analysis discussed for decalin, the *cis* differed from the *trans* by three skew interactions, in the 9-series it will differ by only one since there will be five in the *cis* and four in the *trans*. Thus, the effect of the substituent would be to lower the difference between these two isomers from 2.4 kcal. in decalin to 0.8 in the 9-methyl compound. This reduction in the energy difference would mean that the equilibrium mixture of 9-methyldecalins should contain a higher percentage of *cis* isomer than in decalin itself, but no accurate equilibrium data have been reported.

This whole problem is worthy of reexamination since it may allow one to evaluate the ability of a cyclic system to relieve steric strain due to non-bonded atoms by small distortions of the various bond angles involved in the ring. Since all the steric interactions in the *trans*-9-methyldecalin are on one side of the molecule, any puckering to relieve these would not greatly affect the other side of the molecule; however, in the *cis*-decalin there are two skew interactions on one side and three on the other, and any distortion to relieve one side would serve to increase the interactions on the other side.

It was reported in 1954, however, that such a stability of a *trans* ring juncture is not found with a perhydroheterocyclic ring system.[49] With decahydroisoquinoline-1,3-dione derivatives, it was found that, in the compound having two angular hydrogens, the equilibrium was in favor of the *trans* but when one of the hydrogens was replaced by an angular methyl group the *cis* form was favored at equilibrium. The applicability of this study to carbocyclic rings is not clear.

Polycyclic perhydroaromatic systems

The extension of the conformational concepts to this system of fused ring hydroaromatic compounds has resulted in a better understanding of the relative stabilities of the isomers and the critical stereochemical requirements involved in certain bonding. By utilizing the concepts discussed for cyclohexane and decalin, i.e., (*a*) the chair conformation is more stable than the boat, (*b*) the conformation with the larger number of equatorial substituents is the more stable, and (*c*) substituents in the 1,3 position to each other when forced to occupy a diaxial conformation bring about more steric interaction than when in a 1,4-diaxial arrangement, it has been possible to estimate the relative energy differences of the isomeric perhydrophenanthrenes and anthracenes.[50]

[49] W. E. Bachmann, A. Ross, A. S. Dreiding, and P. A. S. Smith, *J. Org. Chem.*, *19*, 222 (1954).

[50] W. S. Johnson, *Experientia*, *8*, 315 (1951); *J. Am. Chem. Soc.*, *75*, 1498 (1953).

A study of the stereochemistry of the perhydrophenanthrenes by Linstead and his colleagues [51] has furnished data which permit the testing of these conformational postulates. For example, they found that the *cis-syn-cis*-9-ketophenanthrene (XLVI) could be isomerized to and was consequently less stable than the *cis-syn-trans* ketone

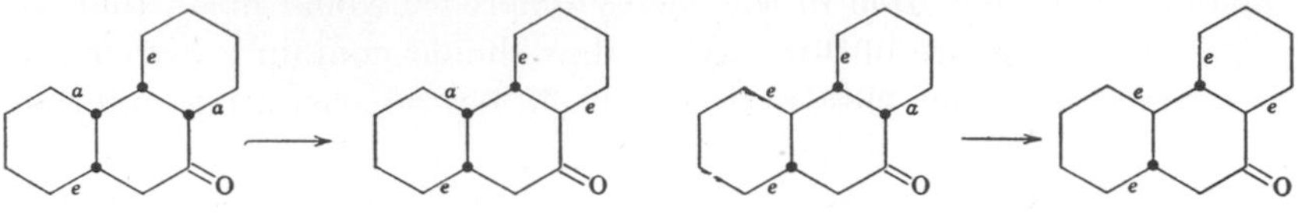

XLVI   XLVII   XLVIII   XLIX

(XLVII). Similarly, the *trans-anti-cis* ketone (XLVIII) could be converted to the *trans-anti-trans* compound (XLIX). From models, it is to be seen that XLVI can be viewed as a 1,2,3,4-tetrasubstituted cyclohexane, and, as in any *cis*-1,2-disubstituted cyclohexane, adjacent linkages must be equatorial and axial, respectively. The system XLVI has two equatorial and two axial substituents, whereas, in XLVII, one ring being *trans* and hence fused by two equatorial bonds, the system has three equatorial and one axial substituent. Similarly, XLVIII contains three equatorial and one axial, whereas XLIX is fused with four equatorial substituents. It was also reported [51] that the *cis-syn-trans*-10-ketoperhydrophenanthrene (L) was stable and would not isomerize to the *trans-syn-trans* form (LI). This stability of a *cis* ring juncture, however, should be expected only if all the cyclohexane rings remain in a chair conformation, since in such an arrange-

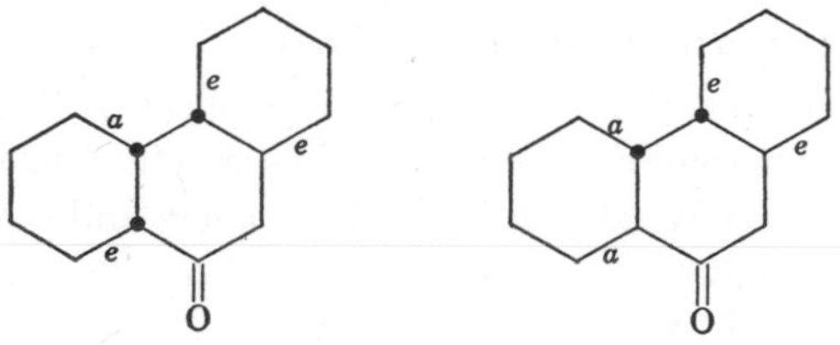

L   LI

ment the bond to be isomerized is equatorial and any change would transform it into an axial type. As the carbon atom in the backbone (C_{12}) is already axial it would mean a ring fusion by two axial bonds; the reasons for this not being possible have been discussed earlier. The bonds of *trans-syn-trans* molecule (LI) will not join unless the central ring is transformed into a boat conformation. It is not sur-

[51] R. P. Linstead et al., *J. Am. Chem. Soc.*, *64*, 1985 (1942), and papers in that series; *J. Chem. Soc.*, *1950*, 1428.

prising that this latter perhydro isomer is not favored energetically because the strain energy expected for conversion of one ring to the boat form is much larger than that for an axial substituent in an all-chair system.

These perhydro compounds also have been analyzed in a more quantitative manner [50] following the generalized scheme developed in the decalins, i.e., by counting the number of skew butane type of steric interactions. The notations used in the following figures are e for equatorial, a for axial, e-b for an equatorial bond on a boat conformation, and a-b for an axial bond on a boat conformation. Examination of the bonds from the central ring of the most stable of the perhydro-phenanthrenes, *trans-anti-trans* (LII), shows that all rings are fused by equatorial bonds. In addition, however, there is one skew butane interaction resulting from the hydrogens on C_4 and C_5. Such an interaction has previously been assigned a value of 0.8 kcal./mole, and this value has been assigned arbitrarily to LII. The *trans-anti-cis* (LIII) and the *cis-syn-trans* (LIV) both have three equatorial and one axial fusion, or one additional *cis*-decalin interaction, or a total of four skew interferences, and have been assigned the arbitrary value of

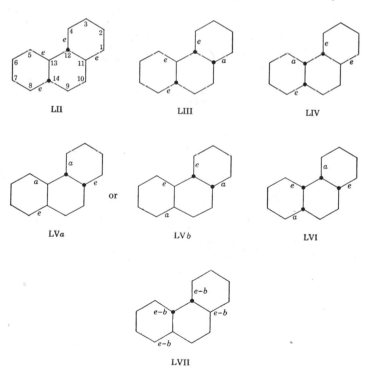

LII   LIII   LIV

LVa   LVb   LVI

LVII

3.2 kcal. In the *cis-anti-cis* compound (LV*a* or LV*b*), there are two possible arrangements of the atoms since the ring fusions are two equatorial and two axial bonds and these can be arranged so that the two axial bonds are 1,2 or 1,4 to each other. In LV*a* there are six skew interactions, and in LV*b* there are seven, and so the 1,2 arrangement should be preferred and the isomers assigned an arbitrary energy value of 4.8 kcal. In the *cis-syn-cis* isomer (LVI), likewise fused by two equatorial and two axial bonds, there are the equivalent of two *cis*-decalin structures. The *cis* interactions are further complicated by the fact that the carbon atoms extending from C_{11} and C_{13} of the compound are forced into a 1,3 diaxial conformation, and such an arrangement has been shown on 1,3-dimethylcyclohexane to introduce an energy factor of at least 5.4 kcal. Johnson has postulated that since in the phenanthrene case it is the methylene and not the methyl group interaction the value should be about $\frac{8}{9}$ as large, or 4.8 kcal. A more reasonable estimate, however, which takes into account the greater rigidity of the methylene groups in this structure and the extreme steric interference resulting, would seem to be 8–9 kcal. In addition to this steric interference there are still two skew interactions involving C_7,C_9 and C_1,C_9, and so the assigned energy should be greater than 9 kcal. The *trans-syn-trans* structure (LVII), as mentioned before, required that the central ring adopt a boat conformation, and in addition there are two skew interferences involving C_4 and C_5, and so the assigned energy should be approximately 7.2 kcal. The additional interaction of C_4 and C_5 has not been evaluated previously, and the value used in the present discussion can be arrived at by simply assuming that the major energy contributor is the boat conformation and that the other non-bonded atom steric interferences are less than that of a *cis*-butane since the carbon-carbon bond interaction has already been considered in the value assigned to the boat conformation; the value of the residual interaction can be approximated as being similar to two skew butane steric interferences since there are two such hydrogen-hydrogen interactions.

In a similar manner the isomeric perhydroanthracenes can be arranged in the order of their stability, and it is found that the most stable should be the *trans-syn-trans* compound (LVIII) since all ring junctures are equatorial and there are no skew interactions; this compound has been assigned a zero energy on the arbitrary scale employed in this discussion. Next, the *cis-syn-trans* (LIX) with three equatorial and one axial juncture and three skew interactions resulting from the *cis* ring fusion can be assigned a value of 2.4 kcal., and the *cis-anti-cis* (LX) with two equatorial and two axial linkages and two *cis*-decalin types of interactions can be given a value of 4.8 kcal. The *trans-anti-trans* (LXI) is another isomer which requires that the central ring adopt a boat conformation and accordingly can be assigned a value

LVIII   LIX   LX

LXI   LXII

of ≥ 5.6 kcal. The *cis-syn-cis* (LXII) displays the 1,3 diaxial type of interaction discussed in the phenanthrenes and in addition possesses two skew interferences and thus can be assigned a value of ≥ 9 kcal.

Cyclopentanes

The saturated five-membered ring also is an important unit in organic chemistry, being of particular interest because the torsional forces about single bonds are in opposition to the forces tending to retain tetrahedral bond angles. Thus, the latter forces act to keep all five carbon atoms coplanar while the torsional forces tend to pucker the ring. Measurement of the entropy of gaseous cyclopentane [52] and calculations [53] based on normal values of the force constants indicate a puckered ring. Hassel and Viervoll [54] investigated this molecule by the electron diffraction method, and although they assumed a planar model to obtain bond length values, a small puckering would have only a minor effect and indeed would appear to improve the fit at larger distances. The thermodynamic functions have been calculated [55] using a method similar to that described for cyclohexane. It was concluded that the potential energy of the molecule is at a maximum when the molecule is planar. Also the ring-puckering motions

[52] J. G. Aston, S. C. Schumann, H. L. Fink, and P. M. Doty, *J. Am. Chem. Soc.*, *63*, 2029 (1941); J. G. Aston, H. L. Fink, and S. C. Schumann, *ibid.*, *65*, 341 (1943); D. R. Douslin and H. M. Huffman, *ibid.*, *68*, 173 (1946).

[53] K. S. Pitzer, *Science*, *101*, 672 (1945).

[54] O. Hassel and H. Viervoll, *Tidsskr. Kjemi Bergvesen Met.*, *6*, 31 (1946).

[55] J. E. Kilpatrick, K. S. Pitzer, and R. Spitzer, *J. Am. Chem. Soc.*, *69*, 2483 (1947).

are, first, an ordinary vibration in which the amount of puckering oscillates about a most stable value and, second, a pseudo one-dimensional rotation in which the phase of the puckering rotates around the ring. This is not a real rotation, since the actual motion of the atom is perpendicular to the direction of rotation and there is no angular momentum about the axis of rotation. In one of its simpler conformations, cyclopentane can be viewed as having four carbon atoms nearly planar and the fifth displaced above or below the plane by about 0.5 A; the displaced atom is not always the same one, but rather the puckering can be regarded as rotating around the ring as the atoms vibrate. Thus a non-planar conformation (LXIII) is favored because

LXIII

the deformation of the tetrahedral valency angle of the non-planar conformation is less serious than the unfavorable opposed orientation of the planar form.

Again, it is of interest to examine the relationship of the physical properties of the 1,3-dimethylcyclopentanes to their stereochemistry. On the basis of physical properties, the compound having the higher boiling point, refractive index, and density had been assigned a *cis* configuration, but Birch and Dean [56] unequivocally prepared an optically active 1,3-dimethylcyclopentane, and the material was found to possess the properties of the previously assigned *cis* isomer. Since only the *trans* compound can be optically active, it requires here, as in the cyclohexane series, that the isomers be reversed and the material with the higher value of physical properties be given a *trans* configuration. Haresnape [57] has attempted to evaluate the energy difference in this series by a method similar to that employed in previous cases, and he has arrived at the conclusion that the molecule possessing the *trans* configuration should be about 0.5 kcal./mole higher in energy than the *cis* isomer. Accordingly, the *cis* should be the more stable, thermodynamically. Haresnape [57] also extended his calculations to the 1,2-dimethylcyclopentanes and found that the *cis* should be of about 1.7 kcal. higher energy than the *trans;* this result is in agreement with the stereochemistry previously assigned on the basis of physical properties.

[56] S. F. Birch and R. A. Dean, *J. Chem. Soc., 1953,* 2477.
[57] J. N. Haresnape, *Chemistry & Industry, 1953,* 1091.

Hydrindanes

A five-membered ring may be fused to a cyclohexane ring in a chair conformation through either a *cis* or a *trans* ring juncture; in the former the fusion would involve an equatorial and an axial bond, and in the latter two equatorial bonds would be utilized. On the basis of previously developed concepts, the isomer with two equatorial bonds would be expected to be more stable, and experiment bears this out.[58] Comparing the energy differences, the lesser value for isomeric hydrindanes (0.74 ± 0.52 kcal./mole) than for isomeric decalins (2.4 kcal./mole) presents a new problem to be evaluated in terms of conformational concepts. Examination of models of isomeric hydrindanes gives some insight into the problem. In order to fuse a five- and a six-membered ring, it is necessary to distort the six-membered ring so as to bring the bonds used in the attachment of the five-membered ring closer together. In the *cis* isomer, the main distortion is a deformation of the chair conformation of the six-membered ring towards that of a boat, a motion readily possible and one not expected to greatly affect the energy content of the compound. In the *trans* isomer, the distortion needed is towards a more severe chair conformation. This introduces additional angle strain into both rings and causes crowding of the axial hydrogen atoms. Such distortions in *trans*-hydrindanes suggest a higher energy content for the molecule than one expects for a strainless structure fused with two equatorial bonds, and would bring the energy of the *trans* isomer closer to that of the *cis* than is found in the decalin series.

These same concepts, however, also have been utilized to account for specific formation of a cyclic ketal from *cis*- but not *trans*-1,2-cyclohexanediol.[59] Evaluation of this type of conformational reasoning must await further work.

It is also interesting to examine the stability of the isomeric *cis*-5-hydrindanols, since here again the same problem with respect to conformational analysis arises as discussed in the *cis*-2-decalols. There are two conformations for each isomer, for the *cis-cis* (LXIV and LXV) and for the *cis-trans* (LXVI and LXVII). In LXV the hydroxyl group is *trans* and axial, and there is steric interaction between the C_5-hydroxyl group and the C_3-hydrogen. Such interference is absent

[58] W. Hückel, M. Sachs, J. Yantschulewitsch, and F. Nerdel, *Ann.*, *518*, 155 (1935), found that the *trans* form of hydrindane was more stable than the *cis* by 2 kcal./mole. F. D. Rossini (private communication) has found that a more accurate value for this energy difference is 0.74 ± 0.52 kcal./mole.

[59] S. G. Angyal and C. G. MacDonald, *J. Chem. Soc.*, *1952*, 686.

when the hydroxyl is *cis* to the ring juncture hydrogen atoms and axial (LXVI). As in the decalols, this latter isomer (LXVI and LXVII) would be expected to be more stable, thermodynamically, than the *cis-cis* (LXIV and LXV). The stereochemistry of the 5-substituted-*cis*-hydrindanes has been assigned on the basis of reactivity.[60]

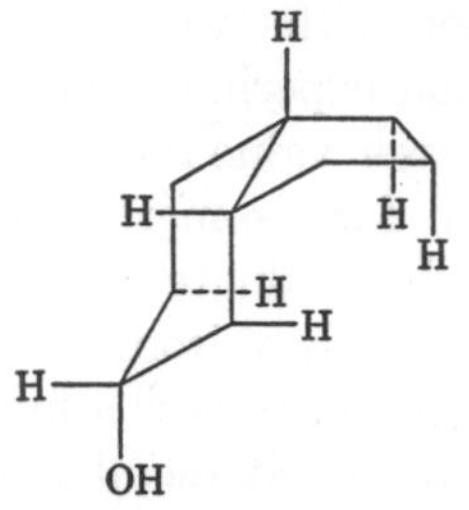

LXIV

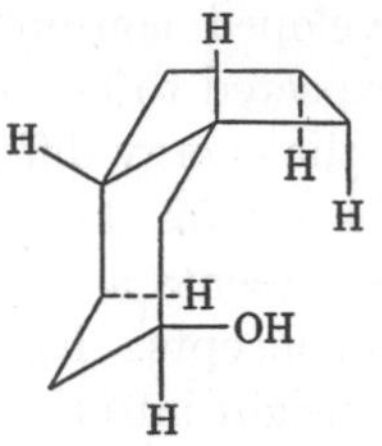

LXV

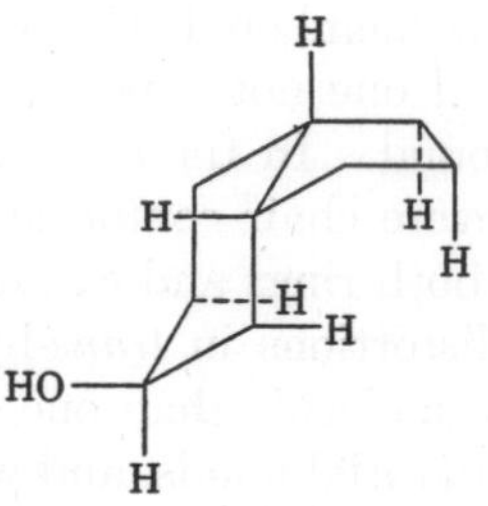

LXVI

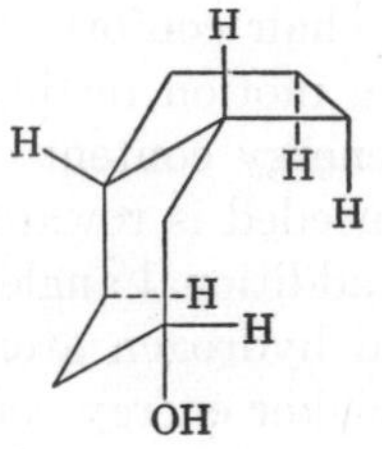

LXVII

It was found that the compound assigned a *cis-trans* (LXVI and LXVII) configuration on this independent basis was the same compound that Hückel [61] had found to be the thermodynamically stable isomer by equilibration experiments. Thus, in the hydrindanes the application of conformational concepts correctly assigns the stereochemistry of the compound whereas in the *cis*-2-decalols the experimental facts are at variance with theory.

Cyclohexene and cyclopentene

Cyclohexene, like cyclohexane, can readily exist in two conformations which closely resemble the boat and chair forms. Both these conformations satisfy the geometrical requirement that the four carbon atoms associated with the olefinic system lie in the same plane. An accurate representation, on a plane surface, of these two conforma-

[60] W. G. Dauben and J. Jiu, *J. Am. Chem. Soc.*, **76**, 4426 (1954).
[61] W. Hückel, *Ann.*, **533**, 1 (1937).

tions presents certain difficulties, but LXVIII and LXIX attempt
to illustrate the geometry of the molecule as viewed along the plane
containing the four atoms of the olefinic system. Beckett, Freeman,
and Pitzer [62] have extended their calculations to this system and have
shown that the chairlike conformation (LXVIII) would be favored

LXVIII   LXIX

by about 2.7 kcal./mole. Also, X-ray data on compounds like choles-
teryl iodide,[63] pentachlorocyclohexene,[64] and naphthalene tetrachloride [65] support such an assigned conformation. The extension of the
equatorial and axial concepts to this and related systems [66] has been
suggested and the utility discussed.

In cyclopentene, again four carbon atoms must be coplanar. If the
fifth carbon atom of the system is placed in this same plane, the bonds
between the three methylene groups are at the maximum torsional
energy since the hydrogen atoms on the methylene groups are in an
opposed configuration. By considering the strain energy as a function
of the distance from the fifth carbon atom to the plane of the four
carbon atoms, it was found [62] that, within the magnitude of thermal
energy at room temperature, the potential energy of cyclopentene is
unchanged by puckering the ring and having the atom out of the
plane by amounts up to about 0.3 A.

Cyclohexanones

The conversion of one of the carbon atoms of a cyclohexane ring
to a carbonyl carbon atom appears to have little effect on the overall
shape of the ring system, and again there are two conformations
analogous to a boat and a chair. Since the usual non-bonded atom

[62] C. W. Beckett, N. K. Freeman, and K. S. Pitzer, *J. Am. Chem. Soc.*, **70**, 4227 (1948).

[63] C. H. Carlisle and D. Crowfoot, *Proc. Roy. Soc.*, *A184*, 64 (1945).

[64] R. A. Pasternak, *Acta Cryst.*, *4*, 316 (1951).

[65] M. A. Lasheen, *Acta Cryst.*, *5*, 593 (1952).

[66] D. H. R. Barton, R. C. Cookson, W. Klyne, and C. W. Shoppee, *Chemistry & Industry*, *1954*, 21, and references therein.

interactions are still present, a cyclohexanone should best be represented as existing in a chair conformation. However, because of the different geometrical requirements of the carbonyl bonded system, the usual staggered arrangement of all atoms bonded to carbon in a chair conformation is changed. Whereas the bonds on the five methylene carbons remain staggered, the oxygen of the carbonyl system is arranged in an opposed configuration with respect to the two adjacent equatorial bonds. This destruction of the symmetry of the chair con-

As viewed down the C–C bond

formation about the carbonyl center thus requires that the carbonyl oxygen bond lie at different distances from the adjacent equatorial and axial bonds.

The importance of this feature of the cyclohexanone ring system can be illustrated by consideration of the conformations of α-halocyclohexanone derivatives. A detailed study of the infrared spectra of α-brominated steroidal ketones,[67] compounds in which the isomeric bromides have a distinct conformation, shows that, when the bromine atom is equatorial [68] and consequently approximately coplanar with the carbonyl grouping, the frequency of the carbonyl vibration is raised about 20 cm.$^{-1}$. When the bromine atom is axial very little displacement occurs. The frequency change of the equatorial bromo ketone has been attributed to a coplanar dipolar-dipolar repulsion between the bromine atom and the carbonyl grouping.

With this method to determine whether the bromine is equatorial or axial with respect to the carbonyl group, the simple α-halocyclohexanones have been studied.[69] Because of the flexibility of this system, the halogen atom can occupy either conformation. From a steric viewpoint the equatorial (LXX) would be favored; from a dipolar repulsion viewpoint the axial (LXXI) would be preferred

[67] R. N. Jones, D. A. Ramsey, F. Herling, and K. Dobriner, *J. Am. Chem. Soc.*, 74, 2828 (1952).

[68] L. F. Fieser and R. Ettorre, *J. Am. Chem. Soc.*, 75, 1700 (1953); L. F. Fieser and X. A. Dominguez, *ibid.*, 75, 1704 (1953); L. F. Fieser and W. Yuang, *ibid.*, 75, 4837 (1953); E. J. Corey, *ibid.*, 75, 4832 (1953).

[69] E. J. Corey, *J. Am. Chem. Soc.*, 75, 2301 (1953).

since the dipoles would be in the most favorable orientation allowed in this structure. From the infrared spectrum of the compound it

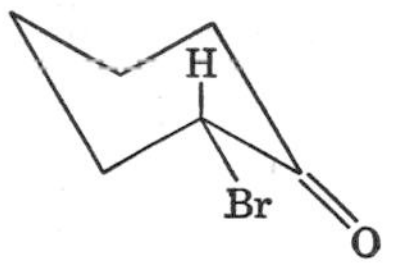

LXX 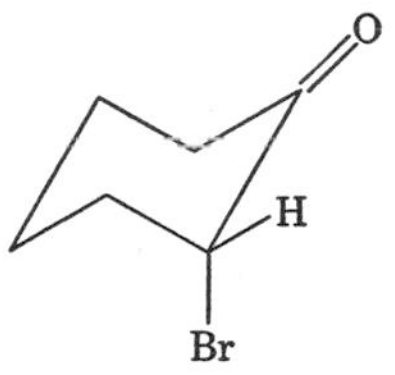   LXXI

was found that the bromine was axial. Calculations showed this conformation to be favored by at least 2.3 kcal. Similarly, the energy of the most stable of the six possible boat conformations of α-bromo-cyclohexanone was estimated to be at least 5 kcal. greater than the chair conformation with the bromine atom axial.[69] It was shown, however, that, upon increasing the magnitude of the steric interaction by placing another substituent in such a position as to create a 1,3 di-axial type of repulsion, the bromine atom could be forced to assume an equatorial conformation. For example, in 2-bromo-4,4-dimethylcyclo-hexanone (LXXII) or in cis-2,6-dibromocyclohexanone (LXXIII) [70] the halogens are in an equatorial conformation. Thus, when dipolar repulsions are more important than non-bonded atom interaction,

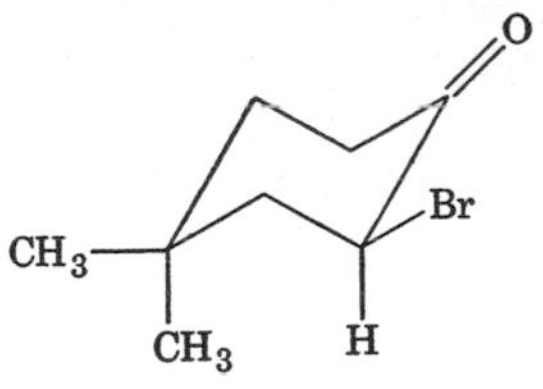

LXXII 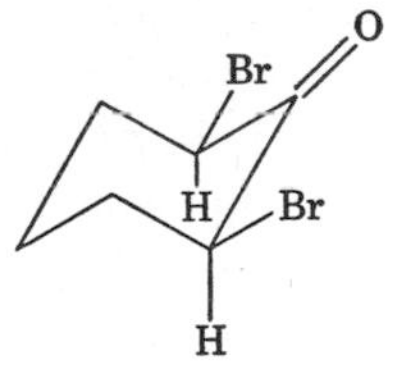   LXXIII

care must be taken in the allocation of the conformation of the groups. Of course, in a cyclohexanone where the substituent added does not display a dipolar repulsion, the grouping would still prefer the equatorial conformation. These concepts have been extended to more complex examples with equally interesting results.[71]

[70] E. J. Corey, J. Am. Chem. Soc., 75, 3297 (1953).

[71] E. J. Corey, J. Am. Chem. Soc., 76, 175 (1954); a similar article appeared in Experientia, 9, 329 (1953).

Medium and large ring compounds

The discovery of the applicability of the acyloin synthesis for the preparation of ring compounds [72] has made available compounds containing more than six carbon atoms in the ring and has allowed more thorough study of these systems. Early workers did not critically investigate the influence of ring size on the physical and chemical properties of such cyclic systems but assumed that these higher homologs, being free from Baeyer ring strain, should not differ from cyclohexane more than the higher acyclic homologs differ from the lower. The more recent work of Prelog, Ruzicka, and their colleagues, however, has shown that the properties do exhibit a peculiar dependence on ring size. With regard to the physical properties, such as density and refractive index of the cyclanol acetates,[73] it was noted that, whereas acyclic systems showed a steady increase in the density with molecular weight, the alicyclic compounds showed a maximum density when the ring was medium sized.[74] Furthermore, a study of the equilibrium constant for the reaction between a cyclanone and hydrogen cyanide in alcoholic solution [75] and the dissociation constants of polymethyleneimines [76] again showed abnormality in the medium-sized ring compounds. In the respective reactions, the ketone is stabilized with respect to the cyanohydrin and the imine with respect to the ammonium salt.

One possible explanation for these phenomena is that in these compounds the nucleophilic center is shielded by the hydrogens of the polymethylene chain.[73] Such a proximity of the hydrogen atoms to the carbonyl group would be possible only in certain conformations. By considering the usual non-bonded eclipsed interactions, rings containing 8–12 carbon atoms can be built only when they contain several such unfavorable conformations whereas rings containing 5–7 or 13 or more carbon atoms can be arranged so that all or almost all the

[72] V. Prelog, L. Frenkiel, M. Kobelt, and P. Barman, *Helv. Chim. Acta*, *30*, 1741 (1947); M. Stoll and J. Hulstkamp, *ibid.*, *30*, 1815, 1837 (1947); V. L. Hansley, U. S. pat. 2,226,268.

[73] For an excellent review covering this material in detail, see V. Prelog, *J. Chem. Soc.*, *1950*, 420.

[74] Prelog and Brown (see footnote 21), *J. Am. Chem. Soc.*, *73*, 212 (1951), have provided the following definition of ring size: small, 3–4; normal, 5–7; medium, 8–12; large, 13 and up.

[75] L. Ruzicka, Pl. A. Plattner, and H. Wed, *Helv. Chim. Acta*, *28*, 613 (1945); V. Prelog and M. Kobelt, *ibid.*, *32*, 1187 (1949).

[76] L. Ruzicka, M. Kobelt, O. Häfliger, and V. Prelog, *Helv. Chim. Acta*, *32*, 544 (1949).

C—C bonds have the normal staggered configuration. Accordingly, the much higher energy content of medium-sized rings is reflected in the physical properties. With regard to the effect on chemical reactivity, let us consider cyclodecanone. In this molecule there are two important conformations to consider: in one the oxygen atom of the carbonyl group lies as a peripheral substituent to the ring (see Fig. 11) called "O-outside" (LXXIV); in the other it is perpendicular to the plane of the ring surrounded by "axial-like" hydrogen atoms (see Fig. 12) and is called "O-inside" (LXXV). The "O-outside" conformation is that usually encountered in a normal ring ketone, and this conformation in cyclodecanone has eight methyl hydrogen eclipsed

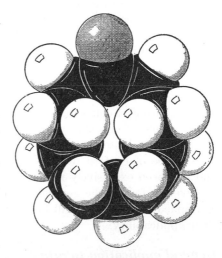

Fig. 11. Cyclodecanone, "O-outside" conformation.

interactions while the "O-inside" has only six such eclipsed arrangements and two staggered orientations. Thus, the reactions of cyclodecanone should be examined on the basis that the "O-inside" confor-

Fig. 12. Cyclodecanone, "O-inside" conformation.

mation is favored. This "O-inside" conformation of an oxygen atom flanked by hydrogen atoms at a very close distance is favored in all medium-sized-ring ketones. Studies on the solvolysis of the epoxide of cyclooctene,[77] cyclononene, and cyclodecene,[78] and on the carbonyl reactivity in ring-closure reactions of medium-sized ring ketones, have yielded some confirmation of this transannular hydrogen effect. It is of passing interest to note that these transannular effects are absent in cycloheptene.[79] The above reactions are discussed in Chapter 4.

GENERAL RULES OF REACTIVITY

The concept of equatorial and axial bonds in the study of the chemical reactions of alicyclic systems has enabled workers to better understand and evaluate the steric characteristic of certain configurations. This phase of conformational analysis is discussed in other chapters and has been extensively reviewed.[80] For the sake of easy reference, however, a few of the generalizations of the conformational concept as applied to reactivity will be discussed briefly in order to illustrate their applicability.

General application to rate

The rate of a reaction of a compound which can react from either of two conformations, such as Equatorial (E) and Axial (A), can be expressed as in the diagram, where K is the equilibrium constant for

$$A \underset{}{\overset{K}{\rightleftarrows}} E$$

$$K_A^{\ddagger} \downarrow \qquad \downarrow K_E^{\ddagger}$$

$$A^{\ddagger} \qquad E^{\ddagger}$$

$$kt/h \downarrow \qquad \downarrow kt/h$$

Products

the ground-state conformations and $K_A^{\ddagger}$ and $K_E^{\ddagger}$ are related to the free energies of activation from the axial and equatorial conformations, respectively. For a unimolecular reaction, the rate of formation of products, dP/dt, is

$$\frac{dP}{dt} = \frac{kt}{h} K_A^{\ddagger}[A] + \frac{kt}{h} K_E^{\ddagger}[E]$$

[77] A. C. Cope, S. W. Fenton, and C. F. Spencer, *J. Am. Chem. Soc.*, *74*, 5884 (1952).

[78] V. Prelog and K. Schenker, *Helv. Chim. Acta*, *35*, 2044 (1952); *36*, 471, 896 (1953).

[79] A. C. Cope and W. N. Baxter, *J. Am. Chem. Soc.*, *76*, 276 (1954).

[80] D. H. R. Barton, *J. Chem. Soc.*, *1953*, 1027; S. J. Angyal and J. A. Mills, *Revs. Pure and Appl. Chem.*, *2*, 185 (1952).

where the concentration of the ground-state conformations is expressed in square brackets. Division of this equation by the total concentration of reacting species, $[A + E]$, gives

$$\frac{dP/dt}{[A + E]} = \frac{[A]}{[A + E]} \frac{kt}{h} K_A^{\ddagger} + \frac{[E]}{[A + E]} \frac{kt}{h} K_E^{\ddagger}$$

Since the left-hand side of this equation is simply a first-order rate constant, k, and on the right-hand side the concentration terms are mole fractions of the ground-state conformations, N_A and N_E, and the other terms are rate constants, k_A and k_E, corresponding to a pure A or a pure E reacting through an A-type transition state, $A^{\ddagger}$, and an E-type transition state, $E^{\ddagger}$, respectively, the expression can be simplified to read

$$k = N_A k_A + N_E k_E$$

The observed rate constant k is a weighted average of the rate constants characteristic of the conformational isomers A and E. Thus, the rate of reaction is dependent upon the concentration of each ground-state conformation and the specific rate of reaction of each conformation. The former is a reflection of the free-energy difference between each ground state, and the latter a reflection of the free-energy difference between the individual ground state and its corresponding transition state. If the total rate of reaction and the individual rate constants for each pure conformation are known, then the mole fraction of each conformation in the ground state can be calculated. This type of calculation offers another method of obtaining the free-energy differences of the conformations of a compound. In addition, if the compound contains two or more groupings at such a distance that there is no interaction and each grouping is functioning as if in an individual compound, then the overall free-energy difference of the ground-state conformations can be viewed as being a simple additive function of the free-energy differences between the axial and the equatorial conformations of each substituent. In this manner if the free-energy difference between two conformations for one group of a disubstituted compound is known, that for the other group can be calculated from the overall free-energy difference of the two conformations of the disubstituted compound obtained from the above equation.

Next let us consider the type of free-energy information that can be obtained by an examination of the composition of the product of such a reaction as outlined above. For information about the composition of a product to be useful, it is essential that the product of reaction of each conformation be an individual compound which is not in rapid equilibrium with the product from the reaction of the other conformation. The composition of the product then will be determined by the ratio of the individual rates of reaction of each conformation, and, since these rates depend both upon the free energy of activation and the ground-state concentration, no discrete information with regard to either can be obtained. Such a product analysis does, however, yield information with respect to the difference in free energy between the two transition states. For example, the ratio of the rate of reaction of each conformation is

$$\frac{-d[E]/dt}{-d[A]/dt} = \frac{N_E k_E}{N_A k_A}$$

but $N_E/N_A = K$, the equilibrium constant for the ground-state conformations. Accordingly, the ratio of the rates can be expressed as $(k_E/k_A)K$. If we call the ground-state free energies F_E and F_A, and the transition-state free energies $F_E^{\ddagger}$ and $F_A^{\ddagger}$, then, neglecting transmission coefficients, the rate ratio can be expressed as

$$\frac{-d[E]/dt}{-d[A]/dt} = \frac{(kt/h)\exp-(F_E\ddagger-F_E)/RT \exp-(F_E-F_A)/RT}{(kt/h)\exp-(F_A\ddagger-F_A)/RT}$$

$$= \exp(F_A\ddagger-F_E\ddagger)/RT$$

The distinction between the expression of the ratio of the rates in terms of specific rate constants and an equilibrium constant and in terms of transition-state theory is a result of the basic assumptions employed in the development of each expression. In the former, the reaction of each conformation has been considered to proceed independently from ground states of different free energies. Thus, the population of each ground state, as expressed by the equilibrium constant, must be considered. This population ratio as such does not enter the transition-state expression since in this latter treatment the reaction is viewed as path independent and all reaction is assumed to begin from a common ground state. This last restriction inherently takes into account a population ratio since it states that, for a molecule in state A in going to transition state $E^{\ddagger}$, the free energy required in going from ground state A to ground state E (or $F_E - F_A$) as well as the free energy required to go from ground state E to transition state $E^{\ddagger}$ must be considered. This free-energy difference $(F_E - F_A)$ is the same free-energy difference considered in the equilibrium constant.

It should be reemphasized that, in contrast to the ratio of the rates of reaction of the individual conformations being only dependent upon the free-energy difference of the transition states, the actual rate of a reaction of a compound is dependent upon the energy of activation and the exact values of F_A and F_E. Accordingly, the ground-state conformational energies (and thus the ground-state concentrations) must be considered. In addition, when the actual rates of two different compounds are to be compared, both ground-state and transition-state energies must be taken into account, since the rate for each compound will be dependent upon different ground states.

Stability

Generally, at a given carbon atom in a cyclohexane ring system an equatorial substituent is more stable than an axial substituent. The reasons for this follow directly from the earlier discussion with regard to the energies related to these two types of bonds. Thus, when a substituted cyclohexane is subjected to equilibration conditions, that isomer in which the substituent affected is equatorial will be favored. The equilibration of an alcohol or a carboxylic ester with base, reduction of a ketone with sodium and alcohol, and reduction of an unhindered ketone with lithium aluminum hydride or sodium borohydride illustrate this concept. An extension of this rule is that when a hindered ketone is reduced with the above hydrides, or when a relatively unhindered ketone is reduced with aluminum isopropoxide, the axial isomer is favored. Of equal utility with regard to this generalization is the restatement by Barton [80] of the classical von Auwer-Skita rule of catalytic hydrogenation. Accordingly, catalytic hydrogenation of all ketones in a strongly acid media (rapid hydrogenation) gives rise to the axial isomer whereas hydrogenation in neutral medial (slow hydrogenation) forms an equatorial alcohol if the ketone is unhindered or an axial isomer if the ketone is greatly hindered. Illustrations of the concepts are to be found in the formation of substituted cyclohexanols.[81]

Rate of reaction

At a given carbon atom in a cyclohexane ring system, an axial hydroxyl group is more hindered towards acylation than an equatorial grouping, and, also, the ester of an axial alcohol is more slowly hydrolyzed. This concept as it applies to alcohols in nonrigid systems has been discussed by Eliel,[82] who has postulated that in such cases the reaction proceeds via the conformation of the molecule in which the reactive hydroxyl group is equatorial and that the rate differences in isomers should be attributed to that energy necessary to place the other substituent, if necessary, into an axial conformation. For exam-

[81] For leading references, see D. S. Noyce and D. B. Denney, *J. Am. Chem. Soc.*, *72*, 5743 (1950).

[82] E. L. Eliel, *Experientia*, *9*, 91 (1953).

ple, the rates of esterification of the isomeric menthols, based upon the postulates of Eliel, would be in the order of menthol, isomenthol, neoisomenthol, and neomenthol, and the relative rates actually found are 16.5:12.3:3.1:1.0, respectively.[83]

In addition to the foregoing, it must be realized with a more complex rigid system, such as a compound of the *trans*-decalin type, that in order to make predictions as to the relative reactivities at centers, all steric factors must be taken into account and the equatorial and axial nature not only of the reacting group but also of all other groups in the molecule must be evaluated. This aspect of steric hindrance will be considered in other chapters.[84]

A related generalization is that the rate of oxidation of any hydroxyl group on a cyclohexane ring system with chromic acid or hypobromous acid is more rapid with the axial than with the equatorial isomer. The rationale for this rule is to be found in the fact that, in such a reaction, the rate-determining step is not the formation of the corresponding ester but the attack on the C—H bond of the alcoholic carbon being oxidized.[85]

When such concepts are applied to systems of unknown configuration, the stereochemistry of the center can be determined.

Ionic eliminations

As discussed earlier in this chapter with regard to acyclic systems, a planar, four center transition state is preferred in a 1,2 ionic elimination. This condition is fulfilled in a cyclohexane system when 1,2-*trans* substituents assume the axial conformation (or are free to adopt such a conformation). Since the diaxial conformation is preferred over a diequatorial in such a reaction, it is found that, with a rigid system of the *trans*-decalin type, the rate of *trans* elimination of the two *trans* substituents in the diaxial conformation is more rapid than when the two *trans* substituents are in the diequatorial conformation. For example, the rate of elimination of *p*-toluenesulfonic acid to form an olefin from a 3α-tosyloxycholestane [3α-OTs (*a*) and 2β and/or 4β-H (*a*)] is more rapid than from the 3β isomer [3β-OTs (*e*) and 2α and/or 4α-H (*e*)].[86]

[83] J. Read and J. Grubb, *J. Chem. Soc.*, *1934*, 1779.

[84] Barton (see reference 80) has made semiquantitative estimates of the relative degree of hindrance of the different positions in steroids by consideration of the conformation of the groupings surrounding the reaction center.

[85] M. Cohen and F. H. Westheimer, *J. Am. Chem. Soc.*, *74*, 4387 (1952), and earlier papers.

[86] H. R. Nace, *J. Am. Chem. Soc.*, *74*, 5937 (1952); see also D. H. R. Barton and W. J. Rosenfelder, *J. Chem. Soc.*, *1951*, 1048.

Pyrolytic eliminations

The formation of an olefin by pyrolysis of an ester has been shown to proceed preferentially via a planar cyclic transition state.[87] This condition requires that the groups of a cyclic compound to be eliminated be in an equatorial-axial arrangement. In a cyclic series, it is theoretically possible for this condition to be fulfilled also by a diequatorial arrangement of groupings since one of the features of the cyclohexane system is that an equatorial substituent on one carbon atom is equidistant (but not coplanar) from either an axial or an equatorial substituent on an adjacent carbon atom. However, only the equatorial-axial arrangement of a *cis* configuration can readily achieve coplanarity, since only slight distortion of the ring system from a true chair form is required. On the other hand, to achieve planarity of an equatorial-equatorial *trans* system requires distortion of the chair conformation in such a manner as to increase the axial-axial interactions between other atoms in the molecule, and apparently such an increased energy requirement tends to inhibit the *trans* elimination. See Chapter 6.

Rearrangements

In most rearrangements the groups participating are *trans* with respect to one another and the steric requirement for facile rearrangement is that the centers involved be in a plane. There are two possible conformations for a departing group in any rearrangement. When the group is axial, the only other groups in the molecule capable of meeting the preferred steric requirement for migration are those attached to the ring (peripheral substituents). When the departing group is equatorial, only a carbon atom of the ring system itself fulfills the preferred orientation. Thus, if a system is rigid, prediction can be made as to the migrating group, whereas in a non-rigid system the energy differences of the separate conformations and the migration aptitude of the groups also must be considered. This option in a non-rigid system is clearly illustrated by work on the isomeric 2-aminocyclohexanols.[88] Upon reaction with nitrous acid the *cis* isomer (LXXIV) yields both cyclopentanecarboxaldehyde and cyclohexanone and the *trans* (LXXV) gives only the cyclopentanealdehyde. The geometry of these molecules is readily seen by looking down the C_2-C_1 axis of the molecule.

[87] D. H. R. Barton, *J. Chem. Soc.*, *1949*, 2174; E. R. Alexander and A. Mudrak, *J. Am. Chem. Soc.*, *72*, 1810 (1950).

[88] G. E. McCasland, *J. Am. Chem. Soc.*, *73*, 2293 (1951).

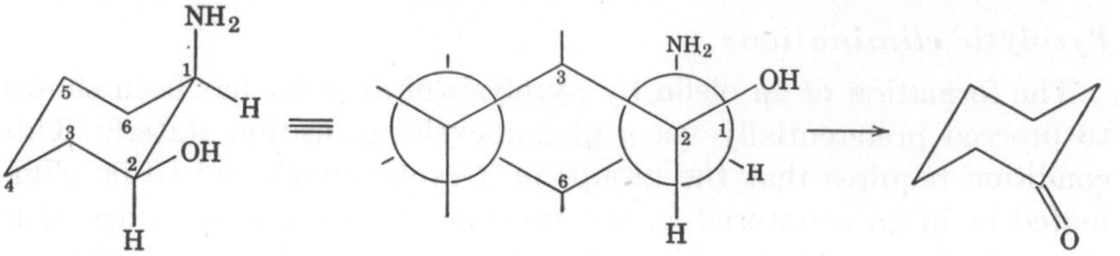

LXXIVa

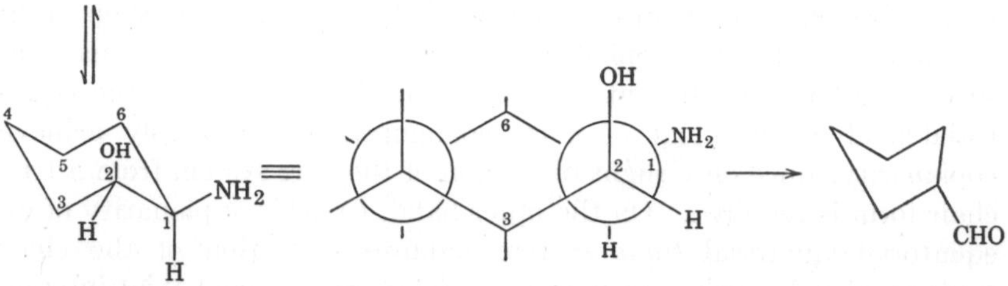

LXXIVb

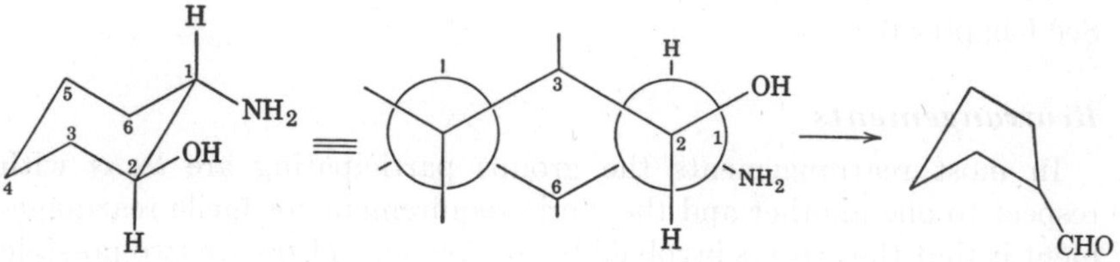

LXXV

In the *cis* isomer two *e, a* conformations of about equal energy exist and two products are obtained. From the diagram it is seen that, for a preferred planar transition state when the departing group is axial, the adjacent axial hydrogen atom is best suited for migration, whereas, when the amino group is equatorial, the ring carbon atom fulfills the requirement. In the *trans* isomer, since the diequatorial is energetically favored over the diaxial conformation, the molecule will preferably react with the amino group in the equatorial conformation, and it is seen here again that the ring carbon atom is that which best forms a *trans*, planar transition state.

Miscellaneous

In addition to the above generalizations, some specific rules have been developed that apply only to certain reactions or groupings, and it might be of interest to present a few examples. First, it has been shown that, when an alicyclic amine of equatorial conformation is deaminated with nitrous acid, the resulting alcohol is of equatorial conformation, whereas, when the amino group is axial, the major product also is the equatorial isomer.[45, 46, 60, 89] Second, it has been found that alcohols of equatorial conformation are absorbed more strongly [90] on paper in chromatography than their axial epimers. Third, in steroidal systems it has been shown that, for alcohols,[91] the band in the infrared at 1000 cm.$^{-1}$ is dependent upon the conformation of the hydroxyl group, being 1030–1040 cm.$^{-1}$ when equatorial and 1000–1010 cm.$^{-1}$ when axial. Furthermore, it has been shown that the bands at 1240 cm.$^{-1}$ for the acetates of these alcohols also are affected by conformation, the band being composed of a single maximum for the equatorial and a series of maxima for the axial. These generalizations are not directly applicable to less complex cyclic compounds like the 2-decalols.[92]

QUANTITATIVE ENERGY VALUES

In order to simplify the preceding sections, the more detailed consideration and the tabulation of quantitative energy values were postponed to this point. For many purposes the order of magnitude or even the sign of the given energy difference is sufficient to allow useful conclusions to be drawn. The more detailed knowledge of the energy of various conformations and of intermediate orientations, however, is needed for the complete understanding of the properties of the molecule.

Conformation energies

Conformations (as defined here) constitute definite chemical species which, however, are not separable by presently available methods. Nevertheless, any rapid physical method of analysis can, in principle, yield a measurement of the concentration of a given conformation. The method which has been used most extensively depends on the Raman or the infrared spectrum.

[89] J. A. Mills, *J. Chem. Soc., 1953*, 260; A. K. Bose, *Experientia, 8*, 458 (1952); *9*, 256 (1953).

[90] K. Savard, *J. Biol. Chem., 202*, 457 (1953).

[91] R. N. Jones, P. Humphries, F. Herling, and K. Dobriner, *J. Am. Chem. Soc., 75*, 3215 (1951); A. R. H. Cole, R. N. Jones, and K. Dobriner, *ibid., 74*, 5571 (1951); A. Furst, H. H. Kuhn, R. Scotoni, and Hs. H. Gunthard, *Helv. Chim. Acta, 35*, 951 (1952); H. Rosenkrantz, A. T. Milhorat, and M. Farber, *J. Biol. Chem., 195*, 509 (1952).

[92] W. G. Dauben, E. Hoerger, and N. K. Freeman, *J. Am. Chem. Soc., 74*, 5206 (1952).

It was shown [93] that in many 1,2 disubstituted ethanes the spectrum of the liquid contained bands from two conformations (see Fig. 2 and adjoining text), while in the solid the bands of only one conformation remained. Thus the bands associated with each conformation may be selected unequivocally. Although it is difficult to obtain the absolute intensities of Raman bands, the relative intensity of a *trans* band and a *gauche* or skew band yields a measure of the relative concentration of the two conformations. Thus for the reaction

$$trans\ CH_2X\!\!-\!\!CH_2Y = gauche\ CH_2X\!\!-\!\!CH_2Y$$

$$K = (\text{constant})\ [I_g/I_t]$$

where K is the usual equilibrium constant and I is the appropriate measure of intensity of the given Raman band.

If these measurements are made as function of temperature,[94] the heat of reaction may be obtained from the equation

$$\Delta H = R\,\frac{d \ln K}{d(1/T)} = R\,\frac{d \ln (I_g/I_t)}{d(1/T)}$$

Most of the values in Table II were obtained by methods equivalent to the one just described, although, for a few, more complex calculations were used to obtain the heat from less closely related experimental data.

In addition to the values given in Table II for acyclic compounds, there are some relatively accurate values for the cyclohexane system. The values for methylcyclohexane were given earlier. Winstein and Holness [95] have obtained a number of additional conformational free-energy differences for the cyclohexane system. They used the *t*-butyl group to fix the conformation of cyclohexane compounds. It is assumed very reasonably that this grouping can exist only in the equatorial conformation as long as other substituents are relatively small. Thus, it is possible to determine the properties characteristic of various functional groups in the axial and equatorial positions (see p. 44). For example, *cis*-4-*t*-butylcyclohexanol may be assumed to have an equatorial *t*-butyl group and an axial hydroxyl group. Since the *t*-butyl group is in a remote location, the reactions of the hydroxyl

[93] K. W. F. Kohlrausch, *Z. physik. Chem.*, *B18*, 61 (1932), and many later papers by Kohlrausch and by S. Mizushima.

[94] A. Langseth and H. J. Bernstein, *J. Chem. Phys.*, *8*, 410 (1940).

[95] S. Winstein and N. J. Holness, *J. Am. Chem. Soc.*, *77*, 5562 (1955).

TABLE II

ENERGY DIFFERENCES BETWEEN CONFORMATIONS

Substance	State	Conformations	ΔH, cal./mole	Ref.
n-Butane	Liquid	trans → gauche	770 ± 90	a, b
n-Butane	Gas	trans → gauche	~800	c
n-Pentane	Liquid	trans → gauche	450 ± 60	b, j
n-Hexane	Liquid	trans → gauche	500 ± 70	b
n-Paraffin	Gas	trans → gauche	~500	d
1,2-Dichloroethane	Gas	trans → gauche	1140 ± 20	e, f, g
1,2-Dichloroethane	Liquid	trans → gauche	0 ± 50	e, i
1,2-Dibromoethane	Gas	trans → gauche	1700 ± 40	e, f, h
1,2-Dibromoethane	Liquid	trans → gauche	730 ± 50	e, i
1-Chloro-2-bromoethane	Gas	trans → gauche	1460 ± 30	e
1-Chloro-2-bromoethane	Liquid	trans → gauche	410 ± 50	e
Bromoacetyl chloride	Gas	trans → gauche	1000 ± 100	k
Bromoacetyl bromide	Gas	trans → gauche	1900 ± 300	k
n-C_5F_{12}	Liquid	trans → gauche	400 ± 100	l
2-Methylbutane	Gas	(t, g) * → (g, g) *	Large	m, o
1,1,2-Trichloroethane	Gas	(t, g) * → (g, g) *	>2300	n
2,3-Dimethylbutane	Gas	trans → gauche	0 ± 100	m, o
1,1,2,2-Tetrachloroethane	Gas	trans → gauche	0 ± 200	n
1,1,2,2-Tetrachloroethane	Liquid	trans → gauche	−1100	p
1,1,2,2-Tetrabromoethane	Liquid	trans → gauche	−910 ± 50	q

* The (t, g) or trans, gauche conformation contains the indicated relationships between methyl groups or chlorine atoms and has symmetry C_1. Likewise the (g, g) conformation has symmetry C_s.

a G. J. Szasz, N. Sheppard, and D. H. Rank, J. Chem. Phys., 16, 704 (1948).
b N. Sheppard and G. J. Szasz, ibid., 17, 86 (1949).
c K. S. Pitzer, ibid., 8, 711 (1940); also Chem. Revs., 27, 39 (1940).
d W. B. Person and G. C. Pimentel, J. Am. Chem. Soc., 75, 532 (1953).
e K. Kuratani, T. Miyazawa, and S. Mizushima, J. Chem. Phys., 21, 1411 (1953).
f W. D. Gwinn and K. S. Pitzer, ibid., 16, 303 (1948).
g H. J. Bernstein, ibid., 17, 258 (1949).
h H. J. Bernstein, ibid., 18, 897 (1950).
i D. H. Rank, R. E. Kagarise, and D. W. E. Oxford, ibid., 17, 1354 (1949).
j S. Mizushima and H. Okasaki, J. Am. Chem. Soc., 71, 3411 (1949).
k I. Nakagawa, I. Ichishima, K. Kuratani, T. Miyazawa, T. Simanouchi, and S. Mizushima, J. Chem. Phys., 20, 1720 (1952).
l G. J. Szasz, ibid., 18, 1417 (1950).
m D. W. Scott, J. P. McCullough, K. D. Williamson, and G. Waddington, J. Am. Chem. Soc., 73, 1707 (1951).
n J. R. Thomas and W. D. Gwinn, ibid., 71, 2785 (1949).
o N. Sheppard and G. J. Szasz, J. Chem. Phys., 18, 145 (1950).
p A. Langseth and H. J. Bernstein, ibid., 8, 410 (1940).
q R. E. Kagarise and D. H. Rank, Trans. Faraday Soc., 48, 394 (1952).

group should be those characteristic of an axial hydroxyl on cyclohexane.

Following the argument developed on p. 44, the relative concentration of equatorial and axial conformations in cyclohexanol, itself, can be evaluated. In Table III are given the values of the free-energy differences $(a - e)$ for various groups on a cyclohexane ring.

TABLE III

ΔF (Axial-Equatorial) for the Given Substituent on a Cyclohexane Ring

(Data for the given solvent at 25–50°)

Group	Solvent	$\Delta F\ (a - e)$, kcal./mole
t-C$_4$H$_9$	—	$\sim$5.4
i-C$_3$H$_7$	H$_2$O	3.3
n-C$_4$H$_9$	H$_2$O	2.1
n-C$_3$H$_7$	H$_2$O	2.1
C$_2$H$_5$	H$_2$O	2.1
CH$_3$	—	1.8
OTs	EtOH	1.7
OCOC$_6$H$_4$COO$^{\ominus}$	H$_2$O	1.2
OH	75% HOAc	0.8

Potential barriers

The heights of the potential maxima which separate the various conformations are also known quantitatively in some cases. These heights are essentially activation energies but are not obtained commonly from rate data because the rates of conversion are usually too fast for measurement. Rather, these barrier energies are usually inferred indirectly from the thermodynamic properties or from the spectral data on the torsional energy levels.

Since the potential function for an internal rotation must be periodic and must have certain symmetry properties it may be expanded in a Fourier series involving only cosine terms. Also it is convenient to arrange the terms so that the potential is zero at the lowest minimum. Thus we have

$$V(\phi) = \sum_{n=1}^{\infty} \tfrac{1}{2} V_n (1 - \cos n\phi)$$

In the rotation of a symmetrical group such as a methyl group, symmetry considerations eliminate many terms. Also, sparsity of experimental data may force the elimination of higher terms. Indeed most calculations have been made for the one-term formula

$$V(\phi) = \tfrac{1}{2}V_0(1 - \cos n\phi)$$

wherein V_0 is now the height of the barrier peaks above the minima and n is number of peaks (and minima) per revolution.

The procedure is to calculate by quantum mechanics the energy levels corresponding to the molecule at hand with the assumed potential barrier. If spectral data are available, the various V_n values may be adjusted until agreement is obtained. In the case of methyl chloroform [96] it was possible to evaluate two terms as follows: $V_3 = 2910$, $V_6 = 57$ cal./mole. In most cases only a single term is evaluated. For example, Dennison and his collaborators [97] have studied methyl alcohol very extensively and obtained $V_0 = 1072$ cal./mole.

In many cases internal rotational motion itself is inactive spectroscopically. It is still possible, however, to find the potential barrier from thermodynamic data. The equations of statistical mechanics permit the thermodynamic properties to be calculated from the energy level pattern. Indeed, general tables are available [98] which give the heat capacity or entropy as a function of the potential barrier height, the temperature, and such molecular properties as the moment of inertia and the number of minima per revolution.

It must be remembered that the observed thermodynamic properties are the sum over all types of motion that the molecule possesses. Thus the internal rotation can be studied by this method only after all other motions are well enough understood. The contributions of translation and of rotation of the entire molecule are large but are easily calculated with adequate accuracy. High-frequency vibrational motions make a negligible contribution at moderate temperatures. The problem usually lies in the assignment of the correct frequencies to all low-frequency vibrations of the molecule. Tables IV and V give two examples wherein the vibration frequencies are divided into the ranges 0–600 cm.$^{-1}$, 600–1200 cm.$^{-1}$, and above 1200 cm.$^{-1}$ It may also be noted that the medium-frequency vibrations (600–1200 cm.$^{-1}$) contribute much less to the entropy than to the heat capacity.

The data for ethane are more extensive than are given in Table IV. These have been evaluated elsewhere [99] in greater detail, and it was

[96] K. S. Pitzer and J. L. Hollenberg, *J. Am. Chem. Soc.*, *75*, 2219 (1953).

[97] E. V. Ivash and D. M. Dennison, *J. Chem. Phys.*, *21*, 1804 (1953), and preceding papers.

[98] K. S. Pitzer, *Quantum Chemistry*, section 9h and appendix 18, Prentice-Hall, New York, 1953.

[99] K. S. Pitzer, *Discussions Faraday Soc.*, *10*, 66 (1951).

TABLE IV

Thermodynamic Properties of Ethane and the Potential Barrier
Calculated Therefrom

(Units for C and S, cal./deg. mole; for V_0, cal./mole)

	C_v at		S at
	93.1°K.	193°K.	184.1°K.
Translation and rotation (overall)	5.961	5.961	48.634
Vibration			
5 modes (600–1200 cm.$^{-1}$)	0.002	0.439	0.058
12 modes (above 1200 cm.$^{-1}$)	0.000	0.030	0.000
Total, less internal rotation	5.963	6.430	48.692
Experimental value	6.51	8.02	49.54
Internal rotation term	0.55	1.59	0.85
Barrier height V_0	2750	2870	2830

TABLE V

Entropy of Methyl Chloroform and the Potential Barrier
Calculated Therefrom

	S at 286.5°K.
Translation	40.38 cal./deg. mole
Rotation (overall)	25.60
Vibration	
6 modes (less than 600 cm.$^{-1}$)	8.03
5 modes (600–1200 cm.$^{-1}$)	0.04
6 modes (above 1200 cm.$^{-1}$)	0.00
Total, less internal rotation	74.05
Experimental value	76.22 ± 0.16
Internal rotation term	2.17
Barrier height V_0	2940 ± 300 cal./mole

concluded that the one-term cosine formula was satisfactory with $V_0 = 2875 \pm 125$ cal./mole. Also it should be noted that spectral data, as mentioned above, give a more precise value for methyl chloroform.

In Table VI are given values of the barrier height V_0 for a number of substances.

TABLE VI

BARRIER HEIGHTS FOR INTERNAL ROTATION

Substance	n	V_0, cal./mole	Ref.
$H_3C—CH_3$	3	2875 ± 125	a
$H_3C—CF_3$	3	3000 ± 200	b
$H_3C—CCl_3$	3	2910	c
$H_3C—C_2H_3$	3	1950	d
$H_3C—C_6H_5$	6	500 ± 500	e
$H_3C—C≡C—CH_3$	3	<500	f
$H_3C—C≡C—CF_3$	3	<1200	g
$H_3C—OH$	3	1072	h
$H_3C—SH$	3	1460 ± 270	i
$H_3C—SiH_3$	3	1300 ± 300	j
$H_3C—OCH_3$	3	3100 (av.)	k
$H_3C—SCH_3$	3	2000 (av.)	l
$H_3C—CHO$	3	1000	m
$H_3C—NO_2$	6	6.00 ± 0.30	n

a K. S. Pitzer, *Discussions Faraday Soc.*, *10*, 66 (1951).

b H. S. Gutowsky and H. B. Levine, *J. Chem. Phys.*, *18*, 1297 (1950).

c K. S. Pitzer and J. L. Hollenberg, *J. Am. Chem. Soc.*, *75*, 2219 (1953).

d J. E. Kilpatrick and K. S. Pitzer, *J. Research Natl. Bur. Standards*, *37*, 163 (1946).

e K. S. Pitzer and D. W. Scott, *J. Am. Chem. Soc.*, *65*, 803 (1943).

f G. B. Kistiakowsky and W. W. Rice, *J. Chem. Phys.*, *8*, 618 (1940); D. M. Yost, D. W. Osborne, and C. S. Garner, *J. Am. Chem. Soc.*, *63*, 3492 (1941).

g B. Bak, L. Hansen, and J. Rastrup-Andersen, *J. Chem. Phys.*, *21*, 1612 (1953).

h E. V. Ivash and D. M. Dennison, *ibid.*, *21*, 1804 (1953).

i H. Russell, Jr., D. W. Osborne, and D. M. Yost, *J. Am. Chem. Soc.*, *64*, 165 (1942).

j D. R. Lide and D. K. Coles, *Phys. Rev.*, *80*, 911 (1950).

k R. M. Kennedy, M. Sagenkahn, and J. G. Aston, *J. Am. Chem. Soc.*, *63*, 2267 (1941).

l D. W. Osborne, R. N. Doescher, and D. M. Yost, *ibid.*, *64*, 169 (1942).

m K. S. Pitzer and W. Weltner, Jr., *ibid.*, *71*, 2842 (1949).

n E. Tannenbaum, R. D. Johnson, R. J. Myers, and W. D. Gwinn, *J. Chem. Phys.*, *22*, 949 (1954).

Multiple internal rotations

Many new problems arise when there are two or more internal rotations in the same molecule. It is beyond the scope of this section to discuss them all.[100] In the simplest case, the two or more rotating

[100] See reference 94 and the following papers for more extensive discussion of multiple rotation problems: J. F. Kilpatrick and K. S. Pitzer, *J. Chem. Phys.*, *17*, 1064 (1949); K. S. Pitzer, *ibid.*, *14*, 239 (1946); K. S. Pitzer and W. D. Gwinn, *ibid.*, *10*, 428 (1942).

groups are light and widely separated in the molecule. Examples include *trans*-2-butene, *p*-xylene, and mesitylene. In these cases one may ignore interactions between the various internal rotations in fair approximation.

In *cis*-2-butene the two methyl groups are sufficiently close together that there can be interference between the hydrogen atoms in certain positions, as is apparent in Figs. 13, 14, and 15. Thus it is not sur-

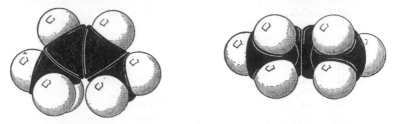

FIG. 13.   *Cis*-2-butene, both methyls staggered with respect to double bond.

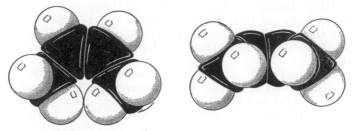

FIG. 14.   *Cis*-2-butene, both methyls staggered with respect to single bond.

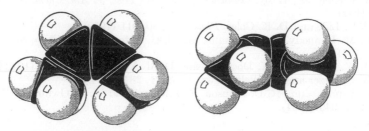

FIG. 15.   *Cis*-2-butene, alternate methyl group staggering.

prising that the energy content (at 0°K.) of *cis*-2-butene is 1.29 kcal./mole higher than that of the *trans* isomer. More surprising initially is the fact that the restriction to methyl group rotation is less in *cis*- than in *trans*-2-butene. In both, the data are from thermodynamics and include both entropies and heat capacities. For the *trans* isomer, the data are consistent with simple cosine potential barriers of 1950 cal./mole for each methyl group, and this value agrees with that found for the single rotation in propylene. If the thermodynamic data on *cis*-2-butene are arbitrarily interpreted on the basis of two independent rotations subject to simple cosine barriers, then a barrier height of 450 cal./mole is obtained.

There is no simple basis for decision as to the location of the potential minimum for the single methyl rotation in propylene. However, if we use also the data for the 2-butenes, then a conclusion is possible. The value for the *trans* isomer merely confirms the absence of differences from propylene unless there is actual interference between the hydrogen atoms of the rotating groups.

The potential minimum for a methyl adjacent to a double bond may be either staggered with respect to the single bond (LXXVI) or

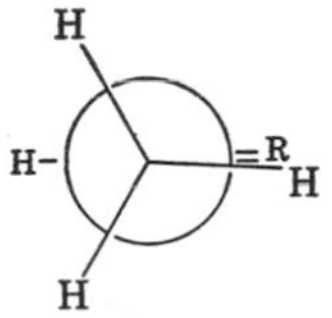

LXXVI 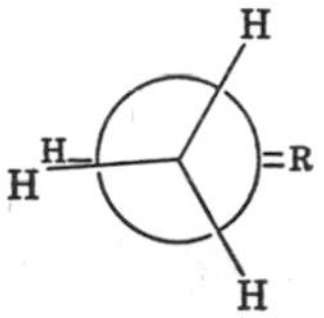   LXXVII

the double bond (LXXVII). Referring back now to Figs. 13, 14, and 15 for *cis*-2-butene, one can see that if LXXVII were the low energy position for a single group then the orientation in Fig. 13 should be an essentially strain free conformation for the whole molecule. In that event the hindrance apparent in the orientation in Fig. 15 should increase the restriction to rotation as compared to independent methyl groups, in contrast to the observed facts.

With the alternate assumption of LXXVI as the low energy position for a single methyl group, then the interference apparent in the orientation in Fig. 15 for *cis*-2-butene will have the effect of raising the energy of the potential minimum whereas the energy of the maxima are left unchanged. This is in agreement with the observed results that the restriction of rotation is decreased as compared to propylene and *trans*-2-butene and with the higher overall energy content of the *cis* isomer.

It seems safe to conclude that methyl groups adjacent to a C=C double bond have their potential minimum in the position staggered with respect to the single bond and opposed to the double bond. This result is consistent with the strain energy data on unsaturated ring molecules such as cyclopentene, cyclohexene, cyclopentadiene and 1,3-cyclohexadiene.

Although values of average apparent potential barriers could be given for many molecules having multiple rotations, it is apparent that the interpretation of such data is complicated and requires particular consideration of the special circumstances in each case. Consequently, potential energy data from single internal rotations should be taken for molecular structure discussions whenever possible.

Chapter 2

by *Ernest L. Eliel*

Substitution at Saturated Carbon Atoms

INTRODUCTION

NUCLEOPHILIC SUBSTITUTION

Duality of Mechanism
Stereochemistry
The S_N1 Reaction—Polar and Solvent Effects
The S_N1 Reaction—Steric Effects
The S_N2 Reaction—Polar and Steric Effects
The S_Ni Reaction
General Survey
Alternation Effects in Nucleophilic Displacement Reactions

FREE-RADICAL SUBSTITUTION

Optical Stability of Free Radicals
Mechanistic Types in Free Radical Reactions
The Stereochemistry of Catalytic Reductions
Steric Effects in Free-Radical Reactions
Steric Effects in Oxidation Reactions

STERIC INFLUENCES ON THE REACTIVITY OF ANIONS

Optical Stability of Carbanions
Steric Effects Involving Anions and Other Bases
61

Chapter 2

INTRODUCTION

This chapter is concerned with reactions of the type $RR'R''CX + Y \rightarrow YCRR'R'' + X$ regardless of the detailed mechanism of this transformation. The main effect of steric factors in such reactions is on the rate of substitution, which depends on the difference in free energy between the ground state and the transition state and is independent of the energy of the final state (product), except in so far as free-energy effects in the final state may also manifest themselves in the transition state.[1a] Any effect (steric or polar) that tends to destabilize the transition state only will retard the rate of the reaction under consideration by increasing the activation energy; in contrast an effect which destabilizes the ground state only (thus bringing its energy level closer to that of the transition state) will decrease the activation energy and therefore increase reaction rate.[1b] Thus steric effects may either slow down a reaction ("steric hindrance") or make it easier ("steric assistance" [1b]), notwithstanding the fact that, unlike polar effects, steric effects (at least primary ones *) generally destabilize a given state (ground or transition) rather than stabilize it.

In many cases of substitution at saturated carbon atoms, a clean-cut distinction between polar and steric factors does not appear possible at present (see Chapter 13 for attempts to make such a distinction in certain instances). Therefore polar factors as well as steric factors will frequently be discussed in this chapter. On occasions, the relative importance of the two factors is either not well understood or even highly controversial; in such cases both factors will be presented and

[1a] G. S. Hammond, *J. Am. Chem. Soc.*, **77**, 334 (1955).

[1b] The idea that reaction may be *assisted* as well as hindered by steric factors was first clearly implied by H. C. Brown, *Science*, **103**, 385 (1946).

* By "primary steric effect" is meant one which affects the energy level of the ground or transition state *directly* rather than by modification of an already existing polar factor.

an evaluation of their relative importance attempted in the light of all experimental evidence that appears relevant.

Substitution reactions at saturated carbon atoms are usually divided into nucleophilic substitution reactions, electrophilic substitution reactions (carbanion reactions), and homolytic or free-radical substitution reactions, depending on whether the carbon atom at which substitution occurs bears a positive (or partly positive) charge, a negative charge, or is electrically neutral. This division will be used here, nucleophilic reactions being dealt with first because of their importance, and because steric effects in nucleophilic substitution have been studied much more extensively and are understood much better than corresponding effects in the other two types of substitution reaction.

There is another way of subdividing substitution reactions at saturated carbon atoms, using the geometry of the transition state as a criterion rather than the nature of the charge distribution. Thus the reaction of $CRR'R''X$ with Y may involve either a separation of X [1c] followed by combination of the intermediate so formed with Y (path A) or X may disengage itself simultaneously as Y forms the new bond (path B). These hypothetical paths differ in that in path A only three groups are bonded to the central carbon atom in the transition state, but in path B five atoms are so bonded.[2] (In both cases the central

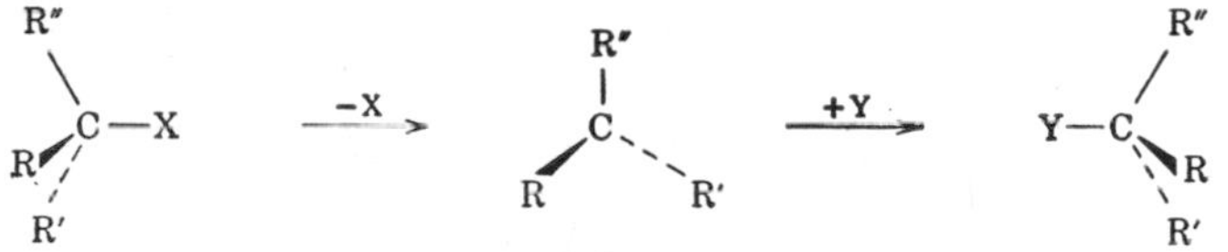

Path A

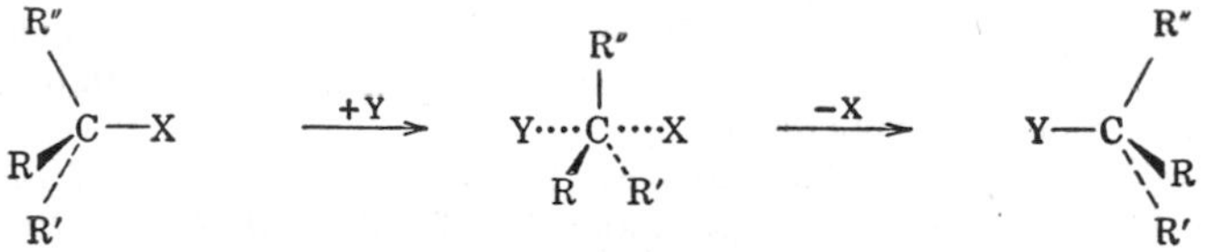

Path B

carbon atom and the groups R, R', and R'' are coplanar in the activated complex.) Accordingly, steric effects in the transition state would be expected to be much more significant in path B than in path A. Whether these two paths represent actual reaction mechanisms, or

[1c] Separation of X may involve its combination with solvent, reagent, or catalyst.

[2] For a possible interpretation of the unusual pentacovalent state of the central carbon atom in path B, see R. J. Gillespie, *J. Chem. Soc.*, *1952*, 1002; M. J. S. Dewar, *ibid.*, *1953*, 2885; H. H. Jaffé, *J. Chem. Phys.*, *21*, 1618, 1893 (1953).

whether they are only hypothetical extremes (the actual reaction path being intermediate between the two) is as yet undecided. In any event nucleophilic displacement reactions may proceed by paths resembling either A or B, while free-radical and carbanion displacement reactions usually proceed by path A (although in a few reactions there is evidence for path B). It follows that steric effects are of much greater significance in nucleophilic displacement reactions than in the other two types; this is another reason why nucleophilic substitution is considered first.

NUCLEOPHILIC SUBSTITUTION

Duality of mechanism

Although systematic quantitative data on substitution reactions have been available for over half a century,[3] rationalization of the data has come about only since the 1930's, largely as the result of the pioneering work of Polanyi [4] and Hughes and Ingold [4] and their respective schools.

Nucleophilic substitution reactions are of four different types, depending on the charge of the displacing group Y and the group displaced X (see introduction), namely:

(i) $$Y^- + R_3CX \rightarrow YCR_3 + X^-$$

(ii) $$Y + R_3CX \rightarrow YCR_3^+ + X^-$$

(iii) $$Y^- + R_3CX^+ \rightarrow YCR_3 + X$$

(iv) [5] $$Y + R_3CX^+ \rightarrow YCR_3^+ + X$$

[3] The earlier literature has been reviewed by E. Wilson, *Chem. Revs.*, *16*, 149 (1935). This review also reveals how little the experimental data were understood in the early 1930's. One of the earliest quantitative studies appears to be that of J. Wislicenus, *Ann.*, *212*, 239 (1882).

[4] Early references: (a) N. Meer and M. Polanyi, *Z. physik. Chem.*, *19B*, 164 (1932); (b) E. D. Hughes, C. K. Ingold, and C. S. Patel, *J. Chem. Soc.*, *1933*, 526. Much of the work of Polanyi's school has been summarized by (c) A. G. Evans, *The Reactions of Organic Halides in Solution*, Manchester University Press, Manchester, England, 1946, and *Trans. Faraday Soc.*, *42*, 719 (1946). Hughes and Ingold have summarized the work of their school at frequent intervals; for more recent discussions see (d) E. D. Hughes, *Quart. Revs. London*, *5*, 245 (1951), and (e) C. K. Ingold, *Structure and Mechanism in Organic Chemistry*, Cornell University Press, Ithaca, N. Y., 1953, Chapter 7.

[5] Notwithstanding widely held views to the contrary, reactions of this type have been known for a long time, e.g., J. von Braun, M. Kühn, and O. Goll, *Ber.*, *59*, 2330 (1926). Cf. J. H. Brewster and E. L. Eliel in R. Adams' *Organic Reactions*, Vol. 7, Chapter 3, p. 138, John Wiley & Sons, New York, 1953.

Examples are

(i) $$C_2H_5Br + I^- \rightarrow C_2H_5I + Br^-$$

(ii) $$C_6H_5CH_2N(CH_3)_2 + CH_3I \rightarrow C_6H_5CH_2\overset{+}{N}(CH_3)_3I^-$$

(iii) $$C_6H_5CH_2\overset{+}{N}C_5H_5 + C_2H_5O^- \rightarrow C_6H_5CH_2OC_2H_5 + C_5H_5N$$

(iv) $$C_6H_5CH_2\overset{+}{N}(CH_3)_3 + C_6H_5CH_2NH_2 \rightarrow$$

$$(C_6H_5CH_2)_2\overset{+}{N}H_2 + N(CH_3)_3$$

Despite the superficial difference in these four charge types, they are all nucleophilic in that the C—X bond breaks so as to leave the electron pair of the bond with the atom or group X while Y contributes the electron pair of the new C—Y bond. Moreover, the steric effects in the four types are so similar that they can all be considered together for the present purpose.

In contradistinction, there is another type of division of nucleophilic displacement reactions, more significant from the steric point of view, according to whether the reaction takes place in two stages (path A, p. 63) or in one stage (path B, p. 63). This division was first made by Hughes and Ingold, who labeled the two-stage reaction S_N1 and the one-stage reaction S_N2 (the numerals 1 and 2 designate unimolecular and bimolecular reactions, respectively).[6] Since this definition of S_N1 and S_N2 is a mechanistic rather than an operational one, it had to be supplemented by a set of rules of how the S_N1 or S_N2 nature of a given displacement was to be established experimentally, e.g., by kinetic or optical criteria, solvent effects, etc.[7] Unfortunately, the application of the various criteria sometimes does not give a consistent answer as to the nature of the reaction. This may be because in a given reaction some molecules undergo substitution via path A and others via path B, or it may be that some path intermediate between A and B is actually followed by all molecules. Both points of view have been affirmed by different investigators and at different times.[8]

[6] For a detailed discussion, see C. K. Ingold, reference 4e, Chapter 7. A somewhat briefer discussion by P. D. Bartlett is found in Chapter 1, Vol. 3 of H. Gilman's *Organic Chemistry*, pp. 25–45, John Wiley & Sons, New York, 1953. The reader is referred to these chapters for essential background information.

[7] Ingold, reference 4e, has a thorough discussion of these criteria.

[8] (a) E. D. Hughes and C. K. Ingold, *Trans. Faraday Soc.*, 37, 657 (1941); (b) S. Winstein, E. Grunwald, and H. W. Jones, *J. Am. Chem. Soc.*, 73, 2700 (1951); (c) C. G. Swain, *Rec. Chem. Progr. Kresge-Hooker Sci. Lib.*, 12, 21 (1951); (d) C. G. Swain and W. P. Langsdorf, *J. Am. Chem. Soc.*, 73, 2813 (1951); (e) D. A.

The controversy cannot be entered upon here; however, since path A (the S_N1 mechanism) and path B (the S_N2 mechanism) show rather different behavior from the point of view of steric effects, the two mechanisms will be dealt with separately in the following, with the realization that intermediate behavior may sometimes be encountered.

Stereochemistry

As a general rule,[9] the S_N2 process involves inversion of configuration at the central carbon atom ("Walden inversion") and the S_N1 process involves some inversion accompanied by more or less extensive racemization.[9] Since this subject has been summarized in several other places,[10] only a few select examples, such as Walden inversion at primary and at tertiary centers and Walden inversion involving onium ions, can be discussed here.

WALDEN INVERSION AT PRIMARY AND AT TERTIARY CARBON ATOMS. Displacement reactions of the S_N2 type involve inversion not only when the central carbon atom is secondary [11] but when it is primary as well. Experimental verification of this fact was delayed by the obvious difficulty of inducing asymmetry at a primary center, but was realized in 1953 by a study of optically active deuterium compounds of the type RCHDX. Thus, 1-deuterobutanol, n-C_3H_7CHDOH, synthesized in optically active form by asymmetric reduction of n-butyraldehyde with optically active 2-deuterooctanol-2 in a reaction of the Meerwein-Ponndorf type,[12] has been converted to active 1-deutero-1-bromobutane by means of phosphorus tribromide. The bromo-

---

Brown and R. F. Hudson, *J. Chem. Soc.*, *1953*, 3352; (*f*) M. L. Bird, E. D. Hughes, and C. K. Ingold, *J. Chem. Soc.*, *1954*, 634; (*g*) E. Gelles, E. D. Hughes, and C. K. Ingold, *J. Chem. Soc.*, *1954*, 2918; (*h*) V. Gold, J. Hilton, and E. G. Jefferson, *J. Chem. Soc.*, *1954*, 2756; (*i*) M. F. Hawthorne and D. J. Cram, *J. Am.* Chem. Soc., *76*, 3451 (1954); (*j*) C. G. Swain and R. B. Mosely, *ibid.*, *77*, 3727 (1955).

[9] Reference 4e, pp. 377, 381.

[10] E.g., K. Freudenberg and Th. Wagner-Jauregg in K. Freudenberg's *Stereochemie*, Vol. 2, Chapters 3 and 8, Franz Deuticke, Leipzig, Germany, 1932; R. L. Shriner and R. Adams in Gilman's *Organic Chemistry*, Vol. 1, Chapter 4, p. 264, John Wiley & Sons, New York, 1943; E. E. Turner in E. H. Rodd's *Chemistry of Carbon Compounds*, Vol. 1A, p. 107, Elsevier Publishing Co., New York, 1951; C. K. Ingold, reference 4e, p. 372; W. Klyne, *Progress in Stereochemistry*, pp. 94, 194, Butterworths Publications, London, 1954.

[11] Ingold, reference 10; J. Kenyon, *Bull. soc. chim. France*, *1951*, 64C; H. Phillips, *J. Chem. Soc.*, *123*, 44 (1923); J. Kenyon and H. Phillips, *Trans. Faraday Soc.*, *26*, 451 (1930); E. D. Hughes, F. Juliusburger, S. Masterman, B. Topley, and J. Weiss, *J. Chem. Soc.*, *1935*, 1525; E. D. Hughes, F. Juliusburger, A. D. Scott, B. Topley, and J. Weiss, *J. Chem. Soc.*, *1936*, 1173; W. A. Cowdrey, E. D. Hughes, T. P. Nevell, and C. L. Wilson, *J. Chem. Soc.*, *1938*, 209.

[12] A. Streitwieser, *J. Am. Chem. Soc.*, *75*, 5014 (1953).

butane was racemized by boiling with a solution of lithium bromide
in acetone [12] at a rate equal to that observed in the reaction of n-butyl
bromide with radioactive bromide ion under the same conditions.[13]
It follows that the displacement of the organic bromide by bromide
ion involves rearward attack. Walden inversion has also been demonstrated for the reaction of the p-toluenesulfonate of optically active
1-deuteroethanol with base.[14] The active alcohol was synthesized
enzymatically and converted to the tosylate. It was shown by enzy-
matic methods that the alcohol resulting from the reaction of the
tosylate with sodium hydroxide had a configuration opposite to that
of the starting material.

Displacement at tertiary centers may also involve substantial inversion.[15] Thus, reaction of the resolved acid phthalate of 2,4-dimethyl-
4-hexanol (I) with methanol gives the methyl ether of 2,4-dimethyl-
4-hexanol with at least 76% inversion of configuration, the reaction
being one in which the nucleophilic reagent (methanol) breaks the
alkyl-oxygen bond of the rather hindered ester.[15a] Replacement of

the isobutyl group in compound I by a phenyl group leads to a considerable increase (from 48% or less to 88% or more) of racemization
in the methanolysis,[16] presumably owing to greater stability of the

carbonium ion $C_6H_5\overset{+}{C}\overset{CH_3}{\underset{C_2H_5}{}}$ due to resonance.

[13] L. J. Le Roux and S. Sugden, *J. Chem. Soc.*, *1939*, 1279.

[14] F. A. Loewus, F. H. Westheimer, and B. Vennesland, *J. Am. Chem. Soc.*, *75*, 5018 (1953); see also A. Streitwieser, *ibid.*, *77*, 1117 (1955).

[15] (a) W. v. Doering and H. H. Zeiss, *J. Am. Chem. Soc.*, *75*, 4733 (1953). (b) See also E. D. Hughes, C. K. Ingold, R. J. L. Martin, and D. F. Meigh, *Nature*, *166*, 679 (1950); C. A. Bunton, E. D. Hughes, C. K. Ingold, and D. F. Meigh, *ibid.*, *166*, 680 (1950).

[16] H. H. Zeiss, *J. Am. Chem. Soc.*, *75*, 3154 (1953).

WALDEN INVERSION IN REACTIONS OF ONIUM SALTS. The illustration on p. 63 for the geometry of the S_N2 reaction involves maximum separation of the incoming group Y and the outgoing group X. In reactions of charge-type i (p. 64), both X and Y are negatively charged, and it was believed at one time that electrostatic repulsion of the two groups was responsible for their separation. That this is not so has since been demonstrated by a consideration of reactions of charge type iii (reaction of onium salts with bases) and of charge type ii (the Menshutkin reaction); such reactions also involve Walden inversion. Thus the decomposition of optically active N,N,N-trimethyl-α-phenylethylammonium acetate gives rise to α-phenylethyl acetate with 98–100% inversion.[17]

$$
\begin{array}{c}
\text{H} \\
| \\
\text{C}_6\text{H}_5\overset{|}{\text{C}}\text{CH}_3 \\
| \\
\text{N(CH}_3)_3{}^+
\end{array}
\quad + \text{ OAc}^- \longrightarrow
\begin{array}{c}
\text{OAc} \\
| \\
\text{C}_6\text{H}_5\overset{|}{\text{C}}\text{CH}_3 \; + \; \text{N(CH}_3)_3 \\
| \\
\text{H}
\end{array}
$$

Inversion was also observed in the reaction of α-phenylethyl bromide with dimethyl sulfide and in the decomposition of the resulting sulfonium bromide.[18a] Other examples have been reported.[18b]

$$
\begin{array}{c}
\text{H} \\
| \\
\text{C}_6\text{H}_5\overset{|}{\text{C}}\text{CH}_3 \; + \; \text{(CH}_3)_2\text{S} \longrightarrow \\
| \\
\text{Br}
\end{array}
\quad
\begin{array}{c}
\text{S(CH}_3)_2{}^+\text{Br}^- \\
| \\
\text{C}_6\text{H}_5\overset{|}{\text{C}}\text{CH}_3 \longrightarrow \\
| \\
\text{H}
\end{array}
$$

$$
\begin{array}{c}
\text{H} \\
| \\
\text{C}_6\text{H}_5\overset{|}{\text{C}}\text{CH}_3 \; + \; \text{(CH}_3)_2\text{S} \\
| \\
\text{Br}
\end{array}
$$

It is somewhat unfortunate that in all these examples either X or Y (though not both) are still negatively charged, so that the geometry of the transition state may have been conditioned by the ion-dipole repulsion of Y$^-$ and the Lewis base X (or X$^-$ and the Lewis base Y). It would still seem desirable to undertake an optical study of a reaction of charge-type iv (p. 64) in which *neither* X *nor* Y bears a negative charge.

[17] H. R. Snyder and J. H. Brewster, *J. Am. Chem. Soc.*, **71**, 291 (1949). For a possible explanation of the complete racemization observed in the reaction of the quaternary ammonium acetate with the anion of malonic ester described in the same reference see J. H. Brewster and E. L. Eliel, reference 5.

[18] (a) S. Siegel and A. F. Graefe, *J. Am. Chem. Soc.*, **75**, 4521 (1953); (b) J. Read and J. Walker, *J. Chem. Soc.*, **1934**, 308; S. H. Harvey, E. D. Hughes, and C. K. Ingold quoted in reference 4e, p. 380.

The S_N1 reaction—polar and solvent effects

Among the factors that determine whether a displacement reaction will follow the S_N1 mechanism and, if so, at what rate, are stability of the carbonium ion intermediate, solvation of the ion, and destabilization of the ground state due to steric factors. The first factor has been discussed extensively elsewhere.[4c, 4e] Inductive, resonance, and hyperconjugation effects seem to be most significant in the stabilization of the carbonium ion. Regarding solvent effects, it has been pointed out [19] that in reactions of charge type i and ii (p. 64) solvation of the carbonium ion greatly increases reaction rate in S_N1 reactions. It is therefore important to establish a measure of "solvating power" of a given solvent; this has been done by Grunwald and Winstein, who use $Y = \log k/k_0$ as an index of solvating power, where k_0 is the rate of solvolysis of t-butyl chloride in 80% ethanol-water and k is the rate of solvolysis of the same halide in the given solvent. Y values for a number of solvents and solvent mixtures [20] are listed in Table I; from the definition it follows that the "best" solvents (i.e., those best able to solvate the carbonium ion) have the highest positive Y value. A similar measure of solvating power is given in Table II, which lists relative rates (and their logarithms) of quaternization of tertiary amines with alkyl halides in a variety of solvents.[21]

TABLE I

Solvent	Y-Value [20]	Relative Rate *
Ethanol	−2.03	0.0093
90% dioxane	−2.03	0.0093
90% acetone	−1.85	0.014
Acetic acid	−1.64	0.023
Methanol	−1.09	0.081
90% ethanol	−0.78	0.17
80% ethanol	0.00	1.00
50% ethanol	+1.64	44
Formic acid	+2.08	120
Water	+3.56	3630

* Solvolysis rate of t-butyl chloride in given solvent relative to 80% ethanol taken as unity.

[19] E. D. Hughes, C. K. Ingold, et al., J. Chem. Soc., 1935, 252; 1948, 2043; summarized in reference 4e, pp. 345ff.; see also A. A. Frost and R. G. Pearson, Kinetics and Mechanism, pp. 121ff., John Wiley & Sons, New York, 1953.

[20] E. Grunwald and S. Winstein, J. Am. Chem. Soc., 70, 846 (1948); S. Winstein, private communication.

[21] L. Bock and P. deBenneville, Circular, Rohm & Haas Co., Philadelphia, Pa.; cf. N. Menschutkin, Z. physik. Chem., 6, 43 (1890); E. Tommila and P. Kauranen,

TABLE II

Relative Quaternization Rate [21]

Solvent	Number	log
Hexane	1.0	0.00
Diethyl ether	4.2	0.62
Benzene	38.2	1.58
Chloroform	100	2.00
Ethanol	203.3	2.31
Methanol	286.6	2.46
Acetone	337.7	2.53
Acetonitrile	373	2.57
Nitromethane	516	2.71
Dimethylformamide	975	2.99
Ethylene glycol	1290	3.11
Formamide	ca. 4000	ca. 3.60

Since solvation of the carbonium ion is important, at least in S_N1 reactions of charge type i and ii, steric inhibition of solvation should lead to a drop in rate. Although instances where such an effect is important have been observed (cf. Chapter 11), no clear-cut case of steric inhibition of solvation has been demonstrated in the displacement reaction, and the subject remains to be explored.

The S_N1 reaction—steric effects

Little is known about steric hindrance in the S_N1 reaction. The failure of triphenylmethyl bromide to react with triphenyl carbinol or with pyridine in benzene solution has been ascribed to inability of the carbinol or the base to form an ion pair with the bromide ion, owing to steric interference of the triphenylmethyl group.[22] Steric hindrance may be responsible for the high proportion of olefin found in the solvolysis products of highly branched trialkylcarbinyl halides; [23, 24b] here the bulk of the alkyl groups seems to prevent covalent combina-

Acta Chem. Scand., *8*, 1152 (1954). The reaction of tertiary amines with alkyl halides does not normally follow the S_N1 mechanism, but the solvent effects in this reaction are the same, at least qualitatively, as in S_N1 reactions of charge-type i and ii.

[22] (a) C. G. Swain, *J. Am. Chem. Soc.*, *70*, 1119 (1948). (b) See also H. A. Smith and G. Thompson, *ibid.*, *77*, 1778 (1955).

[23] (a) H. C. Brown and R. S. Fletcher, *J. Am. Chem. Soc.*, *72*, 1223 (1950); (b) H. C. Brown and H. L. Berneis, *ibid.*, *75*, 10 (1953); (c) H. C. Brown and R. B. Kornblum, *ibid.*, *76*, 4510 (1954).

[24] (a) H. C. Brown and R. S. Fletcher, *J. Am. Chem. Soc.*, *71*, 1845 (1949); (b) see also H. C. Brown and M. Nagakawa, *ibid.*, *77*, 3610, 3614 (1955), and H. C. Brown and Y. Okamoto, *ibid.*, *77*, 3619 (1955).

tion of the carbonium ion with the solvent to form alcohols. (See, however, reference 29. This matter is discussed in detail in Chapter 6.)

Steric assistance has been called on [23a, 24] to explain the abnormally fast rate of solvolysis of highly branched tertiary alkyl halides, according to the equation $RR'R''CCl + H_2O \rightarrow RR'R''COH$ + olefins + HCl. The rates, relative to t-butyl chloride taken as unity, are summarized in Table III.

TABLE III

RELATIVE RATES OF SOLVOLYSIS OF CHLORIDES $RR'R''CCl$

Entry No.	R	R'	R''	A	B	C
1	Me	Me	Me	1.00	1.00	1.00
2	Me	Me	Et, n-Pr, i-Pr, n-Bu, t-Bu, n-Am, 3-Me-2-Bu	0.87–1.67	0.86–1.61 [25]	1.8–2.5
3	Et	Et	Me, Et, i-Pr	1.73–3.00	2.0–2.60 [25]	—
4	Me	Me	t-Am	5.7 [23c]		—
5	Me	Me	Neopent	21 [23b]	—	—
6	Me	Et	t-Bu *	6.9 [23c]	—	—
7	Et	Et	t-Bu *	48.1; 12.0 †	(13.8 [27])	—
8	Me	i-Pr	i-Pr *	14	—	—
9	i-Pr	i-Pr	i-Pr *	—	—	5; 252 †
10	i-Pr	i-Pr	t-Bu *	—	—	1280
11	Me	t-Bu	t-Bu *	—	—	24; 27,900 †
12	i-Pr	t-Bu	t-Bu *	—	—	194; 450; 50,400 †
13	t-Bu	t-Bu	t-Bu *	—	590 [28]	136; 2700 †
14	Me	Neopent	Neopent	580 [23b]	—	—

A: at 25° in 80% ethanol; reference 24a unless otherwise indicated.
B: at 35° in 80% ethanol.
C: at 25° in 90% acetone; reference 26.

* Structure of alcohol from which chloride was prepared; see text.
† See text for reason why several figures appear here.

Thus, when the alkyl groups attached to the tertiary carbon bearing the halogen are not very branched (entries 1–3), the effect of structure on rate is slight; e.g., t-butyldimethylcarbinyl chloride, t-BuMe$_2$CCl, solvolyzes only 20% faster than t-butyl chloride, Me$_3$CCl.[24] The small acceleration *may* be due to polar causes,[25, 29] although this seems unexpected, in view of the fact that vinylogs of t-butyldimethylcarbinyl chloride, such as (t-butylethynyl)dimethylcarbinyl chloride, t-BuC≡CCMe$_2$Cl, and the corresponding vinyl compound,

[25] J. Shorter and C. Hinshelwood, *J. Chem. Soc.*, *1949*, 2412.

[26] P. D. Bartlett and M. S. Swain, *J. Am. Chem. Soc.*, 77, 2801 (1955).

[27] P. D. Bartlett and L. Knox, *J. Am. Chem. Soc.*, 61, 3184 (1939). Cf. reference 24a for correction.

[28] F. Brown, T. D. Davies, I. Dostrovsky, O. J. Evans, and E. D. Hughes, *Nature*, 167, 987 (1951).

[29] E. D. Hughes, C. K. Ingold, and V. J. Shiner, Jr., *J. Chem. Soc.*, *1953*, 3827. See, however, H. C. Brown and I. Moritani, *J. Am. Chem. Soc.*, 77, 3623 (1955).

t-BuCH=CHMe$_2$Cl, solvolyze *more slowly* than the homologous methyl compounds, MeC≡CCMe$_2$Cl and MeCH=CHCMe$_2$Cl (Table X, p. 86). One would expect any polar effect to be transmitted across the unsaturated system. Steric assistance (see below) is not so transmitted, of course, and therefore may provide a more satisfactory explanation of the observed order of solvolysis rates.[23, 24]

As the alkyl groups are more branched, the solvolysis rate increases markedly (entries 4, 6, and especially 5 and 7–14), in some cases to enormous values (entries 11, 12), although there is not necessarily an exact correlation between rate and degree of branching (compare 12 with 13). Two explanations have been suggested for this phenomenon. According to one,[29] solvolysis is assisted by neighboring group participation.[30] Rearrangements often accompany the formation of chlorides from highly branched tertiary alcohols, as evidenced by the presence of two and sometimes three chlorides in the product obtained by the action of hydrogen chloride on these alcohols (entries 7, 9, 11–13). Thus, not only are the structures of some of the chlorides in Table III in doubt, but also it is likely that further rearrangements might take place in the solvolysis reactions. In at least one instance where a p-nitrobenzoate of a highly branched alcohol was solvolyzed, the product was entirely a rearranged olefin; in this case at least rearrangement must have taken place during solvolysis of the ester rather than during its formation.[31] These rearrangements suggest anchimeric assistance, but do not prove it, since rearrangement may *follow* rather than accompany formation of the carbonium ion.

A more likely explanation of the enhanced solvolysis rates of highly branched halides is the strain caused by steric interference of the alkyl groups in a tertiary halide RR′R″CCl when the R groups are very bulky.[23, 24] This strain has been termed B strain (cf. Chapter 9) because it affects mainly the alkyl groups on the backside of the alkyl halide. B strain is relieved in the (trigonal) carbonium ion and therefore facilitates its formation from the (tetrahedral) halide. Anchimeric assistance may be a contributing factor to some of the high rates shown in Table III, but it should be noted that enhancement of solvolysis rate has been observed even where the absence of rearrangement has been demonstrated (entries 4–6).[32a]

[30] This effect is called "anchimeric assistance" by S. Winstein, C. R. Lindegren, H. Marshall, and L. Ingraham, *J. Am. Chem. Soc.*, **75**, 147 (1953), and "synartetic acceleration" by F. Brown, E. D. Hughes, C. K. Ingold, and J. F. Smith, *Nature*, **168**, 65 (1951).

[31] P. D. Bartlett and M. Stiles, *J. Am. Chem. Soc.*, **77**, 2806 (1955).

[32] (a) For an interesting discussion of the solvolysis of a hindered chloride (longibornyl chloride) derived from a sesquiterpene (longifolene) see P. P. Ourisson

Steric strain has also been suggested [32b] as a *contributing* factor to the well-established fact [32c] that alkyl iodides react faster than alkyl bromides in S_N1 reactions and bromides, in turn, react faster than chlorides. In support of this suggestion it is pointed out [32b] that the *ratio* of the solvolysis rate of a tertiary alkyl bromide or iodide, RR'R''CX (X = Br or I) to that of the corresponding chloride RR'R''CCl *increases* as the size of the R groups (and therefore the degree of interference of these groups with the halogen atom in the halide molecule) increases. The extreme variation of this ratio is from 39 for *t*-butyl to 63 for dimethylneopentylcarbinyl in the bromides, and from 100 for *t*-butyl to 237 for dimethyl-*t*-butylcarbinyl in the iodides.

The S_N2 reaction—polar and steric effects

Crowding in the transition state is more likely to occur in reaction path B (p. 63) than in path A. Therefore it is not surprising that steric hindrance is more common in S_N2 reactions than in S_N1. Thus it has long been known [33] that reactivity in the S_N2 reaction of A—X decreases in the series A = methyl > ethyl > *i*-propyl and is probably even less for A = *t*-butyl. For example, the following relative rates have been measured for the reaction of alkyl bromides with chloride ion: [34a] Me, 100; Et, 1.65; *i*-Pr, 0.022; *t*-Bu, 0.0048; and a similar sequence was established for the reaction of alkyl bromides with iodide,[34b] alkyl iodide with bromide,[34c] alkyl bromide with radioactive bromide ion,[34d] alkyl chloride with radioactive chloride,[34e] alkyl iodide with radioactive iodide,[34f] and alkyl iodide with chloride ion.[34g, 35]

---

and G. Ourisson, *Bull. soc. chim. France*, *1954*, 1415. (b) H. C. Brown and A. Stern, *J. Am. Chem. Soc.*, *72*, 5068 (1950). The major part of the increase in rate (which also occurs in S_N2 reactions) is attributed to the decrease in the carbon-halogen bond strength from chlorides to iodides. As has been pointed out in reference 4c, p. 18, the latter explanation by itself is not satisfactory, since the decrease in bond strength is more than compensated by the decrease in electron affinity and the solvation energy from chloride to iodide. (c) K. A. Cooper and E. D. Hughes, *J. Chem. Soc.*, *1937*, 1183; E. D. Hughes and U. G. Shapiro, *ibid.*, *1937*, 1177.

[33] For a summary, cf. reference 4e, pp. 316ff.

[34] (a) E. D. Hughes, C. K. Ingold, and J. H. D. Mackie, *J. Chem. Soc.*, *1955*, 3173. (b) L. Fowden, E. D. Hughes, and C. K. Ingold, *ibid.*, 3187. (c) *ibid.*, 3193. (d) P. D. B. de la Mare, *ibid.*, 3180. See also reference 34h. (e) *ibid.*, 3169. (f) *ibid.*, 3196. (g) E. D. Hughes, C. K. Ingold, and J. H. D. Mackie, *ibid.*, 3177. (The reader should not be misled by an error in the title and abstract of this paper.) (h) L. J. le Roux and E. R. Swart, *ibid.*, 1475.

[35] W. Reeve, E. L. McCaffery, and T. E. Kaiser, *J. Am. Chem. Soc.*, *76*, 2280 (1954).

Other investigators, while confirming the trend in the methyl, ethyl, i-propyl series, have reported a higher rate for t-butyl than for i-propyl: for example, in the reaction of alkyl chlorides with iodide,[36] of bromides with radiobromide,[37] and of iodides with radioiodide;[38] but these results may have been affected by the incursion of the S_N1 mechanism[34h, 39] or elimination reactions,[34g] or both.

Whether the drop in rate in the series methyl, ethyl, i-propyl, t-butyl is due to polar factors, to steric factors, or to a combination of the two is controversial. Polanyi has ascribed the entire effect to the crowding of the five groups attached to the central carbon atom in the transition state, i.e., to a steric factor.[4c, 40] Hughes and Ingold, on the other hand, calculate that the drop in rate is partly due to polar factors, since steric hindrance is insufficient to account for the entire effect.[4e, 41]

There appears to be no way of settling this point experimentally, since steric factors cannot be removed without changing the nature of the alkyl group, which, in turn, may affect the polar factors in an unpredictable way. However, there is much circumstantial evidence to suggest that polar factors in the series methyl, ethyl, i-propyl are too small and possibly not in the right direction to account for the observed drop in rate. Thus in the reaction of allyl chlorides $RR'C{=}CH{-}CH_2Cl$ with potassium iodide in acetone and sodium ethoxide in ethanol—reactions which would appear to be of the typical S_N2 type (see, however, reference 8d)—substitution of one or two methyl groups in the γ position (R and/or R' methyl instead of hydrogen) leads to an *increase* in rate (cf. Table IX, p. 84). Here the steric factor is excluded by the remoteness of the methyl groups from the site of the reaction, but the polar factors are presumably transmitted across the vinyl group.[42, 43] Similar arguments apply to p-alkyl substituted benzyl halides (Table XII, p. 90).

---

[36] J. B. Conant and R. E. Hussey, *J. Am. Chem. Soc.*, *47*, 476 (1925).

[37] L. J. Le Roux, C. S. Lu, S. Sugden, and R. H. K. Thompson, *J. Chem. Soc.*, *1945*, 586.

[38] H. A. C. McKay, *J. Am. Chem. Soc.*, *65*, 702 (1943).

[39] Cf. M. Polanyi and J. L. Tuck, *Trans. Faraday Soc.*, *34*, 222 (1938).

[40] E. C. Baughan and M. Polanyi, *Trans. Faraday Soc.*, *37*, 648 (1941).

[41] I. Dostrovsky, E. D. Hughes, and C. K. Ingold, *J. Chem. Soc.*, *1946*, 173; P. B. D. de la Mare, L. Fowden, E. D. Hughes, C. K. Ingold, and J. D. H. Mackie, *ibid.*, *1955*, 3200.

[42] R. C. Fuson, *Chem. Revs.*, *16*, 1 (1935).

[43] It may be claimed that the polar factor is weakened by transmission through the vinyl system and that therefore its effect is reversed. Although it is true that the polar effect of the methyl group in S_N2 reactions is ambiguous (cf. Table XII, p. 90) the argument is invalidated by the fact that introduction of a *second* methyl

Positive evidence for steric effects in the series ethyl, isopropyl, t-butyl comes from a study of the reaction of phenacyl chlorides $C_6H_5COCClRR'$ with iodide ion.[35] One would expect the strong accelerating effect of the phenacyl group (cf. p. 103) in S_N2 reaction, which is presumably due to the carbonyl dipole, to be offset only partially by the weak electron-donation of methyl groups in the R and R' positions. However, the effect of methyl groups is enormous, as evidenced by the relative rates R = R' = H, 100; R = CH_3, R' = H, 0.6; R = R' = CH_3 ca. 0.0003. In fact the drop in rate here is greater[44] than a typical drop for an S_N2 reaction in the $CH_3CCClRR'$ series (p. 73), which might be R = R' = H, 100; R = CH_3, R = H, 1.33; R = R' = CH_3, 0.29. The magnitude of the drop in the phenacyl series suggests a large steric effect of a methyl group attached to the reaction center.

TABLE IV

REACTION OF ALKYL HALIDES WITH BASES OF DIFFERENT STRENGTHS AND STERIC REQUIREMENTS

$$R'_3N + RI \rightarrow R'_3NR^{\oplus}I^{\ominus}$$

Activation Energy (in Kcal) for Reaction with

Amine	p_{ka} 25°	CH_3I	C_2H_5I	i-C_3H_7I	Difference between C_3H_7I and CH_3I
Et$_3$N	10.64	9.7	12.5	16.0	6.3
Pyridine	5.17	13.9	16.0	17.7	3.8
Quinuclidine	10.58 [47]	9.5	10.9	13.6	4.1

Further evidence for steric effects in the series methyl, ethyl, isopropyl comes from a study of the reaction of appropriate alkyl iodides with triethylamine, quinuclidine, and pyridine.[45] The activation energies for these reactions[45, 46] are summarized in Table IV. Triethylamine and quinuclidine are organic bases of comparable strength and therefore, presumably, of comparable nucleophilic character (cf.

---

group in the γ position, which should offset the weakening of the polar factor, brings about a further increase in rate. Again it may be claimed (cf. reference 8d) that the reaction of allyl halides with iodide or ethoxide ion is more "S_N1-like" than the corresponding reactions of alkyl halides, and that therefore the polar effect of methyl may be acceleration in the former case and retardation in the latter. This argument is set aside by the fact that α-methylallyl chloride reacts considerably more slowly with either iodide or ethoxide ion than allyl chloride does.

[44] Phenacyl chloride reacts about 10,000 times as fast as n-butyl chloride; α-chloroisobutyrophenone actually reacts somewhat more slowly than t-butyl chloride.

[45] H. C. Brown and N. R. Eldred, J. Am. Chem. Soc., 71, 445 (1949).

[46] K. J. Laidler and C. N. Hinshelwood, J. Chem. Soc., 1938, 858.

[47] V. Prelog and Ingold quoted by B. M. Wepster, Rec. trav. chim., 71, 1171 (1952).

p. 157); accordingly they react with methyl iodide with about the same activation energy. Pyridine, a weaker base, requires higher activation energy. As the halide is changed to ethyl iodide and then to isopropyl iodide, the activation energy increases. If this were due largely or entirely to a polar factor, the change should be about the same for triethylamine and quinuclidine and presumably different for pyridine. Actually the change in activation energy in going from methyl iodide to isopropyl iodide is greater for triethylamine, a base of high steric requirement (cf. p. 157), than for quinuclidine, a base of the same strength but low steric requirement. On the other hand, the corresponding change is about the same for pyridine and quinuclidine, both bases of low steric requirement, though of different strength.

A striking drop in rate in the S_N2 reaction is observed in the series ethyl, n-propyl, i-butyl, neopentyl, as indicated in Table V. The

TABLE V

RELATIVE REACTION RATES OF β-SUBSTITUTED ALKYL HALIDES *

R Group	Cl⁻ + RBr[34a]	Br⁻ + RBr[34d]	I⁻ + RBr[34b]	Cl⁻ + RI[34g]	OEt⁻ + RBr[48]
Et	100	100	100	100	100
n-Pr	65	65	82	58	28
i-Bu	15	3.3	3.6	3.8	2.98
Neopentyl	0.0026	0.0015	0.0012	0.0014	0.000424
			0.0053 [49,50]		

* Only complete reaction series are listed. For other less complete data, see references 34c, 34f, 51, 52.

most spectacular member of this series is neopentyl, the lack of reactivity of whose halides was first pointed out by Whitmore and coworkers.[53] It is generally agreed that the drop in rate is due entirely to steric factors, since the methyl substituents are too far from the

[48] I. Dostrovsky and E. D. Hughes, J. Chem. Soc., 1946, 157.

[49] I. Dostrovsky and E. D. Hughes, J. Chem. Soc., 1946, 161.

[50] P. D. Bartlett and L. J. Rosen, J. Am. Chem. Soc., 64, 543 (1942), give a higher value, but Dr. Bartlett has suggested an impurity might have been present in the neopentyl halide used.

[51] T. I. Crowell and L. P. Hammett, J. Am. Chem. Soc., 70, 3444 (1948); P. M. Dunbar and L. P. Hammett, J. Am. Chem. Soc., 72, 109 (1950).

[52] T. I. Crowell, J. Am. Chem. Soc., 75, 6046 (1953).

[53] F. C. Whitmore et al., J. Am. Chem. Soc., 55, 4161 (1933); 61, 1586 (1939); 63, 124 (1941). Under suitable conditions, neopentyl halides may undergo S_N1 reactions with rearrangement; cf. Chapter 5.

center of reaction to exert an appreciable polar effect.   This is borne out both by calculation [41] and, experimentally, by the fact that the retarding effect of the t-butyl group disappears when either an ethynyl [50] or a phenyl group [54] is placed between it and the halomethylene group, as shown in Table VI.

TABLE VI

RELATIVE RATE OF REACTION WITH POTASSIUM IODIDE IN ACETONE

Compound	Relative Rate	Reference
n-C_4H_9Br	1.00	
$(CH_3)_3CCH_2Br$	0.000064	49
n-$C_4H_9C\equiv CCH_2Br$	38.4	50
$(CH_3)_3CC\equiv CCH_2Br$ (II)	48.5	50
$CH\equiv CCH_2Br$	90	55
⬡CH_2Br	200	56
$(CH_3)_3C$—⬡—CH_2Br (III)	260	54

If the effect of the t-butyl group in neopentyl halides were polar rather than steric, it should be relayed by the ethynyl group or the benzene ring sufficiently to make the rate of displacement of the bromine in compounds II and III abnormally slow.   Such, however, is not the case.

It must not be concluded from these results that S_N2 reactions in the neopentyl system are entirely impractical.   The retarding effect of steric hindrance can sometimes be compensated by the use of high reaction temperatures and highly nucleophilic reagents (cf. p. 157). Thus, under suitable conditions, neopentyl p-toluenesulfonate will react normally with morpholine, thiourea, thiophenolate ion, benzyl mercaptide ion, iodide ion, or sulfhydride ion,[57] and neopentyl alcohol will react normally with phosphorus tribromide and with thionyl chloride in the presence of quinoline to give the corresponding neopentyl halide provided that high enough reaction temperatures and

[54] C. W. L. Bevan, E. D. Hughes, and C. K. Ingold, *Nature, 171*, 301 (1953).
[55] T. L. Jacobs and W. F. Brill, *J. Am. Chem. Soc., 75*, 1314 (1953).
[56] A. G. Evans and S. D. Hamann, *Trans. Faraday Soc., 47*, 25 (1951).
[57] F. G. Bordwell, B. N. Pitt, and M. Knell, *J. Am. Chem. Soc., 73*, 5004 (1951). Similar observations in the case of pentaerythritol derivatives have been made by B. P. Fedorov and I. S. Savel'eva, *Izvest. Akad. Nauk S.S.S.R., Otdel. Khim. Nauk*, 223 (1950); *C. A., 45*, 1501g (1951).   See also p. 118.

long enough reaction times are employed.[58]   Neopentyl iodide can also be obtained in good yield by the reaction of the alcohol with the triphenyl phosphite–methyl iodide complex.[59]   Other interesting synthetic applications of S_N2 reactions in the neopentyl system have been reported.   Thus, while the tosylate of 9-hydroxymethyl-3-benzyloxydecalin (IV) when reduced with lithium aluminum hydride merely underwent sulfur-oxygen fission and reverted to the parent alcohol,

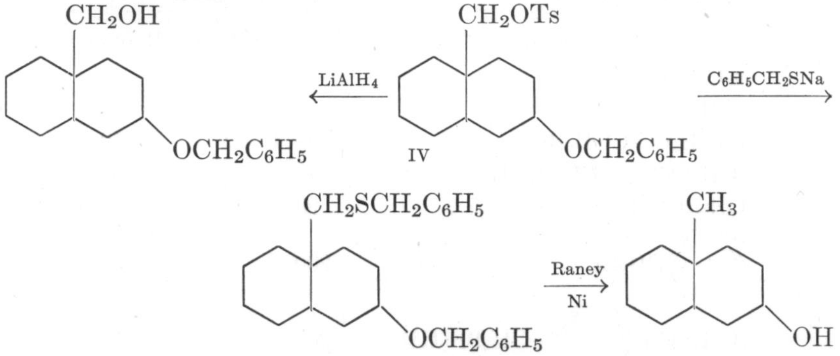

it could be reduced indirectly through displacement by the highly nucleophilic benzyl mercaptide ion followed by desulfurization by Raney nickel.[60]   A similar reaction sequence had previously been used in the synthesis of cantharidin.[61]   In a bicyclic tosylate of the isobutyl type it was observed that normal reduction (alkyl oxygen fission) with lithium aluminum hydride could be forced by using a large excess of the reagent in hot, concentrated tetrahydrofuran solution, when the ordinary ether solution of the hydride would produce sulfur-oxygen fission.[62]

The effect of methyl substituents in an alkyl halide becomes slight in the 3 position and disappears in the 4 position, as shown in Table VII.

[58] L. H. Sommer, H. D. Blankman, and P. C. Miller, J. Am. Chem. Soc., 73, 3542 (1951); 76, 803 (1954); cf. W. Gerrard and P. Tolcher, J. Chem. Soc., 1954, 3640, for the course of the reaction of triethylneopentoxysiloxane with thionyl chloride.

[59] S. R. Landauer and H. N. Rydon, J. Chem. Soc., 1953, 2224; N. Kornblum and D. C. Iffland, J. Am. Chem. Soc., 77, 6653 (1955).

[60] A. S. Hussey, H. P. Liao, and R. H. Baker, J. Am. Chem. Soc., 75, 4727 (1953); cf. W. G. Dauben, R. C. Tweit, and R. L. MacLean, ibid., 77, 48 (1955); A. S. Dreiding and A. J. Tomasewski, ibid., 77, 168 (1955).

[61] G. Stork, E. E. van Tamelen, L. J. Friedman, and A. W. Burgstahler, J. Am. Chem. Soc., 75, 384 (1953).

[62] H. M. Walborsky, Helv. Chim. Acta, 36, 1251 (1953).

TABLE VII

RELATIVE REACTION RATE WITH POTASSIUM IODIDE IN ACETONE

Halide	Rate	Reference
$CH_3CH_2CH_2CH_2Br$	100	
$(CH_3)_3CBr$	0.07 *	33
$(CH_3)_3CCH_2Br$	0.0064	49
$(CH_3)_3CCH_2CH_2Br$	4.15	50
$(CH_3)_3CCH_2CH_2CH_2Br$	100	50

* Relative to n-propyl bromide = 100. There is little difference, in rates of other reactions, between n-propyl and n-butyl halides.

A similar trend has been observed in the isobutyl, isoamyl, isohexyl bromide series, the rate for isohexyl being the same as that for straight-chain alkyl bromides in reaction with sodium thiocyanate.[52] Nothing appears to be known about highly substituted alkyl halides with substituents larger than methyl. In the rate of S_N2 reactions of primary aliphatic alkyl halides, little change occurs as the chain is lengthened beyond n-propyl.[52, 63]

In the series ethyl, n-propyl, i-butyl, neopentyl, by far the greatest drop in rate comes between the isobutyl and neopentyl halides. This discontinuity is typical of steric effects. In this particular instance, it comes about because the methyl groups in n-propyl and i-butyl halides can be so oriented in the transition state that the rear of the carbon atom at which displacement occurs is quite accessible. In neopentyl halides, however, the rear of this atom is inaccessible, regardless of orientation of the methyl groups; therefore much more activation energy is required to bring about displacement by path B (p. 63).[64]

The S_Ni reaction

It has been pointed out before (p. 66) that S_N2 and S_N1 reactions proceed with inversion and/or racemization. Reactions are known, however, where retention of configuration is observed. Sometimes this is due to participation of a neighboring group (cf. Chapter 5), but it cannot always be so explained. Nucleophilic displacement reactions

[63] Reference 4e, p. 319. A slight minimum in rate for n-butyl is indicated in reference 52.

[64] For a detailed discussion, see reference 4e, pp. 403ff. It is of interest that the activation *energy* required for displacement on n-propyl halides is about the same as for ethyl halides. However, because of the more stringent requirement for the orientation of the extra methyl group in the transition state, the *entropy* of activation is less favorable for n-propyl than for ethyl, and this accounts for the observed drop in rate in this particular case.

in which there is retention of configuration without participation of a neighboring group are called $S_N i$ reactions.[65, 66]   Examples are the reaction of alcohols of the type $C_6H_5\overset{\displaystyle |}{\underset{\displaystyle |}{C}}$—OH with hydrogen halide at low temperature,[67] thionyl chloride in the absence of pyridine hydrochloride,[68] phosgene,[69] and phosphorus chlorides [68] to give halides, the cleavage of α-phenethyl aryl ethers with hydrogen halide,[70] the reaction of α-phenethylamine with nitrous acid [71a] and nitrosyl chloride [71b] and the thermal rearrangement of N-nitrosoamides.[71c]   ($S_N i$ reactions in alicyclic compounds are referred to on p. 128.)

Hughes, Ingold, and coworkers [65] considered that, in contrast to the $S_N 1$ and $S_N 2$ reactions, the $S_N i$ reaction involves front-side attack of the reagent, as exemplified in the following formulations for the reaction of an alcohol with thionyl chloride:

$$R\text{—}O\text{—}H \xrightarrow{\text{SOCl}_2} R\text{—}O\text{—}\overset{\displaystyle O}{\overset{\uparrow}{S}}\text{—}Cl$$

$$R\text{—}O\text{—}\overset{\displaystyle O}{\overset{\uparrow}{S}}\text{—}Cl \rightarrow R\text{—}O\text{—}\overset{\displaystyle O}{\overset{\uparrow}{S^+}} + Cl^- \rightarrow$$

$$R^+ + SO_2 + Cl^- \rightarrow SO_2 + RCl \quad S_N 1$$

$$R\text{—}O\text{—}\overset{\displaystyle O}{\overset{\uparrow}{S}}\text{—}Cl \rightarrow Cl^- + R\text{—}O\text{—}\overset{\displaystyle O}{\overset{\uparrow}{S^+}} \longrightarrow Cl\text{—}R + SO_2 \quad S_N 2$$

$$\underset{\underset{Cl}{}}{\overset{\displaystyle O}{\overset{R}{\diagup\diagdown}}} S{\rightarrow}O \rightarrow \underset{\underset{Cl}{\diagdown}}{R} + SO_2 \qquad\qquad S_N i$$

---

[65] W. A. Cowdrey, E. D. Hughes, C. K. Ingold, S. Masterman, and A. D. Scott, *J. Chem. Soc.*, *1937*, 1252.   See also reference 41 and reference 4e, p. 392.   The qualification is pointed out in reference 66.   Since the exact mechanism of the $S_N i$ reaction is as yet uncertain, it is best to adhere to the present operational definition, even though it is of necessity limited to optically active systems.

[66] D. J. Cram, *J. Am. Chem. Soc.*, *75*, 332 (1953).

[67] P. A. Levene and A. Rothen, *J. Biol. Chem.*, *127*, 237 (1939); P. H. Wilken, Ph.D. thesis, University of Notre Dame, Notre Dame, Indiana, 1954.

[68] See references 65, 66 for bibliography.

[69] M. B. Harford, J. Kenyon, and A. H. Phillips, *J. Chem. Soc.*, *1933*, 179; K. B. Wiberg and T. M. Shryne, *J. Am. Chem. Soc.*, *77*, 2774 (1955).

[70] H. Hart and H. S. Eleuterio, *J. Am. Chem. Soc.*, *76*, 1379 (1954).

[71] (a) E. Ott, *Ann.*, *488*, 186 (1931); (b) H. Felkin, *Compt. rend.*, *236*, 298 (1953); (c) E. H. White, *J. Am. Chem. Soc.*, *77*, 6014 (1955).

The formation of chlorosulfites as intermediates in the thionyl chloride reaction appears to be well established.[72,73] Unfortunately, the simple picture of the $S_N i$ process shown above [65] fails to explain why neopentyl alcohol $(CH_3)_3CCH_2OH$ [74] and 1-apocamphanol (V) [27] do

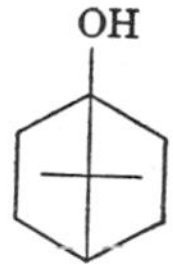

OH

V

not react with thionyl chloride in the normal way. Neopentyl alcohol does yield a chlorosulfite, which, however, on thermal decomposition gives a mixture containing neopentyl sulfite, thionyl chloride, t-amyl chloride, and very little, if any, neopentyl chloride.[75] Apocamphanol yields only a sulfite.[27] Yet, by analogy with ring-closure reactions (p. 117), a cyclic mechanism of the type shown above should be insensitive to steric hindrance and presumably it should not be affected either by the rigidity (cf. p. 135) of compound V. The picture of the $S_N i$ reaction has been modified by Cram [76] by an extrapolation of information obtained in more complex systems (Chapter 5). The observed retention is interpreted through formation of a complex ion pair from the chlorosulfite; the anion of this pair then rearranges to give sulfur dioxide and chloride ion, and finally the simple ion pair so formed collapses to form covalent chloride:

$$—C—O—SOCl \rightarrow —C^+OSOCl^- \rightarrow$$
(Ion pair)

$$—C^+Cl^- + SO_2 \rightarrow SO_2 + —C—Cl$$
(Ion pair)

This picture also explains why phenyl-substituted carbinols, $Ph—C—OH$, are more likely to use the $S_N i$ mechanism than others, since the carbonium part of the ion is stabilized by benzylic resonance. It further explains why primary chlorosulfites, such as neopentyl chlorosulfite, do not easily decompose thermally to give chlorides

[72] E.g., P. Carré, *Bull. soc. chim. France*, [4], *53*, 1075 (1933); W. E. Bissinger and F. E. Kung, *J. Am. Chem. Soc.*, *69*, 2158 (1947); P. D. Bartlett and H. F. Herbrandson, *ibid.*, *74*, 5971 (1952).

[73] E. S. Lewis and C. E. Boozer, *J. Am. Chem. Soc.*, *74*, 308 (1952); C. E. Boozer and E. S. Lewis, *ibid.*, *75*, 3182 (1953).

[74] F. C. Whitmore and H. S. Rothrock, *J. Am. Chem. Soc.*, *54*, 3431 (1932).

[75] W. Gerrard, A. Nechvatal, and B. M. Wilson, *J. Chem. Soc.*, *1950*, 2088. The preparation of neopentyl chloride from the alcohol and thionyl chloride in the presence of quinoline is probably an $S_N 2$ reaction; cf. p. 77.

[76] D. J. Cram, *J. Am. Chem. Soc.*, *75*, 332 (1953).

TABLE VIII

STEREOCHEMICAL RESULTS OF THE DECOMPOSITION OF ALKYL
CHLOROSULFITES IN VARIOUS SOLVENTS

Solvent	Alkyl Group	% Preservation of Activity	Optical Course
Dioxane	sec-Butyl	96.5	Retention
Tetrahydropyran	sec-Butyl	98.2	Retention
Ethylene chloride	sec-Butyl	55	Retention
Tetrahydrofuran	sec-Octyl	35	Retention
Dioxolane	sec-Octyl	20	Retention
Acetophenone	sec-Octyl	18	Inversion
Acetal	sec-Octyl	27	Inversion
Cyclohexanone	sec-Butyl	36	Inversion
Isoöctane	sec-Octyl	43	Inversion
Thiophene	sec-Octyl	49	Inversion
Acetonitrile	sec-Butyl	64	Inversion
Dioxane and pyridine hydrochloride	sec-Butyl	67	Inversion
Kerosene	sec-Octyl	78	Inversion
Toluene	sec-Butyl	95	Inversion
No solvent	sec-Octyl	93	Inversion

(primary carbonium ions are high in energy) and why apocamphanol
(V) does not give the corresponding chloride with thionyl chloride
(the carbonium part of the ion pair cannot flatten out; cf. p. 135).
Lewis and Boozer [73] have extended the ion-pair mechanism, drawing
attention to the importance of the solvent. These authors discovered
that even secondary *aliphatic* chlorosulfites, which ordinarily decompose to chlorides with predominant inversion of configuration, can
be made to react with retention when ethers or alkyl halides are used
as solvents, as shown in Table VIII. They explain retention of configuration as being due to backside participation of solvent, as shown.

This formulation may explain further why, where backside participation of the solvent is difficult or impossible, as in the neopentyl and apocamphyl system, the $S_N i$ reaction fails. (For a discussion of the rather more complex order of solvents in the *inversion* reaction, the reader is referred to the original papers.[73])

What has been said regarding the $S_N i$ reaction of alcohols with thionyl chloride would seem to apply, with little change, to other $S_N i$ reactions producing halide. A slightly different picture, however, must be drawn for the $S_N i$ reaction of amines with nitrous acid and its chloride. Usually this reaction involves racemization and some inversion $(S_N 1)$: [77,78]

$$R\text{—}NH_2 + NOX \rightarrow R\text{—}N_2^+X^- \rightarrow N_2 + R^+X^- \rightarrow RX$$

(X may be Cl or Br as well as OH.) However, there are cases of retention of configuration, in cyclic systems [79] (p. 128). Moreover, 1-phenylethylamine, which reacts with nitrous acid in aqueous medium slowly and with predominant inversion of configuration, in acetic acid reacts rapidly and with predominant retention.[71a] There appears to be a correlation of the stereochemistry with the reaction rate, since addition of sodium acetate to the acetic acid medium, which slows down the reaction, also changes its steric course from retention to inversion. An $S_N i$ mechanism also appears to be involved in the decomposition, with rearrangement, of 2-phenyl-(p-tolyl)ethylammonium nitrite in dry butanol which yields an alcohol as a product rather than a butyl ether.[80] The reaction of amines with nitrous acid is discussed further in connection with cyclic systems (p. 128).

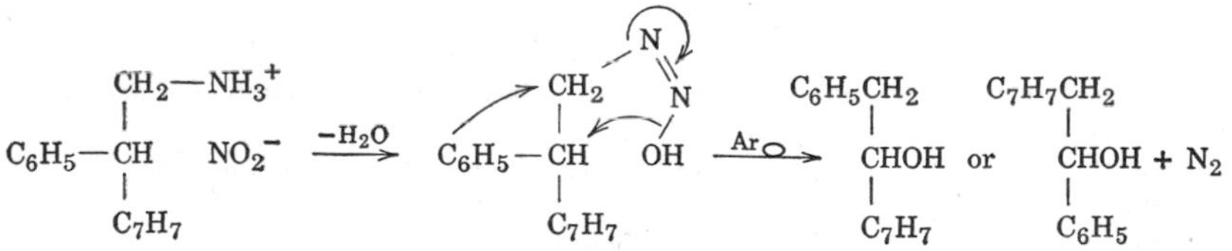

[77] P. Brewster, F. Hiron, E. D. Hughes, C. K. Ingold, and P. A. D. Rao, *Nature*, *166*, 178 (1950); Ingold, reference 4e, p. 395.

[78] Cf. J. D. Roberts and J. A. Yancey, *J. Am. Chem. Soc.*, *74*, 5943 (1952); J. D. Roberts and M. Halmann, *ibid.*, *75*, 5759 (1953); C. C. Lee and J. W. T. Spinks, *Can. J. Chem.*, *31*, 761 (1953); M. B. Watson and G. W. Youngson, *J. Chem. Soc.*, *1954*, 2145.

[79] W. G. Dauben, R. C. Tweit, and C. Mannerskantz, *J. Am. Chem. Soc.*, *76*, 4420 (1954).

[80] P. S. Bailey and J. G. Burr, *J. Am. Chem. Soc.*, *75*, 2951 (1953).

General survey

In the following pages, substitution reactions of various alkyl halides and related compounds will be considered, with special emphasis on steric effects influencing the reactivity of such compounds.

ALLYL, PROPARGYL, AND BENZYL HALIDES. These halides seem to provide a particularly clear instance where S_N1 and S_N2 reactions tend to merge into each other gradually.[8d] Caution must therefore be used in interpreting their reactions in terms of these prototypes, and some inconsistencies are perhaps to be expected because of the inadequacy of the mechanistic picture.

TABLE IX

RELATIVE REACTION RATES OF VARIOUS SUBSTITUTED ALLYLIC HALIDES

Entry No.		KI-Acetone	NaOEt-EtOH	LiCl-Acetone [83a]	H_2O-EtOH [82]	H_2O-HCO$_2$H [82]	AgNO$_3$-EtOH [81]
1	$CH_3CH_2CH_2Cl$	0.013 [83]	0.027 [83a]	0.072	0.052	0.04	—
2	CH_2=$CHCH_2Cl$	1.00	1.00	1.00	1.00	1.00	1.00
3	"CH_3CH=$CHCH_2Cl$"	2.37 [84]	3.71; [84] 3.18; [85] 2.62 [83a]	2.52	91.3; 93 [85]	3550	321
4	cis-CH_3CH=$CHCH_2Cl$	8.35 [86]	5.1 [86]	—	—	—	—
5	trans-CH_3CH=$CHCH_2Cl$	1.56 [86]	4.4 [86]	—	—	—	—
6	$(CH_3)_2C$=$CHCH_2Cl$	28 [87]	Very fast; [87] † 15.0 [83a] †	21.3	2.5×10^5	1.5×10^7	—
7	CH_2=$CHCHClCH_3$	0.023 [81]	0.063; [85] ca. 0.049 [83a]	—	81.5; 77 [85]	5670	187
8	CH_2=$CHC(CH_3)_2Cl$	—	—	0.043	1.35×10^6	8×10^7	—
9	CH_2=$CHCHCl_2$	ca. 0.014 *	0.0060 [88]	—	1.01 [88]	65.4	2.44
10	cis-$ClCH$=$CHCH_2Cl$	8.6 [89]	2.86; [88] 2.78 [90]	—	0.98; 1.00 [88]	2.1	1.42
11	trans-$ClCH$=$CHCH_2Cl$	2.9 [89]	3.25; [88] 3.47 [90]	—	0.98; 1.01 [88]	3.09	1.48
12	CH_2=$C(CH_3)CH_2Cl$	1.58 [89]	1.03; [89] 0.89 [83a]	—	1.53	0.05	—

* Rate at 25° relative to that of allyl chloride at 20°.

† The high rate reported in reference 87 may have been caused by solvolysis during the quenching process.

[81] S. Oae and C. A. VanderWerf, J. Am. Chem. Soc., 75, 2724 (1953).

[82] In 50% ethanol and 99.5% formic acid. Data of C. A. Vernon, J. Chem. Soc., 1954, 423, except where noted otherwise.

[83] J. B. Conant, W. R. Kirner, and R. E. Hussey, J. Am. Chem. Soc., 47, 488 (1925).

[83a] C. A. Vernon, J. Chem. Soc., 1954, 4462.

[84] M. Tamele, C. J. Ott, K. E. Marple, and G. Hearne, Ind. Eng. Chem., 33, 115 (1941).

[85] W. G. Young and L. J. Andrews, J. Am. Chem. Soc., 66, 421 (1944).

[86] L. F. Hatch and S. S. Nesbitt, J. Am. Chem. Soc., 73, 358 (1951).

[87] L. F. Hatch and L. S. Gerhardt, J. Am. Chem. Soc., 71, 1679 (1949).

[88] L. J. Andrews and R. E. Kepner, J. Am. Chem. Soc., 69, 2230 (1947); 70, 3456 (1948).

[89] L. F. Hatch, L. B. Gordon, and J. J. Russ, J. Am. Chem. Soc., 70, 1093 (1948); L. F. Hatch and R. H. Perry, Jr., J. Am. Chem. Soc., 71, 3262 (1949).

[90] L. F. Hatch and H. E. Alexander, J. Am. Chem. Soc., 71, 1037 (1949).

The reaction rates for a number of substituted allyl halides are summarized in Table IX. Columns 5, 6, and 7 list reactions which are probably largely S_N1. One would expect these reactions to be considerably faster than corresponding reactions of primary alkyl halides, because of the resonance stabilization of the allyl carbonium ion,

$$CH_2\!\!=\!\!CH\!\!-\!\!CH_2{}^{\oplus} \leftrightarrow {}^{\oplus}CH_2\!\!-\!\!CH\!\!=\!\!CH_2$$

In fact, however, the increase in rate from n-propyl to allyl (entries 1 and 2) is only by a factor of about 20–25.[82, 91] Perhaps the hydrolysis rate of the n-propyl chloride in aqueous formic acid is enhanced by the incursion of the S_N2 mechanism.[93] Alternatively (or in addition) the inductive electron withdrawal of the vinyl group may destabilize the allyl carbonium ion.[94] A comparison of allyl chloride with its 3-methyl and 3,3-dimethyl homologs (entries 2–6, Table IX) in S_N1-type reactions indicates a very large accelerating effect of the additional methyl groups; a still slightly larger effect is observed in the 1-methyl and 1,1-dimethyl homologs (entries 7, 8). This large effect of methyl groups, presumably polar in nature, is observed in other reaction series as well; it is striking how its magnitude varies with reaction series and with solvent, as shown in Table X. Since the effect of a methyl substituent in the 1 and 3 positions of the allyl system is much the same (entries 3 and 7, 6 and 8, Table IX), steric hindrance of solvation cannot be of great importance here, unless one wants to ascribe a very different electrical effect to the methyl groups in the two positions. From this and the large effect of the methyl substituent it appears that the hydrolysis of 1- and 3-alkyl substituted allyl halides in formic acid constitutes a rather extreme example of the S_N1 reaction.

[91] A somewhat larger factor, ca. 75, is estimated from the observation (reference 92) that allyl chloride is hydrolyzed in aqueous formic acid about three times as fast as isopropyl chloride and that isopropyl *bromide* (at a higher temperature) solvolyzes about 25 times as fast as ethyl bromide, which, in turn, would be expected to react about as fast as n-propyl bromide. See, however, references 93, 99a.

[92] A. G. Evans and S. D. Hamann, *Trans. Faraday Soc.*, *47*, 25 (1951).

[93] S. Winstein and H. Marshall, *J. Am. Chem. Soc.*, *74*, 1120 (1952). A graded range from the extreme S_N2 mechanism (called N by these authors) to the extreme S_N1 mechanism (called *Lim*) is postulated.

[94] J. L. Franklin and H. E. Lumpkin, *J. Chem. Phys.*, *19*, 1073 (1951), have shown that the appearance potentials of n-propyl, allyl, and benzyl ions in the gas phase are equal. The exact significance of this observation to solution kinetics is not clear, since allyl chloride hydrolyzes in formic acid *somewhat* faster than n-propyl chloride (vide supra) and benzyl chloride hydrolyzes about 45 times faster than allyl chloride; reference 84.

TABLE X [95]

RATE OF HYDROLYSIS OF VARIOUS ALKYL HALIDES

Series	Reference	Solvent	Temperature, °C	$k_1 \times 10^4$ in sec.$^{-1}$		
				R = H	R = CH$_3$	R = t-C$_4$H$_9$
(CH$_3$)$_2$RCCl	24, 32b	80% Ethanol	25	0.000019	0.092	0.111
RCH=CHCH$_2$Cl	82	Formic acid	44.6	0.00036 *	2.05	0.91
CH$_2$=CHCHRCl	82	Formic acid	44.6	0.00036 *	1.28	0.82
p-RC$_6$H$_4$CH$_2$Br	54	Formic acid	25.1	0.00368	0.213	0.103
p-RC$_6$H$_4$CHPhCl	96	80% acetone	25	0.728	15.6	7.96
RC≡CC(CH$_3$)$_2$Cl	95	80% acetone	25	0.00237	5.13	2.80
RC≡CC(CH$_3$)$_2$Cl	95	Formic acid	15	0.075	ca. 400	—

* Corrected value.

In S_N2 reactions, allyl chloride reacts appreciably faster than propyl chloride (entries 1 and 2, columns 2–4, Table IX). This may be partly due to the electron-withdrawing effect of the vinyl group,[97] and partly to overlap of the incipient A—X and A—Y bonds in the transition state Y···A···X with the π orbitals of the vinyl group.[98] Moreover, there is less steric hindrance in the transition state (path B, p. 63) involving an S_N2 reaction of allyl halides, since the vinyl group can be so oriented that it is contained entirely in a plane at right angles to the reaction coordinate. The decrease in rate due to substituents in the 1 position (either chlorine or methyl, entries 7 and 9, Table IX) is clearly due to steric hindrance, since the same substituents in the 3 position produce an increase in rate (entries 3–6, 10, 11). A methyl substituent in the 2 position (entry 12) has little effect on rate in either S_N1 or S_N2 reactions.

The greater reactivity of cis-3-substituted allyl chlorides over the corresponding trans isomers in the reaction with iodide ion (entries 4–5, 10–11) has yet to be explained. It may be a consequence of steric assistance, provided that the chlorine atom interferes more with the cis-methyl group in the ground state than do the chlorine and iodine atoms together in the transition state.

The behavior of propargylic halides in S_N1 reactions is rather different from that of allylic halides. Propargyl chloride [99] and bromide [95]

[95] A. Burawoy and E. Spinner, J. Chem. Soc., 1954, 3752.

[96] E. D. Hughes, C. K. Ingold, and N. A. Taher, J. Chem. Soc., 1940, 949.

[97] K. J. Laidler, Chemical Kinetics, p. 372, McGraw-Hill Book Company, New York, 1950. Cf. C. N. Hinshelwood, K. J. Laidler, and E. W. Timm, J. Chem. Soc., 1938, 848.

[98] M. J. S. Dewar, The Electronic Theory of Organic Chemistry, p. 73, Oxford University Press, London, England, 1949.

[99] L. F. Hatch and V. Chiola, J. Am. Chem. Soc., 73, 360 (1951).

solvolyze too slowly for quantitative study.[99a] The rate of solvolysis of 1,1-dimethylpropargyl chloride, $HC\equiv CC(CH_3)_2Cl$, in 80% ethanol at 25° is only [100-102] 7.4×10^{-4} hr.$^{-1}$ compared to 550×10^{-4} hr.$^{-1}$ for t-amyl chloride, $CH_3CH_2C(CH_3)_2Cl$, in the same solvent and at the same temperature [24] and $138,000 \times 10^{-4}$ hr.$^{-1}$ for 1,1-dimethyl-allyl chloride, $H_2C\!=\!CHC(CH_3)_2Cl$, in 75% ethanol at 25.1°.[103] However, the solvolysis of the tertiary acetylenic chloride is faster than that of isopropyl chloride (6.85×10^{-6} hr.$^{-1}$), suggesting that there is some stabilization of the carbonium ion due to propargylic resonance [104]

$$-C\equiv C-\overset{\oplus}{C}R_2- \;\rightleftarrows\; -\overset{\oplus}{C}\!=\!C\!=\!CR$$

The net effect of this resonance stabilization is small, because it is partly offset by the strong electron-withdrawing effect of the ethynyl group, which would tend to destabilize the carbonium ion.[105] When the electron-withdrawing effect of the ethynyl group is compensated by a methyl substituent, as in 4-chloro-4-methyl-2-pentyne, $CH_3C\equiv CC(CH_3)_2Cl$, the solvolysis rate then becomes very fast (Table X), faster, in fact, than that of the lower vinylog t-butyl chloride $CH_3\!-\!C(CH_3)_2Cl$ which lacks the ethynyl group.

In contrast, typical S_N2 reactions of propargyl halides, such as the reaction with potassium iodide in acetone, are rapid, the rate constants for propargyl chloride and 3-methylpropargyl chloride, $CH_3C\equiv CCH_2Cl$, being comparable to the constants for the corresponding allyl compounds,[99,106] presumably for analogous reasons. Surprisingly, a *tertiary* propargylic halide has been found to react rapidly with sodium hydroxide in 80% ethanol to give the corresponding ethyl ether [95,100] and with sodium acetylide in ammonia to give an *amine*.[107] A special mechanism has been postulated to account for these results.[100]

[99a] P. J. C. Fierens and P. Kruys, *Bull. soc. chim. Belges*, *64*, 542 (1955), report that the rate of solvolysis of propargyl bromide in water at 25° is 57% of the corresponding rate for n-propyl bromide.

[100] G. F. Hennion and D. E. Maloney, *J. Am. Chem. Soc.*, *73*, 4735 (1951).

[101] Similar results were reported independently by A. N. Pudovik, *J. Gen. Chem. U.S.S.R.*, *21*, 1462, 1811 (1951); *C. A.*, *46*, 4467b, 7033h (1952).

[102] A value of 8.54×10^{-4} hr.$^{-1}$ is given in reference 95 without acknowledgment of the earlier value in reference 101.

[103] P. B. D. de la Mare and C. A. Vernon, *J. Chem. Soc.*, *1954*, 2504.

[104] The reality of such resonance is further suggested by the unusually long halogen bond in propargyl halides: L. Pauling, W. Gordy, and J. H. Saylor, *J. Am. Chem. Soc.*, *64*, 1753 (1942).

[105] Cf. J. K. Kochi and G. S. Hammond, *J. Am. Chem. Soc.*, *75*, 3452 (1953).

[106] T. L. Jacobs and W. F. Brill, *J. Am. Chem. Soc.*, *75*, 1314 (1953).

[107] G. F. Hennion and E. G. Teach, *J. Am. Chem. Soc.*, *75*, 1653 (1953).

Benzyl halides undergo S_N1 reactions more rapidly than allyl halides. Thus the hydrolysis of benzyl chloride in formic acid is about 45 times as fast as that of allyl chloride.[92, 108] Resonance stabilization of the benzyl carbonium ion appears to be considerable (see, however, reference 94). As one might expect, electron-withdrawing substituents reduce the rate of S_N1 reactions in substituted benzyl halides, and electron-donating substituents enhance it.[109]

Since resonance plays an important part in facilitating S_N1 reactions in benzylic systems, steric inhibition of resonance (cf. Chapter 11) should lead to a drop in rate. This prediction is borne out by a study of solvolysis rates of o-substituted α-phenylalkyl chlorides,[110–112] shown in Table XI. For maximum resonance in the carbonium ion, the ben-

TABLE XI

Effect of Steric Inhibition of Resonance on Solvolysis

Entry No.	Solvent	Rate, $(\text{sec}^{-1}) \times 10^7$	Temperature, °C.	Solvent	E_a, kcal./mole	log PZ	Reference
1	MeCHClPh	1180	45	80% EtOH	20.4	10.00	111
2	EtCHClPh	273	45	80% EtOH	20.7	9.58	111
3	n-PrCHClPh	327	45	80% EtOH	20.3	9.38	111
4	i-PrCHClPh	58.7	45	80% EtOH	22.9	10.40	111
5	Et₂CHCHClPh	145	45	80% EtOH	22.3	10.36	111
6	t-BuCHClPh	2.18	45	80% EtOH	25.4	10.68	111
7	t-AmCHClPh	4.58	45	80% EtOH	24.8	10.59	111
8	C₆H₅CHClCH₃	1.65	25	Abs. EtOH	25.6	11.97	110
9	o-CH₃C₆H₄CHClCH₃	36.7	25	Abs. EtOH	22.8	11.18	110
10	VI, $n = 5$	1450	25	Abs. EtOH	20.0	10.77	110
		1510	25	Abs. EtOH	20.3	11.08	112
11	VI, $n = 6$	400	25	Abs. EtOH	20.2	10.32	110
		363	25	Abs. EtOH	21.6	11.43	112
12	VI, $n = 7$	15.3	25	Abs. EtOH	23.9	11.58	110
		8.13 (60.7)	25 (40)	Abs. EtOH	25.0	12.24	112
13	VI, $n = 8$	7.68	40	Abs. EtOH	25.9	11.97	112
14	2,4,6-Me₃C₆H₂CHClMe	3270	25	Abs. EtOH	21.9	12.46	110

VI

[108] Cf. also H. Burton and D. A. Munday, *J. Chem. Soc.*, *1954*, 1456.

[109] The data are too extensive to be cited here. See, for example, reference 3, p. 182, also references 54 and 122; also S. C. J. Olivier, *Rec. trav. chim.*, *49*, 697, 996 (1930); J. B. Shoesmith and R. H. Slater, *J. Chem. Soc.*, *1926*, 214; G. M. Bennett and B. Jones, *ibid.*, *1935*, 1815; J. W. Baker, *ibid.*, *1934*, 987.

[110] G. Baddeley and J. Chadwick, *J. Chem. Soc.*, *1951*, 368.

[111] G. Baddeley, J. Chadwick, and H. T. Taylor, *J. Chem. Soc.*, *1954*, 2405.

[112] R. Huisgen, W. Rapp, I. Ugi, H. Walz, and E. Mergenthaler, *Ann.*, *586*, 1 (1954).

zene ring and the alkyl group attached to the central carbon atom
should be coplanar, as shown in formula VII. Coplanarity is inter-

VII

fered with when R is larger than methyl, even though R' = H (entries
2–7, Table XI), and, in any event, when R' is methyl or methylene
(entries 9, 12, 13), unless steric interference is minimized by formation
of a five- or six-membered ring (entries 10, 11).[113] That the o-methyl
substituted halide (entry 9) reacts faster than the unsubstituted one
(entry 8) seems confusing at first sight but is presumably due to the
polar effect of the o-methyl group, which more than outweighs steric
inhibition of resonance. The latter is still important, however, even in
o-methyl-α-phenethyl chloride, as suggested by the much slower
solvolysis rate of the o-methyl compound as compared with the cyclic
compounds VI, $n = 5, 6$ (entries 9–11). The same point is brought
out by the ethanolysis rates of substituted benzhydryl chlorides.[114]
2-Methylbenzhydryl chloride solvolyzes 2.9 times as fast as the parent
compound benzhydryl chloride, but the 4-methyl substituted compound is 5.7 times faster still than the 2-isomer.[115]

Steric hindrance to solvation has been suggested as a contributing
factor to the slow solvolysis rate of some of the compounds shown in
Table XI.[116]

The high solvolysis rate of 2,4,6-trimethyl-α-phenethyl chloride
(entry 14, Table XI) requires explanation, since here steric inhibition
of resonance by the *two ortho*-methyl groups should be particularly
significant. It appears that this effect is more than outweighed by
the polar effect of the three methyl groups, possibly augmented here
by steric strain in the ground state (cf. p. 71). The high entropy of

[113] The higher rate of solvolysis of the five-membered ring compound over the
six-membered one may indicate less inhibition of resonance in the smaller ring
system, or it may be due to I strain; cf. p. 121.

[114] J. F. Norris and C. Banta, *J. Am. Chem. Soc.*, **50**, 1804 (1928); J. F. Norris
and J. T. Blake, *ibid.*, **50**, 1808 (1928). See also reference 22b.

[115] Surprisingly, there is no difference in the dissociation constants of 2- and
4-methyl trityl chlorides in nitromethane solution: A. G. Evans, J. A. G. Jones,
and G. O. Osborne, *J. Chem. Soc.*, *1954*, 3803.

[116] S. Winstein and B. K. Morse, *J. Am. Chem. Soc.*, *74*, 1133 (1952).

activation provides added evidence for the latter factor; apparently the molecule is unusually rigid in the ground state because of inability of the chloroethyl side chain to rotate without colliding with the methyl groups. In agreement with entry 14, Table XI, is the fact that 2,4,6-trimethylbenzyl chloride ionizes in liquid sulfur dioxide solution to a greater extent than benzyl chloride does.[117]

In S_N2 reactions, benzyl halides are about 200 to 300 times faster than normal alkyl halides;[3] in fact, their reactivity is about as high as that of the corresponding methyl halides.[92] The reasons for this, polar or steric, are probably analogous to those previously discussed (p. 86) for allylic systems. As illustrated in Table XII, the effect on rate of substituents in the benzene ring is small and ambiguous. The reason for this has been discussed elsewhere.[8d, 97]

TABLE XII

EFFECT OF *para*-ALKYL SUBSTITUENTS IN REACTIONS OF BENZYL HALIDES
AND SIMILAR COMPOUNDS

(The symbol X stands for R—⟨ ⟩—CH₂—.)

Reaction	Solvent	Tempera-ture, °C.	Refer-ence	Relative Reaction Rate			
				R = H	R = Me	R = t-Bu	R = NO₂
XBr + I⁻	Acetone	0.0	54	1.00	1.46	1.35	—
XBr + OEt⁻	EtOH	25.1	54	1.00	1.48	1.38	—
XBr + O-t-Bu⁻	t-BuOH	60.0	54	1.00	1.34	1.19	—
XCl + OEt⁻	EtOH	25.1	54, 118	1.00	1.57	1.46	—
XNC₅H₅ + OEt⁻	EtOH	20.0	54	1.00	0.504	0.691	—
XBr + C₅H₅N	Dry acetone	20	119	1.00	1.66	1.35	0.92
XBr + C₅H₅N	Ethanol, 90%	30.5	120	1.00	2.5	—	0.64
XBr + NO₃⁻	Dry acetone	40	119	1.00	2.0	1.6	2.1
XCl + OH⁻	H₂O-acetone	30	121	1.00	2.17	—	—
XCl + I⁻	Acetone	20	92, 122	1.00	1.47	—	6.2
XBr + aniline	Ethanol, 90%	30.5	120	1.00	2.2	—	0.6

o-Substituents in benzyl halides might be expected, at first sight, to impede S_N2 reactions either by gross steric hindrance or by steric inhibition of resonance. As the data in Table XIII indicate, neither

[117] W. T. Nauta and J. W. Dienske, *Rec. trav. chim.*, **55**, 1000 (1936).

[118] See also H. Franzen, *J. prakt. Chem.*, **97**, 61 (1918); H. Franzen and I. Rosenberg, *ibid.*, **101**, 333 (1921).

[119] (a) J. W. Baker, *Trans. Faraday Soc.*, **37**, 632 (1941); (b) *J. Chem. Soc.*, **1936**, 1448; (c) J. W. Baker and W. S. Nathan, *J. Chem. Soc.*, **1935**, 519, 1840; **1936**, 236.

[120] J. W. Baker, *J. Chem. Soc.*, **1932**, 2631.

[121] S. C. J. Olivier and A. P. Weber, *Rec. trav. chim.*, **53**, 869 (1934).

[122] G. M. Bennett and B. Jones, *J. Chem. Soc.*, **1935**, 1815.

factor can be of major importance, since 2,4,6-trimethylbenzyl bromide undergoes displacement reactions more rapidly than benzyl bromide.

TABLE XIII

TIMES OF HALF REACTION (IN MINUTES) FOR THE REACTION
$R—Br + Ar—NH_2 \rightarrow Ar—NH—R \cdot HBr$ AT 0° IN ABSOLUTE ETHANOL [123]

Amine	Aniline	p-Tolui-dine	o-Tolui-dine	p-Butyl-aniline	o-Butyl-aniline	Mesi-dine
R = benzyl	685	395	1200	360	3120	1740
R = 2,4,6-trimethyl-benzyl	70	45	400	33	550	515
Ratio	9.8	8.8	3.0	10.9	5.7	3.4

Unfortunately it has not been ascertained whether the reaction of 2,4,6-trimethylbenzyl bromide with arylamines (Table XIII) is actually of the S_N2 type,[124] but the dependence in kinetic order on base has been demonstrated for the reaction of 2,4,6-trimethylbenzyl chloride with hydroxide ion in 50% acetone,[125] this being one of the commonly applied criteria for an S_N2 mechanism.[4e] Other displacement reactions of 2,4,6-trimethylbenzyl halides, e.g., with alkylanilines,[126] with cyanide,[127] and with alkoxides,[128] also seem to proceed normally. This may be due in part to an accelerating inductive effect of the three methyl groups (cf. Table XII) and in part to the absence of gross steric hindrance, since the plane of the benzene ring in the transition state is at right angles to the reaction coordinate keeping the ortho-methyl groups out of the way. In fact, there may be steric assistance, just as in the S_N1 reactions of the 2,4,6-trimethylbenzyl halides (p. 89).

In agreement with the above, the failure [129] of 2,4,6-trimethylbenzyl halides to yield aldehyde in the Sommelet reaction [130] is *not* due to

[123] G. Vavon and L. Bourgeois, *Compt. rend.*, *202*, 1446, 1593 (1936).

[124] The fast reaction of p-methoxybenzyl bromide with pyridine (reference 120) has been suspected of being S_N1 (reference 119a).

[125] D. A. Brown and R. F. Hudson, *J. Chem. Soc.*, *1953*, 3352.

[126] R. Levy and J. Bolle, *Mém. services chim. état Paris*, *32*, 62 (1945); *C. A.*, *42*, 4543e (1948).

[127] R. C. Fuson and N. Rabjohn, *Org. Syntheses*, *25*, 65 (1945).

[128] I. I. Lapkin and O. M. Lapkina, *Zhur. Obshcheĭ Khim.*, *21*, 108 (1951); *22*, 1602 (1952); *C. A.*, *45*, 7080h (1951); *47*, 9293f (1953).

[129] R. C. Fuson and J. J. Denton, *J. Am. Chem. Soc.*, *63*, 654 (1941); S. J. Angyal, P. J. Morris, R. C. Rassack, and J. A. Waterer, *J. Chem. Soc.*, *1949*, 2704.

[130] S. J. Angyal in R. Adams' *Organic Reactions*, Vol. 8, Chapter 4, John Wiley & Sons, 1954.

inability to quaternize, but occurs at a later stage of the reaction:

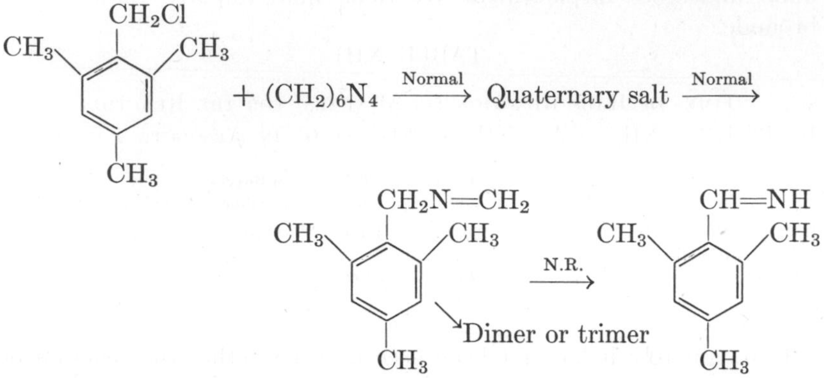

$$\text{(structure)} + (CH_2)_6N_4 \xrightarrow{\text{Normal}} \text{Quaternary salt} \xrightarrow{\text{Normal}}$$

The failure of the last step is probably due to the unfavorable steric situation in the aldimine.

An interesting difference in rate which is due purely to changes in molecular geometry has been reported [131] in the reaction of the *threo* and *erythro* isomers of 1,2-diphenyl-1-propyl bromobenzenesulfonate with lithium halides in acetone. The *threo* compounds invariably reacted much faster (and were also less stable) than the corresponding *erythro* isomers. If it is assumed that, in the transition state, the incoming group (halide, X^-) eclipses the *smallest* group (hydrogen at the other carbon), then an end-on representation of these states along the C_1—C_2 axis will be VIII for the *threo* isomer and IX for the *erythro*.

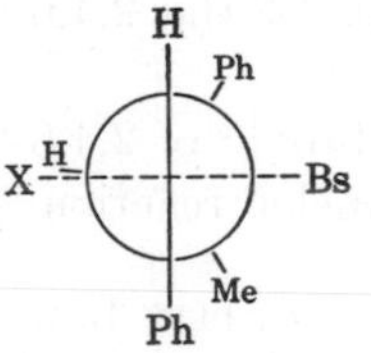

VIII (*threo*) 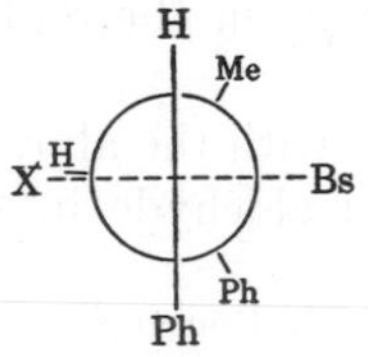   IX (*erythro*)

X = halide   Bs = *p*-bromobenzenesulfonate   Ph = phenyl   Me = methyl

It is evident that, as far as the other groups attached to C_1 and C_2 are concerned, there is less crowding in VIII than in IX; therefore VIII represents the transition state of lower energy.

ALLYLIC REARRANGEMENTS. Rearrangements have been observed in nucleophilic displacement reactions involving allylic systems.[132] Thus,

[131] D. J. Cram and F. A. Abd Elhafez, *J. Am. Chem. Soc.*, **74**, 5851 (1952).

[132] General reviews: (*a*) W. G. Young, *J. Chem. Educ.*, **27**, 357 (1950); (*b*) Ch. Prévost, *Bull. soc. chim. France*, *1951*, C1.

in the S_N1 reaction, the intermediate carbonium ion will have two extreme canonic forms as shown and can give rise to two structurally

$$R—CH{=}CH—\underset{X}{CH}—R' \rightarrow$$

$$X^- + \begin{bmatrix} R—CH{=}CH—\overset{+}{C}H—R' \\ \updownarrow \\ R—\overset{+}{C}H—CH{=}CH—R' \end{bmatrix} \xrightarrow{Y^-} \begin{bmatrix} R—CH{=}CH—\underset{Y}{CH}—R' \\ R—\underset{Y}{CH}—CH{=}CH—R' \end{bmatrix}$$

isomeric products provided $R \neq R'$. (If $R = R'$, the rearrangement can still be followed by tracer methods.[133]) The S_N1 reaction involving allylic rearrangement is often denoted by S_N1'. Similarly there is a bimolecular S_N2' reaction in which the base Y attacks the "far end" of the allylic system with a concomittant shift of the double bond and expulsion of the X group:

$$Y^- + \overset{R}{\underset{|}{C}}H{=}CH—\overset{R'}{\underset{|}{C}}HX \rightarrow Y\overset{R}{\underset{|}{C}}H—CH{=}\overset{R'}{\underset{|}{C}}H + X^-$$

Finally, the S_Ni reaction also has its analog involving allylic shift and denoted by S_Ni'. These types will now be discussed.

Rearrangements in S_N1 reactions of allylic systems have long been known.[132] They involve two interesting steric problems, unfortunately both imperfectly understood as yet. One is the question at which end

TABLE XIV

PRODUCTS OF THE REACTION *

$$R—CH^{..}CH^{..}CH_2{}^+Y^- \rightarrow$$

$$R—CH{=}CH—CH_2Y + R—CHY—CH{=}CH_2 \text{ [132b]}$$

R	Y	% Primary Product	% Secondary Product
Methyl	OH	38	62
Methyl	Cl	55	45
Methyl	Br	95	5
Methyl	OC_2H_5	90	10
Methyl	$OCOCH_3$	98	2
Phenyl	OH	75	25
Phenyl	Cl	97	3
Phenyl	Br	100	?

* No experimental details are available.

[133] E.g., R. F. Nystrom and J. C. Leak, *J. Am. Chem. Soc.*, 75, 3039 (1953).

the allylic carbonium ion is attacked by the Y reagent. Fragmentary data by Prévost [132b] (see Table XIV) indicate that steric factors may play a part here in that the more bulky Y reagents have the greater tendency to attack the ion at the primary (less hindered) end. This tendency is more marked in the phenylallyl than in the methylallyl system, corresponding to the larger bulk of the phenyl group.

Another problem is whether the configuration about the double bond is preserved in this type of allylic rearrangement. Prévost [132b] states that the secondary allyl halide, where it leads to rearranged primary product, gives predominantly the (thermodynamically more stable) *trans* compound but that the reaction of the primary halides is stereospecific in that *cis* product is obtained from *cis* starting material and *trans* product from *trans* starting material.

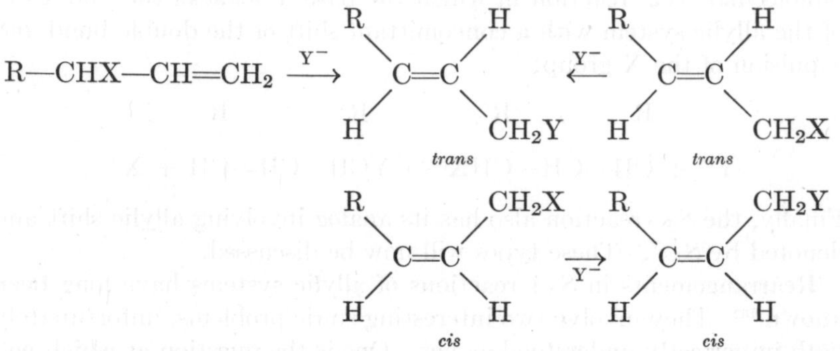

Data from the work of Prévost and of Valette [134] support this view. (See flowsheet below.) The results of the hydrolysis and acetolysis of

$$CH_2{=}CH{-}CHOH{-}CH_2OH$$

$$\downarrow PBr_3$$

$$\underset{trans}{CH_2Br{-}CH{=}CH{-}CH_2Br} \xrightarrow[H_2O]{Na_2CO_3} \underset{trans}{CH_2OH{-}CH{=}CH{-}CH_2OH} + CH_2{=}CH{-}CHOH{-}CH_2OH$$

$$\downarrow NaOAc,\ AcOH$$

$$\underset{trans}{AcOCH_2CH{=}CH{-}CH_2OAc} + CH_2{=}CHCHOAcCH_2OAc$$

$$\underset{cis}{CH_2OHCH{=}CHCH_2OH} \xrightarrow{HBr} \underset{cis}{CH_2BrCH{=}CHCH_2Br}$$

trans-1,4-dibromo-2-butene indicate *either* that the normal product is formed by an S_N2 reaction and that the S_N1 reaction leads *exclusively* to rearranged product, which is unlikely, *or* that, if part of the normal

[134] Ch. Prévost, *Ann. chim.*, [10], *10*, 129 (1928); A. Valette, *ibid.*, [12], *3*, 644 (1948).

(unrearranged) product results from an S_N1 reaction, this reaction leads to the *trans* isomer exclusively. Unfortunately, the more significant results in the *cis* series (more significant, because the *cis* isomers are the less stable and would be readily transformed into the *trans* isomers if the S_N1 reaction were not stereospecific) are scarce. If the results of Prévost and Valette are borne out, it probably means that the geometric configuration of the carbonium ion is locked by π-orbital overlap.

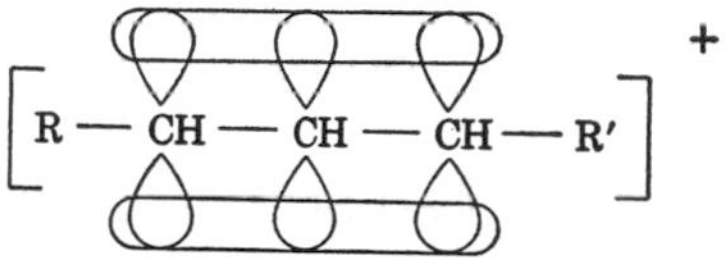

$$\left[R - CH - CH - CH - R' \right]^{+}$$

Although examples of the S_N2' reaction have probably been in the literature for some time,[135] the operation of this mechanism was first demonstrated in 1949 in the reaction of α-methylallyl chloride and α-ethylallyl chloride with sodiomalonic ester.[136] It was established not only that part of the product was rearranged (10% in the case of the methylallyl compound, 23% in the case of ethylallyl) and that the reaction followed second-order kinetics but also that neither the starting chlorides nor the reaction products rearranged under the conditions of the alkylation reaction. From the steric point of view it is interesting that the secondary halides, α-methyl- and α-ethylallyl chloride, gave partially rearranged products, presumably because of steric hindrance to the normal S_N2 reaction, but the primary halides, crotyl chloride and 1-chloro-2-pentene, gave only normal alkylation products: [136]

$$R\!-\!CHCl\!-\!CH\!=\!CH_2 + Na^{+-}CH(CO_2Et)_2 \rightarrow$$

$$CH(CO_2Et)_2$$
$$\mid$$
$$R\!-\!CH\!-\!CH\!=\!CH_2 + R\!-\!CH\!=\!CH\!-\!CH_2\!-\!CH(CO_2Et)_2$$
$$(S_N2) \qquad\qquad\qquad (S_N2')$$
$$\text{10\% (R = CH}_3\text{); 23\% (R = C}_2\text{H}_5\text{)}$$

but

$$R\!-\!CH\!=\!CH\!-\!CH_2Cl + Na^{+-}CH(CO_2Et)_2 \rightarrow$$

$$R\!-\!CH\!=\!CH\!-\!CH_2\!-\!CH(CO_2Et)_2$$
$$(S_N2) \quad \text{only}$$
$$R = CH_3 \quad \text{or} \quad C_2H_5$$

[135] See citations in reference 136; also (a) T. Reichstein, *Ber.*, *63*, 749 (1930); (b) M. M. Runde, E. W. Scott, and J. R. Johnson, *J. Am. Chem. Soc.*, *52*, 1284 (1930); (c) H. R. Snyder and E. L. Eliel, *ibid.*, *70*, 1857 (1948); (d) E. Rothstein, *J. Chem. Soc.*, *1940*, 1550.

[136] R. E. Kepner, S. Winstein and W. G. Young, *J. Am. Chem. Soc.*, *71*, 115 (1949).

The most clean-cut S_N2' reactions are obtained where the competing S_N2 reactions are suppressed by steric factors and S_N1 reactions are minimized by the choice of a highly nucleophilic reagent and a solvent of little ionizing power (low Y value, p. 69). Thus the reaction of 1,1-dimethylallyl chloride with thiophenoxide ion in ethanol gives the rearranged product in 62% yield with little contamination by unrearranged product.[137]

$$CH_2\!\!=\!\!CH\!\!-\!\!C(CH_3)_2Cl + Na^{+-}SC_6H_5 \xrightarrow[\text{kinetics}]{\text{2nd-order}}$$

$$C_6H_5SCH_2\!\!-\!\!CH\!\!=\!\!C(CH_3)_2 + Na^+Cl^-$$

Many other instances of demonstrated or presumed S_N2' reactions in acyclic,[138] alicyclic,[139] and heterocyclic [140] allylic systems are now on record.

Stork and White [139b] found that, stereochemically, the incoming group in an S_N2' reaction approaches the allylic system from the same side from which the departing anion recedes. This is reasonable if the reaction is thought of as a double inversion, involving the two ends of the allylic system: [141]

[137] P. B. D. de la Mare and C. A. Vernon, *J. Chem. Soc.*, *1953*, 3555.

[138] W. G. Young, I. D. Webb, and H. L. Goering, *J. Am. Chem. Soc.*, *73*, 1076 (1951); B. D. England, *J. Chem. Soc.*, *1955*, 1615; P. B. D. de la Mare and C. A. Vernon, *J. Chem. Soc.*, *1952*, 3325, 3331, 3628; L. F. Hatch and J. J. D'Amico, *J. Am. Chem. Soc.*, *73*, 4393 (1951); D. D. Phillips, *ibid.*, *76*, 5385 (1954); R. W. Kierstead, R. P. Linstead, and B. C. L. Weedon, *J. Chem. Soc.*, *1952*, 3610; L. H. Amundsen and W. F. Brill, *Abstracts*, Boston Meeting Am. Chem. Soc., 58M (1951); W. G. Young and J. M. Rule, unpublished experiments; P. B. D. de la Mare and C. A. Vernon, *J. Chem. Soc.*, *1954*, 3679; W. G. Young, R. A. Clement, and Chin-Hua Shih, *J. Am. Chem. Soc.*, *77*, 3061 (1955).

[139] (a) G. Stork in R. H. F. Manske and H. L. Holmes' *The Alkaloids*, Vol. 2, pp. 176, 180, 185, Academic Press, New York, 1952; (b) G. Stork and W. N. White, *J. Am. Chem. Soc.*, *75*, 4119 (1953).

[140] F. G. Bordwell, J. Weinstock, and F. Ross, *Abstracts*, Chicago Meeting Am. Chem. Soc., 60-O (1953); M. J. Kland-English and C. L. Wilson, *Abstracts*, Boston Meeting Am. Chem. Soc., 48M (1951); E. Eliel and P. Peckham, *J. Am. Chem. Soc.*, *72*, 1209 (1950); O. Moldenhauer, G. Trautmann, and R. Pfluger, *Ann.*, *583*, 61 (1953); see also reference 135a–c.

[141] The displacement of the 2,6-dichlorobenzoate ion is interesting. This ion behaves much like an inorganic one because of the high acid strength of 2,6-dichlorobenzoic acid and because the bulk of the chlorine atoms prevents attack of the base at the carbonyl oxygen.

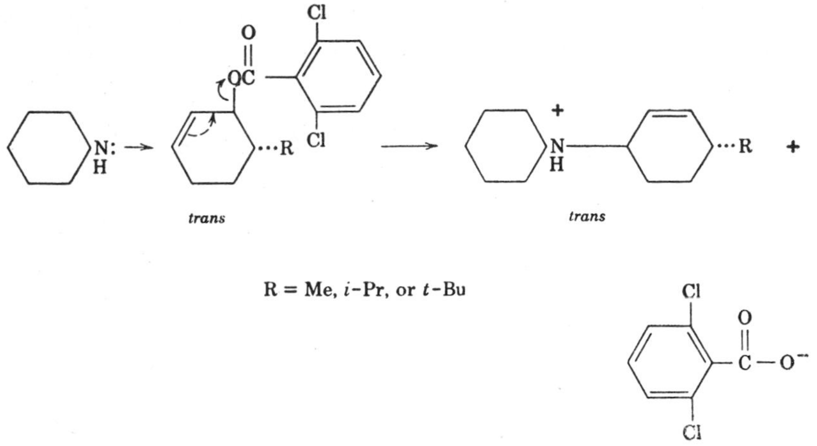

R = Me, i-Pr, or t-Bu

The reaction of 2α-bromocholestanone with potassium acetate in boiling acetic acid which gives rise to 4α-acetoxycholestanone among other products [142] may be another example of an S_N2' reaction with double inversion involving, in this instance, the enol form of the ketone.

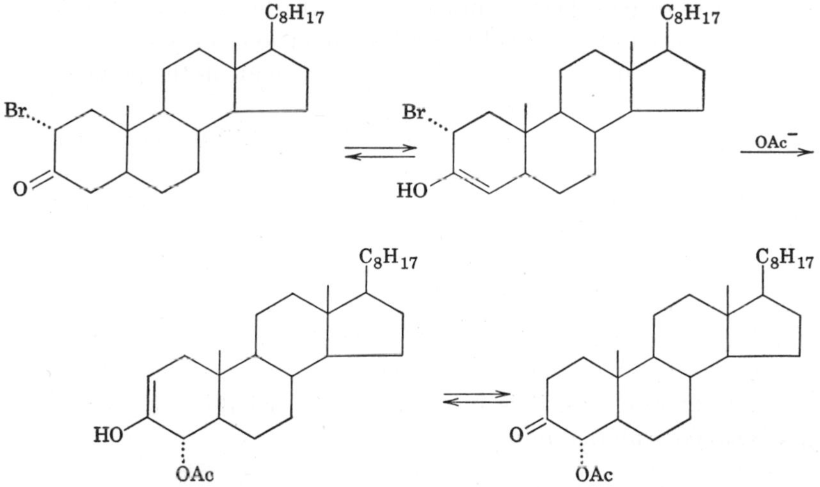

Similarly the reaction of 6β-Δ⁴-cholestene-3-one with potassium acetate which gives 2α-acetoxy-Δ⁴-cholestene-3-one [142] may be an instance of

[142] L. F. Fieser and M. A. Romero, *J. Am. Chem. Soc.*, **75**, 4716 (1953). 2α-Acetoxycholestanone, formed with retention of configuration, is another product of this reaction. Since an S_N1 displacement on an α-haloketone is unlikely (cf. p. 103), the absence of Walden inversion in this instance is very surprising and suggests thermodynamic control of the reaction; see p. 98.

an S_N2' reaction with 1,6 displacement across the conjugated system of double bonds of the enol. The stereochemical result of overall

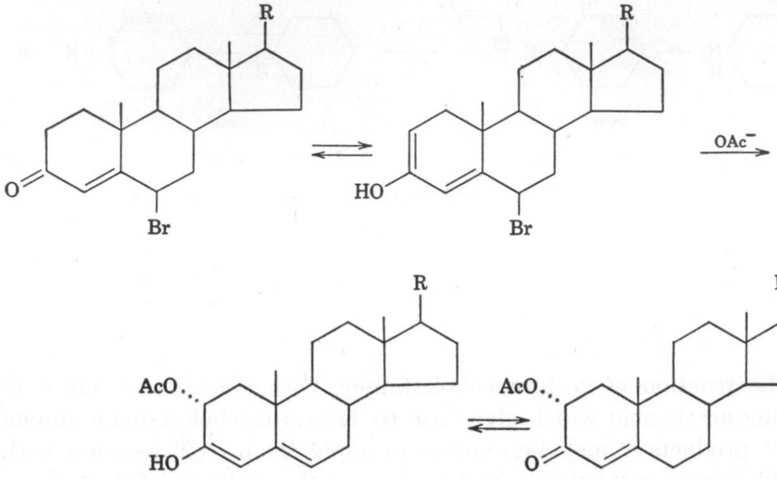

inversion is to be expected, in analogy with the results of Stork and White,[139b] since in the present case *triple* inversion should occur. Analogous stereochemical observations have been made in the progesterone and desoxycorticosterone series.[143]

Since, in all the alicyclic systems studied,[139, 142, 143] the product is the more stable epimer, the possibility that the product is determined thermodynamically rather than kinetically cannot entirely be ruled out.

Internal displacement reactions involving allylic systems are known as S_Ni' reactions. One type of this reaction is involved in the acetolysis of 1,1-dimethylallyl chloride which is accompanied by rearrangement to the 3,3-dimethyl isomer. Since this rearrangement is unaffected by external chloride ions, it is believed to proceed through an ion pair and is called "internal return." [144]

$$CH_2{=}CH{-}CMe_2Cl \rightarrow \text{Ion pair} \rightarrow ClCH_2{-}CH{=}CMe_2$$

Another type of S_Ni' process is involved in the reaction of allyl alcohols (either substituted or tagged) with thionyl chloride which may

[143] F. Sondheimer, St. Kaufmann, J. Romo, H. Martinez, and G. Rosenkranz, *J. Am. Chem. Soc.*, **75**, 4712 (1953).

[144] W. G. Young, S. Winstein, and H. L. Goering, *J. Am. Chem. Soc.*, **73**, 1958 (1951); P. B. D. de la Mare and C. A. Vernon, *J. Chem. Soc.*, *1954*, 2504.

lead to rearrangement.[145] This may proceed through a cyclic intermediate as shown in formula X or, in analogy to what has been postulated for simple $S_N i$ reactions,[73, 76] may involve an ion pair also. Intermediates somewhat similar to X may be involved in the thermal rearrangement of allylic halides.

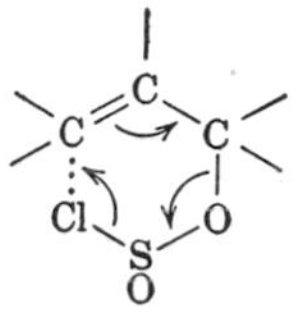

X

GEMINAL POLYHALIDES AND α-HALO ETHERS. Geminal polyhalides might be expected to react by the $S_N 1$ mechanism more readily than corresponding monohalides because of stabilization of the intermediate carbonium ion by resonance:

$$Cl\overset{+}{-}CH_2 \leftrightarrow \overset{+}{Cl}=CH_2$$

Actually, however, solvolysis of the polyhalomethanes is extremely slow (Table XV, column D; also reference 92).

TABLE XV

Compound	A	B	C	D	E	F
CH_3Cl	85	81	83	45	87	—
CH_2Cl_2	8	7	8	2	4	0.001
$CHCl_3$	84	78	85	0	1	1
CCl_4	35	15	24	—	10	0.00

A: % Completion of reaction with sodium ethoxide in absolute ethanol at 90° after 30 minutes.[146]

B: % Completion of reaction with potassium hydroxide in 95% ethanol at 90° after 30 minutes.[146]

C: % Completion of reaction with tetramethylammonium hydroxide in 95% ethanol at 90° after 30 minutes.[146]

D: % Completion of solvolysis in 50% aqueous ethanol at 90° after 12 hours.[146]

E: % Completion of reaction with piperidine in 95% ethanol at 90° after 5 hours.[146]

F: Relative reaction rates with hydroxide ion in 66⅔% aqueous dioxane at 36°.[147]

[145] W. G. Young, *Abstracts*, Twelfth National Organic Chemistry Symposium, Am. Chem. Soc., Denver, Colorado, 23 (1951), and unpublished results; H. L. Goering, T. D. Nevitt, and E. F. Silversmith, *J. Am. Chem. Soc.*, 77, 4042, 5026 (1955), F. F. Caserio, G. E. Dennis, R. H. DeWolfe, and W. G. Young, *ibid.*, 77, 4182 (1955).

[146] P. Petrenko-Kritschenko and V. Opotsky, *Ber.*, 59, 2131 (1926).

[147] J. Hine, *J. Am. Chem. Soc.*, 72, 2438 (1950).

Perhaps the inductive electron-withdrawal by the halogen atoms outweighs any resonance stabilization of the carbonium ion.

On the other hand, in the solvolysis of benzyl halides, where the S_N1 mechanism is already favored by resonance of the carbonium ion, the accumulation of halogen atoms on the benzyl carbon leads to a marked increase in solvolysis rates (Table XVI).

TABLE XVI

RELATIVE RATES OF SOLVOLYSIS IN 50% AQUEOUS ACETONE AT 30° [148]

Compound	Relative Rate
$PhCH_2Cl$	1.0
$PhCHCl_2$	9.90 *
$PhCCl_3$	496 †
$PhCH_2Br$	25.5
$PhCHBr_2$	30.8
$PhCBr_3$	5090
$PhCHClBr$	140
$PhCClBr_2$	8160
$PhCCl_2Br$	9510
$PhCF_2Cl$	0.188 ‡

* Benzal chloride solvolyses 10.5 times as fast as benzyl chloride in 50% aqueous acetone (reference 121) and 203 times as fast in formic acid (reference 92).

† Benzotrichloride reacts 500 times as fast as benzyl chloride in 50% acetone (reference 121) and 10.8 times as fast as benzal chloride in 80% ethanol (reference 92).

‡ Extrapolated from data at higher temperatures.

That B strain (cf. p. 72) is not a *predominant* factor here is indicated by the greater effect of chlorine in accelerating solvolysis as compared with bromine. Bromine is more bulky than chlorine but has less tendency to form double bonds.[149]

S_N2 reactions of geminal polyhalides are retarded by steric interference due to the bulky halogen atoms. Table XV shows that methylene chloride reacts more slowly with bases than methyl chloride does. Surprisingly, chloroform reacts much *faster* than methylene chloride with strong mineral base. Hine [147, 150] has shown that this is due to the

[148] J. Hine and D. E. Lee, *J. Am. Chem. Soc.*, *73*, 22 (1951); *74*, 3182 (1952).

[149] Fluorine, despite its greater tendency to form double bonds as compared with chlorine, is less effective in accelerating the S_N1 reaction. This may be due to the greater inductive electron-withdrawal, and possibly to the smaller size (if B strain is important) of the fluorine atom.

[150] J. Hine and A. M. Dowell, Jr., *J. Am. Chem. Soc.*, *76*, 2688 (1954).

operation of a specific mechanism involving CCl_3^- and CCl_2 as intermediates.[151]

The abnormally high reactivity of carbon tetrachloride is probably due to the fact that it, also, gives rise to CCl_3^- through an oxidation-reduction process involving the ethanol solvent.[152a]

$$CCl_4 + CH_3CH_2OH + 2OH^- \rightarrow CCl_3^- + Cl^- + 2H_2O + CH_3CHO$$

In dioxane medium, carbon tetrachloride reacts with base very slowly (Table XV, column F).

The results of a systematic study of the reaction of methylene halides with iodide and methoxide ion are summarized in Table XVII.[152b]

TABLE XVII

RATES OF REACTION OF METHYLENE HALIDES WITH IODIDE AND METHOXIDE ION AT 50° RELATIVE TO ETHYL BROMIDE TAKEN AS 100

Entry No.	Halide	with I^-	with CH_3O^-
1	CH_2Cl_2	0.0124 *	0.0602 *
2	CH_2ClBr	12.8	5.00
3	CH_2ClI	0.00912	9.35
4	CH_2BrF	79.4	476
5	CH_2Br_2	4.06 *	0.784 *
6	CH_2BrI	5.89	2.16
7	CH_2I_2	—	1.14 *
8	CH_2BrCH_3	100.0	100.0
9	CH_3Br	ca. 19,000 †	1000
10	CH_3I	—	918

* Actual rate divided by a statistical factor of 2.
† At 20°.

α-Haloethers would be expected to resemble geminal dihalides somewhat in their behavior; actually they are subject to very rapid hydrolysis by the S_N1 mechanism because of the more favorable electromeric electron-donating properties of alkoxyl groups as compared to halogen. In contrast to geminal dihalides they also react rapidly in displacement reactions with iodide ion and with other nucleophilic reagents.[153] If

[151] Chemical evidence for the dichlorocarbene (CCl_2) intermediate has been obtained by trapping it through addition to olefins: W. von E. Doering and A. Kentaro Hoffmann, J. Am. Chem. Soc., 76, 6162 (1954).

[152] (a) J. U. Nef, Ann., 308, 329 (1899); see also C. K. Ingold and W. J. Powell, J. Chem. Soc., 119, 1222 (1921). (b) J. Hine, C. H. Thomas, and S. J. Ehrenson, J. Am. Chem. Soc., 77, 3886 (1955).

[153] V. P. Gol'mov and N. M. Afanas'ev, Zhur. Obshchei Khim., 22, 1953 (1952); C. A., 47, 9269a (1953); C. T. Mason, C. W. R. Wade, and H. W. Pouncy, Jr., J. Am. Chem. Soc., 76, 2255 (1954).

these are truly S_N2 reactions, evidently it must be concluded that steric interference due to the methoxyl group is much less severe than that due to halogen and is more than outweighed by a favorable polar effect.

VICINAL POLYHALIDES. A vicinal halogen atom is known to retard the S_N1 reaction; thus the rate of solvolysis of 1,2-dichloroisobutane, $(CH_3)_2CClCH_2Cl$, is only about $1/4000$ of that for 2-chloroisobutane, $(CH_3)_2CClCH_3$.[154] This is to be expected, since the electron-withdrawing effect of the vicinal halogen atom destabilizes the carbonium ion. The situation with respect to the S_N2 reaction was confused for a long time, because in the early work [155] the reaction was followed by the appearance of halide or consumption of nucleophilic reagent and no distinction was made between substitution and accompanying elimination. Hine and Brader [156] have studied the reaction of 2-substituted ethyl bromides with the highly nucleophilic sodium thiophenolate; this reaction is not complicated by elimination. The data (Table XVIII; alkyl substituents studied by the same authors are included

TABLE XVIII

X	H	CH₃	C₂H₅	CH₃O	F	Cl	Br	I	NO₂
A	1.00	0.655	0.689	—	0.124	0.144	0.128	—	—
B	1.00	—	—	1.42 [158]	2.11	2.25	2.22	1.90	5.12

Row A: Relative reaction rates of $X\text{-}CH_2CH_2Br$ with sodium thiophenolate in methanol at 20°.[156]
Row B: Relative reaction rates of $p\text{-}X\text{-}C_6H_4CH_2CH_2Cl$ with potassium iodide in acetone at 75°.[157]

for comparison) prove that a vicinal halogen atom actually has a *retarding* effect on the S_N2 reaction. Since substitution of a halogen atom in the *para* position of 2-phenylethyl chloride has an accelerative effect (Table XVIII), the retarding effect of the halogen in 2-haloethyl bromides may be in part steric. Comparison of the fluoro with the chloro compound indicates that it is not entirely so. Perhaps bond

[154] H. C. Brown, M. Kharasch, and T. H. Chao, *J. Am. Chem. Soc.*, *62*, 3435 (1940).

[155] E.g., (a) V. V. Tronov and A. T. Gershevich, *J. Russ. Phys. Chem. Soc.*, *59*, 727 (1927); *C. A.*, *22*, 3389 (1928); (b) A. Slator, *J. Chem. Soc.*, *85*, 1286 (1904).

[156] J. Hine and W. H. Brader, *J. Am. Chem. Soc.*, *75*, 3964 (1953).

[157] G. Baddeley and G. M. Bennett, *J. Chem. Soc.*, *1935*, 1819.

[158] The retardation by *p*-methoxy as compared with hydrogen in reaction with potassium hydroxide observed by M. Simonetta and G. Favini, *J. Chem. Soc.*, *1954*, 1840, is presumably due to the fact that substitution and elimination were studied together.

breaking in the transition state has proceeded to such an extent in the dihalides that the electrostatic electron-withdrawal of the vicinal halogen has an unfavorable effect on reaction rate also.[8d, 97, 159]

The effect of an alkoxy group resembles that of halogen in that it appears to accelerate the S_N2 reaction when substituted in the *para* position of a β-phenethyl halide (Table XVIII) but retard it when directly attached to the β-carbon atom.[3, 160a] A retarding effect of the vicinal group is also observed with most halohydrins.[3, 160b]

α-HALO KETONES. α-Halo ketones react very slowly in ionization-type reactions (e.g., they fail to react with alcoholic silver nitrate) but quite fast in bimolecular displacement reactions.[3, 160] The slowness of the ionization reaction has been explained by the adverse effect of the positive end of the $\overset{+}{C}=\overset{-}{O}$ dipole on the stability of the carbonium ion. There is, however, no universal agreement on the reasons for the very fast rate of the bimolecular reaction.[161] Hughes [162] has ascribed the accelerative effect of the carbonyl group to its electron-withdrawing properties which facilitate the approach of Y^-. On this basis the same effect should be observed in α-halosulfones and α-halonitro compounds (systems $-SO_2-\overset{|}{\underset{|}{C}}-X$ and $O_2N-\overset{|}{\underset{|}{C}}-X$, respectively); in fact, however, these halides react sluggishly compared with simple alkyl halides.[163] This could be explained by steric interference of the bulky sulfone and nitro groups in the transition state of the S_N2 reaction, and, in accordance with this explanation, p-$CH_3C_6H_4SO_2CH=CHCH_2Cl$ reacts 1400 times as fast as n-butyl chloride. It is less easy to understand why 2,4,6-trimethylphenacyl

[159] Compounds of the type CF_3CH_2X seem to be highly resistant to displacement. Cf. H. M. Walborsky and M. Schwarz, *J. Am. Chem. Soc.*, *75*, 3241 (1953), footnote 12; H. Gilman and R. Jones, *ibid.*, *65*, 1458 (1943); R. N. Haszeldine and A. G. Sharpe, *Fluorine and Its Compounds*, p. 76, Methuen & Co., London, England, 1951; E. T. McBee, D. H. Campbell, and C. W. Roberts, *J. Am. Chem. Soc.*, *77*, 3149 (1955).

[160] (a) F. B. Tutwiler and R. L. McKee, *J. Am. Chem. Soc.*, *76*, 6342 (1954); (b) R. G. Pearson, S. H. Langer, F. V. Williams, and W. J. McGuire, *ibid.*, *74*, 5130 (1952).

[161] Part of the material in the following section has been drawn from the Ph.D. thesis of E. N. Trachtenberg, Harvard University, 1952. The author is indebted to Prof. P. D. Bartlett for permission to use this information.

[162] E. D. Hughes, *Trans. Faraday Soc.*, *37*, 603 (1941).

[163] F. G. Bordwell and G. D. Cooper, *J. Am. Chem. Soc.*, *73*, 5184 (1951), and earlier references cited therein.

halides [119a, 164] and the cyclic bromo ketone XI [165] also are sluggish in S_N2 displacements. The data in Table XIX suggest that the effect

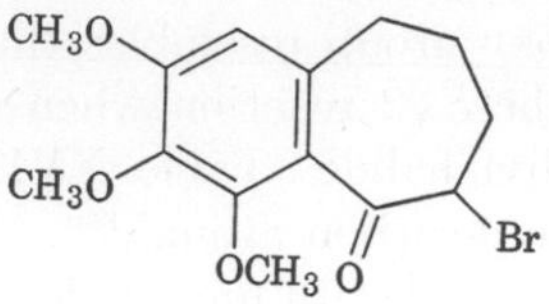

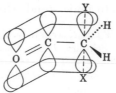

XI

in the 2,4,6-trimethylphenacyl halide at least is a steric one, since the reaction rate with the 2- and 4-monomethyl and 2,4-dimethyl compounds is only slightly less than with the parent compound.

TABLE XIX

RELATIVE RATE OF REACTION OF SUBSTITUTED PHENACYL BROMIDES WITH PYRIDINE IN ACETONE SOLUTION AT $20°$ [119a,164a]

Substituent:	H	p-t-Bu	p-Me	o-Me	2,4-di-Me	2 4,6-tri-Me	p-NO$_2$	o-NO$_2$	p-Cl	p-Br
Rate:	1.0	0.72	0.94	0.70	0.63	ca. 0	2.4	0.30	1.63	2.16

Dewar [98] has explained these facts by postulating that the effect of the carbonyl group is due to overlap of its π orbitals with the p-orbital accommodating the entering and leaving groups. This overlap will be at a maximum when the $Y\cdots C\cdots X$ bond and the $C{=}O$ bond are at right angles to each other, and models indicate that in this position the o-methyl groups in the benzene ring produce very considerable steric interference.

A different explanation of the data has been offered by J. W. Baker,[119a, 164a] who assumes that the Y^- moiety attaches itself to the carbonyl group in the rate-determining step and then shifts to the

[164] (a) J. W. Baker, J. Chem. Soc., 1933, 1128; 1938, 445; (b) D. L. Brebner and L. C. King, J. Am. Chem. Soc., 75, 2330 (1953); (c) S. H. Babcock, F. I. Nakamura, and R. C. Fuson, J. Am. Chem. Soc., 54, 4407 (1932).

[165] P. D. Gardner and W. J. Horton, J. Org. Chem., 19, 213 (1954); D. Caunt, W. D. Crow, R. D. Haworth, and C. A. Vodoz, J. Chem. Soc., 1950, 1631. The parent compound (no methoxyl groups) reacts normally with cyanide: D. S. Tarbell, H. F. Wilson, and E. Ott, J. Am. Chem. Soc., 74, 6263 (1952).

α-carbon with ejection of X$^-$ in a subsequent fast step. This explanation is not tenable as such, since it does not accommodate the very

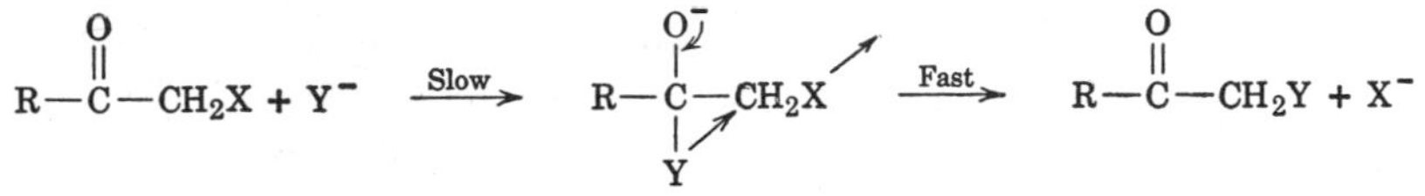

$$R-\overset{\overset{\text{O}}{\|}}{C}-CH_2X + Y^- \xrightarrow{\text{Slow}} R-\overset{\overset{O_2^-}{|}}{\underset{Y}{C}}-CH_2X \xrightarrow{\text{Fast}} R-\overset{\overset{\text{O}}{\|}}{C}-CH_2Y + X^-$$

considerable difference in rate between phenacyl chloride and phenacyl bromide,[159, 166] but it can easily be modified so as to avoid this difficulty by assuming a triangular transition state (XII, resonance hybrid between attack at carbonyl and attack at α-carbon).[161, 167] Methyl

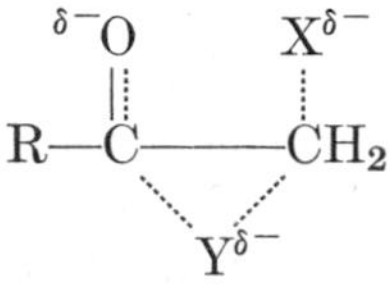

$$R-\overset{\overset{\delta^-O}{\|\|}}{\underset{\underset{Y^{\delta^-}}{\diagup}}{C}}\cdots\cdots\overset{X^{\delta^-}}{\underset{}{CH_2}}$$

XII

substituents in the *ortho* positions of the ring are known to interfere sterically with approach to the carbonyl function (Chapter 4) and would therefore make this transition state unattractive.

Further experiments designed to decide whether the effect of the carbonyl group is mainly electrostatic, or whether a transition state such as XII is involved, are due to Bartlett and Trachtenberg[161] and to Pearson and coworkers,[160] and were interpreted somewhat differently by the two groups of investigators. A study of the open-chain phenacyl halide XIII and its cyclic analog XIV revealed that XIII reacts about 9000 times faster with iodide at 0° than XIV (the data for XIV were extrapolated from rate measurements at higher temperatures).[161] This result cannot easily be accommodated on the

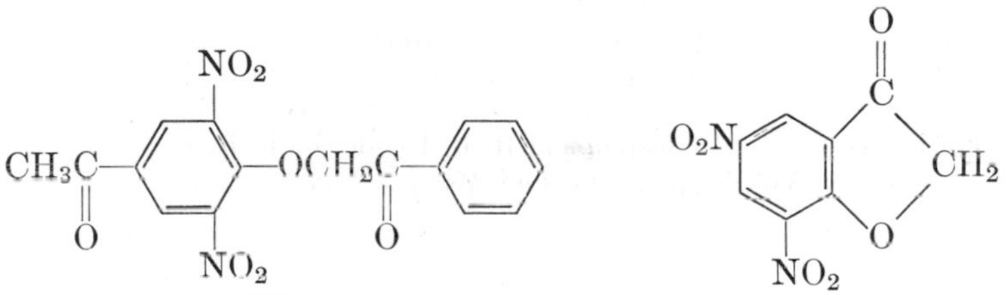

XIII   XIV

166 The bromide reacts faster. If this were an indirect effect on the carbonyl group, the chloride should react faster on either polar or steric grounds, since chlorine is smaller and more electron-withdrawing than bromine.

167 S. Winstein, quoted by P. D. Bartlett in H. Gilman's *Organic Chemistry*, Vol. 3, p. 35, John Wiley & Sons, New York, 1953.

basis of a simple inductive effect, since on that basis the two compounds should differ only slightly.[167a] As the triangular transition state (XII) can be realized with XIII, but not with XIV, the difference in rate of the two compounds seems to provide evidence for such a transition state. On the other side, it was stressed [160] that the accelerative effect of the carbonyl group is greater in displacements involving highly nucleophilic but feebly basic reagents (cf. p. 157) such as thiourea,[160] iodide,[136] and thiosulfate [155b, 168] than in reactions involving the more basic but less nucleophilic agent pyridine.[160, 169] From this it was concluded [160] that covalent attachment of the reagent at the carbonyl function (as in XII) was not of major importance.[169a] It would appear that transition state XII or the picture given by Dewar (p. 104) seems best to account for the reactivity of α-halo ketones, the difference of interpretation [160, 161, 167a] being confined to the ionic or covalent nature of the link between Y and the carbonyl carbon.

RING OPENING OF EPOXIDES. Much has been written regarding the ring opening of epoxides.[170] Nevertheless, the subject is still in a somewhat confused state. Table XX gives a survey of ring-opening reactions of unsymmetrical epoxides with special emphasis on more recent publications not covered in the earlier review.[170] This survey is believed to be representative, but by no means exhaustive; an exhaustive survey is not within the scope of this chapter.

[167a] Professor Pearson, in a personal communication, suggested that the results are not incompatible with an inductive effect, provided that the orientation of the carbonyl dipole with respect to the direction of approach of the nucleophilic agent Y is given consideration. If Y approaches from the direction of the positive end of the carbonyl dipole, displacement will be assisted most effectively. In XIV this is sterically impossible, and therefore there is little assistance of displacement. Similar considerations apply to 2,4,6-trimethylphenacyl halide and to compound XI.

[168] A. Slator and D. F. Twiss, J. Chem. Soc., 87, 481 (1905); 95, 93 (1909).

[169] H. T. Clarke, J. Chem. Soc., 97, 416 (1910).

[169a] The implicit assumption that ease of attack on carbonyl is determined by basicity rather than by nucleophilic character of the anion may not, however, be valid.

[170] For a review, see S. Winstein and R. B. Henderson in R. Elderfield's Heterocyclic Compounds, Vol. 1, pp. 22–46, John Wiley & Sons, New York, 1950.

TABLE XX

RING-OPENING REACTIONS OF EPOXIDES OF THE TYPE

$$R-CH\underset{\displaystyle O}{\overset{\displaystyle \diagup\;\diagdown}{\longrightarrow}}CH_2 + HX \rightarrow \underset{\substack{|\\OH\\ \\A}}{R-CHCH_2X} + \underset{\substack{|\\X\\ \\B}}{R-CH-CH_2OH}$$

Entry No.	R	HX	Added Acid or Base	Yield %A	Yield %B	Reference
1	CH_3	$HOCH_3$	CH_3ONa	63	0	171
2			H_2SO_4	15	6	171
3		HOC_2H_5	NaOH	81	2	172
4			None	56	16	172
5			H_2SO_4	25	31	172
6		$HOCH_2CH{=}CH_2$	$CH_2{=}CHCH_2ONa$	80	0	173
7			H_2SO_4	34	50	173
8		HOC_6H_5	NaOH	90	0	174
9			$C_6H_5SO_3H$	3.3	3.2	174
10		$HCH(CO_2Et)(COCH_3)$	NaOEt	61 *	0	175
11		$HCH(CO_2Et)_2$	NaOEt	Low *	None?	176
12		$HCH(CN)(CO_2Et)$	NaOEt	61 *	0	177
13		NaN_3	None	Only	Trace?	178
14		LiC_6H_5	None	58	0	179
15	C_2H_5	H_4LiB	None	57	0	180
16	$n\text{-}C_4H_9$	HOC_6H_5	BF_3	Much	Little	181
17	$n\text{-}C_6H_{13}$	HSO_3Na	Na_2SO_3	0	14.5	182
18	$n\text{-}C_8H_{17}$	H_4AlLi	None	90	0	183
19	$CH_2{=}CH$	$HOCH_3$	CH_3ONa	Mixture		184
20			H_2SO_4	?	40–63	184
21		$HOCH_2CH{=}CH_2$	$CH_2{=}CH{-}CH_2ONa$	0	66	173
22			H_2SO_4	Little	Much	173
23		$HCH(CO_2Et)(COCH_3)$	NaOEt	ca. 27.5 *	ca. 27.5 *	175
24		$HCH(CO_2Et)_2$	NaOEt	64 *	0	185
25		$HCH(CN)(CO_2Et)$	NaOEt	65–74 *	0	186
26		NaN_3	None	[16] †	23 †	178
27		H_4LiAl	None ‡	70	30	187
28			None §	83	17	187, 188
29	C_6H_5	$HOCH_3$	CH_3ONa	52	27	189, 190
30			H_2SO_4	4	38	189, 191
31		$HOCH_2CH{=}CH_2$	$CH_2{=}CHCH_2ONa$	ca. 73	ca. 8	173, 192
32			H_2SO_4	0	83	173, 192, 193
33		HOC_6H_5	$NaOH, H_2O$	20	65	194, 195

TABLE XX (*Continued*)

RING-OPENING REACTIONS OF EPOXIDES OF THE TYPE

Entry No.	R	HX	Added Acid or Base	% A	% B	Reference
				Yield		
34	C_6H_5	HOC_6H_5	$NaOC_6H_5$, dioxane	41	36	194, 195
35			$p\text{-}CH_3C_6H_4SO_3H$	1	15	196
36		HCH (with CO_2Et and $COCH_3$)	NaOEt	56 *	0	175
37		$HCH(CO_2Et)_2$	NaOEt	72 *	0	185
38		HCH (with CN and CO_2Et)	NaOEt	91.5 ‖	0	186
39		NaN_3	None	None	63	197, 178
40		LiC_6H_5	None	70–72	0	179
41		H_4LiAl	None	94	0	198
42		H_4LiB	None	74	26	180
43		H_3N	None	57	17	199
44		Amines	None	Only	None	191
45		$HNHCH_2C_6H_5$	None	62–63	4	200
46			$C_6H_5CH_2NH_3^+$, No solv.	56–57	8–9	200
47			$C_6H_5CH_2NH_3^+$, CH_3OH	8–18	14–27	200
48		Various tertiary amine salts	None	5–21	52–88	201
49		HSO_3Na	Na_2SO_3	None	91	182
50		Mercaptans	Base	Only?	None?	202
51	$p\text{-}O_2NC_6H_4\text{-}$	HOC_6H_5	NaOH, H_2O	53	26	203
52			$p\text{-}CH_3C_6H_4SO_3H$	?	Some	203
53		$HCH(CO_2Et)_2$	NaOEt	46	0	204
54		H_4LiB	None	38	62	180
55	$m\text{-}O_2NC_6H_4\text{-}$	HOC_6H_5	NaOH, H_2O	63	31	205
56			$p\text{-}CH_3C_6H_5SO_3H$	?	Some	205
57	$o\text{-}O_2NC_6H_4\text{-}$	HOC_6H_5	NaOH, H_2O	69	27	205
58	$p\text{-}CH_3OC_6H_4\text{-}$	HOC_6H_5	NaOH, H_2O or dioxane	?	46	206
59		H_4LiB	None	<5	>95	180
60	$2,4,6\text{-}(CH_3)_3C_6H_2$	HOC_6H_5	NaOH	?	42?	207
61	$p\text{-}BrC_6H_4$	H_4LiB	None	84	16	180
62	$ROCH_2$	¶	NaOEt	Only	None	181, 208
63	ϕOCH_2	$HNaSO_3$	Na_2SO_3	69	None	182
64	$ClCH_2$	Any HX	Acid *or* base	Only	None	209
65	R_2NCH_2	Malonic ester	NaOEt	Only *	None	210

* Lactone.

† The yield refers to the amines produced by reduction of the product azides, the figure in brackets being for the reduction product of N_3—CH_2—CH=CH—CH_2OH presumably formed by an S_N2' reaction.

‡ $\dfrac{LiAlH_4}{Epoxide} = 2:1$ molar ratio.

§ 0.26:1 molar ratio.

‖ Mixture of diastereoisomeric lactones.

¶ Malonate, ethylmalonate, acetoacetate, cyanoacetate.

[171] W. Reeve and A. Sadle, *J. Am. Chem. Soc.*, *72*, 1251 (1950).

[172] H. C. Chitwood and B. T. Freure, *J. Am. Chem. Soc.*, *68*, 680 (1946).

[173] D. Swern, G. N. Billen, and H. B. Knight, *J. Am. Chem. Soc.*, *71*, 1152 (1949).

[174] A. R. Sexton and E. C. Britton, *J. Am. Chem. Soc.*, *70*, 3606 (1948).

[175] R. M. Adams and C. A. VanderWerf, *J. Am. Chem. Soc.*, *72*, 4368 (1950).

[176] J. A. McRae, E. H. Charlesworth, F. R. Archibald, and D. S. Alexander, *Can. J. Research*, *21B*, 186 (1943).

[177] S. A. Glickman and A. C. Cope, *J. Am. Chem. Soc.*, *67*, 1012 (1945).

[178] C. A. VanderWerf, R. Y. Heisler, and W. E. McEwen, *J. Am. Chem. Soc.*, *76*, 1231 (1954).

[179] S. J. Cristol, J. R. Douglass, and J. S. Meek, *J. Am. Chem. Soc.*, *73*, 816 (1951).

[180] R. Fuchs and C. A. VanderWerf, *J. Am. Chem. Soc.*, *76*, 1631 (1954).

[181] G. Van Zyl, G. D. Zuidema, J. F. Zack, and P. B. Kromann, *J. Am. Chem. Soc.*, *75*, 5002 (1953).

[182] R. Ten Eyck Schenck and S. Kaizerman, *J. Am. Chem. Soc.*, *75*, 1636 (1953).

[183] M. S. Newman, G. Underwood, and M. Renoll, *J. Am. Chem. Soc.*, *71*, 3362 (1949).

[184] R. G. Kadesch, *J. Am. Chem. Soc.*, *68*, 41 (1946); P. D. Bartlett and S. D. Ross, *J. Am. Chem. Soc.*, *70*, 926 (1948).

[185] R. R. Russell and C. A. VanderWerf, *J. Am. Chem. Soc.*, *69*, 11 (1947).

[186] G. D. Zuidema, P. L. Cook, and G. Van Zyl, *J. Am. Chem. Soc.*, *75*, 294 (1953).

[187] R. Fuchs and C. A. VanderWerf, *J. Am. Chem. Soc.*, *74*, 5917 (1952).

[188] L. W. Trevoy and W. G. Brown, *J. Am. Chem. Soc.*, *71*, 1675 (1949).

[189] W. Reeve and I. Christoffel, *J. Am. Chem. Soc.*, *72*, 1480 (1950).

[190] A. Kaelin, *Helv. Chim. Acta*, *30*, 2132 (1947).

[191] W. Emerson, *J. Am. Chem. Soc.*, *67*, 516 (1945).

[192] F. N. Hayes and C. Gutberlet, *J. Am. Chem. Soc.*, *72*, 3321 (1950).

[193] M. S. Newman, B. J. Magerlein, and W. B. Wheatley, *J. Am. Chem. Soc.*, *68*, 2112 (1946).

[194] C. O. Guss, *J. Am. Chem. Soc.*, *71*, 3460 (1949).

[195] C. O. Guss and H. R. Williams, *J. Org. Chem.*, *16*, 1809 (1951).

[196] C. O. Guss, H. R. Williams, and L. H. Jules, *J. Am. Chem. Soc.*, *73*, 1257 (1951).

[197] W. E. McEwen, W. E. Conrad, and C. A. VanderWerf, *J. Am. Chem. Soc.*, *74*, 1168 (1952).

[198] R. F. Nystrom and W. G. Brown, *J. Am. Chem. Soc.*, *70*, 3738 (1948).

[199] A. J. Castro, D. K. Brain, H. D. Fisher, and R. K. Fuller, *J. Org. Chem.*, *19*, 1444 (1954).

[200] C. L. Browne and R. E. Lutz, *J. Org. Chem.*, *17*, 1187 (1952).

[201] L. C. King, N. W. Berst, and F. N. Hayes, *J. Am. Chem. Soc.*, *71*, 3498 (1949).

[202] H. Gilman and L. Fullhart, *J. Am. Chem. Soc.*, *71*, 1478 (1949).

[203] C. O. Guss and H. G. Mautner, *J. Org. Chem.*, *16*, 887 (1951).

[204] S. J. Cristol and R. F. Helmreich, *J. Am. Chem. Soc.*, *74*, 4083 (1952).

[205] C. O. Guss, *J. Org. Chem.*, *17*, 678 (1952).

[206] C. O. Guss, *J. Am. Chem. Soc.*, *74*, 2561 (1952).

[207] C. O. Guss, *J. Am. Chem. Soc.*, *75*, 3177 (1953).

[208] R. Rothstein and J. Ficini, *Compt. rend.*, *234*, 1694 (1952); F. G. Ponomarev, *Doklady Akad. Nauk S.S.S.R.*, *87*, 609 (1952); *C. A.*, *48*, 108h (1954).

[209] *Epichlorohydrin*, Technical Booklet SC 49-35, Shell Chemical Corp., 1949.

[210] R. Rothstein, K. Binovic, and O. Stoven, *Bull. soc. chim. France*, *1953*, 401.

In a few cases, confusion has arisen because of contradictory experimental results.[211] These have been due to the difficulty in separating and analyzing for the two isomeric products (sometimes the minor isomer has escaped detection altogether [191, 200]), to difficulties in synthesizing authentic specimens of the possible isomeric products,[212] and perhaps in some instances also to the sensitivity of the product ratio to relatively minor changes in reaction conditions. Thus the product ratio may be affected by changes in solvent (entries 33 and 34, 46 and 47, Table XX) and in proportion of reagents (entries 27 and 28).

The major difficulty, however, has been in the mechanistic interpretation of the ring-opening reactions of unsymmetrical epoxides. Several different mechanisms, S_N1 and S_N2, uncatalyzed or catalyzed by acids have been called into play to explain the divergent results.[170,]

Classification of epoxide ring opening according to the S_N1-S_N2 dichotomy is probably not convenient. Under such a classification, predominant attack at secondary positions in aliphatic epoxides (entries 5, 7), increased substitution at secondary positions in the presence of acids (entries 1, 2, 3; 5; 6, 7; 8, 9; 29, 30; 31, 32; 33, 35; 45, 46) and in the presence of ionizing solvents (entries 33, 34; 46, 47), and the predominant attack at the secondary position in p-methoxystyrene oxide as compared with styrene oxide (entries 58, 34; 59, 42) would all have to be explained by incursion of the S_N1 mechanism. Unfortunately, most of these cases have not been kinetically or stereochemically controlled, but in the few cases where stereochemical studies

[211] For example, references 191 and 189; 193, 173, and 192. M. Mousseron, R. Jacquier, M. Mousseron-Canet, and R. Zagdoun, *Bull. soc. chim. France, 1952*, 1042, have reported that the reduction of ethylidenecyclohexane epoxide (i) with lithium aluminum hydride gives methyl cyclohexyl carbinol (ii), while A. W. Burgstahler, Ph.D. dissertation, Harvard University, 1952, reports 1-ethylcyclohexanol (iii) as the product of this reaction.

[212] For example, it was overlooked (reference 191) that the reaction R'—CHOH—CH$_2$Br + OR$^-$ often does *not* give R'—CHOH—CH$_2$OR, because the epoxide is formed from the bromohydrin first (the internal displacement reaction being very fast) and then opens up to form either R'—CHOH—CH$_2$OR or R'—CHOR—CH$_2$OH. Cf. reference 194; N. H. Cromwell and Kwang-Chung Tsou, *J. Org. Chem., 15*, 1219 (1950); H. Bretschneider and N. Karpitschka, *Monatsh., 84*, 1043 (1953). The latter case is *particularly* surprising since it involves reaction with the highly nucleophilic and feebly basic azide ion. On the other hand, in reference 201 different products are reported from the reaction of isomeric halohydrins with pyridine.

have been carried out, both the uncatalyzed and the acid-catalyzed reactions have been shown to involve extensive, if not complete, inversion of configuration. Thus, the reaction of cyclopentene oxide with sodiomalonic ester gives *trans*-2-hydroxycyclopentylmalonic ester (XV),[213] and the reaction of 1,2-dimethylcyclopentene oxide with lithium aluminum hydride gives *trans*-1,2-dimethylcyclopentanol-1 (XVI).[188] Among acid-catalyzed reactions, the addition of methanol to cyclohexene oxide in the presence of sulfuric acid gives *trans*-2-methoxycyclohexanol,[214] and even the addition of piperidine to the stilbene oxides (XVII) in the presence of piperidine hydrobromide proceeds in stereospecific fashion,[200] although this system might be considered particularly prone to react by an S_N1 mechanism. Thus the *cis* isomer (XVIIa) gives only the *threo* amino alcohol XVIIIa; the *trans* oxide (XVIIb) gives exclusively the *erythro* amino alcohol XVIIIb.[215]

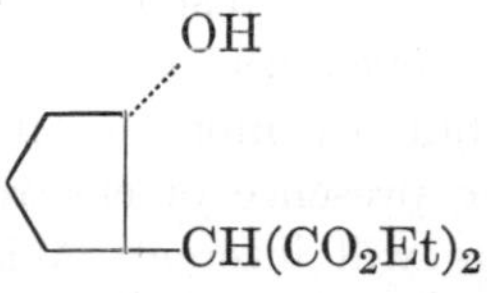

XV

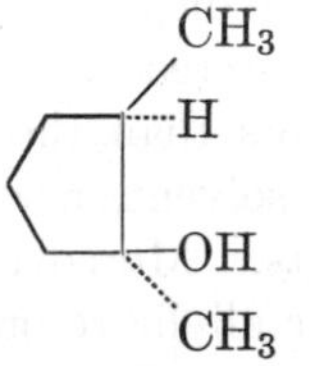

XVI

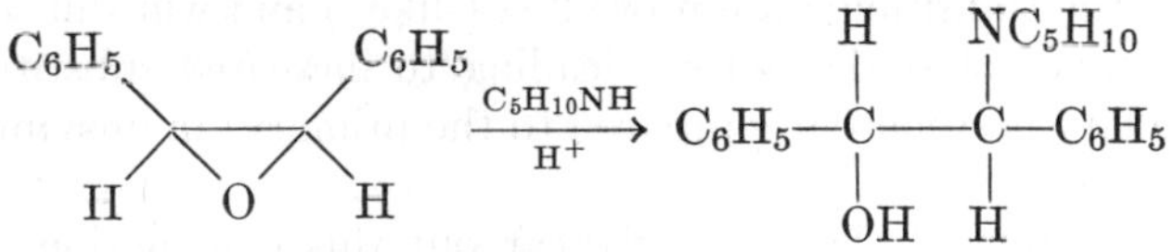

XVIIa (*cis*) $\xrightarrow[\text{H}^+]{\text{C}_5\text{H}_{10}\text{NH}}$ XVIIIa (*threo*)

[213] W. E. Grigsby, J. Hind, J. Chanley, and F. H. Westheimer, *J. Am. Chem. Soc.*, *64*, 2606 (1942).

[214] S. Winstein and R. B. Henderson, *J. Am. Chem. Soc.*, *65*, 2196 (1943).

[215] Reaction with the *trans* oxide (XVIIb) is faster than with the *cis* oxide (XVIIa). This is a typical conformational effect in the transition state (cf. Chapter 5). If the epoxide ring is opened in *trans* fashion (cf. p. 130), then, in the transition state (iv) for the *cis* oxide, the phenyl groups will be *gauche*, but in the transition state (v) for the *trans* oxide, the phenyl groups will be *trans*, and will therefore offer less steric interference. Cf. D. Y. Curtin, *Rec. Chem. Progr. Kresge-Hooker Sci. Lib.*, *15*, 111 (1954).

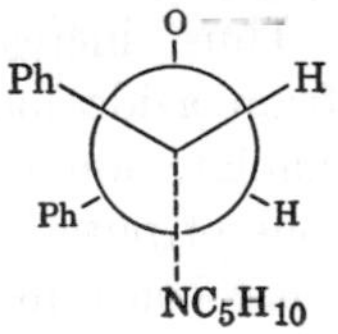

iv 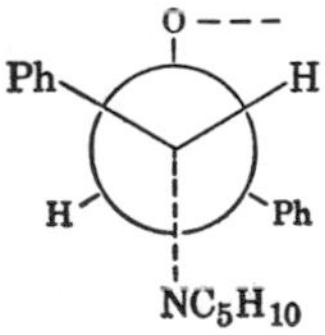   v

$$C_6H_5, \quad H \xrightarrow[\text{H}^+]{C_5H_{10}NH} \quad C_6H_5-\underset{\underset{OH}{|}}{\overset{\overset{H}{|}}{C}}-\underset{\underset{NC_5H_{10}}{|}}{\overset{\overset{H}{|}}{C}}-C_6H_5$$

$$H \quad O \quad C_6H_5$$

XVII*b* (*trans*)   XVIII*b* (*erythro*)

A consistent explanation of the reactivity of epoxides has been given [180, 216] in terms of the unified "push-pull" mechanism of Swain.[8c, d] Because of the strain in the three-membered ring of the epoxide, bond breaking in $R-CH-CH_2$ will be more important than in the corre-

sponding halides $RCHXCH_3$ and RCH_2CH_2X and will be especially important in acid-catalyzed reactions, since the facile coordination of a proton or Lewis acid on the epoxide oxygen provides a strong "pull" in the displacement. As a result, "S_N2" displacement reactions (using the stereochemical criterion) of epoxides are less sensitive to steric factors than those of halides, but are more sensitive to such factors as solvent, resonance, and the presence of electron-releasing substituents. Moreover, these factors will interact: Acid catalysis, benzylic or allylic resonance, electron-releasing substituents, and ionizing solvents will favor bond-breaking in the transition state (i.e., will make the transition state more "S_N1-like") and will thus decrease the importance of steric factors, leading to increased substitution at the secondary position (as compared to the primary) in unsymmetrical epoxides.

Examples from Table XX will bear out this explanation. In aliphatic epoxides (entries 1–18; 54–57) steric factors will direct attack toward the primary position, unless bond breaking is facilitated by acid catalysts (entries 2, 5, 7). In butadiene and styrene oxide, on the other hand, bond breaking is facilitated by resonance of the incipient carbonium ion:

$$C=\overset{+}{C}-C-C-O^- \leftrightarrow \overset{+}{C}-C=C-C-O^-$$

and secondary attack occurs more readily, even in the absence of acids (entries 19, 21, 23, 26, 29, 33, 39). The product ratio may depend on quite delicate steric factors here. Thus, increasing the steric requirement of the nucleophilic agent from azide ion (entry 39) to methoxide ion (entries 19, 29) to the enolate ion of malonic ester (entries 24, 37) shifts the product from one of pure secondary to one of pure primary attack. Keeping the base constant, increasing the

[216] A. Feldstein and C. A. VanderWerf, *J. Am. Chem. Soc.*, **76**, 1626 (1954).

steric requirement from butadiene oxide to styrene oxide again enhances primary attack (entries 21, 31; 23, 36). Sometimes, the effect is so subtle as to elude ready explanation (entries 19 vs. 21, 23 vs. 25). With lithium aluminum hydride, increasing the proportion of the reagent increases the concentration of AlH_4^- (low steric requirement) as an effective reducing agent and decreases the importance of $Al(OR)_nH_{4-n}$ (higher steric requirement), thus increasing attack at the secondary position (entries 27, 28). The greater amount of secondary attack on the styrene oxide with lithium borohydride as compared to lithium aluminum hydride (entries 41, 42) may be due to lesser steric requirements of the borohydride.[217]

More ionizing media should make the transition state more "S_N1-like," i.e., enhance the importance of bond breaking and therefore favor attack at secondary positions; this is indeed the case (entries 33, 34; 46, 47). Indirectly, this may be the reason why reactions commonly carried out in solvents of little ionizing power (low Y-value, cf. p. 69) lead to less secondary attack than those carried out in aqueous media. Thus 1,1-diphenylethylene oxide is attacked at the benzylic (secondary) position by sodium β-naphthoxide in water,[220] but at the primary position by phenyllithium in ether.[179]

[217] It is realized that factors other than steric ones, such as base strength, effects of solvation of ions, presence of Lewis acids in the case of the hydrides, etc., may be important in some or all of these instances (see also 216). However, the importance of steric factors is suggested by the fact that disecondary epoxides, such as 1,2-epoxytetralin (vi) (reference 218) and various ring substituted β-methyl-styrene oxides (vii) (reference 219) are attacked at the benzylic position exclusively.

(vi)

R = R' = CH₃O

or R = CH₃O, R' = H

or R, R' = CH₂

(vii)

[218] E. E. van Tamelen, G. Van Zyl, and G. D. Zuidema, J. Am. Chem. Soc., 72, 488 (1950).

[219] C. Mannich and F. Schmitt, Arch. Pharm., 266, 73 (1928). The compounds actually used as starting materials are the bromohydrins ArCHOHCHBrCH₃, but the reaction undoubtedly proceeds via the epoxide; cf. reference 212. See also E. Fourneau and G. Benoit, Bull. soc. chim. France, 12, 985 (1945).

[220] C. O. Guss, R. Rosenthal, and R. F. Brown, J. Am. Chem. Soc., 75, 2393 (1953).

In styrene oxide, a *para* substituent capable of spreading out positive charge, such as methoxyl or methyl, should favor the "S_N1-like" transition state and therefore encourage attack at the secondary (benzylic) position; this, again, is the case (entries 34, 58; 42, 59). Conversely, a mildly electron-withdrawing substituent, such as *p*-bromo and *m*-nitro (entries 33, 55; 42, 61), will encourage attack at the primary position.[221] This is also evidenced in *para*-substituted stilbene oxides where the *p*-methyl compound is attacked by lithium aluminum hydride predominantly at the substituted ring, but the *p*-chloro compound predominantly at the unsubstituted ring.[216] The effect of the strongly electron-withdrawing *para*-nitro substituent is not so simple. Decreased secondary attack might be expected and is indeed observed in at least one example (entries 33, 51); yet in another (entries 42, 54) secondary attack is *enhanced*. Here the encouragement of bond making by the nitro group may outweigh its adverse effect on bond breaking, the transition state being such that bond breaking has proceeded to a lesser extent than usual. Similar reversals in substituted benzyl halides are known.[8d]

In view of this, it is surprising that epoxyketones are attacked predominantly at the β position by lithium aluminum hydride[222] and exclusively so by amines:[223]

$$C_6H_5CH\!\!-\!\!-\!\!CHCOC_6H_5 + \text{(isoquinoline)NH} \rightarrow$$

$$\text{(isoquinoline)N}\!-\!CH\!-\!CHOHCOC_6H_5 \quad (94\%)$$
$$\underset{C_6H_5}{|}$$

This may be indicative of peculiar geometric restrictions on the transition state. (See the discussion on α-halo ketones, p. 103.)

STERIC EFFECTS IN RING-CLOSURE REACTIONS. Ease of ring closure will be discussed here in so far as it depends on the number and kind of the atoms in the ring and on ring substituents.[224] Little quantitative information is available on the formation of carbocyclic com-

[221] The *o*-nitro group (entry 57) may not be comparable, since it may inhibit attack at the secondary position by steric interference.

[222] W. Herz, *J. Am. Chem. Soc.*, *74*, 2928 (1952).

[223] (a) N. H. Cromwell and N. G. Barker, *J. Am. Chem. Soc.*, *72*, 4110 (1950); (b) N. G. Barker and N. H. Cromwell, *ibid.*, *73*, 1051 (1951).

[224] Dependence on solvent has been discussed by G. Salomon, *Trans. Faraday Soc.*, *32*, 153 (1936), but is outside the scope of this chapter.

pounds by ring closure involving substitution at saturated carbon atoms, but a number of such ring closures have been studied from the preparative point of view.[225] For example, the reaction of a poly-methylene dibromide with acetoacetic ester in the form of its enolate ion gives carbocyclic derivatives except where the ring formed would be four-membered, when ring closure at the oxygen atom takes place instead. This reaction suggests at least qualitatively that the four-membered ring is more difficult to form than a three-, five-, six- or seven-membered one.

$$Br(CH_2)_nBr + CH_3COCH_2CO_2Et \xrightarrow{NaOEt} CH_3CO-C-CO_2Et \quad n = 2, 4, 5, 6$$
$$\underset{(CH_2)_n}{}$$

$$Br(CH_2)_3Br + CH_3-COCH_2CO_2Et \xrightarrow{NaOEt} CH_3-C=CCO_2Et$$
$$\underset{O}{} \quad \underset{CH_2}{}$$
$$H_2C-CH_2$$

Again Gol'mov[226] found that dihalides of the type $X(CH_2)_nX$ in reaction with sodiomalonic ester will give good yields of ω-haloalkyl-malonic ester when $n = 3$, 5 or 6, since the 4-, 6- and 7-membered rings form but slowly. However, when $n = 2$ or 4, the principal product was cyclic, demonstrating the ready closure of cyclopropane and cyclopentane rings.

More quantitative data for the ring closure of ω-haloamines, halo-hydrins, and halosulfides[227] confirm that the ease of ring closure in small and common rings as a function of the number of atoms in the rings is three-membered > four-membered < five-membered > six-membered > seven-membered.

The data on the ring closure of ω-bromoalkylamines[228] are summarized in Table XXI. It is evident that the irregular trend of rates is due to a combination of more regular trends in activation energy and frequency factor. The activation energy decrease from three- to five-membered rings is a measure of the decreased strain involved in

[225] Cf. R. C. Fuson, *Advanced Organic Chemistry*, p. 422, John Wiley & Sons, New York, 1950; W. H. Perkin, *J. Chem. Soc.*, *1929*, 1347.

[226] V. P. Gol'mov, *Zhur. Obshchei Khim.*, *22*, 1944 (1952); *C. A.*, *47*, 9267h (1953).

[227] See the review by G. M. Bennett, *Trans. Faraday Soc.*, *37*, 794 (1941).

[228] (a) H. Freundlich and A. Krestornikov, *Z. physik. Chem.*, *76*, 79 (1911); (b) H. Freundlich and M. B. Richards, *ibid.*, *79*, 681 (1912); (c) H. Freundlich and W. Neumann, *ibid.*, *87*, 69 (1914); (d) H. Freundlich and R. Bartels, *ibid.*, *101*, 177 (1922); (e) H. Freundlich and H. Kroepelin, *ibid.*, *122*, 39 (1926); (f) H. Freundlich and G. Salomon, *ibid.*, *166*, 161 (1933); (g) G. Salomon, *Helv. Chim. Acta*, *16*, 1361 (1933); *17*, 851 (1934); *19*, 743 (1936).

TABLE XXI

RELATIVE RATES OF THE REACTION

$$Br(CH_2)_nNH_2 \longrightarrow (CH_2)_nNH \cdot HBr$$

Atoms in Ring	3	4	5	6	7	10	12	14, 15	17
k (relative)	0.072	0.001	60 *	1.00	0.002	ca. 2×10^{-10}	ca. 10^{-7}	2×10^{-6}	4×10^{-6}
E (kcal.)	24.9	23.2	ca. 16.8	ca. 18.3	24.9	—	—	—	—
log PZ sec.$^{-1}$	14.8	11.4	ca. 12	ca. 11	13.3	—	—	—	—

* Calculated from corresponding chloro compound.

making the ends of the rings approach. It is not immediately obvious why the strain increases in the formation of the six-membered ring. The activation energy for the formation of the seven-membered ring is stated to be anomalously high because of surface-tension effects.[224] The frequency factor is very high in the three-membered ring, since all arrangements of the atoms in a chain of three atoms are equally favorable to ring closure. There is a considerable drop in PZ for the four-membered ring, which accounts for the relative difficulty of closing four-membered rings as compared to three-membered ones. (The ends of a four-atom chain tend to be far apart most of the time.) The slightly higher frequency factor for the five-membered ring has been taken to indicate that the five-atom chain has a greater tendency to exist in a coiled (as distinct from a zigzag) conformation than a four- or six-atom chain. In this conformation, the ends of the chain approach each other readily. Rings between eight- and fourteen-membered are almost impossible to form by any means except the acyloin synthesis [229] because the atomic arrangement in such rings is either such that there is crowding of hydrogen atoms (of CH_2 groups) across the rings or conformational strain due to bond opposition of adjacent methylene groups (cf. Chapter 1) or both. Rings fourteen-membered and larger form more easily, though naturally the probability of the ends of the long chain colliding is quite small.

Data on ring closure of compounds of the type $RS(CH_2)_nCl$ to cyclic sulfonium salts [230] parallel those for the haloamine series. Thus rates of ring closure of five-, six- and seven-membered rings are in the ratio 5700:75:1; eight- through thirteen-membered rings could not be formed, fifteen-, seventeen-, and eighteen-membered rings closed very

[229] For the mechanism of this extremely useful method of making medium and large rings, see V. Prelog, *J. Chem. Soc.*, *1950*, 420.

[230] G. M. Bennett, F. Heathcoat, and A. N. Mosses, *J. Chem. Soc.*, *1929*, 2567; G. M. Bennett and E. G. Turner, *J. Chem. Soc.*, *1938*, 813; G. M. Bennett and H. Gudgeon, *J. Chem. Soc.*, *1938*, 1891.

slowly in a high-boiling solvent (acetophenone) in the presence of sodium iodide.

Turning next to the influence of the nature of the atoms in the ring on the ease of ring closure, one finds that medium-sized rings with one or two oxygen atoms, unlike those with one nitrogen or sulfur atom, can be synthesized readily, as is shown in Table XXII.[231]

TABLE XXII [231]

n	6	7	8	9	10	11	12	13	14
Yield %	100 *	50 †	40 †	69 †	90	71	70	42	51
$t\frac{1}{2}$ (20°) min.‡	0.5	60	1150						
$t\frac{1}{2}$ (78°) min.‡			2	9	23	44	47.5	53	75

  * Non-standard conditions, yield not comparable with others.
  † Probable loss due to volatility.
  ‡ Half-time of reaction at temperature specified.

There is no minimum in yield or reaction rate in the region of the medium-sized rings, perhaps because the bare oxygen atoms, unlike methylene groups, do not give rise to bond oppositions of CH-bonds or transannular hydrogen repulsion. Comparison of the ease of ring closure with the strictly analogous carbocyclic system XIX is, however, lacking.

XIX

A third interesting effect observed in the formation of small rings is the absence of steric hindrance due to substituents. In fact, alkyl substituents at either end of the closing chain will facilitate ring formation. Thus $ClCH(CH_3)CH_2NH_2$ closes about four times as rapidly as $ClCH_2CH_2NH_2$, and $ClCH_2CH(CH_3)NH_2$ closes about 30 times as fast as the unsubstituted compound.[228f, 232] More complete data are available for the ring closure of halohydrins (Table XXIII).[233]

[231] K. Ziegler, A. Lüttringhaus, and K. Wohlgemuth, *Ann.*, *528*, 162 (1937).

[232] L. Smith and B. Platon, *Ber.*, *55*, 3143 (1922). See also R. F. Brown and N. M. van Gulick, *J. Am. Chem. Soc.*, *77*, 1079, 1083, 1089 (1955).

[233] H. Nilsson and L. Smith, *Z. physik. Chem.*, *166A*, 136 (1933). For ring closure of α,γ-dibromides to cyclopropanes, see R. G. Kelso, K. W. Greenlee, J. M. Derfer, and C. E. Boord, *J. Am. Chem. Soc.*, *77*, 1751 (1955).

TABLE XXIII

RELATIVE RATE OF FORMATION OF EPOXIDES FROM HALOHYDRINS IN ALKALI AT 18°C.[233]

Compound	Relative Rate
$HOCH_2CH_2Cl$	1
$HOCH_2CHClCH_3$	5.5
$CH_3CHOHCH_2Cl$	21
$HOCH_2CCl(CH_3)_2$	248
$(CH_3)_2COHCH_2Cl$	252
$(CH_3)_2COHCHClCH_3$	1360
$CH_3CHOHCCl(CH_3)_2$	2040
$(CH_3)_2COHCCl(CH_3)_2$	11600

The absence of steric hindrance is still noticeable in the four-membered ring, as evidenced by the ready cyclization of $CH_3CHBrCH_2$-

$$C(CH_3)_2NH_2 {}^{234} \quad and \quad (BrCH_2)_2C \underset{CH_2Br}{\overset{CH_2OH}{<}} ,{}^{235} \quad and \quad the \quad surprisingly$$

high reactivity of pentaerythrityl tetrabromide, $C(CH_2Br)_4$, in the formation of bicyclic compounds such as XX.[236] The formation of

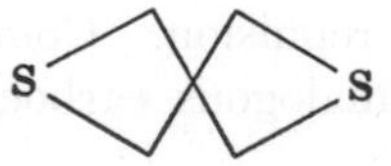

XX

three- and four-membered rings through ring-chain tautomerism,[237] exemplified in formulas XXI–XXII, should also be mentioned here.

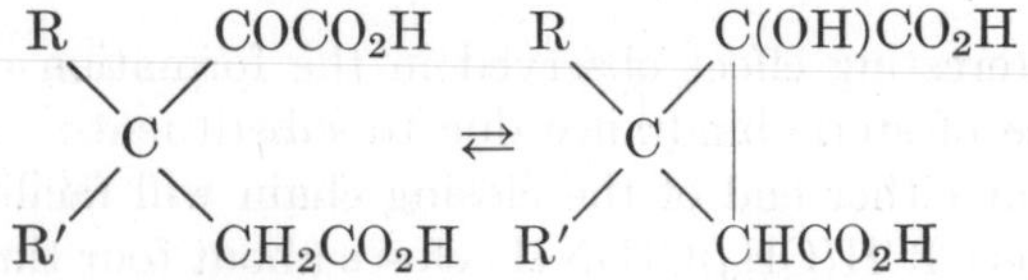

XXI   XXII

[234] M. Kohn, Ann., 351, 134 (1907).

[235] F. Govaert and M. Beyaert, Natuurw. Tijdschr. Belg., 22, 73 (1940); C. A., 37, 3054 (1943).

[236] See, for example, H. J. Backer and K. J. Keuning, Rec. trav. chim., 52, 499 (1933); H. J. Backer and N. Evenhuis, ibid., 56, 129 (1937). Ring closure reactions of pentaerythritol derivatives have been summarized by S. F. Marrian, Chem. Revs., 43, 149 (1948).

[237] This interesting topic has been reviewed by J. W. Baker, Tautomerism, Chapter 10, D. Van Nostrand Co., New York, 1934.

When R and R' are hydrogen, or when R is methyl and R' is methyl or ethyl, only the open-chain tautomer XXI is obtained; but, when R and R' are both ethyl or both n-propyl, the major part of the product exists in the cyclic form XXII. When RR' are pentamethylene (cyclohexane derivative), the equilibrium is entirely on the side of XXII; but, when they are hexamethylene (cycloheptane derivative), it is almost entirely on the side of XXI.

In the five- and six-membered rings the situation is not so clear. 2-Amino-5-chlorohexane, $H_2NCH(CH_3)CH_2CH_2CH(CH_3)Cl$ (of unknown configuration), cyclizes only at about one-tenth the rate for the corresponding unsubstituted compound 4-chlorobutylamine, $H_2NCH_2CH_2CH_2CH_2Cl$.[228b] On the other hand, tetramethylsuccinic acid cyclizes to the anhydride on steam distillation,[238] and dimethyl-maleic acid forms an anhydride spontaneously.[239] Moreover, the Perkin ring closure of dihalides with sodiomalonic ester to form five- and six-membered rings has been accomplished successfully in compounds where steric hindrance might have been expected to prevent reaction.[240]

The reasons why alkyl substituents, far from preventing the closure of small rings, actually seem to assist it are not entirely clear. Thorpe and Ingold [241] postulated many years ago that the deformation of the normal tetrahedral angle of the atoms in the ring of, let us say, 1,1-dimethylcyclopropane to a much smaller angle (60°) would produce an *increase* in the angle between the exocyclic dimethyl groups. This spread might result in a relief of steric strain (compression or B strain) and thus assist ring formation. Physical evidence on the reality of this spread is ambiguous. Electron diffraction measurements on cyclopropane [242] and [2.2.0]-bicyclopentane [243] indicate that the H—C—H angle in these compounds is increased to 118–120°, and other evidence has been cited for an unusual bond structure in

[238] K. Auwers and V. Meyer, *Ber.*, *22*, 2011 (1889); *23*, 293 (1890); P. E. Verkade, *Rec. trav. chim.*, *40*, 199 (1921).

[239] *Beilstein*, Vol. 2, p. 780; cf. A. C. D. Rivett and N. V. Sidgwick, *J. Chem. Soc.*, *97*, 1677 (1910).

[240] V. P. Golmov, *Zhur. Obshchei Khim.*, *23*, 1162 (1953); *C. A.*, *47*, 12255d (1953). E. van Heyningen, *J. Am. Chem. Soc.*, *76*, 2241 (1954).

[241] E.g., R. M. Beesley, C. K. Ingold, and J. F. Thorpe, *J. Chem. Soc.*, *107*, 1080 (1915); C. K. Ingold, *ibid.*, *119*, 305, 951 (1921).

[242] O. Bastiansen and O. Hassel, *Tidsskr. Kjemi Bergvesen Met.*, *6*, 71 (1946); via P. W. Allen and L. E. Sutton, *Acta Cryst.*, *3*, 46 (1950).

[243] J. Donohue, G. L. Humphrey, and V. Schomaker, *J. Am. Chem. Soc.*, *67*, 332 (1945).

cyclopropane.[244]   On the other hand, the Cl—C—Cl angle in 1,1-dichlorocyclopropane has been reported [245] as 112°, the same as in methylene chloride; [246] and the H—C—H angle in cyclopentane is reported [247] to be tetrahedral.   However, regardless of what the Me—C—Me angle in 1,1-dimethylcyclopropane may turn out to be, the very fact that the two methylene groups in this compound are tied into a small ring should, by itself, relieve the compression at the quaternary carbon atom and therefore favor the formation of the cycle from a suitable open-chain compound in which the steric compression is not so relieved.   The same effect might be expected in a substituted cyclobutane; but in cyclopentane, because of the small deviation of the ring angle (108°) from tetrahedral, the effect should become very minor and might be outweighed by ordinary steric hindrance (F strain) to ring closure.

Another type of steric effect in ring closure has been pointed out by Curtin.[215]   When a three-, four- or five-membered ring is formed in such a way that two bulky substituents will be placed *cis* to each other (i.e., in an eclipsed position), then ring closure will be slow as compared to one involving the corresponding groups in a *trans* position. Thus *trans*-stilbene oxide is formed from *erythro*-stilbene bromohydrin more rapidly than *cis*-stilbene forms from the *threo* bromohydrin.[248] Again *dl*-dimethylsuccinic acid forms the anhydride (methyl groups *trans*) with cold acetyl chloride, but *meso*-dimethylsuccinic acid is not affected by the same conditions.[249, 250]   The above-cited extraordinarily facile ring closure of tetramethylsuccinic acid is so much more remarkable in comparison and reemphasizes the importance of relief of steric strain in ring formation as a driving force.[251]

[244] E.g., C. L. Arcus, *Chemistry & Industry, 1947*, 646; A. D. Walsh, *Nature, 159*, 712 (1947); *Trans. Faraday Soc., 45*, 179 (1949).   See, however, J. P. Fried, R. F. Schneider, and B. P. Dailey, *J. Chem. Phys., 23*, 1557 (1955).

[245] J. M. O'Gorman and V. Schomaker, *J. Am. Chem. Soc., 68*, 1138 (1946).

[246] L. O. Brockway, *Revs. Mod. Phys., 8*, 231 (1936).

[247] O. Hassel and H. Viervoll, *Tidsskr. Kjemi Bergvesen Met., 6*, 31 (1946); via reference 242.

[248] H. W. Holly, Ph.D. dissertation, Rutgers University, 1952; via reference 215.

[249] W. A. Bone and C. H. G. Sprankling, *J. Chem. Soc., 75*, 839 (1899); cf. A. Werner and M. Basyrin, *Ber., 46*, 3229 (1913).

[250] For other examples see reference 215.

[251] Steric strain in *meso*-dimethylsuccinic acid (viii, R = H) would be expected to be very slight in comparison to tetramethylsuccinic acid (viii, R = CH₃).

(viii)

DISPLACEMENT REACTIONS IN RING COMPOUNDS. This section is concerned with reactions of the type

which, in some respects, differ significantly from corresponding reactions of acyclic compounds. The subject matter will be taken up under three different headings: reactivity as a function of ring size, reactivity in cyclohexane derivatives as a function of conformation (cf. Chapter 1), and reactivity at bridgehead carbons.

Effect of ring size. The effect of ring size on ease of displacement has been rationalized by H. C. Brown in terms of I strain, which is defined as "change in internal strain which results from change in coordination number of a ring atom involved in chemical reaction." [252] The concept was first proposed to explain certain anomalies in the base strength of cyclic amines.[253] Its basis is as follows: In a saturated carbon atom the normal bond angles are 109° 28′, corresponding to sp^3 hybridization.[254] In a doubly bonded carbon atom or carbonium ion, however, the bonds are coplanar, corresponding to sp^2 hybridization, and the normal bond angle is 120°; the same is true for the three fixed groups in the transition state of the S_N2 reaction (see p. 63). In three- and four-membered ("small") rings, the actual bond angles are close to 60° or 90°, respectively. Since this is closer to 109° than to 120°, there will be less deformation if the hybridization of the ring carbons is sp^3 than if it is sp^2; in other words the atoms in such rings will be reluctant to form carbonium ions or to undergo S_N2 displacement reactions, and if they are doubly bonded (as in carbonyl compounds) they will be very ready to undergo addition reactions to the double bond. In five-membered rings a different situation pertains, and for different reasons. In the tetrahedrally bonded cyclopentane, there are ten C—H bond oppositions which give rise to considerable conformational strain (cf. Chapter 1), approximately 1 kcal. per bond opposition. When there is a change from sp^3 to sp^2 at one of the carbon atoms, four bond oppositions will disappear, corresponding to a gain in energy of 4 kcal. This relief of conformational strain presumably more than outweighs the angular strain involved in the change from

[252] H. C. Brown, R. S. Fletcher, and R. B. Johannesen, *J. Am. Chem. Soc.*, *73*, 212 (1951).

[253] H. C. Brown and M. Gerstein, *J. Am. Chem. Soc.*, *72*, 2926 (1950). See also Chapter 9.

[254] L. Pauling, *Nature of the Chemical Bond*, p. 81, Cornell University Press, Ithaca, N. Y., 1945.

sp^3 to sp^2.[255] In the seven-membered ring and medium-sized rings (eight- to twelve-membered) the situation is the same as in the five-membered ring, since, as was mentioned on p. 116 in connection with the difficulty of forming medium-sized rings, bond oppositions in these systems are quite pronounced. Such bond oppositions can be relieved by the $sp^3 \rightarrow sp^2$ change. In the six-membered ring, the situation is completely different, however. In the chair form of cyclohexane (cf. Chapter 1) there is complete staggering of the CH (or CX) bonds, with no bonds in opposition. When the configuration of one of the carbon atoms is changed from sp^3 to sp^2, two bond oppositions will be engendered, as can be easily seen from consideration of models. This change will therefore cost energy and will be resisted. Therefore, in a cyclohexyl system, carbonium ion and S_N2 reactions are discouraged, but additions to exocyclic double bonds (as in cyclohexanone) are favored. These predictions [256] are summarized in Table XXIV.

TABLE XXIV

Effect of Ring Size on Reaction Rates

Ring Size	Small		Common			Medium	Large
Reaction Type	3	4	5	6	7	8–12	>12
S_N1	VS	S	F	S	F	F	M
S_N2	VS	S	F	S	F	F	M
Radical *	VS	S	F	S	F	F	M
Carbanion †	VS	S	F	S	F	F	M
Carbonyl ‡	VF	F	S	F	S	S	M

S = slow.   F = fast.   V = very.   M = moderate.

* See p. 148 for discussion.
† See p. 162 for discussion.
‡ Cf. Chapter 4.

Some pertinent data are summarized in Table XXV. The first three columns are concerned with S_N1 reactions, the remaining ones with S_N2 reactions. The first entry in each column refers to a non-cyclic (isopropyl or t-butyl) compound included for comparison. The

[255] The normal angle in cyclopentane is 108°—very close to the tetrahedral angle, but not so close to the 120° angle in the sp^2 configuration. Thus angular strain should work *against* change to sp^2. Since in fact the $sp^3 \rightarrow sp^2$ change takes place easily, angular strain can be of minor importance only as compared to conformational strain, if one is to follow Brown's argument. The slight puckering of the cyclopentane ring, first reported by J. G. Aston, S. C. Schumann, H. L. Finck, and P. M. Doty, *J. Am. Chem. Soc.*, *63*, 2029 (1941), is assumed not to affect the bond-opposition argument significantly.

[256] H. C. Brown, *Rec. Chem. Progr. Kresge-Hooker Sci. Lib.*, *14*, 83 (1953).

TABLE XXV

EFFECT OF I STRAIN ON NUCLEOPHILIC REACTIVITY IN RING COMPOUNDS

Relative Rate in Reaction Studied

Compound	n *	A	B	C	D	E	F	G
$(CH_3)_2CXY$	—	1.00	ca. 1.00	—	>5.7 †	1.00	1.00 ‡	—
$(CH_2)_2CXY$	3	—	2×10^{-5}	0.015	0	0	—	—
$(CH_2)_3CXY$	4	0.974	14	41.2	1.43	0.0075	—	—
$(CH_2)_4CXY$	5	43.7	16	14.5	>5.7 †	1.6	1.14	84; 84
$(CH_2)_5CXY$	6	0.35	1.00	1.00	1.00	0.01	0.0109	19; 10
$(CH_2)_6CXY$	7	38.0	31	—	—	0.98	1.56	73; 35
$(CH_2)_7CXY$	8	100	285	—	—	0.23	0.36	—
$(CH_2)_8CXY$	9	15.4	266	—	—	—	—	—
$(CH_2)_9CXY$	10	6.22	539	—	—	—	—	—
$(CH_2)_{10}CXY$	11	4.21	67	—	—	—	—	—
$(CH_2)_{12}CXY$	13	1.00	—	—	—	—	—	—
$(CH_2)_{14}CXY$	15	0.64	—	—	—	—	0.13	—
$(CH_2)_{16}CXY$	17	0.67	—	—	—	—	—	—

* n = number of carbon atoms in ring.

† 5.7 is the rate at 60° or 60.5° relative to cyclohexyl bromide at 90°. The value for isopropyl bromide is that of reference 56.

‡ Value for 2-iodoöctane.

A. X = CH_3; Y = Cl. Solvolysis of methyl cycloalkyl chlorides in 80% ethanol at 25°.[252,257]

B. X = H; Y = $OSO_2C_6H_4CH_3$-p. Solvolysis of cycloalkyl p-toluenesulfonates in acetic acid containing acetic anhydride and potassium acetate at (or extrapolated to) 60°.[258]

C. X = H; Y = Cl. Solvolysis of cycloalkyl chlorides in 50% ethanol at 95°.[258]

D. X = H; Y = Br. Reaction of cycloalkyl bromides with potassium iodide in acetone at 90°.[258]

E. X = H; Y = Br. Reaction of cycloalkyl bromides with lithium iodide in dry acetone at (or extrapolated to) 25°.[260]

F. X = H; Y = I. Exchange reaction of cycloalkyl iodides with radioiodide at (or extrapolated to) 25°.[261]

G. First figure: per cent Br⁻ produced with β-naphthylamine at reflux in 1 hour. Second figure: per cent Br⁻ produced with 28.5% aqueous potassium carbonate at reflux in 24 hours.[262]

predictions of Table XXIV are frequently borne out, but there are also a few difficulties. Thus, although in the solvolysis of the tertiary cycloalkyl halides the prediction that the C_4 compound should react more slowly than the C_5 compound is borne out, the same is not true of the solvolysis of the corresponding secondary halides and p-toluenesulfonates. Cyclobutyl p-toluenesulfonate solvolyzes at about the same rate as the cyclopentyl homolog in acetic acid, and solvolysis of cyclobutyl chloride in 50% ethanol is actually faster than that of cyclo-

[257] H. C. Brown and M. Borkowski, J. Am. Chem. Soc., 74, 1894 (1952).

[258] J. D. Roberts and V. C. Chambers, J. Am. Chem. Soc., 73, 5034 (1951). Similar data for the cyclopentyl and cyclohexyl case are reported in reference 259.

[259] S. Winstein, B. K. Morse, E. Grunwald, H. W. Jones, J. Corse, D. Trifan, and H. Marshall, J. Am. Chem. Soc., 74, 1127 (1952).

[260] P. J. Fierens and P. Verschelden, Bull. soc. chim. Belg., 61, 427, 609 (1952).

[261] S. F. Van Straten, R. V. V. Nicholls, and C. A. Winckler, Can. J. Research, 29, 372 (1951).

[262] J. Loevenich, H. Utsch, P. Moldrickx, and E. Schaefer, Ber., 62, 3084 (1929).

pentyl chloride. Since the reactions of the cyclobutyl compounds give rise, in part, to rearranged products (allylcarbinyl and cyclopropyl-carbinyl derivatives), their unexpectedly high rate may be due to neighboring group assistance [257] (cf. Chapter 5). It must then be assumed that the slow solvolysis of the cyclopropyl compounds, which also yield rearranged products (allyl derivatives), proceeds without such assistance.

An alternative explanation for the slowness of the nucleophilic displacement reaction in cyclopropyl compounds has been offered on the basis of an analogy between the cyclopropyl and vinyl systems.[258] On this basis cyclopropyl halides should react slowly, just as vinyl halides, but cyclopropylcarbinyl halides should react rapidly in analogy with allyl halides. This latter prediction has been verified experimentally.[263]

A more serious discrepancy with predictions based on I strain occurs in the reaction rates of cyclopentyl and cyclohexyl halides and p-toluenesulfonates. According to the I-strain concept, cyclopentyl compounds should react fast in both S_N1 and S_N2 reactions. However, whereas cyclopentyl compounds do indeed react appreciably faster than open-chain compounds in S_N1 reactions, the reactivity of cyclohexyl compounds is normal or nearly normal rather than diminished. In S_N2 reactions, on the other hand, the cyclopentyl halides react normally rather than fast, though the cyclohexyl halides show the expected sluggishness.[36, 50, 264] The reasons for the behavior of cyclohexyl halides will be discussed further in conjunction with conformational considerations. The failure of cyclopentyl halides to show the increase in S_N2 reactivity predicted on the basis of I strain has been explained [260] as being due to an unfavorable steric situation in the transition state when the position of the groups X and Y relative to the ring is taken into account. This crowding of X and Y by the ring offsets any gain in energy due to diminished bond oppositions in the five-membered ring and more than offsets this gain in the eight-membered ring; this accounts for the unexpected slowness of S_N2 reactions in the latter.

It is evident, then, that the concept of I strain has made possible an understanding of otherwise enigmatic trends of substitution rates in cyclic systems, but that, for a complete interpretation of the rates, other important contributing factors must be taken into account.[257]

An interesting effect of I strain in a bridged ststem has been observed by Walborsky and Baum [264a] in the solvolysis of [2.2.2]-bicy-

[263] J. D. Roberts and R. H. Mazur, *J. Am. Chem. Soc.*, *73*, 2509 (1951).

[264] A. L. Solomon and H. C. Thomas, *J. Am. Chem. Soc.*, *72*, 2028 (1950).

[264a] H. M. Walborsky, private communication.

cloöctyl-2 p-bromobenzenesulfonate (XXIII). The acetolysis rate of this compound at 25° is 7.44×10^{-6} sec.$^{-1}$, or about 43 times larger than the corresponding rate for cyclohexyl p-bromobenzenesulfonate.[259] Since anchimeric assistance is apparently not of importance in the bicyclooctyl system,[264b] the enhancement in rate appears to be

−OBs

2

3

XXIII

due to eclipsing of the groups attached to carbons 2 and 3 in compound XXIII which is relieved in the carbonium ion. In fact, the ratio in acetolysis rate between XXIII and cyclohexyl brosylate (43) is similar to that (32) between cyclopentyl tosylate (eclipsed) and cyclohexyl tosylate (not eclipsed),[259] as one might expect.

Conformational effects. The effect of conformational factors (cf. Chapter 1) in displacement reactions in cyclic systems is not yet well understood. Before a discussion of experimental results, it might be well to summarize what effects would be expected, on the basis of present theory, in substitution reactions in six-membered rings.[265]

H   H   H   H   H   H

|4 |6 |4 |6 |4 |6

H   H   H   H   H   H

|5 |2 $+X^-$ |5 |2 $+Y^-$ |5 |2

H $\rightleftarrows$ H ...X $\rightleftarrows$ H

|3 $-X^-$ |3 $-Y^-$ |3

H   Y   H Y... H   H   H

−H   −X   −X

Transition state

In a symmetrical S_N2 displacement of the type $I^{-*} + RI \rightarrow I^*R + I^-$ the transition state looks the same, regardless of whether the substituent originally present is equatorial or axial. There is bond opposition, in the transition state, between the hydrogen atom on adjacent carbons (2, 1, and 6), and this bond opposition gives rise to I strain, as indicated above. In addition, however, one of the groups I^- or I^{-*} will be in a considerably more crowded position, with respect to the axial hydrogen atoms on carbon atoms 3 and 5, in the transition state than in either the starting material or the product. If the original substituent was axial (Y above), then it (i.e., the leav-

[264b] H. M. Walborsky, *Experientia*, 9, 209 (1953).

[265] This subject has been reviewed briefly by S. J. Angyal and J. A. Mills, *Revs. Pure and Appl. Chem.*, 2, 185 (1952).

ing group) will be so crowded; but, if the original substituent was equatorial (X above), the entering group will be so crowded. There is a third type of crowding. If the leaving group is axial (Y), then the entering group (X) will be crowded slightly by the axial hydrogen atoms on carbon atoms 2, 4, and 6; and if the leaving group is equatorial (X), then it itself will be crowded by these hydrogen atoms. As a result of all these effects, the activation energy for S_N2 displacement reactions in six-membered saturated rings will be considerably higher than that for corresponding reactions in acyclic systems, which is in agreement with the facts.[36, 50, 264, 266]

Since, then, the transition state in a symmetrical S_N2 substitution (and, to a first approximation, in any S_N2 substitution) is the same, regardless of whether the substituent displaced is equatorial or axial, an axial substituent should be displaced more easily, because of its higher ground-state energy. (This is a case of steric assistance.) In fact, cis-4-t-butylcyclohexyl tosylate (axial tosyl) undergoes displacement with thiophenoxide ion about 19 times as fast as the trans isomer (equatorial tosyl).[267]

Another consequence of the above argument is that replacement of a methylene group in a six-membered ring by oxygen should greatly facilitate the S_N2 reaction by diminishing the repulsion of non-bonded atoms in the transition state (through removal of axial hydrogen atoms). This effect is observed in compounds XXIV [268] and XXV,[269]

XXIV   XXV

which undergo facile displacement with iodide ion. This is a remarkable circumstance, for, if the p-toluenesulfonate is assumed to be axial for easy displacement,[267] the "missing" axial hydrogens are on the same

[266] However, cyclohexyl halides can alkylate even strong bases; thus cyclohexyl malonic ester has been made from cyclohexyl bromide and sodiomalonic ester: E. Hope and W. H. Perkin, J. Chem. Soc., 95, 1360 (1909); Th. Wagner-Jauregg and H. Arnold, Ann., 529, 274 (1937); J. V. Braun and P. Kurtz, Ber., 70, 1224 (1937); F. F. Blicke and F. Leonard, J. Am. Chem. Soc., 68, 1934 (1946); N. D. Zelinski, L. S. Bondar, V. N. Kost, and B. V. Lifshits, Izvest. Akad. Nauk S.S.S.R., Otdel. Khim. Nauk, 96 (1951); C. A., 45, 10205e (1951).

[267] E. L. Eliel and R. S. Ro, Chemistry & Industry, 1956, 251.

[268] N. K. Matheson and S. J. Angyal, J. Chem. Soc., 1952, 1133.

[269] O. Heuberger and L. N. Owen, J. Chem. Soc., 1952, 910.

side in one case and on the opposite side in the other; but it is in complete agreement with the arguments advanced above.

In the S_N1 reaction, bond opposition leading to I strain, as explained earlier, should again be engendered in the transition state. However, since the transition state is reached before the carbonium ion is formed, bond opposition in this state is not yet complete, which may explain in part why the S_N1 reaction is not retarded very significantly.[260] Moreover, where the departing group is axial, there is a compensating steric acceleration, due to relief of crowding between the axial substituent and the axial hydrogens on carbon atoms 3 and 5. As a result of this, S_N1 reactions (usually accompanied by E_1 elimination) should be quite facile for axial substituents, or substituents that can be switched readily to the axial position. It seems, however, that the difference in S_N1 rate between substituents restricted to equatorial positions and substituents in axial positions is not as large as might have been expected, for it was found [270] that cis-4-t-butylcyclohexyl tosylate (tosylate group axial) is solvolyzed in ethanol, acetic acid, or formic acid at a rate only 3–4 times as fast as the corresponding trans isomer (tosylate group equatorial). The interpretation of this result is complicated by the fact that solvolysis is certainly not a simple "carbonium ion process," since the trans (equatorial) tosylate yields (besides olefin) almost exclusively the inverted (cis) solvolysis product.[271] The cis (axial) tosylate yields a mixture of the inverted (trans), uninverted (cis), and rearranged (trans-3-t-butyl substituted) solvolysis product. The result has been interpreted in terms of tight ion pairs.[270, 272]

In so far as the difference in rate between an equatorial and an axial halide or sulfonate in S_N1 reactions depends on the difference in energy of the ground states, rather than the transition states (the less stable axial compound reacting faster), this difference should disappear in a tertiary halide, such as the 1,2-dimethylcyclohexyl bromides (XXVIa, b). Here both isomers contain two equatorial groups

XXVIa   XXVIb

[270] S. Winstein and N. J. Holness, J. Am. Chem. Soc., 77, 5562 (1955).

[271] If a carbonium ion were intermediate, the product should presumably be largely the more stable trans isomer.

[272] Cf. S. Winstein, E. Clippinger, A. H. Fainberg, and G. C. Robinson, Chemistry & Industry, 1954, 664.

and one axial group of nearly equal steric requirement and are therefore equal in energy content. In fact, the two isomers do not differ significantly in rate of hydrolysis in aqueous methylethyl ketone.[273] The isomeric 1,3-dimethylcyclohexyl chlorides also appear to solvolyze at the same rate.[252]

A somewhat different situation exists in reactions which might be classified grossly as "$S_N i$" (cf. p. 80), such as reactions of cyclic alcohols with thionyl chloride, chlorides of phosphorus, and hydrogen halides [274] and reactions of cyclic amines with nitrous acid.[265, 275–277] Although no rate studies appear to be available in these systems, product studies indicate that the equatorial isomers react with predominant or exclusive retention of configuration, while the axial isomers tend to give much elimination product, a mixture of the two possible substitution products with the equatorial one predominating, and sometimes products of rearrangement. Thus menthol (OH equatorial) reacts with phosphorus pentachloride to give predominantly menthyl chloride,[274a, c] but neomenthol (OH axial) with the same reagent gives a mixture of neomenthyl chloride, menthyl chloride, 4-chloromenthane, and menthene as might be expected if the carbonium ion were an intermediate.[278] Similarly, menthylamine in aqueous solution gives only menthol when treated with nitrous acid, but neomenthylamine gives a mixture of 2-menthene, 3-menthene, and menthanol-4.[279] A detailed study has been made of the reaction of all the decalylamines

[273] T. D. Nevitt and G. S. Hammond, J. Am. Chem. Soc., 76, 4124 (1954).

[274] (a) W. Hückel and H. Pietrzok, Ann., 540, 250 (1939); (b) G. Tsatsas, Ann. chim., 19, 217 (1944); (c) J. G. Smith and G. F. Wright, J. Org. Chem., 17, 1116 (1952); R. J. Cremlyn and C. W. Shoppee, J. Chem. Soc., 1954, 3794.

[275] (a) J. A. Mills, J. Chem. Soc., 1953, 260; (b) A. K. Bose, Experientia, 9, 256 (1953).

[276] See also: O. Wallach, Ann., 276, 296 (1893); 300, 278 (1898); 397, 181 (1913); J. Gutt, Ber., 40, 2061 (1907); J. Read and G. J. Robertson, J. Chem. Soc., 1927, 2168; J. Read, W. J. Grubb, and D. Malcolm, ibid., 1933, 170; J. Read and R. G. Johnston, ibid., 1934, 226; J. Read and W. J. Grubb, ibid., 1934, 1779; G. Komppa and S. Beckmann, Ann., 512, 172 (1934); W. Hückel, R. Mentzel, E. Brinkmann, and E. Kamenz, Ann., 451, 109 (1927); W. Hückel, R. Schlüter, W. Doll, and F. Reimer, Ann., 530, 166 (1937); W. Hückel, Ann., 533, 1 (1937); W. Hückel, A. Gross, and W. Doll, Rec. trav. chim., 57, 555 (1938); W. Hückel, W. Tappe, and G. Legutke, Ann., 543, 191 (1940); W. Hückel and E. Wilip, J. prakt. Chem., 158, 21 (1941); P. Anziani and R. Cornubert, Bull. soc. chim. France, [5], 15, 857 (1948); R. Cornubert and P. Hartmann, ibid., [5], 15, 867 (1948); W. Dauben and E. Hoerger, J. Am. Chem. Soc., 73, 1504 (1951); also reference 280b.

[277] W. G. Dauben, R. C. Tweit, and C. Mannerskantz, J. Am. Chem. Soc., 76, 4420 (1954).

[278] W. Hückel and K. Kümmerle, Ber., 75, 115 (1942).

[279] W. Hückel, W. Tappe, and G. Legutke, Ann., 543, 198 (1940).

with nitrous acid.[277] It has been postulated [275a] that retention of configuration in the equatorial isomer is due to the operation of the $S_N i$ mechanism as pictured on p. 80.[65] A cyclic transition state is attractive for an equatorial substituent, but not (because of crowding) for an axial one. A different interpretation [277] which has been put on the amine-nitrous acid reaction is somewhat analogous to the ion-pair mechanism of the $S_N i$ reaction.[66] According to this interpretation, the solvated diazonium ion loses nitrogen to give a solvated carbonium ion. In the equatorial isomer, the carbonium ion collapses by frontside attack of solvent to give the equatorial product. In the axial isomer, front-side attack is slowed by crowding and the carbonium ion survives long enough to undergo rearward attack by solvent thus giving largely the more stable equatorial isomer or (presumably) undergoing rearrangement where the system is favorably disposed towards rearrangement.

Less clear-cut results are obtained in the reactions of the methylcyclohexanols (where conformational isomers are quite readily interconvertible) with hydrogen halide and phosphorus halides.[280, 281]

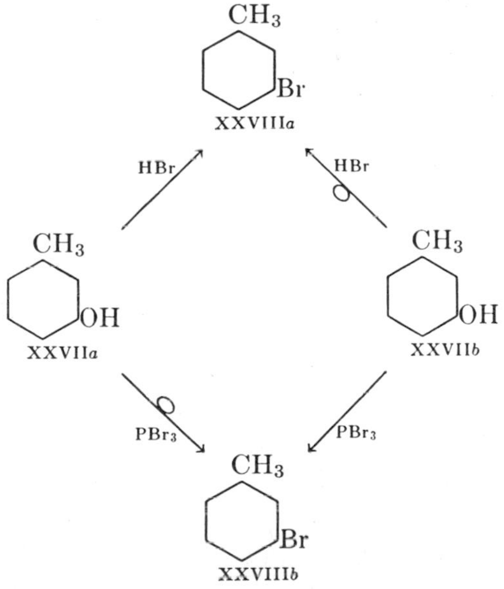

(XXVIIa and b and XXVIIIa and b are epimeric)

[280] (a) M. Mousseron, R. Granger, and J. Valette, *Bull. soc. chim. France, 1946,* 244; (b) M. Mousseron and R. Jacquier, *ibid., 1951,* 80C.

[281] See also P. Sabatier and A. Mailhe, *Compt. rend., 140,* 840 (1903); J. Gutt, *Ber., 40,* 2069 (1907); N. Zelinsky, *Ber., 41,* 2676 (1908); A. Skita and H. Ritter, *Ber., 44,* 668 (1911); A. Mailhe and Murat, *Bull. soc. chim. France,* [4], *9,* 216 (1911).

These results are summarized in the formulations for the 3-isomers.
The implication of this scheme is that the configuration of the product depends only on the reagent and is independent of the configuration of the starting material; no explanation has been advanced for
this. Which of the two isomers (*cis* or *trans*) of 3-methylcyclohexanol
reacts with inversion with a given reagent and which one reacts with
retention is impossible to say in the absence of reliable information on
the configuration of the 3-methylcyclohexyl bromides.[282] Unexplained
differences in the rate of hydrolysis (S_N1) [283] and of aminolysis (both
S_N1 and S_N2) [284] of various epimeric sugar halides may also have
their origin in conformational effects, since a six-membered ring is
present in the pyranose form of the sugars.

Interesting conformational effects are observed in the ring-opening
reactions of cyclohexene epoxides which have been extensively studied
in the steroid field.[285] It is always found that nucleophilic reagents
attack the epoxide ring from the axial side so that the equatorial
bond [286] of the oxide is broken and the oxygen atom remains attached

to the axial position. Thus, for example, 3α,4α-epoxycholestane
(XXIX) reacts with lithium aluminum hydride to give the 3α-hy-
droxycholestane (XXX) (*epi*-cholestanol) in which the OH group is
axial, and the same epoxide reacts with acetic acid to give 3α-hydroxy-
4β-acetoxycholestane (XXXI) (both substituents axial). In turn, 3β,-
4β-epoxycholestane (XXXII) gives 4β-hydroxycholestane (XXXIII)

[282] The assignment made in reference 280 on the basis of carbonation of the
Grignard reagent is probably unreliable; cf. G. Roberts and C. W. Shoppee, *J.
Chem. Soc.*, *1954*, 3418, and Chapter 8.

[283] F. H. Newth and G. O. Phillips, *J. Chem. Soc.*, *1953*, 2896, 2900, 2904.

[284] N. B. Chapman and W. E. Laird, *Chemistry & Industry*, *1954*, 20.

[285] T. F. Gallagher and W. P. Long, *J. Biol. Chem.*, *162*, 495 (1946); W. P. Long
and T. F. Gallagher, *ibid.*, *162*, 511 (1946); Pl. A. Plattner, H. Heusser, and A. B.
Kulkarni, *Helv. Chim. Acta*, *31*, 1885 (1948); *32*, 265, 1070 (1949); Pl. A. Plattner,
H. Heusser, and M. Feurer, *ibid.*, *31*, 2210 (1948); *32*, 587 (1949); A. Fürst and
Pl. A. Plattner, *ibid.*, *32*, 275 (1949); G. Roberts, C. W. Shoppee, and R. J. Stephen-
son, *J. Chem. Soc.*, *1954*, 3178; reference 288.

[286] Actually the cyclohexane chair in an epoxide is quite deformed; cf. B. Ottar,
Acta Chem. Scand., *1*, 283 (1947).

with lithium aluminum hydride, and 3α-acetoxy-4β-hydroxycholes-
tane (XXXIV) with acetic acid; again, all substituents are axial.[287]

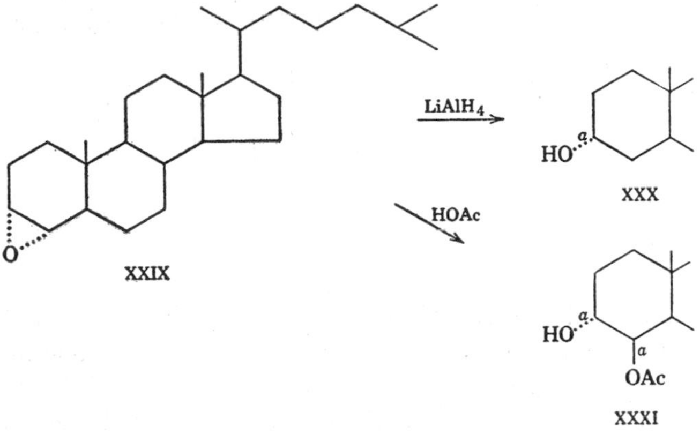

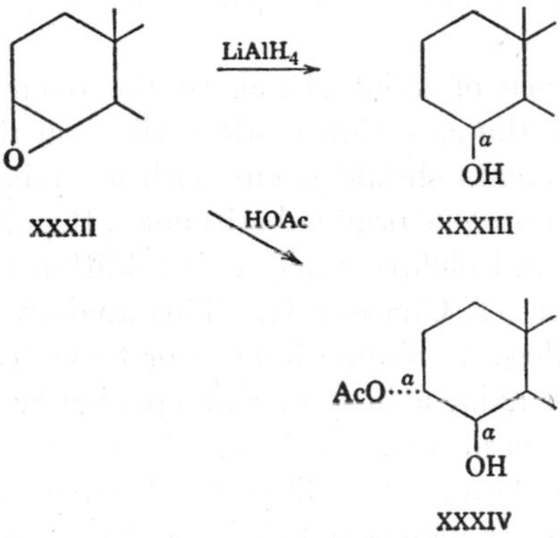

That the conformational effect in the reduction of epoxides with
lithium aluminum hydride is very powerful is demonstrated in the direction of ring opening of 3α-hydroxy-5β,6β-epoxycholestane [288] and
the corresponding 3β compound (XXXV).[289] These compounds are
secondary-tertiary epoxides, and, in analogy with acyclic examples (p.
106), should yield exclusively tertiary alcohols by attack of lithium
aluminum hydride at the secondary position; actually, however, they

---

[287] Ralph Scotoni, doctoral dissertation, Eidgenössische Technische Hochschule,
Zurich, Switzerland, 1953.

[288] Pl. A. Plattner, H. Heuser, and M. Feurer, Helv. Chim. Acta, 32, 587 (1949).

[289] A. Fürst, Habilitationsschrift, Eidgenössische Technische Hochschule, Zurich,
Switzerland, 1952.

yield mixtures of the two alcohols. With the 3α compound, the secondary alcohol product, formed by attack of the reagent at the tertiary carbon, predominates by a ratio of 3:1. This "anomalous" ring opening is evidently due to the fact that in the secondary alcohol

| | Major | | Minor |
| XXXV | XXXVI | | XXXVII |

product ($3\alpha,6\beta$-dihydroxycholestane, XXXVI) the substituent in position 6 is axial, while in the tertiary alcohol product ($3\alpha,5\beta$-dihydroxycoprostane, XXXVII) the alcohol group in position 5 is equatorial with respect to ring B. It should be mentioned that the formation of secondary alcohols in this type of situation is not usual with lithium aluminum hydride, though it is generally observed in catalytic reduction.

The predominance of axial attack in the opening of the epoxide ring is contrary to the assertion made earlier, on theoretical grounds, that S_N2 displacements should occur with an axial substituent more readily than with an equatorial substituent. It points out an analogy between epoxides and olefins, since ionic addition to olefins also gives the diaxial product (cf. Chapter 1). This analogy is evidently closer here than the analogy to simple halides or tosylates.

The principle of axial attack in ring-opening reactions of epoxides fused to six-membered rings has also been observed in the sugar series.[290] There is, however, a difference between the sugars and the steroids in that the six-membered rings in the steroids are rigid whereas in the sugars they are not rigid, unless there is an additional ring (such as a benzylidene bridge) which prevents interconversion of the two chair forms. Therefore the sugar epoxides can normally exist in two conformations, and, even though one form may be much more stable than the other, they can be interconverted during reaction.[291] If this happens, prediction of the product by the principle of axial attack becomes impossible, since either point of attachment of the

[290] E.g., (a) F. H. Newth, W. G. Overend, and L. F. Wiggins, *J. Chem. Soc.*, *1947*, 10; (b) F. H. Newth and R. F. Homer, *ibid.*, *1953*, 989; (c) V. Y. Labaton and F. H. Newth, *ibid.*, *1953*, 992. For a review, see W. G. Overend and G. Vaughn, *Chemistry & Industry*, *1955*, 995.

[291] F. H. Newth, *Chemistry & Industry*, *1953*, 1257; R. C. Cookson, *ibid.*, *1954*, 223; cf. A. K. Bose, D. K. R. Chaudhuri, and A. K. Bhattacharyya, *ibid.*, *1953*, 869.

epoxide ring may become axial. Thus the reaction of 4,6-benzylidene-2,3-anhydro-α-methylalloside (**XXXVIII**), which, because of the *trans* fusion of the two six-membered rings must be entirely in the conformation shown, with potassium hydroxide gives 84% 4,6-benzylidene-α-methylaltroside (**XXXIX**) (axial attack) and only 7% 4,6-benzylidene-α-methylglucoside (**XL**) (equatorial attack).[292] On the other hand, in reaction with hydrochloric acid, where the benzylidene bridge may be cleaved before opening of the epoxide ring, the major product (40%) is 3-chloro-α-methylglucoside (**XLI**) formed by *apparent* equatorial attack and only 20% 2-chloro-α-methylaltroside (**XLII**) is formed by axial attack.[290a, 293] It is evident that the product of the

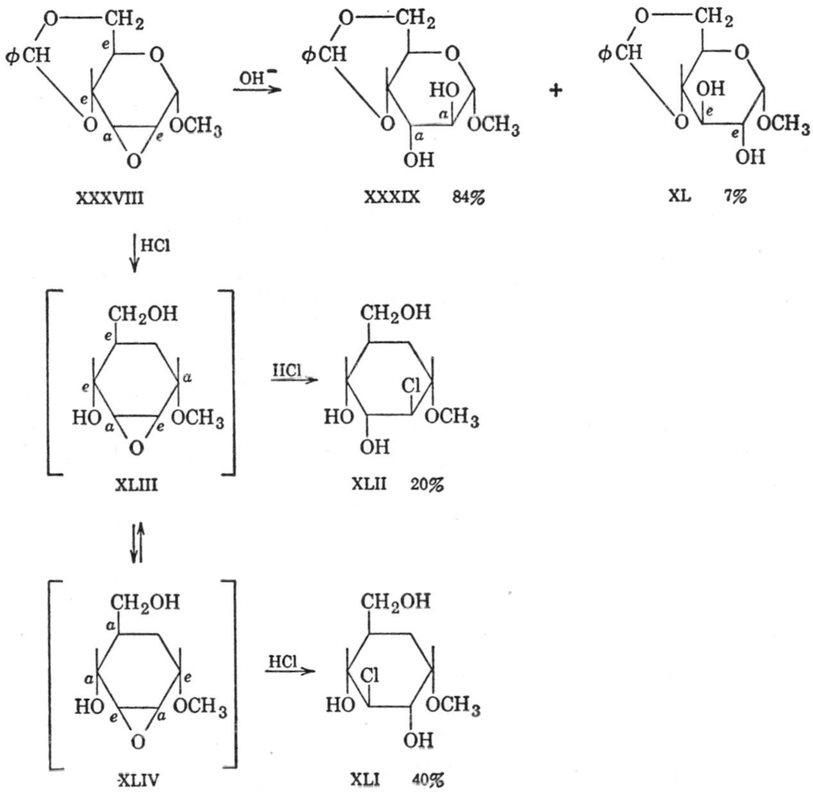

removal of the benzylidene group from **XXXVIII** may react in form **XLIII** or **XLIV**, and if axial attack is general, it must be concluded that it reacts mainly as **XLIV**. The directive influence of the methoxyl

[292] N. K. Richtmeyer and C. S. Hudson, *J. Am. Chem. Soc.*, *63*, 1727 (1941).
[293] S. Mukherjee and H. C. Srivastava, *Proc. Indian Acad. Sci.*, *35*, 178 (1952).

group (encouraging attack on the oxide remote from it; cf. entry 62, Table XX, p. 108) is apparently strong enough to outweigh the fact that XLIV (because of the larger number of axial substituents) is present in smaller concentration than XLIII in the equilibrium mixture of the two. A similar effect of methoxyl has been noticed elsewhere.[294]

Steric effects at exocyclic positions. In three-, four-, and five-membered rings, where adjacent *cis* positions are eclipsed, one would expect steric hindrance to substitution in exocyclic halides, provided that the halogen is not far from the ring and that there is a bulky *cis* substituent in an adjacent position on the ring. Little is known about such halides, but it has been found [295] that compound XLV will readily undergo substitution by aniline to give XLVI, whereas the geometrical isomer XLVII does not react under the same conditions.

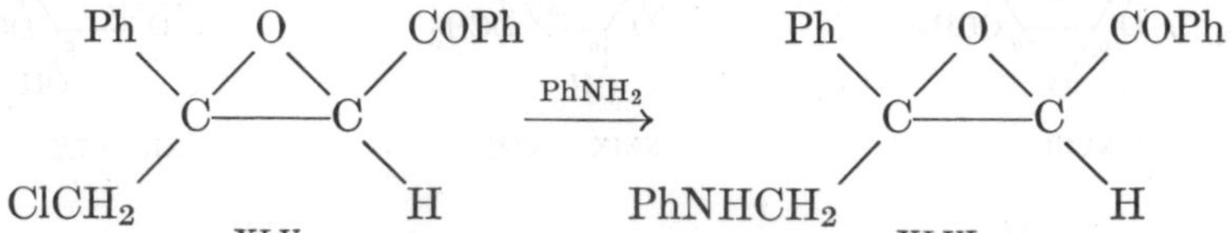

*Reactions at bridgehead carbon atoms.** The reactivity of substituents at bridgehead carbons toward nucleophilic reagents has long been a matter of theoretical interest. The impossibility of bringing about a Walden inversion at such centers would seem to exclude the S_N2 reaction, and the S_N1 reaction should be retarded, if not prevented, by the difficulty of forming a planar carbonium ion and possibly by the lack of opportunity for rearward solvent participation in the transition state.

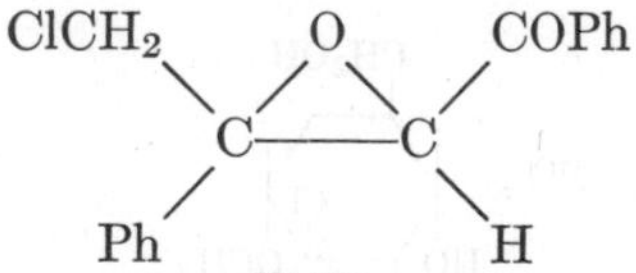

A system illustrating these effects has long been known. β-Caryophyllene alcohol (XLVIII) on treatment with phosphorus pentachloride,[296] is reported to give the chloride which reacts with sodium acetate in acetic acid (S_N1?) to give β-caryophyllene acetate. Yet the

* Reviewed by D. E. Applequist and J. D. Roberts, *Chem. Revs.*, *54*, 1065 (1954).
[294] G. Charalambous and E. Percival, *J. Chem. Soc.*, *1954*, 2443.
[295] H. H. Wasserman and J. B. Brous, *J. Org. Chem.*, *19*, 515 (1954).
[296] O. Wallach and W. Walker, *Ann.*, *271*, 285 (1892).

chloride is inert to boiling quinoline and to boiling concentrated ethanolic sodium ethoxide, reagents which might be expected to bring
about S_N2 attack.[297] However, the implications of this work could

XLVIII

not be understood until the structure of β-caryophyllene alcohol was
established.[298]

The first systematic study of the bridgehead carbon system was
undertaken by Bartlett and Knox.[299] These authors obtained 1-apo-
camphylamine from the corresponding acid by a Hofmann reaction
and were readily able to convert the amine to the corresponding chloride by treatment with nitrosyl chloride and to the corresponding alcohol by treatment with nitrous acid. Failure of the S_N2 reaction at
the bridgehead was demonstrated by complete inertness of 1-chloro-
apocamphane towards 30% aqueous alcoholic potassium hydroxide
(24 hours' reflux) and of the corresponding p-toluenesulfonate toward
the highly nucleophilic lithium iodide in acetone. The S_N1 reaction
failed also: 1-chloroapocamphane did not react with alcoholic silver
nitrate during 48 hours' reflux.

Surprisingly, certain reactions which might have proceeded by the
S_Ni path, such as the reaction of 1-apocamphanol with hydrogen
bromide, phosphorus pentachloride, and thionyl chloride, also failed
(only complexes and sulfites, but no halides were obtained). The contrast between these reactions and the above-mentioned successful reaction of 1-apocamphylamine with nitrous acid or nitrosyl chloride
suggests that the overall classification of all these types as S_Ni (cf.
p. 80) is less than satisfactory. Apparently apocamphyl chlorosulfite
does not give the apocamphyl carbonium ion pair required for transformation to the chloride, but the diazonium salt from apocamphyla-
mine may give a solvated apocamphyl carbonium ion. Perhaps this
is because diazonium salts are particularly good sources of carbonium
ions (which are formed from them by simple loss of the rather stable
nitrogen molecule), as evidenced by the ready formation of phenol

[297] G. G. Henderson, J. M. Robertson, and C. A. Kerr, J. Chem. Soc., 1926, 62.
[298] D. H. R. Barton, T. Bruun, and A. S. Lindsey, J. Chem. Soc., 1952, 2210.
[299] P. D. Bartlett and L. H. Knox, J. Am. Chem. Soc., 61, 3184 (1939).

from benzenediazonium salts as compared to the failure of phenol to give chlorobenzene with thionyl chloride. An alternative, but probably less likely, interpretation of the amine reactions is that they proceed by a free-radical mechanism (cf. p. 149).

The behavior of the apocamphyl system is summarized in the chart.

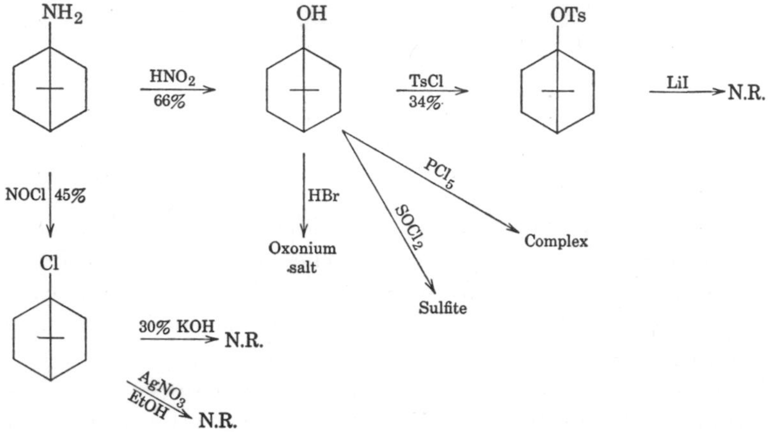

Similar observations were made with the maleic anhydride adduct of 9-bromoanthracene (XLIX) [300] with 1-bromotriptycene (L, X = Br) [301] and with 1-iodotriptycene (L, X = I).[302] 1-Bromotriptycene,

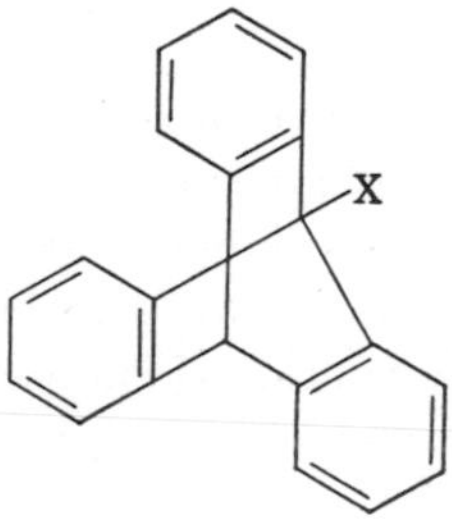

L 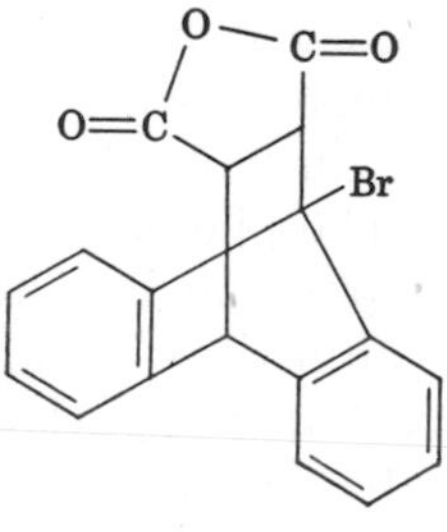   XLIX

though of the triphenylmethyl halide type, shows no sign of ionization in liquid sulfur dioxide (indicating absence of tendency to form a carbonium ion) and is unaffected by prolonged boiling with alcoholic sodium hydroxide or sodium sulfide. 1-Iodotriptycene is inert to sil-

[300] E. Barnett, N. F. Goodway, A. G. Higgins, and C. A. Lawrence, *J. Chem. Soc.*, *1934*, 1224; P. D. Bartlett and S. G. Cohen, *J. Am. Chem. Soc.*, *62*, 1183 (1940).

[301] P. D. Bartlett and E. S. Lewis, *J. Am. Chem. Soc.*, *72*, 1005 (1950).

[302] P. D. Bartlett and F. D. Greene, *J. Am. Chem. Soc.*, *76*, 1088 (1954).

ver nitrate in boiling aqueous ethanol. Evidently these compounds have no resemblance whatsoever to triphenylmethyl halides because of complete steric inhibition of resonance in the carbonium ion (Bredt rule [303]); their diminished reactivity as compared with even 1-bromo-[2.2.2]-bicycloöctane, mentioned below, has been ascribed [302] to the inductive electron-withdrawing effect of the phenyl groups which destabilizes the carbonium ion and to the greater rigidity of the triptycyl as compared to the [2.2.2]-bicycloöctyl system which makes it more difficult for the ion even to approach planarity.

It was mentioned before that, whereas complete inertness of bridgehead halides in S_N2 reactions is to be expected, complete inertness in S_N1 reactions cannot be predicted with confidence, since there is the possibility of formation of a non-planar or partly planar carbonium ion. Thus 4-chlorocamphane (LI), though inert to ethanolic sodium ethoxide during 2 days at 205° and to alcoholic silver nitrate during 21 hours at 160°, does produce silver chloride with aqueous silver nitrate after 19.5 hours at 205°.[304] Similarly, the compound releases part or all of its halogen on boiling with aluminum bromide in cyclohexane or on heating with zinc chloride in water or di-n-butyl ether at 200°. These reactions point to the formation of the carbonium ion, though no pure organic products could be isolated. More conclusively, it has been shown that 1-bromobicyclo-[2.2.1]-heptane (LII) is converted to the corresponding alcohol in 2 days with aqueous silver nitrate at 150°.[305]

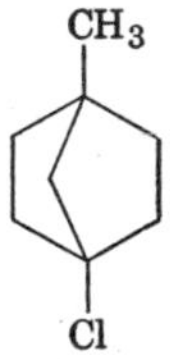

LI 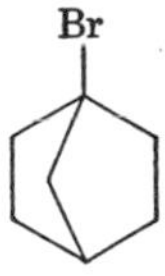   LII 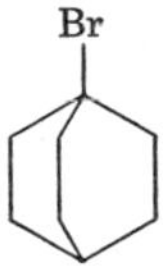   LIII 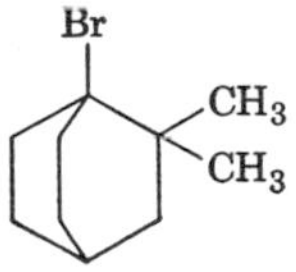   LIV

The S_N1 reaction at the bridgehead becomes easier as the ring system is made larger and more flexible, presumably because the transition state can then approach the planar form. Thus 1-bromobicyclo-[2.2.2]-octane (LIII) and 1-bromo-2,2-dimethylbicyclo-[2.2.2]-octane (LIV) react with aqueous silver nitrate to give the corresponding alcohols in 4 hours.[305] LIV also undergoes ethanolysis to give the corre-

[303] F. S. Fawcett, Chem. Revs., 47, 219 (1950).

[304] W. v. E. Doering and E. F. Schoenewaldt, J. Am. Chem. Soc., 73, 2333 (1951).

[305] W. v. E. Doering, M. Levitz, A. Sayigh, M. Sprecher, and W. P. Whelan, J. Am. Chem. Soc., 75, 1008 (1953).

sponding ethyl ether; the rate of this reaction is unaffected by added sodium ethoxide, which is typical of an S_N1 reaction. The rates of solvolysis of LIII and LIV in 70% aqueous dioxane at 100° are slower by a factor of ca. 10^5–10^6 than the rate of solvolysis of t-butyl bromide in 80% ethanol (a solvent of about the same ionizing power; cf. p. 69) calculated at the same temperature.

Another instance of successful displacement in the [2,2,2]-bicyclooctane system is the conversion of 1-bromo-4-carbethoxy-[2,2,2]-bicyclooctane (LV) to the sodium salt of the corresponding hydroxy acid (LVI) by 24 hours' boiling with 1% aqueous sodium hydroxide.[306]

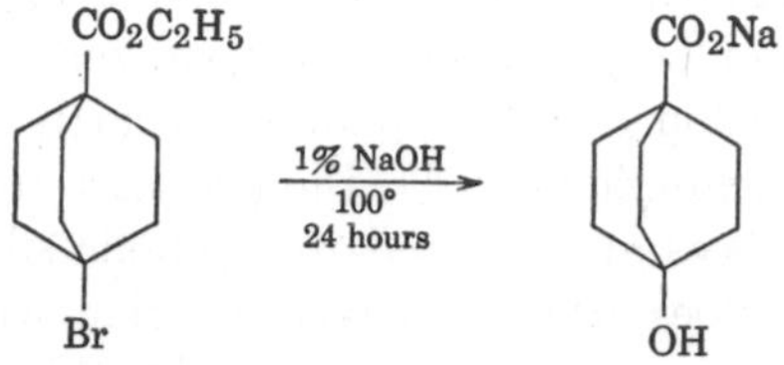

$$CO_2C_2H_5 \xrightarrow[\substack{100° \\ 24 \text{ hours}}]{1\% \text{ NaOH}} CO_2Na$$

Br   OH

LV   LVI

The already-mentioned acetolysis of the chloride corresponding to β-caryophyllene alcohol also fits into the picture, since the relatively flexible [4,3,1]-bicyclodecane system is involved.

Alternation effects in nucleophilic displacement reactions

In concluding this section on nucleophilic displacement reactions, mention is made of some curious alternation effects observed in some homologous series; they are summarized in Table XXVI.

Although an extensive study of most of the homologous series indicated in Table XXVI is lacking, a "zigzagging" of the rates from the odd to the even members of the series seems to be indicated in all series except the last two. This effect appears to be steric in origin. It has been postulated [161] that the enhanced rate in the series C_6H_5CO-$(CH_2)_nX$ is due to a transition state of type LVII which is most

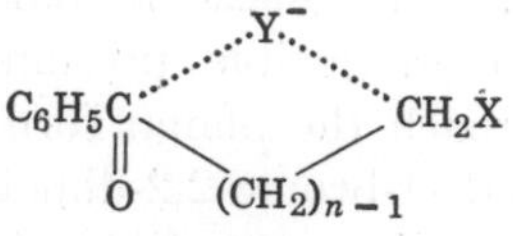

$$C_6H_5C \underset{\substack{\| \\ O \quad (CH_2)_{n-1}}}{\overset{Y^-}{\diamond}} CH_2\overset{\cdot}{X}$$

LVII

favored when $n = 1$ (three-membered ring), less so when $n = 3$ (five-membered ring) and still less when $n = 2$ (four-membered ring). A

[306] J. D. Roberts, W. T. Moreland, and W. Frazer, *J. Am. Chem. Soc.*, **75**, 637 (1953).

TABLE XXVI

RATE CONSTANTS IN HOMOLOGOUS SERIES OF HALIDES

(Relative to n-Butyl Halide as Unity)

n	0	1	2	3	4	5	6	7
A	—	79 [83]	3.97	4.01	—	—	—	—
B	0.0020	64 [50]	0.319	0.415	—	—	—	—
C	—	195	1.12	1.72	1.49	1.42	1.46	1.40
D	700	105,000	86.7	230	—	—	—	—
E	0	782	0.48	1.9	—	—	—	—
F	—	270	0.45	39.5	—	—	—	—
G	—	59.1	0.45	1.57	—	—	—	—
H	42.0	2,800	1.61	1.65	1.35	—	—	—
I	—	—	0.30	1.67	1.37	—	—	—
J	—	2.52	1.08	1.00	1.35	1.30	1.25	1.35
K	—	1.46	1.01	1.00	1.05	1.07	1.09	1.11

A: Reaction of chlorides CH_2=$CH(CH_2)_nCl$ with iodide ion in dry acetone at 15°.[307]
B: Reaction of Bromides CH_2=$CH(CH_2)_nBr$ with iodide ion in dry acetone at 15°.[307]
C: Reaction of chlorides $C_6H_5(CH_2)_nCl$ with iodide ion in dry acetone at 50°.[308]
D: Reaction of chlorides $C_6H_5CO(CH_2)_nCl$ with iodide ion in dry acetone at 50°.[83,308]
E: Reaction of chlorides C_6H_5C≡$C(CH_2)_nCl$ with iodide ion in dry acetone at 60°.[309]
F: Reaction of chlorides $CH_3CO_2(CH_2)_nCl$ with iodide ion in dry acetone at 50°.[83]
G: Reaction of chlorides $C_6H_5CO_2(CH_2)_nCl$ with iodide ion in dry acetone at 50°.[310]
H: Reaction of chlorides $Cl(CH_2)_nCO_2C_2H_5$ with iodide ion in dry acetone at 50°.[308]
I: Reaction of chlorides $C_6H_5O(CH_2)_nCl$ with iodide ion in dry acetone at 50°.[310]
J: Reaction of chlorides $CH_3(CH_2)_nCl$ with iodide ion in dry acetone at 50°.[36]
K: Reaction of bromides $CH_3(CH_2)_nBr$ with thiocyanate ion in ethanol at 25°.[52]

similar explanation may obtain in the series $C_6H_5(CH_2)_nX$, provided that the rate enhancement in this series is accounted for by overlap of the electrons of the benzene ring with the electrons of the C—X bond being broken and the C—Y bond which is formed. Field effects depending on the relative orientation of the functional group (phenyl, acyloxyl, carbethoxyl, etc.) to the carbon atom at which displacement occurs may contribute to the alternation in rate.[311]

The alternation effect has also been explained on the basis of second-order hyperconjugation,[312] but, in view of the finding [313] that *no* alternation is observed in S_N1 type reactions such as the reaction of phenyl-substituted alkyl bromides with mercuric nitrate, such an explanation appears unlikely.

In the rates of displacement of normal alkyl bromides with sodium thiocyanate there is no alternation effect, but a slight minimum is ob-

[307] A. Juvala, *Ber.*, *63*, 1989 (1930).
[308] J. B. Conant and W. R. Kirner, *J. Am. Chem. Soc.*, *46*, 232 (1924).
[309] M. J. Murray, *J. Am. Chem. Soc.*, 60, 2662 (1938).
[310] W. R. Kirner, *J. Am. Chem. Soc.*, *48*, 2745 (1926).
[311] D. J. Cram, private communication.
[312] Reference 98, p. 158.
[313] S. Oae and C. A. VanderWerf, *J. Am. Chem. Soc.*, *75*, 5037 (1953).

served for *n*-butyl bromide.[52] No complete explanation for the observed minimum has been advanced;[314] it is of interest, however, that in the above-mentioned reaction of the phenylalkyl bromides with mercuric nitrate there is a minimum in rate for γ-phenylpropyl bromide, though no corresponding minimum occurs with *n*-butyl bromide.[313]

FREE-RADICAL SUBSTITUTION

Optical stability of free radicals [315]

Predictions regarding the optical stability of radicals are uncertain. Since the central carbon atom in a carbon free radical carries seven electrons, its configuration may be either planar (sp^2) with the odd electron occupying a *p*-orbital above or below the plane of the central atom and its neighbors, or tetrahedral (sp^3), in which case, because of the vacant orbital, it would probably oscillate rapidly and easily between the two possible configurations.[316] In either case, the radical should be incapable of exhibiting optical activity. This conclusion appears to be well founded in fact. Thus phenylbiphenyl-α-naphthyl-thioglycollic acid (LVIII) is racemized by treatment with triphenyl-

LVIII

[314] See Chapter 4 for similar effects in ester hydrolysis.

[315] For a review, see R. L. Shriner and R. Adams in H. Gilman's *Organic Chemistry*, 2nd ed., Vol. 1, p. 383, John Wiley & Sons, New York, 1943.

[316] No definite decision between these two possibilities seems to be possible at this time. G. Karagunis and G. Drikos, *Z. physik. Chem.*, *26B*, 428 (1934), preferred the tetrahedral configuration, since they observed that phenylbiphenyl-α-naphthyl radicals as well as phenyl-*p*-tolyl-*p*-ethylphenyl radicals give slightly *active* triarylmethyl chlorides when treated with chlorine in the presence of circularly polarized light (asymmetric induction). Later, however, G. Karagunis and T. Jannakopoulus, *Z. physik. Chem.*, *47B*, 343 (1940), favored the planar configuration on the basis of absence of dipole moment in triarylmethyl radicals. Actually, both pieces of evidence would seem to be compatible with both configurations. G. Karagunis (reference 319) states that oscillation between two pyramidal configurations involves an improbably large motion of atoms.

methyl radicals,[317] presumably because of formation of phenylbiphenyl-α-naphthylmethyl free radicals incapable of maintaining optical activity. Similarly, the fact that the potassium salt of active 2-methylbutyric acid upon Kolbe electrolysis gives inactive 3,4-dimethylhexane (either *dl* or *meso* or a mixture of the two) may be reasonably ascribed to the intervention of free-radical intermediates.[317] Again, active 2-

$$
\begin{array}{ccc}
\text{CH}_3 & \text{CH}_3 & \text{CH}_3 \quad \text{CH}_3 \\
| & | & | \qquad | \\
2\text{C}_2\text{H}_5\text{—CHCOOK} \xrightarrow{\text{Electrolysis}} 2\text{C}_2\text{H}_5\text{CH•} \rightarrow \text{C}_2\text{H}_5\text{CH—CHC}_2\text{H}_5 \\
\text{Active} & \text{Inactive} & \text{Inactive}
\end{array}
$$

phenylbutane when treated with acetyl peroxide yields a mixture of *meso* and racemic 3,4-diphenyl-3,4-dimethylhexane.[318]

The failure, despite many attempts, to resolve phenylbiphenyl-α-naphthylmethyl radicals by chromatography on a variety of optically active adsorbents [319] constitutes further negative evidence for the optical stability of free radicals.[320]

The fact that the photochemical chlorination of optically active 1-chloro-2-methylbutane gives *inactive* 1,2-dichloro-2-methylbutane [321] has been taken to indicate the intervention of free radicals as reaction intermediates:

$$
\begin{array}{cc}
\text{ClCH}_2\text{CHC}_2\text{H}_5 + \text{Cl•} \rightarrow \text{HCl} + \text{ClCH}_2\overset{\bullet}{\text{C}}\text{C}_2\text{H}_5 \\
| & | \\
\text{CH}_3 & \text{CH}_3 \\
\text{Active} & \text{Inactive}
\end{array}
$$

$$
\begin{array}{cc}
\text{ClCH}_2\overset{\bullet}{\text{C}}\text{C}_2\text{H}_5 + \text{Cl}_2 \rightarrow \text{ClCH}_2\text{CClC}_2\text{H}_5 + \text{Cl•} \\
| & | \\
\text{CH}_3 & \text{CH}_3 \\
& \text{Inactive}
\end{array}
$$

Contradicting evidence seems to come from the pyrolysis of optically active *dl*-(α-methyl)butyryl peroxide (LIX), which gives rise to optically *active sec*-butyl α-methylbutyrate (LX), which can be hydrolyzed, in turn, to *sec*-butyl alcohol and α-methylbutyric acid of re-

[317] E. S. Wallis and F. H. Adams, *J. Am. Chem. Soc.*, *55*, 3838 (1933).

[318] P. H. Wilken, Ph.D. thesis, University of Notre Dame, 1955.

[319] G. Karagunis, *Helv. Chim. Acta*, *32*, 1840 (1949).

[320] Triarylmethyl and simple alkyl free radicals do not necessarily have the same configuration, however. The situation with the triarylmethyl radicals is complicated by resonance and by steric interference of the *ortho*-hydrogen substituents when the radical is planar.

[321] H. C. Brown, M. S. Kharasch, and T. H. Chao, *J. Am. Chem. Soc.*, *62*, 3435 (1940).

tained configuration.[322] The retention of activity in the alcohol part
of the ester may, however, be ascribed to intervention of the cyclic
transition state LXI.[323]

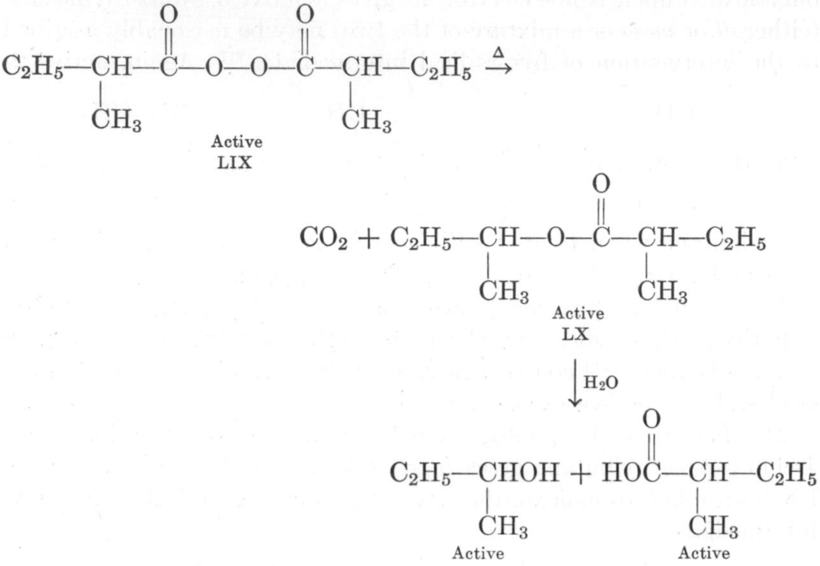

$$C_2H_5-\overset{\underset{|}{CH_3}}{CH}-\overset{\overset{O}{\|}}{C}-O-O-\overset{\overset{O}{\|}}{C}-\overset{\underset{|}{CH_3}}{CH}-C_2H_5 \overset{\Delta}{\rightarrow}$$

Active
LIX

$$CO_2 + C_2H_5-\overset{\underset{|}{CH_3}}{CH}-O-\overset{\overset{O}{\|}}{C}-\overset{\underset{|}{CH_3}}{CH}-C_2H_5$$

Active
LX

$$\downarrow H_2O$$

$$C_2H_5-\overset{\underset{|}{CH_3}}{CHOH} + HO\overset{\overset{O}{\|}}{C}-\overset{\underset{|}{CH_3}}{CH}-C_2H_5$$

Active   Active

LXI

Preliminary reports [324] to the effect that optically active α-methyl-
butyric acid reacts with acetyl peroxide to give slightly *active sym*-
dimethyldiethylsuccinic acid have not yet been confirmed in detail.

Mechanistic types in free-radical reactions

The chlorination of 1-chloro-2-methylbutane involves a free radical
as an intermediate, and its mechanism thus resembles that of path A
(p. 63). It might be termed an S_H1 reaction in analogy to the S_N1

[322] M. S. Kharasch, J. Kuderna, and W. Nudenberg, *J. Org. Chem.*, *19*, 1283
(1954).
[323] P. D. Bartlett and J. E. Leffler, *J. Am. Chem. Soc.*, *72*, 3030 (1950). Alternatively, for a "cage effect" interpretation, see F. D. Greene, *ibid.*, *77*, 4869 (1955).
[324] M. S. Kharasch and W. H. Urry, quoted by L. E. Sutton, *Discussions Faraday
Soc.*, *2*, 62 (1947); M. S. Kharasch, J. G. Kuderna, and W. H. Urry, quoted by
G. W. Wheland, *Advanced Organic Chemistry*, 2nd ed., p. 714, John Wiley & Sons,
New York, 1949.

reaction in nucleophilic substitution. Similarly the pyrolysis of α-methylbutyryl peroxide might be called an $S_H i$ reaction. There is also an $S_H 2$ mechanism, analogous to $S_N 2$, exemplified in the thermal racemization of 2-iodobutane by iodine in which one iodine atom displaces another.[325] A similar mechanism has been postulated [326] for the chlorination with sulfuryl chloride of diethyl *cis*- and *trans*-hexahydrophthalates.

The stereochemistry of catalytic reductions

Some interesting observations on the stereochemistry of catalytic reductions are recorded here, though it is recognized that these may bear little or no mechanistic relation to free-radical reactions in homogeneous systems. Among catalytic reductions leading to loss of activity (formally similar to $S_H 1$) are the desulfurization by Raney nickel of derivatives of active 2-phenyl-2-phenylmercaptopropionic acid (e.g., LXII) and of the corresponding sulfoxide (e.g., LXIII) which give rise to racemic 2-phenylpropionic acid derivatives (e.g., LXIV) [327] and the deuteration of 1-phenyl-1-chloroethane over Raney nickel which gives rise to inactive 1-phenyl-1-deuteroethane [328] despite the fact that the latter compound is capable of exhibiting optical activity.[329] Retention of configuration (analogous to $S_H i$) has

$$\underset{\substack{\text{Active}\\ \text{LXII}}}{\overset{\text{Ph}}{\underset{\text{SPh}}{\text{CH}_3\text{CCONH}_2}}} \xrightarrow{\text{Ni}} \underset{\substack{\text{Inactive}\\ \text{LXIV}}}{\overset{\text{Ph}}{\underset{\text{H}}{\text{CH}_3\text{CCONH}_2}}} \xleftarrow{\text{Ni}} \underset{\substack{\text{Active}\\ \text{LXIII}}}{\overset{\text{Ph}}{\underset{\text{SOPh}}{\text{CH}_3\text{CCONH}_2}}}$$

$$\underset{\text{Active}}{\text{PhCHClCH}_3} \xrightarrow[\text{Ni}]{\text{D}_2} \underset{\text{Inactive}}{\text{PhCHDCH}_3}$$

been observed in the catalytic hydrogenolysis of methyl atrolactate (LXV) to methyl 2-phenylpropionate (LXVI) [330] and of 2-phenyl-2-

[325] R. Ogg and M. Polanyi, *Trans. Faraday Soc.*, *31*, 482 (1935); R. Noyes, private communication. See also D. Clark, H. O. Pritchard, and A. F. Trotman-Dickenson, *J. Chem. Soc.*, *1954*, 2633, for the reaction of methyl iodide with radioiodine.

[326] C. C. Price and M. Schwarcz, *J. Am. Chem. Soc.*, *62*, 2891 (1940).

[327] W. A. Bonner, *J. Am. Chem. Soc.*, *74*, 1034, 5089 (1952).

[328] E. R. Alexander, A. G. Pinkus, and F. W. Stone, *Brookhaven Conf. Rept.*, *4*, 100 (1950).

[329] E. L. Eliel, *J. Am. Chem. Soc.*, *71*, 3970 (1949).

[330] W. Bonner, J. A. Zderic, and G. A. Casaletto, *J. Am. Chem. Soc.*, *74*, 5086 (1952).

chloropropionic acid.[331] Inversion of configuration (analogous to S_H2) has been observed in the reduction of derivatives of active 2-phenyl-

$$\underset{\underset{\underset{\text{LXV}}{}}{\overset{\text{Ph}}{\underset{\text{OH}}{CH_3\overset{|}{\underset{|}{C}}CO_2CH_3}}} \rightarrow \underset{\underset{\text{LXVI}}{}}{\overset{\text{Ph}}{\underset{\text{H}}{CH_3\overset{|}{\underset{|}{C}}CO_2CH_3}}}$$

2-benzenesulfonylpropionic acid (LXVII) by means of Raney nickel, which gives the corresponding derivatives of 2-phenylpropionic acid of about 90% of the original activity and apparently inverted configuration.[327] Chemical reduction of 2-phenyl-2-chloropropionic acid

$$\underset{\underset{\text{LXVII}}{}}{\overset{\text{Ph}}{\underset{\text{SO}_2\text{Ph}}{CH_3\overset{|}{\underset{|}{C}}CONH_2}}} \longrightarrow \overset{\text{H}}{\underset{\text{Ph}}{CH_3\overset{|}{\underset{|}{C}}CONH_2}}$$

with zinc and acetic acid also leads to 2-phenylpropionic acid of inverted configuration.[331]

The reaction of optically active lactic acid with deuterium oxide at 120–130° in the presence of a platinum catalyst gives α-deuterolactic acid of partially preserved activity,[332] but whether this reaction involves retention or inversion is not known.

Steric effects in free-radical reactions

Since so many free-radical reactions proceed by the S_H1 path, primary steric effects, i.e., effects directly attributable to the bulk of the reactants, are, in general, not to be expected. A primary steric effect has been claimed in the chlorination of 2,3,4,5,6-pentachloroethylbenzene (LXVIII).[333] Photochemical chlorination of this material at 180° gives predominantly the β-chloroethyl product (LXX, 4.6 parts) and only minor amounts of the α-chloroethyl product (LXIX, 1 part); [334]

---

[331] E. Ott and K. Krämer, *Ber.*, *68*, 1655 (1935); cf. E. L. Eliel and J. P. Freeman, *J. Am. Chem. Soc.*, *74*, 923 (1952).

[332] J. Bell, K. A. Macdonald, and R. I. Reed, *J. Chem. Soc.*, *1953*, 3459.

[333] S. D. Ross, M. Markarian, and M. Nazzewski, *J. Am. Chem. Soc.*, *71*, 396 (1949).

[334] Since the α-chloro compound was too unstable for isolation, the mixture was allowed to react with benzene in the presence of aluminum chloride, and the resulting mixture of 1-phenyl-1-pentachlorophenylethane and 2-phenyl-1-pentachlorophenylethane was analyzed by fractional crystallization and weighing of the products.

at 70–75° the ratio of the two products was only 1.6:1. Chlorination of pentachloroethylbenzene with sulfuryl chloride and benzoyl peroxide proceeded sluggishly and gave exclusively the β-chloro compound;[335] photochemical bromination gives exclusively the α-bromide in nearly quantitative yield.[336] These facts, summarized in Table

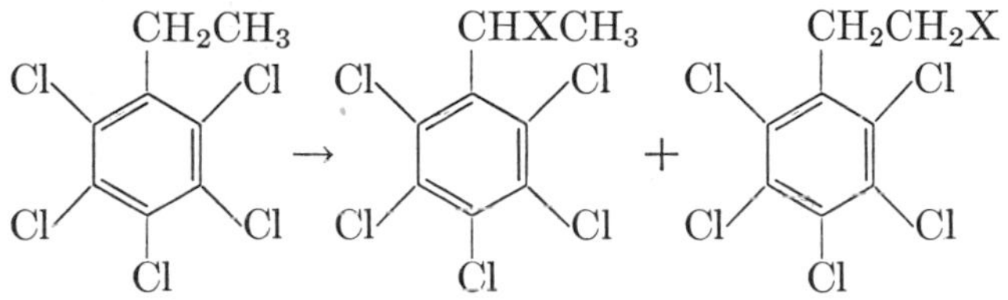

XXVII, have been accounted for by postulating screening of the α-

TABLE XXVII

PRODUCTS FROM THE HALOGENATION OF 2,3,4,5,6-PENTACHLOROETHYLBENZENE

Reagent	X	LXIX	LXX
Cl_2, 75°	Cl	1 part	1.6 parts
Cl_2, 180°	Cl	1 part	4.6 parts
SO_2Cl_2	Cl	None	ca. 40%
Br_2	Br	ca. 100%	None

hydrogen atoms in the side chain by chlorine atoms in the *ortho* position of the ring.[333]

It is of interest to compare pentachloroethylbenzene (LXVIII) with the parent compound ethylbenzene. In ethylbenzene, chlorination with molecular chlorine [337] (though not chlorination with sulfuryl chloride [338] or bromination [318]) affects the β position to a substantial extent. Moreover, in competitive chlorination of toluene-cyclohexane mixtures with chlorine *or* sulfuryl chloride (but not in photobromination of such mixtures) the hydrogen atoms in cyclohexane are replaced faster (3.75

---

[335] S. D. Ross, M. Markarian, and M. Nazzewski, *J. Am. Chem. Soc.*, **69**, 1914 (1947).

[336] S. D. Ross, M. Markarian, and M. Nazzewski, *J. Am. Chem. Soc.*, **69**, 2468 (1947).

[337] R. Fittig and J. Kiesow, *Ann.*, **156**, 246 (1870); R. Anschütz, *Ann.*, **235**, 329 (1886); J. Schramm, *Monatsh.*, **8**, 102 (1887); *Ber.*, **26**, 1706 (1893); E. B. Evans, E. E. Mabbott, and E. E. Turner, *J. Chem. Soc.*, **1927**, 1159, 1163; S. Hanai, *J. Chem. Soc. Japan*, **63**, 187 (1942); *C. A.*, **41**, 3437a (1947); Brit. pat. 609,482 (1948); *C. A.*, **43**, 2636g (1949); R. Pieck and J. C. Jungers, *Bull. soc. chim. Belges*, **60**, 377 (1951).

[338] M. S. Kharasch and H. C. Brown, *J. Am. Chem. Soc.*, **61**, 2142 (1939).

times as fast for chlorine at 55°) than the hydrogen atoms in toluene.[339] At 80° the corresponding ratio drops to 2.8, indicating that the greater reactivity of cyclohexane is largely a function of lower activation energy, not of an enhanced frequency factor. It has been concluded [339] that while photobromination is of the S_H1 type, i.e., involves a transition state resembling a free radical and is therefore greatly assisted by benzylic resonance, the same is not true of free-radical chlorination. The transition state for the latter reaction is assumed to involve only ca. 10% bond breaking and might be termed "S_H2-like." [340] The reaction is therefore not substantially assisted by benzylic resonance but is actually retarded by the inductive electron withdrawal of the phenyl group. The more strongly electron-withdrawing effect of the pentachlorophenyl group should retard the reaction even further; moreover, in view of the nature of the transition state, steric hindrance may be quite important in the pentachloro compound LXVIII. That such hindrance does indeed play a part is suggested by the temperature dependence of the isomer ratio in the chlorination of LXVIII (Table XXVII). At the higher temperature (where the product ratio depends to a greater extent on the frequency factor) the proportion of β attack is enhanced.

A simple bulk effect (F strain) appears to be involved in the side-chain chlorination of o-xylene, which yields the pentachloro derivative (LXXI).[341] Since $\alpha,\alpha,\alpha,\alpha',\alpha'$-pentafluoro-o-xylene (LXXII) can be readily chlorinated further in the side chain,[341a] the inability of the pentachloro compound to undergo further chlorination to a hexachloro derivative must be ascribed to steric hindrance.[342]

A subtle primary steric effect is noted in the dimerization of dimethyl succinate (LXXIII) which yields the two diastereoisomeric tetramethyl butane-1,2,3,4-tetracarboxylates (LXXIV) in the ratio 98 parts meso to 2 parts dl.[343] Provided that the carbomethoxy and car-

[339] G. A. Russel and H. C. Brown, J. Am. Chem. Soc., 77, 4578 (1955).

[340] Under the circumstances, the complete loss of optical activity in chlorination (p. 141) is surprising.

[341] (a) I.G. Farbenindustrie, A.G., Brit. pat. 465,885 (1937); C. A., 31, 7667 (1937); (b) N. Rabjohn, J. Am. Chem. Soc., 76, 5479 (1954).

[342] H. C. Brown et al., J. Am. Chem. Soc., 75, 1 (1953).

[343] M. S. Kharasch, H. C. McBay, and W. H. Urry, J. Org. Chem., 10, 394 (1945). The configurations of the diastereoisomeric products were not assigned, but were correctly guessed by the abstractor [C. A., 40, 1783 (1946)] and have since been

$$2 \; \underset{\text{LXXIII}}{\overset{\displaystyle CH_2{-}CH_2{-}CO_2Me}{\underset{|}{CO_2Me}}} \; \xrightarrow{Ac_2O_2}$$

$$MeO_2C{-}CH_2{-}CH{-}CH{-}CH_2{-}CO_2Me$$
$$\underset{\text{LXXIV}}{\overset{|\qquad\quad|}{MeO_2C \quad CO_2Me}}$$

bomethoxymethyl groups differ sufficiently in size (and regardless of which one is bulkier), it is reasonable that the *meso* form (preferred conformation LXXV) should fit together better than the *dl* (preferred conformation LXXVI shown for one enantiomorph), since the former avoids the *gauche* position of the two bulkiest groups.[344]

LXXVa *meso* (98 parts)   LXXVb *dl* (2 parts)

Secondary steric effects in free-radical reactions are more frequent. They are rationalized most easily if it is assumed that the radical is planar. Factors such as B strain and I strain which facilitate formation of a planar radical (see below) will give rise to steric assistance; factors impeding planarity (such as molecular rigidity and steric inhibition of resonance) will produce steric hindrance.

Thus it is well established that tertiary free radicals are formed more easily than secondary, which, in turn, are formed more easily than primary ones.[345]   B strain may be a contributing factor to this order

proved: K. Alder and M. Schumacher, *Ann.*, *564*, 96 (1949); also A. I. Korolev and V. I. Mur, *Akad. Nauk S.S.S.R., Inst. Org. Sintezy Org. Soedinenii Sbornik* I; *C. A.*, *47*, 8003a (1953).

[344] A misinterpretation by H. C. McBay, O. Tucker, and A. Milligan, *J. Org. Chem.*, *19*, 1003 (1954), in terms of the unlikely *eclipsed* conformations is based on an erroneous assignment of the *meso* and *dl* configurations.

[345] See, for example, J. S. Roberts and H. A. Skinner, *Trans. Faraday Soc.*, *45*, 339 (1949); M. Szwarc, *Chem. Revs.*, *47*, 124 (1950), and *Discussions Faraday Soc.*, *10*, 336 (1951).   See, also, the following reviews: Abstraction of hydrogen by methyl radicals: A. F. Trotman-Dickenson, *Quart. Revs.*, *7*, 198 (1953).   Abstraction of hydrogen by chlorine: H. B. Hass in *The Science of Petroleum*, Vol. 4, p. 2787, Oxford University Press, London, England, 1938; A. B. Ash and H. C. Brown, *Rec. Chem. Progr. Kresge-Hooker Sci. Lib.*, *9*, 81 (1948); also reference 346a.   Abstraction of chlorine by sodium: E. Warhurst, *Quart. Revs.*, *5*, 44 (1951).   Abstrac-

—the more highly substituted the radical-forming carbon atom, the more likely is there to be relief of strain due to the change from tetrahedral to planar configuration. More commonly, however, the order of reactivity is attributed to radical hyperconjugation.[346] An answer

$$(CH_3)_3CX \rightarrow (CH_3)_3C\cdot \leftrightarrow (CH_3)_2C{=}CH_2H\cdot$$
$$\text{(tetrahedral)} \qquad \text{(planar)} \qquad \text{(9 forms)}$$

as to the relative importance of these factors must await investigation of more highly substituted radicals such as tri-*t*-butyl carbinyl.[346a]

Steric acceleration due to B strain seems to appear in the thermal decomposition of *trans*-azo-*bis*-nitriles, $RR'C(CN)N{=}NC(CN)RR'$, to give nitrogen and the radical $RR'C(CN)$—. The rate of decomposition is substantially enhanced when R and/or R' is isobutyl or neopentyl as compared to cases where the R groups are methyl, ethyl, *i*-propyl, or *n*-amyl.[347] Evidence for I strain in radical reactions [348] comes from work on the reaction of cycloalkanes with methyl radicals [349] and on the decomposition of azo-*bis*-nitriles.[350] These data (Table XXVIII) indicate an increase in rate from cyclopropyl to cyclopentyl, followed by a decrease for cyclohexyl and a further increase for cycloheptyl and cyclooctyl, then a drop for cyclodecyl. The trend of these rates is similar to that observed in the S_N1 reaction (p. 122).

Qualitative observations on the low reactivity of cyclopropane derivatives towards free radicals are in agreement with the concept of I strain.[257, 351]

---

tion of hydrogen by deuterium: B. de B. Dawent and R. Roberts, *Discussions Faraday Soc.*, *14*, 55 (1953). Abstraction of hydrogen by trichloromethyl radicals: E. C. Kooyman, *Discussions Faraday Soc.*, *10*, 163 (1951). General: E. W. R. Steacie, *Atomic and Free Radical Reactions*, Reinhold Publishing Corp., New York, 1954; A. G. Evans, reference 4c, pp. 10, 59–61, 64–66.

[346] E. C. Baughan, M. G. Evans, and M. Polanyi, *Trans. Faraday Soc.*, *37*, 377 (1941); E. T. Butler and M. Polanyi, *ibid.*, *39*, 19 (1943).

[346a] No B-strain effects have been observed in the chlorination of branched hydrocarbons: G. A. Russel and H. C. Brown, *J. Am. Chem. Soc.*, *77*, 4031 (1955). However, in view of the nature of the transition state in free-radical chlorination (p. 146) this is perhaps not unexpected.

[347] C. G. Overberger, W. F. Hale, M. B. Berenbaum, and A. B. Finestone, *J. Am. Chem. Soc.*, *76*, 6185 (1954).

[348] Cf. Table XXIV, p. 122. The application of the I-strain concept to radicals involves the assumption that the radicals are planar or can be considered planar for practical purposes.

[349] A. F. Trotman-Dickinson and E. W. R. Steacie, *J. Chem. Phys.*, *19*, 329 (1951).

[350] C. G. Overberger, H. Biletch, A. B. Finestone, J. Lilker, and J. Herbert, *J. Am. Chem. Soc.*, *75*, 2078 (1953).

[351] G. S. Hammond and R. W. Todd, *J. Am. Chem. Soc.*, *76*, 4081 (1954).

TABLE XXVIII

Ease of Formation of Cycloalkyl Radicals

Radical Formed	Relative Rate A (per CH_2 group)	Relative Rate B
Isopropyl	—	1.41
Cyclopropyl	0.085	—
Cyclobutyl	0.60	0.00238
Cyclopentyl	1.00	1.00
Cyclohexyl	0.79	0.087
Cycloheptyl	—	16.9
Cyclooctyl	—	115
Cyclodecyl	—	25.4

A: Reaction of cycloalkane with methyl radicals from acetone or acetone-d_6.[349]

B: Thermal decomposition of azo-*bis*-nitrile.[350]

Radicals at bridgeheads cannot become planar and, if pyramidal, cannot oscillate between two opposite configurations. It might therefore be expected that such radicals would be less stable than nonbridgehead radicals of similar structure. That they are nevertheless capable of formation is shown by the thermal decomposition of diapocamphoyl peroxide (LXXVI) in carbon tetrachloride which gives rise to apocamphyl chloride, diapocamphyl and apocamphyl apocamphylcarboxylate among other products [352] and by the similar decomposition of ditriptoyl peroxide (LXXVII).[353] As expected, however, this decomposition is slower than the decomposition of simple trialkylacetyl peroxides.[353] Although the triptyl radical (LXXVIII) bears a formal resemblance to a triphenylmethyl radical, its benzylic resonance is completely inhibited by steric considerations,[303] which explains why triptycene cannot be chlorinated with sulfuryl chloride in the presence of benzoyl peroxide,[354] and why the anthracene–maleic anhydride adduct is only very slowly attacked by trichloromethyl radicals.[355]

[352] M. S. Kharasch, F. Englemann, and W. H. Urry, *J. Am. Chem. Soc.*, 65, 2428 (1943).

[353] P. D. Bartlett and F. D. Greene, *J. Am. Chem. Soc.*, 76, 1088 (1954).

[354] P. D. Bartlett, M. J. Ryan and S. G. Cohen, *J. Am. Chem. Soc.*, 64, 2649 (1942).

[355] E. C. Kooyman and A. Strang, *Rec. trav. chim.*, 72, 329 (1953).

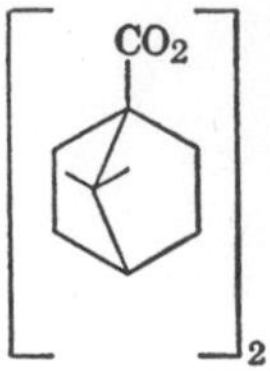

LXXVI 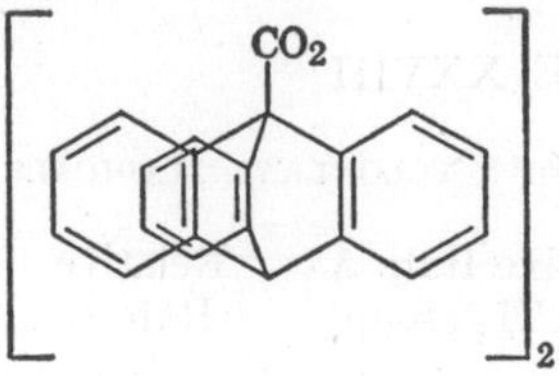   LXXVII 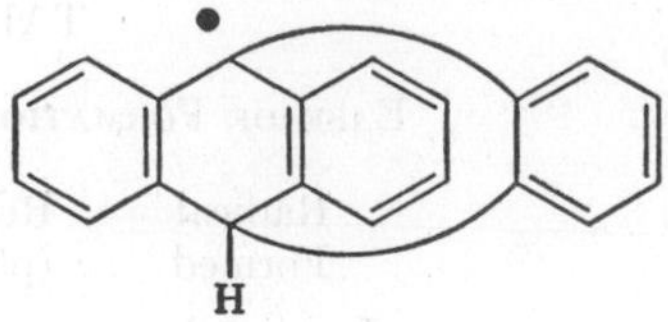   LXXVIII

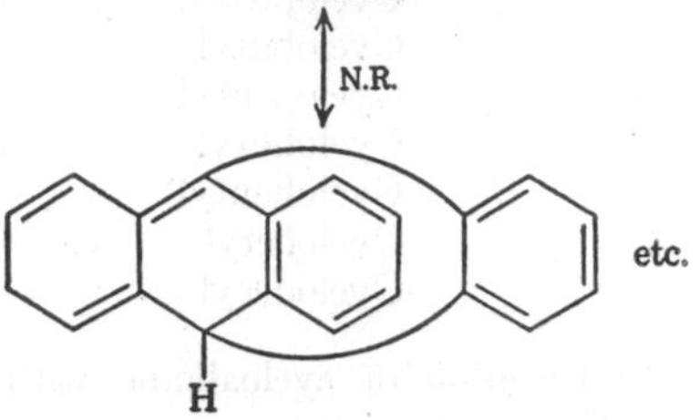

N.R.

etc.

Steric inhibition of resonance by itself may affect the rate of radical reactions, as evidenced by the relative rate of reaction of a series of alkylbenzenes with trichloromethyl radicals [ArCHRR′ + $^\bullet$CCl$_3$ → Ar$\overset{\bullet}{C}$RR′ + CHCl$_3$], shown in Table XXIX.[355]

TABLE XXIX

RELATIVE RATE OF HYDROGEN ABSTRACTION BY TRICHLOROMETHYL RADICALS [355]

Entry	Compound	Relative Rate Found	Relative Rate Calculated
1	Toluene	0.42	(0.42)
2	Ethylbenzene	1.30	(1.30)
3	Isopropylbenzene	1.75	(1.75)
4	m-Methylisopropylbenzene	2.0	2.17
5	p-Methylisopropylbenzene	2.5	2.17
6	o-Methylisopropylbenzene	0.44	2.17
7	2,5-Dimethylisopropylbenzene	0.78	2.59
8	p-Diisopropylbenzene	4.0	3.50
9	1,4-Diisopropyl-2,5-dimethylbenzene	0.74	4.34
10	1,2,3,4-Tetraisopropylbenzene	0.48	7.00
11	Hexaethylbenzene	0.68	7.80

The last column in Table XXIX shows the calculated rate, assuming that the rates for each group are additive. This is shown to be approximately true when the groups are non-adjacent (entries 4, 5, and 8); however, when the two groups larger than methyl are adjacent, steric inhibition of benzylic resonance of the incipient radical reduces the rate considerably below the expected value (entries 6, 7, 9,

10, and 11). (The three xylenes, not shown in the table, have approximately the expected rates; thus steric inhibition of resonance of a *benzyl* radical by a *methyl* group *ortho* to it is not appreciable.)

As one might expect (cf. p. 89), side chains locked in six- and especially five-membered rings are less prone to produce steric inhibition of resonance than acyclic side chains.[356]

Steric inhibition of resonance may be responsible for bromination of $CH_2=C(CH_3)CH_2C(CH_3)_3$ with N-bromosuccinimide at the allylic *methyl* group, despite the fact that this reagent ordinarily attacks an allylic methylene group in preference to a methyl group.[357]

In concluding this section it might be pointed out that, although homolytic reactions do not involve charged intermediates, inductive effects may nevertheless have an important influence on reaction rate.[339, 358]

Steric effects in oxidation reactions

Oxidation reactions may be ionic in mechanism or involve free-radical intermediates; both types will be considered here.

In the oxidation of an alcohol to a carbonyl compound by chromic acid, the rate-determining step is the abstraction of the hydrogen atom bonded to the carbinol carbon.[359] Steric accessibility of this hydrogen might thus be expected to influence the rate of oxidation. It has been reported[360] that 2-methyl-1-naphthylcarbinol (LXXIX) could not be oxidized to the corresponding aldehyde by means of

LXXIX

[356] E. C. Kooyman and A. Strang, *Rec. trav. chim.*, **72**, 342 (1953).

[357] K. Ziegler, A. Späth, E. Schaaf, W. Schumann, and E. Winkelmann, *Ann.*, **551**, 80 (1942). That bromination with N-bromosuccinimide is largely of the S_H1 type is suggested by results of P. Couvreur and A. Bruylants, *Bull. soc. chim. Belges*, **61**, 253 (1952), and W. J. Bailey and J. Bello, *J. Org. Chem.*, **20**, 525 (1955). See also N. P. Buu-Hoi and J. Lecoq, *Compt. rend.*, **226**, 87 (1948).

[358] See also E. C. Kooyman, R. van Helden, and A. F. Bickel, *Koninkl. Ned. Akad. Wetenschap. Proc.*, **56B**, 75 (1953); *C. A.*, **48**, 4456a (1954); R. van Helden and E. C. Kooyman, *Rec. trav. chim.*, **73**, 269 (1954); C. C. Price and H. Morita, *J. Am. Chem. Soc.*, **75**, 3686 (1953); F. R. Mayo and C. Walling, *Chem. Revs.*, **46**, 269 (1950); C. Walling and E. A. McElhill, *J. Am. Chem. Soc.*, **73**, 2927 (1951); H. C. Brown and A. G. Ash, *ibid.*, **77**, 4019 (1955).

[359] F. H. Westheimer and N. Nicolaides, *J. Am. Chem. Soc.*, **71**, 25 (1949).

[360] K. Ziegler and P. Tiemann, *Ber.*, **55**, 3406 (1922).

chromic acid, although oxidation of the 4-methyl isomer proceeded readily. Among substituted cyclohexyl alcohols, compounds having axial hydroxyl groups and equatorial carbinol hydrogen, such as *cis*-4-*t*-butylcyclohexanol (LXXX), are oxidized more readily than the isomers with equatorial hydroxyl and axial carbinol hydrogen, such as *trans*-4-*t*-butylcyclohexanol (LXXXI).[270, 361]

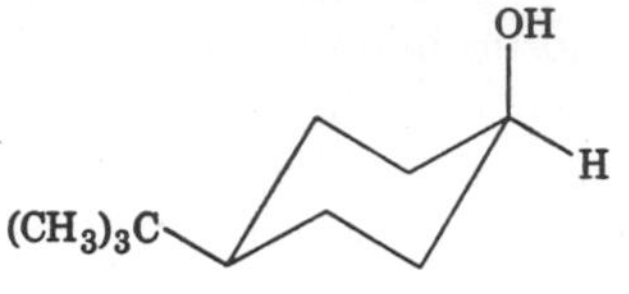

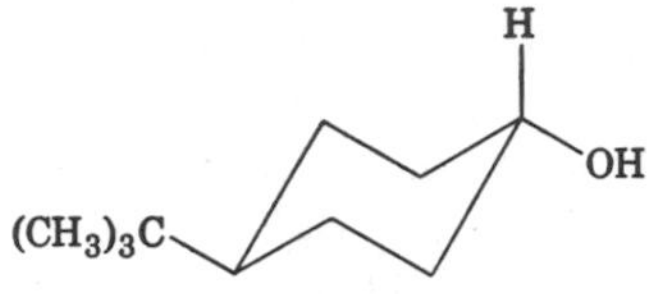

Steric inhibition of resonance seems to impede the normal (allylic)[362] oxidation of 2,4,4-trimethylpentene-1 (LXXXII) by means of air at 130–140° to the expected peroxide LXXXIII; instead, the epoxide LXXXIV is obtained in up to 56% yield.[363]

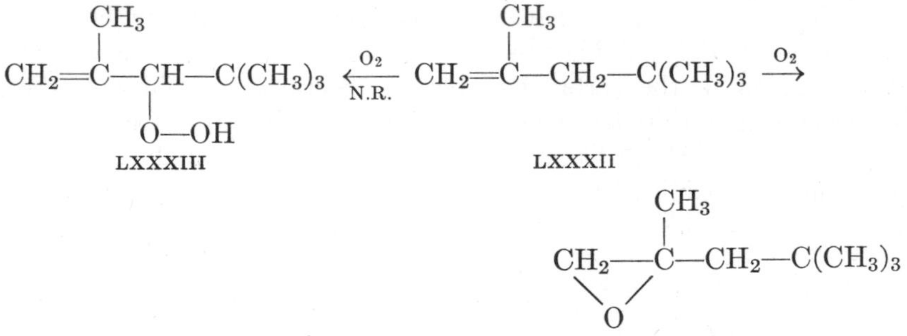

STERIC INFLUENCES ON THE REACTIVITY OF ANIONS

Optical stability of carbanions

The electronic configuration of a saturated carbanion is presumably similar to that of a tertiary amine. Tertiary amines of the type RR′R″N containing no other centers of asymmetry have never been

[361] G. Vavon and C. Zaremba, *Bull. soc. chim. France*, [4] *49*, 1953 (1931); D. H. R. Barton, *Experientia*, *6*, 316 (1950). See also J. Schreiber and A. Eschenmoser, *Helv. Chim. Acta*, *38*, 1529 (1955).

[362] W. A. Waters in H. Gilman's *Organic Chemistry*, Vol. 4, p. 1141, John Wiley & Sons, New York, 1953.

[363] E. J. Gasson, A. F. Millidge, G. R. Primavesi, W. Webster, and D. P. Young, *J. Chem. Soc.*, *1954*, 2161.

resolved.[364] The situation with respect to carbanions is not so clear-cut.[365]

Early claims for the existence of optically stable carbanions were based mainly on the lack of complete racemization of optically active aliphatic nitro compounds when converted to their salts.[366] However, these claims were later disproved when it was shown that the residual activity is due to impurities in the original nitro compound.[367] Other claims to the preparation of optically active salts of nitro compounds [368] should probably be reexamined. A claim that an optically stable carbanion is formed by treatment of the active thioglycollic acid LXXXV with sodium in liquid ammonia [369a] was likewise shown

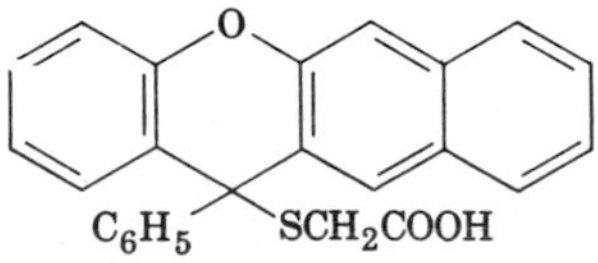

Active

LXXXV

to be unfounded.[369b] Evidence that carbanions may maintain their configuration at low temperatures, however, is found in the reaction of active 2-iodoöctane (LXXXVI) with 2-butyllithium followed by carbonation.[370] The 2-methyloctanoic (LXXXVII) acid obtained was

$$CH_3CHIC_6H_{13} \xrightarrow{CH_3CHLiCH_2CH_3} CH_3CHLiC_6H_{13} \xrightarrow{CO_2} \overset{\overset{\displaystyle CO_2Li}{|}}{CH_3CHC_6H_{13}}$$

LXXXVI   LXXXVII

partly active (20% retention of configuration) when the reaction was carried out at −70°. When the intermediate organometallic compound was allowed to warm to 0°, however, the product LXXXVII

---

[364] An exception is known where the nitrogen atom occupies a bridgehead: V. Prelog and P. Wieland, *Helv. Chim. Acta*, *27*, 1127 (1944).

[365] For a review of early work, see reference 315, p. 388.

[366] R. Kuhn and H. Albrecht, *Ber.*, *60*, 1297 (1927); R. L. Shriner and J. H. Young, *J. Am. Chem. Soc.*, *52*, 3332 (1930).

[367] N. Kornblum, N. N. Lichtin, J. T. Patton, and D. C. Iffland, *J. Am. Chem. Soc.*, *69*, 307 (1947); N. Kornblum, J. T. Patton, and J. B. Nordmann, *ibid.*, *70*, 746 (1948).

[368] W. H. Mills, *J. Soc. Chem. Ind.*, *51*, 750 (1932); J. T. Thurston and R. L. Shriner, *J. Am. Chem. Soc.*, *57*, 2163 (1935).

[369] (a) E. Wallis and F. H. Adams, *J. Am. Chem. Soc.*, *55*, 3838 (1933); (b) G. Wittig, F. Vidal, and E. Bohnert, *Ber.*, *83*, 359 (1950).

[370] R. L. Letsinger, *J. Am. Chem. Soc.*, *72*, 4842 (1950). See also D. J. Cram, J. Allinger, and A. Langemann, *Chemistry & Industry*, *1955*, 919.

obtained on carbonation was inactive. At $-70°$ either the two steps shown involve retention or both steps involve inversion of configuration.

Another instance of stereospecificity in what appears to be a carbanion intermediate has been claimed in certain reactions of organomercury compounds,[371a] but it is quite likely that these reactions are of the S_E2 type and do not actually involve free carbanions.[371b]

More clear-cut evidence for retention of configuration of carbanions comes from the reactions of organometallic compounds derived from olefins. Carbanions so obtained are of the type $RR'C{=}CH^{\ominus}$, and, being similar in configuration to oximes $RR'C{=}NOH$, might be expected to exist in stable *cis* and *trans* forms. When *cis*-1,2-diphenyl-2-*p*-chlorophenyl-1-bromoethylene (LXXXVIII) was treated with *n*-butyllithium at $-20°$ followed by carbonation, *cis*-1,2-diphenyl-2-*p*-chlorophenyl-1-carboxyethylene (XC) was obtained in 82% yield.[372] Decomposition of the intermediate lithium compound (LXXXIX) with methanol gave *cis*-1,2-diphenyl-2-*p*-chlorophenyl-ethylene (XCI) in nearly quantitative yield. Similarly the *trans* isomer (XCII) gave a lithium intermediate (XCIII) which afforded mainly *trans* products on reaction with methanol and carbon dioxide. These results indicate that the intermediate carbanions maintain their configurations, and that both formation and further reaction of the ions involve retention (or, much less likely, inversion) of geometric configuration.

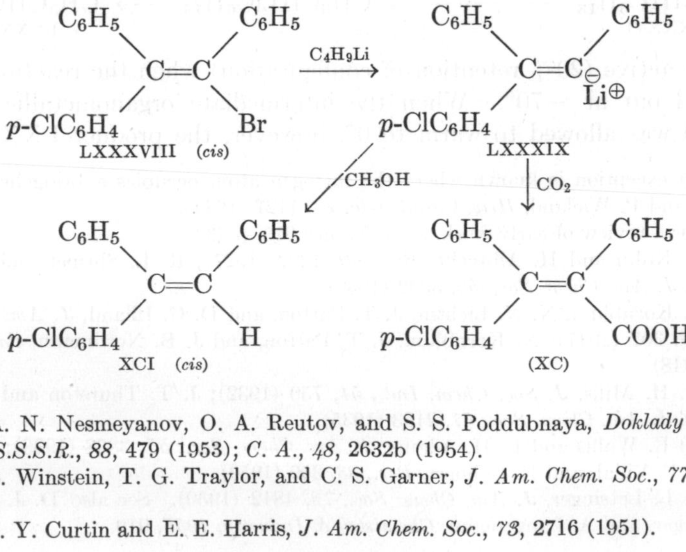

[371a] A. N. Nesmeyanov, O. A. Reutov, and S. S. Poddubnaya, *Doklady Akad. Nauk S.S.S.R.*, **88**, 479 (1953); *C. A.*, **48**, 2632b (1954).

[371b] S. Winstein, T. G. Traylor, and C. S. Garner, *J. Am. Chem. Soc.*, **77**, 3741 (1955).

[372] D. Y. Curtin and E. E. Harris, *J. Am. Chem. Soc.*, **73**, 2716 (1951).

Similarly

$$\text{XCII} \quad (trans) \qquad \qquad \qquad \text{XCIII}$$

To trans products

Analogous results have been observed with the bromostilbenes PhCH=CPhBr,[373] propenyl bromide ($CH_3CH=CHBr$) (only the *cis* isomer was investigated),[374] and the 2-bromo-2-butenes ($CH_3CH=CBrCH_3$).[375] In the last case, the reaction was predominantly but not entirely stereospecific in that the *trans* isomer gave 5–6% of *cis*-crotonic acid in addition to 64–74% of the expected *trans*-crotonic acid and the *cis* isomer gave 8–10% of *trans*-crotonic acid in addition to 21–24% of the expected *cis*-crotonic acid. Lack of complete stereospecificity may be due to isomerization of the bromides before reaction or isomerization of the intermediate lithium compounds.[375] The case of *cis*-propenyl bromide is significant in that the lithium derivative was prepared by treatment of the halide with lithium metal in ether rather than by a metal interchange with butyllithium. Even in this case the carbinols obtained by treating the lithium derivative with various aldehydes were exclusively *cis* isomers, though in the similar case of *cis*-β-bromostyrene (*cis*-$C_6H_5CH=CHBr$) the product of treatment with lithium followed by carbonation was *trans*-cinnamic acid.[376] The reason for the difference in results is not entirely clear, but the stereospecificity in the formation of *cis*-propenyllithium has been explained as being due to reaction of the halide on the surface of the metal with retention of configuration.[374]

Stereospecificity has also been observed in reduction of alkenyl halides with sodium amalgam [377] and with sodium in liquid ammonia,[378] reactions which *may* involve alkenylsodium intermediates. On the

[373] D. Y. Curtin and E. E. Harris, *J. Am. Chem. Soc.*, **73**, 4519 (1951). See also D. Y. Curtin, H. W. Johnson, and E. G. Steiner, *ibid.*, **77**, 4500 (1955).

[374] E. A. Braude and J. A. Coles, *J. Chem. Soc.*, **1951**, 2078.

[375] A. S. Dreiding and R. J. Pratt, *J. Am. Chem. Soc.*, **76**, 1902 (1954).

[376] G. F Wright, *J. Org. Chem.*, **1**, 457 (1936). See also D. F. DeTar and Y. Chu, *J. Am. Chem. Soc.*, **77**, 4410 (1955).

[377] (a) A. Michael and O. Schulthess, *J. prakt. Chem.*, **46**, 236 (1892); (b) H. P. Kaufmann and K. Küchler, *Ber.*, **70**, 915 (1937); (c) R. E. Buckles and G. V. Mock, *J. Org. Chem.*, **15**, 680 (1950).

[378] M. C. Hoff, K. W. Greenlee, and C. E. Boord, *J. Am. Chem. Soc.*, **73**, 3329 (1951).

other hand, reduction of *cis*-2-methyl-3-bromo-2-butenoic acid (XCIV) with zinc in ethanol and in acetic acid gave only tiglic acid (XCV); presumably this reaction is non-stereospecific and leads to the more stable stereoisomer.[377b]

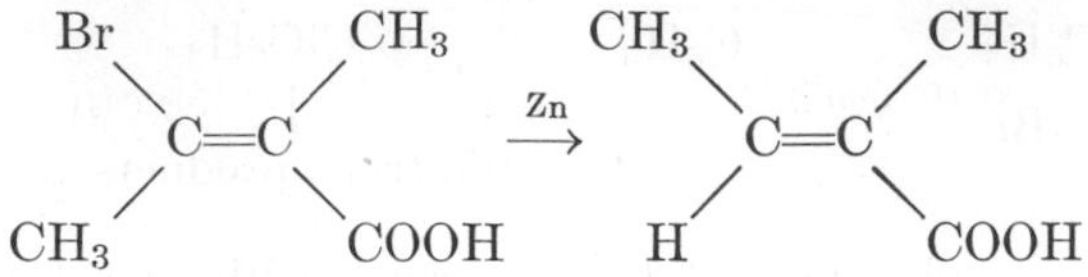

In anionic reductions (with alkali metal and liquid ammonia) leading to *saturated* diastereoisomers, the more stable product results.[379]

Steric effects involving anions and other bases

In this section, steric factors affecting the Y component in the reaction $Y + R - X \rightarrow Y - R + X$ will be considered. Y may be

TABLE XXX

NUCLEOPHILIC CONSTANTS

Base	Nucleophilic Constant
Water	0.00
Picrate ion *	1.9
Sulfate ion *	2.5
Acetate ion	2.72
Chloride ion	3.04
Pyridine *	3.6
Bicarbonate ion	3.8
$HPO_4^=$ *	3.8
Bromide ion	3.89
Azide ion	4.00
Thiourea *	4.1
Hydroxide ion	4.20
Aniline	4.49
Thiocyanate ion	4.77
Iodide ion	5.04
Sulfite ion *	5.1
Acid sulfide ion *	5.1
Cyanide ion [379a]	5.1
Thiosulfate ion	6.36
$HPSO_3^=$ *	6.6

* Value determined indirectly. See reference 380.

[379] D. H. R. Barton and C. H. Robinson, *J. Chem. Soc.*, *1954*, 3045.

[379a] M. F. Hawthorne, G. S. Hammond, and B. M. Graybill, *J. Am. Chem. Soc.*, *77*, 486 (1955).

either an anion or a neutral base. Before steric effects can be discussed intelligently, it is necessary to inquire into the relative reactivity of various bases Y in systems where steric effects are unimportant. This reactivity or "nucleophilic character" of Y parallels the basicity of Y only very roughly; it is better measured by a "nucleophilic constant" [380] defined as $n = \log k/k_0$, where k is the rate constant for the reaction of methyl bromide with the base Y in water solution at 25° and k_0 is the rate constant for hydrolysis of methyl bromide in water at 25° in the absence of extraneous base. Nucleophilic constants are listed in Table XXX.

When Y is an organic base, steric factors depending on its structure may also become important. Such factors have not yet been studied in displacement reactions with alkoxides,[381] but they are well known in displacement reactions of amines of the type

$$RR'R''N + A - X \rightarrow RR'R''NA^+ + X^-$$

In these reactions, as the R groups become more bulky, the reaction is slowed down due to steric hindrance (F strain). As might be expected, the degree of hindrance depends on both the steric requirements of the amine and those of the A group in A − X. The rates of reaction of pyridine, triethylamine, and quinuclidine with methyl, ethyl, and isopropyl iodide (discussed on p. 75) illustrate this point. Further instances are presented here.

Benzyl bromide and substituted benzyl bromides react with pyridine faster than with 2-picoline.[382] Since the electron-donating effect of the methyl group should increase the availability of the free electron pair on the nitrogen atom and therefore increase the rate of quaternization, the observed decrease appears to be due to steric interference.

Rates of quaternization of substituted anilines with methyl and ethyl iodide are summarized in Table XXXI. Again there is a marked steric effect. It is interesting that N-methylindoline (entry 4) reacts more readily with either methyl or ethyl iodide than N,N-dimethyl-

[380] C. G. Swain and C. B. Scott, J. Am. Chem. Soc., 75, 141 (1953). See also J. O. Edwards, ibid., 76, 1540 (1954); C. G. Swain, R. B. Mosely, and D. E. Brown, ibid., 77, 3731 (1955); C. G. Swain, D. C. Ditmer, and L. E. Kaiser, ibid., 77, 3737 (1955).

[381] However, steric factors have been found to influence the course of elimination reactions with alkoxides: H. C. Brown and I. Moritani, J. Am. Chem. Soc., 75, 4112 (1953); cf. Chapter 6. Qualitative observations on steric hindrance in reactions of α-bromo-β-aminoketones with acetate and benzoate ions have been recorded by N. H. Cromwell and F. W. Starks, J. Am. Chem. Soc., 72, 4108 (1950).

[382] J. W. Baker and W. S. Nathan, J. Chem. Soc., 1935, 519.

TABLE XXXI [383]

RELATIVE RATES OF QUATERNIZATION AT 45° IN METHANOL

Entry No.	Base	Rate with CH_3I	Rate with C_2H_5I
1	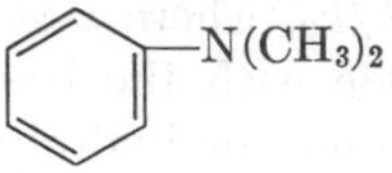 $-N(CH_3)_2$	1.00	0.072
2	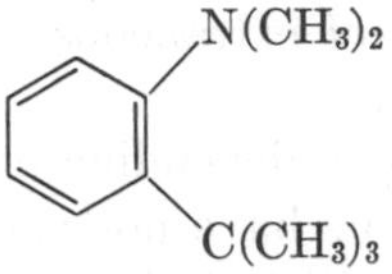 $N(CH_3)_2$ $C(CH_3)_3$	0.0116; * 0 [384]	—
3	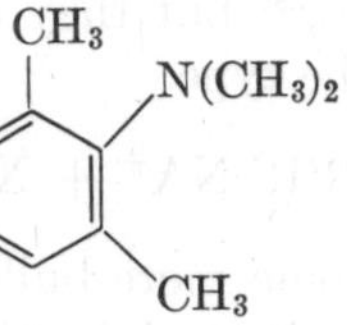 CH_3 $N(CH_3)_2$ CH_3	0.0181; * 0 [384]	—
4	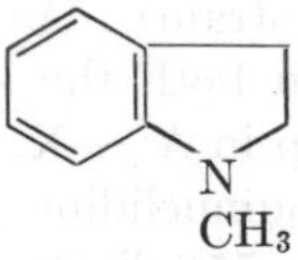 N CH_3	3.87	0.222
5	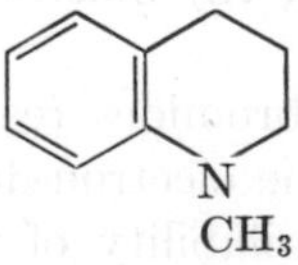 N CH_3	0.82	0.040
6	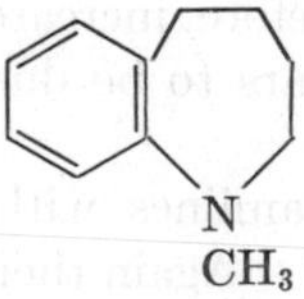 N CH_3	0.0302	0.0093

* This is probably a spurious value due to solvolysis.

aniline (entry 1), presumably because one of the N-alkyl groups is bent back in the form of a ring and therefore presents less steric interference to quaternization. On the other hand, N-methyl-2,3-benzcycloheptylamine (entry 6) quaternizes much more slowly than N,N-dimethylaniline; it behaves like an o-alkyl-N,N-dimethylaniline. The

[383] W. G. Brown and S. Fried, J. Am. Chem. Soc., 65, 1841 (1943), unless indicated otherwise.

[384] H. C. Brown and K. LeRoi Nelson, J. Am. Chem. Soc., 75, 24 (1953); H. C. Brown and M. Grayson, ibid., 75, 20 (1953). (At 25° in acetonitrile.)

puckered cycloheptyl ring gets into the way of the approaching alkyl group, and the benzcycloheptylamine derivative is probably comparable to an *o*-ethylaniline derivative. N-methyl-1,2,3,4-tetrahydroquinoline (entry 5) takes an intermediate position. The relation of N,N-dimethylaniline to the five- and six-membered ring compounds is similar to that observed [253] in the reaction of dimethylamine, pyrrolidine, and piperidine with trimethylboron.

A similar relationship is observed in the reaction of 4-aminoindane, 1-aminotetralin, and 2,3-dimethylaniline with methyl iodide.[385] The first substance yields a mixture of the tertiary amine and the quaternary methiodide, but the last two give the tertiary amines only, and 1-dimethylaminotetralin is not readily quaternized.

A systematic study of the reaction of alkylpyridines with methyl, ethyl, and isopropyl iodide in nitrobenzene solution is summarized in Table XXXII.[256, 386] While substitution of an alkyl group in the 3 or 4 position of the pyridine ring leads to a slight increase in the rate of quaternization because of polar effects, substitution of alkyl groups in the 2 position leads to a decrease in rate (increase in activation energy, decrease in PZ factor) due to steric interference. In attempted

[385] R. T. Arnold, V. J. Webers, and R. M. Dodson, *J. Am. Chem. Soc.*, 74, 368 (1953).

[386] H. C. Brown and A. Cahn, *J. Am. Chem. Soc.*, 77, 1715 (1955).

TABLE XXXII [256, 386]

RATE CONSTANTS ($k \times 10^5$ liter mole^{-1} sec.$^{-1}$) FOR THE QUATERNIZATION OF
ALKYLPYRIDINES WITH ALKYL IODIDES

R' R	CH$_3$ (30°)	C$_2$H$_5$ (60°)	i-C$_3$H$_7$ (80°)
H	50.5	30.9 *	10.0
4-Me	111	67.7	18.8–19.4
4-Et	113.5	67.9	19.0
4-i-Pr	112	68.1	18.7
4-t-Br	111.5	67.6	18.9
3-Me	104.5	62.7	16.9–17.6
3-Et	110.6	64.1	17.5
3-i-Pr	118	63.3	16.5
3-t-Bu	138	67.3	15.5
2-Me	23.9 *	7.85 *	0.813
2-Et	11.4 *	3.77	—
2-i-Pr	3.69	1.15 *	—
2-t-Bu	0.0130	—	—

* Calculated from values at higher temperatures.

reactions of 2-t-butylpyridine with ethyl iodide and 2-ethyl, 2-isopropyl, and 2-t-butylpyridine with isopropyl iodide, steric interference is so severe that the quaternization is attended by a number of complications.[386]

Other reactions in which the rate or course is influenced by steric effects in the base have been reported.[387] An interesting effect of pressure on the rate of the reaction of N,N,o-trimethylaniline with methyl iodide has been observed.[388] At high pressures the reaction rate increases owing to a decrease in activation energy. This is taken to be additional evidence for steric hindrance in the N,N,o-trimethylaniline

[387] W. V. Drake and S. M. McElvain, *J. Am. Chem. Soc.*, *56*, 1810 (1934); reference 223b; H. Stetter, *Ber.*, *86*, 161 (1953); H. C. Brown and W. H. Bonner, *J. Am. Chem. Soc.*, *75*, 14 (1953); A. H. Sommers and S. E. Aaland, *ibid.*, *75*, 5280 (1953); D. P. Evans, *J. Chem. Soc.*, *1954*, 1316; F. H. Mann and F. H. C. Stewart, *ibid.*, *1954*, 4127; Ph. Buu-Hoi, R. Royer, and M. Hubert-Habart, *Rec. trav. chim.*, *73*, 188 (1954). The assumption that o-trifluoromethylaniline is more hindered than o-t-butylaniline made in the last reference is obviously erroneous; the diminished reactivity of the trifluoromethyl compound towards haloquinones must be due to an inductive effect.

[388] K. E. Weale, *J. Chem. Soc.*, *1954*, 2959.

system, since in unhindered systems the activation energy increases with pressure in the Menshutkin reaction.[389]

Steric assistance due to the bulkiness of the amino group is found in carbon alkylations with Mannich bases.[390] Thus the alkylation of 2-nitropropane with 1-diisopropylamino-2-nitrobutane (XCVI, R = $(CH_3)_2CH$—) gives 2-methyl-2,4-dinitrohexane (XCVII) in 44% yield in $3\frac{1}{2}$ hours whereas the reaction with the corresponding dimethylamino compound (XCVI, R = CH_3) takes 8 hours for completion.[391]

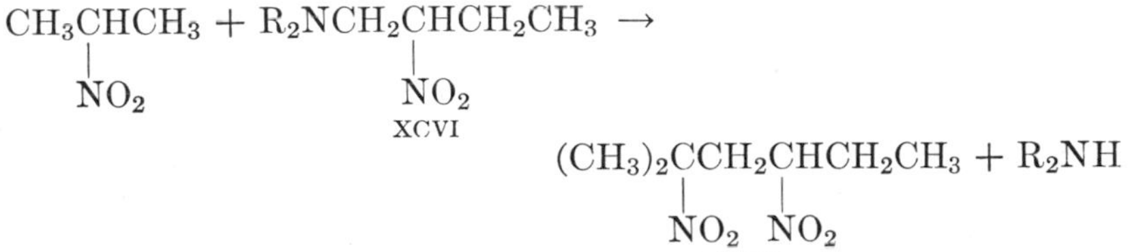

$$\underset{\underset{NO_2}{|}}{CH_3CHCH_3} + \underset{\underset{NO_2}{|}}{R_2NCH_2CHCH_2CH_3} \rightarrow$$

XCVI

$$\underset{\underset{NO_2}{|}\ \underset{NO_2}{|}}{(CH_3)_2CCH_2CHCH_2CH_3} + R_2NH$$

XCVII

Very little is known regarding steric effects on the reactivity of carbanions. Systematic studies regarding the effect of the bulk of the alkyl (R) groups on the reactivity of a carbanion $RR'R''C^-$ seem to be lacking. What little information there is seems to be derived from competition experiments. For example, it is known [392] that the anion derived from Hagemann's ester (XCVIII) is alkylated at the 2 rather

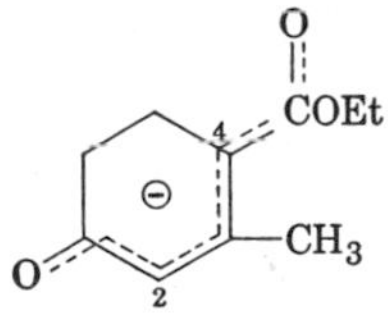

XCVIII

than at the 4 position. The importance of steric factors in this kind of situation is not clear, however.[393] The same applies to the reactions

[389] M. W. Perrin, *Trans. Faraday Soc.*, *34*, 144 (1938). The rate still increases with pressure, owing to an increase in the frequency factor which more than offsets the increase in activation energy

[390] G. L. Shoemaker and R. W. Keown, *J. Am. Chem. Soc.*, *76*, 6374 (1954).

[391] H. R. Snyder and W. E. Hamlin, *J. Am. Chem. Soc.*, *72*, 5082 (1950).

[392] Cf. J. A. Hogg, *J. Am. Chem. Soc.*, *70*, 161 (1948).

[393] For a general discussion of the problem of the alkylation of ambident anions see N. Kornblum, R. A. Smiley, R. K. Blackwood, and D. C. Iffland, *J. Am. Chem. Soc.*, *77*, 6269 (1955) (these authors propose the term "ambident" for the resonating anions with two alternative reactive positions); also H. Henecka, *Chemie der Beta-Dicarbonyl Verbindungen*, Springer-Verlag, Berlin, Germany, 1950; A. Brändström, *Arkiv Kemi*, *6*, 155 (1953), and p. 103 in reference 98.

of unsymmetrical ketones which can form the anions $RR'\overline{C}COCHR''R'''$ and $RR'CHCO\overline{C}R''R'''$; here the problem is further complicated by the fact that both the relative stability and the relative reactivity of the two anions may influence the point of attack.[394]

Turning finally to secondary steric effects in carbanions, one again finds a dearth of information. Thus little seems to be known about steric inhibition of resonance in benzylic carbanions. It has been noted [395] that mesitylacetonitrile (XCIX) and its 3-nitro and 3,5-di-nitro derivatives do not condense with benzaldehyde or p-dimethyl-aminobenzaldehyde under conditions suitable for the condensation of phenylacetonitrile and 2,5-dimethylphenylacetonitrile. Similarly, the ultraviolet spectra of XCIX and its nitro derivatives are unaffected by the addition of sodium ethoxide whereas the spectra of other phen-ylacetonitriles are changed by the addition of base. It is concluded that XCIX and its nitro derivatives fail to form the corresponding anion, C. This is ascribed to the electron-donating effect of the methyl

$$CH_3\text{---}\underset{\underset{CH_3}{|}}{\overset{\overset{CH_3}{|}}{\bigcirc}}\text{---}CH_2CN + Base \xrightarrow{\text{N.R.}} C$$

XCIX

groups, but it might equally well be caused by steric inhibition of res-onance.

I-strain effects have been postulated in carbanions,[256] and the pre-diction has been made that the cyclopropyl carbanion should be of low stability. In this prediction it must be assumed either that the carbanion is planar or that the stability of the ion is diminished, be-cause it cannot readily oscillate from one possible configuration to the other.[396] In an experimental test of this prediction, 2,2-diphenyl-

---

[394] Referring to the aldol condensation (where the situation is further complicated by reversibility), S. G. Powell and A. T. Nielsen, *J. Am. Chem. Soc.*, **70**, 3627 (1948), state that "in alkaline medium, aldehydes condense on the *α-methylene* group of methyl ketones CH_3COCH_2R unless steric factors prevent it, in which case condensation occurs on the methyl group." See, however, H. M. E. Cardwell, *J. Chem. Soc.*, *1951*, 2442. See also earlier papers by S. G. Powell; E. R. Alexander, *Principles of Ionic Organic Reactions*, p. 128, John Wiley & Sons, New York, 1950; A. Nielsen and E. B. W. Ovist, *J. Am. Chem. Soc.*, **76**, 5165 (1954); M. M. Bokadi and Y. Singh, *J. Ind. Chem. Soc.*, **31**, 447 (1954).

[395] A. Bruylants, E. Braye, and A. Schonne, *Helv. Chim. Acta*, *35*, 1127 (1952).

[396] This oscillation may account for the ready racemization at room temperature of carbanions derived from saturated systems.

cyclopropyl cyanide (CI) was converted to its anion by means of lithium diisopropylamide; complete racemization resulted even at −80°, and, even when methyl iodide was added to trap the anion rapidly, the resulting methylated product (CII) was totally racemic.[397]

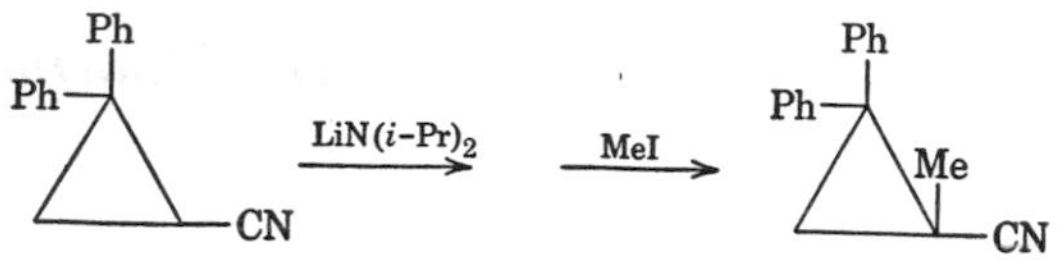

Nevertheless there seems to be some reluctance for the anion of compound CI to form, since CI was racemized by sodium methoxide in methanol at $\frac{1}{88}$ the corresponding rate for methylethylacetonitrile. It must be concluded either that the anion of CI is planar or, if tetrahedral, that it is readily interconverted into its enantiomorph.

The prediction, made on the basis of I strain (cf. p. 122), that phenylcyclopentane should be a stronger acid than isopropylbenzene, but phenylcyclohexane should be weaker, where ionization of the benzylic hydrogen is concerned, has been borne out.[398]

Bridgehead carbanions, though presumably not readily able to become planar, can nevertheless be formed, as evidenced by the fact that the trisulfone CIII (R = H) is soluble, without decomposition, in aqueous sodium bicarbonate whereas the methyl homolog (CIII, R = CH₃) is not.[399]

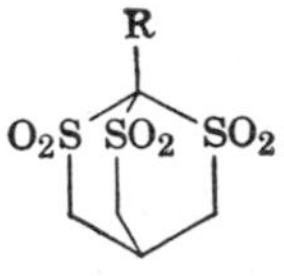

CIII

Acknowledgment. The author is indebted to a number of colleagues, who read all or part of the manuscript, for valuable suggestions. Special thanks are due to Professors Herbert C. Brown and Melvin S. Newman, who gave generously of their time and contributed much helpful advice. The manuscript was typed by Miss Laura Beaulieu and checked by Mr. Arthur Oberster under a grant from the Shell Chemical Company.

[397] H. Walborsky and F. M. Hornyak, *J. Am. Chem. Soc.*, *77*, 6026 (1955); *ibid.*, *78*, 872 (1956).

[398] R. D. Kleene and G. W. Wheland, *J. Am. Chem. Soc.*, *63*, 3321 (1941).

[399] W. v. E. Doering and L. K. Levy, *J. Am. Chem. Soc.*, *77*, 509 (1955).

Chapter 3

by George S. Hammond
and M. Frederick Hawthorne

Steric Effects in Aromatic Substitution

INTRODUCTION

ELECTROPHILIC SUBSTITUTION
    Steric Hindrance to Attachment of the Reagent
    Effect of Steric Interaction among Resident Groups
    Coulombic Interaction between Substituents and Entering Groups

NUCLEOPHILIC SUBSTITUTION
    Mechanism and Steric Effects
    Steric Inhibition of Activation
    Steric Compression at the Reaction Site

SUBSTITUTION BY FREE RADICALS

Chapter 3

INTRODUCTION

The substitution of one group or atom for another on an aromatic nucleus can occur by three mechanisms which are clearly distinct. The most familiar is represented by reactions such as nitration, bromination, and sulfonation in which an electrophilic reagent effects the displacement. The entity displaced is most frequently, but not always, a proton. In addition, the displacement of halide, alkoxide, and various other anions by nucleophilic reagents may be properly regarded as aromatic substitutions. Lastly, free radicals produced in various ways such as by the pyrolysis or photolysis of peroxides or azo compounds may replace hydrogen and possible other substituents attached to aromatic nuclei.

The gross aspects of the mechanism of electrophilic and nucleophilic substitution are rather well understood. The brilliant work of Melander [1] has demonstrated that in bromination and nitration the C—II bond which is being broken has not been sufficiently extended to effect any substantial change in the zero-point vibrational energy. This is most easily interpreted as indicating that the configuration of the transition state is close to I, a possible high-energy intermediate in the displacement of a proton by a reactive electrophilic reagent, X^+. The fact that a kinetic isotope effect is observed in sulfonation

I

reactions indicates that the transition state for such a reaction lies closer to the final configuration. In other words, the C—H bond has been stretched considerably, and the entering SO_3 group has ap-

[1] L. Melander, *Arkiv Kemi*, *2*, 213 (1950).

proached its ultimate position rather closely. For the most part we will regard structures such as I as a logical point of departure for the discussion of steric effects in all electrophilic substitutions.

Similarly, in the nucleophilic displacement reactions of activated aryl halides such as II it is evident that the breaking of the C—X bond has not progressed very far in the transition state. This may be inferred from the usual order of reactivity of similarly constituted halides, which is $F \gg Cl > Br$.[2] In reactions such as nucleophilic

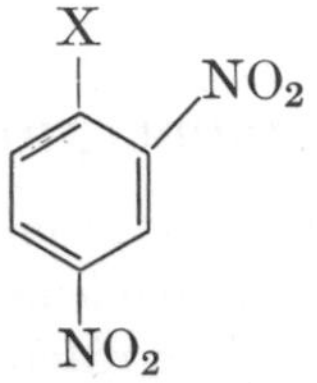

$$X$$

$$NO_2$$

$$NO_2$$

II

displacement at a saturated carbon atom in which the C—X bond is highly extended in the transition state the higher polarizability of the larger halogens increases their reactivity in a striking manner.[3] It therefore follows that reactions in which the smaller halogens are more reactive involve transition states in which the old bond has not been stretched much beyond the normal covalent bond distance. Again, exceptions in which the transition-state configuration is displaced toward that of the products are encountered.[4] In the displacement of halide ions from 2,4-dinitrohalobenzenes by N-methylaniline in nitrobenzene solution, the order of reactivity is $Br > Cl > F$.

$$2,4\text{-}(NO_2)_2C_6H_3Cl + C_6H_5NHCH_3 \xrightarrow{C_6H_5NO_2}$$

$$2,4\text{-}(NO_2)_2C_6H_3N(CH_3)C_6H_5 + HCl$$

While this deviation implies that not all transition states in nucleophilic substitution are close to the configuration III in which the car-

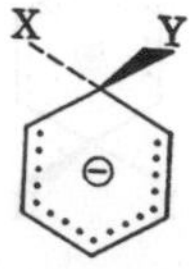

III

[2] J. F. Bunnett and R. E. Zahler, *Chem. Revs.*, *49*, 273 (1951).

[3] C. K. Ingold, *Structure and Mechanism in Organic Chemistry*, p. 338, Cornell University Press, Ithaca, N. Y., 1953.

[4] G. S. Hammond and L. R. Parks, *J. Am. Chem. Soc.*, *77*, 340 (1955).

bon atom undergoing substitution is tetrahedral, this model will be taken as a point of reference in the following discussion.

The advantage of these substitution reactions as a tool in studying steric effects derives from the rigidity of aromatic systems and the fact that the transition states have configurations in which the internuclear distances are usually close to those encountered in stable molecules. This permits relatively accurate estimates as to the actual interatomic distances in both the initial and transition states of the reacting system.

The details of the mechanism of substitution by free radicals are much less evident. Mechanisms which involve the formation of intermediates such as IV as a rate-limiting step do not fit available in-

IV

formation particularly well. It is possible that some radical substitutions involve the reaction of molecular complexes of a radical and the aromatic substrate with a second radical, as has been found to be the case with formally similar reactions of antioxidants with radicals.[5] It seems best to present the empirical observations without attempting to interpret them on the basis of a particular mechanism.

ELECTROPHILIC SUBSTITUTION

The discussion will be divided in such a way as to attempt to illustrate several types of steric effects. Traditionally the term has often carried with it the connotation that steric effects are due alone to the repulsion between non-bonded atoms. It would be entirely satisfactory to adopt this significance of the term as a working definition if it were possible to isolate such effects from certain others. However, such a separation is not possible in general. Therefore, all factors which influence the reactivity of molecules and which arise primarily from the particular geometry of the system must be considered as a group. These effects, as related to the problem of aromatic substitution, include the following.

[5] G. S. Hammond, C. E. Boozer, C. E. Hamilton, and J. N. Sen, *J. Am. Chem. Soc.*, **77**, 3238 (1955).

1. Repulsion between the attacking reagent and groups already attached to the nucleus which arises from overlapping of the van der Waals radii.

2. Interaction which affects the activating or deactivating influences of groups already in the molecule. Such interaction frequently results in "the steric inhibition of resonance."

3. The coulombic interaction of substituents with the entering group. If a large electric moment is associated with the C—Y bond in V the interaction between this moment and X will be quite different for the *ortho* and *para* transition states. It is furthermore probable that the interaction can be either attractive or repulsive and can exert a wide variety of effects on the *ortho/para* ratio in substitutions.

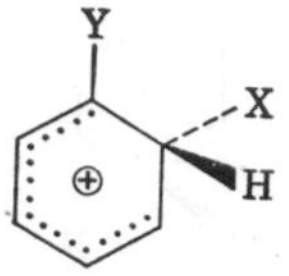

V

Steric hindrance to attachment of the reagent

This influence can be observed with a minimum of complications by studying isomer ratios in the products formed in substitutions on alkylbenzenes. Thus, the variation in the *ortho/para* ratio in attack by a common reagent on monoalkylbenzenes, VI, and the 2/3 ratio in attack on *para*-dialkylbenzenes, VII, can be attributed, in a first approximation, to the variation in the steric requirements of the alkyl groups.

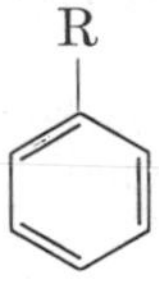

VI    VII

A clear-cut case is found in the nitration of *tert*-butylbenzene with mixed acid.[6] The *ortho/para* ratio is 0.22 as compared to a value of 1.6 found in the nitration of toluene under similar conditions.[7] Since the *para/meta* ratio is decreased only from 8.5 to 6.5 by changing from toluene to *tert*-butylbenzene the large decrease in reactivity at

[6] K. L. Nelson and H. C. Brown, *J. Am. Chem. Soc.*, *73*, 5605 (1951).
[7] W. W. Jones and M. Russell, *J. Chem. Soc.*, *1947*, 921.

the *ortho* position in the latter substrate is not attributable to the differences in hyperconjugation with the two substituents. The results of this and other investigations are summarized in Table I.

TABLE I

ISOMER RATIOS IN THE NITRATION OF ALKYLBENZENES

ortho/para Ratio

Compound	Brown et al.[6, 7a]	Cline and Ried,[8] Vavon and Collier [9]	Cohn, Hughes, Jones, and Peeling [10]	Hansch and Helmcamp [11]
Toluene	1.57	1.5	1.42	1.4
Ethylbenzene	0.93	1.2		1.1
Cumene	0.48	0.16		0.35
tert-Butylbenzene	0.22		0.15	

The monotonic decrease in the *ortho/para* ratio reflects the increase in the bulk of the resident groups. The older data [8, 9] indicate a sharp increase in the difference between ethylbenzene and cumene. Later work, however, showed a smaller difference.[7a, 11] This may indicate that *ortho* attack on ethylbenzene can proceed by way of the relatively strain-free transition-state VIII in which the methyl group is directed away from the entering nitronium ion. The small decrease in the ratio on going from toluene to ethylbenzene would then be due primarily to the lower entropy content of VIII as compared with the ground state of ethylbenzene in which rotation about the C_1—CH_2 bond is less restricted. In cumene both methyl groups cannot be directed away from the entering group, and so the *ortho* transition state has a relatively high potential energy even in the most stable configuration, which may be IX. An even larger increase in the potential

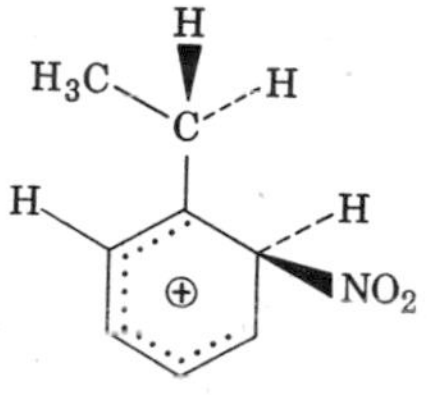

VIII 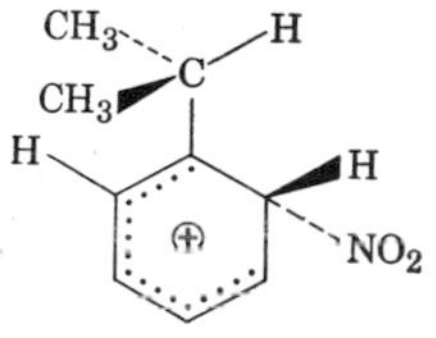   IX

[7a] H. C. Brown and W. H. Bonner, *J. Am. Chem. Soc.*, *76*, 605 (1954).

[8] E. L. Cline and E. E. Ried, *J. Am. Chem. Soc.*, *49*, 3150 (1927).

[9] G. Vavon and A. Callier, *Bull. soc. chim. France*, *41*, 357 (1927).

[10] H. Cohn, E. D. Hughes, M. H. Jones, and M. G. Peeling, *Nature*, *169*, 291 (1952).

[11] C. Hansch and G. Helmkamp, *J. Am. Chem. Soc.*, *73*, 3080 (1951).

energy should be involved in *ortho* substitution on *tert*-butylbenzene since at least one of the three resident methyl groups must be close to the entering group. It would not be surprising to find another large decrease in the ratio on passing from cumene to *tert*-butylbenzene. The results demonstrate that consideration of only the relative strain energies in transition states may lead to seriously incomplete descriptions. Probably the energy of cumene is minimized in conformation X. In *tert*-butylbenzene serious methyl-hydrogen repulsions are unavoidable. Strain in the resting state of the molecule would partially compensate for the strain in the transition state and might tend to equalize the activation energies for *ortho* substitution in cumene and *tert*-butylbenzene.

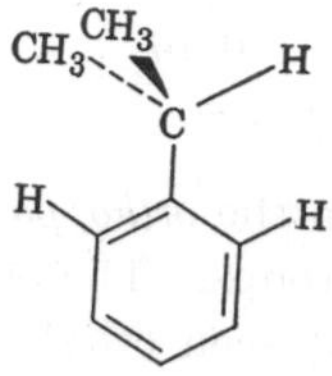

X

The data and the foregoing discussion, which is incomplete because of the neglect of other, closely related rotational states, serves to illustrate the complexity of non-rigid systems. It is a serious oversight to treat alkyl groups as though they were hard spheres with fixed volumes.

Further evidence is obtained by the study of *p*-dialkyl benzenes. *p*-Cymene is attacked primarily in the position *ortho* to the methyl group on sulfonation,[12] bromination,[13, 14] chlorination,[13] and nitration.[14] The yields of derivatives with this orientation which could be isolated by careful fractional crystallization are listed in Table II.

TABLE II

SUBSTITUTION ON *p*-CYMENE

Reaction	Conditions	Per Cent Yield of *ortho* Methyl Derivatives
Bromination	I_2 catalyzed, no solvent, ambient temperature	>54
Chlorination	No solvent, water cooled	>59
Nitration	Mixed acid, $-3°$	>70
Sulfonation	Fuming H_2SO_4 at $0-10°$	>89

[12] R. J. W. LeFevre, *J. Chem. Soc.*, *1934*, 1501.
[13] H. N. Morse and I. Remsen, *Ber.*, *11*, 224 (1878).
[14] E. V. Gerichten, *Ber.*, *10*, 1249 (1877).

The significance of the yield data is uncertain since the losses cannot be easily estimated. The increase in yield in sulfonation is in agreement with the view that the magnitude of the steric effects should be sensitive to increases in the bulk of the attacking reagent. In sulfonation the attacking species is probably SO_3,[15] which is much larger than the species, NO_2^+, involved in nitration.[16]

Contrasting results in the comparison of bromination and nitration are observed with toluene as a substrate.[17] In bromination the *ortho/para* ratio is less than 1.0 and apparently increases somewhat in the temperature interval 25–75°. [17a] In nitration the ratio increases only from 1.33 to 1.42 between −30° and 30°. These data suggest that bromination in toluene involves a relatively bulky attacking reagent such as an aggregate of two or more bromine molecules as has been suggested by kinetic evidence.[17b]

Another perplexing effect which must be called a steric influence is encountered in nitrations with acyl nitrates. *Ortho/para* ratios are often much higher than in other nitrations.[17c] This has been taken as an indication that the attacking reagent under these conditions is not the nitronium ion but is either the acyl nitrate or, more probably, nitrogen pentoxide.[18] Only benzoyl nitrate in carbon tetrachloride was studied in detail, and it was concluded that N_2O_5 was the true reagent in all cases. Since the latter reagent should be more bulky than the nitronium ion and since the ratio is often larger than the statistical value of 2 with toluene as the substrate, there must be some sort of an attractive interaction between the entering reagent and the

[15] C. K. Ingold, *Structure and Mechanism in Organic Chemistry*, p. 299, Cornell University Press, Ithaca, N. Y., 1953.

[16] Even with the precise data available this criterion for the relative steric requirements of attacking reagents should be used with caution. It is based upon a fixed model for the transition-state configuration. Actually, the transition-state configurations undoubtedly vary somewhat, especially as reagents are varied. For example, in sulfonations the transition states are probably unusually close to the final reaction products in that the old C—H bond is probably stretched well beyond the covalent distance (see reference 1) and the entering SO_3 group is nearly in its final position in the plane of the aromatic ring. With very reactive reagents it is likely that contact between the reagent and the aromatic molecule is still relatively loose at the time that the transition state is attained. In the latter case the steric requirements of the reagent could easily be underestimated.

[17] A. F. Holleman, *Die direct Einführung der Substituenten in dem Benzol Kern*, Veit, Leipzig, 1910.

[17a] The occurrence of ω-bromination which becomes the dominant reaction at 75° renders the precision of the determination poor.

[17b] P. W. Robertson et al., *J. Chem. Soc.*, *1948*, 100.

[17c] C. K. Ingold and M. S. Smith, *J. Chem. Soc.*, *1938*, 917.

[18] V. Gold, E. D. Hughes, and C. K. Ingold, *J. Chem. Soc.*, *1950*, 2467.

methyl group. We cannot say whether this interaction should be viewed as a polarization of the methyl group as a whole by the strong dipole of the reagent or as a more localized interaction involving a hydrogen atom of the methyl group. Since the answer is clearly not a routine bulk effect the further elucidation of the problem becomes an attractive prospect.

Effect of steric interaction among resident groups

The interaction of unsymmetrical substituent groups with an aromatic nucleus is a sensitive function of molecular geometry. Thus, the interaction between nitrogen and the nucleus in aniline which is described by structures such as XI will be at a maximum if the nitrogen and its two attached hydrogens are coplanar with the ring.[18a]

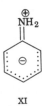

XI

Steric factors which oppose such a configuration would decrease the activating influence of the amino groups toward electrophilic substitution. Similarly, steric strains which twist unsaturated substituents such as $-NO_2$, $-\overset{\overset{\displaystyle O}{\|}}{C}-$, or $-\overset{|}{C}=C<$ from a coplanar configuration will decrease their deactivating influence.

This problem has probably been studied most extensively with aromatic amines. Because of the powerful activating influence of a normal amino substituent a wide spectrum of reactivities can be observed. This makes comparisons relatively clean-cut and endows such studies with unusual precision.

The rates at which a variety of N,N-dialkyl anilines undergo exchange with D_2SO_4 have been measured.[19] The exchange process in-

[18a] The actual configuration of aniline is unknown, but, from the fact that ammonia and aliphatic amines are pyramidal, it can be inferred that in aniline the configuration is that of pyramid with a broad base (i.e., flattened toward the planar configuration).

[19] W. G. Brown, A. H. Widiger, and N. J. Letang, J. Am. Chem. Soc., 61, 2597 (1939).

volves the electrophilic displacement

$$\text{ArH} + \text{D}^+ \rightleftarrows \text{ArD} + \text{H}^+$$

and so the pronounced activating influence of the amine group is readily understood. However, the reactivity of *ortho*-halo-N,N-dimethyl anilines is much lower than that of *meta* and *para* isomers. Furthermore, the deactivation increases with increasing bulk of the halogens as is shown by Table III.

TABLE III

RELATIVE RATES OF DEUTERIUM EXCHANGE *

Compound	Temperature	Time, hours	Number of Hydrogens Exchanged per Mole
2-Fluoro-N,N-dimethylaniline	115	65	0.96
2-Chloro-N,N-dimethylaniline	115	140	0.05
2-Bromo-N,N-dimethylaniline	115	140	0.02
4-Chloro-N,N-dimethylaniline	115	65	1.73
Dimethyl-o-toluidine	115	90	0
Dimethylaniline	60	24	1.73
N-Methylindoline	60	24	1.58
N-Methyl-1,2,3,4-tetrahydroquinoline	60	24	0.87
N-Methyl-2,3-benzo-1-azacycloheptane †	60	44	0

* Exchanges carried out by heating standard amount of the base in C_2H_5OD containing D_2SO_4. The concentration of acid in the first five experiments was twice that in the last four.

† Substantial exchange resulted from heating at 120° for 70 hours.

The striking superiority of indoline over the other heterocyclic bases is attributed to the minimizing of the strain in the configuration in which nitrogen and its attached groups are coplanar with the benzene ring. The strain, similar to that in dimethyl-o-toluidine, involving interaction with the other methylene groups is minimized by the spreading of the bond angles in the unsaturated, five-membered ring. More extensive puckering of the six- and seven-membered rings apparently brings the methylene groups too close to the N-methyl group to permit the coplanar arrangement. The argument is not, however, as elementary as was assumed by the original investigators. Their assignment of a completely coplanar structure to the five-membered ring with a trigonal nitrogen atom seems dubious because such an arrangement would involve the compression of the bond angles at the two methylene groups to 90° each.

Other scattered examples of steric inhibition of resonance are of interest. It has been reported [20] that 2,6,N,N-tetramethylaniline, XII, does not couple with diazotized amines and that XIII and XIV react very slowly. It is likely that the configuration of XII is one in which

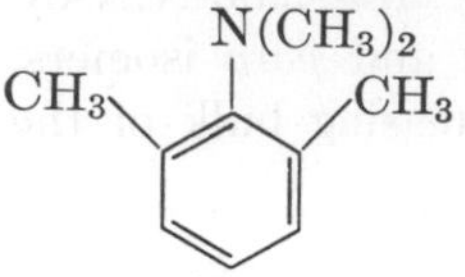

the dimethyl amino group is nearly planar but in a plane perpendicular to the plane of the benzene ring.

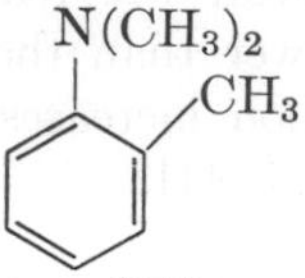

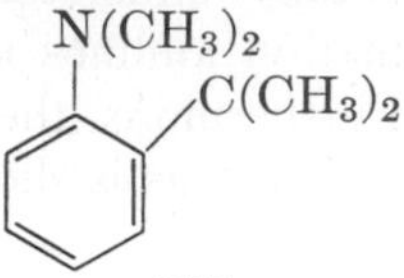

Braun [21] observed similar results in the reaction of aromatic bases with formaldehyde. His technique involved the comparison of the yields of hydroxymethyl products isolated after heating an excess of formaldehyde with the aromatic compound for a standard period of time. The pertinent results are presented in Table IV. It is interest-

TABLE IV

YIELDS IN THE REACTION

$$ArH + CH_2O \rightarrow ArCH_2OH *$$

ArH	Yield	ArH	Yield
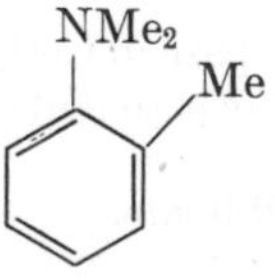	6%	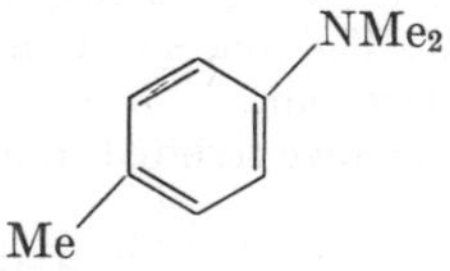	45%
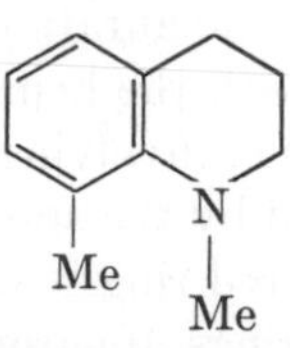	40%	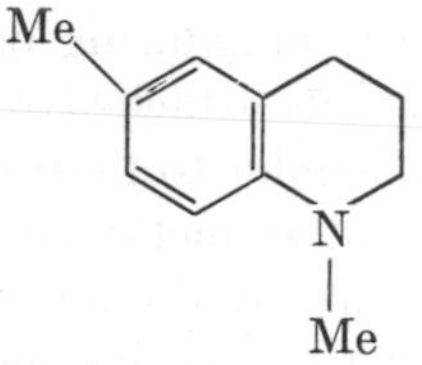	100% †

* Heated 100 hours at 90° with tenfold excess of CH_2O.
† Complete in 22 hours.

ing to note the high relative reactivity of N,6-dimethyl-1,2,3,4-tetrahydroquinoline, in which the nuclear methyl group is out of steric

[20] P. Friedlander, *Monatsh.*, *19*, 627 (1898).
[21] J. von Braun, *Ber.*, *49*, 1101 (1916).

range and in which the coplanar arrangement is favored by the alicyclic structure.

A number of other, less straightforward examples of the same phenomenon have been recognized. Surprisingly, it has been found [22] that mesitylene, durene (XV), and isodurene (XVI) could be diacety-

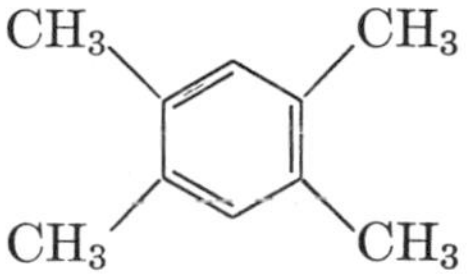

XV 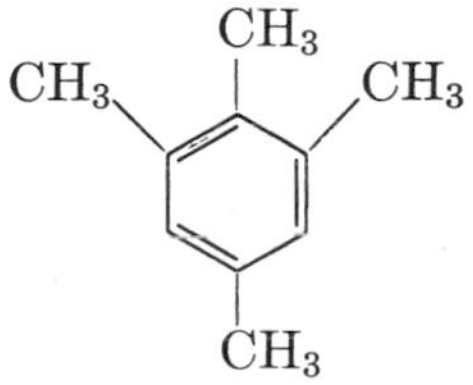   XVI

lated with acetyl chloride and aluminum chloride whereas *meta*-xylene forms only a monoacetyl derivative. It is improbable that this behavior is due to activation by the extra methyl groups. The deactivation by the first acetyl group must be reduced in a remarkable manner when the carbonyl function is forced out of the plane of the ring by two *ortho* methyl groups. Furthermore, deactivation of unhindered ketones is increased by formation of the complexes such as XVII between the monoketone and aluminum chloride. Complexes may be formed from the hindered ketones, but the contributions of structures such as XVIII should be reduced considerably in the presence of two *ortho* methyl groups.

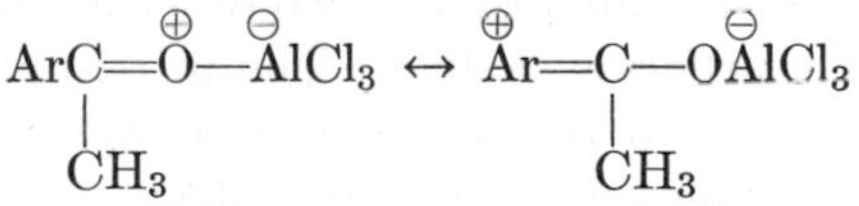

XVII   XVIII

There is another consequence of the steric inhibition of the interaction of substituent carbonyl groups with aromatic rings if they are flanked by a pair of *ortho* substituents. Schubert and coworkers [23] have made a careful study of the acid-catalyzed cleavage of such compounds to the parent hydrocarbons. The reaction is unique, or at least remarkably easy, with diorthosubstituted ketones and acids. This is probably due to the decrease in resonance energies in the ground states as compared with less hindered compounds rather than to anything having to do with the transition states.

[22] V. Meyer and G. Pavia, *Ber.*, *29*, 2564 (1896); G. Baddeley, *Nature*, *144*, 444 (1939).

[23] W. M. Schubert and J. D. Gardner, *J. Am. Chem. Soc.*, *75*, 1401 (1953); W.M. Schubert and H. K. Latourette, *ibid.*, *74*, 1829 (1952). See Chapter 7.

Still another interesting type of effect associated with "steric inhibition of resonance" is encountered in the nitration of 2,6-dimethylacetanilide,[24] which gives mainly the 3-nitro derivative. The orienting influence of the acetamido function, which usually outweighs that of methyl groups, is sufficiently damped by the adjacent methyl group to permit the formation of the highly hindered product, a 1,2,3,4-tetrasubstituted benzene.

Still another variation on this type of effect is found in another "reverse" substitution. The cleavage of p-iodoanilines to anilines by acidic reagents has been studied [25] with the results shown in Table V.

TABLE V

CLEAVAGE OF p-IODOANILINES

| | Yield | |
Compound	HCl-SnCl$_2$	Br$_2$
p-Iodoaniline	46	58
p-Iodo-N,N-dimethylaniline	55	65
2,4,6-Iodoaniline	90	100
2,4,6-Triiodo-N,N-dimethylaniline	5	18

The low reactivity of the trisubstituted dimethylaniline is readily understandable. However, the high reactivity of triiodoaniline presents an enigma. One would expect that the rate of cleavage of the *para* iodine would be inhibited by the two other iodines because of the electron-withdrawing effect of iodine. The intriguing possibility that the iodine atoms *ortho* to the amino groups are replaced the most rapidly because of some obscure steric effect is worthy of further study.

Coulombic interaction between substituents and entering groups

If it were not for the very large electrical moment associated with the C—F bond it would be expected that the *ortho/para* ratio in substitutions on fluorobenzene would be close to the statistical value because of the small volume of the fluorine atom. Furthermore, it would be expected that the ratio would decrease as fluorine is replaced by the larger halogens. That neither expectation is fulfilled is demonstrated by the data from Table VI.

[24] C. E. Ingham and G. C. Hampson, *J. Chem. Soc.*, *1939*, 981.
[25] R. B. Sandin and J. R. L. Williams, *J. Am. Chem. Soc.*, *69*, 2747 (1947).

TABLE VI [25]

ortho/para RATIO IN THE NITRATION OF HALOBENZENES IN HNO_3 AT 0°

Per Cent Yield

Compound	*ortho*	*para*	*ortho/para*
C_6H_5F	12.6	87.4	0.14
C_6H_5Cl	30.1	73.1	0.41
C_6H_5Br	37.2	62.5	0.59
C_6H_5I	34.2	65.8	0.52

This trend has long been recognized and has been explained several times in generally satisfactory terms. Lapworth and Robinson [26] noted that the increase in the relative yield of the *ortho* product parallels the decrease in the negative inductive influence of the halogens. On the basis of this information it was then assumed, quite logically, that the inductive effect, which opposes substitution, is felt most strongly at the *ortho* positions. This is virtually the equivalent of the statement that in the transition state, XIX, the C—X dipole repels the nitro group because it is close to the positive (nitrogen) end of the

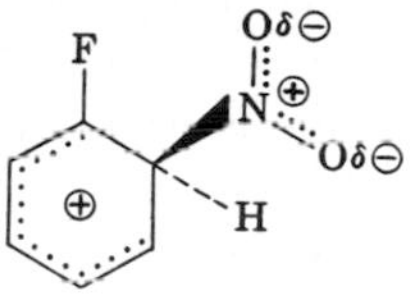

XIX

NO_2 group moment. As the larger halogens are introduced two factors will tend to decrease this effect. First, the magnitude of the C—X bond moment is decreased, and, second, the increase in the bond length will move the center of the moment farther out so that it interacts less effectively with the NO_2 moment. One would also expect that a steric repulsion of some significance would be built up.

Ingold and Ingold [27] have also discussed the effect in terms of a "space field effect." It is apparent that again there is a fundamental agreement among the various authors, although Ingold maintains that his view is substantially different from that of Lapworth and Robinson.

[26] A. Lapworth and R. Robinson, *Mem. Proc. Manchester Lit. & Phil. Soc.*, 72, 43 (1928).
[27] C. K. Ingold and E. H. Ingold, *J. Chem. Soc.*, 75, 1388 (1953).

The data in Table VII serve to illustrate the assertion that bulk effects cannot be cleanly separated from the variation in electrostatic effects due to orientation.

TABLE VII

NITRATION [17] OF ω-CHLOROTOLUENES IN HNO_3 AT 0°

Compound	ortho/para Ratio
$C_6H_5CH_2Cl$	0.75
$C_6H_5CHCl_2$	0.54
$C_6H_5CCl_3$	0.24

The *ortho/para* ratio decreases as the total bulk of the substituent is increased. However, the fact that the absolute yield of *meta*-substituted product also increases in the series is usually attributed to an increasing inductive effect as the number of halogens is increased. It would be consistent with the precedent established with the halobenzenes if this effect were, in itself, enough to cause a decrease in the *ortho/para* ratio. Added to this is the complex problem of deciding the preferred rotational arrangement of the three groups in the transition states. Since this last problem precludes the possibility of carrying out reliable theoretical calculations of the magnitude of either influence it must be granted that the two are inseparable.

It has been suggested [28] that certain substituent groups can exert the opposite electrostatic influence in *ortho* transition states because of their special steric configuration. The *ortho/para* ratios are usually exceedingly large in electrophilic substitutions on compounds bearing substituents such as —NO_2, COR, CHO, CO_2H, and CO_2R. The data presented in Table VIII illustrate the point. Furthermore, a

TABLE VIII

NITRATION [29] OF C_6H_5X

X	Reaction	ortho/para Ratio
NO_2	Nitration	11.7–25.6
CO_2H	Nitration	18.6–22
CO_2CH_3	Nitration	5.7–11.8

very large number of observations based upon either product isolation or semiquantitative fractionation of products leads to the same

[28] G. S. Hammond, F. J. Modic, and R. M. Hedges, *J. Am. Chem. Soc.*, 75, 1388 (1953).

[29] A. F. Holleman, *Chem. Revs.*, 1, 197 (1924).

sort of observation, sometimes with dramatic effects on the isolated yields of products. The examples of Table IX are representative although by no means exhaustive. (See p. 181.)

There are two common characteristics of these groups: they are unsaturated electron-withdrawing functions; and all are non-linear. Several accounts have been given of the orientation phenomena which are based entirely on the former, electronic characteristic. Branch and Calvin [30] have suggested that *ortho* attack interferes less with the normal interaction of the nitro group with the ring than does *para* attack. The interaction is depicted in structures XX–XXII and by structures XXIII and XXIV for the *ortho* and *para* transition, re-

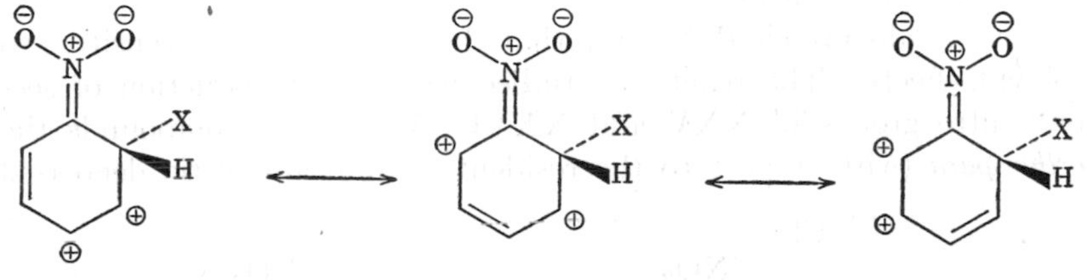

XX   XXI   XXII

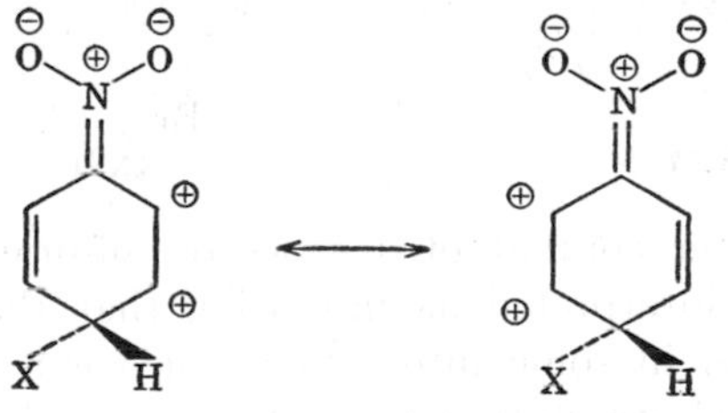

XXIII   XXIV

spectively. The explanation may well be correct, but it is difficult to evaluate theoretically. The question arises whether any of the structures should be assigned an appreciable weight in view of the fact that they indicate a rather high concentration of charge in the ring. Dewar [31] has rationalized the result by semiempirical molecular orbital calculations utilizing the method of Wheland.[32] However, the method does not carry heavy weight in matters of controversy since it is necessary to make an arbitrary assignment of parameters correcting the Coulomb integrals at substituted atoms and relating the

[30] G. E. K. Branch and M. Calvin, *The Theory of Organic Chemistry*, p. 476, Prentice-Hall, New York, 1941.

[31] M. J. S. Dewar, *J. Chem. Soc.*, *1949*, 463.

[32] G. W. Wheland, *J. Am. Chem. Soc.*, *64*, 900 (1942).

resonance integrals involving hetero atoms to those involving carbon atoms. Ingold [33] has commented on the problem and argued that the high values of the *ortho/para* ratio are due to the specific deactivation of the *para* position rather than to the activation of the *ortho* position. The specific *para* deactivation is attributed to a particularly effective resonance interaction with the *para* position. This argument is based upon the observation that the substituents in question give much smaller *para/meta* ratios than do substituents such as —CHCl$_2$, —CCl$_3$, and —CH$_2$N$^+$(CH$_3$)$_3$, which are deactivating by virtue of an inductive effect. To the writer it seems that this contrast is to be expected but that a qualitatively similar behavior should be shown in the *ortho/meta* ratios.

A study already cited [28] shows that the "*ortho* effect" is sensitive to solvent effects. The reactions studied were the introduction of second nitro groups in XXV and XXVI. With both compounds the *ortho/para* (with respect to the resident nitro group) ratio decreased

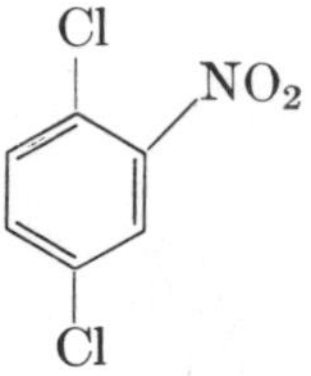

XXV 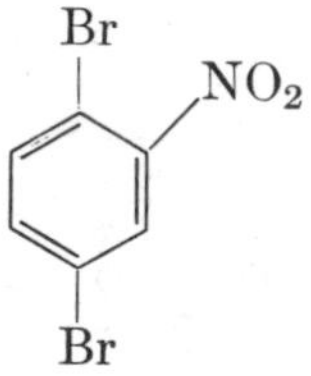   XXVI

with decreasing water content of a series of sulfuric acid solutions. This behavior was interpreted as indicating that the source of the effect is to be found in some interaction which can be described in terms of long-range electrostatic forces. If one considers the geometry of the *ortho* transition state shown it appears that such an interaction might account for the assistance of *ortho* substitution by the groups in

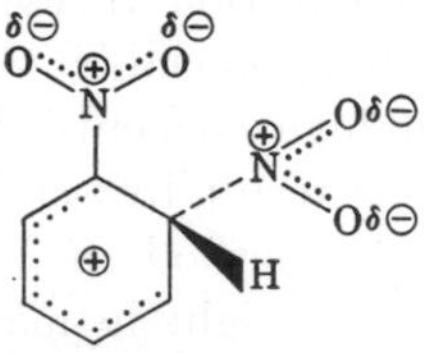

question. By proper rotation of the two groups it is possible to place one of the negatively charged oxygens of the resident group rather close to the positive nitrogen of the entering group. This is not true

[33] C. K. Ingold, *Structure and Mechanism in Organic Chemistry*, Chapter 6, Cornell University Press, Ithaca, N. Y., 1953.

TABLE IX

ortho ORIENTATION BY ELECTRON-WITHDRAWING SUBSTITUENTS

Compound	Product(s) and Relative Yields *		Reference
NO_2 / Cl (3-chloronitrobenzene)	NO_2, Cl, Cl — **M**	NO_2, Cl, Cl — I	17
CO_2H / Cl	O_2N, CO_2H, Cl — **M**	CO_2H, NO_2, Cl — I	17
CHO / Cl	O_2N, CHO, Cl — **M**	CHO, NO_2, Cl	
CH_3 / Br	CH_3, NO_2, NO_2, Br — **M**		34
SO_3H / Br	O_2N, SO_3H, Br — **M**		17
CH_3 / NO_2	CH_3, NO_2, NO_2 — **M**	CH_3, NO_2, NO_2 — I ; CH_3, O_2N, NO_2 — I	17
 CH_3 / CH_3	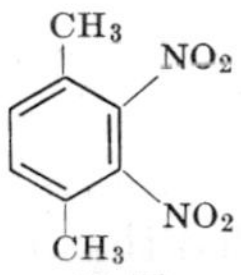 CH_3, NO_2, NO_2, CH_3 — 60–80	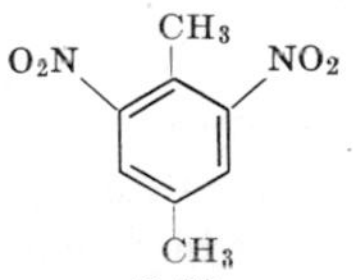 O_2N, CH_3, NO_2, CH_3 — 40–20	35
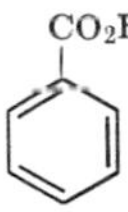 CO_2H	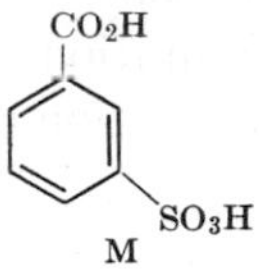 CO_2H, SO_3H — **M**	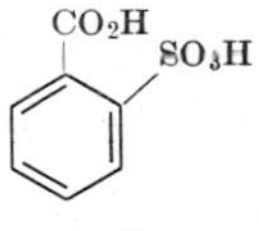 CO_2H, SO_3H — I	17

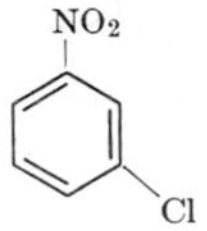

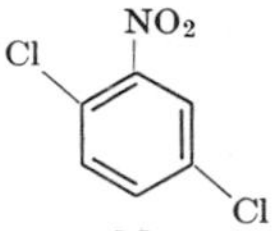

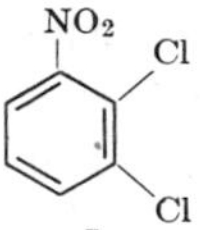

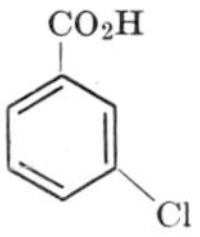

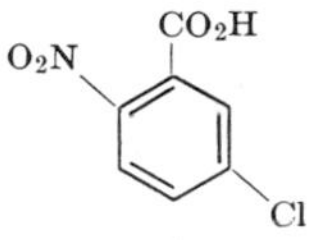

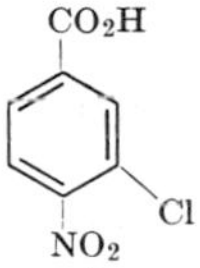

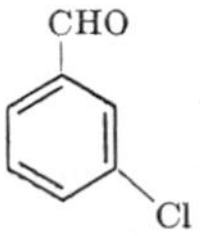

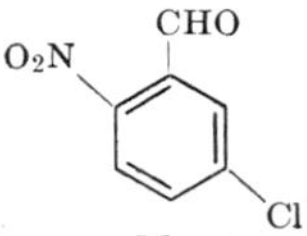

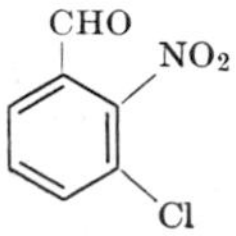

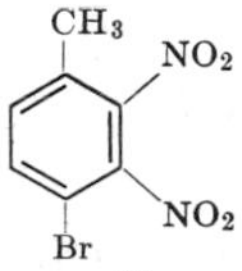

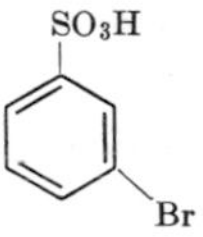

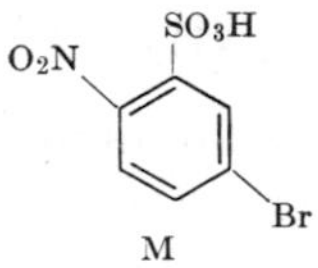

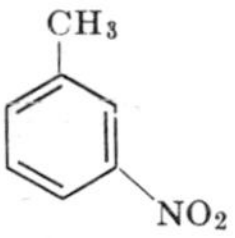

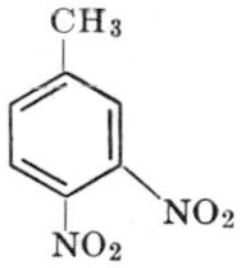

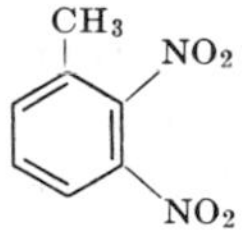

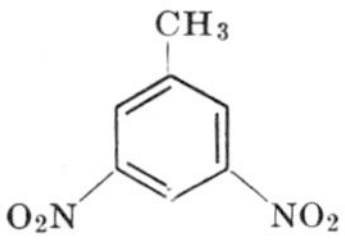

* M indicates major product, and I indicates product isolated in small yield.

[34] R. D. Kleene, *J. Am. Chem. Soc.*, 71, 2259 (1949).
[35] K. A. Kobe and H. Levin, *Ind. Eng. Chem.*, 42, 352, 356 (1950).

of the final product in which the C—N bonds have become coplanar with the aromatic ring. A high *ortho/para* ratio is obtained in the nitration of benzonitrile in which the substituent group is linear.[36] We must therefore conclude that some stereoelectronic effect is making a genuine contribution since dipole-dipole interaction should oppose *ortho* substitution in this system.

NUCLEOPHILIC SUBSTITUTION

Mechanism and steric effects

In addition to the type of aromatic substitution discussed above there exist many examples of the displacement of substituent groups from aromatic systems by nucleophilic reagents. These reactions, termed nucleophilic aromatic substitution reactions, are of two general types, "unactivated" and "activated." These two types of reaction are exemplified by the following equations and are characterized by the absence or presence of an *ortho* or *para* electron-withdrawing substituent, respectively.

$$C_6H_5Cl + NH_2^- \xrightarrow{NH_3} C_6H_5NH_2 + Cl^-$$

$$p\text{-}NO_2C_6H_4Cl + 2NH_3 \longrightarrow p\text{-}NO_2C_6H_4NH_2 + Cl^- + NH_4^+$$

Although reactions of the unactivated type are quite useful in certain synthetic sequences and are well known, too little systematic work has been done to permit an elucidation of their sensitivity to steric effects. Fortunately, reactions of the activated type have been extensively studied, and certain of their characteristics must be clearly attributed to steric interactions, which are discussed below.

Two mechanisms have been proposed for activated nucleophilic substitution reactions. Berliner, Quinn, and Edgerton [37] prefer to consider these reactions as proceeding through an intermediate (A) which has the tetrahedral configuration at the site of the substitution and whose formation or decomposition controls the rate of the reaction.

Chapman and coworkers [38] have concluded that these reactions proceed by the rate-controlling formation of one transition state (B) which has a more or less tetrahedral configuration about the reaction center. The three general types of these transition states are depicted

[36] G. S. Hammond and K. J. Douglass, unpublished observations.

[37] E. Berliner, M. J. Quinn, and P. J. Edgerton, *J. Am. Chem. Soc.*, 72, 5305 (1950).

[38] N. B. Chapman and R. E. Parker, *J. Chem. Soc.*, *1951*, 3301; R. R. Bishop, E. A. S. Cavell, and N. B. Chapman, *ibid.*, *1952*, 437; E. A. S. Cavell and N. B. Chapman, *ibid.*, *1953*, 3392.

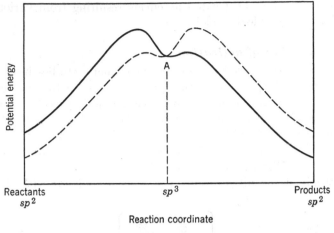

Fig. 1.

in Fig. 2 as B, B', or B'', in which only B' is truly tetrahedral, B and B'' being somewhat more planar at the reaction center. Regardless

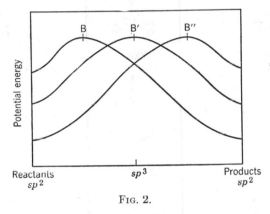

Fig. 2.

of the precise, and as yet undemonstrated, mechanism of these reactions it is clear that the transition state XXVII whose formation is

XXVII

rate controlling must have a geometry best described as near tetrahedral with X and Y the leaving and entering groups and P the coplanar activating group, respectively. The steric effects discussed

below will therefore be treated as effects resulting from various perturbations of this ideal model.

Steric inhibition of activation

Synthetic work as well as more refined kinetic studies have shown
that the most effective activating groups are those that are capable
of stabilizing a negative charge by an electromeric process. This fact
is readily explained by consideration of the reaction of p-nitrobromo-
benzene with a nucleophilic reagent, X^-. The rate-controlling transition state is represented by XXIXa ↔ XXIXb. Structures XXVIIIb,
XXIXb, and XXXb may make their maximum contribution to these
hybrids only if the nitro group may become coplanar with the ring.

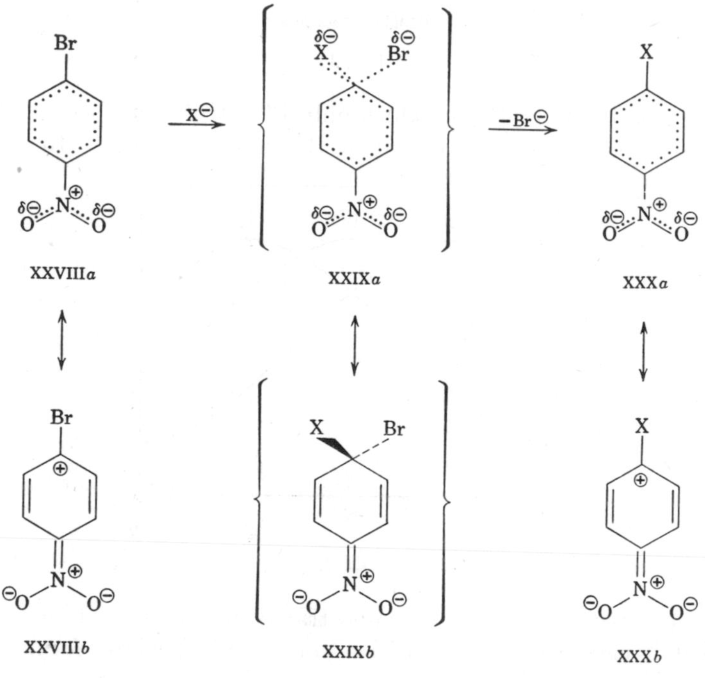

This steric requirement is much more important to the stabilization of
the transition state than to the reactants or products. Thus, the
more nearly planar the activating group may become with the ring
in the transition state, the lower the energy of that transition state
and the faster the reaction proceeds. Many cases have been reported
in which the steric requirements of the activating group are not met.
For purposes of discussion they may be divided into two groups: (1)

those in which the activating group is *para* to the reaction center, and (2) those in which the activating group is *ortho* to the reaction center.

Perhaps the most elegant work which has been carried out with the compounds of group 1 is the study of the rates of reaction of piperidine in hydrocarbon solvents with *p*-nitrobromobenzenes and *p*-bromobenzonitriles summarized in Table X.[39]

TABLE X [39]

STERIC HINDRANCE TO ACTIVATION BY A NITRO GROUP

	 C	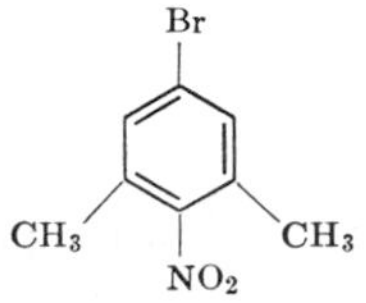 D	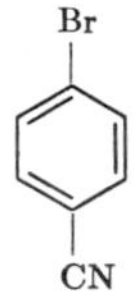 E	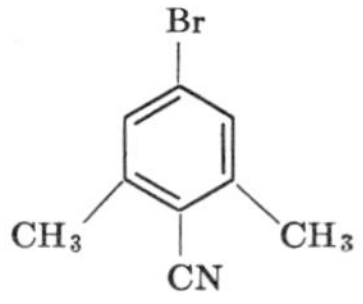 F
Structure	Br on ring, NO₂ para	Br on ring, CH₃, CH₃, NO₂	Br on ring, CN para	Br on ring, CH₃, CH₃, CN
Temperature, °C.	80	80	135	135
1st order $k \times 10^3$	54	2.0	13	3.8

$$k_D/k_C = 0.04 \qquad k_F/k_E = 0.25$$

Comparison of k_F/k_E and k_D/k_C indicates that the introduction of two methyl groups *ortho* to the cyano group of *p*-bromobenzonitrile decreases the rate to 25% of its original value, and a similar introduction of methyl groups into *p*-nitrobromobenzene decreases the rate to 4% of its original value. It is at once apparent that the *p*-nitrobromobenzene reaction is much more sensitive to the presence of di-*ortho* methyl substituents than is that of *p*-bromobenzonitrile. Since the introduction of methyl groups into positions *meta* to the reaction center should have only a feeble effect on the electronic nature of the molecules under discussion, it must be concluded that their effect is predominantly that of forcing the *p*-nitro group into a position perpendicular to the ring in the reactant and transition state. The linear *p*-cyano group is, as predicted, much less affected by this change in steric environment.

A qualitative observation by LeFevre [40] illustrates the same type of steric inhibition of activation. This author observed that XXXI reacted very sluggishly with piperidine while 2,4,6-trinitroanisole reacted violently under the same conditions. Again, the deactivation

[39] W. C. Spitzer and G. W. Wheland, *J. Am. Chem. Soc.*, *62*, 2995 (1940).
[40] R. J. W. LeFevre, *J. Chem. Soc.*, *1933*, 977.

of XXXI by large *o*-alkyl groups may be attributed to the nearly perpendicular relation of the nitro groups to the ring in both the reactant and transition state.

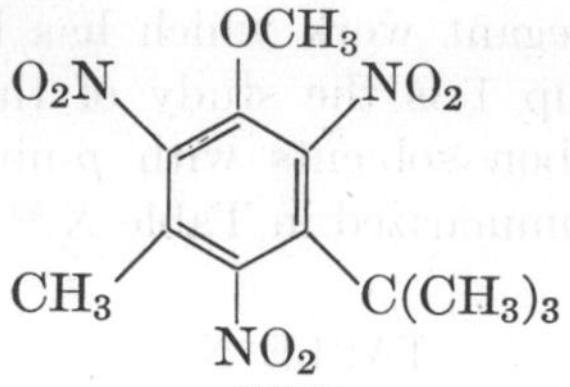

XXXI

Table XI records three examples of the displacement of nitro groups as nitrite ion from reaction centers activated by *p*-nitro groups. In

TABLE XI *

Substrate	Nucleophile	Reference
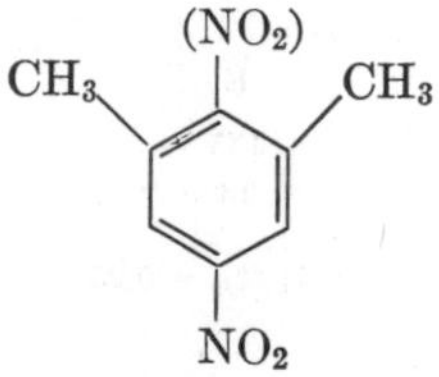	NH_3	41
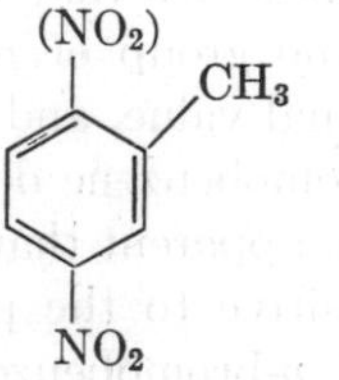	NH_3	42
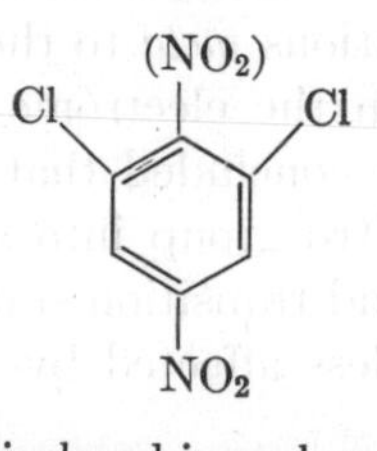	CH_3O^-	43

* The group displaced is enclosed in parentheses.

these cases the nitro group which is displaced is most likely perpendicular with the aromatic ring while the nitro group *para* to it is free

[41] K. Ibbotson and J. Kenner, *J. Chem. Soc.*, **123**, 1260 (1923).
[42] J. Kenner and M. Parkin, *J. Chem. Soc.*, **117**, 852 (1920).
[43] A. F. Holleman, *Rec. trav. chim.*, **39**, 435 (1920).

to become planar with the ring in the transition state. Thus, for example, 2,5-dinitro-*m*-xylene may be cleaved by way of the two possible transition states XXXII or XXXIII. Since XXXII may have a coplanar nitro group and a lower potential energy than XXXIII, the reaction proceeds through XXXII.

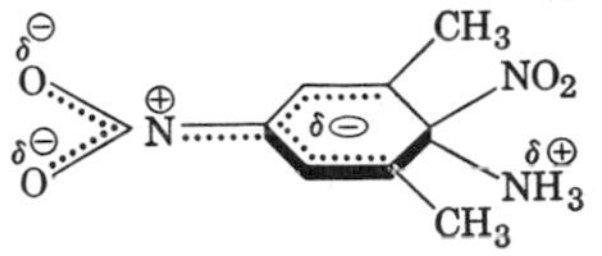

XXXII 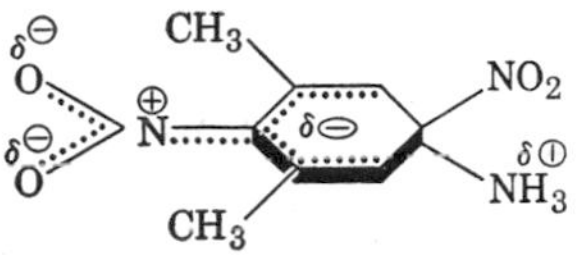   XXXIII

The Arrhenius activation energies, $\Delta E\ddagger$, for the reaction of 1-halo-2-nitro- and 1-nitro-2-halonaphthalenes [44] with piperidine are recorded in Table XII. Comparison of each isomeric pair of halonitronaphtha-

TABLE XII

RATES OF REACTION OF HALONITRONAPHTHALENES WITH PIPERIDINE

1-Substituent	—I	—NO$_2$	—Br	—NO$_2$	—Cl	—NO$_2$
2-Substituent	—NO$_2$	—I	—NO$_2$	—Br	—NO$_2$	—Cl
$\Delta E\ddagger$, kcal.	13.5	14.8	10.4	12.3	10.9	11.6

lenes reveals that the 1-halo-2-nitro compounds always react with the smaller energy of activation. This is no doubt due to the greater steric compression of the nitro group when in the 1 rather than the 2 position of the naphthalene nucleus. Interaction with the *peri* hydrogen is responsible for the larger steric factor.

A perusal of the literature with regard to displacements involving *o*-activated reactions gives the overall impression that transition states of the type XXXIV are nearly as stable as their *p*-analogs represented by XXVII.

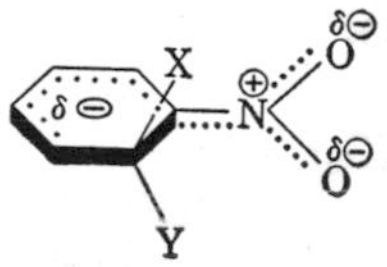

XXXIV

This conclusion is justified if the *o*-nitro group may sandwich itself between the groups X and Y attached to the reaction center. The ground state of the reactant and product molecules, however, must necessarily have a non-coplanar activating group. Thus, the *increase*

44 E. Berliner, M. J. Quinn, and P. J. Edgerton, *J. Am. Chem. Soc.*, 72, 5305 (1950).

TABLE XIII *

ortho Displacements

Substrate	Nucleophile	Reference
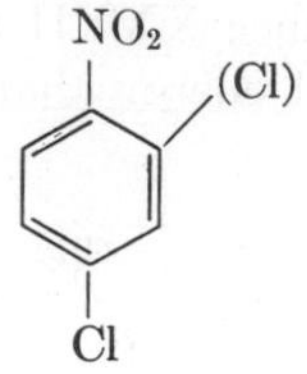 NO_2 / (Cl) / Cl	$\xrightarrow[NH_3]{RNH_2;\ CH_3O^-}$	45, 46
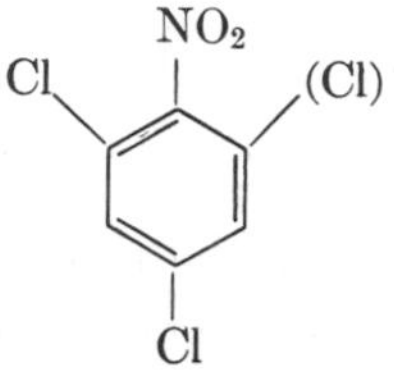 Cl / NO_2 / (Cl) / Cl	$\xrightarrow{CH_3O^-}$	45
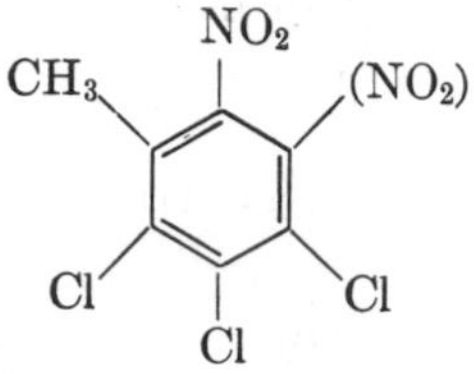 CH_3 / NO_2 / (NO_2) / Cl / Cl / Cl	$\xrightarrow{NH_3}$	47
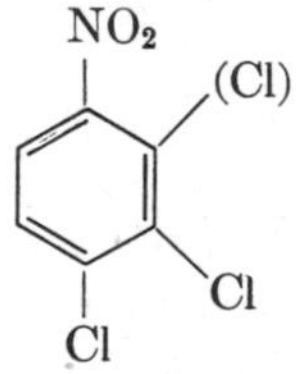 NO_2 / (Cl) / Cl / Cl	$\xrightarrow[NH_3]{CH_3O^-}$	45, 46
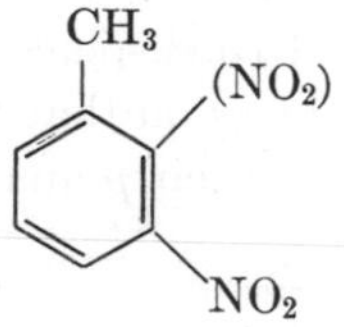 CH_3 / (NO_2) / NO_2	$\xrightarrow{NH_3;\ CH_3O^-}$	43
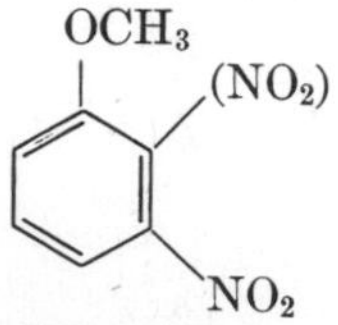 OCH_3 / (NO_2) / NO_2	$\xrightarrow{CH_3O^-}$	48

* The group displaced is enclosed in parentheses.

[45] A. F. Holleman and M. A. J. D. Hollander, *Rec. trav. chim.*, *40*, 67 (1921).
[46] F. Beilstein and A. Kurbatow, *Ann.*, *192*, 235 (1878).
[47] E. Seelig, *Ann.*, *237*, 140 (1887).
[48] M. H. Vermeulen, *Rec. trav. chim.*, *25*, 12 (1906).

in resonance energy on going to the transition state may be greater in an *ortho* displacement. This factor may, however, be more or less compensated by steric repulsion between the nucleophile and the nitro group. Table XIII records examples of relevant competitive reactions.

Another example that points to the stability of transition states related to XXXIV is the failure of compounds of the type XXXV to undergo the von Richter reaction [49] with cyanide ion to produce *o*-

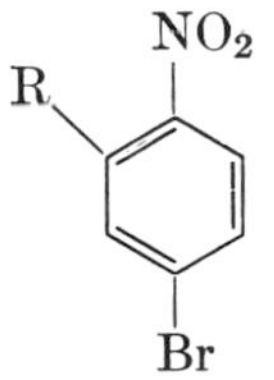

XXXV    XXXVI

nitrocarboxylic acids. Compounds such as XXXVI which have no *ortho* substituent react readily. This may be attributed to the formation of an intermediate, XXXVII, which requires a planar nitro group *ortho* to the position attacked by cyanide ion.

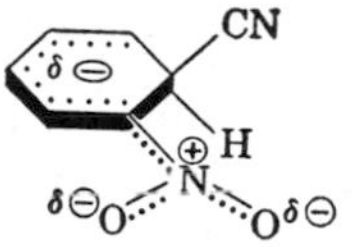

XXXVII

Table XIV records data for the rate of reaction of *o*-chloronitrobenzene and *p*-chloronitrobenzene with methoxide ion and piperidine. The same table includes the relative rates of reaction of *o*-bromonitrobenzene, *o*-bromobenzonitrile, their *para* isomers, and related derivatives, XXXVIII and XXXIX.

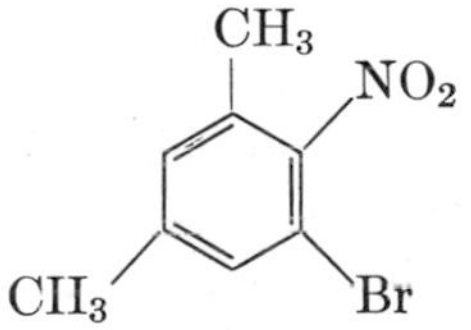

XXXVIII 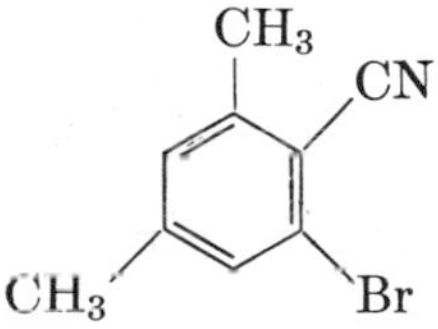   XXXIX

Examination of Table XIV reveals three facts: (1) that *ortho*- and *para*-bromobenzonitriles react at the same rate with piperidine whereas the corresponding *ortho* nitro compound reacts 17 times faster than

[49] J. F. Bunnett, J. F. Cormack, and F. C. McKay, *J. Org. Chem.*, 15, 481 (1950).

TABLE XIV

Substrate	Temperature, °C.	Solvent	Nucleophile	Rate Constant $\times 10^3$	Reference
o-ClC$_6$H$_4$NO$_2$	85	CH$_3$OH	CH$_3$O$^-$	0.0062 *	50
	100	C$_2$H$_5$OH	C$_5$H$_{10}$NH	43.8 †	51
p-ClC$_6$H$_4$NO$_2$	85	CH$_3$OH	CH$_3$O$^-$	0.0231 *	50
	100	C$_2$H$_5$OH	C$_5$H$_{10}$NH	10.5 † ‡	51
o-BrC$_6$H$_4$NO$_2$	80	Benzene	C$_5$H$_{10}$NH	1730 †	39
p-BrC$_6$H$_4$NO$_2$	80	Benzene	C$_5$H$_{10}$NH	100 †	39
XXXVIII	80	Benzene	C$_5$H$_{10}$NH	16.0 †	39
o-BrC$_6$H$_4$CN §	135	Ethyl benzene	C$_5$H$_{10}$NH	17.0 †	39
p-BrC$_6$H$_4$CN §	135	Ethyl benzene	C$_5$H$_{10}$NH	17.0 †	39
XXXIX §	135	Ethyl benzene	C$_5$H$_{10}$NH	5.9 †	39

* Second-order constants (l. mole^{-1} min.$^{-1}$).

† First-order constant (hr.$^{-1}$).

‡ Per cent reaction at standard conditions.

§ Methoxide rates are not reported for these compounds since they exist as imino esters in alcohol solution in the presence of alkoxides.

its *para* isomer; (2) the introduction of a methyl group *ortho* to the *o*-nitro and *o*-cyano analogs has a larger inhibitory effect in the former than in the latter; (3) *o*-chloronitrobenzene reacts faster with piperidine than the *p* isomer and slower than the *p* isomer with alkoxides in alcoholic solvents.

The first observation is in keeping with the previously cited examples of steric acceleration of displacement *ortho* to an activating group having large steric requirements for planarity. The cyano group provides an exception to this rule since its linear nature results in a low steric requirement.

The second fact is obviously related to the first, and it will suffice to say that an additional substituent *ortho* to the activating cyano group has little steric effect, and conversely for the nitro group.

Two arguments may be applied, however, to the inversion of reactivity of *ortho*- and *para*-chloronitrobenzenes when the nucleophile is changed from an amine to alkoxide ion.

Chapman and coworkers [38] have observed that 2,4-dinitrochlorobenzene reacts faster with aniline than with pyridine even though they consider pyridine the more nucleophilic reagent of the two. This anomaly is explained by them as being due to the formation in the transition state of a hydrogen bond between an oxygen of the non-planar *ortho*-nitro group and the amino hydrogen of the aniline molecule. Such a hydrogen-bonded transition state is represented by

[50] A. F. Holleman, M. W. J. DeMooy, and M. J. TerWeel, *Rec. trav. chim.*, *35*, 1 (1915).

[51] H. Franzen and E. Bockhacker, *Ber.*, *53*, 1175 (1920).

XL and should have a considerably lower energy content (ca. 5 kcal./ mole) than the similar pyridine transition state. In addition, this

XL

latter transition state should be of higher energy content owing to steric repulsion of the pyridine ring with the substrate. If this hypothesis is extended to include all primary and secondary amines one could say that o-chloronitrobenzene reacts faster with piperidine than with methoxide ion because of hydrogen bond formation with the piperidine molecule and o-chloronitrobenzene. However, such an argument can hardly be applied to the case at hand since, in order for the system to generate a partial hydrogen bond in the transition state, the o-nitro group must be nearly perpendicular to the aromatic ring, for steric reasons, and this non-coplanarity of the sole activating group should more than cancel the stabilization afforded by the hydrogen bond.

There is, however, an explanation for this rate inversion which considers the change of the position of a transition state along the reaction coordinate as the relative energies of the reactants, transition state, and products are changed. For purposes of discussion it will be assumed that both the reactions in question proceed by way of two transition states from reactants to products as in Fig. 1 with the bond-making transition state being rate-controlling.[51a] These reaction paths are represented by Figs. 3 and 4, Fig. 3 representing the methoxide reaction and Fig. 4 the piperidine reaction. The tetrahedral intermediates are proposed to have the geometry of XXVII and XXXIV for para- and ortho-chloronitrobenzene, respectively, regardless of the nature of the attacking nucleophile. The intermediates for the methoxide reactions should be of much lower energy content than those for the piperidine reactions, which contain separated charges. Also, the ortho and para intermediates should be about equal in energy content for any one nucleophile and are represented as equal. Since the amine reaction is the more endothermic the transition state should

[51a] Even if this assumed mechanism is not correct, in that the reaction may be a one-transition-state process, the arguments about to be presented will still be essentially valid.

be nearer the tetrahedral configuration than in the case of displacements with methoxide.[52] Since the methoxide intermediates are as-

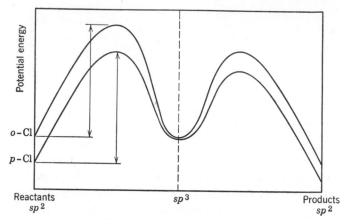

FIG. 3.   Methoxide reaction.

sumed to be about the energetic equals of the reactants, the rate-controlling transition states leading to the formation of the intermediates must have a configuration about halfway between the trigonal and

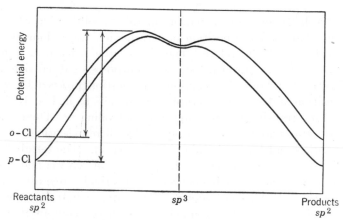

FIG. 4.   Piperidine reaction.

tetrahedral configurations. If this is the proper transition-state configuration for the methoxide reaction, then the *ortho* compound cannot have as planar a nitro group as the *para* compound since the departing halide will not have moved far enough from the plane of the

[52] G. S. Hammond, *J. Am. Chem. Soc.*, 77, 334 (1955).

ring to permit the nitro group to assume the planar configuration. Thus, even though the *ortho* and *para* transition states have nearly the same configuration, the *ortho* transition state must be of higher energy content than its *para* isomer.

In the piperidine reactions the transition state occurs at such a configuration as to allow the *ortho*-nitro group to become "sandwiched" and coplanar. This, in turn, allows the *ortho* transition state to assume an energy nearly identical with that of its *para* isomer. The *ortho* reactant isomer is assigned a higher internal energy than its *para* isomer in each reaction owing to van der Waals repulsive forces and the steric inhibition of the stabilization afforded by structures such as XXVIII*b* or XXX*b* in the *para* compound (see p. 184).

It has been found that no kinetic isotope effect results from the substitution of N-D-piperidine for piperidine in the reaction with *ortho*-chloronitrobenzene.[53] This makes the possibility that hydrogen bonding is a factor of importance seem remote and strongly favors the view that the inversion in rate is due to variation in the configuration of the nitro group. The report [54] that the ratio k_o/k_p for the reaction of piperidine with *ortho*- and *para*-chloronitrobenzenes is largest in media of low dielectric constant is consistent with this explanation. The lowering of the dielectric constant should increase the potential energy of the dipolar intermediate and thereby shift the transition state toward the tetrahedral configuration.

Steric compression at the reaction site

As a general rule, every displacement reaction which has at some point in or prior to the rate-controlling transition state a covalent bond-making process which precedes or occurs concertedly with a bond-breaking process should be quite sensitive to the mutual van der Waals repulsions of the attacking nucleophile and the substrate. Thus, reactions of this type, such as S_N2 displacements, normal esterifications, and the hydrolysis of esters, are retarded by an increase of bulk at the reaction site. This phenomenon was observed long ago and gave rise to the classical meaning of the term "steric hindrance."

Since nucleophilic aromatic substitution is normally observed as an essentially bond-making process, one would expect to find that steric repulsions between the substrate and the approaching reagent molecules are sometimes serious enough to greatly retard such a reaction. The results are not at all convincing except in the reactions of bulky,

[53] M. F. Hawthorne, *J. Am. Chem. Soc.*, *76*, 6358 (1951).

[54] J. F. Bunnett and R. J. Morath, *Abstracts 126th Meeting Am. Chem. Soc.*, 15-O, *1954*.

well-shielded nucleophiles. This probably is a consequence of the tetrahedral nature of the transition states. In such a model *ortho* substituents are, as previously noted, sandwiched between the entering and leaving groups. This minimizes the repulsion involving the nucleophile and may even decrease steric strain involving the substituent and the leaving group. This situation is obviously not clean-cut since the *ortho* substituents clearly influence the substrate molecule electronically, and this usually obscures the smaller steric effect. However, two examples may be given in which the steric effect of *ortho* substituents has been demonstrated. The data pertaining to the first example are given in Table XV.

TABLE XV

STERIC EFFECTS OF *ortho* SUBSTITUENTS [55]

Compound	% Removal of Iodine in Benzene at 80° by Piperidine
 NO_2 (benzene ring) I	12
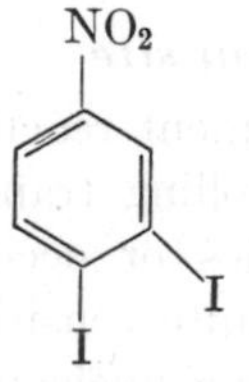 NO_2 (benzene ring) I, I	55
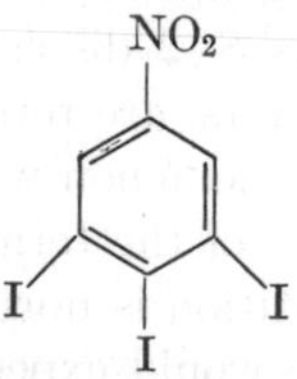 NO_2 (benzene ring) I, I, I	39

Examination of the relative rates for the displacement of iodine from the compounds in Table XV illustrates that one *ortho*-iodine atom accelerates the relative rate from 12 to 55 whereas the addition of one more *ortho*-iodine atom, which should also accelerate the reac-

[55] R. B. Sandin and M. Liskear, *J. Am. Chem. Soc.*, *57*, 1304 (1935).

tion, actually causes retardation. This reversal of effect by the extra iodine substituent must be attributed to a steric repulsion of piperidine and the *ortho* substituents.

The second example [56] has the advantage of comparison of electronically identical processes. These processes yield the two diastereomeric amines (L,D-XLI) and (L,L-XLI) from the competitive reaction of equimolar L-(+)-α-phenylethylamine and *dl*-2-(*s*-butyl)-4,6-

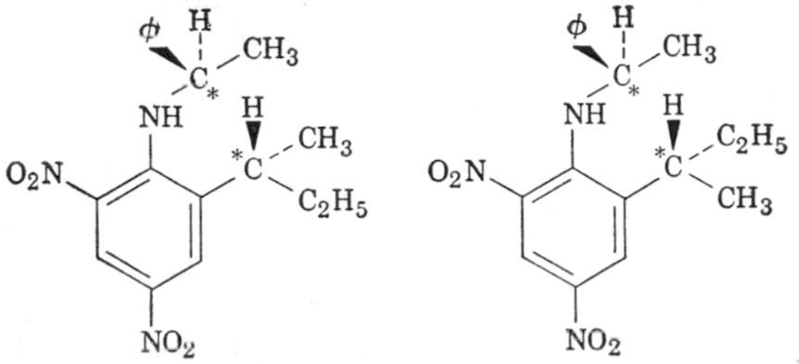

D,L-XLI   L,L-XLI

dinitrochlorobenzene in benzene at 100°. The ratio of (L,L-XLI) to (D,L-XLI) was found to be 1.22. This represents a difference in the free energies of activation of only 150 cal./mole. The subtle difference must arise from the difference in repulsive forces between the L-(+)-α-phenylethylamine and the D- and L-*ortho*-*s*-butyl groups as the amine enters the transition state. Another explanation, which still requires a steric interaction of the amine and the *ortho*-*s*-butyl group, is that the *ortho*-nitro group may be allowed to become coplanar in the transition states more easily in one diastereomer than in the other. This only casts doubt on the direct origin of the 150 cal./mole difference in free energies of activation observed.

The most exhaustive study of the effect of the bulk of an attacking nucleophile on the rate of nucleophilic aromatic substitution is that of Brady and Cropper.[57] Table XVI records a few representative results obtained by these investigators for the reaction of various alkyl and cycloalkyl amines with 2,4-dinitrochlorobenzene in ethanol. For purposes of comparison Table XVI also includes the pK_a values of the amines which were examined kinetically. These pK_a values point out that the ease of coordination of these amines with a proton is about equal in each case, owing to the small steric requirements of a hydrogen atom. However, if the electrophile is changed from a proton to 2,4-dinitrochlorobenzene, the sensitivity of the amine nucleo-

[56] M. F. Hawthorne and D. J. Cram, *J. Am. Chem. Soc.*, *74*, 5859 (1952).
[57] O. L. Brady and F. R. Cropper, *J. Chem. Soc.*, *1950*, 507.

philicity to its steric character is greatly enhanced. This point is nicely illustrated [58] by the fairly regular correlation between the basicity of these amines toward trimethylboron and their rates of reaction indicated in Table XVI. The principal structural characteristic

TABLE XVI *

BASICITIES AND RATES OF REACTION OF AMINES WITH 2,4-DINITROCHLORO-BENZENE REACTION RATE WITH 2,4-DINITROCHLOROBENZENE, l. mole^{-1} min.$^{-1}$ × 10^2

Amine	k, l. mole^{-1} min.$^{-1}$ × 10^2	pK_a
n-Propyl	5.8	10.6
Isopropyl	0.60	10.6
n-Butyl	6.0	10.6
sec-Butyl	0.55	10.6
tert-Butyl	0.023	10.6
Diisopropylamine	0.006–0.004	11.0

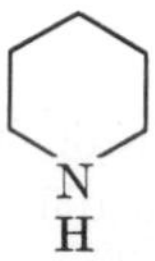	92	11.1

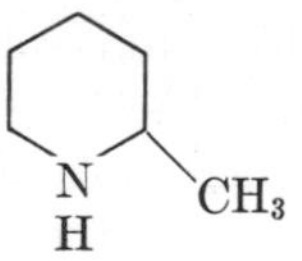	0.13	Not given

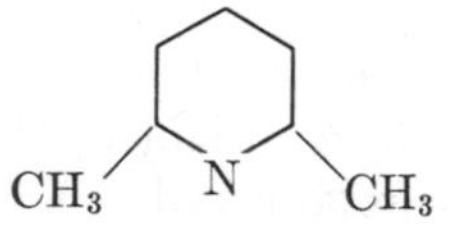	0.006–0.004	Not given

* Data of Brady and Cropper (see reference 57) at 25° in ethanol.

of these amines which appears to limit their reactivity toward 2,4-di-nitrochlorobenzene is the number and bulk of groups attached to α-carbon atoms. It is also interesting to find that α- and β-naphthyl amines [59] react with 2,4-dinitrochlorobenzene in ethanol at the relative rates of 21 and 182, respectively.

McClement and Smiles [60] have observed that the sulfone XLII rearranges much more rapidly than the sulfone XLIII in basic solution. This was interpreted [58] as an example of steric acceleration of reaction

[58] J. F. Bunnett and R. E. Zahler, Chem. Revs., 49, 273 (1951).
[59] H. J. Van Opstall, Rec. trav. chim., 52, 901 (1933).
[60] C. S. McClement and S. Smiles, J. Chem. Soc., 1937, 1016.

rate due to a compression effect involving the sulfone bridge and the *ortho* substituents of both rings as follows.

The rotational conformations which must be obtained in order for the rearrangement of either XLII or XLIII to proceed are repre-

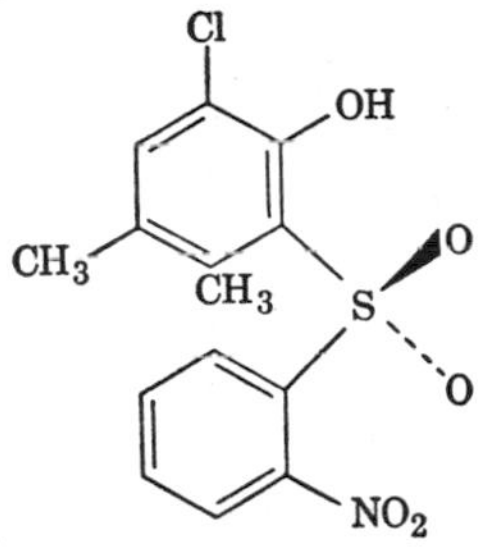

XLII

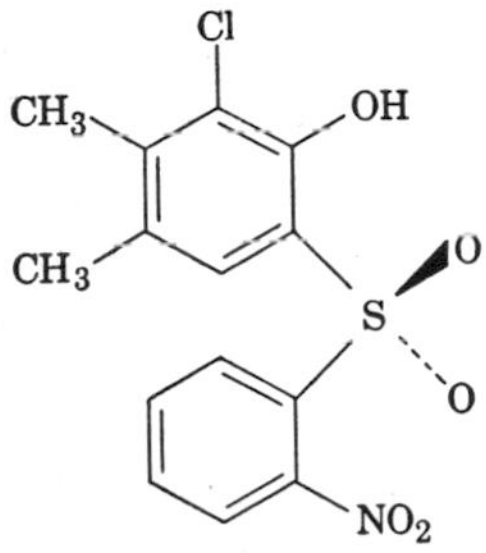

XLIII

sented by XLIV and XLV, respectively. Because of the presence of the adjacent methyl group the anion from XLIII should be constrained to lie near constellation XLIV at all times. This should lead to a low entropy of activation for XLIII as compared to XLII which can assume constellations such as XLVI without undue strain.

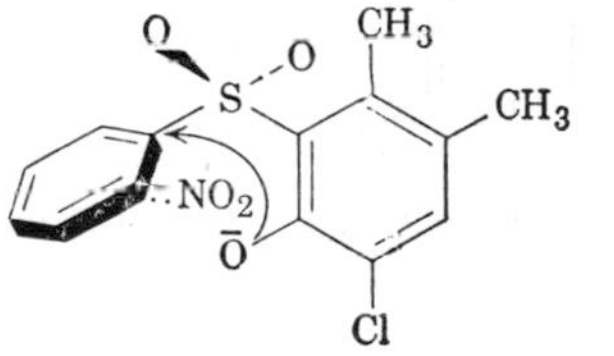

XLIV

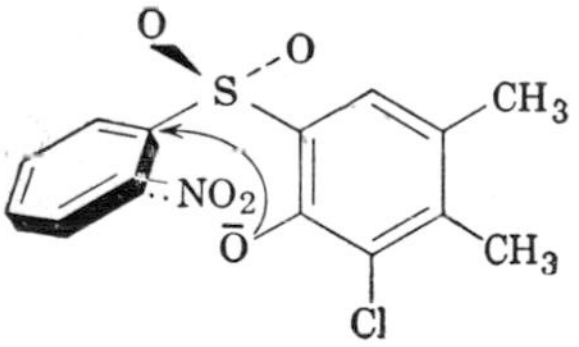

XLV

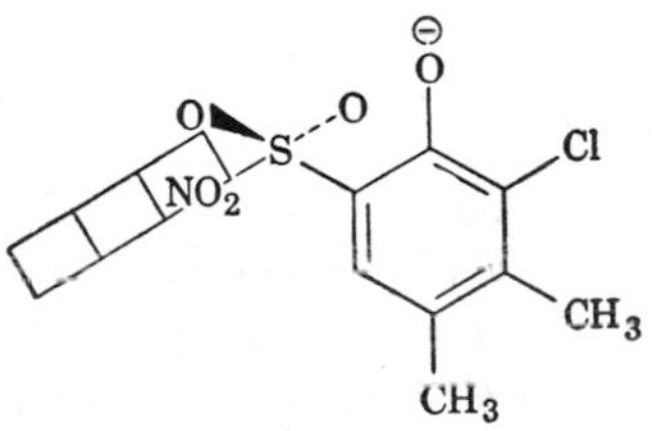

XLVI

Another type of compression effect that has been reported often leads to facilitation of nucleophilic aromatic substitution although an entirely different reaction would be expected on purely electronic grounds. This sterically favored reaction is that of Grignard reagents and substituted benzophenones which have two *ortho*-alkyl substituents in one ring and an *ortho* or *para* substituent in the other ring which has anionic stability. Such a compound is represented by XLVII, which has been found [61] to react with the *tert*-butyl magnesium chloride to produce XLVIII. The explanation of these novel

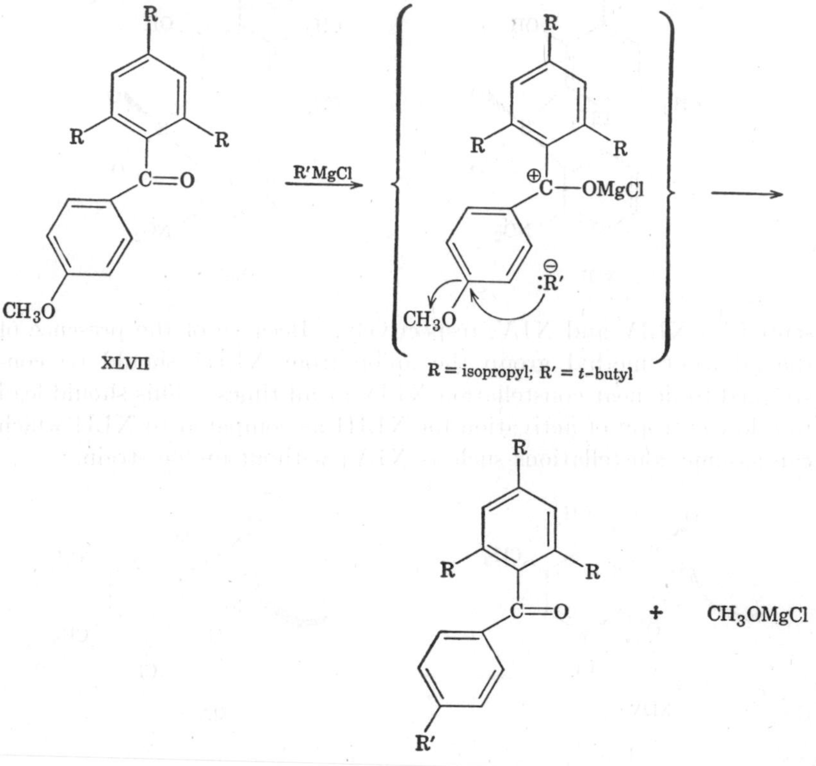

XLVII

R = isopropyl; R' = *t*-butyl

XLVIII

reactions is that the carbonyl bridge when complexed by the Grignard reagent becomes an electrophilic center. This center is, however, hindered to attack by the nucleophilic part of the Grignard reagent by the *ortho* substituents on the neighboring ring. Thus, the normal production of a tertiary alcohol is sterically forbidden. However, the ring which carries the methoxyl or other stable anionic leaving group (—CN, OAc, etc.) may become coplanar with the complexed carbonyl group and thus activate its *ortho* or *para* positions for nucleophilic attack by the *tert*-butyl group of the Grignard.

[61] R. C. Fuson and W. S. Friedlander, *J. Am. Chem. Soc.*, **75**, 5410 (1953).

SUBSTITUTION BY FREE RADICALS

Only fragmentary evidence is available concerning isomer ratios in radical substitution reactions. Indications based upon isolation experiments should be regarded with extreme caution because of the high probability that fractionation occurs during the work-up. Waters [62] has indicated that he regards the common belief that radical substitution is a rather random affair as an unfounded bit of folklore despite the fact that the misconstruction, by others, of statements found in the pioneering review in the field [63] is largely responsible for the myth.

The best studies in the field concern the phenylation of nitrobenzene [64, 65] the halobenzenes,[65] and tert-butylbenzene and p-di-tert-butylbenzene [66] by the thermal decomposition of N-nitrosoacetanilide, benzoyl peroxide, and benzene diazonium chloride. The results are further amplified by competitive experiments which relate the reactivity at the various positions of the benzene derivatives to that of a single position in the benzene nucleus. The results are summarized in Table XVII.

TABLE XVII

PARTIAL RATE FACTORS * FOR PHENYLATION [64, 66]

Compound	F_o	F_m	F_p
C_6H_5F	2.20	1.25	1.20
C_6H_5Cl	2.7	1.03	1.2
C_6H_5Br	2.59	1.75	1.83
C_6H_5I	2.79	1.70	1.80
$C_6H_5NO_2$	6.9	1.2	7.9
$C_6H_5C_4H_9$	0.63	1.28	1.41
p-di-tert-$C_4H_9C_6H_4$	F	= 0.93	

* F = rate at position relative to benzene rate with both corrected by statistical weight.

The studies with the halobenzenes do not reveal any obvious steric hindrance to *ortho* substitution. The reason for the high relative reactivity at the *ortho* positions in these compounds is somewhat obscure. The data are in qualitative agreement with the theoretical calculations of Wheland.[67] However, the method requires the arbi-

[62] W. A. Waters, *Nature, 162,* 183 (1948).

[63] D. F. Hey and W. A. Waters, *Chem. Revs., 21,* 169 (1937).

[64] D. F. DeTar and H. J. Scheifele, *J. Am. Chem. Soc., 73,* 1442 (1951).

[65] D. H. Hey and G. H. Williams, *Discussions Faraday Soc., 14,* 216 (1953).

[66] J. I. G. Cadogan, D. H. Hey, and G. H. Williams, *J. Chem. Soc., 1954,* 3352.

[67] G. W. Wheland, *J. Am. Chem. Soc., 64,* 900 (1942).

trary assignment of values to several of the parameters involved in the calculation, and so the agreement cannot be construed as giving great weight to the mechanism assumed as basis for the calculations. If, as was assumed, the phenyl radical adds to the ring in the rate-determining step it might well be anticipated that a large iodine atom would discourage attack at an adjacent position. Similarly, the failure of the nitro group to offer a substantial steric barrier is rather surprising. It is possible that the transition state allows the nitro group to sandwich between the entering group and the departing hydrogen in the same way as was suggested for nucleophilic displacements *ortho* to a nitro group (p. 187).

Recent work [68] has shown that the reaction of alkylperoxy radicals with aromatic amines and phenols probably involves the reaction of a molecular complex between one radical and the substrate with another radical. If the obvious similarity in the net process to aromatic

substitution is reflected in a similarity in mechanism one would anticipate that the substitution reaction would show very limited sensitivity to steric effects. The orientation would be largely determined by the orientation of the radical with respect to the substrate in the complex since the actual substitution would be exceedingly fast and would go through a transition state which is closely related to the complex.

Considering the problem from an empirical point of view there can be little doubt that, irrespective of mechanism, there is modest steric hindrance to substitution *ortho* to a *tert*-butyl group. This is demonstrated by the results shown in Table XVII for both mono- and di-*tert*-butylbenzene. Another interesting observation included in the same report shows that the steric requirements of the attacking radical also exert an influence on the substitution reaction. An attempt to prepare *o-tert*-butylbiphenyl was frustrated when the decomposition of *o-tert*-butyl-N-nitrosoacetanilide in benzene led to the formation of *tert*-butylbenzene and biphenyl rather than to the expected product.[66]

[68] G. S. Hammond, C. E. Boozer, C. E. Hamilton, and J. N. Sen, *J. Am. Chem. Soc.*, 77, 3238 (1955).

Chapter 4

by Melvin S. Newman

Additions to
Unsaturated Functions

INTRODUCTION

ESTERIFICATION
      Aliphatic Acids
      Aromatic Acids

ESTER HYDROLYSIS
      Acidic Hydrolysis
      Basic Hydrolysis

REACTIONS OF OTHER ACID DERIVATIVES
      Acid Chlorides
      Amides
      Anhydrides
      Nitriles

KETONES

    Intramolecular Acylation
    Acyclic Ketones
    Cyclic Ketones
    Aromatic Ketones

ALDEHYDES

OLEFINS

ACETYLENES

Chapter 4

INTRODUCTION

The addition of reagents to carbon-containing doubly bonded functions probably takes place by approximately the same geometrical path regardless of the nature of the reaction.[1] Accordingly the steric factors influencing the rate of addition for different reactions should be approximately the same. Unfortunately not enough addition reactions have been studied quantitatively with respect to steric factors to tell whether or not this generalization is accurate. Nevertheless, this hypothesis is attractive because it offers some way of predicting the magnitude of steric effects when a standard has been chosen. For example, t-butylacetic acid esterifies more slowly than trimethylacetic acid.[2] Hence one would predict that neopentylethylene would add reagents more slowly than t-butylethylene. In bromination, the relative rates accord with this prediction.[3] Similar predictions might be made about the rates of reactions of aldehydes, ketones, Schiff bases, etc.

The reaction path for addition to unsaturated functions is envisaged below. In a function in which a carbon atom C is doubly bonded to A and singly bonded to B and D, the atoms A, B, C, and D all lie in a plane and the bond angles are about 120° (Ia). After addition of the reagent, NE, has occurred, a new atom, N, is attached to carbon, C, and the familiar tetrahedron with C at the center is obtained (Ib).

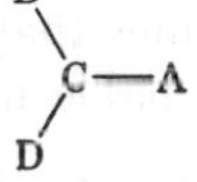

$$\begin{array}{cc} \begin{array}{c} B \\ \diagdown \\ C{-}A \\ \diagup \\ D \end{array} & \begin{array}{c} N \\ | \\ B{-}C{-}A{-}E \\ | \\ D \end{array} \\ \text{I}a & \text{I}b \\ (\pi \text{ electrons not shown}) & \end{array}$$

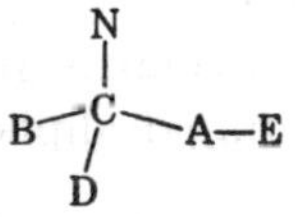

---

[1] This statement applies only to reactions in homogeneous solution and not to *cis* hydroxylations of olefins.

[2] K. L. Loening, A. B. Garrett, and M. S. Newman, *J. Am. Chem. Soc.*, **74**, 3929 (1952).

[3] P. W. Robertson, J. K. Heyes, and B. E. Swedlund, *J. Chem. Soc.*, *1952*, 1014.

In going from Ia to Ib two stepwise [4] paths will be considered. If the attacking reagent is electron-supplying (nucleophilic) the attack is directly on the carbon, C, as this is the positive end of the dipole in the unsaturated function. As the electron-rich atom, N, approaches C it does so from above (or below) the plane of the paper, and the atoms A, B, and D move below (or above) the plane of the paper, until a tetrahedral structure, Ib, is obtained. The reaction is completed by adding E to A. If the addition product thus formed eliminates a molecule to return to some other doubly bonded function the kinetics is not affected since the slow step is the addition. For alkaline and acid hydrolysis of esters, Bender [5] has shown conclusively that a tetrahedral intermediate is formed.

$$R'-\underset{\underset{OR}{\big\backslash}}{\overset{\overset{OH}{\big/}}{C}}-OH$$

Alternately, if the attacking group is electron-seeking (electrophilic) the attack is on the atom A, the negative end of the dipole in the unsaturated function. After this first step (addition of E to A) the carbon atom C and the atoms A, B, and D are still in the same plane, and completion of the reaction involves approach of N essentially as described above for nucleophilic attack.[6]

For a discussion of the steric effects in addition reactions the acid-catalyzed esterification of carboxylic acids has been chosen because a large number of acids have been studied. Furthermore, from the observed lack of sensitivity of acid-catalyzed esterification rates to polar influences (see Taft, Chapter 13), one can be fairly sure that differences in rates are due mainly to steric factors.

ESTERIFICATION

Aliphatic acids

SATURATED ACYCLIC ACIDS. If one assumes that the ionization constant of a saturated aliphatic acid is a reliable measure of the polar

---

[4] The evidence in favor of stepwise addition to olefins is summarized in L. P. Hammett, *Physical Organic Chemistry*, pp. 147–151, McGraw-Hill Book Co., New York, 1940.

[5] M. Bender, *J. Am. Chem. Soc.*, *73*, 1626 (1951).

[6] The timing of these steps conceivably varies from two entirely distinct steps to one concerted step, but the geometry involved is about the same. One can also think of slightly different geometrical approaches depending upon whether E bonds only with A or bonds with C and A as in the case of the hypothetical bromonium ion; I. Roberts and G. E. Kimball, *J. Am. Chem. Soc.*, *59*, 947 (1937).

effects in the chain then one can feel safe in discussing the variations in rate of esterification in terms of steric effects since the ionization constants for a fairly large number of such acids do not vary greatly.[7] In Table I are collected data for the esterification of a number of saturated aliphatic acids.

TABLE I

DATA ON ACID-CATALYZED ESTERIFICATION OF ALIPHATIC ACIDS

$(0.005\ M\ HCl)$ *

	Atoms in Position 6			$k\dagger \times 10^8$	$k\dagger \times 10^8$	$k\dagger \times 10^8$	$\dfrac{k^{40°}\ CH_3COOH}{k^{40°}\ RCOOH}$
Acid	C	H	Total	20°	30°	40°	
1. CH_3COOH	0	0	0	44.0	81.4	132	1
2. CH_3CH_2COOH	0	0	0	40.0	67.0	111	1.19
3. $CH_3CH_2CH_2COOH$	0	3	3	21.1	37.2	65.2	2.02
4. Higher alkanoic	1	2	3				2.02 ave.
5. $(CH_3)_2CHCOOH$	0	0	0	14.7	26.3	44.0	3.00
6. $(CH_3)_3CCOOH$	0	0	0	1.40	2.68	4.93	26.8
7. $(CH_3)_2CHCH_2COOH$	0	6	6	4.88	8.77	15.4	8.57
8. $(CH_3)_3CCH_2COOH$	0	9	9	0.814	1.59	3.09	42.7
9. $(CH_3)_2CHCH_2CH_2COOH$	2	1	3	22.4	38.3	63.4	9.6
10. $(CH_3)_3CCH_2CH_2COOH$	3	0	3	20.4	35.9	61.1	2.16
11. $CH_3CH_2CH(CH_3)COOH$	0	3	3	4.05	7.20	13.1	10.1
12. $(CH_3)_3CCH(CH_3)COOH$	0	9	9		0.0397	0.0817	1616
13. $(CH_3)_3CC(CH_3)_2COOH$	0	9	9			0.0170	7765
14. $(CH_3)_3CCH_2CH(CH_3)COOH$	3	0	3	0.629	1.13	2.03	65.0
15. $(CH_3)_3CCH_2C(CH_3)_2COOH$	3	0	3	0.106	0.22	0.435	303
16. $(CH_3)_2CHCH(C_2H_5)COOH$	0	9	9		0.0380	0.0780	1692
17. $(CH_3CH_2)_3CCOOH$	0	9	9			0.0214	6170
18. $(CH_3CH_2)_2CHCOOH$	0	6	6	0.351	0.711	1.32	100
19. $[(CH_3)_2CH]_2CHCOOH$	0	12	12	Too slow			
20. $(CH_3CH_2CH_2)_2CHCOOH$	2	4	6	0.297	0.631	1.22	108
21. $(n\text{-}C_4H_9)_2CHCOOH$	2	4	6	0.267	0.553	1.10	120
22. $[(CH_3)_2CHCH_2]_2CHCOOH$	4	2	6	0.140	0.278	0.547	241
23. $[(CH_3)_3CCH_2]_2CHCOOH$	6	0	6	0.0274	0.0562	0.115	1150
24. $(CH_3)_3CCH(C_2H_5)COOH$	0	12	12	Too slow			
25. $(CH_3)_3CCH_2C[C(CH_3)_3]COOH$	3	9	12	Too slow			
26. $(CH_3)_3CCH(C_2H_5)CH_2CH_2COOH$ (with CH_3 branch)	3	1	3	4.34	7.70	13.4	9.85 ‡

* Organic acid 0.5 mole/l.

† k expressed in liters per mole per second.

‡ This table is reproduced from the publication cited in reference 2 with the permission of the Editor of the *Journal of the American Chemical Society*.

[7] See J. F. J. Dippy, *Chem. Revs.*, **25**, 151 (1939). The $K^{25°}_{Ion.\ H_2O}$ for trimethylacetic acid is 0.891×10^{-5}; for acetic acid, 1.76×10^{-5}; and for diethylacetic acid, 1.77×10^{-5}; yet diethylacetic acid is esterified about 100 times more slowly than acetic. The rate for trimethylacetic is intermediate. The ionization constants for highly hindered aliphatic acids are significantly smaller than those of unhindered acids. See G. S. Hammond and D. H. Hogle, *J. Am. Chem. Soc.*, **77**, 338 (1954); see Chapter 9.

Although there is little change in rate in going from acetic to propionic acid there is a significant drop in rate of esterification in going from propionic to butyric. If one numbers the atoms in an acid consecutively, starting with the carbonyl oxygen as one, it is seen that the feature present in butyric acid and higher homologs that is absent in the lower members is the presence of atoms in the six position (see Fig. 1). The following empirical rule may then be proposed: *In*

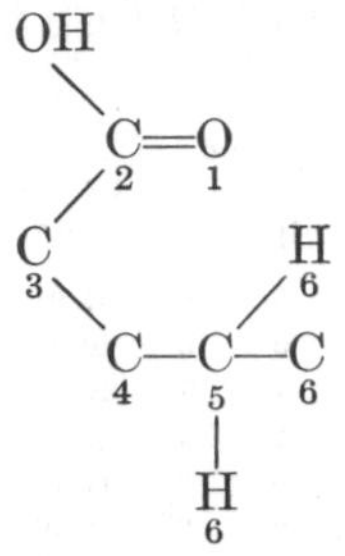

FIG. 1. Coiled structure for acids, numbering shown.

reactions involving addition to an unsaturated function containing a double bond, the greater the number of atoms in the six position the greater will be the steric effect. This rule will be referred to as the *rule of six*, and the number of atoms in the six position will be called the *six-number*.[8] Examination of the data in Table I reveals that the number of atoms in other positions is also a contributing factor, but the most highly hindered acids are those with the highest six-number. For analysis of the rates of esterification reference will be made to the column in Table I which gives the ratio of the rate of esterification of acetic acid to that of substituted acid at 40°. The higher the number, the more slowly the acid is esterified relative to acetic acid.

Perhaps the most significant result is the finding that substitution of methyl groups for hydrogen causes a greater decrease in rate when at the β-carbon than when at the α- or γ-carbon. Note that in going from acetic acid, 1, to trimethylacetic acid, 6, the rate is decreased 26.8 fold. In going from propionic, 2, to *t*-butylacetic acid, 8, the rate is decreased 36 fold. In going from butyric acid, 3, to neopentylacetic acid, 10, the rate is almost unchanged. The importance of sub-

---

[8] M. S. Newman, *J. Am. Chem. Soc.*, 72, 4783 (1950). It should be emphasized that the rule of six is empirical and is to be used only as a substitute for molecular models. The examination of models is the best way of estimating steric factors.

stitution on the β-carbon has been referred to previously,[9] but the general impression gained on reading a variety of textbooks on advanced organic chemistry is that branching at the α-carbon is the most important factor.[10] Actually, branching at the α-carbon is very important, but the importance is based upon the fact that such branching *permits more atoms to be in the six position.*

The reason why atoms in the six position are more effective in providing steric hindrance is undoubtedly associated with the fact that when the atoms in a chain are arranged in a coiled structure the atoms in the six position (see Fig. 1) approach the oxygen most closely. In such a coiled position the chain is sterically effective in hindering addition for two reasons: the addition to the carbonyl group is blocked in certain directions; and, when addition occurs from other directions, the increased spatial requirements involved in going from the starting acid to the tetrahedral intermediate are more easily met in an uncoiled, rather than a coiled, state.[11]

From the fact that neopentylacetic acid, 10, is esterified at the same rate as butyric acid, 3, it should not be inferred that branching at the γ position is unimportant. A comparison of the ratio of rates for acids 10 and 14 (30-fold decrease) to the ratio for acids 3 and 11 (5-fold decrease) reveals that a similar structural change (replacing one α-hydrogen by a methyl group) has a much greater effect in an acid completely branched at the γ-carbon than in one which is unsubstituted at this position. Note that in these four acids (3, 10, 11, and 14) the six-number is constant at 3.

That an ethyl group has a greater effect than a methyl on the α-carbon is well illustrated by comparing the decrease in going from 2 to 3, from 5 to 18, from 6 to 17, and from 12 to 24, and noting that

[9] (a) B. V. Bhide and J. J. Sudborough, *J. Indian Inst. Sci.*, *8A*, 89 (1925), were probably the first to note the importance of substitution on the β-carbon in decreasing the rate of esterification, but they did not emphasize the generality or significance of their results. See also (b) reference 7, p. 212. (c) H. A. Smith and J. Burn, *J. Am. Chem. Soc.*, *66*, 1494 (1944). (d) J. Cason and H. Wolfhagen, *J. Org. Chem.*, *14*, 155 (1949).

[10] For example, G. Vavon, in V. Grignard's *Traité de chimie organique*, Vol. 2, part 42, p. 863, Masson et Cie, Paris, France, 1936, states in italics, "Un petit radical ramifié au point d'attache apportera un empêchement stérique supérieur à celui d'un gros radical non ramifié au point d'attache . . ." [example cited]

$$(CH_3)_3C-\ >\ (CH_3)_3C-CH_2-\ >\ (CH_3)_3C-CH_2CH_2-$$

[11] See H. A. Smith and J. P. McReynolds, *J. Am. Chem. Soc.*, *61*, 1963 (1939), for a more detailed discussion of coiled structures in esterification and other reactions.

as the rest of the chain becomes more branched the ethyl group is more and more effective in its hindering action. The balance between acids 12 and 16 is noteworthy. The effect of an ethyl group is strikingly illustrated by a comparison of acids 8, 13, and 24. Here, an ethyl group on the α-carbon (24) has a greater effect than two methyl groups (13), although the magnitude is impossible to judge because the rate of 24 is too slow for measurement under the conditions chosen. In these cases, each substitution of an ethyl for a methyl group increases the six-number by 3.

In the series of acids 8, 12, and 13 (all of six-number 9); 10, 14, 15 (all of six-number 3), a greater decrease in rate is made when the first α-hydrogen is substituted by methyl (8/12, 37.8 fold; 10/14, 30 fold) than when the second α-hydrogen is substituted (12/13, 4.7 fold; 14/15, 4.6 fold). (This is not the case in the less highly branched series 2, 5, and 6.)

An interesting series is provided by the disubstituted acetic acids. Of those which have a six-number of 6, the rate decreases as the atoms in the six position change from hydrogen to carbon (i.e., 18, 20, 21, 22, and 23 in order of decreasing rate). As the six-number increases to 9 (acid 16) the rate drops markedly, and when the six-number reaches 12 (acids 19 and 24) the rate becomes too slow to measure.

The importance of branching in cases where the six-number does not change is illustrated by the series 8, 16, and 17 (in which the rate decreases in the order with increasing branching) and the series 10, 14, and 15.

To summarize, one can readily see that the estimation of steric effects from structure is a difficult task. However, in all cases where the six-number is 9 (with the exception of acid 8) the acid is moderately well hindered, whereas when the six-number is 12 a severely hindered acid is at hand. With the use of the six-number and attention to the branching involved it should prove possible to estimate the hindrance to be expected in addition reactions of other unsaturated functions involving saturated chains. However, many interesting problems await solution. For example, in a ketone, RCOR, the six-number and branching effects may be concentrated on one side or distributed between the two R groups. As far as serious steric hindrance is concerned, which arrangement is more effective? In olefins of the type $(R)_2C{=}C(R)_2$ the variables can be distributed in four chains. Here again the same question and others might be asked.

Still another steric factor to consider in acid-catalyzed esterification is the steric requirements of the alcohol involved. The results in Table I were obtained with methanol. A fairly large number of acids has been studied in ethanol,[12] and in Table II enough data are collected to show that for the same series of acids the rates are decreased more in ethanol than in methanol. It would be interesting to study the rates of series of acids with neopentyl alcohol, a primary alcohol with large steric requirements, which has already been shown to undergo acid-catalyzed esterification in the normal way.[13]

TABLE II

ACID-CATALYZED ESTERIFICATION IN METHANOL AND ETHANOL

$$\text{Ratio } \frac{k_{CH_3COOH}}{k_{RCOOH}}$$

RCOOH	CH_3OH,* 25° 0.005 M HCl	C_2H_5OH,† 25° 0.1 M HCl	$\dfrac{k_{MeOH}}{k_{EtOH}}$
CH_3COOH	1	1	1
CH_3CH_2COOH	1.03	1.45	1.40
$CH_3CH_2CH_2COOH$	2.04	2.94	1.44
$(CH_3)_2CHCOOH$	3.04	5.10	1.67
$(CH_3)_2CHCH_2COOH$	9.1	15.3	1.68
$(CH_3CH_2)_2CHCOOH$	118	257	2.18

* Data taken from H. A. Smith et al., see Newman, *J. Am. Chem. Soc., 72* 4783 (1952).

† Data taken from Bhide and Sudborough, *J. Indian Inst. Sci., 8A,* 89 (1952).

SATURATED CYCLIC ACIDS. The rates for the acid-catalyzed esterification of a number of cyclic acids with ethanol are listed in Table III. The rates for the unsubstituted cycloalkylcarboxylic acids decrease with increasing size of ring from cyclobutanecarboxylic through cycloheptanecarboxylic. This behavior is consistent with that to be expected from the larger steric requirements of the larger rings. However, the rate for cyclopropanecarboxylic acid is slower than would be expected on steric grounds. Undoubtedly a polar factor is involved here; hence a discussion of cyclopropanecarboxylic acid will be included in the analysis of the behavior of unsaturated acids (see below). An interesting discussion of polar effects in cycloalkanecarboxylic acids and related compounds has been published.[14]

With respect to the rule of six as applied to cyclic acids, one can conclude that atoms in the six position but in a cyclic structure or directly attached to it (i.e., hydrogen atoms or the carbon atoms of al-

[12] B. V. Bhide and J. J. Sudborough, *J. Indian Inst. Sci., 8A,* 89 (1925).
[13] O. R. Quayle and H. M. Norton, *J. Am. Chem. Soc., 62,* 1170 (1940).
[14] J. D. Roberts and V. C. Chambers, *J. Am. Chem. Soc., 73,* 5030 (1951).

TABLE III

ACID-CATALYZED ESTERIFICATION OF SATURATED CYCLIC ACIDS

RCOOH	Ratio $\dfrac{CH_3COOH}{RCOOH}$
$CH_2{=}CHCOOH$	54.8 *
Cyclopropanecarboxylic	24.9 *
Cyclobutanecarboxylic	1.46 *
Cyclopentanecarboxylic	4.06 *
Cyclohexanecarboxylic	9.83 *
Cycloheptanecarboxylic	15.91 *
Isobutyric	5.11 *
Diethylacetic	257 *
Trimethylacetic	1.0 †
2,5-Dimethylcyclopentanecarboxylic,	
meso trans	1.1 †
racemic	9.0 †
meso cis	240 †
1,2,2-Trimethylcyclopentanecarboxylic	Too slow
2,2,6-Trimethylcyclohexanecarboxylic	Too slow

* The rate at 25° for acetic acid in ethanol (0.1 N HCl) is taken as unity; B. V. Bhide and J. J. Sudborough, *J. Indian Inst. Sci.*, *8A*, 89 (1925).

† The rate at 40° for trimethylacetic acid in methanol containing about 0.06 N HCl is taken as unity; T. L. Jacobs and W. H. Florsheim, *J. Am. Chem. Soc.*, *72*, 261 (1950).

kyl groups attached to the ring) are relatively ineffective from a steric point of view and should be disregarded. Note that the rate for iso-butyric acid (six-number 0) approximates the rate for cycloalkane-carboxylic acids, whereas the rate for diethylacetic acid (six-number 6) is much smaller than that of cyclohexanecarboxylic acid [15] (six-number 5, if ring atoms and hydrogens attached to them are counted).

The steric factors in the three 2,5-dimethylcyclopentanecarboxylic acids are important in their effect on the rate of esterification. These acids have the same six-number (6, counting only those atoms on the methyl groups), yet the rate for the *meso cis* isomer is 218 times less than the rate for the *meso trans* isomers.[16] In the *meso cis* case, the carboxyl group is held between the two methyl groups, which are extremely effective in hindering action. This steric effectiveness is similar to the situation in diorthosubstituted aromatic acids (see below).

[15] See H. A. Smith and H. S. Levenson, *J. Am. Chem. Soc.*, *62*, 2733 (1940), for a more detailed analysis of this situation.

[16] T. L. Jacobs and W. H. Florsheim, *J. Am. Chem. Soc.*, *72*, 261 (1950).

The extremely slow rate of esterification has been used to effect separation of naphthenic acids from petroleum.[17] From the mixture of acids which were not esterified by several 24-hour periods of refluxing in methanol containing 2% by weight of hydrogen chloride, *trans*-2,2,6-trimethylcyclohexanecarboxylic acid was separated in addition to other unidentified acids. Previously,[18] camphanonic acid [19] (1,2,2-trimethylcyclopentanecarboxylic acid) had been isolated in a similar way, and its reported [19] failure to esterify was confirmed.[18]

UNSATURATED ACIDS. Unfortunately too few unsaturated acids have been studied to warrant an extensive discussion of steric effects on rate of esterification. Some generalizations can be made, however, from a study of those acids listed in Table IV.

Long ago it was pointed out that *trans* α,β-unsaturated acids are more rapidly esterified than the *cis* isomers.[20] For tiglic (6) and angelic (7) acids the ratio is about 3.5, but for methyl hydrogen fumarate and methyl hydrogen maleate it is about 2.1 and for cinnamic (10) and allocinnamic (11) acids almost unity. Thus the relative retarding effect of the group in the *cis* position is $CH_3 > COOCH_3 > C_6H_5$. No simple explanation in terms of polar or steric effects is apparent.

Furthermore, α,β-unsaturated acids are esterified from 30 to 60 times more slowly, whereas β,γ-unsaturated acids are esterified somewhat more rapidly [21] than their saturated analogs.[20] Since all the acids involved were probably *trans* no explanation in terms of steric effects is applicable.

Use of the ionization constant of an acid as a basis for estimation of polar effects in rate measurements is frequently made but is not theoretically justified. For example, the ρ value for the esterification of *m*- and *p*-substituted benzoic acids with methanol [22] is -0.53. The negative sign indicates that the weaker the acid the greater is the rate. For the esterification of the same acids with cyclohexanol,[23] ρ is 0.262 (rate larger for stronger acid). Thus, although the Hammett equation is obeyed for both series (an indication of a correlation of acid

[17] B. Shive, J. Horeczy, G. Wash, and H. L. Lochte, *J. Am. Chem. Soc.*, **64**, 385 (1942).

[18] K. Hancock and H. L. Lochte, *J. Am. Chem. Soc.*, **61**, 2448 (1939).

[19] H. Appel, *Z. physiol. Chem.*, **218**, 202 (1933).

[20] (a) J. J. Sudborough and M. J. P. Davies, *J. Chem. Soc.*, **1909**, 975. (b) B. V. Bhide and J. J. Sudborough, *J. Indian Inst. Sci.*, **8A**, 89 (1925).

[21] This difference in rate has been used to effect separation of α,β- from β,γ-unsaturated acids; J. J. Sudborough and E. R. Thomas, *J. Chem. Soc.*, **99**, 2307 (1911).

[22] R. J. Hartman and A. M. Borders, *J. Am. Chem. Soc.*, **59**, 2107 (1937).

[23] Hartman, Storms, and Gassman, *J. Am. Chem. Soc.*, **61**, 2167 (1939).

TABLE IV

RATES OF ESTERIFICATION OF UNSATURATED ACIDS IN METHANOL

Acid	Ratio $\dfrac{CH_3CH_2CH_2COOH}{RCOOH}$ *
1. $CH_3CH_2CH_2COOH$	1.00 †
2. CH_2=$CHCOOH$	16.6 ‡
3. CH_3CH=$CHCOOH$, *trans*	39.6 ‡
4. $CH_3(CH_2)_{14}CH$=$CHOOH$, *trans*	37.8 ‡
5. CH_2=$C(CH_3)COOH$	59.4 ‡
6. CH_3CH=$C(CH_3)COOH$, *trans*	123 ‡
7. CH_3CH=$C(CH_3)COOH$, *cis*	431 ‡
8. $(CH_3)_2C$=$CHCOOH$	175 ‡
9. $(CH_3)_2C$=$C(CH_3)COOH$	1180 ‡
10. C_6H_5CH=$CHCOOH$, *trans*	53.2 †
11. C_6H_5CH=$CHCOOH$, *cis*	55.6 †
12. $(CH_3)_2CHCOOH$	1.49 ‡
13. $(CH_3)_2CHCH(CH_3)COOH$	40.0 ‡
14. CH_3CH=$CHCH_2COOH$ §	0.68 †
15. CH_3CH_2CH=$CHCH_2COOH$ §	0.72 †
16. C_6H_5CH=$CHCH_2COOH$ §	0.58 †
17. $C_6H_5CH_2CH$=$CHCH_2COOH$ §	0.61 †
18. CH_2=$CHCH_2CH_2COOH$	1.10 †
19. C_6H_5CH=$CHCH$=$CHCOOH$ ‖	67.6 †
20. CH_3CH=$CHCH$=$CHCOOH$ ‖	68.5 †
21. $C_6H_5CH_2CH_2CH_2COOH$	0.89 †
22. Oleic, etc.¶	0.92 †
23. CH_3C≡$CCOOH$	38.8 †
24. C_6H_5C≡$CCOOH$	78.0 †
25. Cyclohexanecarboxylic	2.59 †
26. C_6H_5COOH	198 †

* The esterification constants were obtained in methanol at 15°. Corrections were applied for the amount of hydrogen chloride used. Some difficulty was experienced because of the different batches of methanol used by the investigators listed below.

† Data from J. J. Sudborough and J. M. Gittins, *J. Chem. Soc.*, *95*, 315 (1909).

‡ Data from J. J. Sudborough and M. J. P. Davies, *J. Chem. Soc.*, *95*, 975 (1909).

§ Not stated but probably *trans*.

‖ Geometry unknown.

¶ A number of other unsaturated acids, such as elaidic, undecylenic, eurcic, and brassidic, had approximately the same values, almost identical to those of the higher fatty acids.

strength with rate of reaction), the two series lead to opposite conclusions about the polar effects of substituents on rate of esterification.

For aliphatic unsaturated acids, use of the ionization constant in prediction of rate of esterification seems unrewarding. For example, the ionization constants ($\times 10^5$) for butyric (1), crotonic (3), allylacetic (18), and tetrolic (23) acids [7] are 1.50, 2.03, 2.11, and 2.23, respectively, whereas the esterification ratios (see Table IV) compared to butyric acid are 1.00, 39.6, 1.10, and 38.8. The decreased rate for α,β-unsaturated acids is probably caused by the increase in activation energy dependent on loss of conjugation of the carbonyl group with the α,β unsaturation which occurs when the tetrahedral transition state is formed. This explanation is also applicable to the rate of cyclopropanecarboxylic acid, which is much smaller than that of cyclobutanecarboxylic acid and approaches that of acrylic acid (see Table III). In cyclopropanecarboxylic acid the conjugation exists between the three-membered ring and the carbonyl group. Other examples of the ability of a cyclopropyl group to conjugate with other unsaturated functions are known.[24]

For the purpose of predicting steric hindrance to esterification of unsaturated acids the rule of six is probably generally applicable with the reservation that atoms on a *trans* branching are almost ineffective from a steric point of view. Examples of highly hindered unsaturated acids are α- and β-cyclogeranic acids [20b] (2,6,6-trimethylcyclohexene-1-carboxylic acids, effective six-number 9).

Aromatic acids

One field in which steric effects were early recognized as important is the acid-catalyzed esterification of substituted benzoic acids. Victor Meyer and his collaborators [25] studied the esterification of a large number of polysubstituted benzoic acids and noted that when a carboxyl group was flanked by two *ortho* substituents no ester was formed even on refluxing for long periods of time.[26] Since electron-attracting

[24] M. T. Rogers, *J. Am. Chem. Soc.*, *69*, 2544 (1947).

[25] In many textbooks the priority for the concept of steric hindrance is given to Victor Meyer, who published on this subject in 1894 and later. However, Vavon in V. Grignard's *Traité de chimie organique*, Vol. 2, p. 852, Masson et Cie., Paris, France, 1936, points out that the explanation for the lesser reactivity of the *ortho*-substituted carbonyl group in a series of quinones was explained by F. Kehrmann in 1890, who used arguments based on steric factors.

[26] See V. Meyer et al., *Ber.*, *27*, 510, 1580, 3146 (1894); *28*, 182, 1254, 2776, 3197, 3219 (1895). In this work the acids were treated with alcoholic hydrogen chloride under a variety of standard conditions, and the yields of ester were compared. Mesitoic acid was said to yield 2–9% of ester. Later studies showed that pure

as well as electron-repelling groups were equally effective he ascribed the results to the bulk of the groups and stated his esterification law, that aromatic acids having both *ortho* hydrogens substituted by other groups are not esterified by refluxing with alcoholic hydrogen chloride. This law is still essentially valid, only a few exceptions being recognized.[27]

Broadly speaking the exceptions fall into two classes: one in which at least one of the *ortho* groups is small [28] and the other in which an *ortho* carbonyl group is involved. An example of the latter type is tetrachlorophthalic acid, which forms a monoester on treatment under ordinary esterification conditions.[29] Presumably, the monoester is formed from the reaction of the anhydride with alcohol. The monoester cannot be converted to the diester under the usual conditions for acid-catalyzed esterification. Another example of this class is 2-benzoyl-1-naphthoic acid, IIa, which has been shown to yield the pseudo ester, IIb, on acid-catalyzed esterification.[30]

IIa   IIb

When one or more carbon atoms separate the carboxyl group in di-orthosubstituted acids from the ring,[31] the resulting acid is readily esterified. When only a single *ortho* substituent [32] is present, the acid

mesitoic acid yielded no trace of ester. A fused aromatic ring was also found to be effective; e.g., anthracene-9-carboxylic acid could not be esterified.

[27] M. A. Rosanoff, *J. Am. Chem. Soc.*, *30*, 1895 (1908), showed that 2,4,6-trichloro- and 2,4,6-tribromobenzoic acids could be esterified by heating with alcohol in sealed tubes at 183° and concluded that Meyer's esterification law was invalid. Although the measurements were crude, Rosanoff's work is important because it provides the only kinetic study of rates of reaction of highly hindered acids. He also showed that the equilibrium constants for hindered and unhindered halogenated benzoic acids were of the same magnitude.

[28] For example, 2-fluoro-6-nitrobenzoic acid, J. van Loon and V. Meyer, *Ber.*, *29*, 839 (1896). The corresponding 2-chloro acid does not esterify.

[29] V. Meyer and J. J. Sudborough, *Ber.*, *27*, 3146 (1894). See also E. Rupp, *Ber.*, *29*, 1625 (1896).

[30] L. F. Fieser and M. S. Newman, *J. Am. Chem. Soc.*, *58*, 2376 (1936). See also M. S. Newman and C. W. Muth, *J. Am. Chem. Soc.*, *73*, 4627 (1951), and references therein for a discussion of normal and pseudo ester formation.

[31] V. Meyer and J. J. Sudborough, *Ber.*, *27*, 1580 (1894).

[32] For example see J. J. Sudborough and M. K. Turner, *J. Chem. Soc.*, *101*, 237 (1912).

is readily esterified but at a slower rate than the corresponding *para* isomer. In Table V are listed the comparative rates for a number of *ortho* and a few *para* substituted benzoic acids. The size of the k_{para}/k_{ortho} ratio (Table V) increases with increasing bulk of the *ortho* group.[33]

TABLE V

ACID-CATALYZED ESTERIFICATION OF SUBSTITUTED BENZOIC ACIDS

Benzoic Acid o-Substituent	$\dfrac{k_{benzoic}}{k_{o\text{-}benzoic}}$ *	$\dfrac{k_{p\text{-}benzoic}}{k_{o\text{-}benzoic}}$ †
H (Benzoic)	1.00	
CH_3	3.08	3.08
C_2H_5	5.05	
$n\text{-}C_3H_7$	5.77	
C_6H_5	5.55	
OH	21.9	
Cl	2.70	1.46
Br	3.33	2.22
I	4.52	
NO_2	32.2	15.9
OC_6H_5	0.6	
$COCH_3$	0.037	

* Rates measured in ethanol at 15° using HCl; J. J. Sudborough and Turner, *J. Chem. Soc.*, **101**, 237 (1912).

† Rates measured in methanol at 25° using HCl; R. J. Hartman and A. M. Borders, *J. Am. Chem. Soc.*, **59**, 2107 (1937). The $k_{benzoic}/k_{o\text{-}toluic}$ ratio is 3.

[33] The steric effectiveness of a group *ortho* to a carboxyl group as distinct from its polar effect may never be estimated because of the inherent interdependence of these factors (see Chapter 13). Indeed, the estimation of the steric effectiveness of groups in any rate or equilibrium study will always be difficult. One study of interest involves the racemization of optically active biphenyls. Since bulky groups have to swing past each other in the rate-determining step, the smaller the rate the greater the effectiveness of the groups in question. Two series are noteworthy. In one, III, the order found was $Br > CH_3 > Cl > NO_2 > COOH > OCH_3 > F$. In the other, IV, the order was $NO_2 > Br > Cl > CH_3 > OCH_3$. (See R. L. Shriner, R. Adams, and C. S. Marvel in H. Gilman, *Organic Chemistry*, 2nd ed., Vol. 1, pp. 362–368, John Wiley & Sons, New York, 1943.

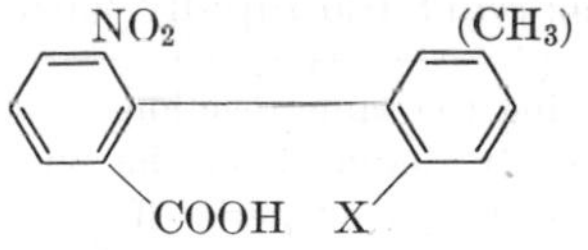

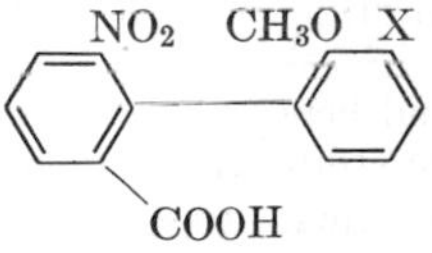

The validity of any conclusions drawn from these studies is clouded by uncertainty about the transition state for racemization. Since two different groups provide the hindrance in the left rings, different transition states (geometrical) may be

In the aromatic series the rule of six is inadequate to explain the extreme unreactivity of diorthosubstituted compounds such as mesitoic acid. The non-reactivity of 2,6-disubstituted acids in particular and of 2,6-disubstituted functions bearing a double bond in general can be explained in two ways. Kadesch [34] pointed out that, where addition to such functions occurs, the attacking reagent must approach the unsaturated linkage from a direction perpendicular to the plane defined by the function. As long as this plane is essentially coplanar with the ring there is little steric hindrance from the *ortho* groups, since the reagent has an unhindered avenue of approach perpendicular to the benzene ring. However, if the *ortho* groups are large enough to prevent free rotation about the bond connecting the unsaturated function to the ring then the plane containing this function must lie at an angle to the ring. In this orientation a perpendicular approach is hindered by the *ortho* groups. One sufficiently large *ortho* group is able to prevent coplanarity of a function with the ring. Reaction with such a monosubstituted derivative is still possible by a perpendicular approach from the side opposite to the *ortho* group. This explanation is consistent with the fact that monoorthosubstituted functions react at a lower rate than the corresponding unsubstituted functions and diorthosubstituted functions do not react at all.[35] The above explanation is based on the collision theory of reaction rates. An alternative explanation in terms of the activated-state theory involves the concept that the steric requirements for the activated state in addition reactions make for a high activation energy for monoorthosubstituted functions and a prohibitively high activation energy for diorthosubstituted functions.

In conclusion of the survey of what is known about steric effects in the acid-catalyzed esterification of acids, it is apparent that, although fairly detailed knowledge of the structural features leading to moderate steric hindrance exists, very few qualitative and no quantitative data on highly hindered acids are available. Furthermore, our knowledge of steric effects among highly hindered acids is not likely to be augmented by esterification studies, for, at the higher temperatures needed to effect esterification, alcohols react too rapidly with catalyst.

---

involved and hence one may not be comparing the same reaction. Repetition of this type of study with compounds more ideally designed for the purpose might prove interesting. (See Chapter 12 for calculation of steric effects in biphenyl racemization studies.)

[34] R. G. Kadesch, *J. Am. Chem. Soc.*, **66**, 1207 (1944); see also W. G. Brown and S. Fried, *ibid.*, **65**, 1841 (1943).

[35] It should be emphasized that this explanation applies only to addition to doubly bonded functions.

The conclusion should not be drawn that highly sterically hindered acids cannot be esterified. In addition to the generally applicable esterifications involving diazomethane, the reaction of sodium or silver salts with alkyl halides, and of acid chlorides with alcohols, a number of other methods can be listed.

PYROLYSIS OF TETRAMETHYLAMMONIUM SALTS.[36]

$$\overset{-}{RCOO}\overset{+}{N}(CH_3)_4 \underset{}{\overset{\Delta}{\rightleftarrows}} RCOOCH_3 + (CH_3)_3N$$

This seldom-used method, not limited to sterically hindered acids, has been applied mainly to the preparation of methyl esters. With regard to mechanism this method is similar to the esterifications involved in the reaction of salts of acids with alkyl halides.

100% SULFURIC ACID METHOD.[37] In this method the acid is dissolved in 100% sulfuric acid and this solution is poured into the alcohol desired. This procedure is neither limited, nor always applicable, to sterically hindered acids. An acid which gives an i factor of 4 in sulfuric acid [38] is required. For example, 2,4,6-tribromobenzoic acid is not esterified by this method, whereas o-benzoylbenzoic acid [39] is. Hindered aliphatic acids, such as triethylacetic acid,[40] are not esterified by this procedure. Triphenylacetic acid is decarbonylated in 100% sulfuric acid,[41] probably in accord with the following equation:

$$(C_6H_5)_3CCOOH + 2H_2SO_4 \rightarrow$$

$$CO + (C_6H_5)_3C^+ + H_3O^+ + 2HSO_4^-$$

ALKYL CHLOROSULFITE METHOD. Only one [42] study of this reaction

$$RCOONa + C_4H_9OSOCl \xrightarrow{100-150°} RCOOC_4H_9 + SO_2 + NaCl$$

has been reported. Good yields of butyl ester were obtained with 2,4,6-trialkylbenzoic acids and tri-n-butylacetic acid, but the reaction failed with 2,4,6-tribromobenzoic acid.

[36] (a) V. Prelog and M. Piantanida, Z. physiol. Chem., 244, 56 (1936); (b) R. C. Fuson, J. Corse, and E. C. Horning, J. Am. Chem. Soc., 61, 1290 (1939); (c) M. S. Newman and H. A. Lloyd, ibid., 74, 2672 (1952); (d) E. L. Eliel and R. P. Anderson, ibid., 74, 547 (1952).

[37] M. S. Newman, J. Am. Chem. Soc., 63, 2431 (1941).

[38] M. S. Newman, H. G. Kuivila, and A. B. Garrett, J. Am. Chem. Soc., 67, 704 (1945).

[39] M. S. Newman, J. Am. Chem. Soc., 64, 2324 (1942). The pseudo ester is formed.

[40] C. Schuerch, Jr., and E. H. Huntress, J. Am. Chem. Soc., 71, 2233 (1949); see footnotes 13 and 14.

[41] H. A. Smith and R. J. Smith, J. Am. Chem. Soc., 70, 2400 (1948).

[42] M. S. Newman and W. S. Fones, J. Am. Chem. Soc., 69, 1046 (1947).

ESTER HYDROLYSIS

Acidic hydrolysis

ACYL-OXYGEN FISSION. The expectation that steric effects on hydrolysis of methyl esters would parallel those in acid-catalyzed esterification in methanol is confirmed by study of the recorded rates.[43] Indeed, the hypothesis that steric factors in a given compound are the same for esterification and hydrolysis under acidic and basic conditions forms the basis for attempts at quantitative evaluation of polar and steric effects in the aliphatic series.[44]

Esters of certain highly hindered acids, such as mesitoic acid, which under ordinary conditions are completely resistant to hydrolysis, can be readily hydrolyzed by dissolution in concentrated sulfuric acid and addition of this solution to water.[45] The success of this hydrolytic procedure is explained by the fact that methyl mesitoate ionizes in sulfuric acid according to the following equation.[46]

$$(CH_3)_3C_6H_2COOCH_3 + 3H_2SO_4 \rightarrow$$

$$(CH_3)_3C_6H_2C\overset{+}{O} + H_3O + CH_3HSO_4 + 2HSO_4^-$$

By taking advantage of the structural similarity of diethyl isopropylidenemalonate, Va, to ethyl mesitoate, Vb, Corey [47] was led to hydrolyze Va to the corresponding half ester in 65% yield by the 100% sulfuric acid method, a result not attainable by the usual hydrolytic

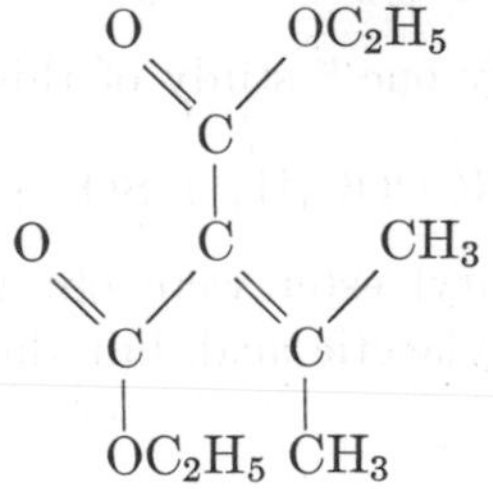

Va   Vb

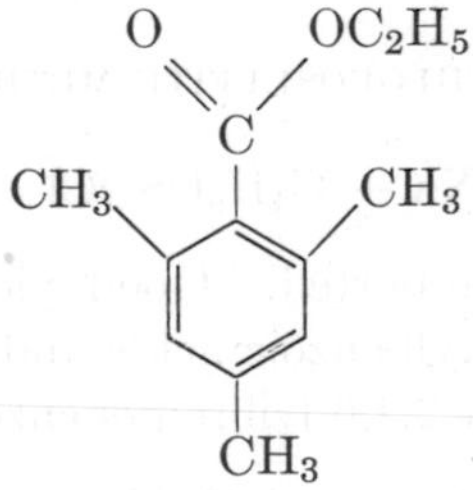

[43] See for example H. A. Smith et al., *J. Am. Chem. Soc.*, *62*, 1556 (1940); *63*, 3465 (1941).

[44] See Chapter 13.

[45] H. P. Treffers and L. P. Hammett, *J. Am. Chem. Soc.*, *59*, 1708 (1937). The esters hydrolyzed by this procedure are probably limited to esters of acids esterified by the 100% sulfuric acid method; see reference 37.

[46] M. S. Newman, H. G. Kuivila, and A. B. Garrett, *J. Am. Chem. Soc.*, *67*, 704 (1945). The varying behavior of methyl esters of 2-benzoyl-6-methylbenzoic acid and 2-benzoyl-3-methylbenzoic acid towards sulfuric acid proved useful in separating mixtures of the two acids. See M. S. Newman and C. D. McCleary, *J. Am. Chem. Soc.*, *63*, 1539 (1941).

[47] E. J. Corey, *J. Am. Chem. Soc.*, *74*, 5902 (1952).

methods. Diethyl isopropylmalonate was not readily hydrolyzed by this method.

ALKYL-OXYGEN FISSION. Acidic and alkaline hydrolysis of esters of unhindered acids generally proceeds with acyl-oxygen fission.[48] However, under suitable conditions alkyl-oxygen fission can be the main reaction path. The use of sterically hindered acids in mechanism studies in this field is illustrated below.

When t-butyl benzoate was refluxed with methanol for 4 days, there was isolated 61.9% of methyl benzoate and 60.7% of t-butyl methyl ether.[49] These products might have been formed by course A or B.

$$C_6H_5COOC(CH_3)_3 + CH_3OH \rightarrow$$

$$\left. \begin{array}{c} C_6H_5COOCH_3 + (CH_3)_3C\!-\!OH \\ CH_3OH + (CH_3)_3COH \rightarrow (CH_3)_3COCH_3 + H_2O \end{array} \right\} A$$

$$\left. \begin{array}{c} C_6H_5COOC(CH_3)_3 + CH_3OH \rightarrow C_6H_5COOH + (CH_3)_3COCH_3 \\ C_6H_5COOH + CH_3OH \rightarrow C_6H_5COOCH_3 + H_2O \end{array} \right\} B$$

When t-butyl mesitoate was refluxed with methanol for 7 days only t-butyl methyl ether, t-butyl mesitoate, and mesitoic acid were obtained. These results indicated that the reaction must have followed course B for t-butyl mesitoate and that path B for the methanolysis of t-butyl benzoate was possible. A further experiment, which showed that when a solution of benzoic acid, t-butyl alcohol, and methanol was refluxed for 7 days no t-butyl methyl ether was produced, indicated that path B is correct.[50]

Basic hydrolysis

ACYL-OXYGEN FISSION. As mentioned above, steric effects in the alkaline hydrolysis of esters parallel those in acidic hydrolysis, with regard to structure of the acyl component. Less is known about steric effects in the alkyl portion.

In discussion of the effect of structure on rate of acid-catalyzed esterification it was assumed (see p. 205) that polar effects were not involved because the ionization constants of saturated aliphatic acids do not vary greatly with structure. However, in alkaline hydrolysis,

[48] See *Ann. Repts. J. Chem. Soc.*, *38*, 229ff (1941), for a review of ester hydrolysis and examples of known types.

[49] S. G. Cohen and A. Schneider, *J. Am. Chem. Soc.*, *63*, 3382 (1941).

[50] Other evidence that the acidic hydrolysis of t-butyl esters proceeds by alkyl-oxygen fission is provided by the more rapid hydrolysis of t-butyl esters as compared to methyl esters; reference 49, and others. A synthetic application involving facile cleavage of t-butyl esters is given by G. S. Fonken and W. S. Johnson, *J. Am. Chem. Soc.*, *74*, 831 (1952).

a distinction should be drawn between primary, secondary, and tertiary alkyl esters, since the basicity of the corresponding alkoxide ions varies considerably, the order of decreasing basicity being t-alkoxide > sec-alkoxide > pr-alkoxide.

In general, esters of primary alcohols are hydrolyzed more rapidly than the corresponding esters of secondary alcohols, which in turn are hydrolyzed more rapidly than esters of tertiary alcohols. Undoubtedly polar and steric effects are involved. If discussion is limited to one type of ester at a time, polar effects may be disregarded and differences in rate attributed to steric factors.

Primary alkyl esters. With regard to steric effects in alkaline hy-

$$
\underset{\gamma}{C}-\underset{\beta}{C}-\underset{\alpha}{\overset{\overset{\displaystyle O}{\|}}{C}}-C-OH
\qquad\qquad
CH_3\overset{\overset{\displaystyle O}{\|}}{C}-O-\underset{\alpha}{C}-\underset{\beta}{C}-C
$$

VIa   VIb

drolysis of esters, it should be pointed out that if primary alkyl acetates are considered the branching can take place only on the β-carbon or at a carbon further removed. An examination of Table VI shows

TABLE VI

ALKALINE HYDROLYSIS OF PRIMARY ALKYL ACETATES

Alkyl	$\dfrac{k_{CH_3CO_2C_2H_5}}{k_{CH_3CO_2R}}$ *	Ref.	Alkyl	$\dfrac{k_{CH_3CO_2C_2H_5}}{k_{CH_3CO_2R}}$	Ref.
1. CH_3-	0.58	1	13. $[(CH_3)_2CH]_2CHCH_2-$ ‡	17.8	4
2. CH_3CH_2-	1.00	1	14. $CH_2=CHCH_2CH_2-$	0.8	3
3. $CH_3CH_2CH_2-$	1.08	1, 2	15. $CH_2=CHCH_2-$	0.5	3, 5
4. $CH_3CH_2CH_2CH_2-$	1.18	1, 2	16. $HC\equiv CCH_2-$	0.15 †	6
5. $(CH_3)_2CH_2CH_2-$	1.28	2, 3	17. $(CH_2)_2CHCH_2-$ ‡	1.5	4
6. $(CH_3)_2CHCH_2-$	1.40	1, 2	18. $(CH_2)_3CHCH_2-$ ‡	2.2	4
7. $CH_3CH_2CH(CH_3)CH_2-$ ‡	3.4	4	19. $(CH_2)_4CHCH_2-$ ‡	3.0	4
8. $(CH_3)_2CHCH(CH_3)CH_2-$ ‡	4.6	4	20. $(CH_2)_5CHCH_2-$ ‡	4.9	4
9. $(C_2H_5)_2CHCH_2-$ ‡	6.7	4	21. $(CH_3)_3CCH_2-$ ‡	5.7	4
10. $(CH_3)_2CHCH(C_2H_5)CH_2-$ ‡	7.0	4	22. $C_2H_5C(CH_3)_2CH_2-$ ‡	7.6	4
11. $n\text{-}C_4H_9CH(C_2H_5)CH_2-$ ‡	10.7	4	23. $CH_3C(C_2H_5)_2CH_2-$ ‡	13.3	4
12. $t\text{-}C_4H_9CH(C_2H_5)CH_2-$ ‡	26.7	4	24. $(C_2H_5)_3CCH_2-$ ‡	32.0	4

* The rate constants were determined in water at 20° for all esters unless otherwise indicated. The rate constant for ethyl acetate in water at 20° is 4.8 g. mole^{-1} min.$^{-1}$; H. Olsson, *Z. physik. Chem.*, *125*, 243 (1927).

† The ratio for propargyl alcohol is relative to ethyl acetate at 25°.

‡ Because of insolubility in water these esters were measured in 70% dioxane-30% water (by volume at 20°). In order to correct for the change in reaction velocity in going from water to 70% dioxane, the reaction ratios are divided by 3. This value was taken because the ratio of the rates in water compared to those in 70% dioxane for neopentyl, 2,2-dimethylbutyl, and 2-methylbutyl acetates were 3.07, 3.37, and 3.02, respectively.

1. L. Smith and H. Olsson, *Z. physik. Chem.*, *118*, 99 (1925).

2. H. Olsson, *ibid.*, *118*, 107 (1925).

3. H. Olsson, *ibid.*, *125*, 243 (1927).

4. Unpublished results, S. Sarel and M. S. Newman.

5. H. Olsson, *Z. physik. Chem.*, *133*, 233 (1928).

6. R. T. Myers, A. R. Collett, and C. L. Lazzell, *J. Phys. Chem.*, *56*, 461 (1952).

that when the three hydrogens on the β-carbon of the ethyl group are replaced by ethyl groups (compound 24) the maximum steric hindrance is provided. Since the rate ratio is only 32 one can assume that prohibitive steric hindrance to carbonyl addition will not be observed with any primary alkyl acetate.

The effect of branching at the β-carbon of the alkyl group of an ester, VI_b, may be compared with branching at the γ-carbon of the acyl group of an acid, VI_a, in acid-catalyzed esterification (see Table I). The only strictly comparable case involves neopentylacetic acid (No. 10, Table I) and neopentyl acetate (No. 21, Table VI). Since neopentylacetic acid is esterified at the same rate as acetic acid and neopentyl acetate is hydrolyzed 5.7 times more slowly than ethyl acetate, one might conclude that, in carbonyl addition reactions of esters, the rates of reaction are more sensitive to substitution on the third atom from the carbonyl group in the alkyl component than in the acyl. However, inasmuch as only one such comparison can at present be made, this generalization must be regarded as tentative.[51]

The rates for cycloalkylcarbinyl esters follow the order one would expect if purely steric factors were involved; i.e., the larger the ring the slower the rate. The more rapid rate for propargyl acetate, 16, as compared to allyl acetate, 15, may be due in part to its smaller steric requirements.

Secondary alkyl esters. The rate of hydrolysis of esters of acyclic secondary alcohols has not received much study. Steric effects in this series can be expected to be larger than in the primary series, since branching occurs nearer the carbonyl group. The rate ratios compared to ethyl acetate (see Table VII), for isopropyl, *sec*-butyl, and 3-pentyl acetates are 3.65, 5.7, and 13.3, respectively. The acid phthalate of di-*t*-butylcarbinol is reported to be hydrolyzed from 140 to 400 times more slowly than that of di-*n*-butylcarbinol, with change of the solvent used.[52] A few other scattered comparisons of rates of secondary alkyl ester hydrolyses can be found, but no significant body of comparable data is available.

[51] Further comparisons of the sort discussed are not possible with regard to substitutions at the β-carbon of VI_a and the α-carbon of VI_b because rate measurements on the necessary acids have not been made. An interesting comparison would be that of the rate of esterification of $(CH_3)_2CHCH_2COOH$ with that of $(C_2H_5)_2CHCH_2COOH$ in contrast to the known rates of hydrolysis of 2-propyl and 3-pentyl acetates (esters 2 and 4, Table VII). Furthermore, the effect on such ratios of replacement of the connecting oxygen atom in VI_b by S and NH would be of interest.

[52] G. Vavon and C. Zaremba, *Bull. soc. chim. France*, [4], *49*, 1853 (1931).

TABLE VII

RATES OF SAPONIFICATION OF SECONDARY AND TERTIARY ALKYL ESTERS

Alkyl	$\dfrac{k_{CH_3COOC_2H_5}}{k_{CH_3COOR}}$ *	Ref.†	R		Ref.
1. CH_3CH_2—	1.00	1	9. CH_3—, cis	1.00 ‡	4
2. $(CH_3)_2CH$—	3.65	2	10. CH_3—, trans	0.36 ‡	4
3. $C_2H_5(CH_3)CH$—	5.7	1, 2	11. C_2H_5—, cis	2.7 ‡	4
4. $(C_2H_5)_2CH$—	13.3	3	12. C_2H_5—, trans	0.74 ‡	4
5. $(CH_3)_3C$—	57 ‖	1, 2	13. C_3H_7—, cis	4.6 ‡	4
6. $C_2H_5(CH_2)_2C$—	124	3	14. C_3H_7—, cis	1.00 §	4
7. $C_3H_7(CH_3)_2C$—	135	3	15. i-C_3H_7—, cis	22.3 §	4
8. $CH_3(C_2H_5)_2C$—	270	3	16. C_3H_7—, trans	0.3 §	4
			17. i-C_3H_7, trans	0.64 §	4

* The rate constants were determined in water at 20° for all esters unless otherwise noted.
† References 1, 2, 3 same as in Table VI.
4. G. Vavon, *Bull. soc. chim. France*, [4], *49*, 937 (1931).
‡ The rate ratios are those for alkaline hydrolysis in water at 39° of *cis*-2-methylcyclohexyl acid phthalate divided by 2-alkylcyclohexyl acid phthalate.
§ These rate ratios are for half phthalates in water at 69°; the rate for *cis*-2-propylcyclohexyl acid phthalate is the numerator.
‖ If the rate of hydrolysis of *t*-butyl acetate at 30° in 70% dioxane-30% water is taken as unity, the rate ratio, $k_{CH_3COO\text{-}t\text{-}bu}/k_{CH_3COOR}$, for pinacolyl acetate is 0.71 and that for diisobutylcarbinyl acetate is 1.61 (unpublished results of S. Sarel and M. S. Newman).

More information exists on rates of hydrolysis of cyclic secondary alcohols. As a general rule, the rate is slower for *cis*-2-alkylcyclohexyl esters than for the *trans* isomers, and the difference is greater the larger the alkyl group. Isopropyl is considerably more sterically effective than normal propyl or higher *n*-alkyl in this series.[53] The differences in rate of hydrolysis of epimeric esters in the steroid [54] series can be traced to differences in the type of bond (equatorial or axial) involved (see Chapter 1).

A subtle steric effect is to be found on study of the relative rates of hydrolysis of the half phthalates of a series of *cis* and *trans* 2-alkylcyclohexanols (see Table VII.) There is only a moderate drop in rate in going from 9 to 11 to 13. However, the rate for 15 at 39° was so slow that comparison of the rate of *cis-i*-propyl (15) to *cis*-propyl (14) acid phthalate was made at 69°. The rate ratio found, 22, is too large to be accounted for by size alone, for in the *trans* series the ratio between 16 and 17 is only about 2. An explanation based on differ-

[53] G. Vavon et al., *Bull. soc. chim. France*, [4], *41*, 357, 1638 (1927).
[54] D. H. R. Barton, *Experientia*, *6*, 316 (1950).

ences in reactivity of the conformations VII and VIIa for the *cis* acid phthalates and VIII and VIIIa for the *trans* isomers can be advanced.

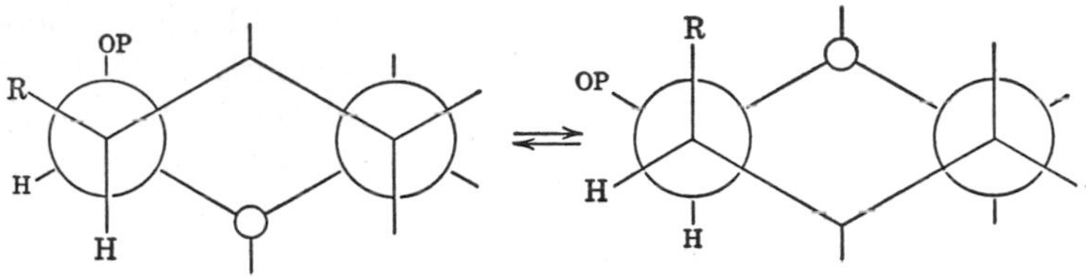

One can assume that the total rate of hydrolysis of a *cis*-2-alkylcyclohexyl acid phthalate is the sum of the rates which proceed from VII and VIIa. Since the hydrolysis of an equatorial ester is favored over that of an axial ester, one might argue that the preferred conformation for hydrolysis is VIIa, and that little, if any, hydrolysis proceeds via VII. However, as R becomes more bulky the tendency for the alkylcyclohexyl ester to exist in the form VII will increase. Hence one would expect the rate of hydrolysis to decrease for two reasons: (1) because R is becoming larger; and (2) because a greater contribution to the total rate of hydrolysis will involve VII. In the *cis* series there is a significantly great change when R is isopropyl as indicated by the fact that the ratio of the rates for *cis*-propyl and -isopropyl esters, compounds 14 and 15, is large. This ratio cannot be explained by the first reason, mere bulk, because if this were responsible one would expect a similar large difference in the *trans* pair, compounds 16 and 17. However, such a large effect is not found. Hence the second reason is indicated; that is, more hydrolysis occurs via that form, VII, in which the ester group is axial. Such an explanation is made more plausible by examination of scale models, which show considerable crowding when the isopropyl group is in the axial position.[55]

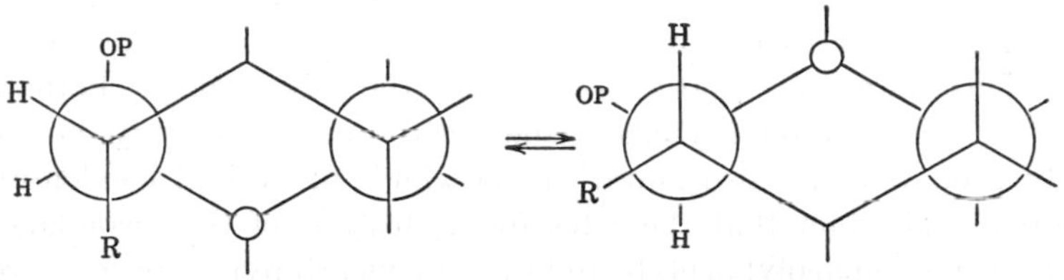

[55] For a theoretical discussion of the validity of arguments based on conformational distribution see Chapter 1.

Tertiary alkyl esters. As a class, *t*-alkyl esters are hydrolyzed considerably more slowly than secondary or primary alkyl esters. The rate ratios for esters 5, 6, 7, and 8 (Table VII) indicate that rather serious hindrance to hydrolysis is likely to occur with further branching of the *t*-alkyl group. Further work is obviously needed in this area. An isolated fact of interest is the inertness of di-*t*-butyl carbonate (six-number 18) to concentrated ammonium hydroxide at 150° and to phenylhydrazine at 185°.[56]

The use of di-*t*-butyl succinate in the Stobbe condensation has marked advantages when slowly reacting ketones are involved. Since *t*-butyl succinate undergoes self-condensation much less readily than methyl or ethyl succinates, higher yields of desired condensation products may readily be obtained.[57] The difficulty in preparation of di-*t*-butyl succinate somewhat detracts from the advantages. Perhaps a properly sized secondary alkyl succinate would not only be more easily prepared but also afford higher yields of desired condensation product. The fact that the rates for hydrolysis of the secondary alkyl acetates, pinacolyl acetate and diisobutylcarbinyl acetate, approximate that of *t*-butyl acetate (see Table VII, footnote ‖) indicates that these esters (or esters having comparable rates of hydrolysis) might be used to advantage.

ALKYL-OXYGEN FISSION. In the hope that quantitative rate measurements on addition reactions of highly hindered carbonyl-containing compounds might be obtained, the rates of alkaline hydrolysis of methyl 4-*x*-2,6-dimethylbenzoates were measured.[58] An analysis of the results indicated that these hydrolyses might have occurred by an attack of hydroxide ion on the alkyl carbon of the ester group with displacement of the substituted benzoate anion, as shown.

$$OH^- + CH_3OOC-\!\!\!\bigcirc\!\!\!-X \rightarrow HOCH_3 + \bar{O}OC-\!\!\!\bigcirc\!\!\!-X$$

Examples of similar displacement reactions are provided by the reaction of hindered methyl esters with methoxide ion to form di-

[56] A. R. Choppin and J. W. Rogers, *J. Am. Chem. Soc.*, **70**, 2967 (1948).

[57] G. H. Daub and W. S. Johnson, *J. Am. Chem. Soc.*, **72**, 501 (1950).

[58] H. L. Goering, T. Rubin, and M. S. Newman, *J. Am. Chem. Soc.*, **76**, 787 (1954), X = NH₂, Br, H, NO₂, OCH₃. However, M. L. Bender and R. S. Dewey, *J. Am. Chem. Soc.*, **78**, 317 (1956), show conclusively that methyl mesitoate (X = CH₃) is saponified by acyl-oxygen cleavage at 126°.

methyl ether [59] and with N-methylpiperidine to form quaternary ammonium salts,[37c] and of substituted benzyl acetates to form benzyl methyl ethers.[60]

REACTIONS OF OTHER ACID DERIVATIVES

Acid chlorides

A study of steric factors in reactions of acid chlorides is interesting because both steric hindrance and steric assistance have been observed. Whether steric factors will hinder or assist depends on the mechanism involved. Two paths can be operative in most reactions of acid halides: path A involves carbonyl addition, and path B ionization.[61]

$$RCOCl + CH_3OH \rightarrow \underset{\underset{OCH_3}{|}}{\overset{\overset{OH}{|}}{RC}} —Cl \rightarrow R \cdot COOCH_3 + HCl \qquad A$$

$$RCOCl \rightarrow R\overset{+}{C}O + Cl^- \xrightarrow{CH_3OH} RCOOCH_3 + HCl \qquad B$$

Reactions occurring by path A are subject to steric hindrance, the magnitude of which is probably best estimated by the assumption that a parallelism exists with hindrance in esterification as outlined earlier in this chapter (see Table I). However, no comparable data are available for aliphatic acid chlorides. For substituted benzoyl chlorides, all groups except para-methyl increase the rate of reaction with alcohols (see Table VIII).

The interpretation of the results listed in Table VIII is difficult, since the contribution to the observed rate made by each of the paths A and B is unknown. In several cases steric effects are apparently operative. For both the ortho-methyl and ortho-methoxy compounds the rates are significantly higher than for the meta or para isomers. The steric assistance probably operates on that portion of the total rate which proceeds by the ionization mechanism (path B) and reaches its maximum with mesitoyl chloride, which is reported to react too rapidly with methanol at 0° for rate measurement.[62] Undoubtedly

[59] J. F. Bunnett, M. M. Robison, and F. C. Pennington, J. Am. Chem. Soc., 72, 2378 (1950).

[60] R. Barthel, Ber., 76, 573 (1943).

[61] G. E. K. Branch and A. C. Nixon, J. Am. Chem. Soc., 58, 2499 (1936).

[62] J. F. Norris and H. H. Young, J. Am. Chem. Soc., 57, 1420 (1935). Undoubtedly the ability of the methyl groups to release electrons is important too.

TABLE VIII

REACTIONS OF SUBSTITUTED BENZOYL CHLORIDES WITH ALCOHOLS

X =	$\dfrac{k_{XC_6H_4COCl}}{k_{C_6H_5COCl}}$ *	X =	$\dfrac{k_{XC_6H_4COCl}}{k_{C_6H_5COCl}}$ *
1. H	1.00	12. o-CH$_3$	5.2
2. o-Cl	2.8	13. m-CH$_3$	1.1
3. m-Cl	3.3	14. p-CH$_3$	0.68
4. p-Cl	1.6	15. o-OCH$_3$	66.0 †
5. o-Br	2.8	16. m-OCH$_3$	2.3 †
6. m-Br	3.5	17. p-OCH$_3$	1.8 †
7. p-Br	1.8	18. o-NO$_2$	1.8
8. o-I	6.6 †	19. m-NO$_2$	12.4
9. m-I	9.3 †	20. p-NO$_2$	15.6
10. p-I	4.3 †	21. 2,4,6-triNO$_2$	Too slow
11. 2,4,6-triBr	Very slow	22. 2,4,6-triCH$_3$	Too fast

* The rate for C$_6$H$_5$COCl in methanol at 0° is taken as unity; see J. F. Norris and H. H. Young, *J. Am. Chem. Soc.*, *57*, 1420 (1935).

† The rate for C$_6$H$_5$COCl in ethanol at 0° is taken as unity; see J. F. Norris, E. V. Fasce, and C. J. Stand, *J. Am. Chem. Soc.*, *57*, 1415 (1935).

this acid chloride reacts by path B.[63] The high reactivity of mesitoyl chloride brings to mind the fact that mesitoic acid has an *i* factor of 4 in sulfuric acid, which indicates the formation of the 2,4,6-trimethylphenyl oxocarbonium ion.[39]

The hindering steric effect of groups is exerted mainly on reactions occurring by path A and reaches its maximum in the tribromo and trinitro compounds. Pentachlorobenzoyl chloride reportedly can be recrystallized from ethyl alcohol and requires 30 hours at reflux to be esterified by methanol.[64]

Studies on the hydrolysis of benzoyl chloride and substituted benzoyl chlorides in water-acetone mixtures in the presence of variable amounts of hydroxide ion have clarified the mechanistic picture.[65] Hydrolysis by the ionization path (similar to B) is favored by an increase of the water content of the medium. 2,4,6-Trinitrobenzoyl chloride hydrolyzes mainly by an S_N2 type reaction (similar to path A), whereas 2,4,6-trimethylbenzoyl chloride hydrolyzes mainly by ionization (path B).

[63] Dr. N. N. Lichtin, Boston University, reports that conductance measurements on a solution of mesitoyl chloride in liquid sulfur dioxide indicated no appreciable ionization.

[64] A. Kirpal and H. Kunze, *Ber.*, *62*, 2102 (1929).

[65] D. A. Brown and R. F. Hudson, *J. Chem. Soc.*, *1953*, 3352. Also, see C. A. Bunton, T. A. Lewis, and D. R. Llewellyn, *Chemistry & Industry*, *1954*, 1154.

From the above facts it should not be concluded that mesitoyl chloride is always more reactive than benzoyl chloride. In the reaction with diazomethane, benzoyl chloride is reactive whereas mesitoyl chloride is inert.[66] This behavior indicates that the reaction of acid chlorides with diazomethane proceeds by carbonyl addition.

Little is known about the effect of steric factors in an alcohol on its rate of reaction with acid chlorides. In general, primary alcohols react more rapidly than secondary, and secondary more rapidly than tertiary, but how much of the overall effect is due to steric factors is not known. An interesting analysis of the rates of reaction of the four isomeric menthols with p-nitrobenzoyl chloride has been made.[67] The relative rates are explained by the assumption that the rings are always in a chair form and that all four isomers react only when the hydroxyl group is in an equatorial position. Analysis of the steric factors involved in the ground and transition states then permits rationalization of the known results. In this connection analysis of the relative rates of hydrolysis of *cis*- and *trans*-propyl and -isopropyl cyclohexyl acid phthalates (see p. 223) should be consulted.[68]

Amides

The hydrolysis of amides has received very little attention from a quantitative point of view. The studies reported agree with results to be expected by application of the rule of six (see p. 206). The most comprehensive data have been produced by Cason and his coworkers,[69] who studied the rate of alkaline hydrolysis of a number of branched long-chain amides, $RCONH_2$, with the object of using the data to estimate the type of branching of the chain in the region of the amide function. From the rate of hydrolysis of C_{27}-phthianamide, it was concluded that this amide has a methyl branch on the α-carbon and not on the β-carbon.[70]

Hydrolysis of more highly hindered aliphatic amides, such as trialkylacetamides, is extremely sluggish under both acidic and basic

[66] W. E. Bachman and J. Sheehan, unpublished results.

[67] E. Eliel, *Experientia*, *9*, 91 (1953). See A. K. Macbeth, J. A. Mills, and W. G. P. Robertson, *J. Chem. Soc.*, *1951*, 2971, for a criticism of the work of Read and Grubb, *J. Chem. Soc.*, *1934*, 1779, discussed by Eliel.

[68] For a theoretical discussion of the validity of arguments based on conformational distribution see Chapter 1.

[69] (*a*) J. Cason and H. J. Wolfhagen, *J. Org. Chem.*, *14*, 155 (1949). (*b*) J. Cason, C. Gastaldo, D. L. Glusker, J. Allinger, and L. B. Ash, *ibid.*, *18*, 1129 (1953).

[70] J. Cason, N. K. Freeman, and G. Sumrell, *J. Biol. Chem.*, *192*, 415 (1951).

conditions.[71] To remove the amino group, diazotization is preferable to hydrolysis.[72] We have found that slow addition of sodium nitrite to a well-stirred solution of amide in strong sulfuric acid (ca. 70–80%) at temperatures of 80–100° affords excellent yields of acids,[73] although others have reported [71a] the failure of this procedure.

In the aromatic series few data are available for the estimation of steric effects. In one study of acidic and basic hydrolysis of benzamides, o-methylbenzamide hydrolyzed at 80° about 20 times more slowly than p-methylbenzamide under alkaline conditions and about 26 times more slowly under acid conditions.[74] More serious steric hindrance has been met with certain bulky monoorthosubstituted benzamides.[75] In studies on the extremely sluggish alkaline hydrolysis of diorthosubstituted benzamides in ethylene glycol solution near 200°, a base-catalyzed dehydration to nitrile has been observed.[76] A similar dehydration does not occur with highly hindered aliphatic amides.[76]

$$ \text{R—CONH}_2 \xrightarrow{\text{OH}^-} \text{RCN} + \text{H}_2\text{O} $$

Anhydrides

Unsymmetric aliphatic anhydrides may react to give isomeric products with a variety of reagents. In general, that product arising from addition to the carbonyl group with the greater branching on the α-carbon is formed in the lesser amount. The larger the groups, the greater the selectivity in such reactions. For example, the isomeric half esters of an unsymmetrical dibasic acid [77] can be made by: (a) reaction of the anhydride with neutral alcohol; or (b) hydrolysis of the diester with one equivalent of alkali.

[71] (a) N. Sperber, D. Papa, and E. Schwenk, J. Am. Chem. Soc., 70, 3091 (1948), contains references to much previous work on synthesis and hydrolysis of hindered amides. (b) F. C. B. Marshall, J. Chem. Soc., 1930, 2754.

[72] L. Bouveault, Bull. soc. chim. France, [3], 9, 368 (1893). See also G. Heyl and V. Meyer, Ber., 28, 2776 (1895).

[73] Unpublished observations of Dr. S. Sarel. A two-step conversion of triethylacetonitrile to the amide (75% H_2SO_4 at 155° for 55 minutes) and amide to acid (cooling to 70° and addition of sodium nitrite over 60 minutes) afforded pure triethylacetic acid in 80% overall yield.

[74] I. Meloche and K. J. Laidler, J. Am. Chem. Soc., 73, 1712 (1951).

[75] L. F. Fieser and J. Cason, J. Am. Chem. Soc., 62, 432 (1940). J. Cason and J. D. Wordie, J. Org. Chem., 15, 617 (1950).

[76] L. Tsai and M. S. Newman, unpublished experiments.

[77] Half esters are frequently converted to acid chlorides for further synthetic use. The fact that isomeric half ester acid chlorides frequently yield the same product or mixtures of products is reviewed and discussed by B. H. Chase and D. H. Hey, J. Chem. Soc., 1952, 553. Also see J. Cason and R. D. Smith, J. Org. Chem., 18, 1201 (1953).

$$\underset{\text{Y}}{\overset{\text{X}}{>}}\text{C}\underset{\substack{|\\ \text{CH}_2-\text{CO}}}{\overset{-\text{CO}}{}}\!\!\!\!\!\!\!\!\!\!\!\!\!\!\text{O} \quad \xrightarrow{\text{CH}_3\text{OH}} \quad \underset{\text{Y}}{\overset{\text{X}}{>}}\text{C}\underset{\text{CH}_2\text{COOCH}_3}{\overset{-\text{COOH}}{}}$$

$$\underset{\text{Y}}{\overset{\text{X}}{>}}\text{C}\underset{\text{CH}_2\text{COOCH}_3}{\overset{-\text{COOCH}_3}{}} \quad \xrightarrow[\text{2. H}^+]{\text{1. NaOH}} \quad \underset{\text{Y}}{\overset{\text{X}}{>}}\text{C}\underset{\text{CH}_2\text{COOH}}{\overset{-\text{COOCH}_3}{}}$$

The Friedel-Crafts condensation of unsymmetrical succinic anhydrides has been reviewed.[78] When α,α-disubstituted anhydrides are involved condensation invariably occurs at the carbonyl group farthest removed from the branching. However, with monosubstituted anhydrides the ratio of products varies with experimental conditions, with solvent, and with the substituting group in a seemingly unpredictable way. For the series of condensations of p-chloro-, methoxy-, and nitrophenylsuccinic anhydrides with benzene and toluene in the aromatic hydrocarbon solvent or in nitrobenzene, the observed results can be accounted for by a combination of polar and solvation effects. Since steric factors are seemingly unimportant this analysis is considered outside the scope of this book.[79]

In the aromatic series, 3-substituted phthalic anhydrides react with alcohols to form half esters in a manner not predictable by steric effects, although such effects must be involved. Thus 3-nitrophthalic anhydride reacts with methanol to give mainly methyl 2-carboxy-6-nitrobenzoate,[80] whereas 3-methylphthalic anhydride yields mainly methyl 2-carboxy-3-methylbenzoate.[81]

[78] E. Berliner in R. Adams, *Organic Reactions*, Vol. 5, pp. 242–248, John Wiley & Sons, New York, 1949.

[79] See the Ph.D. thesis of Paul Scheurer, Ohio State University, 1953, for further information.

[80] R. Wegscheider and A. Lipschitz, *Monatsh.*, **21**, 787 (1900), and F. A. A. Elhafez and D. J. Cram, *J. Am. Chem. Soc.*, **74**, 5846 (1952). In the latter article, however, reaction with a larger alcohol, 1,2-diphenyl-1-propanol, produced a mixture of the isomeric esters.

[81] M. Hayashi and S. Tsuruoka, *J. Chem. Soc. Japan*, **56**, 999 (1935). N. Rabjohn and H. H. Farmer, *J. Am. Chem. Soc.*, **77**, 760 (1955), have shown that Hayashi and Tsuruoka were in error in claiming that only the unhindered ester was formed.

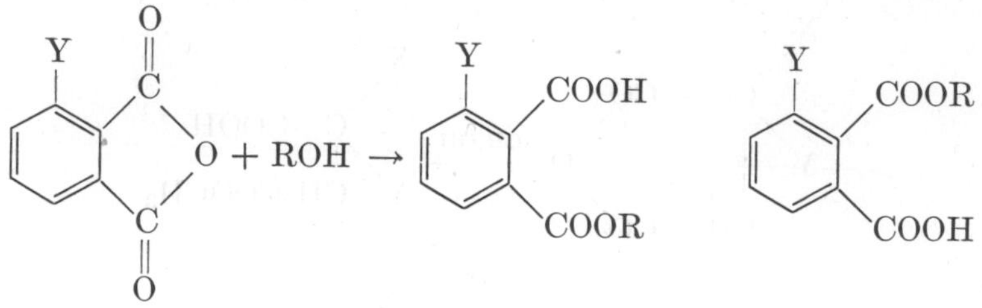

A large number of Friedel-Crafts condensations of 3-substituted phthalic anhydrides (including nitro,[82] bromo,[83] iodo,[84] and acetamido [85]) with various substrates are reported to yield exclusively or predominantly the corresponding 3-substituted-2-aroylbenzoic acids, X. In more complicated 3-substituted anhydrides the same generalization seems to hold.[79]

Careful studies on 3-methylphthalic anhydride and 3-chlorophthalic anhydride have been made in reactions with aromatic Grignard reagents containing 0, 1, and 2 *ortho*-methyl groups and in Friedel-Crafts reactions with aromatic hydrocarbons containing 0, 1, and 2 methyl groups *ortho* to the position forming the new bond.

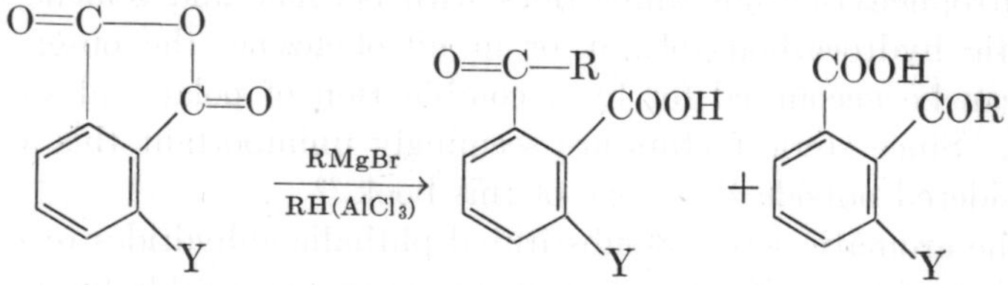

Examination of the data recorded in Table IX reveals that in the Grignard reactions a greater preference is shown for condensation with the unhindered carbonyl to yield compounds of type IX as the number of methyl groups *ortho* to the magnesium atom increases. This is true where Y is methyl [86] and where Y is chlorine.[79] However, in the Friedel-Crafts reaction the situation is quite different. With 3-methylphthalic anhydride there is no preference with benzene and little with *m*-xylene. An appreciable preference for condensation with

[82] P. C. Mitter and P. N. Dutt, *J. Indian Chem. Soc.*, *13*, 231 (1936).

[83] E. H. Huntress, K. Pfister, and K. H. T. Pfister, *J. Am. Chem. Soc.*, *64*, 2846 (1942).

[84] F. F. Blicke and F. D. Smith, *J. Am. Chem. Soc.*, *51*, 1867 (1929).

[85] W. A. Lawrance, *J. Am. Chem. Soc.*, *42*, 1876 (1920).

[86] M. S. Newman and C. W. Muth, *J. Am. Chem. Soc.*, *72*, 5191 (1950). M. S. Newman and C. D. McCleary, *ibid.*, *63*, 1542 (1941).

TABLE IX

REACTIONS OF 3-METHYL- AND 3-CHLOROPHTHALIC ANHYDRIDES IN THE
GRIGNARD AND FRIEDEL-CRAFTS REACTIONS

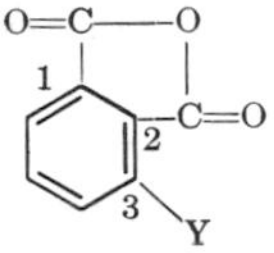

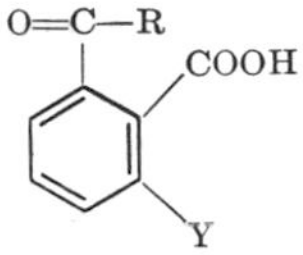

Y	R	IX% G.	IX% F.-C.	X% G.	X% F.-C.	Ratio $\frac{IX}{X}$ G.	Ratio $\frac{IX}{X}$ F.-C.
CH_3	C_6H_5-	43	38	14	37	3	1
CH_3	$2,4-(CH_3)_2C_6H_3-$	39	42	4	32	10	1.3
CH_3	$2,4,6-(CH_3)_3C_6H_2-$	66	68	1	16	66	4.2
Cl	C_6H_5-	52	0	12	96	4.3	0
Cl	$2,4-(CH_3)_2C_6H_3-$	66	0	17	90	4.0	0
Cl	$2,4,6-(CH_3)_3C_6H_2-$	49	18	0	82	High	0.2

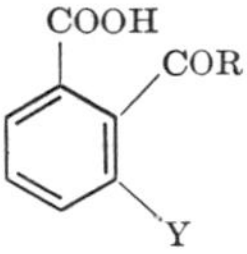

the unhindered carbonyl is shown with mesitylene. With 3-chloro-
phthalic anhydride, however, both benzene and *m*-xylene condense exclusively with the internal carbonyl to yield acids of type X. This
tendency is only partly overcome when the more bulky mesitylene is
involved.[79]

These findings are difficult to interpret. When a 3-substituted
phthalic anhydride reacts with two equivalents of aluminum chloride,
the first equivalent is thought to form an acid chloride-chloroalumi-
num salt. The second equivalent acts in the same way as aluminum
chloride in condensations of acid chlorides.[87] Combining the two
steps, we may indicate the possibilities as follows:

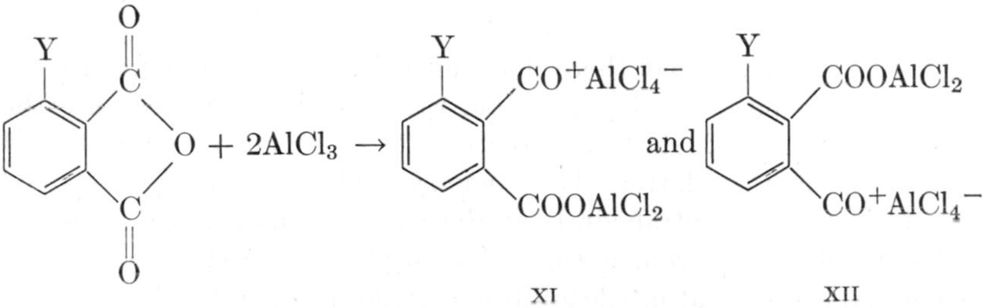

The fact that when Y is Cl and the reactant, benzene or xylene, the
product is exclusively that formed by condensation of XI might be
explained either by assuming that: (*a*) XI is formed exclusively; or
(*b*) XI and XII are in mobile equilibrium and XI is more reactive.

[87] E. Berliner in R. Adams, *Organic Reactions*, Vol. 5, p. 232, John Wiley & Sons,
New York, 1949.

The former explanation seems unlikely in view of the fact that when mesitylene is the reactant an 18% yield of product resulting from XII is obtained. Accordingly, if the second alternative is correct one needs some explanation as to why the reaction proceeds exclusively from XI when Y = Cl and yet, when Y = CH₃, there is little preference. A few probably relevant facts are given below.

1. When 4-chlorophthalic anhydride is condensed with chlorobenzene, the reaction occurs mainly at the carbonyl *meta* to the chlorine.[88]

2. 3-Substituted phthalic acids and anhydrides yield exclusively the corresponding 2-amino-3-substituted benzoic acids, XIII, in the Schmidt reaction.[89]

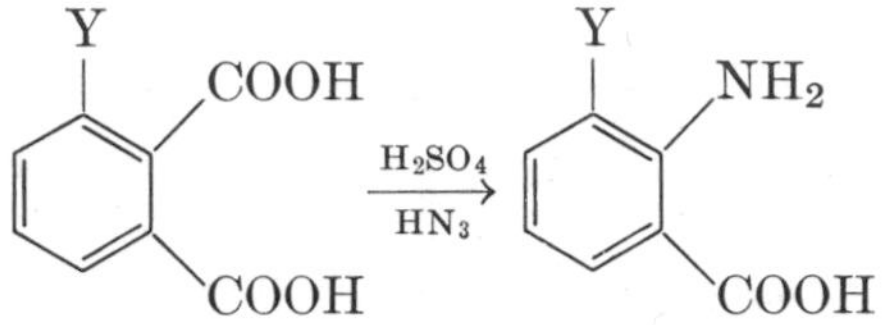

3. 2,6-Dimethylterephthalic acid, XIV, yields only 4-amino-3,5-dimethylbenzoic acid, XV, in the Schmidt reaction.[90]

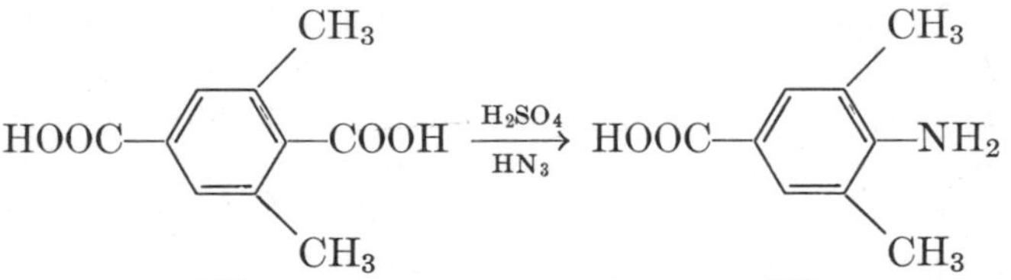

Nitriles

It is unfortunate that there does not exist a large amount of comparative rate data for any addition reaction of nitriles because the geometry involved is different from that of addition to doubly bonded functions. For the latter, the geometry is that previously described (I*a*, planar, to I*b*, tetrahedral) at the start of this chapter. For nitriles the change is from linear, XVI, to planar, XVII. Accordingly one would expect that nitrile additions would in general be less affected by steric factors than addition to doubly bonded functions.

[88] G. Egerer and H. Meyer, *Monatsh.*, *34*, 87 (1913).

[89] Unpublished experiments by Dr. H. Shechter and H. R. Barkemeyer, M.S. thesis, Ohio State University, 1952, Y = OH, OCH₃, F, Cl, CH₃, COOH, and NO₂.

[90] M. S. Newman and H. L. Gildenhorn, *J. Am. Chem. Soc.*, *70*, 317 (1948). The formation of the 4-carboxy-2,6-dimethylphenyl oxocarbonium ion was postulated to account for the result.

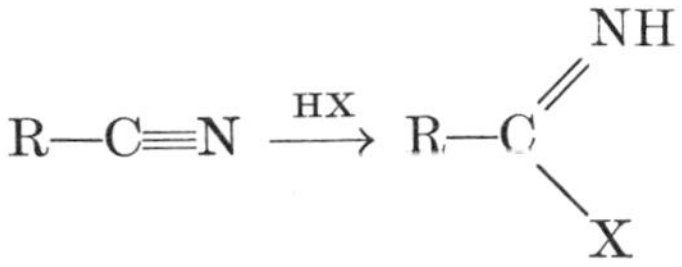

$$R-C\equiv N \xrightarrow{HX} R-C\underset{X}{\overset{NH}{\diagdown}}$$

XVI XVII

That the above conclusion is substantially correct is shown by several cases recorded in which hydrolysis of nitriles proceeds mainly to the amide but not to the acid.[71, 73] For an unhindered nitrile such as octadecanenitrile [91] the rates for nitrile and amide hydrolysis were approximately equal.[92]

The formation of imino ether hydrochlorides by treatment of aromatic nitriles with alcoholic hydrogen chloride,[93] a fairly general reaction, is severely hindered by one *ortho*-methyl group.

$$ArC\equiv N + CH_3OH + HCl \rightarrow ArC\underset{}{\overset{OCH_3}{\diagup}}\!=\!NH\cdot HCl$$

In the reactions of Grignard reagents with trisubstituted acetonitriles,[94] $(R)_3CCN$, the larger the R group the more vigorous the conditions required for addition of Grignard reagent. When the R groups were phenyl, phenyl and isopropyl, the ketimine hydrochloride formed on treatment of the reaction mixture with hydrochloric acid was quite stable and required long boiling to be hydrolyzed into the corresponding ketone. When all the R groups were isopropyl, hydrolysis of the nitrile could not be effected either by heating in concentrated sulfuric acid for 7 days at 90° or by refluxing in a solution of potassium hydroxide in ethylene glycol at 190° for 7 days.[95]

KETONES

Intramolecular acylation

The steric effects in intramolecular acylation to form cyclic ketones have been well summarized.[96] The results indicate that the tendency

[91] J. Cason et al., *J. Org. Chem.*, *18*, 1129 (1953).

[92] If amide and not acid is desired from a nitrile, an alkaline hydrogen peroxide treatment may be used. See L. McMaster and C. R. Noller, *J. Indian Chem. Soc.*, *12*, 652 (1935), and K. Wiberg, *J. Am. Chem. Soc.*, *77*, 2519 (1955).

[93] A. Pinner, *Ber.*, *23*, 2917 (1890). L. Spiegel, *Ber.*, *51*, 296 (1918). P. Pfeiffer, *Ber.*, *51*, 805 (1918).

[94] Ramart-Lucas and F. Salmon-Legagneur, *Compt. rend.*, *184*, 102 (1927).

[95] Unpublished experiments by M. S. Newman and T. Miwa.

[96] W. S. Johnson in R. Adams, *Organic Reactions*, Vol. 2, pp. 144ff, John Wiley & Sons, New York, 1944.

toward ring formation to compounds of type XVIII is as follows:

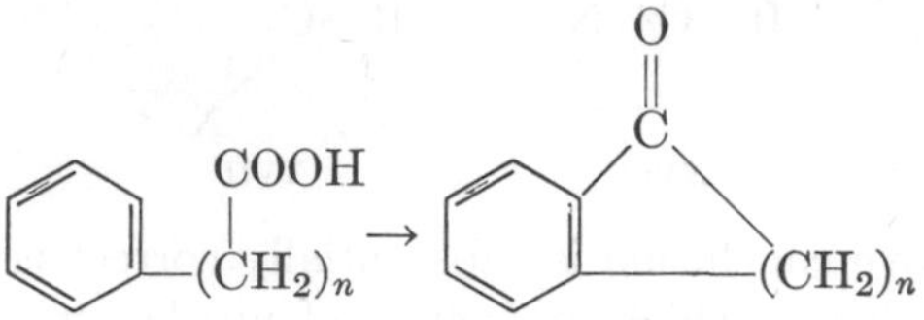

$$n = 3 > 2 > 4$$

This observed preference for ring formation has also been established in a series of competitive intramolecular cyclizations involving appropriately substituted acids. For example, benzylsuccinic acid, XIX, yields only 3-carboxy-1-tetralone, XX; and α-benzyl-γ-phenylbutyric acid, XXI, yields only 2-benzyl-1-tetralone, XXII.[96] These and similar examples may be cited as additional data of interest in connection with some views concerning the lesser stability of six-membered rings with an exocyclic double bond compared to similar five-membered rings.[97] Evidently kinetic factors outweigh thermodynamic ones in these cyclizations.

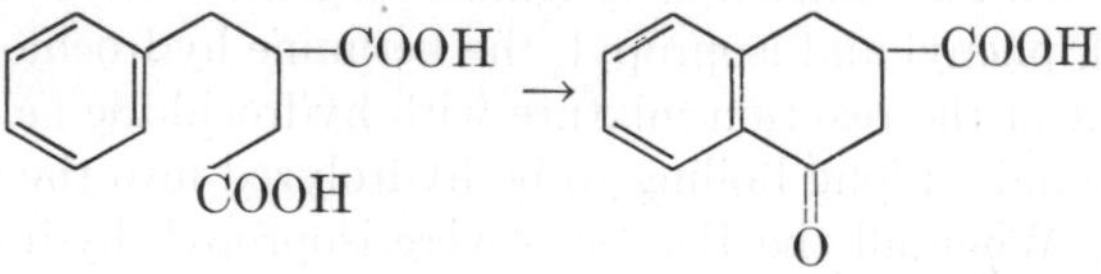

Until recently all attempts to cyclize ω-phenylalkanoic acids, $C_6H_5(CH_2)_nCOOH$, where n was greater than 4 were unsuccessful,[96] and where $n = 4$, the yield of benzosuberone was low. However, by means of a high-dilution technique for carrying out the Friedel-Crafts cyclization, Plattner[98] was able to increase the yield of benzosuberone to 88%. The cyclization of 6-phenylhexanoyl chloride ($n = 5$) to the corresponding cyclic ketone has been effected in 77% yield by a high-

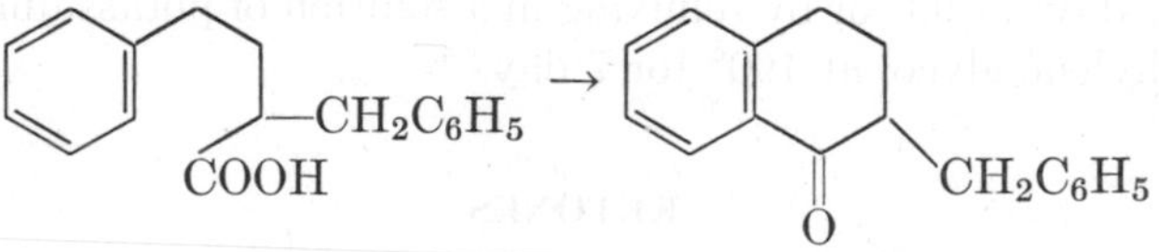

[97] H. C. Brown, J. H. Brewster, and H. Shechter, *J. Am. Chem. Soc.*, **76**, 467 (1954).

[98] Pl. A. Plattner, *Helv. Chim. Acta*, **27**, 801 (1944). See also G. O. Aspinall and W. Baker, *J. Chem. Soc.*, **1950**, 743.

dilution technique.[99]   Where $n = 6$ or 7 no monomeric ketones were obtained, but where $n = 8$–13, inclusive, 21–36% yields of cyclic ketones were obtained in which ring closure occurred *para* to the point of attachment of the acid chain.[99]

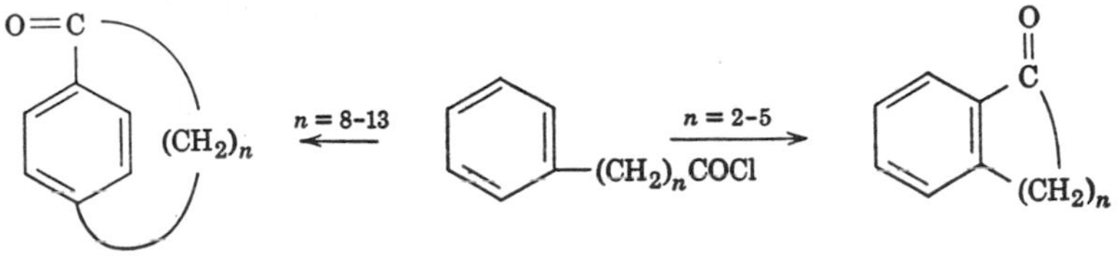

Acyclic ketones

Since no study specifically designed to measure quantitatively the steric effects in addition reactions of a large number of acyclic ketones has been reported, information on steric factors in this field must be gleaned from qualitative and semiquantitative data.   The latter stems mainly from determination of the amounts of addition and enolization in reactions of Grignard reagents.[100]   Qualitative evidence may be gathered from incidental observations regarding ease of formation of derivatives such as oximes and semicarbazones.   However, such data must be interpreted with caution since the ease of formation of derivatives such as bisulfite addition compounds, hydrazones, oximes, and semicarbazones is quite sensitive to experimental variables.[101] Furthermore, the reported failure to obtain a derivative is difficult to interpret as one does not know whether the result was due to a very slow rate of reaction or an unfavorable equilibrium.[102]   It appears that the rule of six together with consideration of the number of methyl groups on the α-carbons can be used to estimate serious steric hindrance in ketones much as in the case of acids and esters (vide infra).

In the generalized formula for a ketone, XXIII, there are two chains in which substitution can occur.   It should prove interesting to deter-

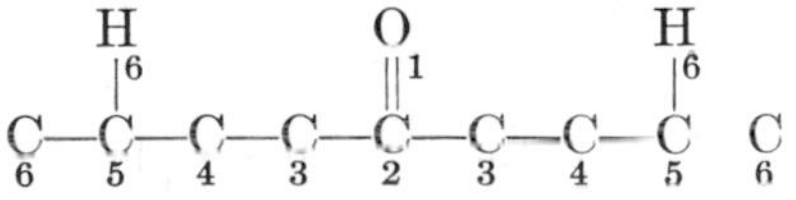

XXIII

[99] See R. Huisgen et al., *Ann., 586*, 52 (1954), for a review of work in this field.

[100] The data up to 1929 are reviewed by J. B. Conant and A. H. Blatt, *J. Am. Chem. Soc., 51*, 1227 (1929).   For later work see F. C. Whitmore and L. P. Bloch, *J. Am. Chem. Soc., 64*, 1619 (1942), and Chapter 8.

[101] (a) See L. Ruzicka and J. B. Buijs, *Helv. Chim. Acta, 15*, 8 (1932), and references therein.   (b) F. H. Westheimer, *J. Am. Chem. Soc., 56*, 1962 (1934).

[102] See J. B. Conant and P. D. Bartlett, *J. Am. Chem. Soc., 54*, 2881 (1932).

mine, for a given six-number, whether it is sterically more effective to concentrate the six-number in one chain or to distribute it between the two chains.

Perhaps the most branched acyclic ketones that have been prepared and studied with regard to oxime formation were those made by alkylation of ketones using sodium amide and alkyl halides.[103] For example, XXIV,[103] XXV,[103] XXVI,[103] and XXVII [104] were reported not to form oximes. In view of a personal communication that the oxime of XXVII could be prepared,[105] the difficulty of arrangement of ketones in any order on the basis of the qualitative results in the literature is apparent.

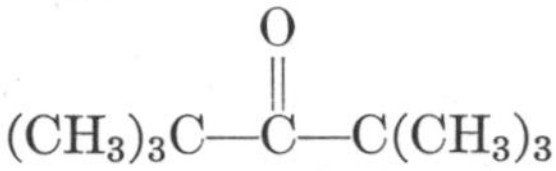

$$(CH_3)_3C-\overset{\overset{\displaystyle O}{\|}}{C}-C(CH_3)_3$$
XXIV

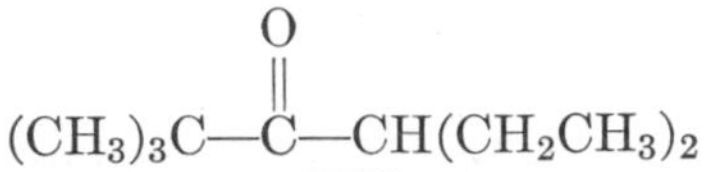

$$(CH_3)_3C-\overset{\overset{\displaystyle O}{\|}}{C}-CH(CH_2CH_3)_2$$
XXV

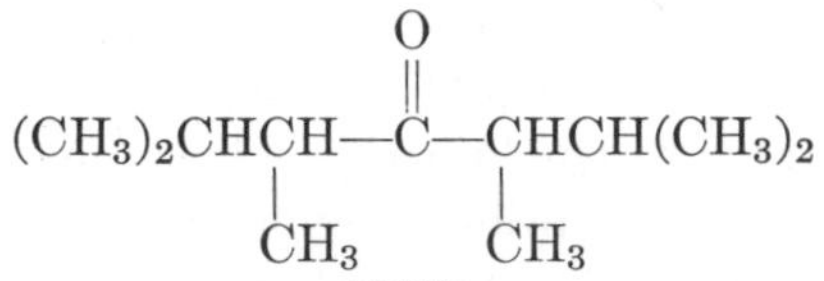

$$(CH_3)_2CHCH-\overset{\overset{\displaystyle O}{\|}}{C}-CHCH(CH_3)_2$$
$$\underset{CH_3}{|} \qquad \underset{CH_3}{|}$$
XXVI

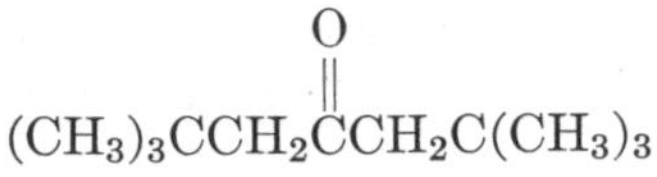

$$(CH_3)_3CCH_2\overset{\overset{\displaystyle O}{\|}}{C}CH_2C(CH_3)_3$$
XXVII

The reactions of a series of highly branched aliphatic ketones and β-diketones were studied by the late F. C. Whitmore and his students (for problems in synthesis of these ketones see Chapter 8). Dineopentylacetone, XXVIII (R = CH_3, six-number 6), could be reduced,

$$[(CH_3)_3CCH_2]_2CHCOR$$
XXVIII

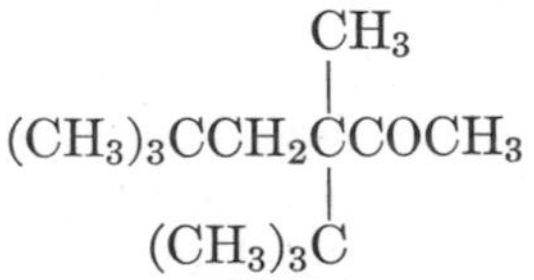

$$(CH_3)_3CCH_2\overset{\overset{\displaystyle CH_3}{|}}{\underset{\underset{\displaystyle (CH_3)_3C}{|}}{C}}COCH_3$$
XXIX

$$[(CH_3)_3CCH_2CO]_2CH_2$$
XXX

albeit with great difficulty, by refluxing 8 days with aluminum isopropylate or by hydrogenation at 200–232° for 6 hours over a copper-zinc-chromite catalyst under 1500 p.s.i.[106] However, methyl-*t*-butyl-

[103] A. Haller and E. Bauer, *Ann. chim. et phys.*, [8], *29*, 318 (1913). See article for behavior of many other ketones.

[104] R. J. McCubbin, *J. Am. Chem. Soc.*, *53*, 356 (1931).

[105] Dr. H. D. Zook, Pennsylvania State College, reported in a letter that the oxime could be made but not the semicarbazone or 2,4-dinitrophenylhydrazone.

[106] F. C. Whitmore and C. T. Lester, *J. Am. Chem. Soc.*, *64*, 1247 (1942).

neopentylacetone, XXIX (six-number 12), could not be reduced by the same reagents under more severe conditions.[107] These ketones reacted with halogens but yielded neither bromoform nor iodoform. Interestingly, dineopentylacetophenone, XXVIII (R = phenyl), would not react with bromine, a fact which supports the concept that there can be steric inhibition of enolization. The same ketone adds methylmagnesium bromide [107] and shows no enolization with this reagent.[108]

The β-diketone, XXX, was not cleaved by refluxing for 24 hours with 60% alkali. However, it did yield a copper chelate derivative.

Cyclic ketones

The assessment of steric effects in substituted cyclic ketones is about the same as that described for acyclic ketones. Branching by methyl groups on the α-carbons affords hindered ketones, but few quantitative data are at hand. For example, 2,2,6-trimethylcyclohexanone forms a semicarbazone and 2,2,6,6-tetramethylcyclohexanone does not,[109] whereas both form oximes.

Aside from the effect of number and size of groups in the ring, the effect of the size of the ring is of considerable interest. The difference in reactivity of cyclic ketones is striking and unexplained in terms of classical structural features. For discussion these ketones will be classified according to the recommendation of H. C. Brown and V. Prelog: [110] small rings, three- and four-membered; common rings, five-, six-, and seven-membered; medium rings, eight- through twelve-membered; and large rings, thirteen-membered and up. A collection of data on these ketones is assembled in Table X.

SMALL RING KETONES (3, 4). No report on the reactivity of a cyclopropanone exists in the literature.[111] The scarcity of data on cyclobutanone makes the assignment of reactivity as compared to cyclopentanone and cyclohexanone difficult. The rate of reaction of cyclobuta-

[107] F. C. Whitmore and D. I. Randall, *J. Am. Chem. Soc.*, *64*, 1242 (1942).

[108] These conclusions were reached by analysis in the Grignard "machine." The corresponding *t*-alcohol was not isolated, and hence the Grignard reagent might have been consumed by addition to the phenyl ring (see Chapter 8).

[109] H. Sobotka and J. D. Chanley, *J. Am. Chem. Soc.*, *71*, 4136 (1949).

[110] H. C. Brown, R. S. Fletcher, and R. B. Johannesen, *J. Am. Chem. Soc.*, *73*, 212 (1951); see footnote 21.

[111] There is some question whether a true cyclopropanone has ever been prepared. The following references may be consulted: C. K. Ingold, *J. Chem. Soc.*, *1921*, 325; Ingold et al., *ibid.*, *1922*, 1177; H. Staudinger and T. Reber, *Helv. Chim. Acta*, *4*, 3 (1921); P. Lipp, J. Buchkremmer and H. Seeles, *Ann.*, *449*, 1 (1932); F. B. LaForge and F. Acree, *J. Org. Chem.*, *6*, 208 (1941); O. R. Quayle and J. F. Cogdell, Jr., *Abstracts* of 118th meeting of the Am. Chem. Soc., Chicago, 1950, p. 6N; Ph.D. thesis of J. F. Cogdell, Jr., Emory University, Georgia, 1950.

TABLE X

Reactions of Ring Ketones

Atoms in Ring	Cyanhydrin * Dissociation Constant	Rate of Formation of Semicarbazones, H_2O, 25° †	Perbenzoic Acid ‡ Oxidation, 25°	Reduction with $NaBH_4$, 25° †
4	0.84 †	26	7.0	1426
5	2.1	81	13.4	38.4
6	0.1 §	949	106	895
7	11.5 ‖	103	1.7	6.69
8	86	19.6 ¶	2.3	6.61
9	170	7.5		0.93
10	— **	6.2	4.0 †	3.6
11	112	5.7 ††		1.1
12	31			4.2
13	26			2.7
14	6			
15–20	10 ‡‡		5.1 †	8.1 §§

* $K = \dfrac{[HCN][ketone]}{[cyanhydrin]}$. The values reported were determined by V. Prelog and M. Kobelt, *Helv. Chim. Acta*, *32*, 1187 (1949), unless otherwise noted.

† Determined by Brown and Wheeler, reference 108. A value of 4.5 was reported by L. Ruzicka et al., *Helv. Chim. Acta*, *28*, 613 (1945), but Brown and Wheeler's value is chosen because their cyclobutanone was very carefully purified.

‡ Data from reference 112.

§ A value of about 0.3 was reported by both Brown and Wheeler and by Ruzicka.

‖ About an average value for all three groups of investigators.

¶ Value in 10% dioxan 19.1; higher ketones in this solvent.

** Too high to measure.

†† The value for 4-heptanone in water is 32.1.

‡‡ The values vary from 7 to 12; di-*n*-octyl ketone, 7; acetone, 3.

§§ Value for C_{15} ketone; for C_{17} ketone, 6.9; for acetone, 70.7.

none with semicarbazide [112] and with perbenzoic acid [112,113] is less than that of cyclopentanone (see Table X), whereas cyclobutanone is reduced by sodium borohydride more rapidly than any other ketone.[108] The dissociation constant of cyclobutanone cyanohydrin lies between that of cyclopentanone and that of cyclohexanone cyanohydrin.[108]

COMMON RING KETONES (5, 6, 7). Of these ketones, cyclohexanone is considerably more reactive than cyclopentanone and cycloheptanone. The latter two alternate in reactivity (see Table X).

[112] Unpublished data, H. C. Brown and O. H. Wheeler, Purdue University.
[113] S. I. Friess and P. E. Frankenburg, *J. Am. Chem. Soc.*, *74*, 2679 (1952).

The reactivity of these ketones has been explained in terms of I-strain.[114] Since a further comprehensive survey of the chemistry of five- and six-membered ring compounds has been made the reader is referred to this article.[115]

MEDIUM AND LARGE KETONES (eight and up). The reactivity of the medium-sized (eight- to twelve-) ring ketones is quite low. A minimum occurs near cyclodecanone. The large ring ketones are more reactive, and when a ring of about thirteen atoms is reached the reactivity parallels that of di-n-alkyl ketone of comparable size. For a complete discussion the reader is referred to the article by Prelog.[116]

It would not be proper to conclude a discussion of steric effects in addition reactions of ketones without mention of attempts to predict the diastereomer produced when a new asymmetric center is formed in the presence of an old one. The fact that the presence of an asymmetric center in a compound influences the proportions of isomers formed when a new asymmetric center is produced in a reaction has long been known. A rule has been proposed [117] by means of which it has been possible to correlate and predict the results in cases where a ketonic group adjacent to an asymmetric carbon is being converted to a secondary or tertiary alcohol in non-catalytic reactions involving (mainly) organometallic reagents. This rule is illustrated by considering formulas XXXI and XXXII. The starting ketone is viewed from

R(R')

R'MgBr

XXXI   XXXII   XXXIII

the extension of the bond joining the carbonyl carbon to the asymmetric carbon which contains the groups L (large steric requirements), M (medium), and S (small). The ketone group is rotated until the carbon oxygen double bond is located between the medium and small groups and the R group is eclipsed with the large group. Cram's rule

[114] See H. C. Brown, R. S. Fletcher, and R. B. Johannessen, *J. Am. Chem. Soc.*, *73*, 212 (1951), for a discussion of I strain in relation to the reactivity of cyclic compounds.

[115] H. C. Brown, J. H. Brewster, and H. Shechter, *J. Am. Chem. Soc.*, *76*, 467 (1954).

[116] V. Prelog, *J. Chem. Soc.*, *1950*, 420. See also reference 99.

[117] D. J. Cram and F. A. A. Elhafez, *J. Am. Chem. Soc.*, *74*, 5828 (1952).

states that that diastereomer, XXXII, will predominate which is formed by the approach of the entering group from the least hindered side (i.e., the group will enter over the S group) of the double bond.

The original article should be consulted for a review of the literature concerning asymmetric induction and for examples of applications of the rule. It is noteworthy that the configuration at the new asymmetric center of the predominating diastereomer can be inverted by changing the order of introduction of the groups R and R' into the compound in question (e.g., XXXIII will result from adding RMgBr to XXXI containing R' instead of R).

Aromatic ketones

In the aromatic series one *ortho* substituent may exert moderate to extreme steric hindrance, depending on the reaction.[118] Two *ortho* groups make for serious steric hindrance, as illustrated by the following examples.

I. Acetomesitylene reacts with Grignard reagents entirely by "enolization" (see Chapter 8). In the Reformatsky reaction enolization occurs exclusively also.[119]

II. With alkaline hypohalite, acetomesitylene is converted into trihaloacetyl mesitylene, but the latter is not cleaved by alkali to mesitoic acid.[120] However, tribromoacetyl derivatives, such as tribromoacetyl mesitylene, may be debrominated one atom at a time by treatment with Grignard reagents, as shown below.[121]

$$RCOCBr_3 + R'MgBr \rightarrow [RCOCBr_2]MgBr + R'Br$$

$$\xrightarrow{\;H_2O\;} RCOCHBr_2$$

III. Phenacyl pyridinium salts are readily cleaved by alkali to the corresponding aromatic acid, but this cleavage fails with the mesityl analog.[122]

$$[ArCOCH_2NC_5H_5]^+Cl^- \xrightarrow{\;OH^-\;} ArCOOH$$

[118] For examples of reactions extremely sensitive to one *ortho* group note imino ester formation, reference 90, and the Stobbe condensation, M. S. Newman and J. Linsk, *J. Am. Chem. Soc.*, *71*, 936 (1949).

[119] M. S. Newman, *J. Am. Chem. Soc.*, *64*, 2131 (1942).

[120] R. C. Fuson and J. T. Walker, *J. Am. Chem. Soc.*, *52*, 3269 (1930). However, J. Houben and W. Fischer, *Ber.*, *63*, 2455 (1930), report a quantitative yield of mesitoic acid on boiling the trichloro ketone with 40% sodium hydroxide for 2 hours. R. T. Arnold and P. N. Craig, *J. Am. Chem. Soc.*, *70*, 2791 (1948), report alcoholic potassium hydroxide to be a superior reagent for this cleavage.

[121] C. H. Fischer, H. R. Snyder, and R. C. Fuson, *J. Am. Chem. Soc.*, *54*, 3665 (1932).

[122] S. H. Babcock, Jr., F. I. Nakamura, and R. C. Fuson, *J. Am. Chem. Soc.*, *54*, 4407 (1932).

IV. Acetomesitylene forms no oxime under the usual conditions. However, on heating at 160° for 6 hours with alcohol and hydroxylamine hydrochloride, acetomesidide is formed in unstated yield.[123] Propiomesitylene was recovered unchanged after 30 hours at 180° under comparable treatment.

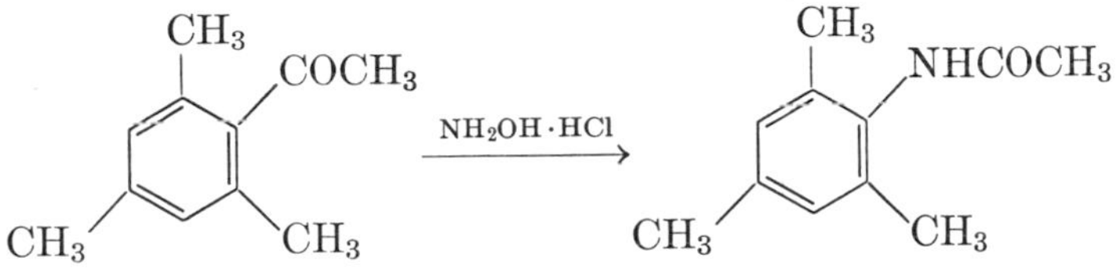

The normal property of ketonic functions of deactivating aromatic rings towards Friedel-Crafts condensations may be greatly reduced by steric factors. Acetomesitylene and analogous diorthosubstituted ketones have been further acylated.[124] Presumably this effect is due to steric inhibition of resonance.

An interesting example of steric hindrance to oxidation is the fact that 4,4'-dihydroxy-2,3,5,6,2',3',5',6'-octamethylbiphenyl, XXXIV, cannot be oxidized to the expected quinone XXXV. Presumably the latter is not formed because of the interference provided by the methyl groups.[125]

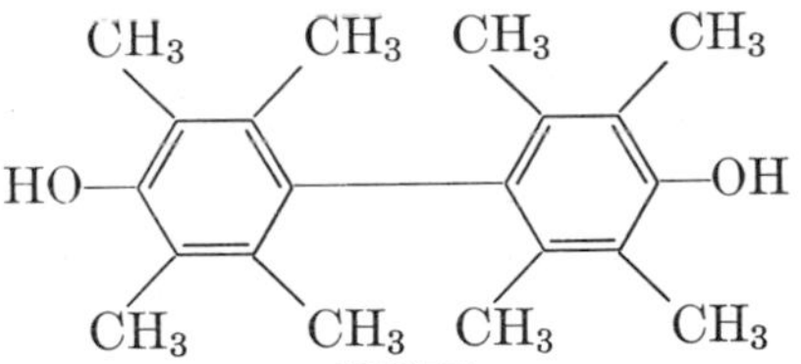

ALDEHYDES

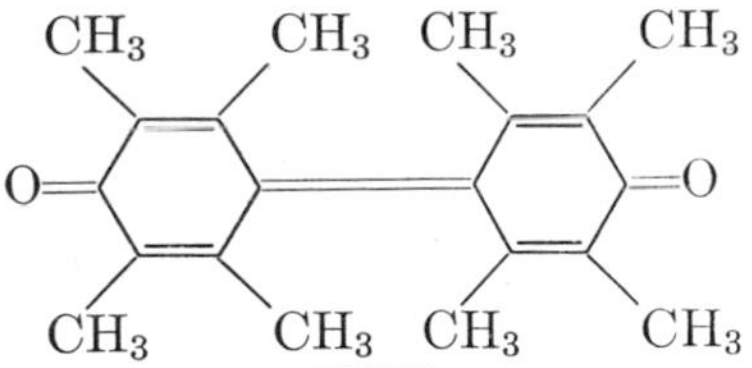

Since aldehydes in general are more reactive than ketones one would expect that steric factors would be of less effect in addition reactions. There are few pertinent data for the aliphatic and cycloaliphatic series. However, in the aromatic series, this generalization is borne out. 2,4,6-Trimethylbenzaldehyde forms no addition product with

[123] E. Feith and S. H. Davies, *Ber.*, *24*, 3546 (1891). However, D. E. Pearson and F. Greer, *J. Am. Chem. Soc.*, *77*, 1294 (1955), have reported the formation of the 2,4-dinitrophenylhydrazone.

[124] See C. A. Thomas, *Anhydrous Aluminum Chloride in Organic Chemistry*, p. 222, Reinhold Publishing Corp., New York, 1941, for a review of such reactions.

[125] Private communication from Dr. B. C. Saunders, Cambridge University, England.

sodium bisulfite whereas 2,3,6- and 2,4,6-trimethylbenzaldehydes and 2,3,4,6- and 2,3,5,6-tetramethylbenzaldehydes do, albeit considerably more slowly (3 days to 3 weeks) than benzaldehyde.[126]

The hindrance to aldehyde addition reactions provided by *ortho*-methyl groups may be overcome by the introduction of suitable polar groups. Thus, although 2,4,6-trimethylbenzaldehyde reacts with sodium acetate and acetic anhydride to give a very small yield of 2,4,6-trimethylcinnamic acid in the Perkin synthesis, 3,5-dinitro-2,4,6-trimethylbenzaldehyde gives a better yield (60%) than benzaldehyde (49%) under comparable conditions.[127]

OLEFINS

Most ionic homogeneous addition reactions of olefins yield products arising from a *trans* course of addition.[128] However, a study of the addition of hydrogen bromide to the isomeric olefins 1,2-dimethylcyclohexene, 2,3-dimethylcyclohexene, and 2-methylmethylenecyclohexane has clarified several aspects of the ionic addition of hydrogen bromide to olefins.[129] Stereochemically, the addition to 1,2-dimethylcyclohexene is predominantly *trans*. However, from the fact that the three olefins yield different proportions of *cis* and *trans* 1,2-dimethyl-1-bromocyclohexane, the classical planar carbonium ion can be ruled out as the only intermediate. If the classical carbonium ion were the only intermediate, all three olefins should yield the same products, since the same carbonium ion should be formed from each. Furthermore, from the fact that the rates of solvolysis of both *cis* and *trans* 1,2-dimethyl-1-bromocyclohexane are almost identical, the stereospecific addition of hydrogen bromide to 1,2-dimethylcyclohexene cannot be the microscopic reverse of the solvolytic elimination of hydrogen bromide, which is best explained by means of a classical carbonium ion.[130]

Free-radical addition to olefins also proceeds stereospecifically and *trans*. Both 1-methylcyclohexene and 1-bromocyclohexene have been shown to add hydrogen bromide (counter Markownikoff) to yield the corresponding products having the added hydrogen and bromine

---

[126] L. I. Smith and J. Nichols, *J. Org. Chem.*, *6*, 489 (1941).

[127] G. Lock and E. Bayer, *Ber.*, *72*, 1064 (1939).

[128] See C. K. Ingold, *Structure and Mechanism in Organic Chemistry*, p. 660, Cornell University Press, Ithaca, N. Y., 1953. Significant exceptions to *trans* addition include oxidation with alkaline permanganate and the addition of hydrogen peroxide catalyzed by osmium tetroxide.

[129] G. S. Hammond and T. D. Nevitt, *J. Am. Chem. Soc.*, *76*, 4121 (1954).

[130] T. D. Nevitt and G. S. Hammond, *J. Am. Chem. Soc.*, *76*, 4124 (1954).

atoms in *trans* orientation.[131]   More examples are needed to establish the generality of this reaction path.

In the absence of quantitative rate data on addition reactions of a large series of olefins, estimation of serious steric effects can be made by application of the rule of six.[8]   By inspection of the generalized formula for an olefin, XXXVI, one can see that the six-number may be increased in any of the four chains attached to the double bond.

$$
\begin{array}{c}
\underset{6}{C}-\underset{5}{C}-\underset{4}{C}-\underset{3}{C} \qquad\qquad \underset{3}{C}-\underset{4}{C}-\underset{5}{C}-\underset{6}{C} \\
\underset{2}{C}=\underset{1}{C} \\
\underset{6}{C}-\underset{5}{C}-\underset{4}{C}-\underset{3}{C} \qquad\qquad \underset{3}{C}-\underset{4}{C}-\underset{5}{C}-\underset{6}{C}
\end{array}
$$

XXXVI

Counting to determine the six-number starts at the carbon of the double bond farthest removed from the chain being considered.   It was seen earlier that in ketones (general formula XXIII, p. 235) the six-number could be distributed between two chains.   In olefins the six-number can be distributed between four chains.   It would be of interest to know, for a given six-number, whether it is more effective to concentrate in one chain or to distribute over two or more chains.

Perhaps the most inclusive study of an addition reaction of a series of olefins is that involving bromination in acetic acid at 25° by Robertson and coworkers.[132]   By suitably weighting inductive and hyperconjugative factors they explained the results without the inclusion of steric factors.   From the fact that *t*-butylethylene is brominated only slightly more slowly than *n*-butylethylene (relative rates 0.70 to 1.05), they argued that steric factors were not involved for the following reason.   The reactive intermediate in bromination is $[(CH_3)_3\overset{+}{C}CH\text{-}CH_2Br]$.   Since the carbonium carbon is of the neopentyl structure, attack should be very slow if steric factors were important.   Since the rate is not slow, steric factors are therefore not important.   One flaw in this reasoning is that the carbonium ion pictured as an intermediate probably goes to a conventional bromonium ion which may be attacked at the terminal carbon.   The fact that mesitylethylene readily adds bromine in the cold [133] may be explained similarly by initial at-

[131] H. L. Goering, P. I. Abell, and B. F. Aycock, *J. Am. Chem. Soc.*, *74*, 3588 (1952).   H. L. Goering, D. I. Relyea, and D. W. Larsen, *ibid.*, *78*, 348 (1956), have shown *cis* addition to *l*-chlorocyclohexene.

[132] For a discussion of the polar effects involved in different bromination mechanisms see P. B. D. de la Mare and P. W. Robertson, *J. Chem. Soc.*, *1950*, 2838.

[133] C. O. Guss, *J. Am. Chem. Soc.*, *75*, 3177 (1953).

tack of positive bromine on the carbon atom farthest removed from the ring, followed by change to a cyclic bromonium ion which in turn may be attacked without serious steric hindrance at either carbon to yield the dibromide. Furthermore, the slow rate (0.10 on same scale as above) for neopentylethylene (six-number 9) is difficult to explain on grounds other than steric. In this connection it is interesting to recall that *t*-butylacetic acid (six-number 9) (acid 8, Table I) is esterified more slowly than trimethylacetic acid (acid 6, Table I), and here the effect is almost certainly steric.

Disubstituted olefins of types $RCH=CHR'$ and $RR'C=CH_2$ are brominated 30 to 40 times more rapidly than 1-hexene, but no highly branched olefins of these types were studied. 1,1-Dineopentylethylene, XXXVII, does not add bromine but reacts with evolution of hydrogen bromide.[134]

The influence of steric factors on the oxidation of olefins is of some interest. 1,1-Dineopentylethylene is extraordinarily resistant to oxidation with strong alkaline permanganate as it is recovered largely unchanged when commercial triisobutylene is heated for 7 hours with this reagent whereas the other isomers present are oxidized.[134] Similarly, on oxidation of commercial triisobutylene with chromic acid, 1,1-dineopentylethylene is recovered unchanged and may thus be easily obtained.[135] This olefin is also very resistant to catalytic hydrogenation; a high pressure of hydrogen (130 atmospheres) and a temperature of 150° for reduction over Raney nickel is required. On the other hand, epoxidation with perbenzoic acid to yield the epoxide, XXXVIII, proceeds normally. On more vigorous oxidation with chromic and sulfuric acids dineopentylethylene is converted mainly into dineopentylacetic acid, XL. Such oxidation of an olefin to an acid of the same carbon content is not new.[136] A mechanism was pro-

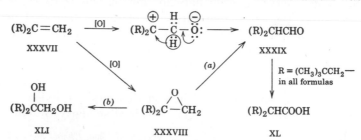

[134] P. D. Bartlett, G. L. Fraser, and R. B. Woodward, *J. Am. Chem. Soc.*, *63*, 495 (1941).

[135] F. C. Whitmore and J. D. Surmatis, *J. Am. Chem. Soc.*, *63*, 2200 (1941).

[136] See F. C. Whitmore and C. D. Wilson, *J. Am. Chem. Soc.*, *56*, 1397 (1934), and references therein.

posed by which attack of oxygen on the terminal carbon made the adjacent carbon electronically deficient. A hydride shift from the end carbon then resulted in the formation of dineopentylacetaldehyde, XXXIX, which was further oxidized to the acid, XL.

This mechanism for olefin oxidation is similar to that [137] which postulates formation of the epoxide, XXXVIII, directly from the olefin, followed by (a) acid-catalyzed rearrangement to the aldehyde, XXXIX, or (b) hydration to the glycol, XLI. The oxidation that proceeds by path b yields products of lower carbon content by further oxidative cleavage of XLI. In most cases an olefin is oxidized by path b, but, in addition to dineopentylethylene, other hindered olefins with terminal methylene groups are oxidized to yield acids (path a).[138] In the case of the epoxide, XXXVIII, treatment with 10% sulfuric acid under conditions which lead to hydration of most epoxides to glycols led exclusively to the aldehyde, XXXIX.[134] If an epoxide is truly an intermediate stage in chromic acid oxidations, then the ratio of further oxidation by paths a or b depends upon the ratio of rearrangement of the epoxide to hydration. Judging from the few results at hand, a highly substituted terminal epoxide is more easily rearranged to aldehyde than hydrated.

Transannular reactions have been noticed on treatment of medium ring olefins with performic acid. In these reactions inspection of models shows that a hydrogen atom across the ring from the electron-deficient reaction center comes very close to the carbon bearing the oxygen. One possible mechanism [139] for such reactions is shown.

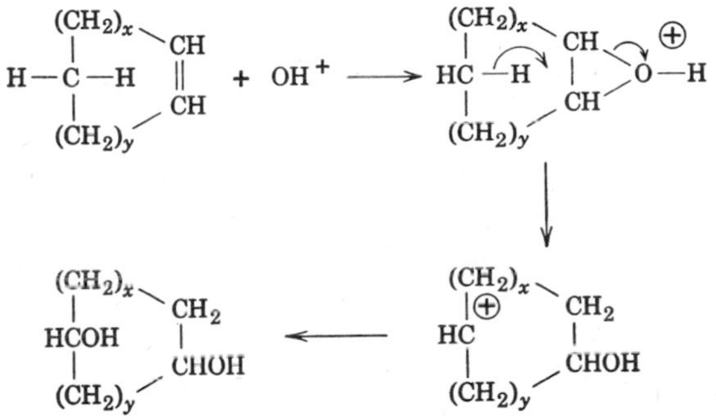

[137] A. Byers and W. J. Hickinbottom, J. Chem. Soc., 1948, 1334.

[138] For other examples see E. H. Farmer and R. C. Pitkethly, J. Chem. Soc., 1938, 287.

[139] A. C. Cope, S. W. Fenton, and C. F. Spencer, J. Am. Chem. Soc., 74, 5884 (1952).

For example, cyclooctene yields more 1,4-cyclooctanediol than the normally expected 1,2-diol;[139] cyclononene yields 1,5-cyclononanediol;[140] and cyclodecene yields 1,6-cyclodecanediol.[141] Cyclooctene oxide also yields 1,4-cyclooctanediol on treatment with formic acid.

In connection with cyclic olefins, it is interesting that cyclooctene is the smallest ring olefin of which the *cis* and *trans* isomers have been isolated.[142] Relative rates of reaction of cyclic olefins with performic acid have been determined for *cis* and *trans* cyclononene [140] and *cis* and *trans* cyclodecene.[141] The values are: C_9, *cis*, 2.60; *trans*, 21.0; C_{10}, *cis*, 1.20; *trans*, 9.50. In acyclic olefins the *trans* isomers are more stable than the *cis;* in the small and medium ring olefins the *cis* form is more stable. It should prove interesting to see at what ring size the *trans* form again becomes the more stable.

The isomerization of a *trans* olefin to the corresponding *cis* olefin has been accomplished by many methods, all of which produce mixtures of the two. The stereospecific conversion of *trans* to *cis* olefin has been accomplished [143] by the following process: (*a*) bromination, (*b*) dehydrobromination, and (*c*) reduction by sodium in liquid ammonia. The stereochemical nature of these conversions is illustrated.

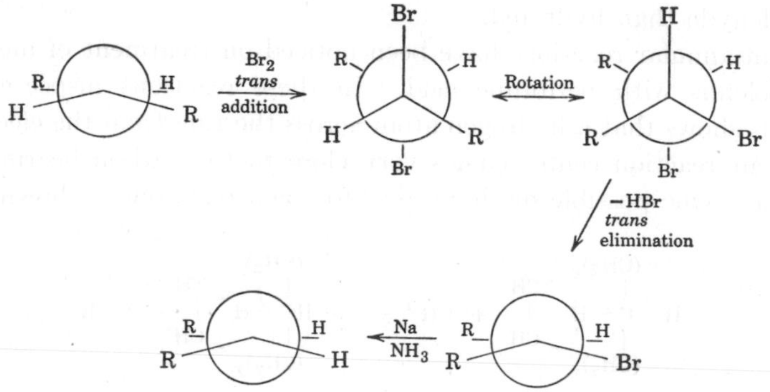

Since pure *trans* olefins may be obtained by the reduction of acetylenes using sodium in liquid ammonia,[144] pure *cis* olefins are most readily prepared from the *trans* compounds by the above isomerization process rather than by catalytic hydrogenation of acetylenes. The latter procedure yields somewhat impure *cis* olefins.[143]

[140] V. Prelog, K. Schenker, and W. Kung, *Helv. Chim. Acta, 36,* 465 (1953).

[141] V. Prelog and K. Schenker, *Helv. Chim. Acta, 35,* 2044 (1952).

[142] A. C. Cope, R. A. Pike, and C. F. Spencer, *J. Am. Chem. Soc., 75,* 3212 (1953).

[143] M. C. Hoff, K. W. Greenlee, and C. E. Boord, *J. Am. Chem. Soc., 73,* 3329 (1951).

[144] K. N. Campbell and L. T. Eby, *J. Am. Chem. Soc., 63,* 216, 2683 (1941).

Although only homogeneous reactions have been considered in this chapter, the classic work of Linstead et al., on hydrogenation of diphenic acid, phenanthrene, etc., should be mentioned,[145] as the steric factors involved are discussed in the light of the experimental results. The essential feature of their findings is that hydrogen is added to that side of a ring undergoing hydrogenation which is absorbed on the catalyst. Intelligent application of the principles outlined in these papers should aid in working out the stereochemistry of reduction products in many syntheses of compounds containing multiple ring fusions.

ACETYLENES

As in the case of the nitrile function (see p. 233) the transition state in reactions involving addition to the acetylene function probably is planar and has three atoms attached to that carbon undergoing attack. The change from a linear function (similar to XVI) to a planar function (similar to XVII) occurs when reagents add to the acetylenic function. Accordingly one would expect that addition to the acetylenic function would be less affected by steric factors than comparable addition to the olefinic function. Unfortunately few data are available to discuss.

Since the electrons in the π bonds of an acetylenic function are held much more firmly than those in an ethylenic function the former is less easily polarized in approach to the activated state. Hence one would expect that addition of polar reagents to a triple bond would occur less rapidly than to an ethylenic bond. The relative rates (second-order constants) of bromine addition at 25° in acetic acid to the following pairs have been determined: [146] styrene to phenylacetylene, ca. 3000; *trans* stilbene to diphenylacetylene, 250; ethyl fumarate to ethyl acetylenedicarboxylate, 60; and 10-undecenoic acid to 10-undecynoic acid, 9000. However, rates for highly branched acetylenes and olefins are not available.

Perhaps the most hindered acetylene that has been prepared is di-*t*-butyl acetylene.[147] This compound is not hydrated under conditions suitable for the conversion of other disubstituted acetylenes into ketones. It adds bromine with difficulty and is oxidized to di-*t*-butyl

[145] R. P. Linstead, W. Doering, S. B. Davis, P. Levine, and R. Whetstone, *J. Am. Chem. Soc.*, *64*, 1985–2026 (1942). R. P. Linstead and R. R. Whetstone, *J. Chem. Soc.*, *1950*, 1428, and several papers between these two.

[146] P. W. Robertson, W. E. Dasent, R. M. Milburn, and W. II. Oliver, *J. Chem. Soc.*, *1950*, 1628.

[147] G. F. Hennion and T. F. Banigan, Jr., *J. Am. Chem. Soc.*, *68*, 1202 (1946)

diketone in high yield by potassium permanganate under conditions which ordinarily lead to cleavage [148] into acids. Reduction of the acetylene by means of sodium in liquid ammonia was not accomplished. On catalytic hydrogenation over Raney nickel at 40 p.s.i., di-*t*-butylacetylene is slowly reduced to an olefin, presumably *cis*-di-*t*-butylethylene. On further reduction 1,2-di-*t*-butylethane is obtained. The di-*t*-butylethylene obtained by catalytic reduction of di-*t*-butylacetylene [147] is different from that formed by vapor phase dehydration of 1,2-di-*t*-butylethanol. The latter olefin was proved to be a di-*t*-butylethylene by the fact that only trimethylacetaldehyde is obtained on ozonization [149] and di-*t*-butylethane on reduction. Since the olefin of Howard et al. is undoubtedly the *trans* isomer, that obtained by reduction of the acetylene must be the *cis* isomer. This finding is of importance in view of the conclusions of H. C. Brown and coworkers about the magnitude of strain to be expected for a compound which is really an analog of *o*-di-*t*-butylbenzene.[150] As pointed out in this article no homomorph of *o*-di-*t*-butylbenzene has ever been prepared.

$$(CH_3)_3CC \equiv CC(CH_3)_3 \xrightarrow{H_2} (CH_3)_3CCH = CHC(CH_3)_3$$
$$\text{\emph{cis}}$$

$$\searrow H_2$$

$$(CH_3)_3CCH_2CH_2C(CH_3)_3$$

$$\nearrow H_2$$

$$(CH_3)_3CCH_2CHOHC(CH_3)_3 \xrightarrow{-H_2O} (CH_3)_3CCH = CHC(CH_3)_3$$
$$\text{\emph{trans}}$$

Mesitylacetylene adds bromine to form the expected dibromide, but the latter does not add bromine under conditions more drastic than those suitable for the conversion of phenylacetylene to tetrabromophenylethane.[151] Furthermore, mesitylacetylene adds only one molecule of methanol under conditions that obtain when phenylacetylene is converted into the dimethyl ketal of acetophenone.[151]

Dimesitylacetylene has been synthesized,[152] but no studies of its reactivity were reported.

[148] Compare N. A. Khan and M. S. Newman, *J. Org. Chem.*, *17*, 1063 (1952).

[149] F. L. Howard, T. W. Mears, A. Fookson, and P. Pomerantz, *J. Am. Chem. Soc.*, *68*, 2121 (1946). See also the Ph.D. thesis of G. W. Moersch, Pennsylvania State College, 1942.

[150] H. C. Brown et al., *J. Am. Chem. Soc.*, *75*, 1 (1953).

[151] M. S. Newman and H. E. Connor, *J. Am. Chem. Soc.*, *72*, 4002 (1950).

[152] R. C. Fuson, P. L. Southwick, and S. P. Rowland, *J. Am. Chem. Soc.*, *66*, 1109 (1944).

Chapter 5

by Donald J. Cram

Intramolecular Rearrangements

THE 1,2 REARRANGEMENTS

    The Nucleophilic 1,2 Rearrangement
    The Electrophilic 1,2 Rearrangement
    The Homolytic 1,2 Rearrangement

TRANSANNULAR REARRANGEMENTS

ACYL AND RELATED REARRANGEMENTS

REARRANGEMENTS INTO AROMATIC RINGS (CLAISEN)

Chapter 5

Most rearrangements are either *internal* substitution (and) or elimination reactions, and, as a result, some of the terminology applied to the latter reactions [1] can be profitably applied to rearrangements. An identification and analysis of steric effects in molecular rearrangements is dependent on an understanding of reaction mechanism, and consequently much space will be occupied with that subject. Much of the material selected for discussion has been drawn from the recent literature since the general subject of rearrangements has been reviewed in the past in other books.[2]

Steric effects will be treated as including the following phenomena: (1) the stereochemistry of the reaction at all sites where bonds are made and broken; (2) non-bonded interactions in both the starting and transition states of the reaction; (3) strain involving the deformation of bond angles in both starting and transition states of the transformation.

THE 1,2 REARRANGEMENTS

A large proportion of intramolecular rearrangements can be summarized in a formal sense by an equation in which Z (oxygen, nitrogen, sulfur, halogen, carbon, or hydrogen) migrates from A to B.[3]

[1] E. Eliel, Chapter 2 of this book.

[2] (a) E. S. Wallis in H. Gilman, *Organic Chemistry*, 1st ed., Vol. 1, Chapter 8, John Wiley & Sons, New York, 1938; (b) G. W. Wheland, *Advanced Organic Chemistry*, Chapter 12, John Wiley & Sons, New York, 1949; (c) M. J. S. Dewar, *Electronic Theory of Organic Chemistry*, Chapter 10, Oxford University Press, 1949; (d) E. R. Alexander, *Principles of Ionic Organic Reactions*, Chapter 5, John Wiley & Sons, New York, 1950; (e) P. D. Bartlett in H. Gilman, *Organic Chemistry*, Vol. 3, Chapter 1, John Wiley & Sons, New York, 1953; (f) C. K. Ingold, *Structure and Mechanism in Organic Chemistry*, Chapter 9, Cornell University Press, Ithaca, N. Y., 1953.

[3] This type of correlation was first made by Whitmore, *J. Am. Chem. Soc.*, *54*, 3274 (1932), as applied to those reactions in which A and Z were carbon, and B was carbon or nitrogen.

$$A—B \rightarrow A—B$$

In all but a few of these rearrangements, A is carbon, and B is carbon, oxygen, or nitrogen. Of course, rearrangements involving many of the above possible combinations of atoms in the Z—A—B sequence are as yet unknown. The generalized concept is profitable because of the many similarities found between individual examples of the generalized reaction and because of the ease of recognition of reaction type when new rearrangements are discovered. For purposes of discussion, Z will be referred to as the *migrating group*, A as the *migration origin*, and B as the *migration terminus*.[2f]

Rearrangements of this type naturally fall into three general mechanistic categories, depending on the nature of the bond-making and bond-breaking at Z—B and Z—A, respectively. By far the most common type is the *nucleophilic rearrangement* [2f] in which Z acts as a nucleophile, and the reaction is initiated by B becoming deficient in electrons, usually by the loss of some group (a "leaving group," not included in the generalized formula). A second, less common type is the *electrophilic rearrangement* [2f] in which Z acts as an electrophile,[1] and the reaction is initiated by B becoming rich in electrons. The third class might be termed a *homolytic rearrangement*, in which the reaction is initiated by B becoming a radical, and Z forming a bond at B by donating one electron to the incipient covalent link.

The nucleophilic 1,2 rearrangement

STEREOCHEMISTRY. The stereochemistry of these rearrangements has been determined in one reaction or another at all three sites of the bond-making and -breaking processes. The stereochemistry at Z has been studied only for those reactions in which Z is an alkyl group, and, to the extent that information is available, the reactions are intramolecular and configuration is retained.[4] The system in which the

---

[4] Wallis and coworkers first demonstrated this retention of configuration with the appropriate derivatives of α-benzylpropionic acid in the Curtius [L. W. Jones and E. S. Wallis, *J. Am. Chem. Soc.*, *48*, 169 (1926)], Hofmann [E. S. Wallis and S. C. Nagel, *ibid.*, *53*, 2787 (1931)], and Lossen [E. S. Wallis and R. D. Dripps, *ibid.*, *55*, 1701 (1933)] rearrangements to give ultimately α-benzylethylamine. Employing the same system, J. V. Braun and E. Friehmelt [*Ber.*, *66*, 684 (1933)] observed the same stereochemical results in the Schmidt reaction. J. Kenyon and D. P. Young [*J. Chem. Soc.*, *1941*, 263] demonstrated a like stereochemical result for the Beckmann rearrangement, and J. F. Lane and E. S. Wallis [*J. Am. Chem. Soc.*, *63*, 1674 (1941)] for the Wolff rearrangement. Evidence for retention of configuration for Z in the Baeyer-Villiger rearrangement was first obtained by R. B. Turner [*ibid.*, *72*, 878 (1952)]. Many other examples are also available.

most data have been obtained is that in which Z is the α-phenylethyl group, and, in the reactions formulated, Z always migrated with complete retention of configuration.[5]

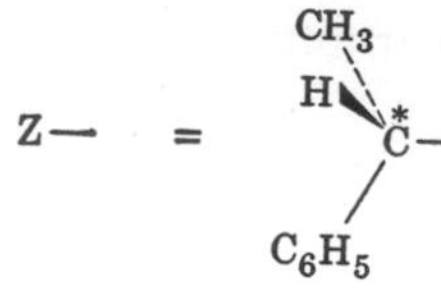

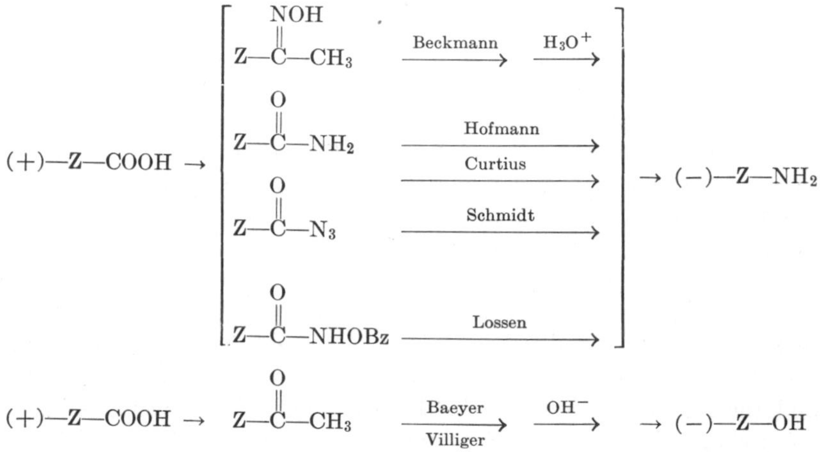

$$Z— \quad = \quad \begin{array}{c} CH_3 \\ H \diagdown \overset{*}{C}— \\ \diagup \\ C_6H_5 \end{array}$$

Further evidence for the intramolecular character of the 1,2-nucleophilic rearrangements is found in the results of rearrangements involving asymmetric molecules. For example, optically active substituted biphenyl (I) when submitted to the Wolff rearrangement gave optically active acid, a result inconsistent with the loss of the blocking ability of the —COCHN₂ group.[6] A still different approach to the

I

[5] For the first five cases formulated, see C. L. Arcus and J. Kenyon, *J. Chem. Soc.*, *1939*, 916, and A. Campbell and J. Kenyon, *ibid.*, *1946*, 25. For the last case, see K. Mislow and J. Brenner, *J. Am. Chem. Soc.*, *75*, 2318 (1953).

[6] J. F. Lane and E. S. Wallis, *J. Org. Chem.*, *6*, 443 (1941). See also E. S. Wallis and W. W. Mayer, *J. Am. Chem. Soc.*, *35*, 2598 (1933), and F. Bell, *J. Chem. Soc.*, *1934*, 835.

stereochemical problem of the migrating group is found in the facile Hofmann rearrangement of II.[7] Inversion at the bridgehead carbon is impossible, and the ease of the reaction coupled with the reluctance of this bridgehead carbon to become deficient in electrons [7] points strongly to the migration of R with its pair of electrons.

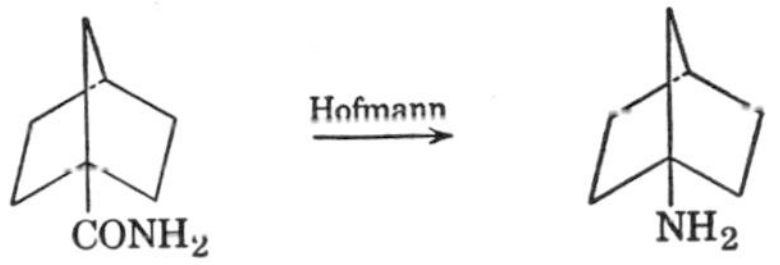

$$\text{(bicyclic structure)} \xrightarrow{\text{Hofmann}} \text{(bicyclic structure)}$$

CONH$_2$ $\qquad\qquad$ NH$_2$

II

The next simplest problem is that of the stereochemistry at atom B, the *migration terminus*. This question can be clearly answered in those cases where B and Z are carbon (pinacol types and Wagner-Meerwein rearrangements), and only partially in one case where B is nitrogen and Z is carbon. The Beckmann rearrangement has been demonstrated [8] to occur only by the migration of Z (formulas) from the side *trans* (anti) to the leaving group, the strong implication being that X is displaced from the back side of N by Z carrying an electron

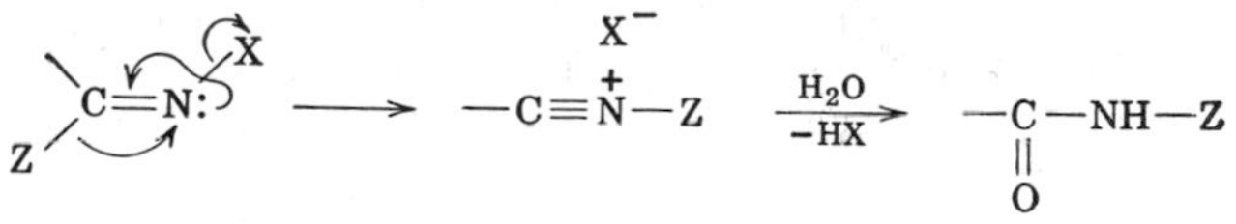

$$\underset{Z}{\overset{X}{>}}C{=}\overset{..}{N}{:} \longrightarrow -C{\equiv}\overset{+}{N}-Z \xrightarrow[-HX]{H_2O} -\underset{\overset{\|}{O}}{C}-NH-Z$$

pair. The cyclic chain of reactions completed by Bernstein and Whitmore [9] demonstrates that inversion occurred at C_α in the semipinacolic

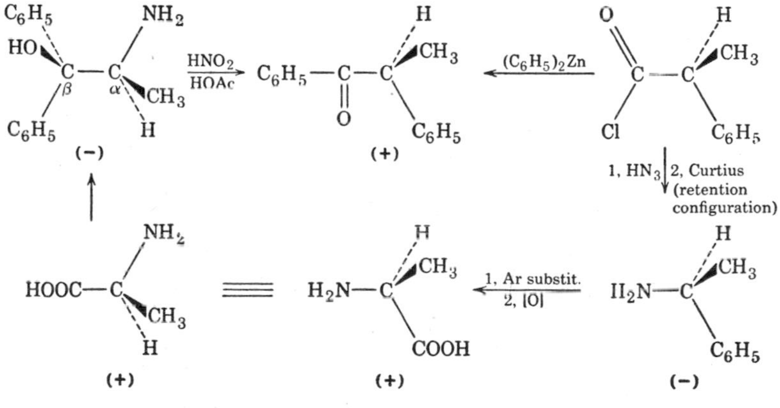

$$
\begin{array}{cccc}
\text{C}_6\text{H}_5 & \text{NH}_2 & & \text{H} \\
\text{HO} \backslash \; / & & & / \text{CH}_3 \\
\quad \text{C}-\text{C} & \xrightarrow[\text{HOAc}]{\text{HNO}_2} & \text{C}_6\text{H}_5-\text{C}-\text{C} & \xleftarrow{(\text{C}_6\text{H}_5)_2\text{Zn}} \\
/\beta \quad \backslash \alpha \backslash \text{CH}_3 & & \| \quad \backslash & \\
\text{C}_6\text{H}_5 \quad \text{H} & & \text{O} \quad \text{C}_6\text{H}_5 & \\
(-) & & (+) & \\
\end{array}
$$

O
||
C — C / CH$_3$
/ \ C$_6$H$_5$
Cl H

1, HN$_3$ | 2, Curtius
(retention configuration)

HOOC—C(NH$_2$)(CH$_3$)(H) (+) ≡ H$_2$N—C(CH$_3$)(H)(COOH) (+) $\xleftarrow[2, [O]]{1,\text{ Ar substit.}}$ H$_2$N—C(CH$_3$)(H)(C$_6$H$_5$) (−)

[7] P. D. Bartlett and L. H. Knox, *J. Am. Chem. Soc.*, **61**, 3184 (1939).

[8] J. Meisenheimer, *Ber.*, **54**, 3206 (1921); O. L. Brady and G. Bishop, *J. Chem. Soc.*, *1925*, 127, 1357.

[9] H. I. Bernstein and F. C. Whitmore, *J. Am. Chem. Soc.*, **61**, 1324 (1939).

deamination reaction. Bartlett and Brown [10] found that, although both *cis*- and *trans*-7,8-diphenyl-7,8-dihydroxyacenaphthene on treatment with aqueous sulfuric acid underwent the pinacol rearrangement to give 8,8-diphenyl-7-ketoacenaphthene (III), the reaction occurred more readily with the *cis*-diol (IV). Furthermore, the *trans*-diol was found to isomerize to IV under the conditions of the experiment.[11]

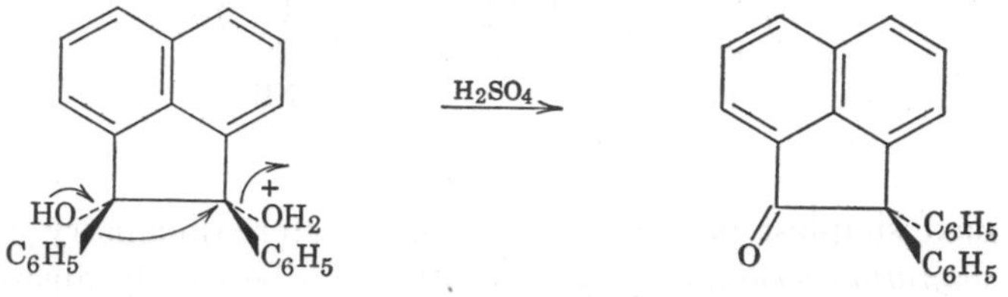

Thus, in both the Beckmann and pinacol rearrangements, that reaction occurs the more readily in which the migrating group approaches the migration terminus from the backside, this site undergoing inversion in the process; this inversion is detectable in the pinacol, but not in the Beckmann, rearrangement.

Of the 1,2 rearrangements, only the Wagner-Meerwein (in the generalized formula, A, B, and Z are carbon) allows the stereochemistry of the atom at the *migration origin* to be examined.

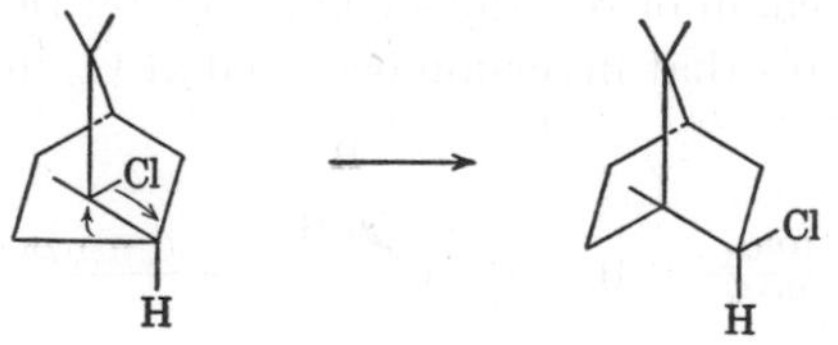

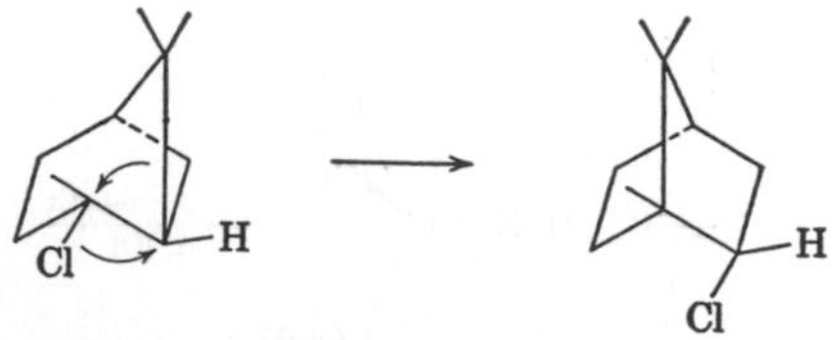

[10] P. D. Bartlett and R. F. Brown, *J. Am. Chem. Soc.*, *62*, 2927 (1940).

[11] For more recent work in this system, see R. F. Brown, *J. Am. Chem. Soc.*, *74*, 428 (1952); R. F. Brown, J. B. Nordmann, and M. Madoff, *ibid.*, *74*, 432 (1952); R. F. Brown, *ibid.*, *76*, 1279 (1954).

In the isomerizations of camphene and pinene hydrochlorides [12] (V and VII) to bornyl and isobornyl chlorides (VI and VIII), respectively, the carbon carrying the chlorine in the product is inverted as compared to the starting material.

In summary, to the extent that the *above reactions* are stereospecific, configuration is retained at Z and inverted at A and B. No clear evi-

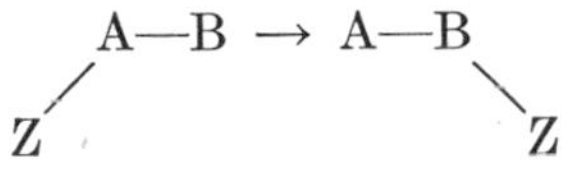

$$A—B \rightarrow A—B$$
$$Z \qquad\qquad Z$$

dence has been obtained that asymmetry has been lost in other than insignificant amounts at Z. However, in appropriate systems, particularly in the Wagner-Meerwein rearrangement,[13] asymmetry can be either completely maintained or lost at A and B. Further discussion of the problem of stereospecificity and steric direction now necessitates a more detailed consideration of the possible mechanisms involved in these reactions.

GENERAL MECHANISM. Of the nucleophilic 1,2 rearrangements, the Wagner-Meerwein offers the best vehicle for discussion and illustration of principles, largely because the migrating group, the migration origin, and terminus are all subject to considerable variation. The migrating group (Z) can be H, R, or Ar; and the migration origin and terminus can be primary, secondary, or tertiary carbon. As a result, systems have been designed for the systematic study of the polar and steric effects on reaction rate and course.

In the following formulation, X is some group capable of leaving

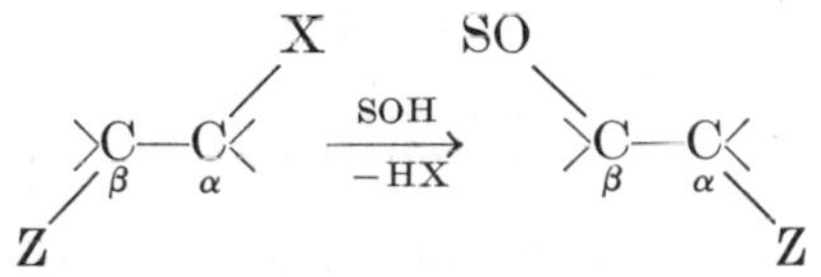

$$>C_\beta—C_\alpha< \xrightarrow[-HX]{SOH} >C_\beta—C_\alpha<$$

the system with its pair of bonding electrons, thereby inducing Z to migrate from C_β to C_α with its bonding electrons. The positive charge thereby induced on C_β is then satisfied by reaction with solvent (SOH) to give the rearranged product (alcohol, ether, or ester). The reactions at C_α and C_β are thus similar to the nucleophilic substitution reaction discussed in Chapter 3, except that a greater variety of

[12] H. Meerwein and K. van Emster, *Ber.*, *53*, 1815 (1920); *55*, 2500 (1922); H. Meerwein and L. Gérard, *Ann.*, *435*, 174 (1923); H. Meerwein, O. Hammel, A. Serini, and J. Vörster, *Ann.*, *453*, 16 (1927).

[13] This reaction is unique because, at least in principle, the stereochemistry of all three sites involved in the bond-making and -breaking processes can be examined.

mechanisms is available for the rearrangement. The mechanisms of the rearrangements of the 3-phenyl-2-butyl and norbornyl systems will illustrate the complexity of the problem.

A study of the 3-phenyl-2-butyl system [14] demonstrated for the first time what had previously been suggested,[15] namely, that discrete, bridged carbonium ion intermediates can intervene between starting material and product in the Wagner-Meerwein rearrangement. Thus the acetolysis of L-*threo*-IX *p*-toluenesulfonate produced racemic *threo*-IX acetate, whereas L-*erythro*-IX *p*-toluenesulfonate gave optically pure L-*erythro*-IX acetate. These results strongly point to

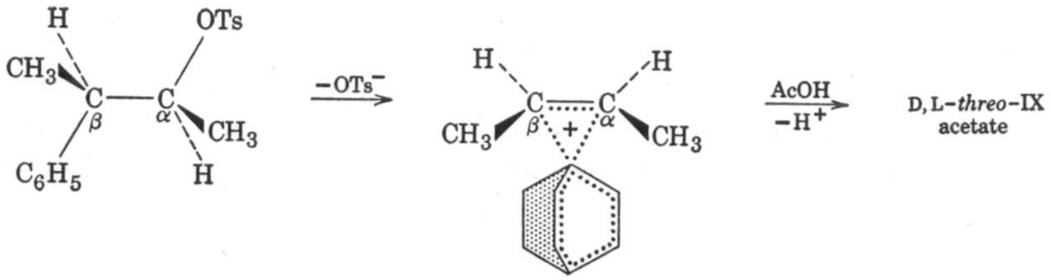

L-*threo*-IX
p-Toluenesulfonate

Internally compensated
bridged carbonium ion

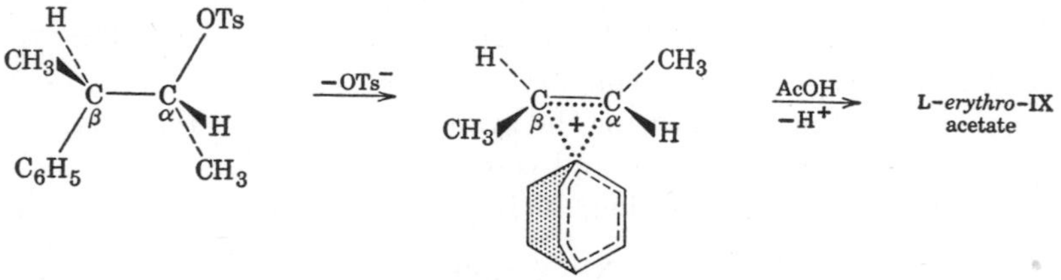

L-*erythro*-IX
p-Toluenesulfonate

Optically active
bridged carbonium ion

the occurrence as intermediates of bridged carbonium ions (ethylene phenonium ions) capable of holding configuration at both C_α and C_β. This ion is internally compensated in the *threo* series and hence can produce only racemic product, since the three-membered ring must open at C_α and C_β with equal probability. In the *erythro* series, the corresponding bridged ion is optically active, and ring opening at either C_α or C_β leads to the same optically active product, which possesses the same configuration as the starting material. The virtual absence of *erythro* product from *threo* starting material and *threo* prod-

[14] D. J. Cram, *J. Am. Chem. Soc.*, **71**, 3863 (1949).

[15] T. P. Nevell, E. de Salas, and C. L. Wilson, *J. Chem. Soc.*, *1939*, 1188, were the first to suggest this phenomena.

uct from *erythro* starting material indicates that C_α was inverted in the ring-closing stage, and that C_α or C_β was inverted in the second (ring-opening) stage. This interpretation successfully predicted the results of the acetolysis of the various stereomers of the p-toluenesulfonates of 3-phenyl-2-pentanol and 2-phenyl-3-pentanol.[16]

Somewhat similar evidence for bridged ions was subsequently obtained [17] in the acetolyses of the optically active *exo-* and *endo*-norbornyl p-bromobenzenesulfonates, both giving racemic *exo*-norbornyl acetate as product, with X as an intermediate. However, from start-

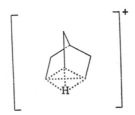

Active *exo*-norbornyl
p-bromobenzenesulfonate

Internally
compensated
X

Active *endo*-norbornyl
p-bromobenzenesulfonate

AcOH

Racemic *exo-*
norbornyl acetate

ing materials containing C^{14} at various positions in *exo*-norbornyl p-bromobenzenesulfonate, it was found [18] that the acetolysis product, *exo*-norbornyl acetate, contained C^{14} shuffled considerably more than can be explained on the simple basis of X as an intermediate. The authors accommodate their results with the suggestion that XI (a nortricyclonium ion) is formed either from or in competition with X.

Three-fold axis of symmetry

XI

[16] D. J. Cram, *J. Am. Chem. Soc.*, *71*, 3883 (1949).

[17] S. Winstein and D. Trifan, *J. Am. Chem. Soc.*, *74*, 1147, 1154 (1952).

[18] (a) J. D. Roberts and C. C. Lee, *J. Am. Chem. Soc.*, *73*, 5009 (1951); (b) J. D. Roberts, C. C. Lee, and W. H. Saunders, Jr., *ibid.*, *76*, 4501 (1954).

A further complication in the Wagner-Meerwein rearrangement is "internal return." [17] The discovery that α,α-dimethylallyl chloride isomerizes predominantly to γ,γ-dimethylallyl chloride during solvolysis [19] anticipated the observation that the first-order rate of racemization of active *exo*-norbornyl *p*-bromobenzenesulfonate was 3.5 times the rate (first-order) of appearance of *p*-bromobenzenesulfonate ion in the acetolysis reaction.[17] That this racemization process was intramolecular was demonstrated by the fact that the rate was not depressed by the addition of *p*-bromobenzenesulfonate ion (no common-ion effect). The suggestion was made that a bridged ion-pair was an intermediate in both the isomerization-racemization reaction (internal return) and the solvolysis-racemization reaction. In the much better ionizing solvent, formic acid, the phenomena of "internal return" virtually disappeared.

The same type of intramolecular isomerization process was found to apply to the acetolysis (and to a far less extent to the formolysis) of the *p*-bromobenzenesulfonates of the stereomers of 3-phenyl-2-butanol,[20a, b] as well as to the stereomers of 3-phenyl-2-pentanol and 2-phenyl-3-pentanol.[21]

The isomerization reaction was demonstrated to involve ionic intermediates as follows.[20a] The *p*-bromobenzenesulfonate of D-*threo*-3-phenyl-2-butanol (1 mole) was partially acetolyzed in the presence of 10 moles of *p*-toluenesulfonate ion. The recovered unsolvolyzed sulfonate was virtually racemic, being a mixture of *threo*-*p*-bromobenzenesulfonate ester and *threo*-*p*-toluenesulfonate ester in the ratio of 3.7/1, respectively. Had a *free*, bridged phenonium ion been an intermediate, the product would have been largely the *p*-toluenesulfonate ester, whereas, if no intermediate had intervened in the intramolecular isomerization reaction, no anion exchange reaction would have been observed.

The explanation of these observations is summarized below. The bridged ion can: (a) collapse (reversibly) to sulfonate ester; (b) undergo anion exchange to give new ester; (c) undergo solvent-anion exchange to give solvolysis product. Thus, the rates of solvolysis, k_s, are not necessarily the same as the rates of ionization, k_1. Rather, $k_s = k_1 \times k_2/(k_{-1} + k_2)$, and, since the balance of all four k's is a

[19] W. G. Young, S. Winstein, and H. L. Goering, *J. Am. Chem. Soc.*, *73*, 1958 (1951). See W. G. Young, K. Nozaki, and R. Warner [*ibid.*, *61*, 2564 (1939)] for earlier indications and discussions of the same sort of phenomena.

[20] (a) D. J. Cram, *J. Am. Chem. Soc.*, *74*, 2129 (1952); (b) S. Winstein and K. Schreiber, *ibid.*, *74*, 2165 (1952).

[21] D. J. Cram, *J. Am. Chem. Soc.*, *74*, 2159 (1952).

$$\text{(a)} \quad \longleftarrow \quad \longrightarrow \text{RX} \\ \text{Racemic}$$

$$\begin{array}{ccc} \text{R—X} & \rightarrow & \text{R}^+\text{X}^- \\ \text{Active} & & \text{Bridged} \\ & & \text{ion-pair} \end{array}$$

(b) $\dfrac{+Y}{-X}$ → R$^+$Y$^-$ ⇌ RY Racemic

+SOH $\Big\downarrow$ −HY

(c) $\dfrac{+SOH}{-HX}$ → ROS Racemic

function of R, X, and SOH, correlations of k_s as a function of R might be misleading without a knowledge of whether ion-pairs are formed and collapse back to starting material. Although some evidence for

$$\text{RX} \underset{k_{-1}}{\overset{k_1}{\rightleftarrows}} \text{R}^+\text{X}^- \xrightarrow[k_2]{\text{SOH}} \text{ROS} + \text{HX}$$

the existence of open (non-bridged) ion-pairs has been adduced,[22] no experimental demonstration that they collapse before solvolyzing has been made, although such a phenomenon has been suggested.[23] Although ion-pairs undoubtedly play a role in a number of rearrangements, the discussion of the reactions can be simplified if these intermediates are referred to only where their presence has proved to affect the results.[24]

The mechanisms of the Wagner-Meerwein rearrangement can be conveniently discussed as formulated. Open ions B and D are assumed to at least partially lose configuration at C_α and C_β, respectively, whereas Z (R, Ar, or H) maintains configurational control at C_β and C_α in intermediate C. Each of the letters represents a discrete entity, and each arrow a transition state. The various mechanisms with their stereochemical consequences are elaborated in Table I, that material returning to unrearranged but solvolyzed product being disregarded.

[22] (a) W. E. Doering and H. H. Zeiss, J. Am. Chem. Soc., 75, 4733 (1953); (b) S. Winstein, E. Grunwald, and H. W. Jones, ibid., 73, 2700 (1951); (c) C. S. Swain and W. P. Langsdorf, ibid., 73, 2813 (1951), and earlier papers.

[23] J. Hine, paper presented before American Chemical Society, Atlantic City, September, 1949, p. 83M of Abstracts.

[24] S. Winstein, E. Clippinger, A. H. Fainberg, and G. C. Robinson [J. Am. Chem. Soc., 76, 2598 (1954), and Chemistry & Industry, 1954, 664] have reported evidence that two types of ion-pairs coexist in certain acetolysis reactions: the "intimate" type consisting of a pair of ions in contact, and the "external" or "solvent-separated" type, the usual concept of a pair of solvated ions held together by coulombic attraction in a solvent of low dielectric constant.

TABLE I

Mechanism *	Stereochemistry at	
	C_α	C_β
A → E	Inv.	Inv.
A → C → E	Inv.	Inv.
A → B → D → E	Ret. + inv.	Ret. + inv.
A → B → C → D → E	Ret. + inv.	Ret. + inv.
A → B → E	Ret. + inv. or ret.†	Inv.
A → B → C → E	Ret. + inv. or ret.†	Inv.
A → D → E	Inv.	Ret. + inv.
A → C → D → E	Inv.	Ret. + inv.

* Account is not taken of ion-pairs, or of material that goes to E but returns to unrearranged solvolysis product.

† Only certain bicyclic systems give only retention.

The use of stereochemical techniques in differentiating between these mechanisms has been particularly useful. No examples of the A → E mechanism are available, but illustrations of many of the other sequences are. The solvolyses of the 3-phenyl-2-butyl [14] and analogous pentyl systems [16] as well as of the *exo*-norbornyl system [17]

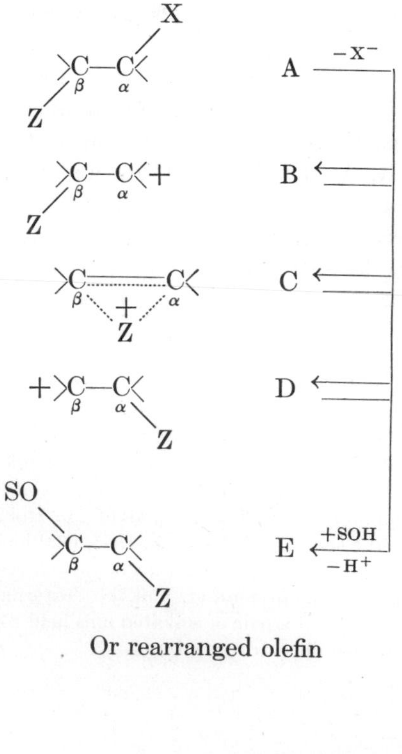

Or rearranged olefin

appear to involve the A → C → E path (or a more complicated equivalent).[25] An illustration of the A → C → D → E (or the less probable A → D → E) sequence is found in the results of the acetolysis of optically pure 1,1-diphenyl-2-propyl p-bromobenzenesulfonate [26] (XII) to give both diastereomers of optically pure 1,2-diphenyl-1-propyl acetate (XIII). The results predicted by the A → B → C

$$(C_6H_5)_2CH-\underset{*}{CH}-CH_3 \quad \xrightarrow[-BsOH]{AcOH} \quad C_6H_5-\underset{*}{CH}-\overset{*}{CH}-CH_3$$

OBs (over second CH of XII); OAc and C_6H_5 (on XIII)

XII   XIII

→ E sequence are found in the endo-norbornyl p-bromobenzenesulfonate (XIV) acetolysis.[17] Retention of configuration at C_α was ob-

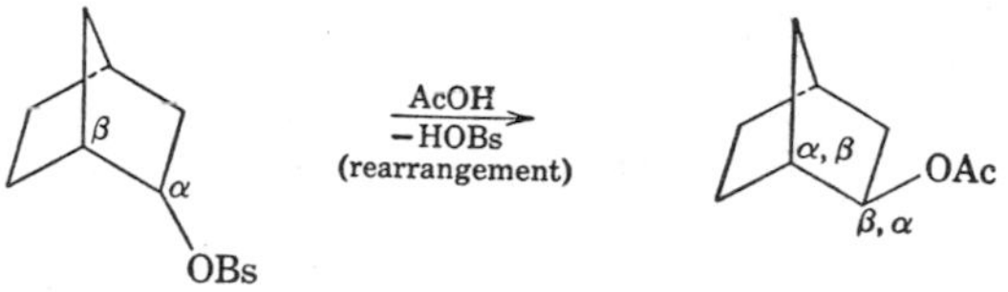

$$\xrightarrow[\substack{-HOBs \\ (rearrangement)}]{AcOH}$$

XIV
Optically pure   Racemic

served in this case, probably a consequence of the rigid geometry of this bicyclic system. The equivalent of this sequence in an open-chain system would probably result in a mixture of retention and inversion at C_α. An example of reaction path A → B → C → D → E (or A → B → D → E) is found in the acetolysis of the various stereoisomers of 3,4-dimethyl-4-phenyl-3-hexyl p-bromobenzoate.[27]

These examples indicate that open ions B and D intervene in the reaction sequences when they can be either ordinary tertiary or secondary benzyl carbonium ions. When B and D are ordinary secondary carbonium ions, their intervention in the Wagner-Meerwein sequence appears to depend on the particular system and on its environment. These results are consistent with those found in the simple solvolytic substitution reaction,[1] where the ability of the system to delocalize

[25] Some evidence for bridged ions in which Z is not halfway between C_α and C_β has been obtained [J. D. Roberts, paper at 120th Meeting of the American Chemical Society, New York, N. Y., September, 1951, p. 2419 of Abstracts; D. J. Cram and F. A. Abd Elhafez, J. Am. Chem. Soc., 75, 3189 (1953)].

[26] (a) D. J. Cram and F. A. Abd Elhafez, J. Am. Chem. Soc., 76, 28 (1954); (b) F. A. Abd Elhafez and D. J. Cram, ibid., 75, 339 (1953).

[27] D. J. Cram and J. D. Knight, J. Am. Chem. Soc., 74, 5839 (1952).

charge measures the relative stability of open carbonium ion intermediates. The occurrence of a C stage (a bridged ion intermediate)
has been demonstrated only for systems in which the migrating group
is aryl or a methylene that is part of a bicyclic system.

The use of the kinetic technique has proved useful in gaining evidence for the absence of the B stage in rearrangements not amenable
to stereochemical scrutiny, as well as for obtaining quantitative data
regarding the tendency for migration to occur as a function of substituents at C_α and C_β. Winstein and coworkers [28] have determined
the first-order solvolysis rates of a large number of systems in various
solvents and interpreted the differences in rates of members of carefully selected series as due to neighboring C and H participation in
the ionization process (anchimeric assistance [28h]).[29] For example,[28a]
the systems formulated undergo rearrangement in acetic acid at widely
differing rates.   In these and other systems,[28] the *rate enhancement*

	Relative Rates (AcOH at 50°)
$(CH_3)_3\underset{\beta}{C}-\underset{\alpha}{CH_2}-OTs$	1
$(C_6H_5)_2\underset{\beta}{CH}-\underset{\alpha}{CH_2}-OTs$	53
$C_6H_5\underset{\beta}{C}(CH_3)_2-\underset{\alpha}{CH_2}OTs$	460
$(C_6H_5)_3\underset{\beta}{C}-\underset{\alpha}{CH_2}OTs$	7.7×10^3

due to neighboring carbon participation in ionization was found to
decrease with increasing substitution at C_α (*p*-bromobenzenesulfonates
in general solvolyze at about three times the rate of the corresponding

[28] (a) S. Winstein, B. K. Morse, E. Grunwald, K. C. Schreiber, and J. Corse,
J. Am. Chem. Soc., *74*, 113 (1952); (b) reference 19; (c) S. Winstein, B. K. Morse,
E. Grunwald, H. W. Jones, J. Corse, D. Trifan, and H. Marshall, *J. Am. Chem.
Soc.*, *74*, 1127 (1952); (d) S. Winstein and B. K. Morse, *ibid.*, *74*, 113 (1952);
(e) S. Winstein, M. Brown, K. C. Schreiber, and A. H. Schlesinger, *ibid.*, *74*, 1140
(1952); (f) reference 15; (g) S. Winstein and K. Schreiber, *J. Am. Chem. Soc.*, *74*,
2165, 2171 (1952); (h) S. Winstein, C. R. Lindegren, H. Marshall, and L. L. Ingraham, *ibid.*, *75*, 147 (1953); (i) S. Winstein, C. R. Lindegren, and L. L. Ingraham,
ibid., *75*, 155 (1953); (j) S. Winstein, *Bull. soc. chim. France*, *18*, C55 (1951).

[29] E. D. Hughes and C. K. Ingold and coworkers have also recognized the phenomena of acceleration of ionization due to carbon participation. (a) F. Brown,
E. D. Hughes, C. K. Ingold, and J. F. Smith, *Nature*, *168*, 65 (1951); (b) J. C.
Charlton, I. Dostrovsky, and E. D. Hughes, *ibid.*, *167*, 986 (1951). These authors
have referred to the effect as "synartetic acceleration," and to bridged ions as
"synartetic ions." The invention of nomenclature should not be confused with
the discovery of the phenomena in question.

p-toluenesulfonates).[28] Thus, the more the substituents at C_α delocalize charge, the less is the *rate enhancement* due to neighboring group participation in ionization. On the other hand, the acetolysis rates increase with successive substitution of R and Ar for hydrogen at C_β in the order $CH_3 < C_6H_5 \cong (CH_3)_2 < (C_6H_5)_2 < (C_6H_5)_3$.[28a] The formulas illustrate one type of series used to determine this order.[28a] Thus, the better the substituents in the β position are at dis-

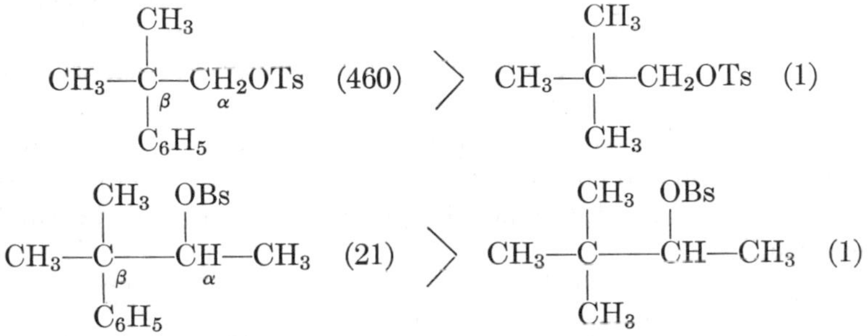

$$\underset{\underset{C_6H_5}{|}}{\overset{\overset{CH_3}{|}}{CH_3-\underset{\beta}{C}-\underset{\alpha}{CH_2}OTs}} \quad (460) \quad > \quad \underset{\underset{CH_3}{|}}{\overset{\overset{CH_3}{|}}{CH_3-C-CH_2OTs}} \quad (1)$$

$$\underset{\underset{C_6H_5}{|}}{\overset{\overset{CH_3 \quad OBs}{| \quad \quad |}}{CH_3-\underset{\beta}{C}\!-\!-\!\underset{\alpha}{CH}-CH_3}} \quad (21) \quad > \quad \underset{\underset{CH_3}{|}}{\overset{\overset{CH_3 \quad OBs}{| \quad \quad |}}{CH_3-C\!-\!-\!CH-CH_3}} \quad (1)$$

tributing charge in the transition state, the greater is the rate enhancement due to participation of groups in the β position in the ionization process.[28a]

A number of difficulties arise in the use of this type of data as a criterion of carbon or hydrogen participation in the ionization process *when the rate differences between systems are small*. Thus Ingold et al.,[2f, 29a] ignoring the stereochemical implications,[14] have interpreted the lack of a marked difference in rate of acetolysis between *threo*-3-phenyl-2-butyl p-toluenesulfonate and 2-butyl p-toluenesulfonate [28a] as evidence that the rearrangement proceeded through two equilibrating open ions.

Actually, the rates of *ionization* of the two systems differ by a factor of about 7, the *ionization* and *solvolysis* rates not being identi-

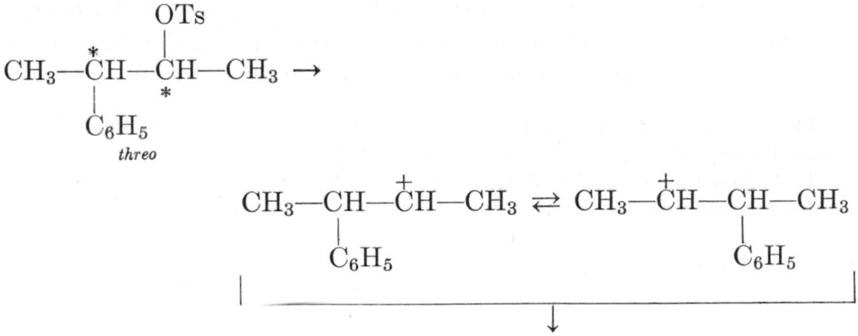

$$\underset{\underset{\underset{threo}{}}{\overset{|}{C_6H_5}}}{\overset{\overset{OTs}{|}}{CH_3-\overset{*}{C}H-\underset{*}{C}H-CH_3}} \rightarrow$$

$$\underset{\underset{C_6H_5}{|}}{CH_3-CH-\overset{+}{C}H-CH_3} \rightleftarrows \underset{\underset{C_6H_5}{|}}{CH_3-\overset{+}{C}H-CH-CH_3}$$

Racemic *threo* product

cal.[20, 28a, 30]   Furthermore, the 2-butyl is a poor model for the 3-phenyl-2-butyl system because the inductive effect of the phenyl group in the latter system tends to slow down the rate of ionization,[8a] and the steric effect tends to inhibit solvent participation.   The rate of C_6H_5 to AcOH involvement in the *ionization* of *threo*-3-phenyl-2-butyl *p*-toluenesulfonate in acetic acid is approximately 66/1.[31]

That solvent competes with neighboring carbon in aiding ionization is illustrated in the solvolysis (without appreciable rearrangement) of optically active benzylmethylcarbinyl *p*-toluenesulfonate.[28e]   The substitution occurring with retention measures phenyl participation, the reaction occurring with inversion probably measuring solvent involvement in the ionization.   As expected, HCOOH < CH_3COOH < C_2H_5OH in ability to compete with a β-phenyl group in aiding ionization.   A study of the 1,2-diphenyl-1-propyl system provided a similar conclusion.[32]

$$C_6H_5-CH_2-\overset{*}{C}H(OTs)-CH_3 \xrightarrow[-HOTs]{+HOS} C_6H_5-CH_2-CH(OS)-CH_3$$

Solvent	Inversion	Retention
EtOH	93%	7%
AcOH	65%	35%
HCOOH	15%	85%

MIGRATORY APTITUDE.   One of the most studied aspects of the 1,2-nucleophilic molecular rearrangement is the problem of the relative ease of migration of groups, most of the investigations employing the pinacol and pinacol-like reactions.[33]   The classical attack on this problem centered about the study of the products of rearrangement of the symmetrical and unsymmetrical glycols, XVA and XVB, respectively.   By examining series of compounds in which *a* and *b* were appropriately varied, the groups could be placed in orders according to their tendency to rearrange and assigned "migratory aptitudes."[34]

[30] D. J. Cram and F. A. Abd Elhafez, *J. Am. Chem. Soc.*, *75*, 3189 (1953).

[31] D. J. Cram, *J. Am. Chem. Soc.*, *74*, 2137 (1952).

[32] F. A. Abd Elhafez and D. J. Cram, *J. Am. Chem. Soc.*, *75*, 339 (1953).

[33] For summaries, see: (a) *Ann. Repts. Chem. Soc. (London)*, *27*, 114 (1930); *30*, 181 (1933); *36*, 195 (1939); (b) G. W. Wheland, *Advanced Organic Chemistry*, pp. 496–519, John Wiley & Sons, New York, 1949.

[34] Examples of these two types of studies are: W. E. Bachmann and J. W. Ferguson, *J. Am. Chem. Soc.*, *56*, 2081 (1934); W. E. Bachmann and H. R. Steinberger, *ibid.*, *56*, 170 (1934).

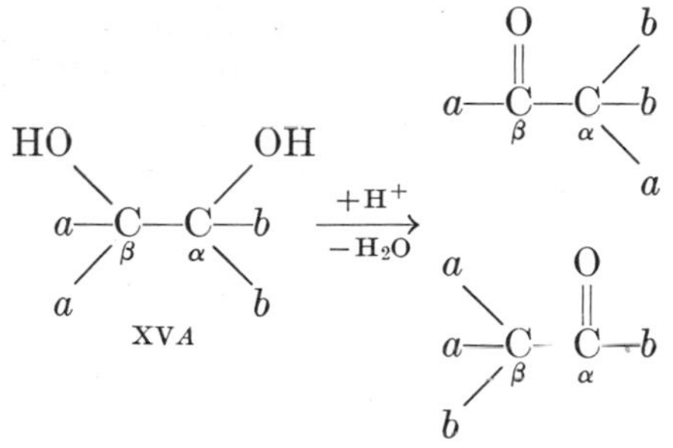

$$
\begin{array}{c}
\overset{\text{HO}}{\diagdown}\ \ \overset{\text{OH}}{\diagup} \\
a-\underset{\underset{a}{\beta}}{C}-\underset{\underset{b}{\alpha}}{C}-b \\
\text{XV}_A
\end{array}
\quad
\xrightarrow[-\text{H}_2\text{O}]{+\text{H}^+}
\quad
\begin{array}{c}
\overset{O}{\underset{\underset{\beta}{\parallel}}{}}\quad \overset{b}{\diagup} \\
a-\underset{\beta}{C}-\underset{\alpha}{C}-b \\
\diagdown a
\end{array}
$$

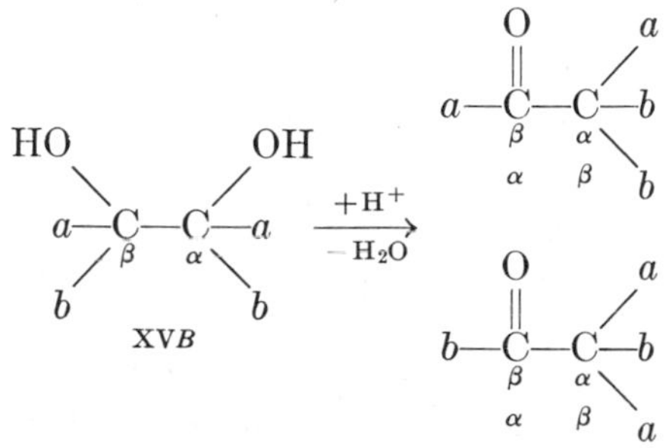

$$
a-\underset{\underset{b}{\beta}}{C}\overset{\displaystyle O}{-}\underset{\alpha}{\overset{\parallel}{C}}\!-b
$$

$$
\begin{array}{c}
\overset{\text{HO}}{\diagdown}\ \ \overset{\text{OH}}{\diagup} \\
a-\underset{\underset{b}{\beta}}{C}-\underset{\underset{b}{\alpha}}{C}-a \\
\text{XV}_B
\end{array}
\quad
\xrightarrow[-\text{H}_2\text{O}]{+\text{H}^+}
$$

Although a limited degree of internal consistency in the data was observed, particularly in the series of the symmetrical glycols,[33] the problems have turned out to be far more complicated than anticipated.

Just as in the Wagner-Meerwein rearrangement, a number of mechanisms are available, some of which involve complex equilibria. In the unsymmetrical pinacols (XV), group a might migrate by one mechanism and b by another, and determination of which group migrates only indicates which mechanism is the more energetically feasible, not that one group has a greater migratory aptitude than a second.[35]

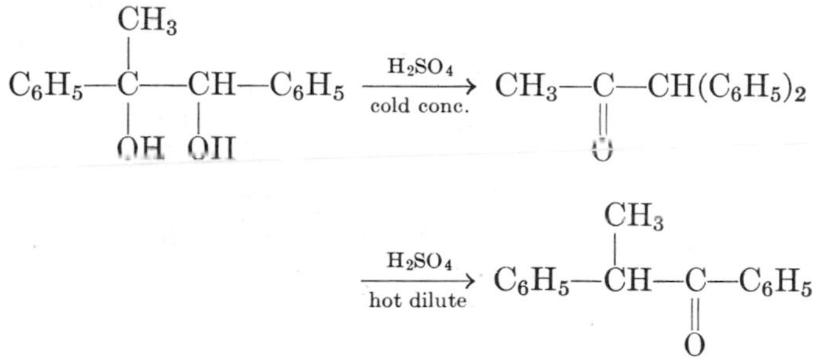

$$
\underset{\underset{\text{OH OH}}{|\ \ \ \ |}}{\overset{\overset{\text{CH}_3}{|}}{C_6H_5-C-CH-C_6H_5}}
\xrightarrow[\text{cold conc.}]{H_2SO_4}
\underset{\underset{O}{\parallel}}{CH_3-C-CH(C_6H_5)_2}
$$

$$
\xrightarrow[\text{hot dilute}]{H_2SO_4}
\underset{\underset{O}{\parallel}}{C_6H_5-CH-\overset{\overset{CH_3}{|}}{C}-C_6H_5}
$$

[35] Reference 33b lists a large number of internal inconsistencies in the assignment of migratory aptitudes, some of which undoubtedly reflect comparisons of groups migrating by way of different mechanisms.

An illustration of the variation of mechanism with conditions is found in the reaction of 1,2-diphenyl-1,2-propanediol with cold concentrated sulfuric acid on the one hand, and with hot dilute sulfuric acid on the other. In the first case, phenyl, and in the second case, hydrogen, migrated.[36]

Even when dealing with symmetrical pinacols (XV), groups a and b might migrate by different mechanisms, although this possibility is much less likely than with the unsymmetrical pinacols.[37] Another difficulty that arises in assigning migratory aptitudes to groups is that the resonance of stabilization of the transition states of the actual migration stage is a function not only of the group that is migrating but also of the other substituents at C_α and C_β. Particularly when aryl groups are involved (either as a migrating group, or one left behind), such phenomena as steric inhibition of resonance and eclipsing effects in the transition state as well as the release of steric compression in destroying the starting material play a role (see later section for discussion).

The most success in assigning migratory aptitude has been found in comparing reactions of individual compounds which possess the general structure XVI and in which the aryl groups are either phenyl or o- or p-substituted phenyl. Here the two OH's are equivalent, the

$$
\begin{array}{cc}
\text{Ar}' & \text{Ar}' \\
| & | \\
\text{Ar}-\text{C}-\!\!-\text{C}-\text{Ar} \\
| & | \\
\text{OH} & \text{OH}
\end{array}
$$

XVI

steric situations from compound to compound are comparable, and probably a common mechanism applies to all the reactions. The following types of orders of decreasing migratory aptitude have been observed (phenyl = 1:[34] p-anisyl, 500; p-tolyl, 15.7; p-isopropylphenyl, 9; p-ethylphenyl, 5; m-tolyl, 1.95; m-anisyl, 1.6; phenyl, 1; p-chlorophenyl, 0.7; o-anisyl, 0.3; m-chlorophenyl, 0. The order for the p substituents is similar to that observed in rates of electrophilic aromatic substitution of the corresponding monosubstituted benzenes. This correlation is to be expected since the nucleophilic 1,2 rearrangement involving aryl as the migrating species is essentially an electro-

[36] (a) A. McKenzie and R. Roger, J. Chem. Soc., 125, 244 (1924); (b) M. Tiffeneau and Dorlencourt, Ann. chim. phys., [8], 16, 252 (1909); (c) A. McKenzie and H. Wren, J. Chem. Soc., 97, 473 (1910).

[37] Although bridged ions may intervene as intermediates in the pinacol as in the Wagner-Meerwein rearrangement, they have not yet been detected.

philic substitution reaction in which one cation is replacing another on a benzene ring. Steric effects play a much more important role, however, in these rearrangements as compared to the simple aromatic substitution, since, in the former, the group being displaced is usually a highly substituted carbon, whereas in the latter the displaced group is hydrogen. The anomalously low migratory aptitudes associated with o-anisyl support this inference.[38]

A special problem in mechanism arises when hydrogen is the migrating group in the pinacol reaction. The reaction can alternatively be considered as a 1,2 elimination to produce the enol of the ketonic prod-

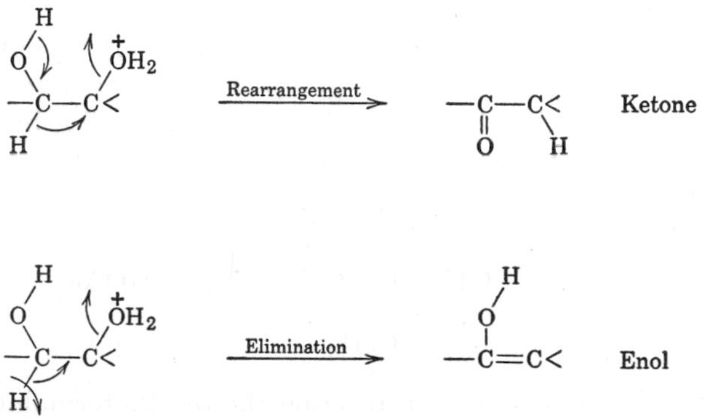

uct (see formulas). In two cases, the reaction has been demonstrated to go by rearrangement. Optically active o- and m-tolylhydrobenzoins (but not the p isomer) were found to give with dilute sulfuric acid the corresponding optically active α-phenyl-α-tolylacetophenones.[39a] The second and better-documented case of a stereospecific hydrogen migration is formulated.[39b] Although the aldehyde produced was appreciably racemized (possibly after its formation), some stereospecificity

[38] R. F. Brown [J. Am. Chem. Soc., 76, 1279 (1954)] observed that cis- and trans-1,2-di-o-tolyl and di-p-tolylacenaphthenediols give the corresponding pinacolone in sulfuric-acetic acid, and, although rates were not run, the o-substituted phenyls appeared to migrate as readily as the para. Brown suggests that the abnormally long C—C bond in the substrate might compensate for the usually observed retardation of the pinacol reaction involving o-substituted phenyl as the migrating group. In the less constrained Beckmann rearrangement, P. T. Scott, W. E. Cole, and D. E. Pearson [Abstracts of papers presented at meeting of the American Chemical Society at Kansas City, March, 1954, p. 25N] found that the effect of substituents in the o position was one of marked acceleration as compared to the corresponding substituents in the p position.

[39] (a) A. McKenzie, R. Roger, and W. B. McKay, J. Chem. Soc., 1932, 2597; R. Roger and W. B. McKay, ibid., 1933, 332; (b) K. Mislow and M. Siegel, J. Am. Chem. Soc., 74, 1060 (1952).

$$\underset{(+)}{\overset{\displaystyle \overset{H}{\overset{|}{O}}\overset{+}{OH_2}}{H-\overset{|}{\underset{|}{C}}-\overset{|}{\underset{|}{C}}-C_6H_5}} \xrightarrow[\text{H}_2\text{SO}_4]{\text{Dilute}} \underset{(+)}{O=CH-\underset{|}{CH}-C_6H_5}$$

for the reaction sequence was established. The question whether the *o* substituent plays some steric role in the preservation of activity in the product is still in doubt.

The migratory aptitude of groups in the Wagner-Meerwein rearrangement has been studied enough to define the types of problems that are involved. In the acetolysis of *threo*-3-phenyl-2-butyl *p*-toluenesulfonate at 75°, the ability of groups to participate in the ionization at C_α was found to be $C_6H_5 > H > AcOH > CH_3$ by factors of 66, 8, 1, and $<.05$, respectively.[31] Roberts and coworkers [40] observed

$$CH_3-\overset{\overset{\displaystyle H}{\overset{|}{}}}{\underset{\underset{\displaystyle C_6H_5}{|}}{C}}-\overset{\overset{\displaystyle OTs}{\overset{|}{}}}{\underset{\alpha}{CH}}-CH_3 + HOAc$$

in the nitrous acid deamination reaction the results formulated below.

$$p\text{-CH}_3\text{OC}_6\text{H}_4-\text{CH}_2-\text{C}^{14}\text{H}_2\text{NH}_2 \xrightarrow[\text{H}_2\text{O}]{\text{HNO}_2} 33\% \quad p\text{-CH}_3\text{OC}_6\text{H}_4-\text{C}^{14}\text{H}_2-\text{CH}_2\text{OH}$$

$$\text{C}_6\text{H}_5-\text{CH}_2-\text{C}^{14}\text{H}_2\text{NH}_2 \xrightarrow[\text{H}_2\text{O}]{\text{HNO}_2} 24\% \quad \text{C}_6\text{H}_5-\text{C}^{14}\text{H}_2-\text{CH}_2\text{OH}$$

$$p\text{-NO}_2\text{C}_6\text{H}_4-\text{CH}_2\text{C}^{14}\text{H}_2\text{NH}_2 \xrightarrow[\text{H}_2\text{O}]{\text{HNO}_2} 5\% \quad p\text{-NO}_2\text{C}_6\text{H}_4-\text{C}^{14}\text{H}_2-\text{CH}_2\text{OH}$$

$$\text{CH}_3-\text{CH}_2-\text{C}^{14}\text{H}_2\text{NH}_2 \xrightarrow[\text{H}_2\text{O}]{\text{HNO}_2} \left[\begin{array}{l} 9\% \begin{cases} \text{CH}_3-\text{C}^{14}\text{H}_2-\text{CH}_2\text{OH} \quad 9\% \\ \text{CH}_3-\text{CH}_2-\text{C}^{14}\text{H}_2\text{OH} \quad 91\% \end{cases} \\ 41\% \quad \text{CH}_3-\underset{\underset{\displaystyle OH}{|}}{CH}-\text{C}^{14}\text{H}_3 \end{array} \right]$$

$$\text{CH}_3-\text{C}^{14}\text{H}_2\text{NH}_2 \xrightarrow[\text{H}_2\text{O}]{\text{HNO}_2} 2\% \quad \text{C}^{14}\text{H}_3-\text{CH}_2\text{OH}$$

Other investigators [41] studied migratory aptitude in the phosphorus

[40] (a) J. D. Roberts and J. A. Yancey, *J. Am. Chem. Soc.*, 74, 5943 (1952); (b) J. D. Roberts and C. M. Regan, *ibid.*, 75, 2069 (1953); (c) J. D. Roberts and M. Halmann, *ibid.*, 75, 5759 (1953).

[41] (a) B. Benjamin and C. J. Collins, *J. Am. Chem. Soc.*, 75, 402 (1953); (b) C. J. Collins, L. S. Ciereszko, and J. G. Burr, *ibid.*, 75, 405 (1953); (c) J. G. Burr and L. S. Ciereszko, *ibid.*, 74, 5426 (1952).

pentoxide dehydration reaction of 2,2-diarylethanols. The values of

$$C_6H_5-\overset{\displaystyle \overset{Ar}{|}}{C}H-C^{14}H_2OH \xrightarrow[\text{Xylene}]{P_2O_5}$$

$$C_6H_5-CH{=}C^{14}H-Ar + C_6H_5C^{14}H{=}CH-Ar$$

Ar migration relative to C_6H_5 (unity) are as follows: $p\text{-}CH_3OC_6H_4{}^-$, 21.2; $p\text{-}t\text{-}but\ C_6H_4{}^-$, 3.2; $p\text{-}C_2H_5C_6H_4{}^-$, 2.18; $p\text{-}CH_3C_6H_4{}^-$, 1.98; 3,4-$(CH_3)_2C_6H_3{}^-$, 1.91; $p\text{-}i\text{-}prop\ C_6H_4{}^-$, 1.82; $m\text{-}CH_3C_6H_4{}^-$, 1.58; $p\text{-}CH_3C_6H_4{}^-$, 1.34; β-naphthyl-, 1.3; α-naphthyl-, 1.1; $o\text{-}CH_3O-$ $C_6H_4{}^-$, 0.8. Finally, a comparison between $CH_3{}^-$ and $C_2H_5{}^-$ is found in formolysis of 3,4-dimethyl-4-phenyl-3-hexyl p-bromobenzo-ate,[27] the ratio being $CH_3/C_2H_5 = 35/1$.

The electronically anomalous position of the o-anisyl group in the above series points strongly to the intervention of a marked steric effect, but one not as dramatic as was observed in the pinacol series quoted above. This difference probably derives from the generally more highly substituted system employed for the pinacol reactions.

One of the serious problems in studying migratory aptitude arises out of the fact that C and H participation in the ionization process does not necessarily result in rearrangement. Thus, in the formolysis of the diastereomeric 1,2-diphenyl-1-propyl p-bromobenzenesulfonates (XVII),[26b] although ionization occurs with participation of the neighboring phenyl group (substitution occurs predominately with preservation of configuration), the product XVIII is unrearranged. A sec-

$$CH_3-\overset{*}{\underset{\underset{\displaystyle XVII}{\overset{*}{|}}{\underset{\displaystyle C_6H_5}{|}}}{\overset{\displaystyle \overset{OBs}{|}}{C}H}-\overset{}{C}H-C_6H_5 \xrightarrow[-\ HOBs]{HCOOH} CH_3-\overset{}{\underset{\underset{\displaystyle XVIII}{\underset{\displaystyle C_6H_5}{|}}}{\overset{\displaystyle \overset{OOCH}{|}}{C}H}}-CH-C_6H_5$$

threo/erythro

erythro →   1/1.6

threo →   2.5/1

ond problem is associated with hydrogen as a participating but non-migrating group. The concept of the protonated double bond [42] has

[42] K. S. Pitzer, *J. Am. Chem. Soc.*, **67**, 1126 (1945); C. C. Price, *Mechanisms of Reactions at Carbon-Carbon Double Bonds*, p. 40, Interscience Publishers, New York, 1946; M. J. S. Dewar, *Electronic Theory of Organic Chemistry*, p. 213; reference 32a, Oxford University Press, London, 1949.

been discussed in connection with a variety of phenomena, in particular with the mechanism of the solvolytic rearrangement (H as migrating group) and elimination reaction, which frequently accompany one another.[31] If such a species is an intermediate in these two reactions (as some results suggest [31]), hydrogen might participate in the ionization at C_α, but the bridged ion produced might dissociate to give

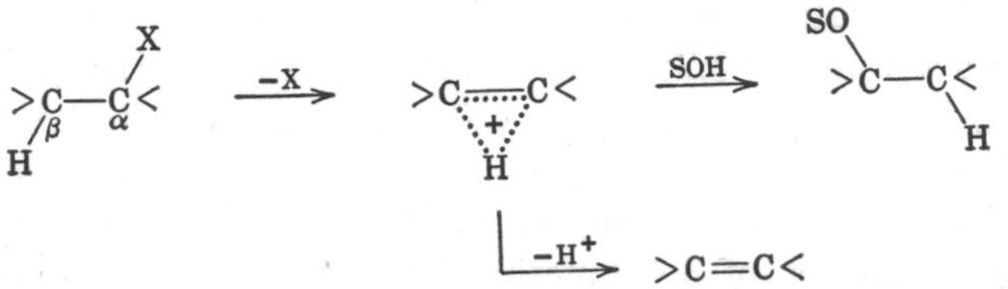

largely olefin. In this connection, it is informative that the rate of acetolysis of the p-toluenesulfonate of neomenthyl (XIX) is 170 times that of menthyl (XX). Although some of this difference is probably

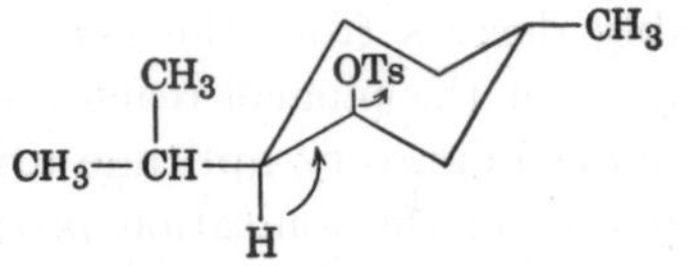

XIX 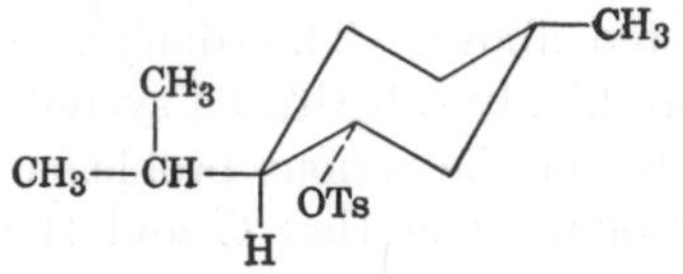   XX

due to steric facilitation of ionization,[8, 43] some may result from the much more favorable geometry for hydrogen participation in ionization in the neomenthyl as compared to the menthyl ester.[28c] Since olefin is the main product, the amount of rearranged material does not measure the degree of involvement of hydrogen in the initial ionization process.

These facts indicate that no such thing as "intrinsic migratory aptitude" exists, which generally applies to the nucleophilic 1,2 rearrangements. In carefully chosen series of compounds whose reactions are mechanistically similar, orders of ease of migration of groups can be developed. However, these orders do not necessarily apply either to other sets of reaction conditions or to other series of compounds carrying the same reference groups.

ECLIPSING EFFECTS. A number of steric consequences are derived from the necessity for the migrating group (Z = R, Ar, or H) to displace the leaving group (X) from the *back side* in those nucleophilic 1,2 rearrangements in which A and B are carbon and the first stage is concerted (synchronous). These consequences derive from a preferred

[43] W. Hückel, *Ber.*, *77B*, 905 (1944).

geometry for the transition state of this first stage wherein Z and X are oriented somewhere between $>90°$ and $180°$ with respect to one another along the axis of the C_β—C_α bond ($180°$ is ideally the most

Transition state

favorable configuration). The problems posed by these requirements center about: (1) the steric compatibility of b, C_β, C_α, and d occupying one plane, and a, C_β, C_α, and c occupying another;[44,45] (2) the extent to which the transition state in question approximates this geometry of maximum steric repulsions.

The common method of studying these effects is to compare the reactivities of two diastereomerically related compounds. Differences in reactivity are functions of the stability of both the starting and the

[44] In this conformation, b and d are said to be eclipsed, the same being true of a and c.

[45] This problem has been recognized in various forms for some time in connection with the bimolecular elimination reaction and various rearrangement reactions, as well as in connection with the relative stability of cis and trans olefins and cis- and trans-1,2-dialkyl cyclopentanes. Although examples of acyclic diastereomers of widely differing reactivity in elimination and rearrangement reactions have been known since almost the beginning of this century, the rationalization of these effects has been given comparatively recently. W. G. Young, D. Pressman, and C. D. Coryell [J. Am. Chem. Soc., 61, 1640 (1939); W. G. Young, Eighth National Organic Symposium, St. Louis, Mo., December, 1939, Abstracts of papers, pp. 92–95] recognized that, in the elimination of bromine with potassium iodide from diastereomeric dibromides (e.g., meso- and dl-stilbene dibromides), that isomer eliminates the faster which gives the trans olefin. The effect of conformation of the starting diastereomers on rate of reaction was explicitly discussed. S. Winstein and D. Seymour [J. Am. Chem. Soc., 68, 121 (1946)] state that conditions are more favorable for participation of the neighboring chlorine atom in meso-stilbene dichloride (as compared to the dl isomer) because the chlorines are situated trans and a ring might close (a chloronium ion with phenyl groups trans to one another) more readily than in the case of the dl isomer. P. I. Pollak and D. Y. Curtin [J. Am. Chem. Soc., 72, 961 (1950)] discuss the differences of the course of semipinacolic deamination reaction for diastereomerically related compounds in terms of three effects: starting conformation, relative steric compatibility of cis and trans transition states, and relative degrees of steric inhibition of resonance in the cis and trans transition states. The phenomenon of eclipsing groups which produce non-bonded interactions has been termed the cis effect by D. Y. Curtin [Thirteenth National Organic Chem. Symposium, Ann Arbor, Mich., June, 1953, Abstract of papers, pp. 40–49] and has been discussed as applied to a variety of reactions.

transition states.   Only three pieces of data are available regarding the relative stability of *acyclic* diastereomers.   The $\Delta F°$ for the transformation of *dl-* into *meso*-stilbene dibromide is at least -800 cal.; [46]

$$\underset{\underset{*}{\overset{|}{C_6H_5}}}{\overset{}{CH_3—\overset{*}{C}H}}—\underset{}{\overset{\overset{\displaystyle O}{\overset{\displaystyle \|}{O—C—H}}}{\overset{|}{CH}}}—C_6H_5 \quad \frac{erythro}{threo} = 1.23 \text{ at equilibrium}$$

complete equilibration of *threo-* and *erythro*-1,2-diphenyl propyl formates in formic acid (25°) gave a $\Delta F°$ of only -120 cal.; [26b] incomplete equilibration of the diastereomeric 3-cyclohexyl-2-butanols indicates that $\Delta F°$ is 0–400 cal. [47]   Thus the differences in stability of the starting states appear to be rather small in those systems that do not carry highly polarized groups on both asymmetric carbon atoms, [48] and therefore attention can be centered on the transition state.

A number of anomalous examples of the semipinacolic deamination reaction are recorded in which the expected group did not migrate. [49] In the system in which $Ar = p\text{-}CH_3OC_6H_4^-$, the β racemate (the

$$\underset{\overset{|}{C_6H_5}}{Ar—\overset{\overset{\displaystyle OH}{|}}{\overset{*}{C}}—\overset{\overset{\displaystyle NH_2}{|}}{\overset{*}{C}}H}—C_6H_5 \quad \xrightarrow{HNO_2} \quad \underset{\overset{|}{C_6H_5}}{Ar—\overset{\overset{\displaystyle O}{\|}}{C}—CH}—C_6H_5$$

One of two racemates
(α isomer)

$$\underset{Ar}{C_6H_5—\overset{\overset{\displaystyle OH}{|}}{\overset{*}{C}}—\overset{\overset{\displaystyle NH_2}{|}}{\overset{*}{C}}H}—C_6H_5 \quad \xrightarrow{HNO_2} \quad \underset{Ar}{C_6H_5—\overset{\overset{\displaystyle O}{\|}}{C}—CH}—C_6H_5$$

Other of two racemates (β)

stereochemical structure was unknown) reacted with nitrous acid to give ketone in which phenyl had migrated, although numerous studies

[46] R. E. Buckles, W. E. Steinmetz, and N. G. Wheeler, *J. Am. Chem. Soc.*, *72*, 2496 (1950).

[47] D. J. Cram and F. D. Green, *J. Am. Chem. Soc.*, *75*, 6005 (1953).

[48] The larger difference in energies between the diastereomers of stilbene dibromide than in the other two cases is probably a result of dipole-dipole interactions in the former system [see S. Mizushima, Y. Morino, and T. Shimanouchi, *J. Phys. Chem.*, *56*, 324 (1952)].

[49] (a) A. McKenzie and A. K. Mills, *Ber.*, *62*, 1784 (1929); (b) A. McKenzie and A. P. Wood, *Ber.*, *71*, 358 (1938); (c) A. McKenzie and A. C. Richardson, *Ber.*, *123*, 79 (1923); (d) A. McKenzie and W. S. Dennler, *Ber.*, *125*, 2105 (1924).

pointed to a much greater migratory aptitude for a p-anisyl group as compared to a phenyl in analogous systems. Where Ar = 1-naphthyl, the α racemate gave [49c, d] product in which phenyl had migrated, whereas, with the β racemate, the 1-naphthyl group migrated. Curtin and coworkers,[50] through a series of studies clearly demonstrated for the first time that the group migrated that gave a transition state in which the bulky (non-migrating) groups attached to the two asymmetric carbon atoms were *distributed trans to one another*. The same

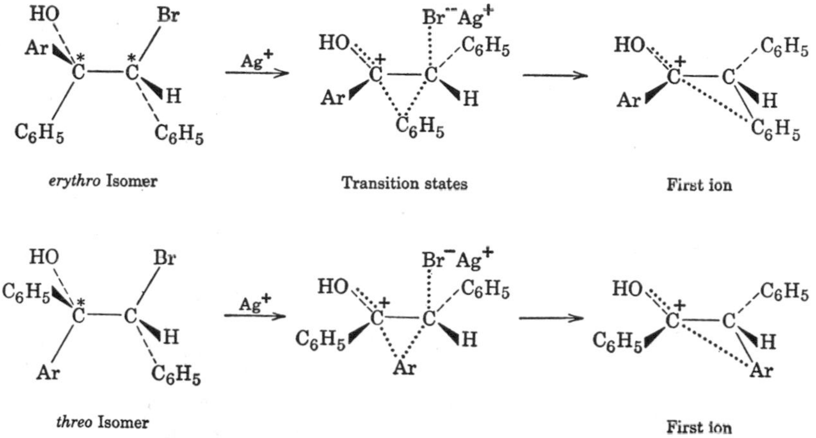

erythro Isomer   Transition states   First ion

threo Isomer   First ion

principles apply to systems in which methyl is substituted for aryl on the carbon at the migration terminus.

Curtin [51] has correlated a large number of examples of bimolecular elimination (see section on elimination reactions), rearrangement, and ring-closure reactions in which observed relative rates can be grossly interpreted in terms of the relative strain involved in eclipsing various groups in the transition states in question.[52] Substituents can be crudely divided into three groups with respect to their ability to provide eclipsing effects: [51] small (S), medium (M), and large (L). Fitting the data available [51] to the above classification, S = H or D; M =

[50] (a) P. I. Pollak and D. Y. Curtin, J. Am. Chem. Soc., 72, 961 (1950); (b) D. Y. Curtin, E. E. Harris, and E. K. Meislich, ibid., 74, 2901 (1952); (c) D. Y. Curtin and E. K. Meislich, ibid., 74, 5518 (1952); (d) D. Y. Curtin and P. I. Pollak, ibid., 73, 992 (1951); (e) D. Y. Curtin and E. K. Meislich, ibid., 74, 5905 (1952).

[51] D. Y. Curtin and M. Crew, Thirteenth National Organic Symposium of the American Chemical Society, June, 1953, Ann Arbor, Michigan, p. 42.

[52] In all of the examples cited in reference 51, the reasonable assumption has been made that the rate of interconversion of various *rotational isomers* in the starting materials is faster than the rate of the reaction in question. See Chapter 1 for a theoretical discussion of this point.

CH_3, OH, Cl, Br, or I; L = Ar, COOH, COOR, or COAr. The importance of eclipsing effects then can be arranged in an order of the importance of repulsions between the various sized groups:

L $\succ\!\!\prec$ L > L $\succ\!\!\prec$ M > M $\succ\!\!\prec$ M > M $\succ\!\!\prec$ S > S $\succ\!\!\prec$ S.

Important eclipsing effects in chemical reactions have been found only for the first three cases, L $\succ\!\!\prec$ L, and L $\succ\!\!\prec$ M, and M $\succ\!\!\prec$ M.

The second problem in connection with eclipsing effects is the extent to which the non-migrating groups are pressed into the same plane in the transition state of the rearrangement stage. In the pinacol and similar rearrangements, the transition state probably occurs somewhere near the point in which the migrating group is halfway between the migration terminus and origin. This geometry would be necessary

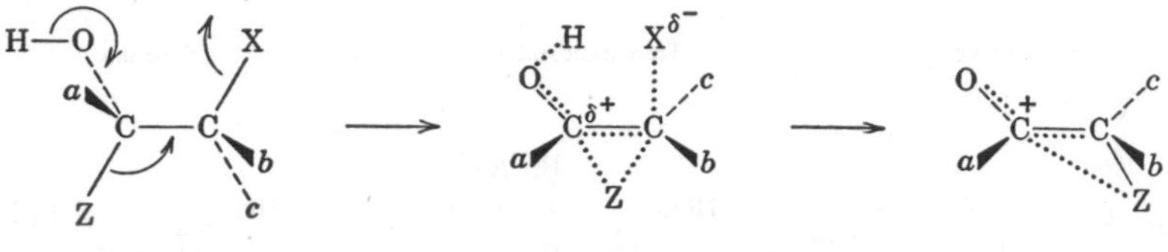

| Starting state | Transition state | Bridged cation if any |

for stabilization of the transition state by delocalization of electrons involving the hydroxyl on the migration origin. As a result, eclipsing effects are important in these rearrangements.

In the Wagner-Meerwein rearrangement, the geometry of the transition state probably varies from system to system, depending on the non-migrating substituents on the migration terminus and origin. The following examples are cited.

The acetolysis rates of *threo*- and *erythro*-3-phenyl-2-butyl *p*-toluenesulfonate differ only slightly, the ratio amounting to only 1.2/1, respectively, at 50°,[28a] in spite of the fact that two methyl groups (R's in the formulation) are becoming eclipsed in the formation of the *cis*

cis Ion from *threo*   *trans* Ion from *erythro*

bridged ion but not in the *trans*. As pointed out earlier, however, the simple *solvolysis rate* data of this type do not represent the relative *rates of ionization* of the two systems, owing to the collapse of intermediate ion-pairs to starting material. Although results are not available to permit calculation of the *rates of ionization* of both isomers of this system, product and anion exchange data [20a] suggest that the *rates of ionization* in acetic acid do not differ by much more than a factor of 2 or 3. In the acetolysis of the far more hindered *threo*- and *erythro*-2,5-dimethyl-4-phenyl-3-hexyl *p*-bromobenzenesulfonates XXI, the rate of appearance of *p*-bromobenzenesulfonic acid from the *erythro* isomer is 5.3 times the analogous rate for the *threo* isomer (50°).[53] Since the polarimetric and titrimetric rates for the *threo* isomer differ only by a factor of 1.2, the phenomena of ion-pair collapse, at least from phenonium ions, does not appear to be important in this system, and the rate of appearance of *p*-bromobenzenesulfonic acid can be used as an indication of the relative rates of ionization of the two isomers. The partial rates of acetolysis leading to XXII (whose configuration is retained) appear to be almost equal [53] for the two diastereomeric esters, even though, with one diastereomer, a *cis*-phenonium

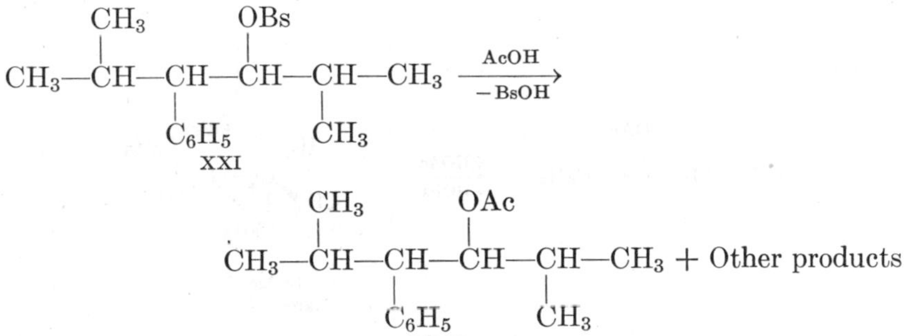

$$CH_3-\underset{\underset{\displaystyle C_6H_5}{|}}{\overset{\overset{\displaystyle CH_3}{|}}{CH}}-CH-\underset{\underset{\displaystyle CH_3}{|}}{\overset{\overset{\displaystyle OBs}{|}}{CH}}-CH-CH_3 \quad \xrightarrow[-\text{BsOH}]{\text{AcOH}}$$

XXI

$$CH_3-\underset{\underset{\displaystyle C_6H_5}{|}}{\overset{\overset{\displaystyle CH_3}{|}}{CH}}-CH-\underset{\underset{\displaystyle CH_3}{|}}{\overset{\overset{\displaystyle OAc}{|}}{CH}}-CH-CH_3 + \text{Other products}$$

XXII

ion is produced, and with the other a *trans*-phenonium ion. Thus the transition states leading to these phenonium ions would appear to be much nearer in geometry to the starting material than to bridged ion, and the eclipsing of groups in going to the *cis*-bridged ion (XXIII) probably occurs *after* the transition state has been passed.

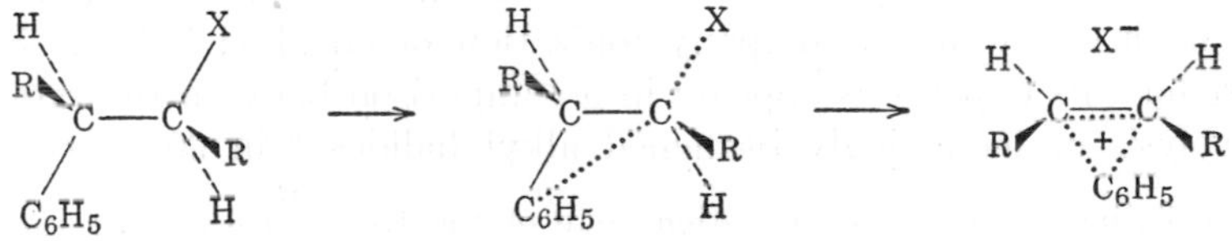

Transition state   Bridged ion-pair

XXIII

In contrast to the systems discussed above, in the acetolytic rearrangement of 1,1-diphenyl-2-propyl *p*-bromobenzenesulfonate into 1,2-

[53] D. J. Cram, F. A. Abd Elhafez, and F. L. Nyquist, unpublished results.

diphenyl-1-propyl acetate, only one of the two phenyls migrated.[26a, b] As would be expected, that phenyl migrated which involved a transition state in which the bulky non-migrating groups (methyl and phenyl) are *trans* to one another.   In this system, the transition state is more like a rigid three-membered ring whose non-migrating substituents are much more eclipsed than in the systems previously discussed.   This interpretation is consistent with the notion that in the

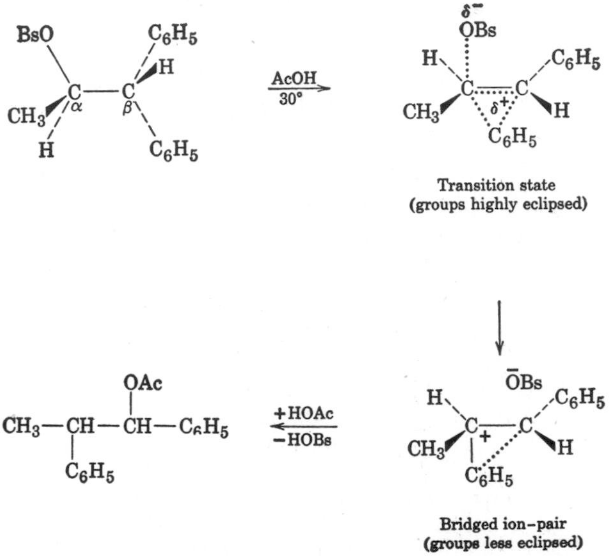

Transition state
(groups highly eclipsed)

Bridged ion–pair
(groups less eclipsed)

transition state the migrating phenyl is much nearer the midpoint between C_α and C_β than in the bridged ion produced.   That the bridging phenyl in the ionic intermediate should be more bonded to C_α than C_β is a consequence of the distribution of positive charge in the non-migrating as well as the migrating phenyl.[54]

RELEASE OF STERIC COMPRESSION.   Brown [55] first recognized the possibility that, in highly hindered systems, relief of compression energy (B strain) [55a] would accompany ionization of an alkyl halide.   Support for this hypothesis appears in a comparison between the rates of solvolysis of increasingly branched alkyl halides [56] in 90% acetone-

    [54] Eclipsing effects in the transition state of the E$_2$ reaction are discussed in Chapter 7.   In this reaction as well, different degrees of eclipsing of groups were observed, depending on how developed the double bond was in the transition state.

    [55] (a) H. C. Brown, *Science*, *103*, 385 (1946); (b) H. C. Brown and R. S. Fletcher, *J. Am. Chem. Soc.*, *71*, 1845 (1949).

    [56] (a) P. D. Bartlett, 10th National Organic Symposium, Boston, Massachusetts, June, 1947, p. 30 of *Abstracts*; (b) P. D. Bartlett, *Bull. soc. chim. France*, *1951*, 18, 101C.

water. Doubt exists about the exact structure of some of these halides [56] because of possible rearrangements during their preparation,
but there is no doubt that the rates of solvolysis increase dramatically

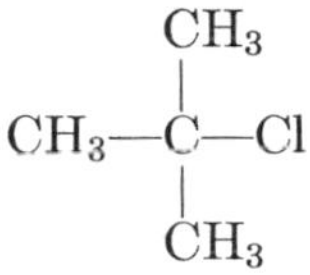

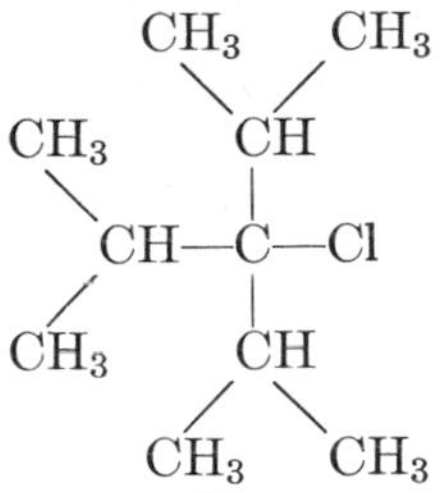

with increased β substitution in this tertiary series.[57] The fact that
kinetic acceleration due to carbon participation also increases with
β substitution in other, less hindered systems suggests that part of
the rate increases of the above chlorides are due to this same polar
effect. Superimposed on this polar effect (at least in the highly ramified systems) is the release of steric compression in the passing of
starting material to the transition state of the Wagner-Meerwein rearrangement or to the transition state leading to the open carbonium
ion. The products of the reactions of the more highly substituted
systems have not yet been reported, but it seems probable that the
products are highly rearranged.[58]

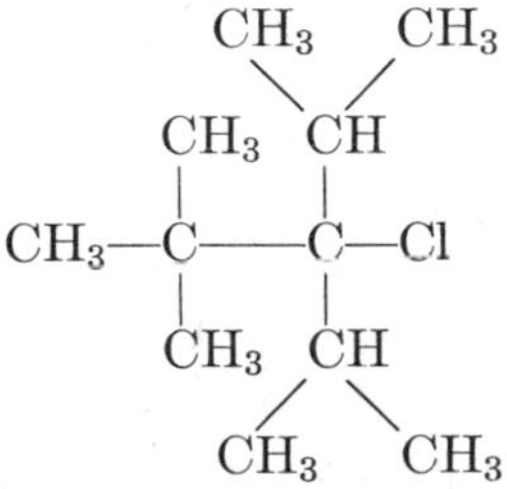

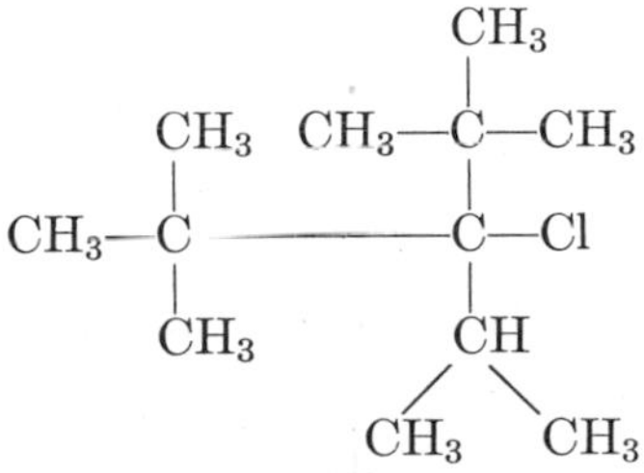

RELEASE OF STRAIN DUE TO ANGLE DEFORMATION. The nucleophilic
rearrangements in small ring compounds involve a number of new
problems.[59] The first-order acetolysis rates (60°) of the p-toluenesulfonates of the three- and four-membered ring carbinols are tabulated

[57] F. Brown, T. D. Davies, L. Dostrovsky, O. J. Evans, and E. D. Hughes
[Nature, 167, 987 (1951)] subsequently recognized this effect.

[58] See Chapter 2 for a more detailed discussion.

[59] For a summary, see J. D. Roberts, 12th National Organic Chemistry Symposium of the American Chemical Society, Denver, Colorado, June, 1951, p. 38 of
Abstracts.

below, as well as the products obtained at those temperatures necessary to drive the reactions to completion.[60, 61] Rearrangement oc-

ACETOLYSIS IN PRESENCE OF NaOAc

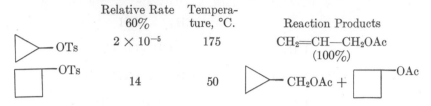

	Relative Rate 60%	Temperature, °C.	Reaction Products
▷—OTs	2×10^{-5}	175	$CH_2{=}CH{-}CH_2OAc$ (100%)
☐—OTs	14	50	▷—CH_2OAc + ☐—OAc

curred with the three- and four-membered rings as starting material,
the reaction being markedly slowed in the former and accelerated in
the latter example. Steric effects may operate which tend to depress
the solvolysis rates of cyclopropyl and cyclobutyl p-toluenesulfo-
nates.[60a, 62] The starting molecules probably possess less bond-angle
strain (I-strain) [62] than the transition states, the effect being greater
for the smaller ring system. The electrical effect in the cyclopropyl

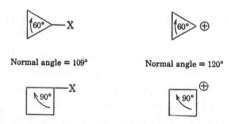

Normal angle = 109°   Normal angle = 120°

system which tends to delocalize the unshared pairs of electrons on X
(and thus strengthen the C—X bond) may be as, or more, important
in decreasing the solvolysis rate.[60a] Although the product of acetoly-

sis of cyclopropyl p-toluenesulfonate is rearranged, it is not yet clear
what type of intermediates, if any, intervene between product and
reactant.

[60] (a) J. D. Roberts and V. C. Chambers, *J. Am. Chem. Soc.*, **73**, 3177 (1951);
(b) J. D. Roberts and V. C. Chambers, *ibid.*, **73**, 5034 (1951).

[61] The rates are calculated relative to that of cyclohexyl p-toluenesulfonate,
which gave 15% cyclohexyl acetate and 85% cyclohexene. Cyclopentyl p-toluene-
sulfonate acetolyzed 16 times as fast as the cyclohexyl compound and gave 61%
cyclopentyl acetate and 39% cyclopentene. See Chapter 3 for more details.

[62] H. C. Brown and M. Gerstein, *J. Am. Chem. Soc.*, **72**, 2926 (1950).

The rate enhancement in the cyclobutyl system is probably due to carbon participation in the ionization to give some kind of bridged carbonium ion or ions which can solvolyze and collapse to either cyclobutyl or cyclopropylcarbinyl acetate. Further support for the intervention of a bridged carbonium intermediate, XXIV, was obtained

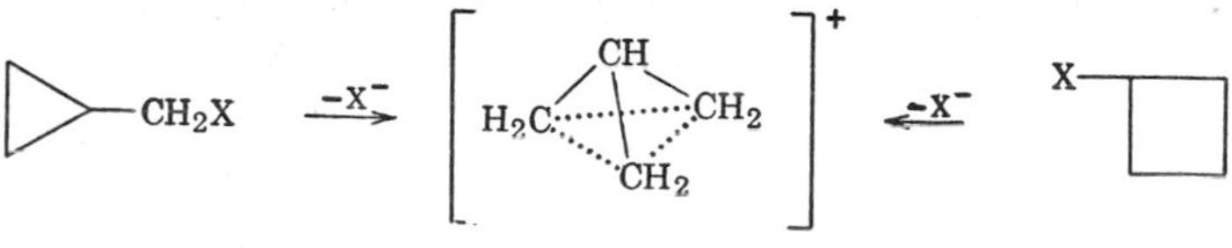

XXIV

from a study of the C^{14} distribution in the cyclopropylcarbinol and cyclobutanol formed when 1-C^{14} cyclopropylcarbinylamine was treated with nitrous acid.[63] The results indicated that the three methylene carbons in the starting amine achieve equivalence in the course of the reaction. Possibly the same bridged ion, XXIV, arises from cyclobutyl starting materials.

The electrophilic 1,2 rearrangement

In this class of rearrangement it is characteristic for Z to act as an electrophile. The reactions (see formulas) are initiated when B becomes rich in electrons. Only two reactions are known that fit this description, the Stevens and the Wittig rearrangements.

$$A—B \rightarrow A—B$$

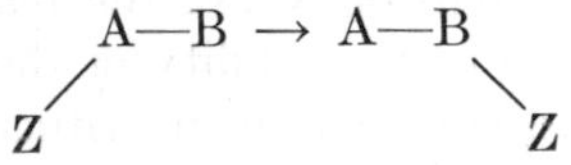

comes rich in electrons. Only two reactions are known that fit this description, the Stevens and the Wittig rearrangements.

STEVENS REARRANGEMENT. In the generalized formulation of this reaction (see below), the migrating group R can be methyl, benzyl, substituted benzyl, phenacyl, allyl, or 3-phenylpropargyl; a and b are methyl or other alkyl substituents; $\ddot{B}$ is a base capable of producing

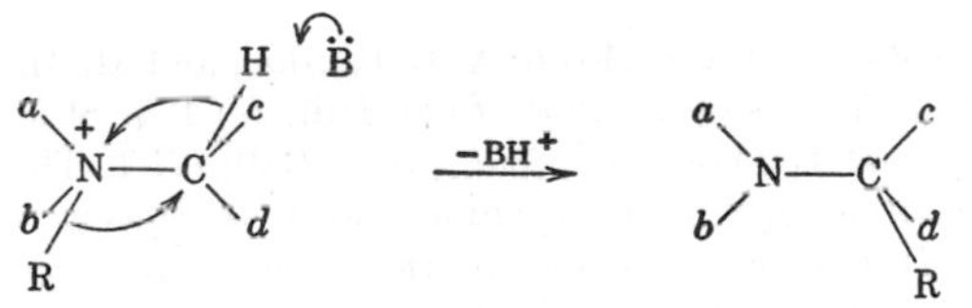

a carbanion at the migration terminus (OH^-, RO^-, NH_2^-, $C_6H_5^-$); and c and d (either one or both) are groups that facilitate anion forma-

[63] (a) J. D. Roberts and R. H. Mazur, J. Am. Chem. Soc., 73, 2509, 3542 (1951); (b) see also the suggestion of C. G. Bergstrom and S. Siegel, ibid., 74, 145 (1952).

tion (e.g., phenyl, vinyl, benzoyl, or acetyl).[64] The reaction has been demonstrated to be intramolecular by applying the reaction simultaneously to two different compounds in the same medium and demonstrating that no interchanges of the migrating group between the two systems occurred.[64b] At least in some systems in some media, the migration stage of the reaction appears to be preceded by the formation of a carbanion. Thus, the rate of reaction of XXV increased but

$$CH_3-\overset{CH_3}{\underset{C_6H_5CH_2}{\underset{|}{\overset{|}{N^+}}}}-\overset{H}{\underset{H}{\overset{|}{C}}}-COC_6H_5 \xrightarrow{OH^-}$$

XXV

$$CH_3-\overset{CH_3}{\underset{C_6H_5CH_2}{\underset{|}{\overset{|}{N^+}}}}-\overset{\ominus}{CH}-COC_6H_5 \rightarrow \overset{CH_3}{\underset{CH_3}{\underset{|}{\overset{|}{N}}}}-\overset{|}{\underset{CH_2C_6H_5}{CH}}-COC_6H_5$$

approached a limit as the concentration of OH^- in the medium was increased.[64d] When various substituents were placed in the m and p positions of the benzyl group of XXV, the reaction rate increased in the order of the *electron-attracting* ability of the substituent ($CH_3O <$ $H < Cl < NO_2$).[64b, d] In contrast, p substituents placed in the phenacyl group of XXV increase the rate of rearrangement in order of their *electron-releasing* ability ($NO_2 < Cl$ or $CH_3O < H < CH_3$), although the effect is less pronounced.[64e]

Although Stevens [64b, d] suggested that R migrates with its bonding electrons, others have suggested [65] that the above data are also consistent with R migrating without its bonding electrons. That the migrating group completely maintains its asymmetry has been dem-

[64] (a) T. S. Stevens, E. M. Creighton, A. B. Gordon, and M. MacNicol, *J. Chem. Soc.*, *1928*, 3193; (b) T. S. Stevens, *ibid.*, *1930*, 2107; (c) T. S. Stevens, W. W. Sneddon, E. T. Stiller, and T. Thompson, *ibid.*, *1930*, 2119; (d) T. Thompson and T. S. Stevens, *ibid.*, *1932*, 55, 69; (e) J. L. Dunn and T. S. Stevens, *ibid.*, *1932*, 1926; and *1934*, 279; (f) T. S. Stevens and B. Heins, *ibid.*, *1937*, 856; (g) G. Wittig, R. Mangold, and G. Felletschin, *Ann.*, *580*, 116 (1948).

[65] (a) G. M. Bennett and A. W. Chapman, *Ann. Repts. Chem. Soc. London*, *27*, 123 (1930); (b) H. B. Watson, *Modern Theories of Organic Chemistry*, p. 205, Oxford University Press, London, England, 1941; (c) C. R. Hauser and S. W. Kantor, *J. Am. Chem. Soc.*, *73*, 1439 (1951); (d) C. K. Ingold, reference 2f, p. 526.

onstrated [66a] with the aid of optically active XXVI as starting mate-

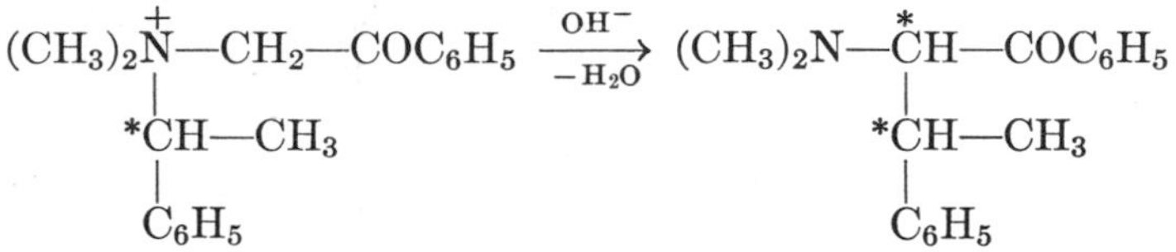

$$(CH_3)_2 \overset{+}{N}—CH_2—COC_6H_5 \xrightarrow[-H_2O]{OH^-} (CH_3)_2N—\overset{*}{C}H—COC_6H_5$$

$$\overset{|}{*CH—CH_3} \qquad\qquad\qquad \overset{|}{*CH—CH_3}$$

$$\overset{|}{C_6H_5} \qquad\qquad\qquad\qquad \overset{|}{C_6H_5}$$

$$\qquad XXVI \qquad\qquad\qquad\qquad XXVII$$

rial. The relative configurations of reactant and product were determined,[66b] and the α-phenylethyl group was found to retain its configuration during the rearrangement. A unique method of forming the starting material for the Stevens rearrangement [67] consists in decomposing aliphatic diazo compounds, XXVIII, with certain tertiary amines. A reaction similar to the Stevens rearrangement has been observed with sulfonium compounds.[64d]

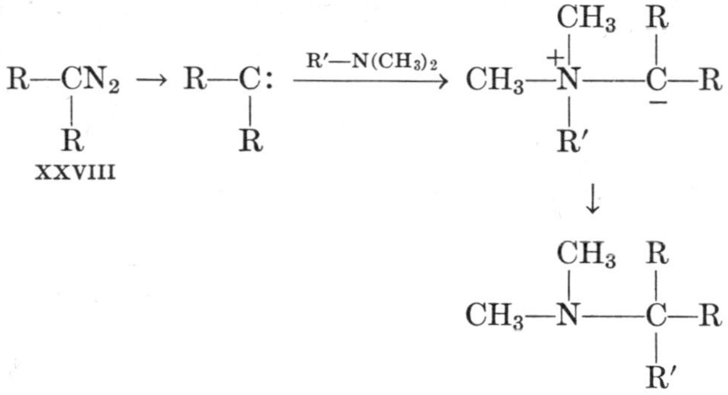

$$R—CN_2 \rightarrow R—C: \xrightarrow{R'—N(CH_3)_2} CH_3—\overset{\overset{\displaystyle CH_3}{|}}{\underset{\displaystyle R'}{N}}\overset{\overset{\displaystyle R}{|}}{\underset{}{—C—R}}$$

$$\overset{|}{R} \qquad \overset{|}{R}$$

$$XXVIII$$

$$\downarrow$$

$$CH_3—\overset{\overset{\displaystyle CH_3}{|}}{\underset{\displaystyle R'}{N}}\overset{\overset{\displaystyle R}{|}}{—C—R}$$

In these rearrangements the question of whether the migrating group (R) migrates with or without its pair of bonding electrons is extremely subtle. Both the rough kinetics [64d] and the fact that in some cases deeply colored solutions develop during the reaction [65c] point to carbanion formation in the first stage. In the ordinary phenacyl systems with OH^- as base, carbanion formation is probably reversible and not rate limiting. The rate-limiting migration stage is accelerated by electron-dispersing substituents (e.g., NO_2 in the p position of the migrating benzyl group), but slowed by delocalization of charge in the carbanion (see above). The bridged species XXIX might represent either an unstable intermediate or the transition state of the reaction.

[66] (a) A. Campbell, A. H. J. Houston, and J. Kenyon, *J. Chem. Soc.*, *1947*, 93; (b) J. H. Brewster and M. W. Kline, *J. Am. Chem. Soc.*, *74*, 5179 (1952).
[67] W. R. Bamford and T. S. Stevens, *J. Chem. Soc.*, *1952*, 4675.

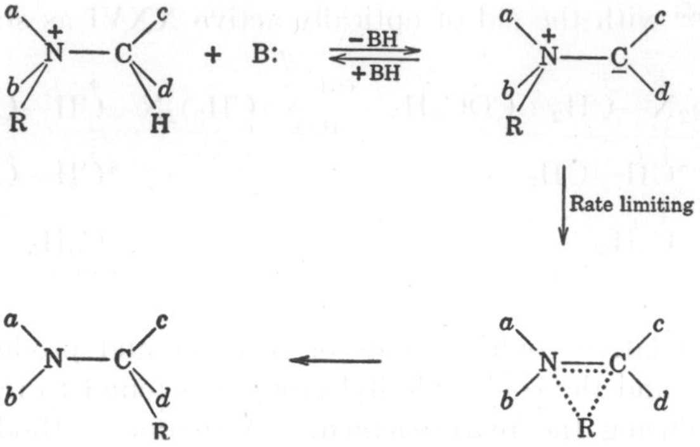

XXIX

In either case, resonance of stabilization due to contributions of A, B, C, and D to the hybrid should apply. Of the dipolar structures (C and D), C must be the more important (delocalization of electrons in

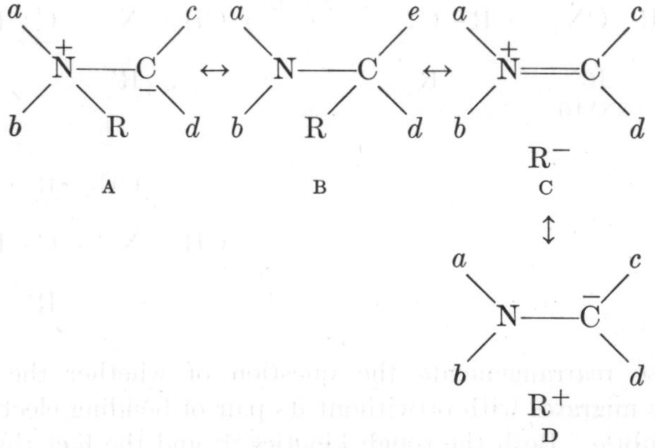

R enhances the rate, delocalization in C_{-d}^{-c} inhibits the rate of rearrangement). Thus, if **XXIX** is an intermediate, it should possess considerable ion-pair character, and if a transition state, considerable dipolar character. In any event, the question whether R migrates with its bonding electrons becomes almost meaningless.

WITTIG REARRANGEMENT. In this reaction, an alkyl group migrates from either oxygen [68] or sulfur [69] to either a carbanion or incipient

[68] (a) G. Wittig and L. Lohman, *Ann.*, *550*, 260 (1942); (b) G. Wittig and W. Happe, *Ann.*, *557*, 205 (1947); (c) C. R. Hauser and S. W. Kantor, *J. Am. Chem. Soc.*, *73*, 1439 (1951).

[69] C. R. Hauser, S. W. Kantor, and W. R. Bransen, *J. Am. Chem. Soc.*, *75*, 2660 (1953).

carbanion bonded to the oxygen or sulfur. The product is an alcoholate or mercaptolate anion. The bases employed are in general stronger ($NaNH_2$ [68c, 69] or C_6H_5Li [68a, b]) than in the Stevens rearrangement, and R has thus far been limited to methyl, benzyl, and allyl. In all the

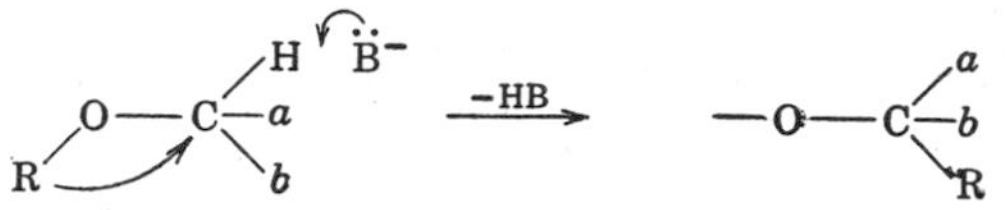

systems studied, either or both *a* and *b* have been aryl groups. The reaction appears to involve the anion-metal cation ion-pair as an intermediate, and is formulated as such.

$$\underset{CH_3}{\diagup}O—CH_2—C_6H_5 \xrightarrow{C_6H_5Li} \underset{CH_3}{\diagup}O—\overset{Li^+}{\underset{-}{C}H}—C_6H_5 \rightarrow LiO—\underset{CH_3}{\underset{|}{C}H}—C_6H_5$$

These two examples of electrophilic 1,2 rearrangements have not been studied in highly enough constrained systems to allow any steric effects to be identified, nor has the stereochemistry of the transformations been thoroughly explored.

The homolytic 1,2 rearrangement

In this group of rearrangements Z migrates as a radical. The reaction (formulas) is initiated when B becomes deficient by one electron. Examples of this class of rearrangement have only been found

$$\underset{Z}{\diagup}A—B \rightarrow A—B\underset{Z}{\diagdown}$$

recently, one set being analogous to the Wagner-Meerwein, a second to the Baeyer-Villiger, and a third to the Wolff rearrangement.

In all the examples similar to the Wagner-Meerwein rearrangement,[70] a phenyl migrated in preference to an alkyl group. The reactions were initiated either by the homolytic cleavage of the C—Cl

[70] (*a*) W. H. Urry and M. S. Kharasch, *J. Am. Chem. Soc.*, *66*, 1438 (1944); (*b*) S. Winstein and F. H. Seubold, *ibid.*, *69*, 2916 (1947); (*c*) W. H. Urry and N. Nicolaides, *ibid.*, *74*, 5163 (1952); (*d*) D. Y. Curtin and M. J. Hurwitz, *ibid.*, *74*, 5381 (1952).

bond at the migration terminus with a cobaltous chloride-Grignard mixture, or by the decarbonylation reaction of an aldehyde with di-*tert*-butyl peroxide. The results formulated have been interpreted to

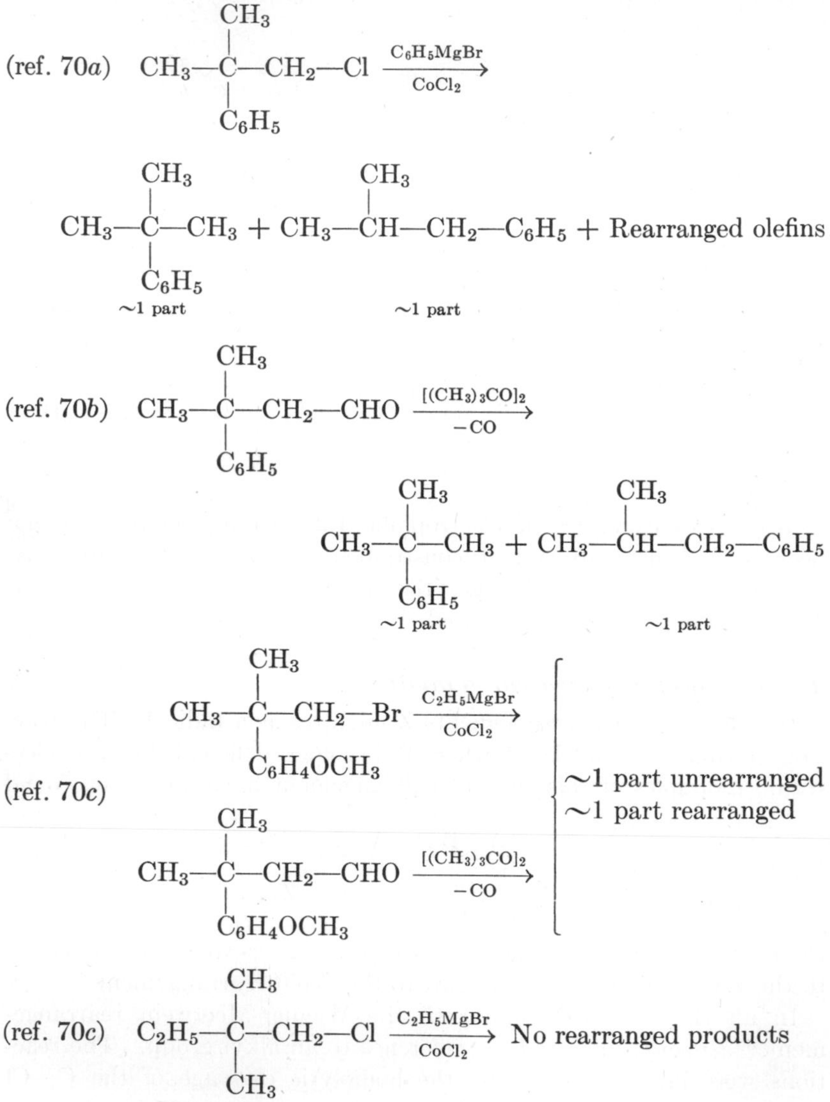

$$(\text{ref. } 70a) \quad CH_3-\underset{\underset{C_6H_5}{|}}{\overset{\overset{CH_3}{|}}{C}}-CH_2-Cl \xrightarrow[CoCl_2]{C_6H_5MgBr}$$

$$CH_3-\underset{\underset{C_6H_5}{|}}{\overset{\overset{CH_3}{|}}{C}}-CH_3 + CH_3-\underset{}{\overset{\overset{CH_3}{|}}{CH}}-CH_2-C_6H_5 + \text{Rearranged olefins}$$

$$\quad\quad\quad\quad \sim1 \text{ part} \quad\quad\quad\quad\quad \sim1 \text{ part}$$

$$(\text{ref. } 70b) \quad CH_3-\underset{\underset{C_6H_5}{|}}{\overset{\overset{CH_3}{|}}{C}}-CH_2-CHO \xrightarrow[-CO]{[(CH_3)_3CO]_2}$$

$$CH_3-\underset{\underset{C_6H_5}{|}}{\overset{\overset{CH_3}{|}}{C}}-CH_3 + CH_3-\overset{\overset{CH_3}{|}}{CH}-CH_2-C_6H_5$$

$$\quad\quad\quad\quad \sim1 \text{ part} \quad\quad\quad\quad \sim1 \text{ part}$$

$$(\text{ref. } 70c)$$

$$CH_3-\underset{\underset{C_6H_4OCH_3}{|}}{\overset{\overset{CH_3}{|}}{C}}-CH_2-Br \xrightarrow[CoCl_2]{C_2H_5MgBr}$$

$$CH_3-\underset{\underset{C_6H_4OCH_3}{|}}{\overset{\overset{CH_3}{|}}{C}}-CH_2-CHO \xrightarrow[-CO]{[(CH_3)_3CO]_2}$$

$$\left. \right\} \quad \begin{array}{l} \sim1 \text{ part unrearranged} \\ \sim1 \text{ part rearranged} \end{array}$$

$$(\text{ref. } 70c) \quad C_2H_5-\underset{\underset{CH_3}{|}}{\overset{\overset{CH_3}{|}}{C}}-CH_2-Cl \xrightarrow[CoCl_2]{C_2H_5MgBr} \text{No rearranged products}$$

involve both unrearranged and rearranged radicals as discrete intermediates, although stereochemical evidence is lacking. In the di-*tert*-butyl peroxide-catalyzed decomposition of β-phenylisovaleralde-

(ref. 70d) $p\text{-}CH_3OC_6H_4\text{—}CH\text{—}CH_2\text{—}CHO \xrightarrow[-CO]{[(CH_3)_3CO]_2}$
$\qquad\qquad\qquad\qquad\quad |$
$\qquad\qquad\qquad\qquad\ C_6H_5$

$$p\text{-}CH_3OC_6H_4\text{—}CH\text{—}CH_3$$
$$|$$
$$C_6H_5$$
(Possibly with H migration)

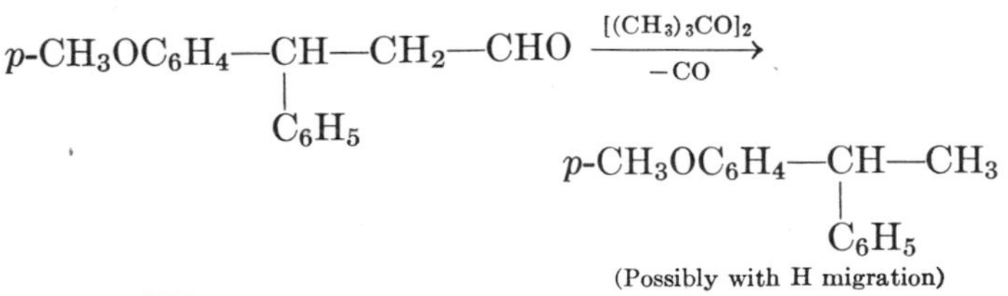

(ref. 70d) $C_6H_5\text{—}\overset{\displaystyle CH_3}{\underset{\displaystyle C_6H_5}{\overset{|}{\underset{|}{C}}}}\text{—}CH_2\text{—}CHO \xrightarrow[-CO]{[(CH_3)_3CO]_2}$

$$C_6H_5CH_2\text{—}\overset{\displaystyle CH_3}{\underset{\displaystyle C_6H_5}{\overset{|}{\underset{|}{C}}}}\text{——}\overset{\displaystyle CH_3}{\underset{\displaystyle C_6H_5}{\overset{|}{\underset{|}{C}}}}\text{—}CH_2\text{—}C_6H_5$$
(100% rearrangement)

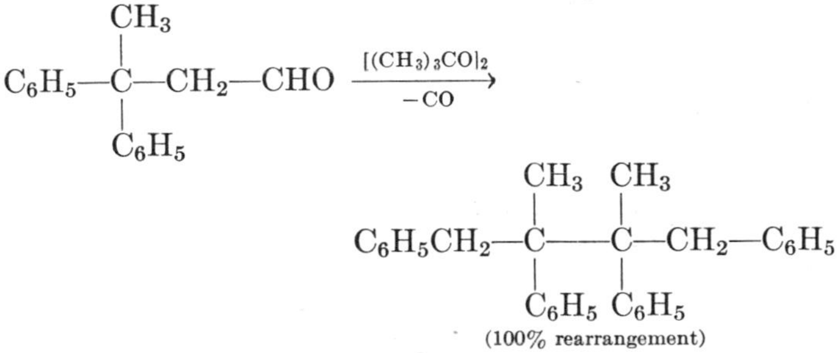

(ref. 70d) $(C_6H_5)_3C\text{—}CH\text{—}CHO \xrightarrow[-CO]{[(CH_3)_3CO]_2}$
$\qquad\qquad\qquad\quad\ |$
$\qquad\qquad\qquad\ CH_3$

$$(C_6H_5)_2CH\text{—}\underset{\displaystyle CH_3}{\overset{|}{C}H}\text{—}C_6H_5 + (C_6H_5)_2\text{—}\underset{\displaystyle CH_3}{\overset{|}{C}}\text{—}C_6H_5$$

Complete rearrangement

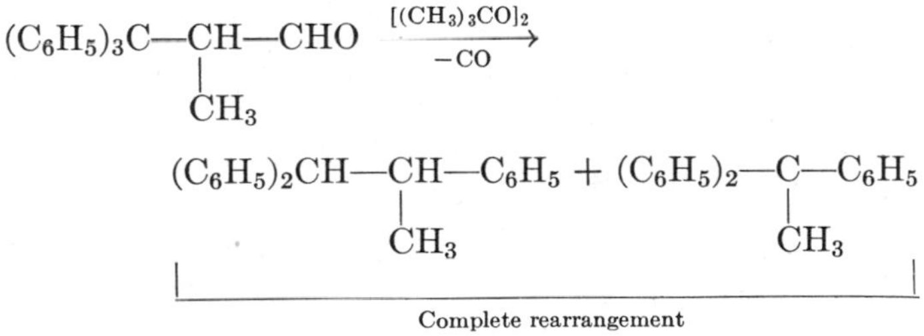

(ref. 70d) $(C_6H_5)_3C\text{—}CH_2\text{—}CHO \xrightarrow[-CO]{[(CH_3)_3CO]_2}$

$$(C_6H_5)_2CH\text{—}CH_2\text{—}C_6H_5$$
(Complete rearrangement)

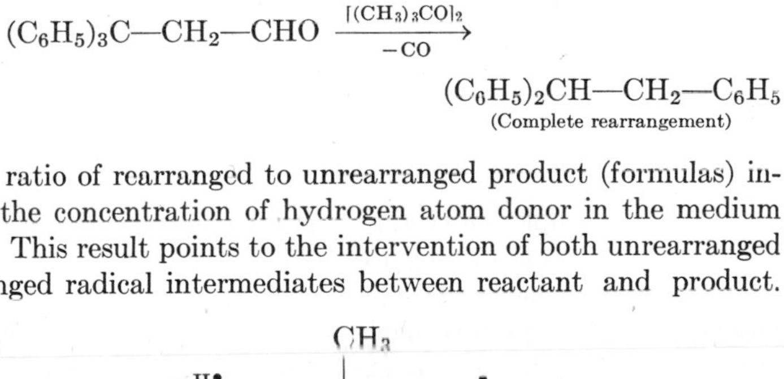

hyde,[71] the ratio of rearranged to unrearranged product (formulas) increased as the concentration of hydrogen atom donor in the medium decreased. This result points to the intervention of both unrearranged and rearranged radical intermediates between reactant and product.

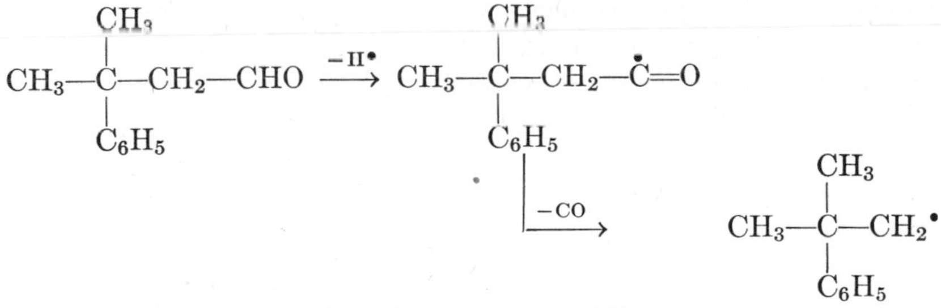

$$CH_3\text{—}\overset{\displaystyle CH_3}{\underset{\displaystyle C_6H_5}{\overset{|}{\underset{|}{C}}}}\text{—}CH_2\text{—}CHO \xrightarrow{-H\cdot} CH_3\text{—}\overset{\displaystyle CH_3}{\underset{\displaystyle C_6H_5}{\overset{|}{\underset{|}{C}}}}\text{—}CH_2\text{—}\overset{\displaystyle\cdot}{C}\!=\!O$$

$$\downarrow -CO$$

$$CH_3\text{—}\overset{\displaystyle CH_3}{\underset{\displaystyle C_6H_5}{\overset{|}{\underset{|}{C}}}}\text{—}CH_2\cdot$$

[71] F. H. Seubold, J. Am. Chem. Soc., 75, 2533 (1953).

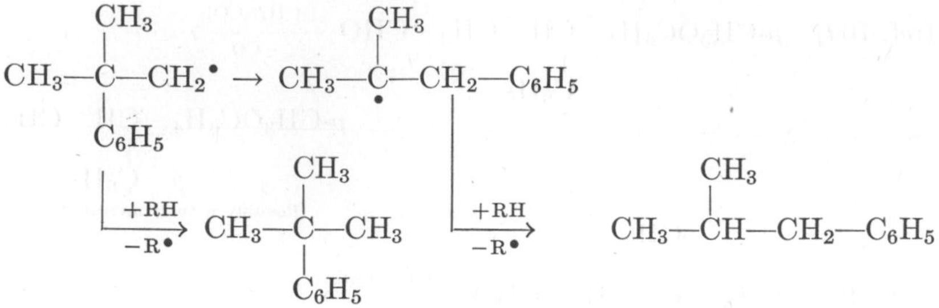

$$CH_3-\underset{\underset{C_6H_5}{|}}{\overset{\overset{CH_3}{|}}{C}}-CH_2\overset{\bullet}{} \rightarrow CH_3-\underset{\underset{\bullet}{}}{\overset{\overset{CH_3}{|}}{C}}-CH_2-C_6H_5$$

$$\xrightarrow[-R^{\bullet}]{+RH} CH_3-\underset{\underset{C_6H_5}{|}}{\overset{\overset{CH_3}{|}}{C}}-CH_3 \qquad \xrightarrow[-R^{\bullet}]{+RH} \qquad CH_3-\underset{}{\overset{\overset{CH_3}{|}}{C}H}-CH_2-C_6H_5$$

The results formulated for the C to O migration of an aryl group [72] indicate that migratory ability in the homolytic 1,2 rearrangements is different from that found in analogous nucleophilic 1,2 rearrangements.

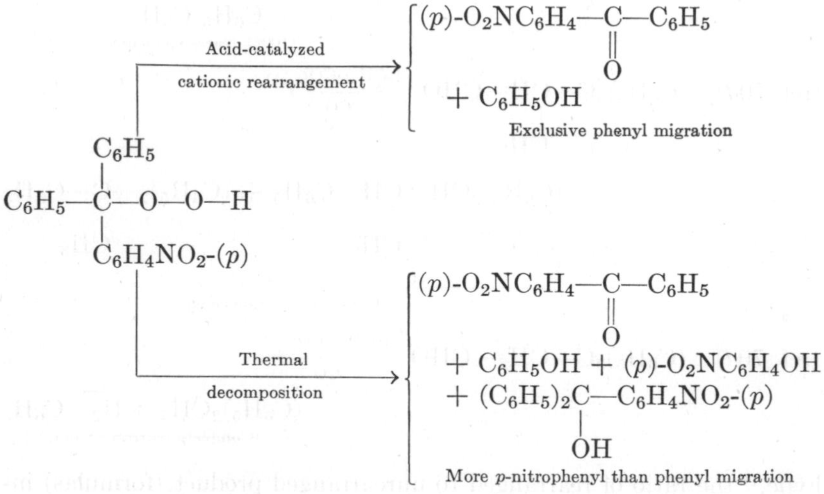

$$\xrightarrow[\text{cationic rearrangement}]{\text{Acid-catalyzed}} \begin{cases} (p)\text{-}O_2NC_6H_4-\underset{\underset{O}{\|}}{C}-C_6H_5 \\ \\ + C_6H_5OH \\ \text{Exclusive phenyl migration} \end{cases}$$

$$C_6H_5-\underset{\underset{C_6H_4NO_2\text{-}(p)}{|}}{\overset{\overset{C_6H_5}{|}}{C}}-O-O-H$$

$$\xrightarrow[\text{decomposition}]{\text{Thermal}} \begin{cases} (p)\text{-}O_2NC_6H_4-\underset{\underset{O}{\|}}{C}-C_6H_5 \\ \\ + C_6H_5OH + (p)\text{-}O_2NC_6H_4OH \\ + (C_6H_5)_2C-C_6H_4NO_2\text{-}(p) \\ \qquad\quad\underset{OH}{|} \\ \text{More } p\text{-nitrophenyl than phenyl migration} \end{cases}$$

In all the examples cited, the relief of compression energy (B strain) might provide some driving force for rearrangement, since in every case a less constrained radical is generated. The discrimination among possible migrating groups suggests, however, that the transition state involved in the migration is one that provides a variable amount of resonance of stabilization, depending on the nature of the migrating groups.

An example of the Wolff rearrangement run in homogeneous medium has been reported,[73] and the catalytic effect of silver ion on the reaction suggests the intervention of radical intermediates.

[72] P. D. Bartlett and J. D. Cotman, *J. Am. Chem. Soc.*, **72**, 3095 (1950).
[73] M. S. Newman and P. F. Beal III, *J. Am. Chem. Soc.*, **72**, 5163 (1950).

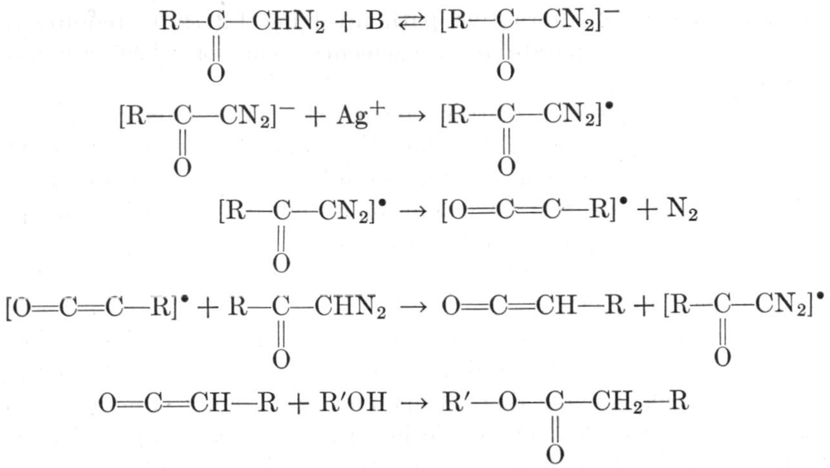

$$R-\underset{\underset{O}{\|}}{C}-CHN_2 + B \rightleftarrows [R-\underset{\underset{O}{\|}}{C}-CN_2]^-$$

$$[R-\underset{\underset{O}{\|}}{C}-CN_2]^- + Ag^+ \rightarrow [R-\underset{\underset{O}{\|}}{C}-CN_2]^\bullet$$

$$[R-\underset{\underset{O}{\|}}{C}-CN_2]^\bullet \rightarrow [O{=}C{=}C-R]^\bullet + N_2$$

$$[O{=}C{=}C-R]^\bullet + R-\underset{\underset{O}{\|}}{C}-CHN_2 \rightarrow O{=}C{=}CH-R + [R-\underset{\underset{O}{\|}}{C}-CN_2]^\bullet$$

$$O{=}C{=}CH-R + R'OH \rightarrow R'-O-\underset{\underset{O}{\|}}{C}-CH_2-R$$

TRANSANNULAR REARRANGEMENTS

A number of examples of transannular rearrangements have been discovered in connection with the study of both large rings and condensed ring systems. Those of the Wagner-Meerwein type with hydrogen as the migrating group are particularly interesting because of the suggestion (implicit in the observation that the reactions occur at all) that the common occurrence of 1,2 shifts is derived largely from the favorable geometry and not necessarily from any intrinsic electronic advantage to a three-membered ring transition state. Although only a relatively small number of examples of transannular migrations are yet available, the recognition of the phenomena will undoubtedly lead to the discovery of many more examples.

The difficulty in identifying migrations more complicated than the 1,2 type is that usually the overall observed results can be interpreted in terms of a series of 1,2 shifts. Thus, the conversion of 4,4-dimethyl-3-ethyl-2-pentanol into 2,4-dimethyl-3-ethyl-2-pentene by the action of acid [74] can be most easily visualized as a direct 1,3 migration of a

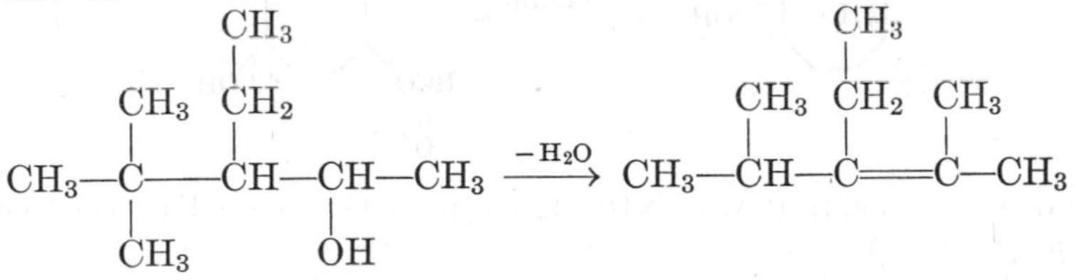

[74] W. A. Mosher and J. C. Cox, *J. Am. Chem. Soc.*, **72**, 3701 (1950). See also W. Herz, *J. Am. Chem. Soc.*, **74**, 3350 (1954).

methyl group. An alternative path involving 1,2 shifts requires a minimum of five separate rearrangements, some of which are improbable.

The first example of a rearrangement that can be interpreted only in terms of 1,3 hydrogen shift is the C^{14} shuffling in the *exo*-norbornyl system.[18] The rearrangements that occur during the dehydration of β-fenchol [75] and the rearrangement of camphenilyl amine to β-isofenchocamphorol [76] provide other examples. In the last three systems, the structures are relatively rigid and the geometries favorable for hydrogen involvement.

Three examples of transannular hydrogen migrations in larger ring compounds have been observed in connection with the solvolytic opening of an ethylene oxide ring. Cope and coworkers [77] observed that the solvolysis of cyclooctene oxide in formic acid gave, after alkaline hydrolysis of the monoformate, a mixture of diols, one of which was identified as 1,4-dihydroxycyclooctane. This result can be accounted

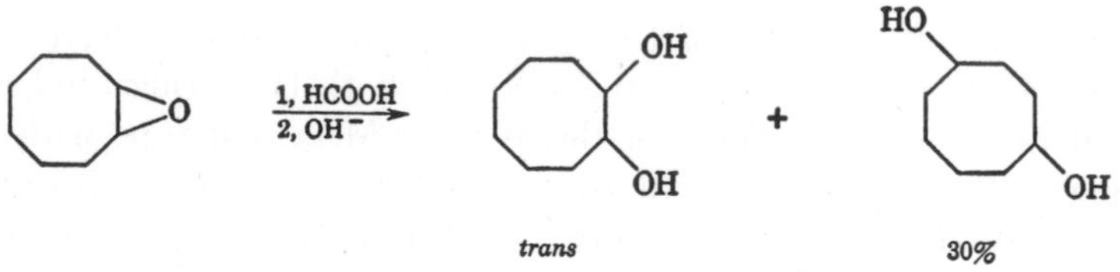

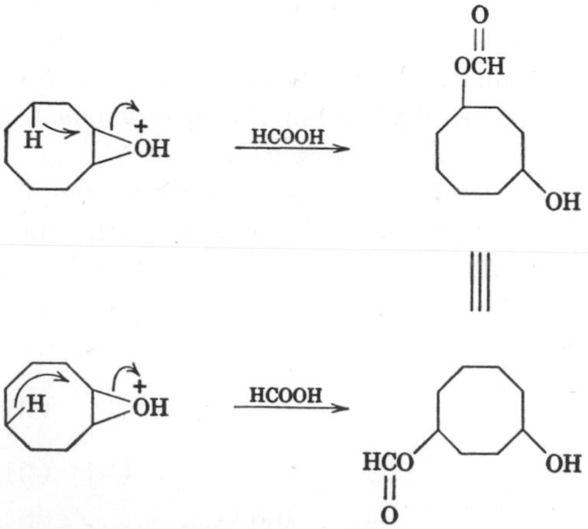

[75] W. Doering and H. P. Wolf, XIIth International Congress of Pure and Applied Chemistry, New York, September, 1951, p. 437 of *Abstracts*.

[76] S. Beckmann and R. Bamberger, *Ann.*, *574*, 65 (1951).

[77] A. C. Cope, S. W. Fenton, and C. F. Spencer, *J. Am. Chem. Soc.*, *74*, 5884 (1952).

for in terms of a 1,3- or a 1,5-hydrogen shift accompanying the opening of the ethylene oxide ring, or a series of 1,2-hydrogen shifts after
the opening. The last possibility is highly improbable. Similarly,
trans-cyclodecene oxide (**XXX**) gave a mixture of one stereoisomer of
1-hydroxydecalin (**XXXI**) and one of 1,6-cyclodecanediol (**XXXII**),
probably the *trans* isomer.[78]   Interestingly, each of these products

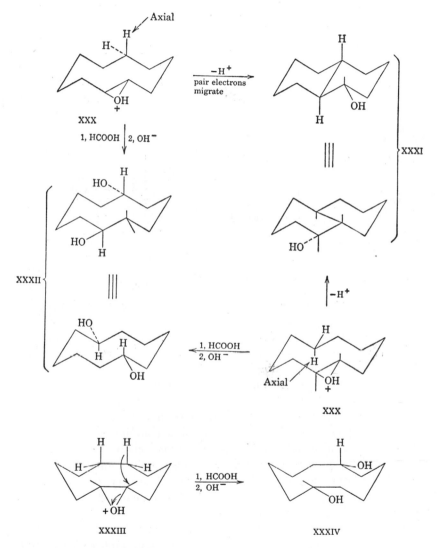

[78] (*a*) V. Prelog and K. Schenker, *Helv. Chim. Acta*, *35*, 2044 (1952); (*b*) V. Prelog,
K. Schenker, and W. Kung, *ibid.*, *36*, 471 (1953).

can arise from a *trans* opening of the oxide ring in either of two directions, the hydride shift in each case opening the three-membered ring in one direction and the electron pair from the C—H bond in the other. From *cis*-cyclodecene oxide (XXXIII) was obtained a second 1,6-cyclodecanediol, probably the *cis* isomer (XXXIV). Again, with XXXIII, either of two hydrogens can migrate, each opening the oxide ring in the opposite direction from the other.

These observations represent the first example in which stereospecificity is encountered at both the carbon atoms *from which* and *to which* a hydrogen migrates. This type of stereospecificity suggests two possible mechanisms: (1) the reactions are completely concerted, all bonds being made and broken in one transition state; (2) the reactions involve a bridged ion intermediate (a protonium ion), such as A, which is separated from both reactant and product by one transition state.

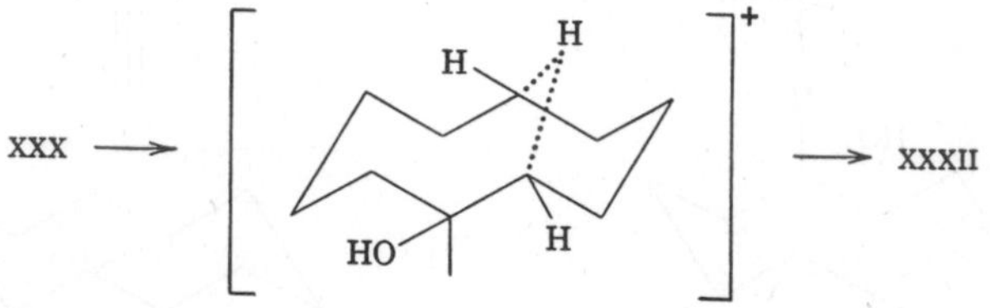

ACYL AND RELATED REARRANGEMENTS

The stereochemistry of and the steric effects associated with the intramolecular acyl-migration reaction have received considerable attention both in the field of natural products and in that of organic reaction mechanisms. Two general formulations illustrate the possible courses (limited to the substituted ethane stysems) that these reactions can assume. In sequence 1, E is usually a good leaving group such as halogen, chlorosulfite, sulfonate ester, or hydroxyl group, and, in principle at least, A and B can be oxygen, sulfur, or nitrogen, although examples of only a few of the possible combinations are known. Similarly, in 2, although all possible combinations of A, B, and E as sulfur, oxygen, or nitrogen can be conceived, only a small number of cases have been investigated. The stereochemistry of sequence 1 varies widely with conditions, whereas, for sequence 2, retention at both C_α and C_β is the rule.

The most studied examples of sequence 1 are those in which E is halogen or an ester function, A = B = oxygen, and R is methyl. The ramifications of the reaction are well illustrated by the various

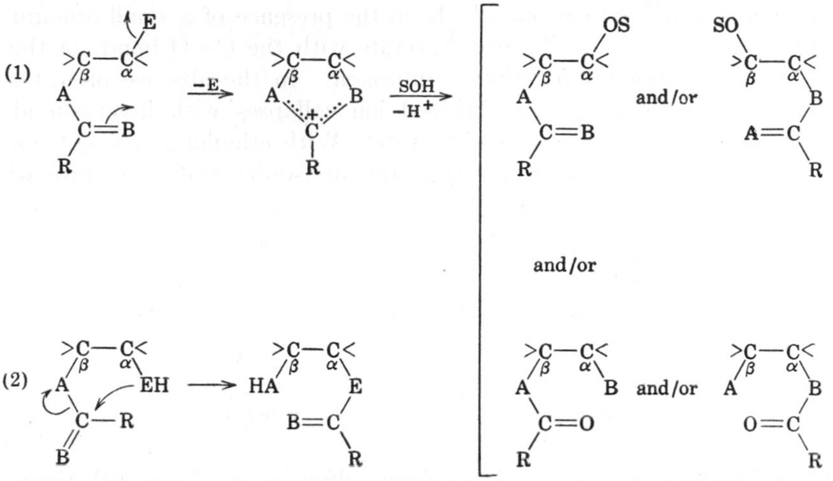

(1) reaction scheme

(2) reaction scheme

courses that the solvolyses of *trans*-2-acetoxycyclohexyl *p*-toluenesulfonate can assume.[79] In acetic acid, the *trans* isomer ionizes to give

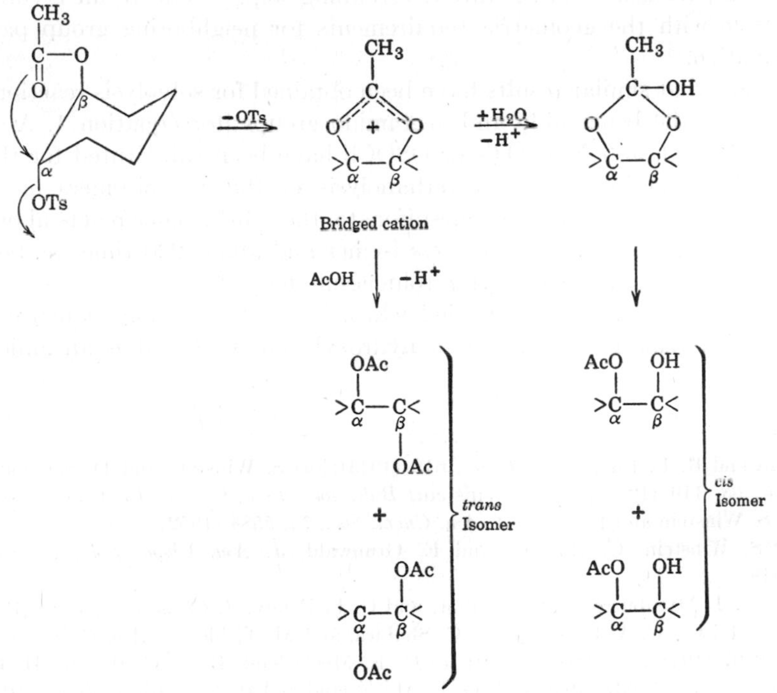

Bridged cation

AcOH | −H+

trans Isomer

cis Isomer

[79] (a) S. Winstein, H. V. Hess, and R. E. Buckles, *J. Am. Chem. Soc.*, *64*, 2796 (1942); (b) S. Winstein and R. E. Buckles, *ibid.*, *64*, 2780, 2787 (1942); (c) S. Win-

an acetoxyl bridged cation, which, in the presence of a small amount of water, can go to *cis* hydroxy acetate with the C—O bonds of the cation at C_α and C_β remaining unbroken. In the absence of water (e.g., dry acetic acid), the bridged ion collapses with inversion at either C_α or C_β to give *trans*-diacetate. With ethanol as solvent, an *ortho* ester results. The fact that the first-order acetolysis rate of

Bridged cation   *ortho* Ester

trans-2-acetoxyl-1-cyclohexyl *p*-toluenesulfonate is about 10^4 times that of the *cis* isomer, coupled with the stereochemical results, points to participation by the acetoxyl group (a complex neighboring group) [79] for the *trans* isomer in the rate-determining step.[80] This result is compatible with the geometric requirements for neighboring group participation.[79]

Somewhat similar results have been obtained for solvolysis reactions in which the benzamido and acetamido groups [for equation 1, A = NH, B = O, and X = OTs or OSOCl] have been substituted for the acetoxyl function.[81] In the ethanolysis of the stereoisomers of 2-benzamidocyclohexyl *p*-toluenesulfonate, the *trans* isomer reacts about 10^3 times as fast (75°) as the *cis* isomer and about 200 times as fast as *trans*-2-acetoxycyclohexyl *p*-toluenesulfonate.[79]

Most of the examples studied which illustrate reaction sequence 2 are in systems in which E is a hydroxyl and A—C—R is an amide

$$\overset{\displaystyle A—C—R}{\underset{\displaystyle B}{\|}}$$

stein and R. E. Buckles, *ibid.*, *65*, 613 (1943); (d) S. Winstein and D. Seymour, *ibid.*, *68*, 119 (1946); (e) S. Winstein, *Bull. soc. chim. France*, *18*, C55 (1951); (f) S. Winstein and R. Heck, *J. Am. Chem. Soc.*, *74*, 5584 (1952).

[80] S. Winstein, C. Hanson, and E. Grunwald, *J. Am. Chem. Soc.*, *70*, 812 (1948).

[81] (a) J. Attenburrow, D. F. Elliot, and G. F. Penny, *J. Chem. Soc.*, *1948*, 310; (b) C. Pfister, C. A. Robinson, A. C. Shabica, and M. Tishler, *J. Am. Chem. Soc.*, *70*, 2297 (1948); *71*, 1101 (1949); (c) G. E. McCasland, R. C. Clark, and H. E. Carter, *ibid.*, *71*, 637 (1949); (d) G. E. McCasland and P. A. Smith, *ibid.*, *72*, 2190 (1950); (e) W. S. Johnson and E. N. Schubert, *ibid.*, *72*, 2187 (1950); (f) S. Winstein and R. Boschan, *ibid.*, *72*, 2311, 4669 (1952). See also reference 59.

group, or E is an amino and A—C—R is an ester function.[82] Welsh [82a]

$$\overset{\parallel}{B}$$

found that the two diasteromerically related N-benzoylephedrines underwent N → O rearrangement at rates that differed by a factor of about 70 in 0.1 N hydrogen chloride in 95% ethanol (~30°) and that the stereochemistry of the reactions was largely that of retention at C_α and C_β, the results predicted by sequence 2. These differences in

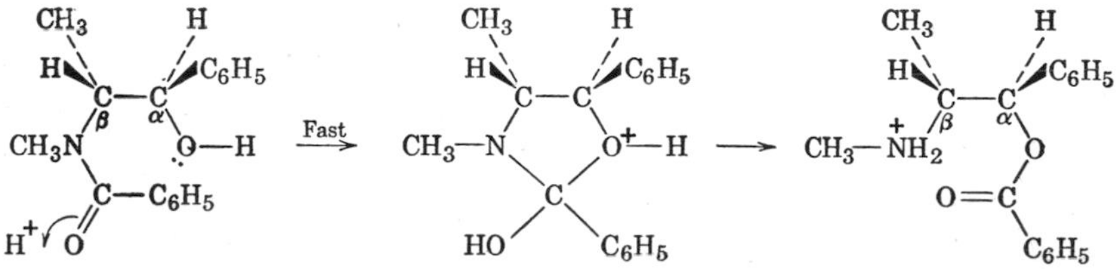

N-Benzoyl-ψ-ephedrine   O-Benzoyl-ψ-ephedrine

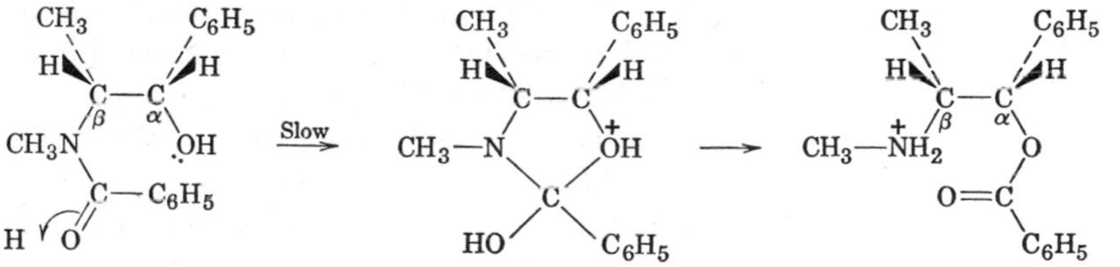

N-Benzoyl ephedrine   O-Benzoyl ephedrine

rate were rationalized [82a] in terms of the steric repulsions between the *cis*-oriented CH_3 and C_6H_5 groups in the transition state in the ephedrine series, an effect that is absent in the *trans*-oriented transition state for ψ-ephedrine series. Under more highly ionizing conditions (hot 5% hydrochloric acid), N-acetylephedrine was found to give about a 2–1 ratio of ψ-ephedrine/ephedrine, whereas, under the same conditions, N-acetyl-ψ-ephedrine gave only ψ-ephedrine. Since

[82] (a) L. H. Welsh, J. Am. Chem. Soc., 69, 128 (1947); 71, 3500 (1949); (b) V. Bruckner, G. Fodor, J. Kiss, and C. Kovaca, J. Chem. Soc., 1948, 885; (c) G. Fodor, V. Bruckner, J. Kiss, and G. Ohegyi, J. Org. Chem., 64, 337 (1949); (d) G. Fodor et al., ibid., 163, 917 (1949); 164, 917 (1949); 167, 690 (1951); (e) G. Fodor, J. Kiss, and I. Sallay, J. Chem. Soc., 1951, 1858; (f) G. Fodor and K. Koezka, ibid., 1952, 850; (g) G. Fodor and J. Kiss, ibid., 1952, 1589; (h) E. E. van Tamelen, J. Am. Chem. Soc., 73, 5773 (1951). See also reference 58.

N → O acyl migration probably occurred before hydrolysis, these stereochemical results are consistent with mechanism 1 controlling the product in the former and 2 in the latter case, in each sequence the CH_3^- and $C_6H_5^-$ groups being oriented *trans* to one another in the stages involving cycles.[82a]

When the stereoisomeric benzamides carrying *o* substituents were treated with hot 5% hydrochloric acid, the same general results were observed as when the phenyl carried no *o* substituent, except that the predominance of inversion to retention in the ephedrine series grew more pronounced as the size of the *o* group became larger. Apparently the steric influence of the *o* substituent augments the tendency of the large, non-migrating groups to be oriented *trans* in the transition states in question.[82a]

The reverse O → N acyl migration can be carried out by treating the stereoisomeric ephedrine ester salts with base.[82a] With both diastereomers, reaction mechanism 2 appears to govern the stereochemistry of the product because all the reactions studied occurred with retention of configuration at both C_α and C_β. That sequence 1 does not compete is undoubtedly derived from the poor ionizing ability of the >C—NH$_2$ bond.

The large volume of work [81c-f, 82d-g] on analogous reactions in cyclic systems points to the essential correctness of Welsh's general interpretations of the C → N and N → O acyl migration reaction.

A number of acyl migrations have been observed to occur in cyclic and bicyclic systems in which the functions involved are not on adjacent carbon atoms, but are transannularly oriented in a geometry advantageous for reaction. Thus, Fodor and coworkers [83] observed N → O and O → N acyl migrations occurred readily for N-benzoyl-nor-ψ-tropine and the respective O-benzoyl derivative. In contrast

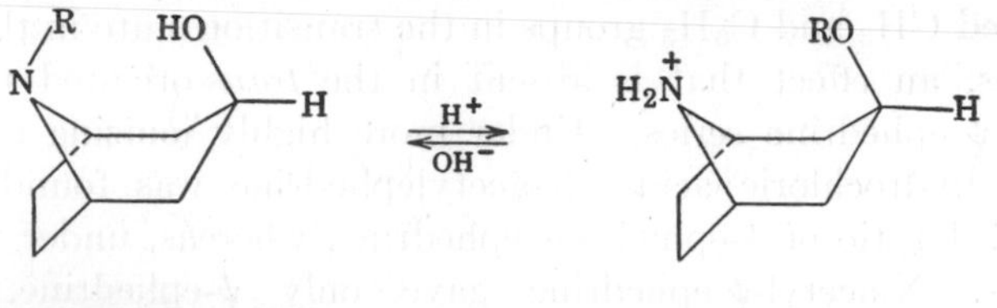

N-Acyl-nor-ψ-tropine,
R = Ac or Bz

O-Acyl-nor-ψ-tropine,
R = Ac or Bz

the diastereomeric N-benzoylnortropine under the same conditions (HCl in dioxane) was recovered unchanged, and no migration was ob-

[83] (a) G. Fodor and K. Nador, *J. Chem. Soc.*, *1953*, 721; (b) G. Fodor and O. Kovacs, *ibid.*, *1953*, 724.

served when O-benzoylnortropine hydrochloride was dissolved in alkali. Apparently, mechanism 2 is the only reaction path available under the conditions of the experiment. On the other hand, although

N-Acyl-nortropine
R = Ac, Bz

the N-acetyl derivative of nor-ψ-tropine behaves similarly to the N-benzoyl derivative, the N-acetyl derivative of nortropine goes to O-acetyl-nor-ψ-tropine. Somewhat similar results were observed with the diastereomeric ecgonine and cocaine series.[83]

A number of acyl migrations and cases of acyl participation in substitution reactions have been observed in the chemistry of the sugars,[84] the results of which can be interpreted in terms of the general reaction sequences 1 or 2.

REARRANGEMENTS INTO AROMATIC RINGS (CLAISEN)

Of the intramolecular rearrangements that go with aromatic substitution (e.g., benzidine, Hofmann, phenylhydroxylamine, Hauser, and Claisen), only the Claisen rearrangement will be discussed.[85]

The intramolecular character of the Claisen rearrangement (formulas) has been demonstrated by the absence of cross products when two compounds involving different substituents are allowed to rearrange in the same reaction mixture.[86] By appropriately labeling the α and γ positions of the migrating allyl group either with alkyl groups or with C^{14}, the two ends have been found to interchange in the *ortho* Claisen but not to interchange in the *para* Claisen rearrangement.

[84] E. L. Hirsh and S. Peat, *Ann. Repts. Chem. Soc. London*, *31*, 172 (1934); H. L. Frush and H. S. Isbell, *J. Research Natl. Bur. Standards*, *27*, 413 (1941); R. U. Lemieux and G. Huber, *J. Am. Chem. Soc.*, *75*, 4118 (1953); B. R. Baker and R. E. Schaub, *J. Am. Chem. Soc.*, *75*, 3864 (1953).

[85] For a review of the older literature, see S. Tarbell in Adams, *Organic Reactions*, Vol. 2, p. 1, John Wiley & Sons, New York, 1944.

[86] C. D. Hurd and L. Schmerling, *J. Am. Chem. Soc.*, *59*, 107 (1937). Implicit in this test for intramolecularity is the assumption that the rates of disappearance of the two starting materials are similar, and that the four rates of possible recombinations of the fragments are of the same order of magnitude.

ortho Claisen

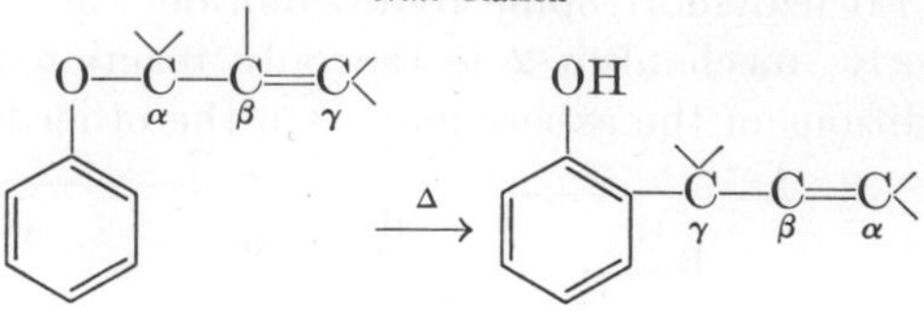

para Claisen

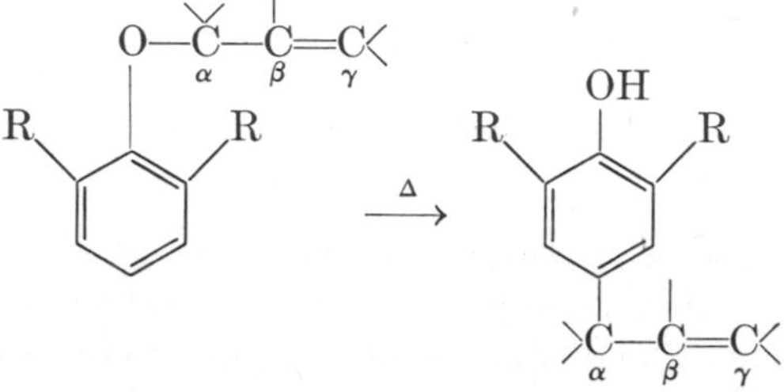

Thus, XXXV and XXXVII gave XXXVI and XXXVIII, respec-

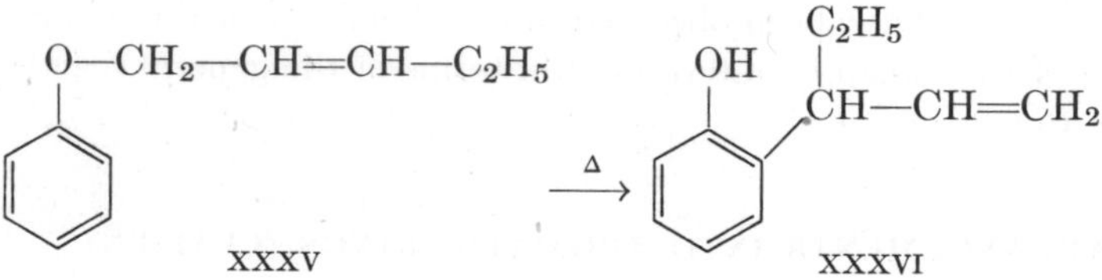

XXXV XXXVI

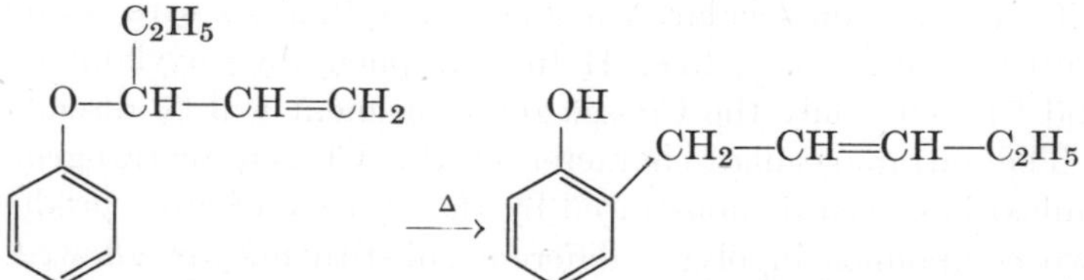

XXXVII XXXVIII

tively,[87] whereas 3-phenoxy-1-propene-1-C^{14} (XXXIX) gave XL.[88] In both cases the ends and points of attachment of the migrating group

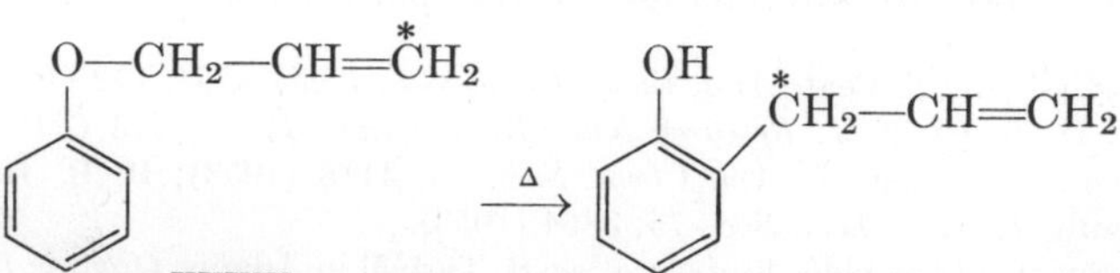

XXXIX XL

[87] (*a*) C. D. Hurd and M. A. Pollak, *J. Org. Chem.*, *3*, 550 (1939); (*b*) W. M. Lauer and W. F. Filbert, *J. Am. Chem. Soc.*, *58*, 1388 (1936).

[88] (*a*) J. P. Ryan and P. R. O'Connor, *J. Am. Chem. Soc.*, *74*, 5867 (1952); (*b*) H. Schmid and K. Schmid, *Helv. Chim. Acta*, *35*, 1879 (1952); *36*, 489 (1953).

were interchanged in the rearrangement to the *ortho* position. In contrast, XLI gave XLII (under the same conditions XLIII did not rearrange) [89] and C^{14}-labeled XLIV gave XLV,[89] the point of attachment of the migrating group being the same in starting material and *para*-rearranged product.

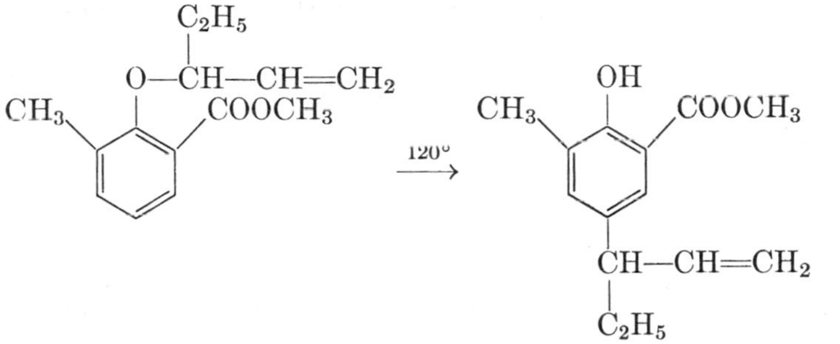

XLI   XLII

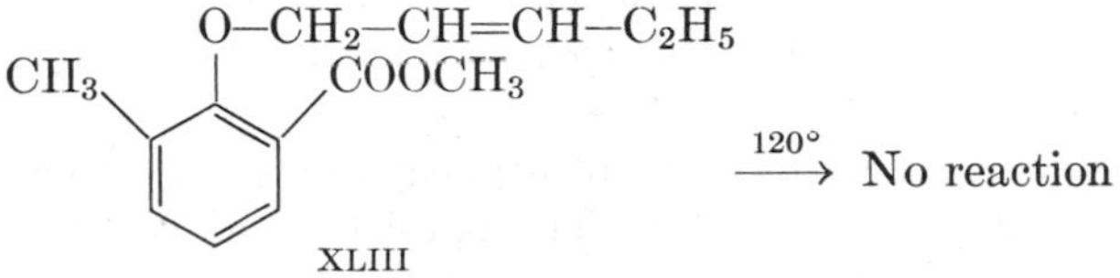

XLIII

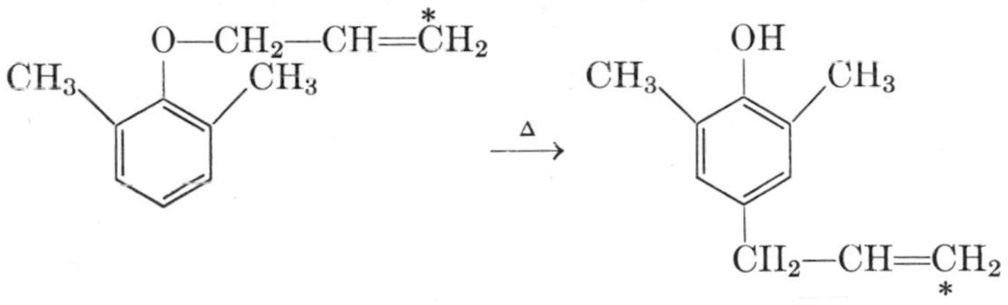

XLIV   XLV

The Claisen rearrangement has been demonstrated to be stereospecific [90] at least in the sense that optically active XLVI and XLVIII

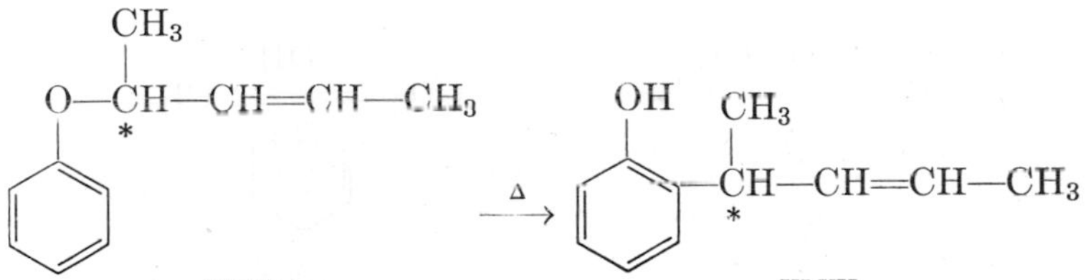

XLVI   XLVII

[89] S. J. Rhoads, R. Raulins, and R. D. Reynolds [*J. Am. Chem. Soc.*, **75**, 2531 (1953)] in a correction of earlier reports [O. Mumm, H. Hornhardt, and J. Diederichsen, *Ber.*, **72**, 100 (1939); O. Mumm and J. Diederichsen, *Ber.*, **72**, 1523 (1939).
[90] E. R. Alexander and R. W. Kluiber, *J. Am. Chem. Soc.*, **73**, 4304 (1951).

gave optically active XLVII and XLIX, respectively. Unfortunately, the degree of stereospecificity and the stereochemical direction of the

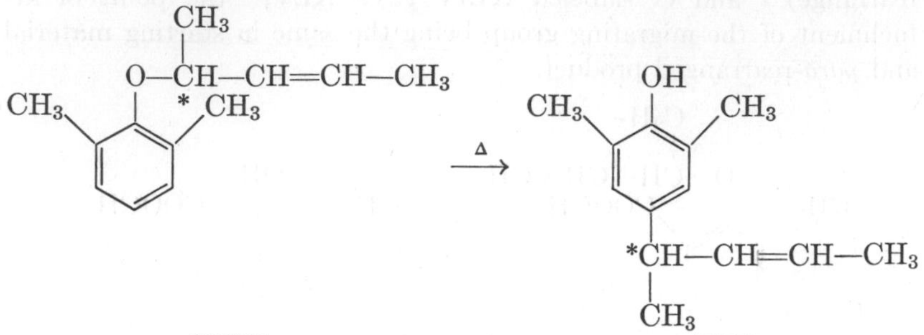

XLVIII   XLIX

reaction are not known because the relative configurations of products and reactants were not established. The stereochemical direction of the asymmetric induction undoubtedly depends on the geometric configuration of the groups attached to the double bond in the starting material.

The stereochemistry of rearrangement of α-phenylethyl aryl ethers has been more thoroughly elucidated.[91] The optically active ethers L and LII gave on thermal rearrangement the optically active prod-

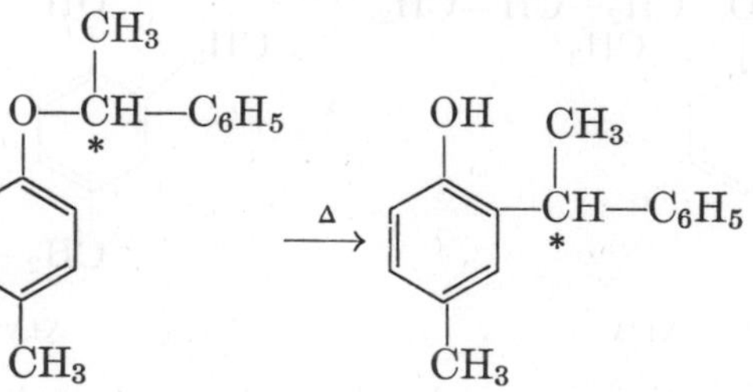

L   LI

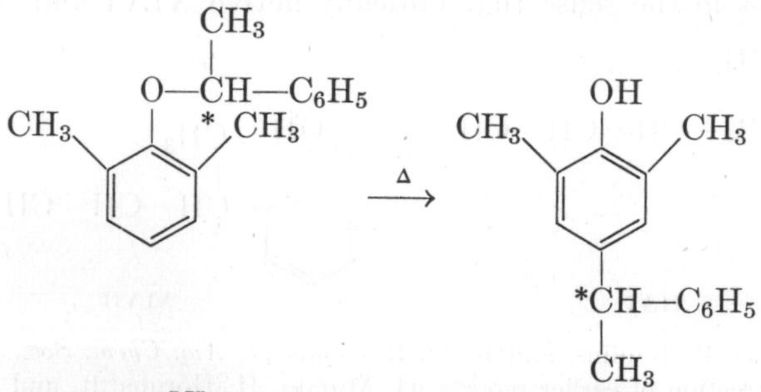

LII   LIII

[91] H. Hart and H. S. Eleuterio, *J. Am. Chem. Soc.*, **76**, 519 (1954).

ucts LI and LIII, respectively. In both cases, the reactions were about 20% stereospecific, and retention of configuration at the asymmetric carbon was predominant. In this particular system, an intermolecular reaction path was also available since, under the rearrangement conditions, optically active LIV gave a 44% yield of C-alkylated

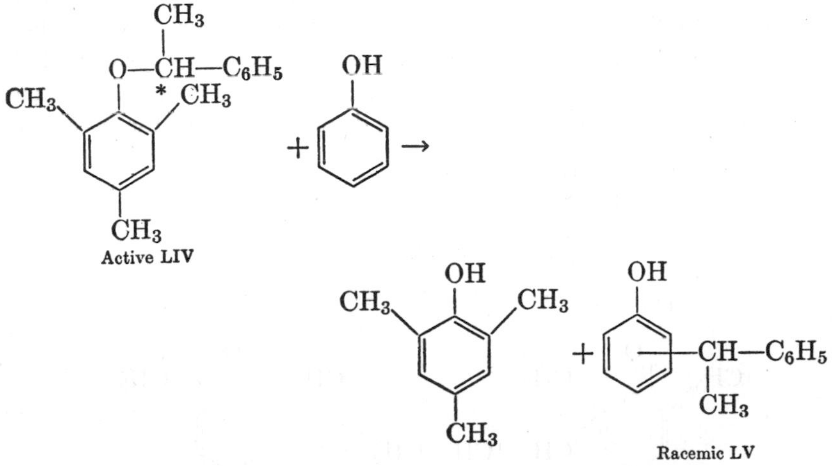

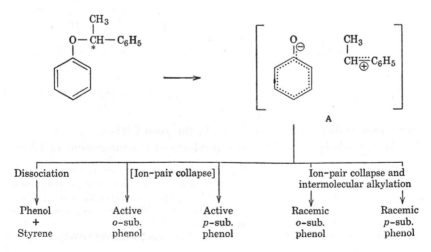

Active LIV

Racemic LV

racemic phenol (LV). When α-phenylethyl phenyl ether was the starting material, both *ortho-* and *para*-rearranged products were found. In all reactions, styrene was a by-product. The partition of starting material between olefin, o-rearranged (racemic and active), p-rearranged (racemic and active) products, as well as products of intermolecular processes, suggests that an ion-pair intermediate is in-

A

Dissociation	[Ion-pair collapse]		Ion-pair collapse and intermolecular alkylation	
Phenol + Styrene	Active o–sub. phenol	Active p–sub. phenol	Racemic o–sub. phenol	Racemic p–sub. phenol

volved.   Ion-pair A could dissociate to give phenol and styrene, collapse to give active *o-* or *p*-alkylated phenol,[92] collapse to give racemic *o-* or *p*-alkylated phenol or disproportionate to give racemic or inverted cross-bred products.

The intervention of a dienone (A) as an intermediate in at least one reaction path available for the *para* Claisen rearrangement was demonstrated as follows.[93]   Allyl 2,6-dimethylphenyl ether (LVI), when caused to rearrange in a solution of maleic anhydride, gave a small amount of a Diels-Alder adduct which, when heated, gave the final rearranged product, LVII.   A striking demonstration of the reversible

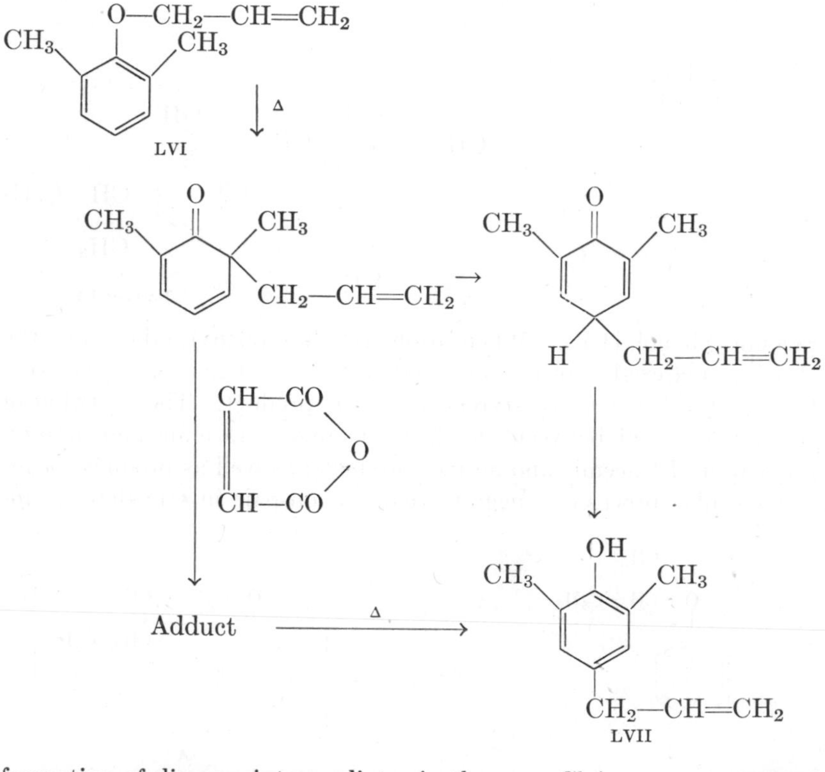

formation of dienone intermediates in the *para* Claisen rearrangement has been made by examining the products of rearrangement of LVIII

[92] The stereochemical capabilities of ion-pairs are not yet clear, but evidence is accumulating that under certain conditions both cation and anion, if potentially asymmetric, are partially capable of maintaining their character, the extent of loss of asymmetry depending on their length of life, their degree of solvation, and the degree of internal delocalization of charge.

[93] H. Conroy and R. A. Firestone, *J. Am. Chem. Soc.*, 75, 2530 (1953).

and LIX.[94] Both starting materials gave a mixture of products LX and LXI, the relations between the product balance obtained from the two starting materials being such as to point to a common intermediate (LXII) for the two reactions. The values calculated for the product balance obtained from LIX (assuming that all product in both experiments funneled through LXII) are shown along with the observed (formulas). The near coincidence of the calculated and ob-

$M = -CH_2-\underset{\underset{CH_3}{|}}{C}=CH_2$

$A = -CH_2-CH=CH_2$

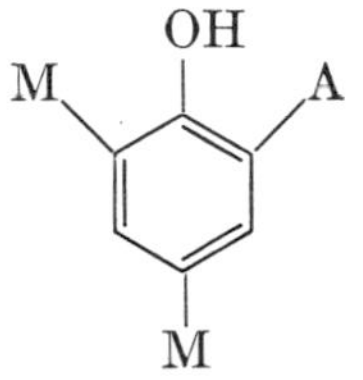

LX	LXI
$\rightarrow$ 40%	60%
$\rightarrow$ 60%	40% (found)
75%	25% (calculated)

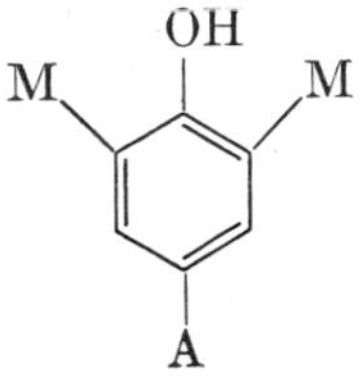

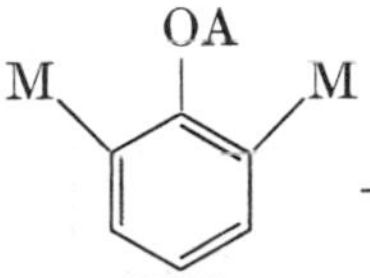

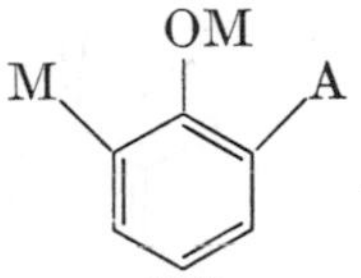

served values indicates that LXII is indeed an intermediate, but not necessarily the *immediate* precursor of LX and LXI. This possible

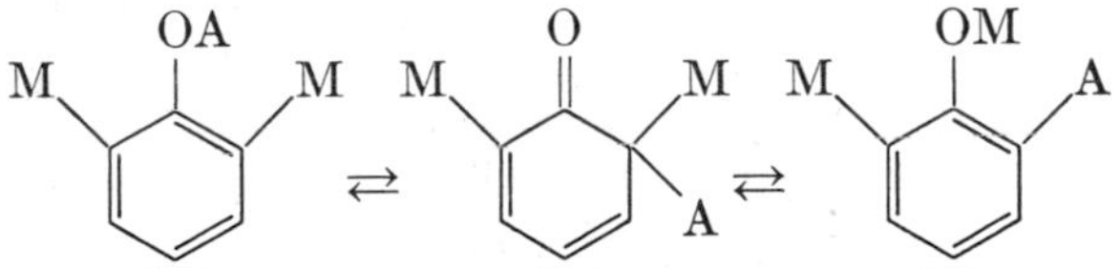

$$LX + LXI$$

ambiguity was removed by allowing LVIII to go only partially to phenolic product and examining the resulting ether and phenol. Although the composition of the phenolic product was the same as when the reaction was allowed to go to completion, the recovered ether was a mixture of LVIII and LIX, with the former predominating. Thus,

[94] D. Y. Curtin and H. W. Johnson, Jr., *J. Am. Chem. Soc.*, **76**, 2276 (1954).

the dienone can partition between four substances, the two starting materials (LVIII and LIX) and the two products (LX and LXI).

These observations taken as a whole lend support to the Hurd-Pollack mechanism [87a] for the Claisen rearrangement that is formulated below. The questions of whether stages B → D and D → E are reversible, or whether ion-pairs (of a highly oriented character) intervene between stages A → B and B → D have not yet been

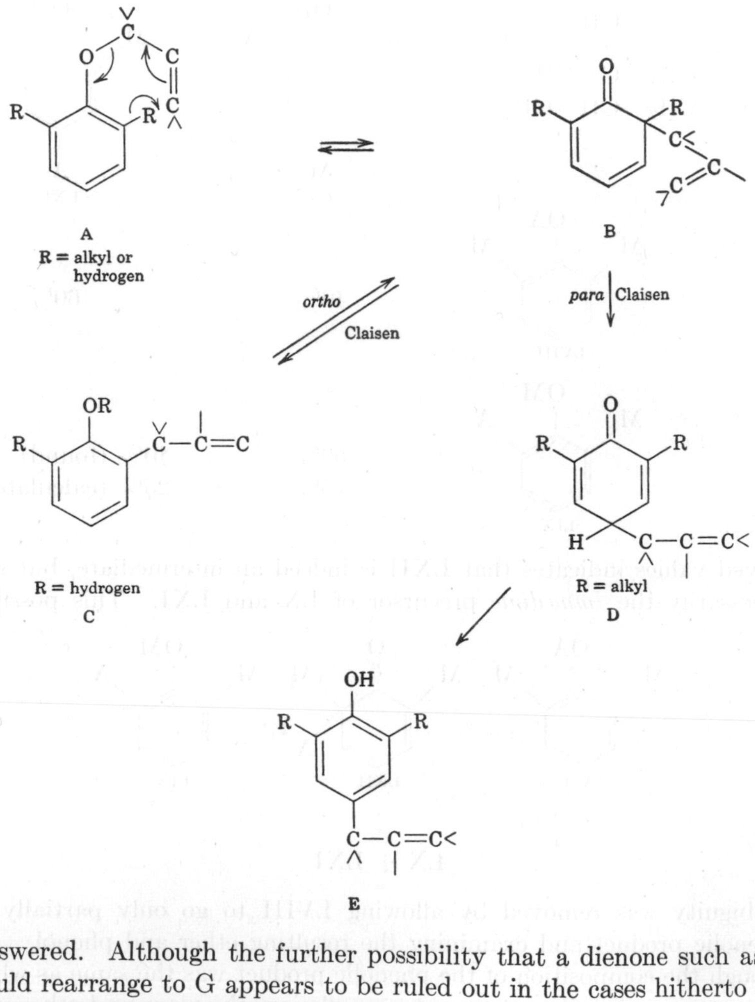

A
R = alkyl or
hydrogen

B

ortho
Claisen

para Claisen

OR

R = hydrogen
C

R = alkyl
D

E

answered. Although the further possibility that a dienone such as F could rearrange to G appears to be ruled out in the cases hitherto described, it is conceivable that, if a system such as LXIII were allowed to react long enough, the radioactive carbon could become distributed not only in both *o* and *p* positions but also at both ends of each allylic

system. A system such as LXIII might also serve as a better source
of a dienone intermediate for a Diels-Alder reaction since the life of
the intermediate might be longer, and it would probably be formed
many times.

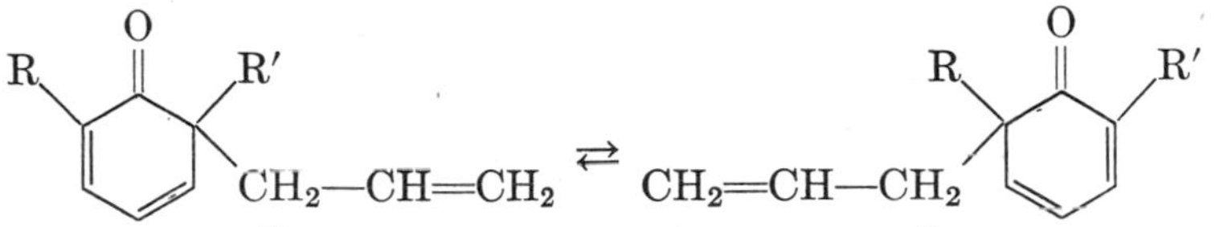

$$F \rightleftarrows G$$

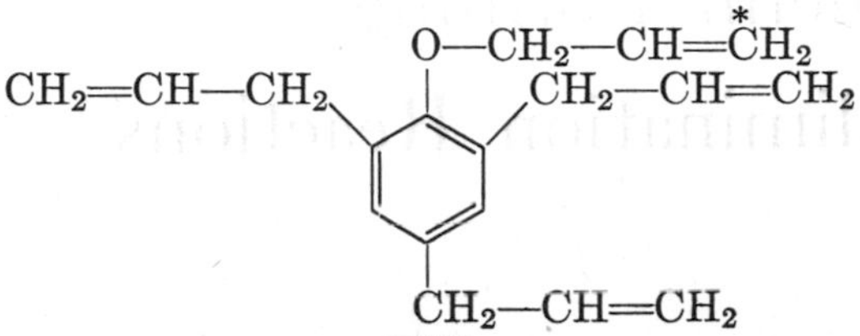

LXIII

Chapter 6

by Donald J. Cram

Olefin Forming
Elimination Reactions

THE INTRAMOLECULAR 1,2 ELIMINATION REACTION

THE HETEROLYTIC ELIMINATION REACTION
    Kinetic Description of Mechanism
    Stereochemistry
    The Stereochemistry of the Monomolecular Reaction
    Orientation in the Heterolytic Elimination Reaction
    Steric Effects in Elimination Reactions

MISCELLANEOUS ELIMINATION REACTIONS

Chapter 6

Steric effects in the 1,2-elimination reaction will be discussed in the context of the mechanism involved. Most of the elimination reactions that result in the formation of a new carbon-to-carbon bond fall into two general categories: those that are intramolecular, are initiated by heat, and proceed by a predominantly unimolecular mechanism; and those that clearly involve heterolytic mechanisms, either unimolecular or bimolecular. Less often studied examples of 1,2 eliminations that fall outside the above categories are discussed in a miscellaneous class.

THE INTRAMOLECULAR 1,2 ELIMINATION REACTION

This class of reaction may be defined by the general formulation in which X may be a variety of functions, most of which are polyatomic. The reaction appears to be intramolecular and occurs under pyrolytic conditions. The Chugaev reaction is perhaps the most widely recognized example of this class of transformation. The ability of this re-

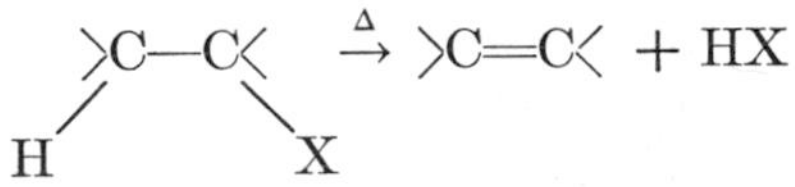

$$\underset{H}{\overset{}{\underset{}{>}}}C-C\underset{X}{\overset{}{<}} \quad \overset{\Delta}{\rightarrow} \quad >C=C< \; + \; HX$$

action to produce olefin without any complicating rearrangements was recognized rather early. For example, although pinacolyl alcohol under acidic conditions gives skeletally rearranged olefins, the pyrolysis of the xanthate provides unrearranged products.[1]

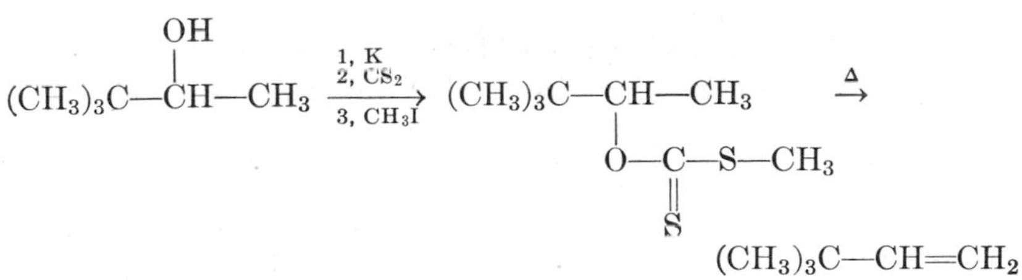

$$(CH_3)_3C-\underset{\overset{|}{OH}}{CH}-CH_3 \quad \xrightarrow[\substack{3,\ CH_3I}]{\substack{1,\ K \\ 2,\ CS_2}} \quad (CH_3)_3C-\underset{\substack{| \\ O-C-S-CH_3 \\ \| \\ S}}{CH}-CH_3 \quad \xrightarrow{\Delta}$$

$$(CH_3)_3C-CH=CH_2$$

[1] W. Formin and N. Sochanski, *Ber.*, *46*, 246 (1913).

Hückel and coworkers [2] observed that the xanthate of menthol gave predominantly 3-menthene, whereas the xanthate of neomenthol gave predominantly 2-menthene.   These results demonstrate the reaction

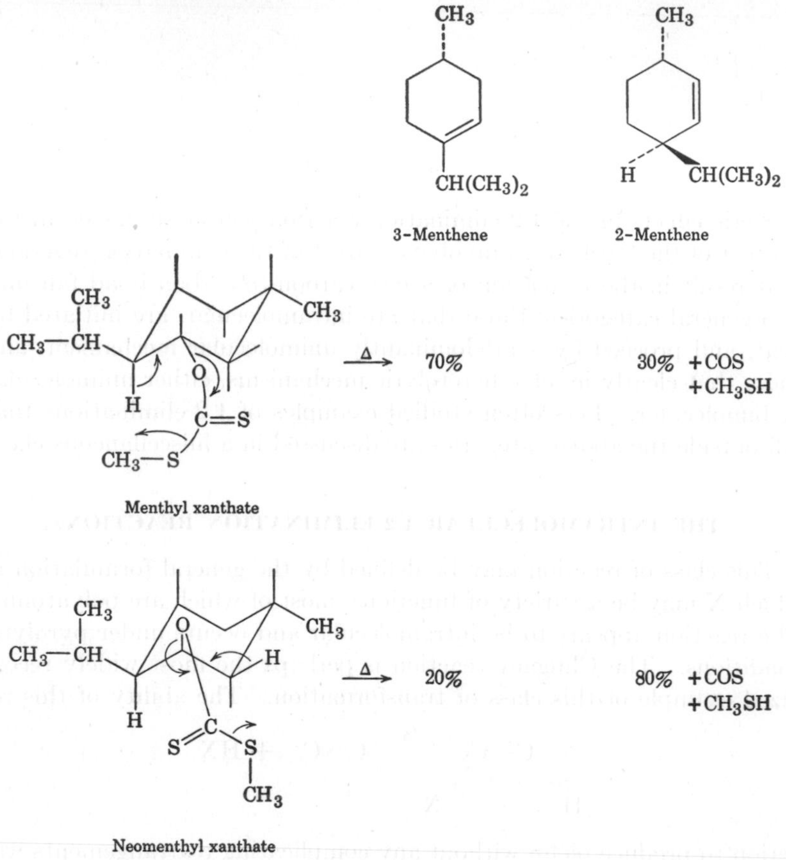

3-Menthene

2-Menthene

$\xrightarrow{\Delta}$ 70%   30% + COS
                                      + CH$_3$SH

Menthyl xanthate

$\xrightarrow{\Delta}$ 20%   80% + COS
                                      + CH$_3$SH

Neomenthyl xanthate

to be predominantly stereospecific and suggest that the preferred course for the reaction involves H and O—C—S—CH$_3$, leaving from

$$\underset{\underset{S}{\parallel}}{}$$

the same side of the incipient double bond [3] (a *cis* elimination reaction).[3]   Hückel's explanation [2] involved hydrogen being abstracted as

[2] W. Hückel, W. Tappe, and G. Legutke, *Ann.*, *543*, 191 (1940).

[3] Difficulties arise in the use of *cis* and *trans* as applied to *processes* as contrasted to *molecules* themselves.   The terms *cis* elimination will be used whenever the leaving groups depart from the same side of the incipient double bond, and *trans* elimination when they leave from the opposite side of the incipient double bond.   In a substituted cyclohexane ring, the loss of two equatorial groups or two axial groups

a proton by the $CH_3\!-\!\overset{..}{\underset{..}{S}}\!-$ function at the same time that the C—O and C—S bonds broke, in each case the electron pair going to the O or S atom. On the other hand,[4] it has been proposed that the thiocar-

$$
\begin{array}{c}
H_2C\!-\!O \\
| \qquad \diagdown \\
\qquad\quad C\!=\!S \\
| \qquad \diagup \\
H_2C\!-\!HS \\
\qquad | \\
\qquad CH_3
\end{array}
\longrightarrow
\begin{array}{c}
H_2C+ \\
| \\
H_2C- \\
\end{array}
\qquad
\begin{array}{c}
O \\
\diagdown \\
\quad C\!=\!S \\
\diagup \\
H\!-\!S \\
| \\
CH_3
\end{array}
$$

bonyl group hydrogen-bonds with and then abstracts the β-hydrogen, and that the lack of rearrangement during the pyrolysis of esters such as acetates, benzoates, phthalates, and oxalates to give olefins points to an analogous reaction mechanism.[5] A similar hypothesis had been

$$
\begin{array}{c}
R\!-\!CH\!-\!CH\!-\!R \\
\;| \qquad\; | \\
\;O \quad\; H \\
\;\diagdown \quad\; \downarrow \\
\;\;C\!=\!S \\
\;| \\
CH_3
\end{array}
\longrightarrow
\begin{array}{c}
R\!-\!CH\!-\!\overset{..}{C}H\!-\!R \\
\;| \\
\;O \\
\;\diagdown\!+ \\
\;\;C\!-\!S\!-\!\boxed{H} \\
\;\;\boxed{S\!-\!CH_3}
\end{array}
\longrightarrow
\left\{
\begin{array}{c}
R\!-\!CH\!=\!CH\!-\!R \\
\updownarrow \\
R\!-\!\underset{+}{C}H\!-\!\underset{-}{C}H\!-\!R
\end{array}
\right.
$$

$$+ \; COS \; + \; CH_3SH$$

advanced earlier [6] as one mechanism for the decomposition of an ester to give olefin.

$$
\begin{array}{c}
H \\
\diagdown \\
O \qquad CR_2 \\
\| \qquad\; | \\
R\!-\!C \quad\; CR_2 \\
\diagdown \quad \diagup \\
O
\end{array}
\rightarrow
\begin{array}{c}
H^- \\
\underset{+}{O}\diagup \quad CR_2 \\
\| \qquad\; | \\
R\!-\!C \quad\; CR_2 \\
\diagdown \quad \diagup \\
O
\end{array}
\rightarrow
\begin{array}{c}
H \\
\diagup \\
O \qquad CR_2 \\
\| \qquad\; \| \\
R\!-\!C \quad\; CR_2 \\
\diagdown \\
O
\end{array}
$$

The Chugaev reaction was demonstrated to assume a predominantly *cis* course [3] in *acyclic* systems through a study of the products of xan-

---

is a *trans* elimination, and the loss of one equatorial and one axial group is a *cis* elimination (see Chapter 1). In both cases, of course, the product is a *cis* olefin, and the starting material may be termed either *cis* or *trans*, depending on the reference substituents. Thus the application of *cis* or *trans* to the elimination reaction always refers to the overall *process*, the leaving groups being the points of reference.

[4] P. G. Stevens and J. H. Richmond, *J. Am. Chem. Soc.*, 63, 3132 (1941).

[5] (a) P. L. Cramer and M. J. Mulligan, *J. Am. Chem. Soc.*, 58, 373 (1936); (b) A. Windaus, H. Lettré, and F. Schenck, *Ann.*, 520, 98 (1935); (c) G. Komppa and G. A. Nyman, *Ann.*, 535, 252 (1938).

[6] C. D. Hurd and F. H. Blunck, *J. Am. Chem. Soc.*, 60, 2419 (1938).

thate decomposition of the diastereomers of 3-phenyl-2-butanol and 1,2-diphenyl-1-propanol.[7] These systems possess the advantage of providing *geometric isomers* as products (thereby allowing comparison between two reactions in which the same bonds are made and broken), rather than the *position isomers* usually found as olefinic products from diastereomerically related *alicyclic* starting materials. The results (see

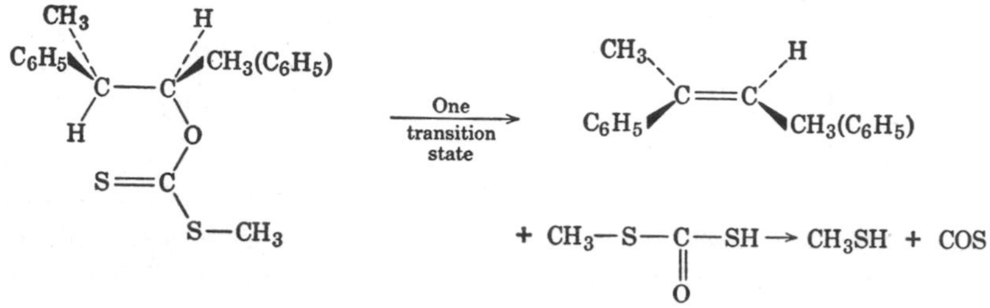

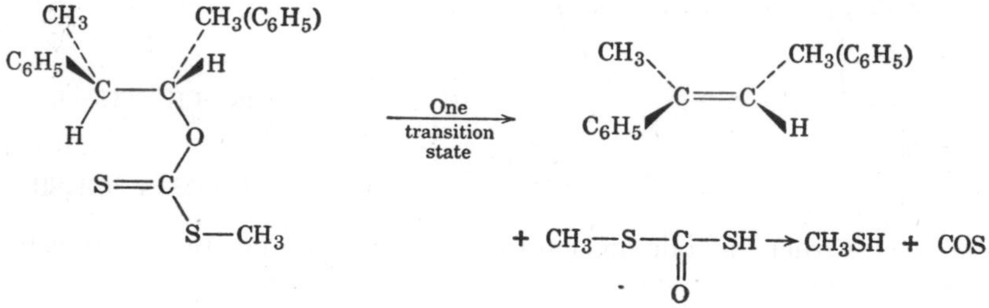

formulations) indicate a high stereospecificity favoring *cis* elimination and point to a concerted mechanism [8] with a transition state of the type formulated.

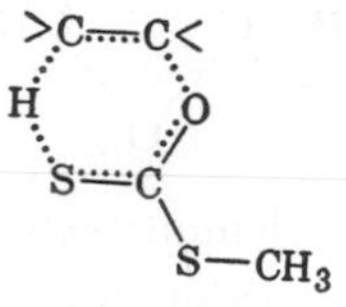

Transition state

Later investigations [9] confirmed the *cis* direction [3] of the Chugaev reaction in a number of other *alicyclic* systems, one of which included

[7] (a) D. J. Cram, *J. Am. Chem. Soc.*, *71*, 3883 (1949); (b) D. J. Cram and F. A. Abd Elhafez, *ibid.*, *74*, 5828 (1952).

[8] A concerted reaction is one in which only one transition state separates reactants and products, all bond-making and -breaking processes occurring simultaneously.

[9] (a) E. R. Alexander and A. Mudrak, *J. Am. Chem. Soc.*, *72*, 1810 (1950); (b) E. R. Alexander and A. Mudrak, *ibid.*, *72*, 3194 (1950); (c) E. R. Alexander and A. Mudrak, *ibid.*, *73*, 59 (1951).

and example of the elimination in a five-membered ring.[9c] Barton [10a, b] correlated and predicted the configurations of a number of natural products of the terpene and steroid class on the basis of the preferred *cis* steric course [3] of the Chugaev reaction.

A number of studies of the stereochemical course of the pyrolysis of esters to give olefins have been reported, all of which point to a preferred *cis* geometry for the H and RCOO groups in the transition state for the reaction.[9, 10a, d, 11] A concerted [8] version of the Hurd mechanism [6] appears to be widely accepted. Further support for this type of mechanism is found in the kinetic study [10d] of the elimination of benzoic acid from menthyl benzoate. The reaction was found to be homogeneous and unimolecular and to give predominantly 3-menthene as product. A completely analogous result was observed for the pyrolysis of menthol chloride in a reactor coated with a carbonaceous film.[10c] The authors suggest a four-center transition for this homogeneous, unimolecular reaction (see formulation). A similar kind of

$$\begin{array}{ccc} >\!C\!-\!C\!<\!\!\!\! & \to\ C\!\cdots\!C\ \to\ & >\!C\!=\!C\!< \\ \ \ |\ \ \ | & \ \ \vdots\ \ \ \vdots & + \\ \text{H}\ \ \text{Cl} & \text{H}\cdots\text{Cl} & \text{HCl} \end{array}$$

Transition
state

kinetic evidence was obtained for the Chugaev reaction [12] as applied to the xanthates of a number of sterols.

Further kinetic studies revealed [12] that a variety of different derivatives of cholesterol underwent a unimolecular elimination similar to

$$>\!C\!=\!C\!<\ +\ \text{Other products}$$

A = O or S
B = O or S
Z = R, Ar, SR, OR, NHC$_6$H$_5$, or Cl

that of the xanthate and acetate and that a number of these, particularly the ethyl carbonate derivative, decomposed to give better yields of olefin than the xanthate or carboxy esters. Although the system

[10] (a) D. H. R. Barton, *J. Chem. Soc.*, *1949*, 2174; (b) D. H. R. Barton and W. J. Rosenfelder, *ibid.*, *1949*, 2459; (c) D. H. R. Barton, A. J. Head, and R. J. Williams, *ibid.*, *1952*, 453; (d) D. H. R. Barton, A. J. Head, and R. J. Williams, *ibid.*, *1953*, 1715.

[11] (a) R. T. Arnold, G. G. Smith, and R. M. Dodson, *J. Org. Chem.*, *15*, 1256 (1950); (b) N. L. McNivan and J. Read, *J. Chem. Soc.*, *1952*, 2067.

[12] (a) G. L. O'Connor and H. R. Nace, *J. Am. Chem. Soc.*, *74*, 5454 (1952); (b) G. L. O'Connor and H. R. Nace, *ibid.*, *75*, 2118 (1953).

did not lend itself to stereochemical study, the kinetic behavior and structural similarities of these systems to those whose stereochemistry has been determined suggest that all these reactions belong to the same mechanistic class.

Most of the reactions discussed above involve temperatures of 150 to 300° C. for their completion. The elimination of the elements of dimethyl hydroxylamine from amine oxides to give olefin (the Cope reaction) was found to go in high yields at much lower temperatures.[13] The mild nature of the reaction conditions is illustrated by the fact that the amine oxide of optically pure 1-N,N-dimethylamino-3-phenyl-butane gives almost a quantitative yield of optically pure 3-phenyl-1-butene when heated to 120°.[14] Particularly interesting is the steric

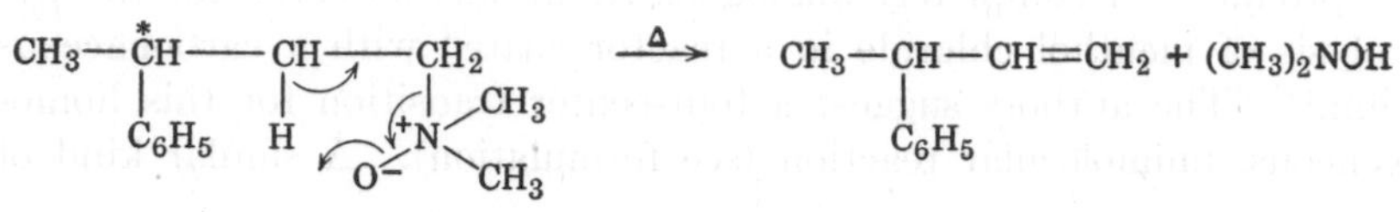

$$CH_3-\overset{*}{C}H\!-\!\!-\!\!-CH\!-\!\!-\!\!-CH_2 \quad\xrightarrow{\Delta}\quad CH_3-CH-CH\!=\!CH_2 + (CH_3)_2NOH$$

course of this reaction in larger ring compounds. From the oxide of N,N-dimethylaminocyclooctane was obtained cis-cyclooctene.[13b, c] However, from the nine- and ten-membered starting materials, the trans cyclic olefins were obtained exclusively.[13c] These results are

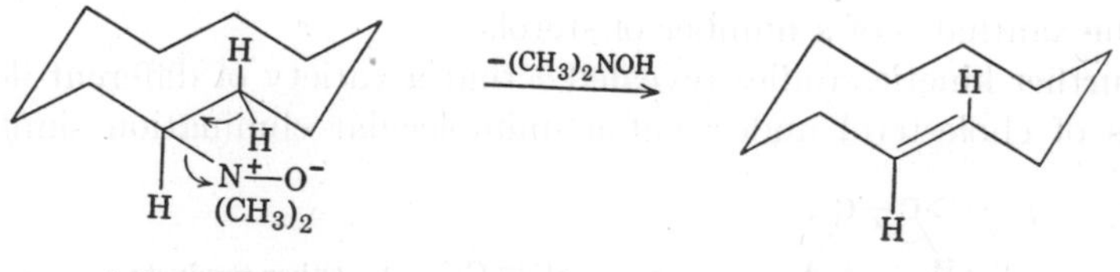

Amine oxide of
N,N-dimethylaminocyclodecane

trans-Cyclodecene

probably due to the tendency of the bulky amine oxide function to be as equatorial as possible and of the elimination reaction to assume a steric course in which the leaving groups are eclipsed or nearly so. The fact that a trans olefin is not likewise obtained from the amine oxide of N,N-dimethylaminocyclooctane (the cis isomer is the exclusive product) must be a consequence of the steric strain involved in

[13] (a) A. C. Cope, T. T. Foster, and P. H. Towle, J. Am. Chem. Soc., 71, 3929 (1949); (b) A. C. Cope, R. A. Pike, and C. F. Spencer, ibid., 75, 3212 (1953); (c) paper before 124th Meeting American Chemical Society, Chicago, Illinois, September, 1953, p. 11F of Abstracts.

[14] (a) D. J. Cram, J. Am. Chem. Soc., 74, 2137 (1952); (b) D. J. Cram and J. Mc-Carty, ibid., 76, 5740 (1954).

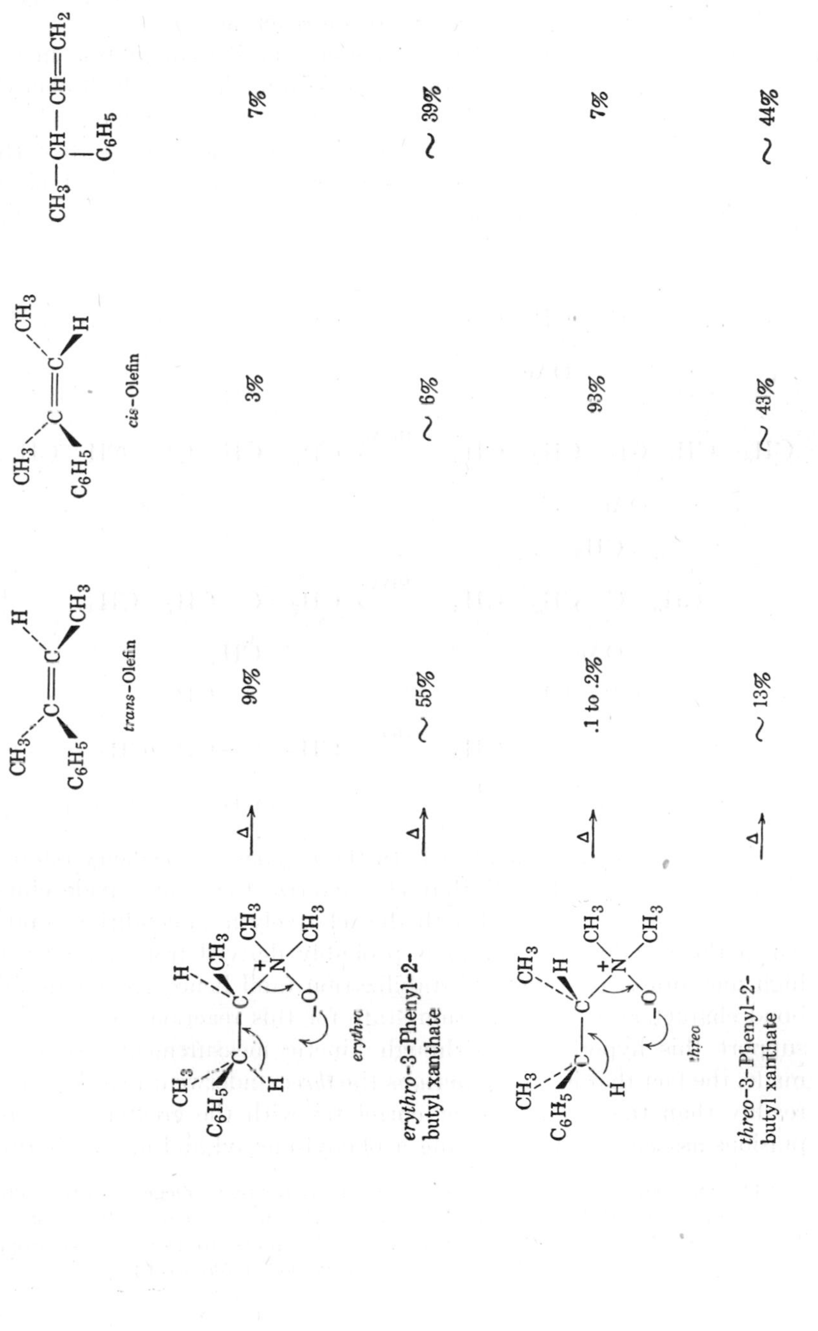

trans-Olefin

cis-Olefin

$CH_3-CH-CH=CH_2$
$\quad\quad |$
$\quad\quad C_6H_5$

erythro

erythro-3-Phenyl-2-butyl xanthate

Δ → 90%   3%   7%

Δ → ~55%   ~6%   ~39%

threo

threo-3-Phenyl-2-butyl xanthate

Δ → .1 to .2%   93%   7%

Δ → ~13%   ~43%   ~44%

putting a *trans* double bond into an eight-membered ring.[15] If this explanation applies, the double bond must be rather well developed in the transition state of the amine oxide reaction.

A comparison of the tendency for stereospecific elimination in the Chugaev and amine oxide reactions has been made [14b] in the 3-phenyl-2-butyl system (formulas). It is noteworthy that the amine oxide reaction assumes a more highly stereospecific reaction course than the Chugaev, and that the ratio of conjugated to unconjugated olefin from the amine oxide is higher (by a factor of about 6) than from the

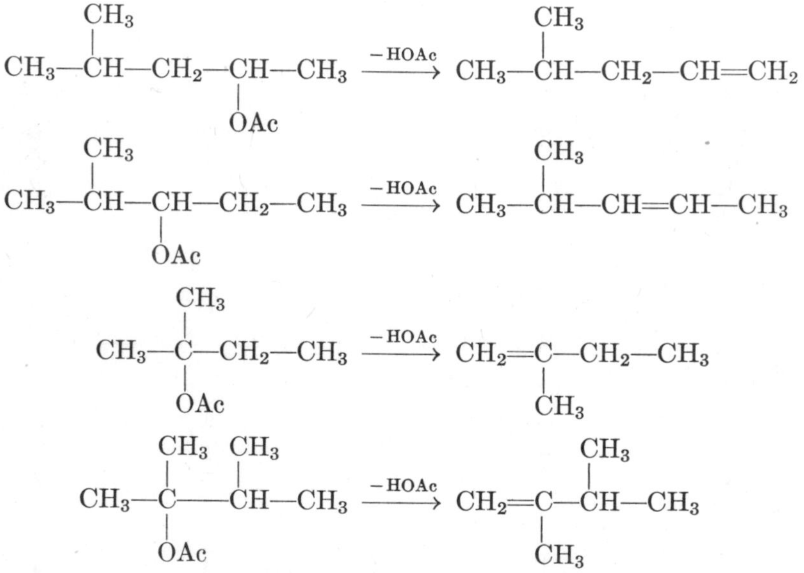

$$CH_3-\underset{\underset{CH_3}{|}}{CH}-CH_2-\underset{\underset{OAc}{|}}{CH}-CH_3 \xrightarrow{-HOAc} CH_3-\underset{\underset{CH_3}{|}}{CH}-CH_2-CH=CH_2$$

$$CH_3-\underset{\underset{CH_3}{|}}{CH}-\underset{\underset{OAc}{|}}{CH}-CH_2-CH_3 \xrightarrow{-HOAc} CH_3-\underset{\underset{CH_3}{|}}{CH}-CH=CH-CH_3$$

$$CH_3-\underset{\underset{OAc}{|}}{\overset{\overset{CH_3}{|}}{C}}-CH_2-CH_3 \xrightarrow{-HOAc} CH_2=\underset{\underset{CH_3}{|}}{C}-CH_2-CH_3$$

$$CH_3-\underset{\underset{OAc}{|}}{\overset{\overset{CH_3}{|}}{C}}-\underset{\overset{|}{CH_3}}{CH}-CH_3 \xrightarrow{-HOAc} CH_2=\underset{\underset{CH_3}{|}}{C}-CH-CH_3$$

xanthate. The enhancement of both these types of specificity (stereochemical and orientational) that characterize the amine oxide elimination is possibly associated with the relatively mild conditions under which the reaction occurs and is probably derived from a relatively high measure of resonance of stabilization (and hence greater double bond character) in the transition state for this reaction. Other facts support this hypothesis. Although kinetic measurements were not made, the fact that in both reactions the *threo* underwent reaction more readily than the *erythro* isomer correlates with the greater steric repulsions associated with eclipsing a phenyl-methyl and methyl-hydro-

[15] The compound *trans*-cyclooctene has been prepared by C. Ziegler and H. Wilms [*Ann.*, *567*, 1 (1950)] by the application of the Hofmann exhaustive methylation procedure to N,N-dimethylcyclooctylamine. Attempts to isomerize *cis*-cyclooctene to the *trans* isomer quite understandably failed (reference 13c).

gen in going to *trans* olefin as compared to eclipsing phenyl-hydrogen and methyl-methyl in going to *cis* olefin. Furthermore, the amine oxide reaction of the *threo* system which goes to the more thermodynamically stable *cis* olefin [14a] is markedly the more stereospecific (a factor of at least ten times) of the reactions of the two diastereomers. Unexpectedly, the result is in the opposite direction for the Chugaev reaction.

In contrast to the Chugaev and amine oxide results, the least substituted olefin predominates in the following high-temperature (500°) acetate pyrolysis reactions.[16] (See p. 312 for formulas.)

Curtin and Kellom [17a] devised a unique system for the study of the stereochemistry of elimination reactions, and particularly for the investigation of eclipsing effects involved in these reactions. Thus racemic *erythro*- and *threo*-2-deutero-1,2-diphenylethanol were prepared, and the pyrolytic elimination reactions of the acetates (and other esters) and derived alkyl halides were studied. In each reaction,

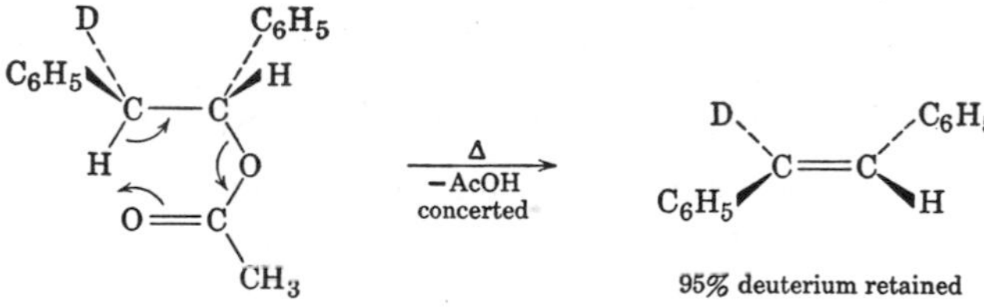

erythro–Acetate

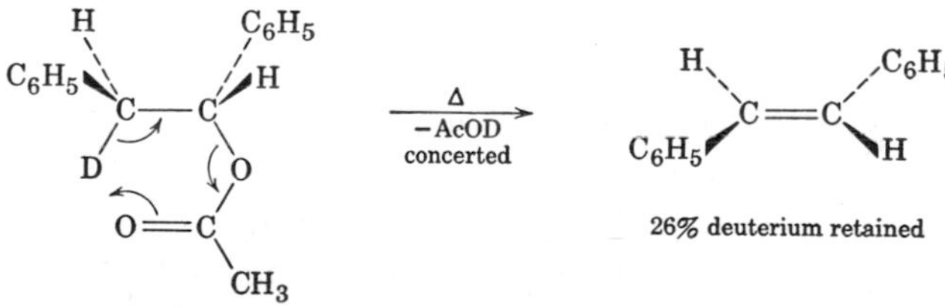

95% deuterium retained

threo–Acetate

26% deuterium retained

three factors operate: (1) the tendency for the reactions to assume a course not involving the eclipsing of two phenyl groups; (2) the tend-

[16] W. J. Bailey and C. King, Meeting of American Chemical Society, Atlantic City, September, 1952, p. 3M of *Abstracts*.

[17] (a) D. Y. Curtin and D. B. Kellom, *J. Am. Chem. Soc.*, *75*, 6011 (1953); (b) F. W. Westheimer and N. Nicolaides, *ibid.*, *71*, 25 (1949); (c) V. J. Shiner, Jr., *ibid.*, *74*, 5285 (1952); (d) V. J. Shiner, Jr., *ibid.*, *75*, 2925 (1953).

ency for hydrogen abstraction to be favored over deuterium (isotope effect); [17b, c] (3) the tendency toward a stereospecific reaction course. Apparently the eclipsing factor plays a dominating role since, although both cis- and trans-stilbene (both deuterated and non-deuterated) are possible products, only the trans isomers were observed. The formulation of the pyrolysis of the acetates indicates a decided tendency for a cis steric course, as well as the expected favoring of hydrogen over deuterium abstraction. The authors [17a] estimated that the rates of H to D abstraction differ by a factor of 2.8 in the acetate pyrolysis reaction and that the stereospecific cis reaction is favored by a factor of about 8 over the trans reaction.

All pyrolytic elimination reactions do not proceed predominantly by a cis stereochemical course. Thus, unlike the Chugaev reaction,[9a] the methyl sulfites of cis- and trans-2-phenyl-1-cyclohexanol both give predominantly conjugated olefin as product, the reaction being stereochemically indiscriminate.[18] It would appear that either radical or intermolecular mechanisms are also available for the production of olefin.

THE HETEROLYTIC ELIMINATION REACTION

The nature of the bimolecular and unimolecular (solvolytic) elimination reactions has been thoroughly discussed from the point of view of polar effects by the Hughes and Ingold school,[19] which is largely responsible for the evolution of the general kinetic framework which defines these transformations. The general kinetic description of the mechanism of these reactions will first be briefly examined, followed by a description of their stereochemistry. Finally, polar and steric effects will be discussed.

Kinetic description of mechanism

Most of the olefin-forming reactions that occur in solution fall into one of two general categories, one proceeding by a unimolecular and multistage sequence, the other by a bimolecular and concerted (synchronous) process.[19] In the E_1 reaction, X = Cl, Br, I, OSO_2R, $O\overset{+}{C}OR$, or $\overset{+}{S}R_2$ and Z = H. For the E_2 reaction, X = Cl, Br, I,

[18] G. Berti, J. Am. Chem. Soc., 76, 1213 (1954). See also C. C. Price and G. Berti, ibid., 76, 1207, 1211, 1219 (1954).

[19] Three general summaries of views have been published: (a) C. K. Ingold, Structure and Mechanism in Organic Chemistry, Chapter 8, p. 420, Cornell University Press, Ithaca, N. Y., 1953; (b) M. L. Dhar, E. D. Hughes, C. K. Ingold, A. M. Mandour, G. A. Maw, and L. I. Woolf, J. Chem. Soc., 1948, 2093; (c) E. D. Hughes and C. K. Ingold, Trans. Faraday Soc., 37, 657 (1941).

OSO_2R, $OCOR$, OR, NR_3, PR_3, SR_2, OOH, or SO_2R; $Z = H$, D, Cl, or $SiCl_3$; $B: = OH_2$, $N(CH_3)_3$, OAc^-, OAr^-, OH^-, OR^-, NH_2^-, $CO_3^=$, or $LiAlH_4$.[20]

Unimolecular (E_1) mechanism, usually fits rate = $k_1[Z-\overset{\vee}{\underset{\wedge}{C}}-\overset{\vee}{C}-X]$

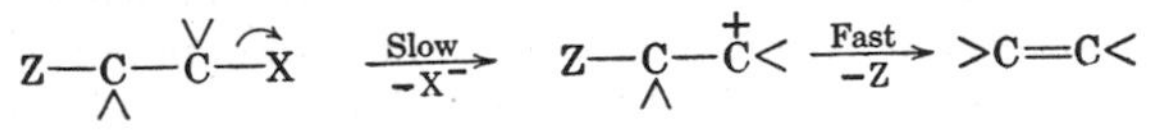

$$Z-\overset{\vee}{\underset{\wedge}{C}}-\overset{\vee}{C}-X \quad \xrightarrow[-X^-]{Slow} \quad Z-\overset{\vee}{\underset{\wedge}{C}}-\overset{+}{C}< \quad \xrightarrow[-Z]{Fast} \quad >C=C<$$

Bimolecular (E_2) mechanism, usually fits rate = $k_2[B:][Z-\overset{\vee}{\underset{\wedge}{C}}-\overset{\vee}{C}-X]$

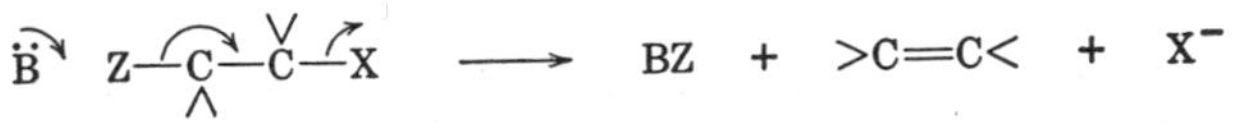

$$B: \quad Z-\overset{\vee}{\underset{\wedge}{C}}-\overset{\vee}{C}-X \quad \longrightarrow \quad BZ \; + \; >C=C< \; + \; X^-$$

Frequently the E_1 mechanism is capable of becoming highly complex by intervention of molecular rearrangements and the phenomenon of "internal return" (Chapter 5), whereas the one-stage E_2 reaction is relatively less complicated.

In giving a mechanistic designation to a transformation, the molecularity of the *rate-determining stage* is always singled out. Only the number of molecules which necessarily undergo covalency change in the transition state determine the molecularity.

Stereochemistry

THE BIMOLECULAR REACTION. The older literature abounds in examples of the base-catalyzed elimination reaction assuming a *trans* steric

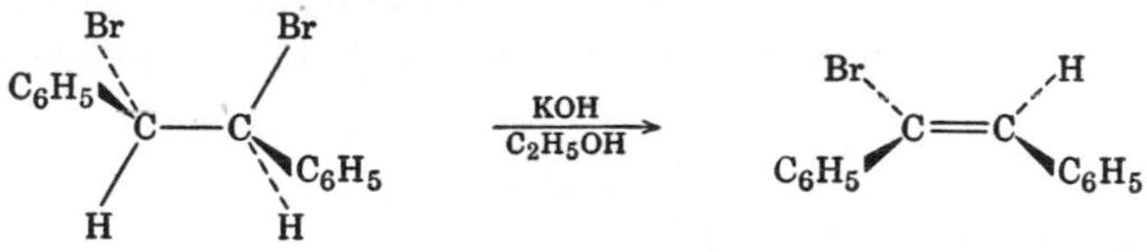

$$I \quad \xrightarrow[C_2H_5OH]{KOH} \quad II$$

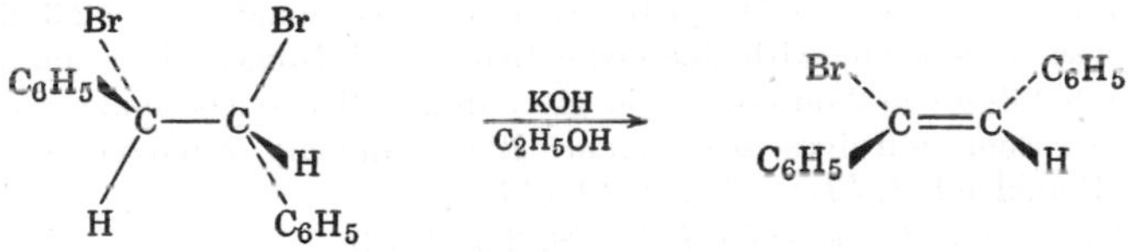

$$III \quad \xrightarrow[C_2H_5OH]{KOH} \quad IV$$

[20] Only a relatively small number of the possible combinations of groups have been investigated, and some of these only cursorily. Summaries of most references to systems involving these substituents are found in references 19a and 19b. Others will be referred to as occasion arises.

course. Michael [21] reported that the base-induced loss of hydrogen chloride from chlorofumaric acid occurs about fifty times as fast as from chloromaleic acid, the product being in each case acetylenedicarboxylic acid. Pfeiffer [22] noted that *meso*-stilbene dibromide (I) gave olefin II, and *d,l*-dibromide (III) gave olefin IV, when treated with ethanolic potassium hydroxide.[23]   In the same paper the results of many authors are summarized, all of which supported the *trans* elimination hypothesis.[24]   Frankland [25] in an extensive review of the literature concludes that usually *trans* elimination occurs more readily than *cis* and that both "chemical forces" and "space limitations" might favor "the process of *trans* extrusion."   Chavanne [26] observed that *trans*-dichloroethylene is consumed by base to give chloroacetylene twenty times as fast as the *cis* isomer.

Regarding the production of olefin from vicinal dihalides, a number of early observations pointed to the fact that diastereomerically related reactants underwent elimination at different rates, but usually the relative stereochemical structures of reactant and product were not known.[27]   In 1939, Young and coworkers [28] demonstrated for the first time the stereochemistry of the reaction (utilized in the earlier studies [27]) of the iodide ion catalyzed loss of bromine from a vicinal dibromide. This transformation was demonstrated to be second order (first order in iodide ion and first order in the vicinal dibromide), to be stereospecific,[27d] and to assume a *trans* steric course [28] (the substituents leave from the opposite side of the incipient double bond). These authors [28] summarized their views as follows: "Iodide ion re-

[21] A. Michael, *J. prakt. Chem.*, *52*, 308 (1895).

[22] P. Pfeiffer, *Z. physik. Chem.*, *48*, 40 (1904).

[23] J. Wislicenus and F. Seeler, *Ber.*, *28*, 2693 (1895).

[24] For example, I with sodium thiophenolate gives *cis*-stilbene, and III gives *trans*-stilbene; *threo*-2,3-dibromo-2-methylbutanoic acid (tiglic acid dibromide) gives with aqueous sodium hydroxide *trans*-2-bromo-2-butene; the *erythro* isomer gives the corresponding *cis* olefin; *trans*-2-bromo-2-butene goes to dimethyl acetylene with potassium hydroxide faster than the *cis* isomer; *trans*-2,3-dibromo-2-butene goes to 2-butyne with zinc faster than the *cis* isomer; the sodium salt of *trans*-2-methyl-3-bromo-2-butenoic acid gives dimethylacetylene under conditions which the *cis* isomer survives (see reference 22 for summary of references).

[25] P. F. Frankland, *J. Chem. Soc.*, *1912*, 654.

[26] G. Chavanne, *Bull. soc. chim. Belg.*, *26*, 287 (1912).

[27] (a) C. F. Van Duin, *Rec. trav. chim.*, *43*, 341 (1924); *48*, 345 (1926); (b) R. T. Dillon, W. G. Young, and H. Lucas, *J. Am. Chem. Soc.*, *52*, 1953 (1930); (c) R. T. Dillon, *ibid.*, *54*, 952 (1932); (d) W. G. Young, D. Pressman, and C. D. Coryell, *ibid.*, *61*, 1640 (1930).

[28] S. Winstein, D. Pressman, and W. G. Young, *J. Am. Chem. Soc.*, *61*, 1645 (1939).

moves a positive bromine atom, and essentially simultaneously with removal, the electron pair which is left unshared by this removal attacks the carbon face opposite the remaining bromine atom forming a double bond and liberating bromide ion." The facts concerning this

$$
\underset{\substack{I^- \; Br}}{\overset{H \qquad Br}{\underset{\displaystyle R}{\overset{\displaystyle R}{\text{C}-\text{C}}}}}\overset{\text{Acetone}}{\longrightarrow}\;\; \underset{R}{\overset{H}{\text{C}}}=\underset{R}{\overset{H}{\text{C}}} \;+\; \text{IBr} \;+\; \text{Br}^-
$$

$$
\underset{\substack{I^- \; Br}}{\overset{H \qquad Br}{\underset{\displaystyle R}{\overset{\displaystyle R}{\text{C}-\text{C}}}}}\overset{\text{Acetone}}{\longrightarrow}\;\; \underset{R}{\overset{H}{\text{C}}}=\underset{H}{\overset{R}{\text{C}}} \;+\; \text{IBr} \;+\; \text{Br}^-
$$

reaction fit the requirements for the widely accepted mechanism for the E_2 reaction,[29] which stresses the (synchronous) nature of all bond-making and bond-breaking processes.

With respect to alicyclic systems, the reaction of neomenthyl chloride with sodium ethoxide gave a 3–1 ratio of 3-menthene to 2-menthene, whereas menthyl chloride gave only 2-menthene.[30] Although a kinetic control was not applied to the experiment, the reaction conditions suggest that the bimolecular mechanism applies.[31] Hückel et al. interpreted these and a number of other observations as evidence for a *preferred trans* orientation of the leaving groups. This specificity was rationalized on the basis of the electrostatic repulsion that would be involved between the alcoholate anion and the negative end of the $\overset{\delta^+}{\text{C}}-\overset{\delta^-}{\text{Cl}}$ dipole were the anion to approach the same side of the six-membered ring on which the chlorine was bonded. Cristol[32] found that the β isomer of benzene hexachloride (Cl's all *trans* to one another) did not undergo a base-catalyzed elimination reaction under

[29] The kinetic aspects and particularly the nomenclature associated with this mechanism were largely developed by the Ingold school (e.g., see W. Hanhart and C. K. Ingold, *J. Chem. Soc.*, *1927*, 997, and reference 19c).

[30] W. Hückel, W. Tappe, and G. Legutke, *Ann.*, *543*, 191 (1940).

[31] E. D. Hughes, C. K. Ingold, and J. B. Rose (*J. Chem. Soc.*, *1953*, 3839) have obtained essentially the same results under kinetically controlled conditions and found the reactions to be bimolecular.

[32] S. J. Cristol, *J. Am. Chem. Soc.*, *69*, 340 (1947).

conditions that consumed the other isomers. This observation was interpreted as a demonstration of a *trans requirement* for the elimina-

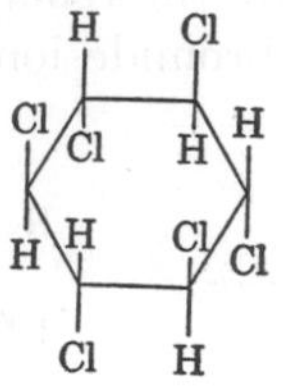

β Isomer

tion of hydrogen halide in a second-order E_2-type reaction. This geometric requirement was considered to arise out of the necessity of the pair of electrons initially in the C—H bond to perform a Walden

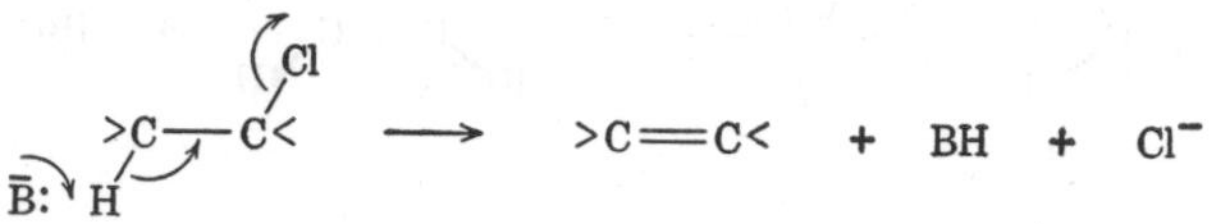

inversion in a one-stage mechanism on the carbon carrying the chlorine substituent. A complete analogy with the S_N2 reaction was thus drawn for the first time. Later, this view was restated in other terms by Hughes and Ingold.[19b, 19a] These last authors' rejection of the electrostatic hypothesis [30] rested on the demonstrated slight preference for *trans* elimination to occur in the bimolecular Hofmann reaction.[33] Here the direction of the electrostatic field due to the C—$\overset{+}{N}$ dipole is the reverse of that found in the C—Cl dipole.[19b]

The stereochemistry of the loss of HX from acyclic systems in the E_2 reaction has been investigated in a number of cases. Treatment of

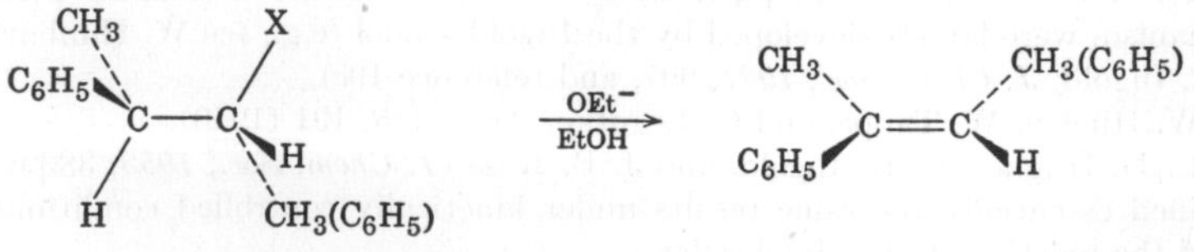

[33] N. L. McNivan and J. Read, *J. Chem. Soc.*, *1952*, 153, 2067.

the diastereomeric 3-phenyl-2-butyl p-toluenesulfonates [34a] or 1,2-diphenyl-1-propyl bromides (or chlorides) [34b] gave in each case an olefin that could arise only by *trans* elimination. The potassium *tert*-butoxide catalyzed elimination of the [hindered] 2,4,6-triethylbenzoates of *threo*- and *erythro*-2-deutero-1,2-diphenylethanol [17a] gave products pointing to a predominating *trans* steric course for the reaction. Similar re-

threo Ester   100% deuterium retained

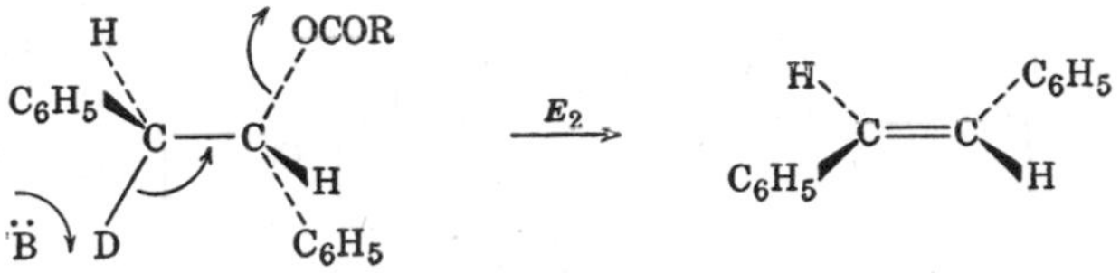

erythro Ester   93% deuterium lost

sults were obtained [35] in the elimination of hydrogen bromide (triethyl amine in benzene) from the diastereomeric benzalacetophenone dibromides to give the isomeric α-bromobenzalacetophenones.

The general question now arises as to the mechanism of the base-induced elimination reactions in which the leaving groups are structurally incapable of assuming a *trans* orientation. The reactions of two systems that fit this condition have been studied, the first of which is the second-order (OH$^-$ in ethanol) elimination of hydrogen chloride from the β isomer (all Cl's *trans*) of benzene hexachloride. Cristol and coworkers [36a, b] demonstrated and Hughes, Ingold, and Pasternack [37] later also found that this isomer is unique among the five known isomers in the sense that, although second-order elimination occurs, the rate is 7000 to 24,000 times slower than that for the other four known diastereomers, each of which possesses at least one

[34] (a) D. J. Cram, *J. Am. Chem. Soc., 74*, 2149 (1952); (b) D. J. Cram and F. A. Abd Elhafez, *ibid., 74*, 5851 (1952).

[35] R. E. Lutz, D. F. Hinkley, and R. H. Jordan, *J. Am. Chem. Soc., 73*, 4647 (1951).

[36] (a) S. J. Cristol, *J. Am. Chem. Soc., 69*, 340 (1947); (b) S. J. Cristol, N. L. Hause, and J. S. Meek, *ibid., 73*, 674 (1951); (c) S. J. Cristol and D. D. Fix, *ibid., 75*, 2647 (1953).

[37] E. D. Hughes, C. K. Ingold, and R. Pasternack, *J. Chem. Soc., 1953*, 3832.

set of vicinal chlorine atoms oriented *cis* to one another. Cristol interpreted [36a, b] (and the latter authors concurred) this dramatic difference in rate as a consequence of the *cis* relation of all 1,2-H and Cl atom-pairs in the β isomer, both sets of authors agreeing that the rate-controlling step is the loss of the first mole of hydrogen chloride from the molecule.

Cristol et al. [36b, c] suggested the following multistage mechanism for the reaction. The ordinary E_2 mechanism is prohibited since, if *trans* elimination were to occur, a *trans* double bond would be introduced into a six-membered ring, which is highly improbable. Therefore, the only alternative to the equally improbable one-stage *cis* elimination mechanism is one in which the first and rate-determining step is the

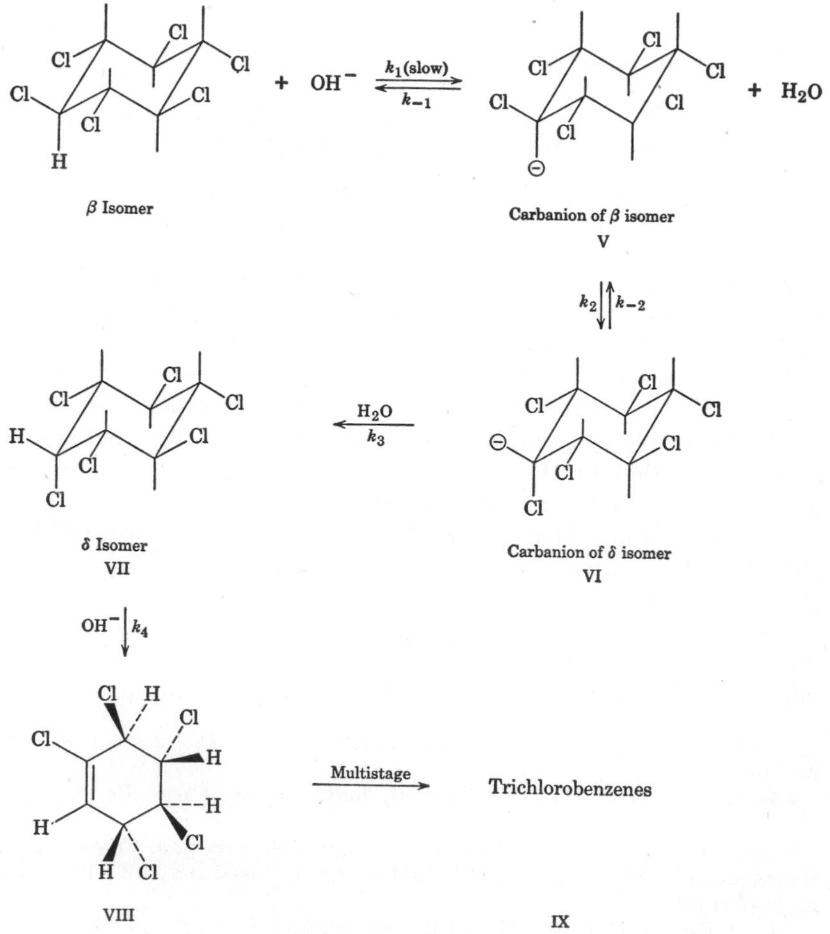

β Isomer

Carbanion of β isomer

V

δ Isomer

VII

Carbanion of δ isomer

VI

VIII

$\xrightarrow{\text{Multistage}}$ Trichlorobenzenes

IX

formation of a carbanion, which can be disposed of in a number of different ways. When run in deuterated solvent for one half-life, the β isomer when recovered contained small amounts of deuterium.[36b, c, 38] This experiment supports the general carbanion mechanism. The most probable path of decomposition of V is for the carbanion to invert to give VI which abstracts a proton from solvent to give δ isomer (VII).[36] This substance contains H and Cl in axial positions on adjacent carbon atoms [39] and has been shown to decompose readily at a much faster rate than the β isomer, and this isomer would not accumulate in the deuterium experiment. However, if the above reaction path applies, deuterated trichlorobenzenes should be produced ultimately when the reaction was run in deuterated solvent since the deuterium that underwent exchange would not be involved in subsequent elimination reactions.[40] Evidence bearing on this point is not available.

The second system in which the leaving groups cannot assume a *trans* configuration is found in the diastereomers of 11,12-dichloro-9,10-dihydro-9,10-ethanoanthracene (X and XI).[41] Both isomers undergo

X    XI

second-order dehydrochlorination with sodium hydroxide in an ethanol-dioxane mixture to give the expected vinyl chloride, but they are both relatively unreactive compared to systems of more adaptable geometry. The unreactivity of X is explained [41] in terms of the constraints that the bicyclic system places on the transition state for elimination, the leaving groups (H and Cl) not being capable of becoming oriented much more than 120° from one another (180° is the ideal orientation) if the other bond angles remain undistorted. This results in an increase in activation energy by 5–8 kcal. over that found in the α, γ, and ϵ isomers of benzene hexachloride which allow direct *trans* elimination.

[38] P. S. Skell and C. R. Hauser [*J. Am. Chem. Soc.*, *67*, 1661 (1945)] were the first to apply this type of isotopic test for a carbanion as an intermediate in the base-catalyzed elimination reaction.

[39] D. H. R. Barton (*J. Chem. Soc.*, *1953*, 1027) cites numerous examples indicating that such geometry is best for the E_2 reaction in the substituted six-membered ring.

[40] Alternative mechanisms involve such improbable steps as *cis* elimination from the carbanion ion itself, or the placing of five chlorines in axial positions.

[41] S. J. Cristol and N. L. Hause, *J. Am. Chem. Soc.*, *74*, 2193 (1952).

The most remarkable feature of this system is that XI, which must undergo overall *cis* elimination, reacts about eight times faster than X, which must undergo overall *trans* elimination. Two factors contribute to this anomalous situation. (1) Although the energy of activation of X and XI is qualitatively what might be expected (energy for *cis* elimination is higher than that for *trans*), this difference is of a smaller magnitude (4 kcal.) than the difference in the less constrained benzene hexachloride systems (9.6–12.5 kcal.), presumably for the reason stated above. (2) The entropy factor in the rates of X and XI favors *cis* elimination (overall) over *trans* elimination by a factor of 2000. In the benzene hexachloride system, the activation energy relationships favoring *trans* elimination more than counterbalance in the rate the entropy relationships that favor *cis* elimination. However, with X and XI, the activation energy relationships favoring *trans* elimination do not quite counterbalance the unfavorable entropy relationships. Thus the paradoxical situation arises in which the rate of *cis* elimination is higher than that of *trans*. The ideal of simplicity is served by the circumstance that only highly specialized systems can be expected to give this type of result.

The stereochemistry of the monomolecular reaction

The steric course of the E_1 reaction is vastly complicated by the multistage nature of the mechanism and by the difficulties of identifying the geometry and capabilities of the intermediates involved. Enough data have now been gathered to at least define the problems and to permit formulation of alternative intimate mechanisms for the transformations.

A number of early observations suggested that the E_1 reaction shows some stereochemical discretion. Thus, *cis*-2-alkylcyclohexanols [42a, b] (H and OH *trans*) undergo acid-catalyzed dehydration to olefin more readily than *trans* (H and OH *cis*). Dehydration with phosphoric acid of *cis*- and *trans*-2-phenylcyclohexanol [43] (XII and XIII) leads to mixtures of olefin which suggest a slight predominance of product that arises by *trans* elimination. The corrected data [9a] are formulated. An interpretation of these findings is rather difficult without a more

[42] (a) W. Hückel, O. Neunhoeffer, A. Gercke, and E. Frank, *Ann., 477*, 131 (1930); (b) G. Vavon and M. Barbier, *Bull. soc. chim. France*, [4], *49*, 567 (1931); (c) G. Vavon, *ibid.*, [4], *49*, 937 (1931). For other references in terpene chemistry, particularly the menthols, see J. L. Simonsen and L. N. Owen, *The Terpenes*, Vol. 1, p. 248, Cambridge University Press, 1947.

[43] C. C. Price and J. V. Karabinos, *J. Am. Chem. Soc., 62*, 1159 (1940).

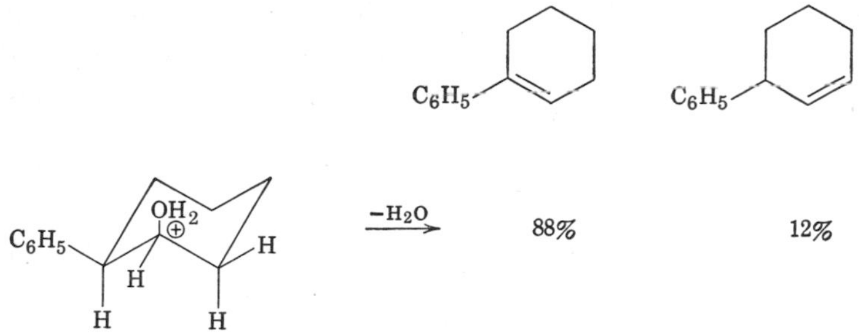

C_6H_5 C_6H_5

$-H_2O \longrightarrow$ 88%   12%

cis Isomer

XII

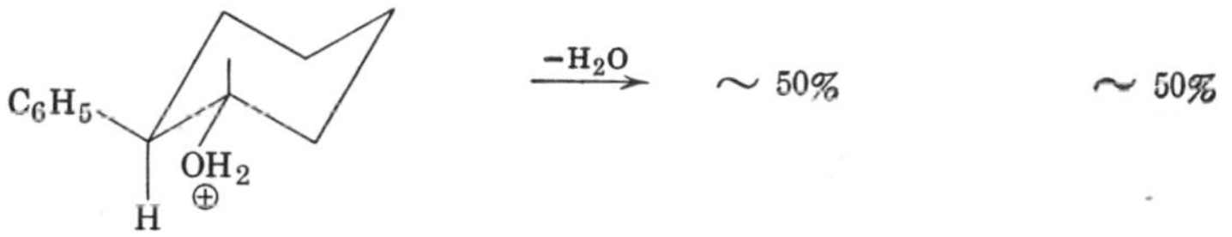

$-H_2O \longrightarrow$ ~ 50%   ~ 50%

trans Isomer

XIII

extensive knowledge of the types of intermediates that intervene between starting material and product.

Only two serious attacks on the problem of the structures of these intermediates have been made, one in an acyclic and the other in an alicyclic system. Each type of system possesses certain advantages. In acyclic systems, stereochemical interpretations can usually be made without any dependence on the Saytzeff rule (see later section), *cis*- and *trans*-related olefins being the products. Since relatively small barriers to rotation in the starting materials are involved, the systems are capable of *adapting to the steric requirements for the reaction, rather than the reaction adapting its orientational course to the geometry of the system*. On the other hand, the five- and six-membered alicyclic systems permit reactivity differences between diastereomerically related compounds to be associated with more nearly rigid and often more easily identifiable geometries. It would appear that the kinetic approach to the problem can be more extensively exploited in alicyclic, and the product balance approach in acyclic, systems.

The acyclic system will be discussed first. Acetolysis of the diastereomers of 3-phenyl-2-butyl *p*-toluenesulfonate (XIV) proceeds by first-order kinetics both in the presence and absence of added sodium acetate, the rates being indifferent (within the range of salt effects) to the concentration of this base.[44] Examination of the acetate products (3-phenyl-2-butyl acetate) from runs made in the presence of added sodium acetate provides convincing evidence that practically none of this ester arises by an S_N2 process involving acetate ion. Since acetate ion is if anything more nucleophilic toward carbon than hydrogen,[45] the absence of S_N2 reaction points to the absence of E_2 reaction involving acetate ion, a conclusion also derived from the kinetic picture.

The balance of the four olefins produced in this solvolysis has been studied in detail as a function of the stereochemistry of the starting material.[46] Evidence was gathered that at least three competing processes were involved in the E_1 reaction. (1) Simple ionization of *erythro*- and *threo*-XIV gave an open (solvated) carbonium ion (XV), which collapsed in a second stage to give about the same ratios of the three unrearranged olefins, XVI, XVII, and XVIII, the process being non-stereospecific. (2) Ionization of both *erythro*- and *threo*-XIV

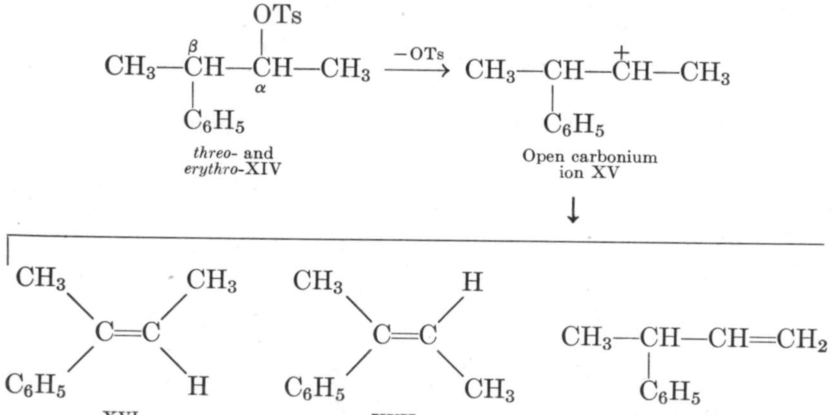

threo- and *erythro*-XIV; Open carbonium ion XV; XVI; XVII; XVIII

occurred with β-H participation and resulted in the production of optically inactive tertiary carbonium ion XIX, which collapsed in each case to the same mixture of olefins XVI, XVII, and the rearranged XX. This process is probably stereospecific in the first stage (that

[44] (*a*) S. Winstein, B. K. Morse, E. Grunwald, K. C. Schrieber, and J. Corse, *J. Am. Chem. Soc.*, *74*, 1115 (1952); (*b*) S. Winstein and K. Schrieber, *ibid.*, *74*, 2165 (1952).

[45] C. K. Ingold, *Structure and Mechanism in Organic Chemistry*, p. 451, Cornell University Press, Ithaca, N. Y., 1953.

[46] D. J. Cram, *J. Am. Chem. Soc.*, *75*, 2137 (1952).

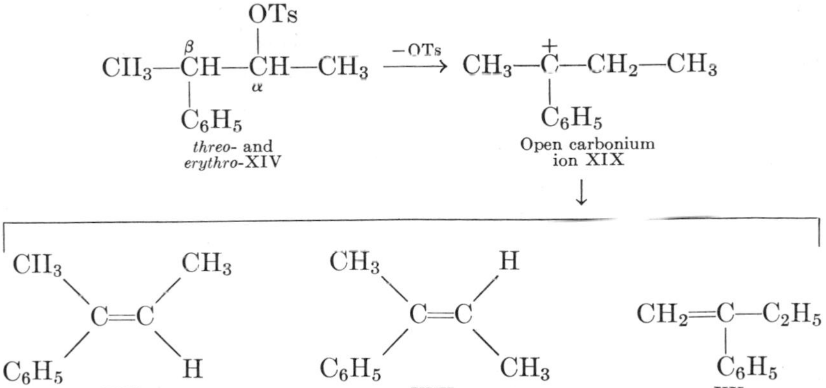

$$CH_3 \overset{\beta}{-}\underset{\underset{C_6H_5}{|}}{CH} \overset{\overset{OTs}{|}}{-}\underset{\alpha}{CH}-CH_3 \xrightarrow{-OTs} CH_3 \overset{+}{\underset{\underset{C_6H_5}{|}}{-}}C-CH_2-CH_3$$

threo- and *erythro*-XIV   Open carbonium ion XIX

↓

$$\underset{C_6H_5}{\overset{CH_3}{\diagdown}}C=C\underset{H}{\overset{CH_3}{\diagup}}$$

XVI

$$\underset{C_6H_5}{\overset{CH_3}{\diagdown}}C=C\underset{CH_3}{\overset{H}{\diagup}}$$

XVII

$$CH_2=\underset{\underset{C_6H_5}{|}}{C}-C_2H_5$$

XX

leading to XIX), but not in the proton-ejecting stage. (3) A *stereo specific process* in which *trans* elimination occurred, XVI resulting from *erythro-* and XVII from *threo*-XIV.

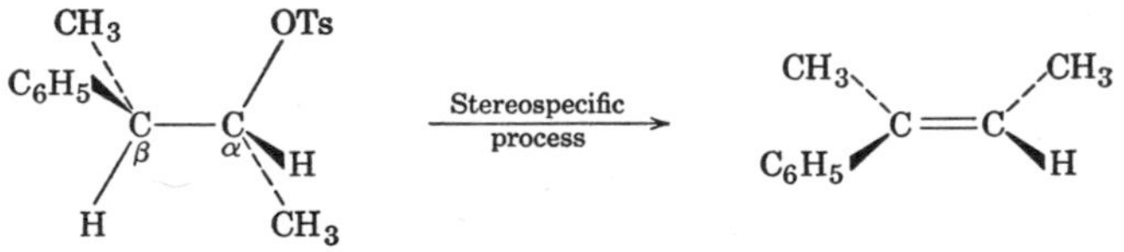

$$\underset{H}{\overset{CH_3}{\underset{C_6H_5}{\diagup}}}\underset{\beta}{C}-\underset{\alpha}{C}\overset{OTs}{\underset{CH_3}{\diagdown}}H \xrightarrow[\text{process}]{\text{Stereospecific}} \underset{C_6H_5}{\overset{CH_3}{\diagdown}}C=C\underset{H}{\overset{CH_3}{\diagup}}$$

erythro-XIV   XVI

$$\underset{H}{\overset{CH_3}{\underset{C_6H_5}{\diagup}}}\underset{\beta}{C}-\underset{\alpha}{C}\overset{OTs}{\underset{H}{\diagdown}}CH_3 \xrightarrow[\text{process}]{\text{Stereospecific}} \underset{C_6H_5}{\overset{CH_3}{\diagdown}}C=C\underset{CH_3}{\overset{H}{\diagup}}$$

threo-XIV   XVII

Three possible mechanisms are available for the last and wholly stereospecific process.[46] The reaction might involve an E_2 mechanism with solvent playing the role of the base. This mechanism is improbable because the solvolytic rate was insensitive to acetate-ion concentration, a stronger base than acetic acid. A second possible mechanism is that each diastereomer of XIV ionized (rate determining) to form an open ion pair capable of holding configuration at C_α long enough for a hydrogen to be lost in a second stage from C_β. This process would be stereospecific if the anion of the ion pair and the hydrogen at C_β left the molecule only from a *trans* orientation. A third and possibly the most attractive mechanism explains not only the stereospecific elimination but the hydrogen migration reaction as well. The facts are accommodated if a hydrogen bridged ion is formed in one stage from starting material, this ion being capable of either dissociating to give olefin, or of completing the migration to give the methyl ethyl phenyl carbonium ion. In this mechanism [46] the reason for the *trans* course of the stereospecific portion of the E_1 reaction lies in the necessity for the hydrogen of the H—C_β becoming bonded at the rear of C_α, the latter becoming inverted as X^- is displaced. This

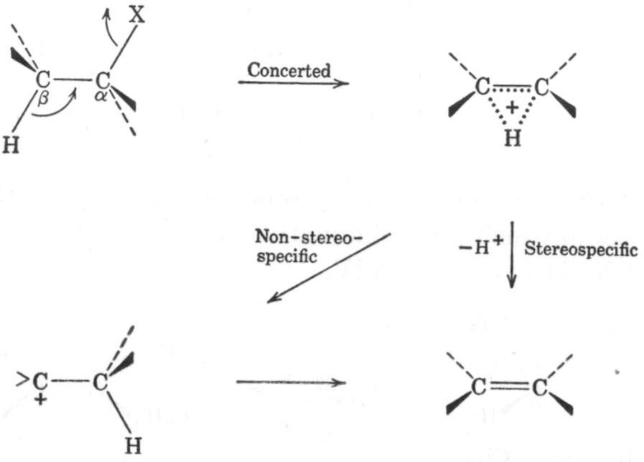

hydrogen bridge would represent a conjugate acid of a weak base and would tend partially to dissociate and partially to go to open carbonium ion, the partitioning between these paths being dependent on ionizing power and nucleophilicity of the solvent. More general support for this hypothesis is found in the fact that systems that provide stereospecificity in the E_1 reaction are those that appear to favor hydrogen migration.

The monomolecular elimination reaction has also been extensively studied from the point of view of its stereochemistry in the alicyclic menthol-neomenthol system. This system is particularly amenable to this type of investigation because the steric requirements of the methyl and isopropyl groups strongly favor their occupation of equatorial positions,[47] a feature that identifies the preferred geometries of the molecules. Although a number of earlier studies [48] had provided evi-

[47] (a) C. W. Beckett, K. S. Pitzer, and R. Spitzer, *J. Am. Chem. Soc.*, *69*, 2488 (1947); (b) O. Hassel and B. Ottar, *Acta Chem. Scand.*, *1*, 929 (1947); (c) D. H. R. Barton, *Experientia*, *6*, 316 (1950).

[48] (a) W. Hückel, W. Tappe, and G. Legutke, *Ann.*, *543*, 191 (1940); (b) W. Hückel and K. Kummerle, *Ber.*, *75B*, 115 (1942); (c) W. Hückel, *ibid.*, *77B*, 805 (1944); (d) J. L. Simonsen and L. N. Owen, *The Terpenes*, Vol. I, p. 248, Cambridge University Press, 1947.

dence that the two diastereomers (X = some leaving group) behaved differently under ionizing conditions, kinetic investigations were not reported until 1952, when Winstein and coworkers [49] found the acetolysis and ethanolysis of menthyl and neomenthyl p-toluenesulfonates to be first order, the latter isomer being consumed 170 times as

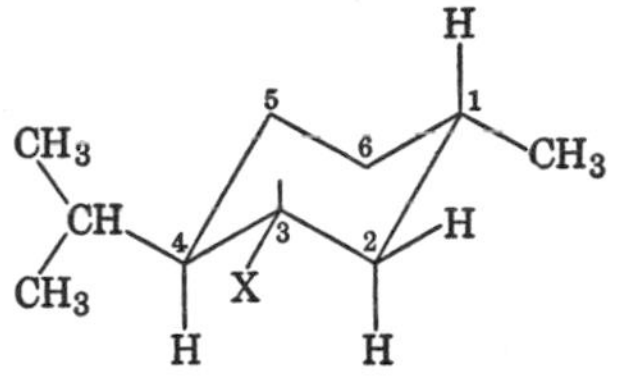

Menthyl-X 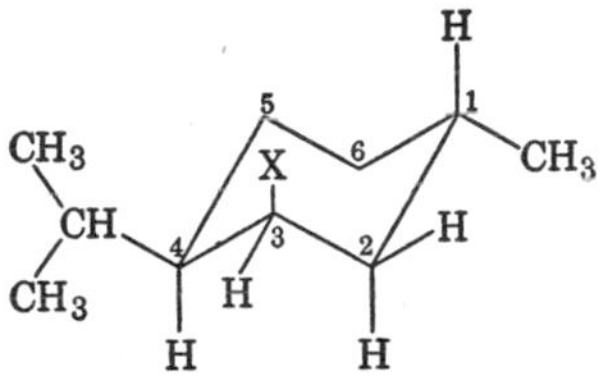   Neomenthyl-X

fast as the former in acetic acid. The facts that this ratio did not change much in going from acetic to formic acids and that the substantial enhancement in rate in going from menthyl to neomenthyl ester is not associated with a closely proportionate increase in the ratio of elimination to substitution were taken as clear evidence that the rates in question in these two solvents measured ionization processes. Although these authors considered that steric facilitation of ionization might contribute substantially to the factor of 170 separating menthyl and neomenthyl p-toluenesulfonate acetolysis rates, they suggest that hydrogen participation in ionization of the neomenthyl system probably accounts for most of the difference. That hydrogen participation in ionization should play a role in the neomenthyl and not the menthyl system is a consequence of the axial-axial relationship of the hydrogen in the 4 position and the p-toluenesulfonate group in the 3 position in the former isomer. The olefinic products of acetolysis are also consistent with this hypothesis, the neomenthyl system giving almost exclusively 3-menthene, the menthyl system a mixture of 2- and 3-menthene with the latter predominant.[49]

Subsequently, Hughes, Ingold, and Rose [31] reported the results of a kinetic and product study of the solvolysis of optically active menthyl and neomenthyl chloride in 80% aqueous ethanol. Again the solvolyses were first order, and again the neomenthyl solvolyzed faster than the menthyl isomer, but in this solvent by only a factor of about 40. The partition of products between 2- and 3-menthene are formulated, as well as the degree of racemization of the latter compound in those

[49] S. Winstein, B. K. Morse, E. Grunwald, H. W. Jones, J. Corse, D. Trifan, and H. Marshall, J. Am. Chem. Soc., 74, 1127 (1952).

runs in which sodium acetate was present to neutralize the acid produced. The degree of racemization of the 3-menthene was used as a

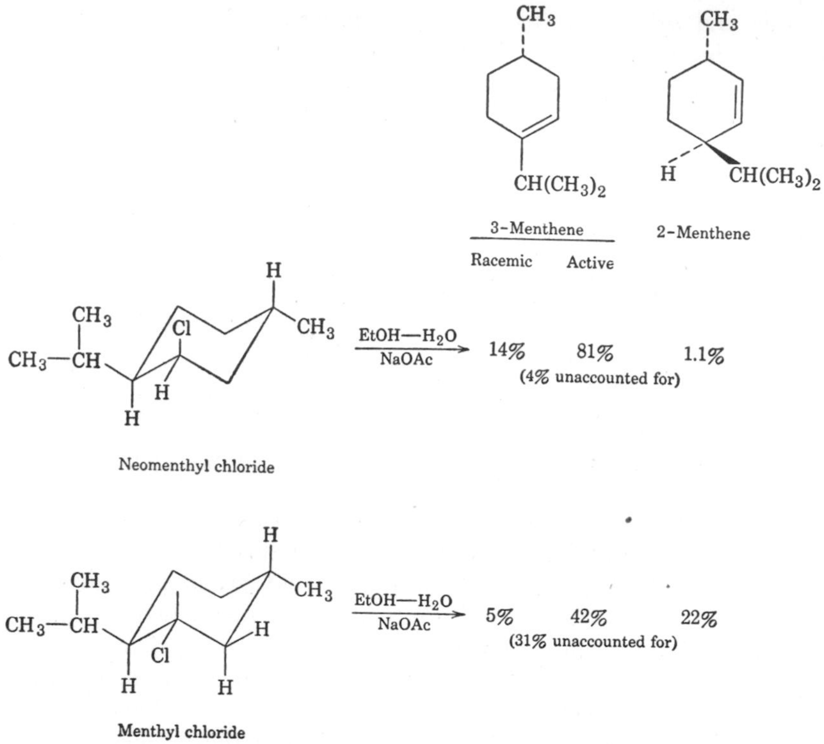

3-Menthene   2-Menthene

Racemic   Active

Neomenthyl chloride

$$\xrightarrow[\text{NaOAc}]{\text{EtOH—H}_2\text{O}}$$

14%   81%   1.1%

(4% unaccounted for)

Menthyl chloride

$$\xrightarrow[\text{NaOAc}]{\text{EtOH—H}_2\text{O}}$$

5%   42%   22%

(31% unaccounted for)

measure of how much of this olefin had arisen from the internally
compensated tertiary carbonium ion, which in turn could have been
produced by a Wagner-Meerwein shift of a hydrogen from the 4- to
the 3-carbon.

The authors [31] interpret these results as follows. The elimination in
the menthyl system is considered to be unimolecular (E_1), the predominant direction of the elimination favoring 3-menthene, as predicted by the Saytzeff rule (see next section). This unimolecular
character of the reaction is associated with the stereochemical constraint (the Cl is not in an axial position) placed on bimolecular elimination. The mildly accelerated first-order reaction of neomenthyl
chloride was considered to arise from a predominating bimolecular
solvolysis, the basic reagent being a solvent molecule. In both reactions, the retention of a high degree of optical activity by the 3-men-
thene produced was taken as evidence that a Wagner-Meerwein type

shift of hydrogen is not an essential feature of the process of elimination.[50]

In another study, Hammond and Nevitt [51] investigated both the E_2 and the E_1 reaction of cis- and trans-1,2-dimethylcyclohexyl bromides. Although the rates of the E_2 reaction with sodium hydroxide in 98% ethanol decrease by a factor of 12 in passing from the trans to the cis isomer, the solvolysis rates in the same solvent (minus the base) were essentially identical. Clearly no hydrogen participation in

trans Isomer   cis Isomer

ionization occurred in the solvolytic experiments.[51] The relatively high stability of a tertiary carbonium ion (as compared to primary and secondary) coupled with the relatively powerful nucleophilic character (compared, e.g., with acetic acid) of aqueous ethanol would both strongly mitigate against hydrogen participation. It has been observed previously (see Chapter 5) that even phenyl participation from a β-quaternary carbon in ionization at an α-tertiary carbon in acetic acid is barely evident.

Orientation in the heterolytic elimination reaction

Two empirical rules have been developed that summarize a large number of observations concerning the direction of elimination in two classes of reactions. The Hofmann rule [52] in a generalized form states that, in the decomposition of a quaternary ammonium hydroxide, the

[50] It is reasonable to assume that just as with other neighboring groups [e.g., see S. Winstein et al., J. Am. Chem. Soc., 74, 1140 (1952)] hydrogen participation in ionization must compete with solvent participation, and that the greatest opportunity to observe the former phenomena would be in less nucleophilic solvents. It is probably significant in this regard that the factor of 170 between the rates of acetolysis of the menthol and neomenthol p-toluenesulfonates (reference 49) drops to about 40 in the solvolysis of the corresponding chlorides in 80% aqueous ethanol (reference 31). Even in ethanol, some hydrogen migration occurs, and the fact that more was not observed might be a consequence of an intermediate bridged hydrogen cation (conjugate acid of 3-methene) giving up a proton to water, rather than the hydrogen migration being completed.

[51] T. D. Nevitt and G. S. Hammond, J. Am. Chem. Soc., 76, 4124 (1954).

[52] A. W. Hofmann, Ann., 78, 253; 79, 11 (1851).

least substituted ethylene is the predominating olefinic product. The Saytzeff rule [53] states that, in the elimination of HX from a secondary or tertiary alkyl halide, the most highly substituted ethylene is the predominating olefinic product. The scope and limitations, and the rationale at the basis of these rules have been elaborated largely by the Hughes-Ingold school,[19] and a brief summary of their views is recorded here.

The correlation stated by the Hofmann rule is considered to arise from a predominating inductive effect operating in the E_2 reaction of substances which carry a leaving group bearing a formal positive charge. An illustration of this rule is found in the bimolecular elimination of XXI to give ethylene and dimethyl propyl amine. The at-

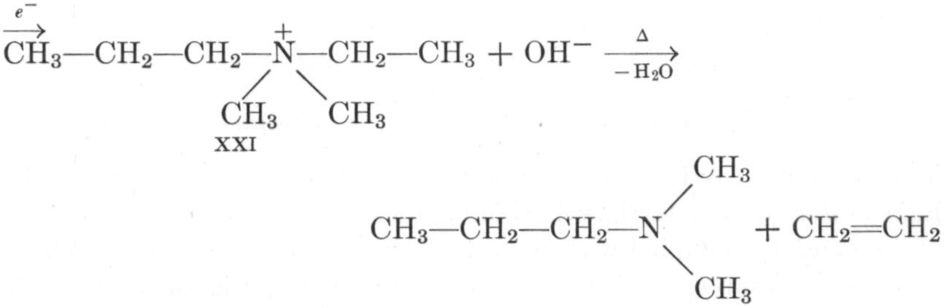

$$\overset{e^-}{\longrightarrow} CH_3-CH_2-CH_2-\overset{+}{N}-CH_2-CH_3 + OH^- \xrightarrow[-H_2O]{\Delta}$$
$$\underset{CH_3 \quad CH_3}{\diagup \quad \diagdown}$$
$$XXI$$

$$CH_3-CH_2-CH_2-N\overset{\diagup CH_3}{\diagdown CH_3} + CH_2\!=\!CH_2$$

tack of base on the hydrogens of the methyl predominates over the attack on the hydrogens of the methylene group because the induced positive charge at the methylene is partially canceled by electron release from the attached methyl group.[19]

When carried to the decomposition of sulfonium hydroxides, the same principle is illustrated by the following order with respect to ease with which alkyl groups split off to form olefins.[19]

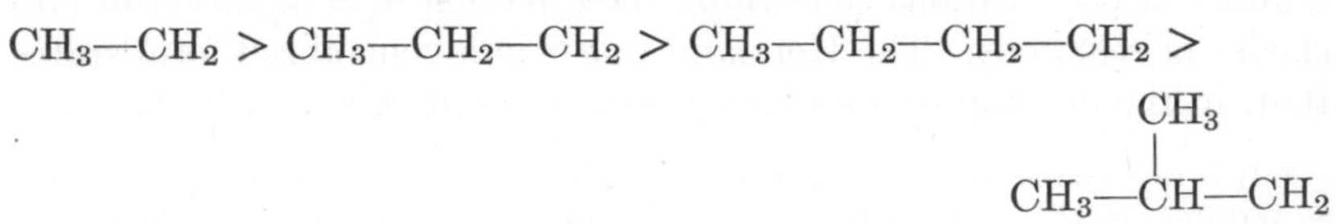

$$CH_3-CH_2 > CH_3-CH_2-CH_2 > CH_3-CH_2-CH_2-CH_2 >$$
$$\underset{CH_3-\overset{\displaystyle CH_3}{\overset{|}{C}H}-CH_2}{}$$

Another application of the principle is the bimolecular elimination of dimethyl sulfide from the 2-n-butyldimethylsulfonium ion to give a mixture of butenes. Again, the hydrogen is lost predominantly

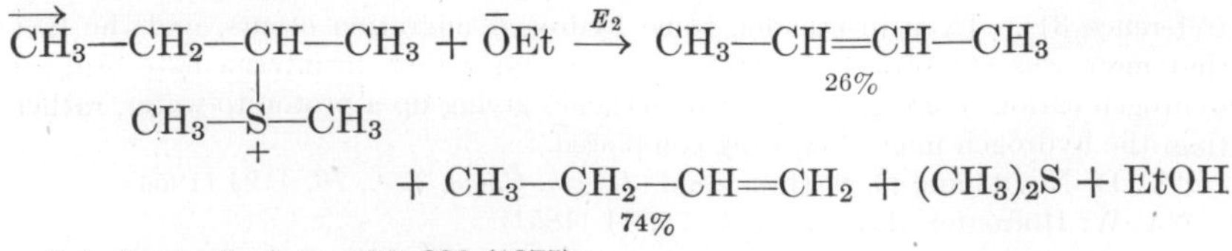

$$\overset{e^-}{\longrightarrow} CH_3-CH_2-\underset{\underset{+}{\overset{|}{S}}-CH_3}{\overset{|}{C}H}-CH_3 + \bar{O}Et \xrightarrow{E_2} CH_3-CH\!=\!CH-CH_3$$
$$26\%$$
$$CH_3-\underset{+}{S}-CH_3$$

$$+ CH_3-CH_2-CH\!=\!CH_2 + (CH_3)_2S + EtOH$$
$$74\%$$

[53] A. Saytzeff, *Ann.*, *179*, 296 (1875).

from the methyl group which is more positive than the methylene group to which is attached an electron-releasing methyl group.[19] Relative rate data support this thesis, the higher alkyl group giving olefin more slowly. It is noteworthy that the rates of loss of a proton from the methyl group were about the same in the two starting materials formulated.[19] Similar data have been obtained for the loss of hydrogen from *tert*-alkyl dimethyl sulfonium ions.[19]

The Hofmann rule appears to be limited to "onium"-type starting materials and to the E_2 reaction. In contrast, the Saytzeff rule applies to most systems in the E_1 and to neutral systems undergoing the E_2 reaction. Just as attention was focused on the starting material in the application of the inductive effect to explain the operation of the Hofmann rule, attention is focused on the transition state in applying resonance effects to explain the operation of the Saytzeff rule.[19]

The bimolecular reaction as applied to the loss of HX from an alkyl halide is formulated, the transition state being drawn to suggest that some delocalization of the electrons in the C_α—a, C_α—b, C_β—c, C_β—d bonds is possible. Groups capable of conjugating or hyperconjugating

with the incipient double bond (whether substituted on C_α or C_β) should facilitate the formation of that double bond. Where a hydrogen can be lost from several different C_β positions in the same molecule, that reaction will predominate which produces the most conjugated transition state. Or, in comparing the reactivity of different molecules, that molecule should react the faster whose transition state is the most stabilized by conjugation with substituents at both C_α and C_β.

In the simple alkyl halides (not carrying unsaturated groups) hyperconjugation effects are dominant. Regarding methyl substitution at C_α, ease of E_2 elimination occurs in the order *tert*-butyl > isopropyl > ethyl (bromide).[19] With respect to methyl substitution at C_β, ease of elimination occurs in the order isobutyl > *n*-propyl > ethyl (bromide).[19] Through a study of the relative rates of elimination (E_2) of a large number of alkyl halides, the ability of different alkyl groups to hyperconjugate with the incipient double bond from either C_α or C_β was found to be methyl > ethyl > propyl > H.[19] This type of order also appears to apply in those E_2 reactions in which two olefins are formed from the same starting material. Thus, *sec*-butyl bromide gives 2-butene at a faster rate than 1-butene because methyl hyper-conjugates with the incipient double bond better than hydrogen. Of

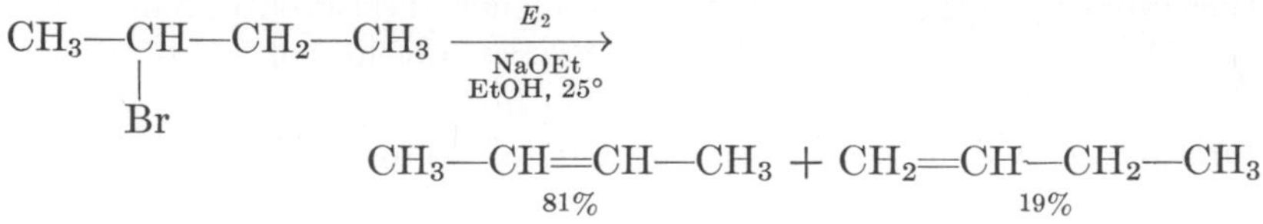

$$CH_3—CH—CH_2—CH_3 \xrightarrow[\substack{NaOEt \\ EtOH, 25°}]{E_2}$$
$$\quad\quad |$$
$$\quad Br$$

$$CH_3—CH{=}CH—CH_3 + CH_2{=}CH—CH_2—CH_3$$
$$\quad\quad\quad 81\% \quad\quad\quad\quad\quad\quad 19\%$$

course, whether dealing with a comparison of rates of formation of olefin along two different chains in the same molecule or in two different molecules, the ability of phenyl in either the α or β position to enhance rate is more marked than that of an alkyl group.[19]

Since the unimolecular elimination reaction is two stages, the balance of isomeric olefins obtained by developing the double bond in different chains of the same molecule should be independent of the nature of the leaving group, at least in those cases uncomplicated by the phenomenon of internal return (see Chapter 5). The same carbonium ion is formed, and its disposition is independent of its source. Similarly, the proportion of products arising by S_N1 and E_1 processes should also be independent of the leaving group for the same reason. The latter has been demonstrated for a number of secondary and tertiary alkyl halides and dimethyl sulfonium compounds in aqueous ethanol.[19] It therefore is logical to expect that the same rule (Saytzeff) applies to the E_1 reaction whether an alkyl halide or a quaternary ammonium compound is the starting material, as has been found to be the case.[19]

In rationalizing orientation effects in the E_1 reaction, attention is focused on the transition state that intervenes between carbonium ion and olefinic product. Again, the substituents on C_β appear to play an important directing role. Thus, tert-amyl bromide in ethanol at 25° produces more 2-methyl-2-butene than 2-methyl-1-butene.

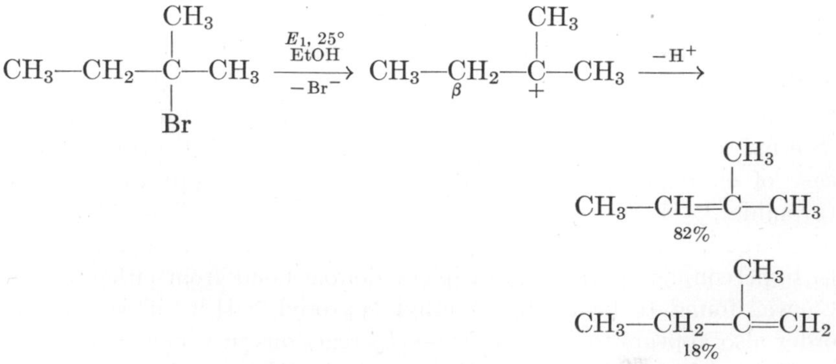

$$\begin{array}{c} CH_3 \\ | \\ CH_3—CH_2—C—CH_3 \\ | \\ Br \end{array} \xrightarrow[-Br^-]{\substack{E_1,\ 25° \\ EtOH}} \begin{array}{c} CH_3 \\ | \\ CH_3—CH_2—C—CH_3 \\ \beta\quad\quad + \end{array} \xrightarrow{-H^+}$$

$$\begin{array}{c} CH_3 \\ | \\ CH_3—CH{=}C—CH_3 \\ 82\% \end{array}$$

$$\begin{array}{c} CH_3 \\ | \\ CH_3—CH_2—C{=}CH_2 \\ 18\% \end{array}$$

Presumably the transition state leading to 2-methyl-2-butene is somewhat stabilized by hyperconjugation of the methyl attached to C_β.[19a]

Similar principles have been applied to explain the enhancement of elimination (E_1) over substitution (S_N1) products where the two spring from the same carbonium ion.[19] Thus olefin formation is enhanced by successive substitution of alkyl groups at both C_α and C_β; the better the hyperconjugative ability of the groups, the greater the enhancement.[19a]

Cases in which both the inductive and conjugative (resonance) effects are supposed to operate have not been discussed here, nor has the semiquantitative empirical application of some of the above principles. These interpretations are elaborated in detail elsewhere.[19a]

Steric effects in elimination reactions

It has been pointed out [19] that steric effects are of considerably less importance in the elimination than in the substitution reaction, particularly with respect to those of the monomolecular variety. This relegation of steric effects to a minor role is attributed to the far more exposed position of hydrogen as compared to carbon with regard to attack by nucleophilic agents.[19] In the ionization and common stage of the E_1 and S_N1 reactions, evidence has accumulated that, as methyl groups are successively substituted for hydrogens in tert-butyl chloride, a point is reached where steric acceleration of ionization becomes important.[54] This section will be devoted to an examination of those cases in which steric effects appear to be operative in the E_2 and E_1 reactions, attention being focused on the second stage (involving proton loss) of the latter.

STERIC EFFECTS IN THE SECOND STAGE OF THE E_1 REACTION. Brown et al.[55a, b] have pointed out that, if R_1, R_2, and R_3 are of sufficient size to release steric compression (B strain) [54] in the ionization stage to give a relatively strainless planar carbonium ion, the reaction of this carbonium ion with solvent in the second stage would involve the recreation of steric compression in going to substitution product. On

[54] (a) H. C. Brown, Science, 103, 385 (1946); (b) H. C. Brown and R. S. Fletcher, J. Am. Chem. Soc., 71, 1845 (1949); (c) P. D. Bartlett, 10th National Symposium, Boston, Massachusetts, June, 1947, p. 30 of Abstracts; (d) P. D. Bartlett, Bull. soc. chim. France, 18, 101C (1951).

[55] (a) H. C. Brown and R. S. Fletcher, J. Am. Chem. Soc., 72, 1223 (1950); (b) H. C. Brown and H. L. Berneis, ibid., 75, 10 (1953); (c) H. C. Brown and I. Moritani, ibid., 77, 3607 (1955); (d) H. C. Brown and M. Nakagawa, ibid., 77, 3610 (1955); (e) H. C. Brown and M. Nakagawa, ibid., 77, 3614 (1955); (f) H. C. Brown and Y. Okamoto, ibid., 3619 (1955).

the other hand, the loss of a proton from a β-carbon to give olefin might be enhanced by a "squeezing-out" process.[55a, b] Either or both

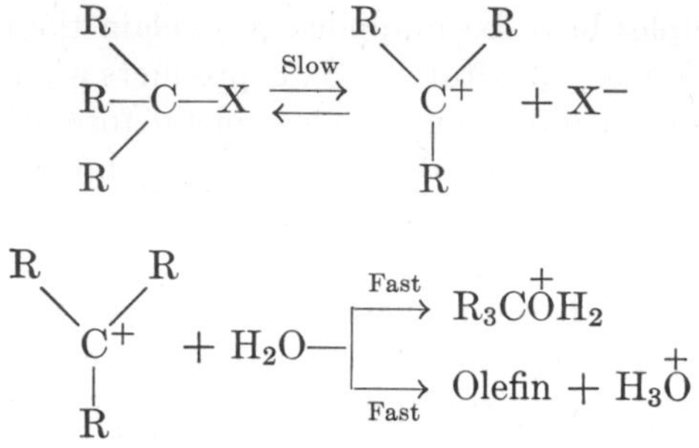

of these effects are said to favor olefin over substitution product. The increase in olefin proportion as the bulk of the R's is gradually increased (see Table I) has been offered [55a, b] as evidence for these ef-

TABLE I

EFFECT OF SIZE OF R ON PER CENT OLEFIN PRODUCED IN SOLVOLYSIS OF
ALKYL CHLORIDES

(25° in 80% Aqueous EtOH)

R_1	R_2	R_3	% Olefin	R_1	R_2	R_3	% Olefin
CH_3	CH_3	CH_3	16	CH_3	CH_3	i-C_3H_7	62
CH_3	CH_3	C_2H_5	34	CH_3	CH_3	t-C_4H_9	61
CH_3	CH_3	n-C_3H_7	33	CH_3	CH_3	neo-C_5H_{11}	65
CH_3	CH_3	n-C_4H_9	35	CH_3	i-C_3H_7	i-C_3H_7	78
CH_3	C_2H_5	C_2H_5	41	C_2H_5	C_2H_5	i-C_3H_7	80
C_2H_5	C_2H_5	C_2H_5	40	C_2H_5	C_2H_5	t-C_4H_9	90

fects, which are considered to supplement the hyperconjugative effects discussed previously.[19] In contrast, Hughes, Ingold, and Shiner [56] claim that the per cent olefin obtained from those compounds in the left column can be predicted purely on the basis of hyperconjugative effects by extending their semiquantitative empirical correlations developed for simpler olefins to these more ramified systems. They suggest (without demonstrating how) that the same thing can be done for three of the compounds of the right-hand column (XXII, XXIII, and XXIV). These authors further suggest that the abnormally high (factor of 4 to 5 based on correlation of hyperconjugative effects) proportion of olefin from dimethyl *tert*-butyl carbinyl chloride might be

[56] E. D. Hughes, C. K. Ingold, and V. J. Shiner, Jr., *J. Chem. Soc.*, *1953*, 3827.

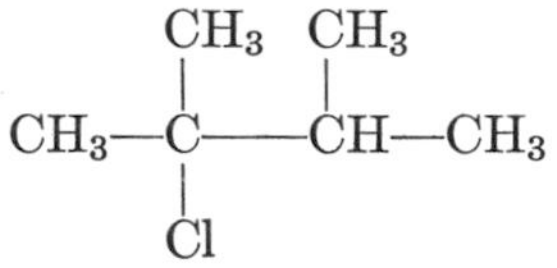

$$CH_3-\underset{\underset{Cl}{|}}{\overset{\overset{CH_3}{|}}{C}}-\underset{}{\overset{\overset{CH_3}{|}}{C}}H-CH_3$$

XXII

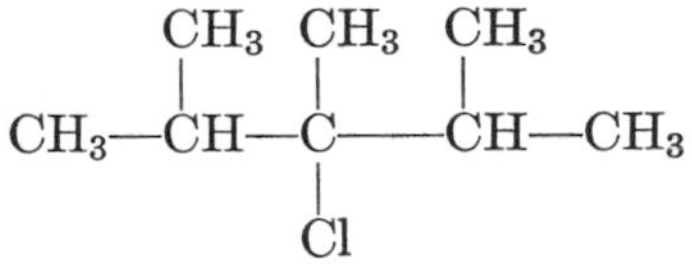

$$CH_3-\overset{\overset{CH_3}{|}}{C}H-\underset{\underset{Cl}{|}}{\overset{\overset{CH_3}{|}}{C}}-\overset{\overset{CH_3}{|}}{C}H-CH_3$$

XXIII

$$CH_3-CH_2-\underset{\underset{Cl}{|}\;\underset{CH_3}{|}}{\overset{\overset{CH_2-CH_3}{|}}{C}}-CH-CH_3$$

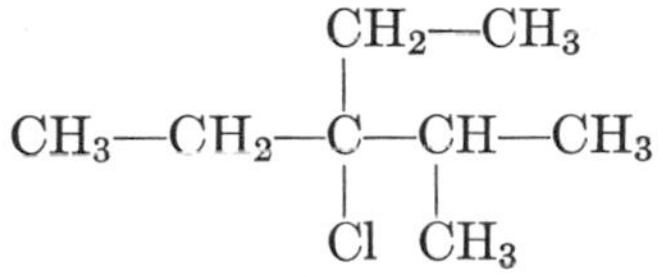

XXIV

due to a disposition of the system to undergo a Wagner-Meerwein rearrangement that somehow enhances olefin production. Similarly, the same possibility would apply to the abnormally high amount of olefin obtained from diethyl *tert*-butyl carbinyl chloride. This possibility was set aside through the work of Roberts and Yancey,[57] who found that C^{14} labeled dimethyl *tert*-butyl chloride could be hydrolyzed with water (non-reversible conditions) without any rearrangement of methyl groups. In connection with the idea that the intervention of Wagner-Meerwein rearrangements (not involving hydrogen migration) might produce either abnormally high proportions of olefin or unexpected orientation of double bonds, results obtained in the 3-phenyl-2-butyl system are pertinent.[46] The possibility that phenonium ions could produce unconjugated olefin directly was eliminated by demonstrating that the degree of optical purity of the 3-phenyl-1-butene produced from active *threo*-3-phenyl-2-butyl *p*-toluenesulfonate in acetic acid was inconsistent with the intervention of an internally compensated intermediate in the reaction.

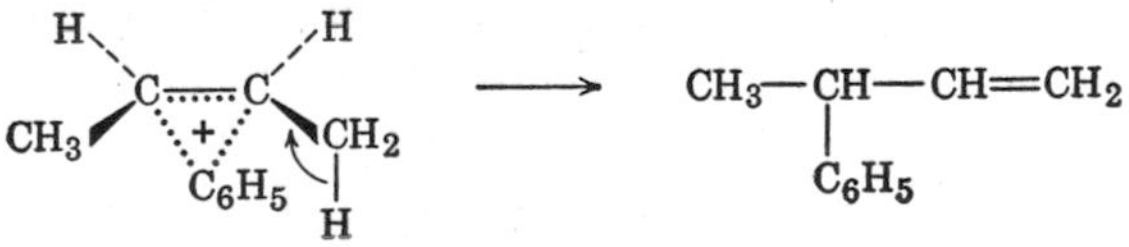

Both the olefin yield and the orientation of the double bond of the predominant unsaturated product from dimethyl *neo*-pentyl carbinyl chloride cannot be explained on the basis of hydrogen hyperconjugative effects.[55b, c, 56] An explanation of these results based on no-bond resonance (carbon-carbon hyperconjugation) has been offered [56] which in essence suggests that the transition state of the proton-ejecting

[57] J. D. Roberts and J. A. Yancey, *J. Am. Chem. Soc.*, **77**, 5558 (1955).

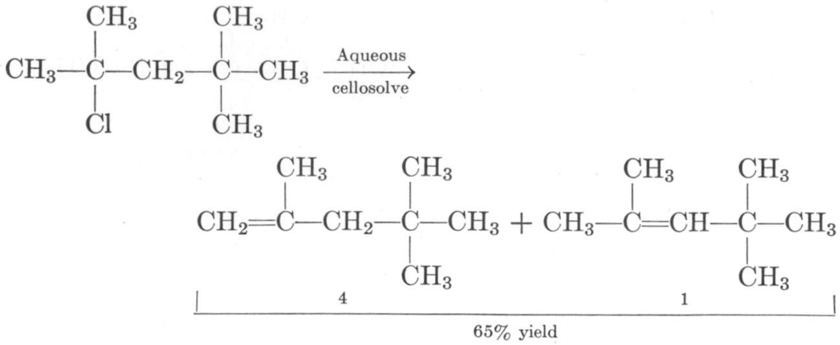

$$CH_3-\underset{\underset{Cl}{|}}{\overset{\overset{CH_3}{|}}{C}}-CH_2-\underset{\underset{CH_3}{|}}{\overset{\overset{CH_3}{|}}{C}}-CH_3 \xrightarrow[\text{cellosolve}]{\text{Aqueous}}$$

$$CH_2=\underset{}{\overset{\overset{CH_3}{|}}{C}}-CH_2-\underset{\underset{CH_3}{|}}{\overset{\overset{CH_3}{|}}{C}}-CH_3 + CH_3-\overset{\overset{CH_3}{|}}{C}=CH-\underset{\underset{CH_3}{|}}{\overset{\overset{CH_3}{|}}{C}}-CH_3$$

| 4 | 1 |

65% yield

stage in this reaction is stabilized by delocalization of charge as suggested in the formulation.

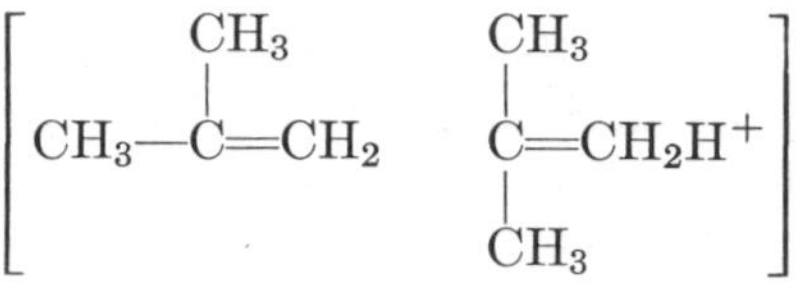

$$\left[CH_3-\overset{\overset{CH_3}{|}}{C}=CH_2 \quad \underset{\underset{CH_3}{|}}{\overset{\overset{CH_3}{|}}{C}}=CH_2H^+ \right] \begin{array}{l}\text{Nine equivalent}\\\text{contributors to}\\\text{hybrid}\end{array}$$

A more plausible steric explanation [55c] for the results obtained from dimethyl *neo*-pentyl carbinyl chloride appears below. In the carbonium ion formed from this system, hydrogen is more exposed than carbon to nucleophilic attack by solvent. Furthermore, as has been pointed out,[55b] compression strain is re-created in the transition state leading to substituted product. Collapse to olefin can occur in two directions to give either the less (Hofmann product) or more (Saytzeff product) substituted olefin, the former predominating by a factor of 4. In the transition state leading to the Saytzeff product, a *tert*-butyl and a methyl group are becoming eclipsed, whereas in the Hofmann product, a hydrogen and a *neo*-pentyl group are becoming eclipsed. Certainly the compression energy involved in the latter process should be less than the former. That eclipsing effects of this sort become controlling only when the bulk of at least one of the eclipsed groups becomes large is demonstrated in Table II.[55e] The data of Table III [55e]

TABLE II

RATIO OF 1- TO 2-OLEFIN PRODUCED IN SOLVOLYSIS OF HALIDES IN 85% *n*-BUTYLCELLOSOLVE AT 25°

Compound	1-Olefin/2-Olefin
$CH_3CH_2CBr(CH_3)_2$	0.27
$C_2H_5CH_2CBr(CH_3)_2$	0.41
$(CH_3)_2CHCH_2CBr(CH_3)_2$	0.70
$(CH_3)_3CCH_2CBr(CH_3)_2$	4.3

TABLE III

RATIOS OF 1- TO 2-OLEFINS AND OF *trans*-2-OLEFIN TO *cis*-2-OLEFIN PRODUCED
IN SOLVOLYSIS OF ARYLSULFONATE ESTERS IN ACETIC ACID AT 70°

Compound	1-Olefin/2-Olefin	*trans*-2-Olefin/*cis*-2-Olefin
$CH_3CH_2CH(OTs)CH_3$	0.11	1.08
$C_2H_5CH_2CH(OBs)CH_3$	0.19	1.38
$(CH_3)_2CHCH_2CH(OBs)CH_3$	0.25	1.94
$(CH_3)_3CCH_2CH(OBs)CH_3$	0.32	83

clearly indicate that eclipsing effects in the second stage of the E_1 reaction can affect the partitioning of the carbonium ion among the 1- and 2-olefins and, more importantly, between the *cis* and *trans* 2-olefins. This effect becomes serious rather suddenly in passing from the substance in which a methyl and an isopropyl group become eclipsed to the substance in which a methyl and a *tert*-butyl group become eclipsed in producing *cis*-2-olefin.

STERIC EFFECTS IN THE E_2 REACTION. In this section the possible operation of three types of steric effects as applied to the bimolecular elimination reaction will be discussed: those arising from the bulk of the base, the bulk of the leaving group, and the bulk of substituents attached to the ethylene in the product.

Evidence that the geometry of the base can play a role in the E_2 reaction was first obtained by Cristol,[58] who identified the only *d,l* isomer of benzene hexachloride (the α isomer) by selectively destroying with brucine (through an elimination reaction) one optical antipode in the presence of the other. Since sufficient brucine was utilized

$+ \tfrac{3}{2}$ Brucine $\longrightarrow \tfrac{3}{2}$ Brucine $\cdot$ HCl $+ \tfrac{1}{2}C_6H_3Cl_3 + \tfrac{1}{2}(-)$ — $C_6H_6Cl_6$

to consume only half of the benzene hexachloride, the reaction was automatically interrupted at the halfway point. The unreacted benzene hexachloride was demonstrated to possess α, $-14.6°$ ($l = 1$ dm., ether), and although the degree of optical purity is unknown, the experiment demonstrates that one enantiomer undergoes (probably an E_2) reaction faster than the other. Since asymmetric induction is most certainly sterically controlled, this observation suggests that the

[58] S. J. Cristol, *J. Am. Chem. Soc.*, *71*, 1894 (1949).

rate of the bimolecular elimination reaction is dependent on the shape of the basic agent employed.

That the bulk of the base involved in an E_2 reaction can play an important role in directing the entrance of a double bond into one or another of two possible positions in an olefin has been demonstrated in Tables IV and V.[59] Thus the larger the base the greater the

	Ratio	1-Olefin/2-Olefin
Alkyl Halide	KOEt	KO—C(CH₃)₃

Alkyl Halide	KOEt	KO—C(CH$_3$)$_3$
CH$_3$—CH—CH$_2$—CH$_3$ (with Br below)	0.23	1.1
CH$_3$—CH—CH$_2$—CH$_2$—CH$_3$ (with Br below)	0.41	1.9
CH$_3$—CH——CH—CH$_2$—CH$_3$ (with CH$_3$ and Br below)	0.41	2.6
CH$_3$—CH——C—CH$_3$ (with CH$_3$ above, CH$_3$ and Br below)	—	6.7
CH$_3$—C—CH$_2$—C—CH$_3$ (with CH$_3$, CH$_3$ above, CH$_3$ and Br below)	5.7	99

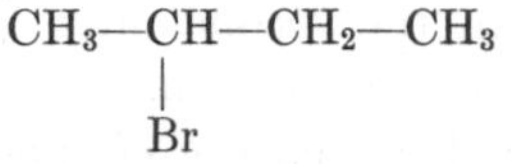

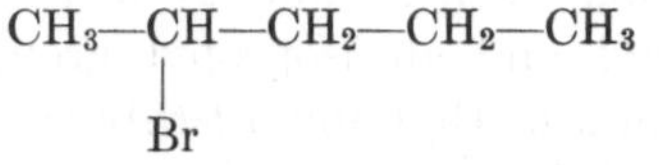

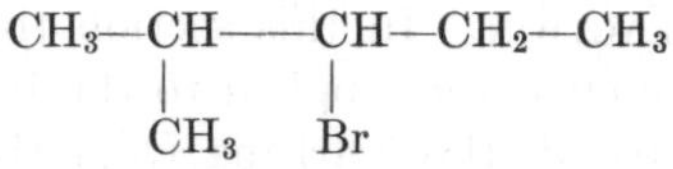

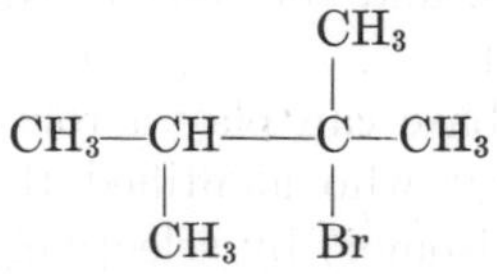

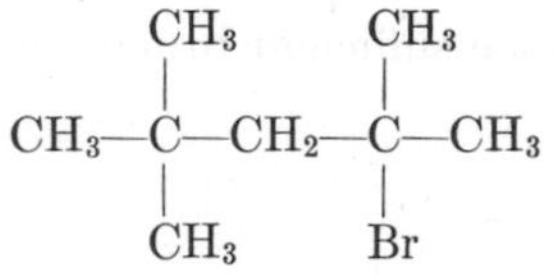

tendency of the least substituted ethylene (Hofmann product) to be formed. With the larger bases, a clear violation of the Saytzeff rule is evident. This effect is much more pronounced in the alkoxide than in pyridine series (Tables IV and V), even though the nitrogen of the latter is probably at least as hindered as the oxygen of the former. These facts indicate that the bulkier bases attack the more exposed hydrogens, the effect being more marked the stronger the base. The claim is also made [59] that, as the bulk of the leaving group is increased in the order Br$^-$, S(CH$_3$)$_2$, RSO$_2$$^-$, and N(CH$_3$)$_3$, a general trend is

[59] H. C. Brown, I. Moritani, Y. Okamoto, M. Nakagawa, and O. H. Wheeler, private communications.

TABLE IV

Olefin Compositions Obtained with Various Bases

Compound	Per Cent of 1-Olefin in Olefinic Product			
	KOC_2H_5	$KOC(CH_3)_3$	$KOC(CH_3)_2C_2H_5$	$KOC(C_2H_5)_3$
$CH_3—CH_2—CH—CH_3$ with Br	18	53	—	—
$CH_3—CH_2$ $CH_2—CH—CH_3$ with Br	29	66	—	—
$CH_3—CH_2—C—CH_3$ with CH_3 and Br	29	72	78	89
$CH_3—CH_2$ CH_2 $C—CH_3$ with CH_3 and Br	50	—	—	—
$CH_3—CH—CH_2—C—CH_3$ with CH_3, CH_3 and Br	54	—	—	—
$CH_3—C—CH_2—C—CH_3$ with CH_3, CH_3, CH_3 and Br	86	98	—	97
$CH_3—CH—C—CH_3$ with CH_3, CH_3 and Br	21	73	81	92

evident for elimination to shift from the Saytzeff to the Hofmann predicted product.[60]

A considerable amount of data has been obtained that points to the importance of eclipsing effects in the E_2 reaction. Since the transition states themselves can never have more double bond character than the olefin they are producing, orientation with respect to the possible importance of eclipsing effects can be gained by examining the thermodynamic stability of pairs of *cis* and *trans* olefins.[61] Heats of combus-

[60] C. H. Schramm [*Science, 112*, 367 (1950)] first suggested that the bulk of the leaving group might be at the basis of the Hofmann rule, but founded his reasoning on the fallacious grounds that, in the E_2 transition state, the leaving group and the substituents attached to the incipient double bond are coplanar.

[61] D. Y. Curtin, *Abstracts* of Thirteenth National Organic Symposium of the American Chemical Society, Ann Arbor, Mich., June, 1953, p. 40.

TABLE V

Olefin Compositions Obtained with Various Bases

	Per Cent of 1-Olefin in Olefinic Product		
Compound	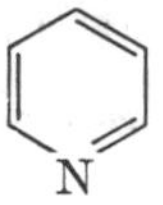	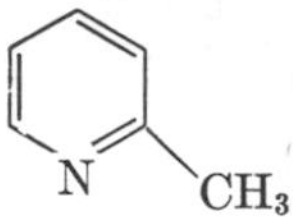	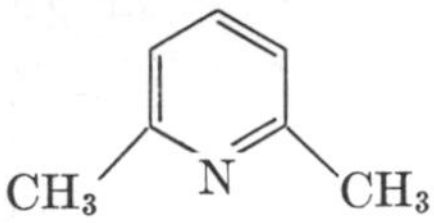
CH₃ CH₃—CH₂—C—CH₃ Br	25	30	45
CH₃ CH₃—CH₂—CH₂—C—CH₃ Br	32	39	48
CH₃ CH₃ CH₃—CH—CH₂—C—CH₃ Br	44	52	58
CH₃ CH₃ CH₃—C—CH₂—C—CH₃ CH₃ Br	70	74	82

tion of three pairs of *cis* and *trans* olefins have been determined [62] and the results are formulated. Equilibrium constants between two

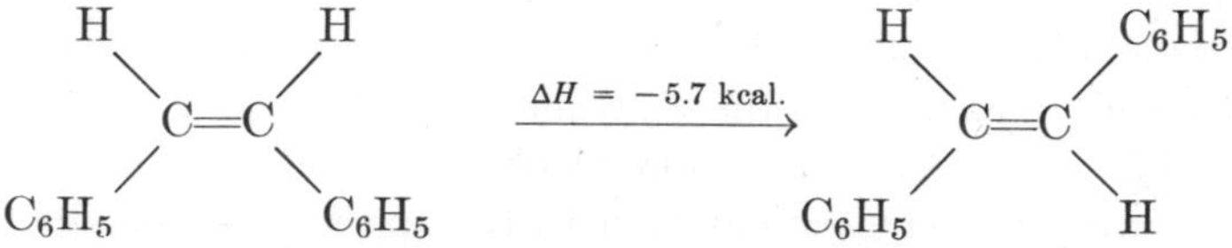

$\Delta H = -5.7$ kcal.   (ref. 62*b*)

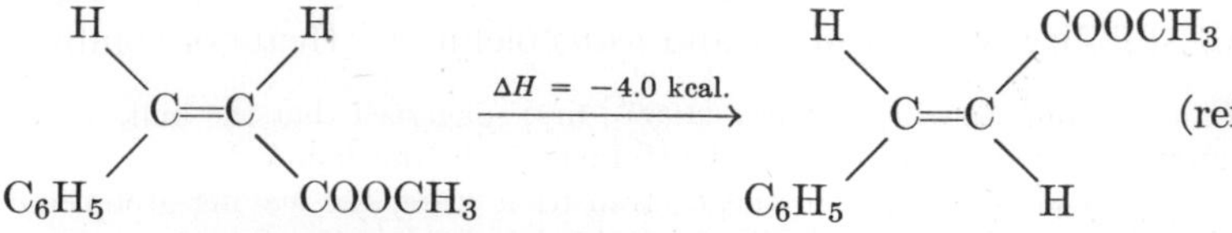

$\Delta H = -4.0$ kcal.   (ref. 62*b*)

[62] (a) G. B. Kistiakowsky, J. R. Ruhoff, H. A. Smith, and W. E. Vaughan, *J. Am. Chem. Soc.*, *57*, 876 (1935); (b) R. B. Williams, *J. Am. Chem. Soc.*, *64*, 1395 (1942).

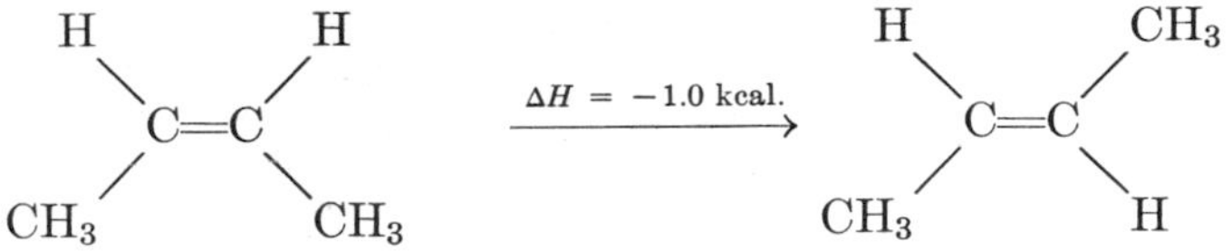

(ref. 62a)

pairs of *cis* and *trans* isomers have also been determined,[63] and the results are indicated.

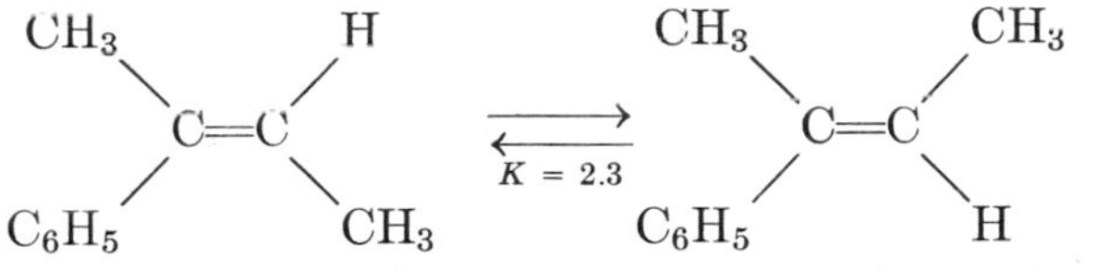

(ref. 63a)

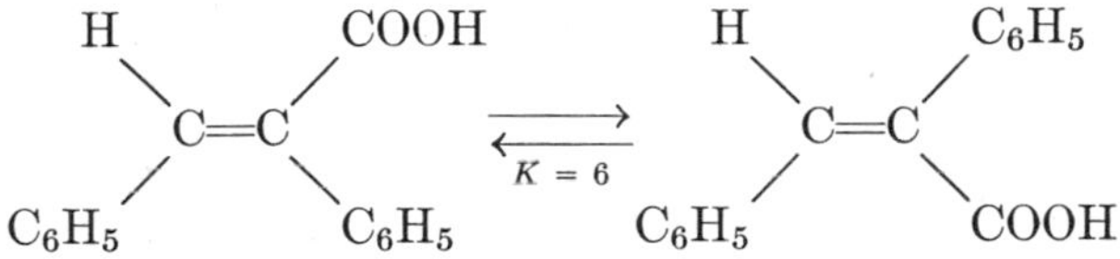

(ref. 63b)

Evidence has accumulated that the transition state of the E_2 reaction possesses enough double bond character to affect rate and product balance seriously. The base-catalyzed elimination of hydrogen bromide from 2-bromobutane gives *trans*-2-butene at a rate approximately six times the rate for the *cis* isomer.[64] The elimination of 2,4,6-triethylbenzoic acid from the 1,2-diphenyl-1-ethyl ester with potassium *t*-butoxide occurs to give *trans*-stilbene at a rate 130 times the

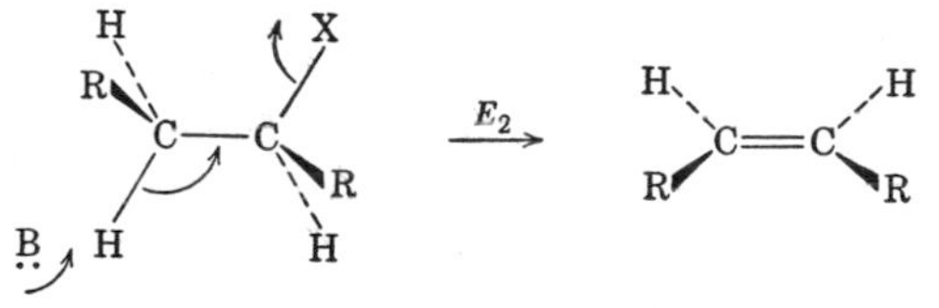

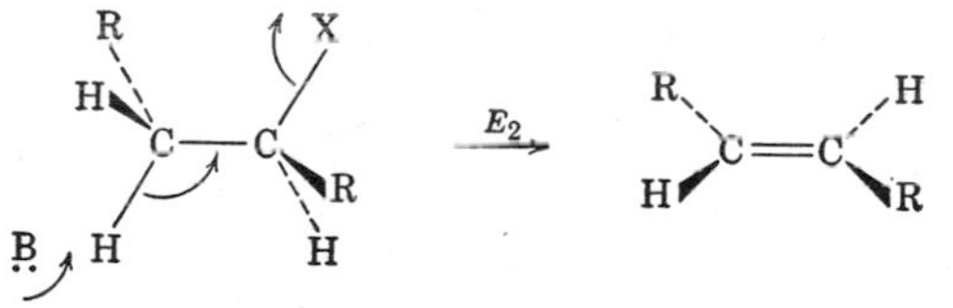

	Relative Rates	
	$R = CH_3$[64]	$R = C_6H_5$[17a]
	1	1
	6	130

[63] (a) D. J. Cram, *J. Am. Chem. Soc.*, **71**, 3883 (1949) and unpublished work; (b) D. Y. Curtin and B. Luberoff, reference 61.

[64] H. J. Lucas, T. P. Simpson, and J. M. Carter, *J. Am. Chem. Soc.*, **47**, 1465 (1925).

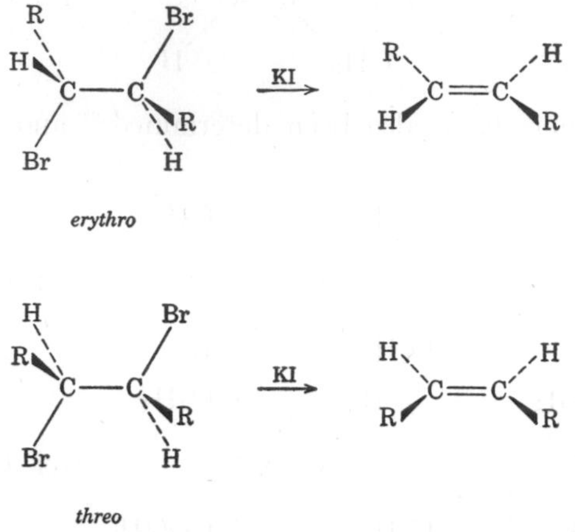

	Relative Rates	
	R = CH$_3$	R = C$_6$H$_5$

erythro   KI →   1.8   100

threo   KI →   1   1

rate for the *cis* olefin.[17a] Similarly, the bimolecular and iodide ion-catalyzed loss of bromine from diastereomerically related vicinal dibromides occurs at different rates.[27d] In the dehydrobromination with triethyl amine in benzene of *threo*- and *erythro*-benzalacetophenone dibromides, one diastereomer reacts faster than the other.[35] The decar-

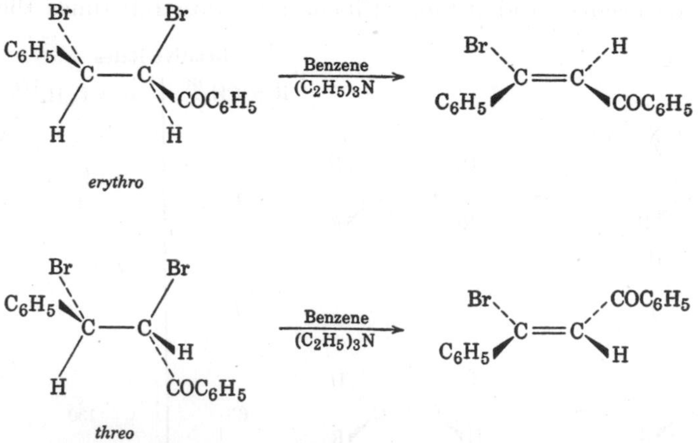

Relative Rates

erythro   Benzene (C$_2$H$_5$)$_3$N →   1

threo   Benzene (C$_2$H$_5$)$_3$N →   100

boxylative dehydrobromination reactions of the two diastereomers of 2,3-diphenyl-3-bromopropionic acid anion also occur at widely differing rates.[65]

[65] See also: (a) P. Pfeiffer, *Ber.*, *45*, 1816 (1912); (b) E. P. Kohler, W. D. Peterson, and C. L. Bickel, *J. Am. Chem. Soc.*, *56*, 2000 (1934).

Finally, eclipsing effects have been observed [59c] in the base-catalyzed elimination of HX from $CH_3CH_2CH_2CHXCH_3$ (Table VI). In all

TABLE VI

RATIOS OF 1- TO 2-OLEFINS AND OF *trans*-2-OLEFIN TO *cis*-2-OLEFIN PRODUCED IN BASIC SOLUTIONS OF $CH_3CH_2CH_2CHXCH_3$

X	Base	1-Olefin/2-Olefin	*trans*-2-Olefin/*cis*-2-Olefin
Br	1 M KOC_2H_5	0.41	2.86
I	1 M KOC_2H_5	0.41	3.44
I	1 M $KO(CH_2)_5$—CH_3	0.96	2.28
OTs	1 M KOC_2H_5	0.89	1.96
$S(CH_3)_2I$	1 M KOC_2H_5	6.1	1.6
SO_2CH_3	4 M KOC_2H_5	9.0	3.6
$N(CH_3)_3I$	4 M KOC_2H_5	44	—

cases the less hindered *trans*-2-pentene dominated in the product over the *cis* isomer. As X was varied both in an electrical and steric sense the extent of this dominance varied within narrow limits in a random way, no clear trends being evident.

A detailed study has been made of this elcipsing effect in the 1,2-diphenyl-1-propyl system XXV.[33b, 66] The rates of E_2 reaction of the

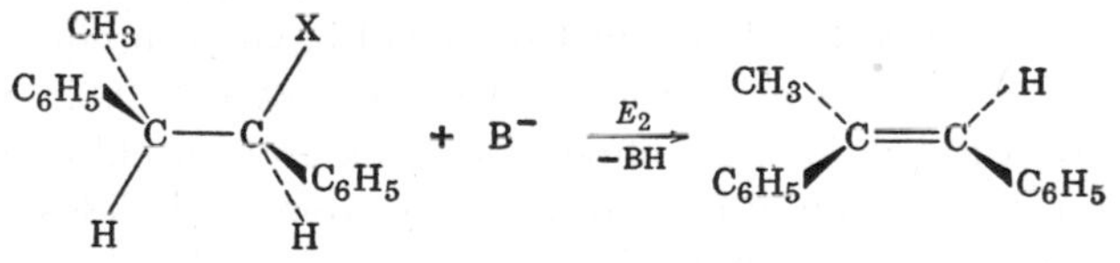

erythro–XXV   *cis*–XXVI

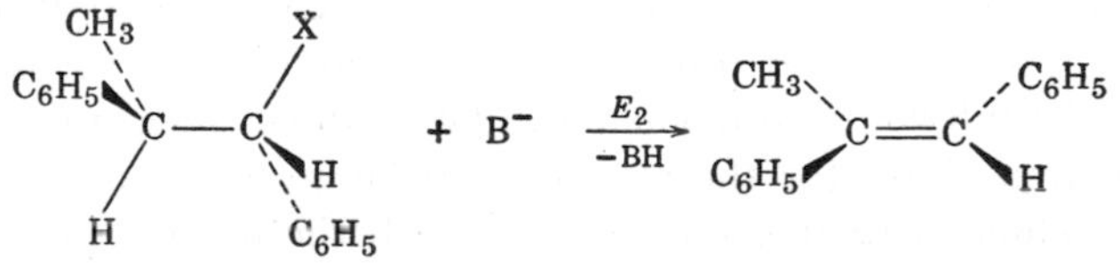

threo–XXX   *trans*–XXVI

threo and *erythro* bromides, chlorides, and trimethyl ammonium iodides with different bases and solvents have been investigated, and the data are presented in Table VII. In representative cases, the reactions

[66] D. J. Cram, F. D. Greene, and C. H. DePuy, *J. Am. Chem. Soc.*, **78**, 790 (1956).

TABLE VII

RATIOS OF ELIMINATION RATES OF DIASTEREOMERIC
1,2-DIPHENYL-1-PROPYL-X

	X	Temperature, C.°	Solvent	Base	$k_{E_2 threo}/k_{E_2 erythro}$
Set 1	Br	50	C_2H_5OH	C_2H_5ONa	0.7
	Cl	50	C_2H_5OH	C_2H_5ONa	1.1
	$\overset{+}{N}(CH_3)_3$	75	C_2H_5OH	C_2H_5ONa	57
Set 2	Br	50	$(CH_3)_3COH$	$(CH_3)_3COK$	5.4
	Cl	50	$(CH_3)_3COH$	$(CH_3)_3COK$	15
	$\overset{+}{N}(CH_3)_3$	30	$(CH_3)_3COH$	$(CH_3)_3COK$	1.1

were found to be second order (first order in base and first order in halide), they are highly stereospecific, and assume a *trans* steric course, except those involving $X = \overset{+}{N}(CH_3)_3$ and potassium *tert*-butoxide as base. Any difference in rate of *threo* and *erythro* compounds under the same conditions should reflect either differences in thermodynamic stability of starting materials or of the transition states of the diastereomers. To differentiate between these two possibilities, the formates of *threo*- and *erythro*-1,2-diphenyl-1-propanol have been equilibrated,[67] and, at 25° in formic acid, the ratio *threo/erythro* $\cong$ 0.8. Since the formyl group is not greatly different in bulk from a chlorine or bromine, the ratios at equilibrium of the diasteromeric halides should be comparable. The trimethylamino group, on the other hand, is probably effectively larger than a phenyl, and therefore probably at equilibrium the ratio *threo/erythro* > 1,[33b] but not by a significant amount.[68] In contrast, at equilibrium, the two olefins (XXVI) exist in the ratio *trans/cis* $\cong$ 50.[66] These results indicate that differences in rates of reaction of the two diastereomers can be used as a measure of whether the transition states for the reactions are more like starting material or like product in their geometry. As with the olefinic products, the diastereomeric transition states differ *only with respect to eclipsing or derived effects.*[69]

[67] F. A. Abd Elhafez and D. J. Cram, *J. Am. Chem. Soc.*, **75**, 339 (1953).

[68] The starting material is undoubtedly an equilibrium mixture of various uneclipsed rotational conformations whereas the olefinic product is frozen into a single eclipsed conformation.

[69] For example, steric inhibition of resonance of eclipsed phenyl groups; the degree of solvation of the leaving groups.

The possible geometries for the transition state are formulated, B representing the base, and HOS the solvent. Transition states a and

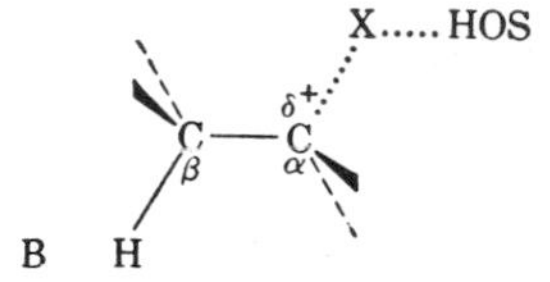

(a)

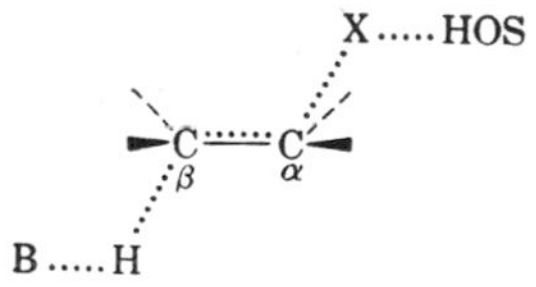

(b)

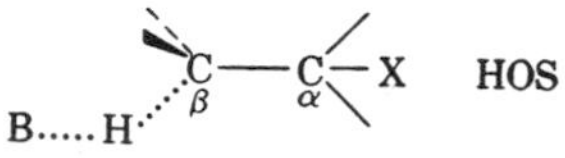

(c)

c [70] resemble starting material with respect to the relative absence of eclipsing effects, and, where these geometries dominate, $k_{threo}/k_{erythro}$ ~ 1. Transition state b resembles product in the sense that the double bond is well developed, and, where this geometry dominates, $k_{threo}/k_{erythro} > 1$. Transition state b might be expected to dominate only in that situation in which the bond-breaking process at C_α was greatly assisted by the electron pair of the C_β—H bond.

The data of Table VII indicate that the rate ratios are sensitive to three effects: the nature of the leaving group, the strength of the base, and the nature of the solvent. [71] In set 1 (Table VII), in which the solvent and base are C_2H_5OH and C_2H_5ONa, respectively, and X is varied, the ratio is 57 when X = $(CH_3)_3N^+$, and about 1 when X = Cl or Br. Thus, structure b dominates when X = $(CH_3)_3N^+$, and structure a with X = Cl or Br. In set 2, when solvent and base are

[70] In these structures, the charges on C_α and C_β are, of course, delocalized by the attached phenyl groups.

[71] Scale molecular models of the alkoxide ions and of the diastereomeric alkyl halides strongly suggest that the bulk of the base plays little or no role in increasing the rate of reaction of one diastereomer over that of the other. Support for this thesis is found in the observation that, in the reaction of the optically pure 2-octylate anion with racemic threo- or erythro-alkyl halide, both enantiomers of each racemate were consumed at the same rate. [33b] The complete absence of asymmetric induction in this reaction coupled with the observed difference in rate at which the threo- and erythro-halides react with 2-octylate anion (factor of 4) indicates that the bulk of the base is not the discriminating factor. Finally, ethylate and n-octylate give the same rate ratios, as do t-butylate and t-amylate (reference 66).

changed to $(CH_3)_3COH$ and $(CH_3)_3COK$, the ratio is about 1 when $X = (CH_3)_3N^+$, and 5.4 and 11.4 when $X = Br$ and Cl, respectively.

These effects are rationalized as follows. The balance between structures a, b, and c in the transition state depends on the relative ease of breaking the C_α—X and C_β—H bonds. If C_β—H is relatively difficult to break compared to C_α—X, then a dominates the transition state. If C_β—H is broken more easily than C_α—X, then either b or c dominates the transition state. If the difference is great, c becomes dominant; if small, b is more important.

In the simple substitution reaction, $Br > Cl > N(CH_3)_3^+$ in ease of replacement.[72] With respect to the C_β—H bond, the hydrogen is much more acidic with $X = N(CH_3)_3^+$ than with $X = $ halogen. Finally, tert-butanol is a poorer solvating medium than ethanol, and tert-butoxide is a stronger base than ethoxide anion.

In set 1 (ethanol and sodium ethoxide), with $X = Cl$ and Br, the C_α—X bond is relatively easily broken because the base is weak, the C_β—H not acidic, and the good solvating medium provides stabilization of a transition state similar to a (charge being created). With $N(CH_3)_3^+$, the C_α—X bond is more difficult to break because solvation energy has to be overcome (charge being destroyed) and the C_β—H is more easily broken because of the presence of the formal charge on nitrogen. Thus, structure b becomes important. In set 2 (tert-butanol and potassium tert-butoxide), with $X = Cl$ or Br, the C_α—X bond becomes more difficult to break (poorer solvating medium), and the C_β—H bond easier to break (increased base strength). Thus, structure b starts to become important in the transition state. With $X = N(CH_3)_3^+$, the combination of the strong base and the formal charge on the nitrogen make anion formation the dominant mechanism and structure c important in the transition state.[73]

MISCELLANEOUS ELIMINATION REACTIONS

Two additional types of elimination reaction will be discussed briefly. Regarding the first of these, Curtin and Kellom [17a] observed that the steric course of the base- (potassium amide-) catalyzed elimination reaction of the acetate of threo- and erythro-2-deutero-1,2-diphenyletha-

---

[72] C. K. Ingold, reference 19a, p. 339.

[73] It is interesting to note that, in $(CH_3)_3COH$, as the bulk of the leaving group gets smaller [$X = (CH_3)_3N^+$, Br^-, and Cl^-], eclipsing effects become less important, whereas in C_2H_5OH, the opposite order is found (see references 59 and 60).

nol was different from that of the 2,4,6-triethylbenzoate. The mechanism suggested [17a] for the predominant *cis* direction of the reaction of the acetate involved first the formation of an acetoxyl anion, followed by an internal and cyclic abstraction of a proton from the β-carbon simultaneously to the breaking of the C—O bond.

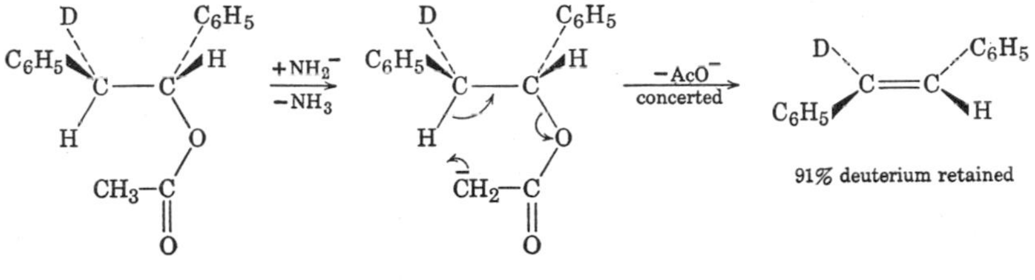
+NH2−
−NH3
−AcO−
concerted
91% deuterium retained

erythro-Acetate

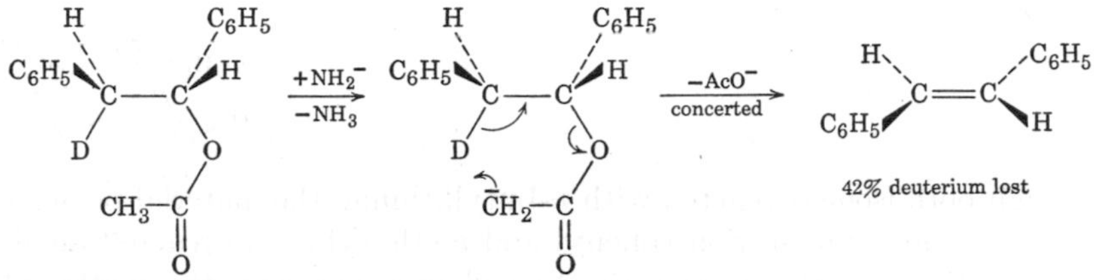
+NH2−
−NH3
−AcO−
concerted
42% deuterium lost

threo-Acetate

Earlier, it had been observed [74] that, although 2-phenylethyl benzoate reacted with potassium amide to form benzamide and 2-phenylethanol, under similar conditions the acetate gave styrene. Similarly, 1,2-diphenylethyl acetate gave *trans*-stilbene. The cyclic process pre-

$$C_6H_5\text{—}CH_2\text{—}CH_2\text{—}O\text{—}\underset{\underset{O}{\|}}{C}\text{—}CH_3 \xrightarrow[-NH_3]{NH_2^-}$$

$$C_6H_5\text{—}CH_2\text{—}CH_2\text{—}O\text{—}\underset{\underset{O}{\|}}{C}\text{—}CH_2^-$$

$$\downarrow +NH_2^- \; -NH_3$$

$$C_6H_5\text{—}CH{=}CH_2 + CH_3\text{—}\underset{\underset{O}{\|}}{C}\text{—}O^-$$

ferred by Curtin to explain the stereochemical course had been previously rejected by Hauser et al.[74] because excess amide ion was re-

[74] C. R. Hauser, J. C. Shivers, and P. K. Skell, *J. Am. Chem. Soc.*, *67*, 409 (1945).

quired to convert 2-phenylethyl acetate to styrene. It is apparent that elucidation of the mechanistic details of this interesting reaction must await a thorough kinetic study.

The second elimination reaction to be considered here is the alkyl lithium-initiated loss of the elements of alcohol from ethers.[75] The stereochemistry of this reaction has been studied [76] with *cis* and *trans* isomers of methyl 2-phenylcyclohexyl ether as starting materials. Al-

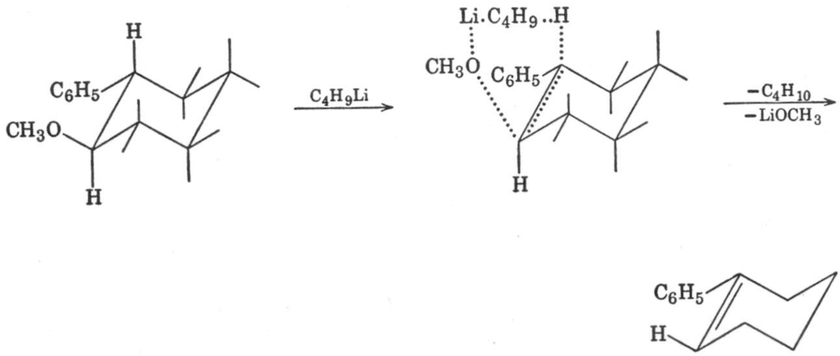

though both isomers reacted with *n*-butyllithium, the material possessing the *trans* configuration (phenyl and methoxyl *trans*) reacted much faster. Since in this isomer the benzyl hydrogen and the methoxyl group are *cis* to one another, the preferred mechanism involves a concerted cyclic process (one transition state) [76] not dissimilar to the Chugaev or acetate pyrolysis mechanisms (see earlier part of chapter). The competing but slower *trans* elimination reaction (that disposing of the *cis* isomer) is probably of the ordinary E_2 variety.

[75] P. Schorigin, *Ber.*, *43*, 1931 (1910).
[76] R. L. Letsinger and E. Bobko, *J. Am. Chem. Soc.*, *75*, 2649 (1953).

Chapter 7

by Harry H. Wasserman

Cleavage Reactions of the Carbon-Carbon Bond

INTRODUCTION

DECARBOXYLATION
    Thermal Decarboxylation of β-Keto Acids and Related Systems
    The Reaction of Silver Salts of Carboxylic Acids with Halogen
    Decarboxylation of Other β,γ Unsaturated Systems
    Decarboxylation of Hindered Aromatic Acids in Strong Acid
    Decarboxylation of β-Halocinnamic Acids
    Decarboxylation of Cinnamic Acids
    Decarboxylation of Optically Active Acids Catalyzed by Optically
        Active Bases
    Decarboxylation of Trihaloacetic Acids

CLEAVAGE OF β-DIKETONES AND RELATED COMPOUNDS

CLEAVAGE OF SUBSTITUTED 1,3-DIOLS AND RELATED
  COMPOUNDS

OXIDATIVE CLEAVAGE OF 1,2-GLYCOLS AND RELATED
  COMPOUNDS

DISSOCIATION OF HEXAARYLETHANES

349

Chapter 7

INTRODUCTION

A number of reactions selected from among those involving cleavage of the carbon-carbon bond will be discussed with special emphasis on the role of steric factors. Among those considered will be decarboxylation, cleavage of 1,2- and 1,3-diols, cleavage of β-diketones, and dissociation of hexaarylethanes. No attempt will be made to give an exhaustive review of the above reactions, nor will there be discussion of all cases where the fission of the carbon-carbon bond may be influenced by steric factors.

The following examples illustrate the types of steric effects to be considered:

(a) In the decarboxylation of β-keto acids, a cyclic, chelate type intermediate is involved. The decomposition of such an intermediate to form the enol of the product takes place through a transition state in which there is a requirement of coplanarity. In those cases where, for steric reasons, coplanarity is difficult to achieve, the parent β-keto acids do not lose carbon dioxide. Analogs of β-keto acids such as β,γ-unsaturated acids and malonic acids, which decarboxylate through related cyclic intermediates, must also be able to accommodate the newly formed double bond in a strain-free environment, and these reactions show a similar dependence on steric factors.

(b) Cyclic intermediates may also be involved in the cleavage of 1,2-glycols and in the cleavage of β-diketones by Grignard reagents. In the above cases, cleavage is suppressed when the particular steric requirement for formation of the intermediate cannot be met.

(c) Steric hindrance to the addition of a solvated proton to an α,β unsaturated system inhibits the decarboxylation of certain substituted arylidenemalonic acids in pyridine. This retarding effect, caused by the presence of bulky groups close to the reactive centers, also explains the exceptional unreactivity of certain highly substituted β-diketones, which are unaffected by long boiling in alkali.

350

Steric hindrance to the approach of the attacking reagent may also explain the inertness toward cleavage of certain glycols in bicyclic systems which are shielded from reaction with glycol-splitting reagents.

(*d*) The transition state for the decarboxylation of salts of β-halocinnamic acids demands a *trans* coplanar arrangement of the groups involved in the decarboxylative elimination. Fixation of the molecule in this arrangement can be hindered by the repulsive interactions of adjacent bulky groups. The latter effect causes a decrease in the rate of decarboxylation or may favor a competing elimination reaction, such as dehydrohalogenation.

The cleavage reactions of 1,3-diols also appear to take place through a rigidly defined transition state, and here, as well, the interactions of neighboring bulky groups may retard the reaction or cause an alternative, less hindered reaction path to be favored.

(*e*) In the decarboxylation of hindered aromatic acids in strong acid, the ground state suffers steric inhibition of resonance, thus reducing the stabilizing influence of the aromatic ring and the alkyl substituents, whereas resonance in the transition state is unaffected by this steric factor. The activation energy for the decarboxylation is thus lowered. Related decarbonylation reactions of hindered aromatic aldehydes and deacylation reactions of hindered ketones can be explained on the same basis.

DECARBOXYLATION

Thermal decarboxylation of β-keto acids and related systems

Studies on the decarboxylation of β-keto acids have shown [1] that it is the keto form of the parent acid which undergoes loss of carbon dioxide, enolization of the acid not being a prerequisite. Thus, α,α-dimethylacetoacetic acid (I), which cannot form an α,β double bond,

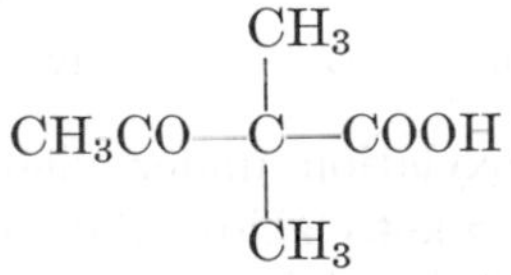

$$
\begin{array}{c}
CH_3 \\
| \\
CH_3CO-C-COOH \\
| \\
CH_3 \\
I
\end{array}
$$

decarboxylates over four times as fast as the unsubstituted acetoacetic acid. Furthermore, since the rate of decarboxylation of I in the presence of bromine or iodine is identical with the rate of halogen uptake,

[1] K. J. Pedersen, *J. Am. Chem. Soc.*, *51*, 2098 (1929); *58*, 240 (1936).

it was concluded that loss of carbon dioxide leads directly to the enol form of the product, which then reacts instantaneously with halogen. Although these facts are consistent with the breakdown of the dipolar form of the parent acid, as suggested by Pedersen, Westheimer [2] has shown that the uncatalyzed decarboxylation of β-keto acids is independent of the dielectric constant of the solvent, and the rate-determining step therefore does not involve a highly polar intermediate. Westheimer's proposal that loss of carbon dioxide takes place through the hydrogen bonded form (II) of the parent β-keto acid yielding the enol of the product is now generally accepted as the mechanism for the decarboxylation of β-keto acids and many related β,γ unsaturated systems.

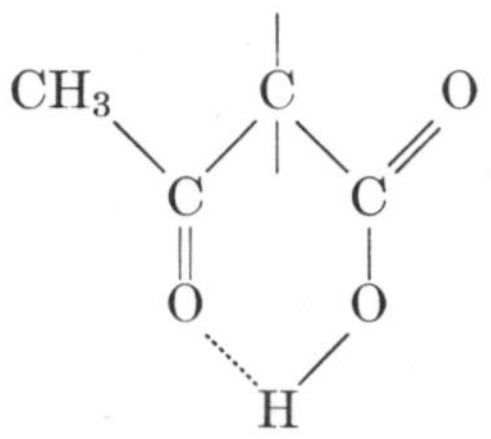

II

The decarboxylation of a β-keto acid by the above process, with formation of the enol of the product, demands that the product be able to accommodate the newly formed double bond in a strain-free environment. Where the formation of the enol involves considerable steric strain, the parent acid is found to be resistant to decarboxylation. Such behavior provides strong support for the proposed mechanism. Thus,[3] both camphenonic acid (III) and ketopinic acid (IV)

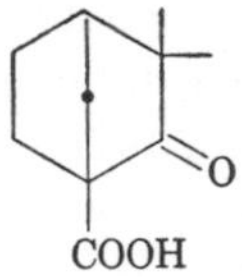

III 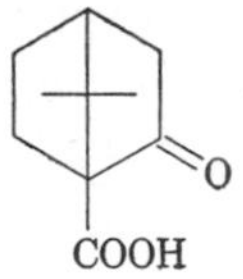   IV

are resistant to decarboxylation under vigorous thermal conditions (above 300°C). Other β-keto acids, the decarboxylation of which would introduce a double bond into a strained situation, have been reported to be thermally stable.[4]

[2] F. H. Westheimer and W. A. Jones, *J. Am. Chem. Soc.*, *63*, 3283 (1941).

[3] (a) O. Aschan, *Ann.*, *410*, 240 (1915); (b) G. Komppa, *Ber.*, *44*, 1536 (1911); (c) von E. Wedekind, *Z. angew. Chem.*, *38*, 315 (1925).

[4] For a number of such cases, see F. S. Fawcett, *Chem. Revs.*, *47*, 219 (1950).

Considering a typical acid in this category, ketopinic acid (IV), it can be seen that the formation of the enol of the decarboxylated product would require the introdution of a double bond at the bridgehead of a small bicyclic system. The geometry of the double bond demands that the four attached atoms lie in one plane and, in this case, would require coplanarity of the atoms at positions a, b, c and d of the 2,2,1-bicyclic system, as shown in the diagram.

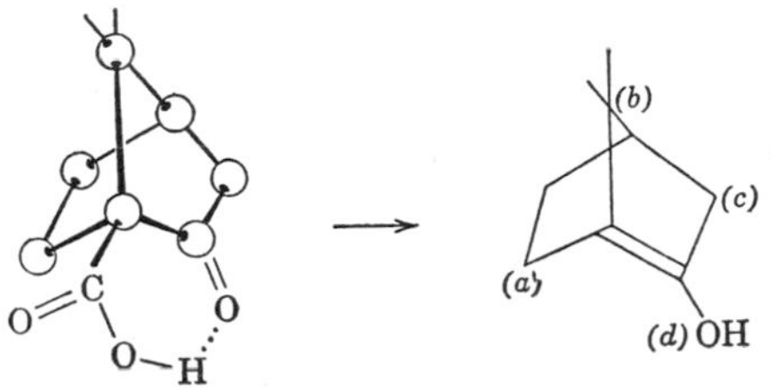

To achieve such a condition of coplanarity demands considerable distortion of bond angles, and in this case must involve prohibitive strain.[5] This is essentially a statement of Bredt's rule prohibiting the introduction of a double bond at the bridgehead of a bicyclic system.[6]

In investigating the limitations of Bredt's rule, Prelog [7] studied the decarboxylation of a number of β-keto acids, in which the carboxyl group is attached to the bridgehead of bicyclic systems of varying size. Whereas the acid V ($n = 3$) in the 3,3,1-bicyclic system is stable on heating in quinoline up to 250°, the analogous acids V ($n = 4$) and

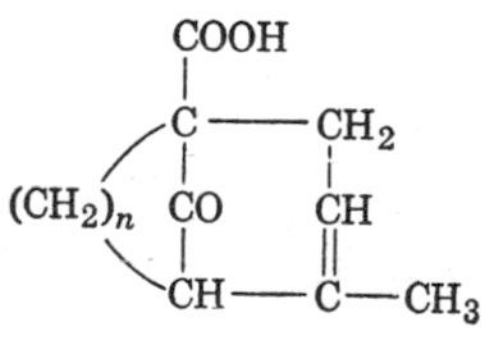

VI ($n = 5$, R = H) containing the 4,3,1- and 5,3,1-bicyclic systems respectively (the latter already accommodating a bridgehead double bond) decarboxylate easily at 240°. The ester (VI, $n = 10$) containing a thirteen-membered ring, decarboxylates spontaneously during saponification.

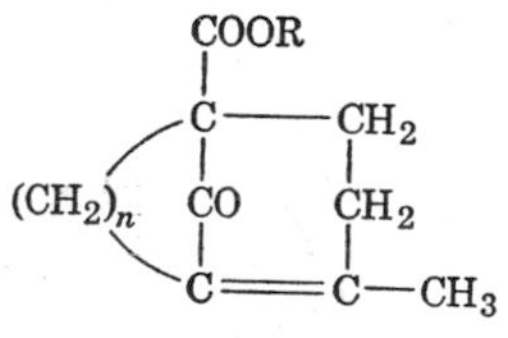

[5] P. D. Bartlett and L. H. Knox, *J. Am. Chem. Soc.*, **61**, 3184 (1939).
[6] J. Bredt, *Ann.*, **437**, 1 (1924).
[7] V. Prelog, L. Ruzicka, P. Barman, and L. Frenkiel, *Helv. Chim. Acta*, **31**, 92 (1948); V. Prelog, P. Barman, and M. Zimmermann, *ibid.*, **32**, 1284 (1949).

In a decarboxylation requiring formation of the enol of the product it appears that a double bond is possible in the 5,3,1-bicyclic system but still prohibited in the 4,3,1 case. As summarized by Prelog,[8] the limit of applicability of Bredt's rule in the 1,3-bicyclic system lies between systems with a seven- and an eight-membered ring.

The reaction of silver salts of carboxylic acids with halogen

Unlike the decarboxylation of β-keto acids which takes place through a precisely defined steric path, the loss of carbon dioxide in the treatment of silver salts of carboxylic acids with bromine [9] seems to be relatively independent of steric factors. Whereas bicyclo-(3,3,1)-nonan-9-one-1-carboxylic acid (VII) is resistant to thermal decarboxylation (owing to steric factors as described above), conversion of VII

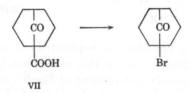

VII

to the bromide with loss of carbon dioxide takes place readily on bromination of the silver salt in carbon tetrachloride.[10] The latter reaction, a general method for the degradation of carboxylic acids to the corresponding bromides, takes place with a large variety of substituted acids [11] in inert solvents through the intermediate acyl hypobromite [9a, 12] as shown.[12a]

$$RCOOAg + Br_2 \rightarrow AgBr + RCOOBr \rightarrow AgBr + CO_2 + RBr$$

During studies on the mechanism of this reaction a variety of model compounds [13,14,15] have been decarboxylated in efforts to distinguish

[8] V. Prelog, *J. Chem. Soc.*, *1950*, 420.

[9] (a) W. Böckemuller and F. W. Hoffman, *Ann.*, *519*, 165 (1935); (b) H. Hunsdieker and C. Hunsdieker, D. R. pat. 695,062 (1935); J. Kleinberg, *Chem. Revs.*, *40*, 381 (1947).

[10] A. C. Cope and M. E. Synerholm, *J. Am. Chem. Soc.*, *72*, 5228 (1950).

[11] H. Hunsdieker and C. Hunsdieker, *Ber.*, *75*, 291 (1942); M. Hauptschein, C. S. Stokes, and A. V. Grosse, *J. Am. Chem. Soc.*, *74*, 848 (1952).

[12] J. W. H. Oldham, *J. Chem. Soc.*, *1950*, 100.

[12a] R. G. Johnson and R. K. Ingham, *Chem. Revs.*, *56*, 219 (1956).

[13] W. T. Smith and R. L. Hull, Jr., *J. Am. Chem. Soc.*, *72*, 3309 (1950).

[14] J. D. Roberts, W. T. Moreland, Jr., and W. Frazer, *J. Am. Chem. Soc.*, *75*, 637 (1953).

[15] P. Wilder, Jr., and A. Winston, *J. Am. Chem. Soc.*, *75*, 5370 (1953).

between a radical and an ionic process. Price originally suggested a radical mechanism taking place essentially as outlined.[16]

$$RCOOBr \rightarrow RCOO\cdot + Br\cdot \quad \text{(initiation)}$$

$$RCOO\cdot \rightarrow R\cdot + CO_2$$

$$R\cdot + Br_2 \rightarrow RBr + Br\cdot$$

$$Br\cdot + RCOOBr \rightarrow RCOO\cdot + Br_2$$

An alternative ionic scheme which features a bimolecular displacement by positive bromine as shown has been proposed [17] chiefly to account

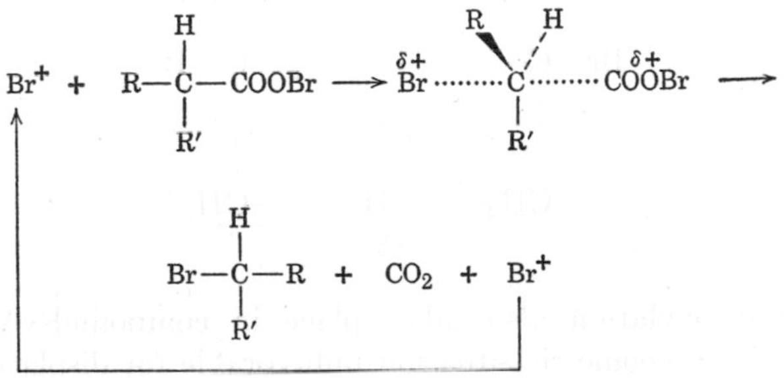

for the inversion of configuration observed in the conversion of optically active 2-phenylpropionic acid to α-phenethyl bromide.[18] Neither mechanism can account for all the reported facts. Price's mechanism does not explain the formation of active bromide,[18, 19] since a free radical would not be expected to maintain asymmetry; on the other hand, the unusual bimolecular ionic mechanism is incompatible with the findings that the reaction is free from certain steric restraints. For example, the fact that the silver salt of adamantane-1,3-dicarboxylic

[16] C. C. Price, *Mechanisms of Reactions at Carbon-Carbon Double Bonds*, p. 55, Interscience Publishers, New York, 1946. The mechanism given in this reference has been slightly modified so as to accommodate formation of the bromide through the (isolated) acyl hypobromite.

[17] C. L. Arcus, A. Campbell, and J. Kenyon, *J. Chem. Soc.*, *1949*, 1510; C. L. Arcus and G. V. Boyd, *ibid.*, *1951*, 1580; J. Kenyon, *Bull. soc. chim. France*, *1951*, 68C.

[18] Other investigators were, however, unable to repeat this reaction, and obtained α-phenethyl-2-phenylpropionate from the silver salt of 2-phenylpropionic acid. See D. C. Abbott and C. L. Arcus, *J. Chem. Soc.*, *1952*, 3195, and J. Cason, M. J. Kalm, and R. H. Mills, *J. Org. Chem.*, 18, 1670 (1953).

[19] F. Bell and I. F. B. Smyth, *J. Chem. Soc.*, *1949*, 2372.

acid (VIII) can be converted to 1,3-dibromoadamantane (IX) [20] makes it very unlikely that the reaction involves a bimolecular displacement, since the cage-like structure of the parent acid would block any approach to the rear of the carbon bearing the carboxyl group. Bromi-

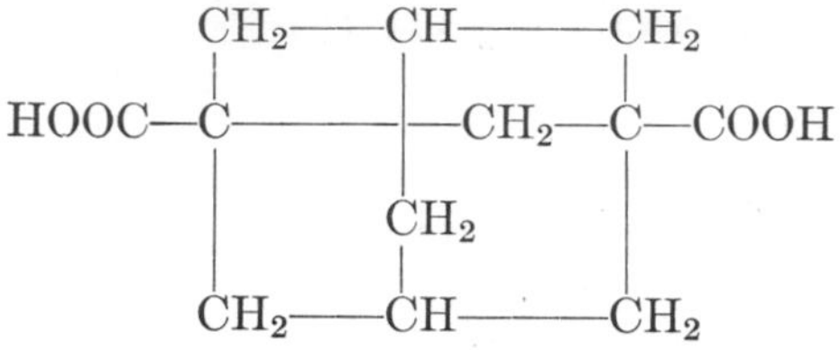

$$\text{HOOC}-\text{C}\begin{array}{c} \text{CH}_2-\!-\!-\text{CH}-\!-\!-\!-\text{CH}_2 \\ \\ -\!-\!-\!-\!-\text{CH}_2-\text{C}-\text{COOH} \\ \\ \text{CH}_2 \\ \\ \text{CH}_2-\!-\!-\text{CH}-\!-\!-\!-\text{CH}_2 \end{array}$$

VIII

$$\text{Br}-\text{C}\begin{array}{c} \text{CH}_2-\!-\!-\text{CH}-\!-\!-\!-\text{CH}_2 \\ \\ -\!-\!-\!-\!-\text{CH}_2-\text{C}-\text{Br} \\ \\ \text{CH}_2 \\ \\ \text{CH}_2-\!-\!-\text{CH}-\!-\!-\!-\text{CH}_2 \end{array}$$

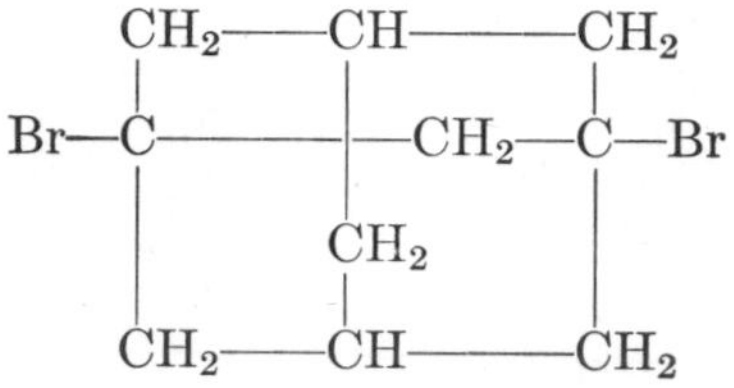

IX

native decarboxylation also takes place in compounds VII [10] and IXb [15] despite a geometric situation unfavorable for displacement.

IXb

The degradation of the silver salt of t-butylacetic acid to neopentyl bromide in good yield [21] is also inconsistent with an ionic mechanism. If a carbonium ion were an intermediate in this process, a rearrangement to t-amyl bromide would be expected. Furthermore, the observation that the bromination of IXb in carbon tetrachloride leads to a mixture of the corresponding bromide and chloride strongly suggests a free-radical mechanism.[22]

[20] V. Prelog and R. Seiwerth, Ber., 74B, 1769 (1941).

[21] W. T. Smith, Jr., and R. L. Hull, J. Am. Chem. Soc., 72, 3309 (1950).

[22] See also the work of D. Bryce-Smith, Nature, 172, 863 (1953); M. Hauptschein, C. S. Stokes, and A. V. Grosse, J. Am. Chem. Soc., 74, 848 (1952); R. A. Barnes and R. J. Prochaska, ibid., 72, 3188 (1950).

Decarboxylation of other β,γ unsaturated systems

The formation of a chelated intermediate has also been suggested as a mechanism for the decarboxylation of other acids containing β,γ unsaturation. Such systems, in addition to the β-keto acids previously discussed, include malonic acid and its half esters, β,γ unsaturated acids, and α,β unsaturated acids capable of isomerizing to the β,γ form.

The fact that the isomeric half esters [23] of 2,5-dimethylcyclopentanedicarboxylic acid (X and XI) decarboxylate on heating to yield the same mixture of monoesters indicates that a common intermediate is

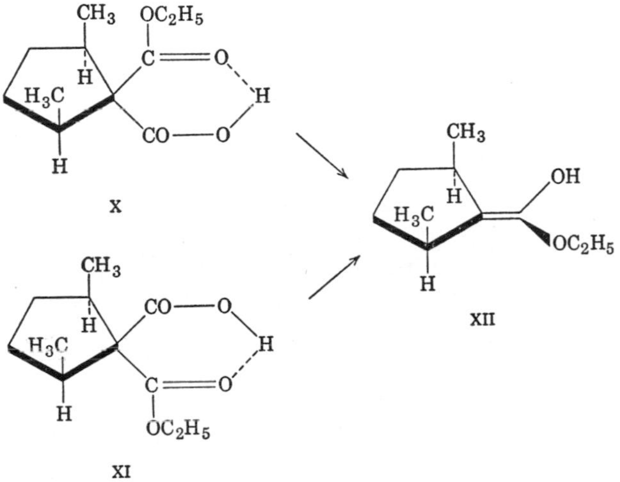

involved in both processes. This intermediate may be shown as the enol (XII) resulting from the decarboxylation of each acid by a cyclic process, analogous to the mechanism for the decarboxylation of β-keto acids.

Whereas decarboxylation of X is essentially complete at 205°, the loss of carbon dioxide from XI requires a temperature of 230–240°. This difference in stability has been explained [23] in terms of the greater strain inherent in the more hindered ester-acid X, where opportunity for interaction between the bulky carbethoxyl and methyl groups exists. Loss of carbon dioxide might provide greater relief from strain in X than in XI. Another explanation [24] for the more facile decarboxylation of X is based on the difference in energy of the two transi-

[23] T. L. Jacobs and W. H. Florsheim, *J. Am. Chem. Soc.*, **72**, 256 (1950).
[24] H. E. Zimmerman, private communication. See also discussion of H. E. Zimmerman on stereochemistry of ketonization, *J. Org. Chem.*, **20**, 549 (1955).

tion states pictured in the diagram. Clearly the transition state derived from X involves less crowding of the departing carbon dioxide molecule and should therefore be lower in energy.

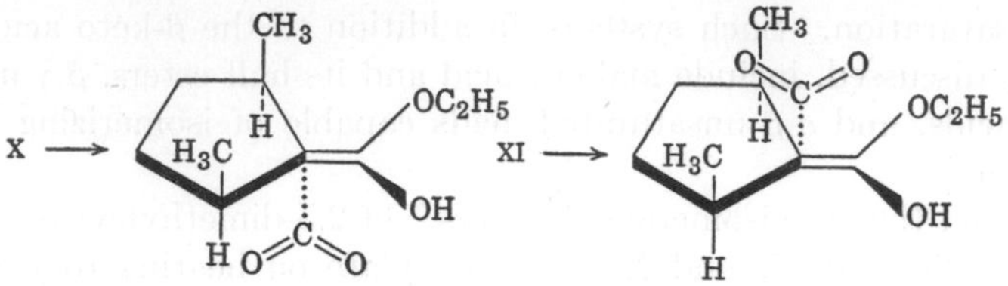

The fact that the mixture of monoesters obtained in the decarboxylation of both X and XI contains about 75–85% of the more hindered isomer XIIa, suggests [23, 24] that the favored formation of XIIa is due to the preferential attack of a proton donor on the less hindered side of the common enol intermediate (XII),[24] presumably as shown.

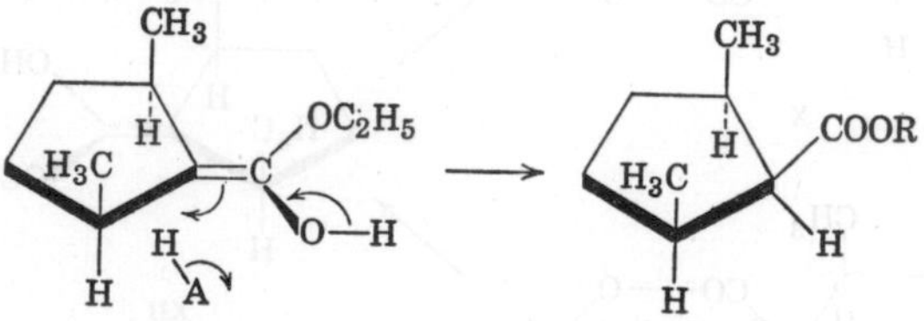

XIIa

The decarboxylation of β,γ unsaturated acids of the vinylacetic acid type has also been pictured [25] in terms of a cyclic intermediate similar to that proposed by Westheimer.[2] The known thermal instability of β,γ unsaturated acids, plus the fact that formation of the decarboxylated product is frequently accompanied by a shift of the carbon-carbon double bond to the α,β position, is in accord with the mechanism shown.

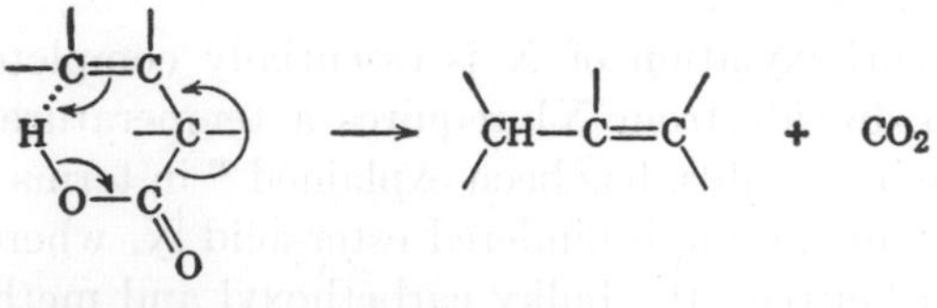

Evidence favoring such a cyclic process for the non-acid-catalyzed decarboxylation of β,γ unsaturated acids has been derived from studies on β,γ-δ,ϵ-dienoic acids.[26] If the mechanism involves the primary

[25] R. T. Arnold, O. C. Elmer, and R. M. Dodson, J. Am. Chem. Soc., 72, 4359 (1950).

[26] D. H. R. Barton and C. J. W. Brooks, J. Chem. Soc., 1951, 257.

addition of a proton to the dienoic acid, the product (due to distribution of the plus charge and accompanying movement of the double bond in the protonated system) would be expected to have a conju-

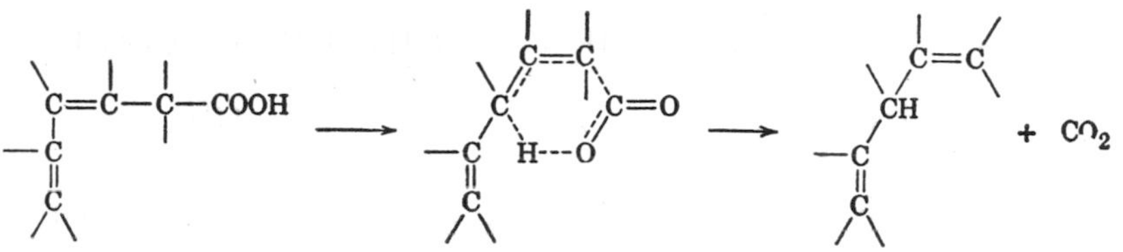

gated pair of double bonds. If, on the other hand, a cyclic mechanism prevails, the double bonds in the decarboxylated product should not be in conjugation, as shown above. Examples chosen from the triterpenoid field [27] show that, in $\beta,\gamma-\delta,\epsilon$-dienoic acid systems, the products of decarboxylation do contain unconjugated double bonds. A mechanism involving a cyclic intermediate as shown is thus favored. Such a mechanism also explains the formation of alkylidenecyclohexanes (B) by the thermal decarboxylation of the corresponding cyclohexeneacetic acids (A).[28,29] This decomposition, in which products

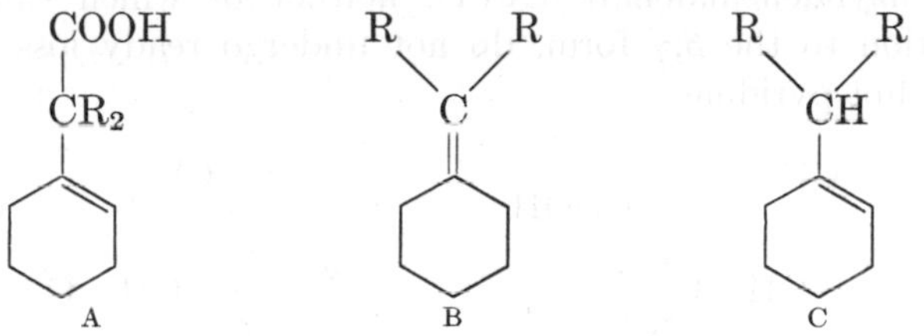

containing double bonds exocyclic to a six-membered ring are formed, is of special interest in view of the fact that such exocyclic compounds are considered to be thermodynamically unstable [30] with respect to the isomeric endocyclic alkylcyclohexenes (C).

It has been further suggested [25,26] that the decarboxylation of a variety of α,β unsaturated acids takes place by a prior isomerization to the β,γ form. Supporting this view is the fact that α,β unsaturated acids in which isomerization to a β,γ form is impossible show marked resistance to decarboxylation. For example, 4,4-dimethylpentene-2-oic acid (XIII) is essentially unchanged after heating at 300° for 5 hours,[25]

[27] L. Ruzicka and O. Jeger, Helv. Chim. Acta, 25, 775 (1942).

[28] O. Wallach, Ann., 360, 26 (1908).

[29] R. P. Linstead, J. Chem. Soc., 1930, 1603.

[30] H. C. Brown, J. H. Brewster, and H. Shechter, J. Am. Chem. Soc., 76, 467 (1954); O. H. Wheeler, Chemistry & Industry, 1954, 900.

whereas, under milder conditions (250°), 75% of 2,2-dimethylbuten-3-oic acid (XIV) undergoes decarboxylation to form 2-methylbutene-2.

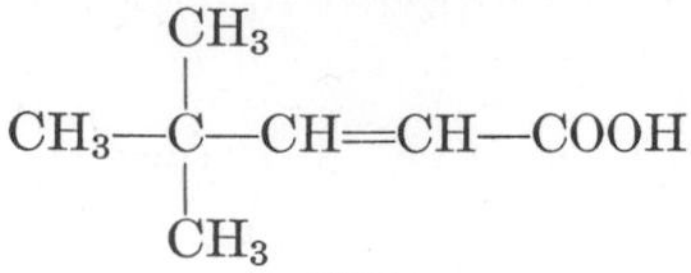

$$CH_3-\underset{\underset{CH_3}{|}}{\overset{\overset{CH_3}{|}}{C}}-CH=CH-COOH \qquad CH_2=CH-\underset{\underset{CH_3}{|}}{\overset{\overset{CH_3}{|}}{C}}-COOH$$

XIII 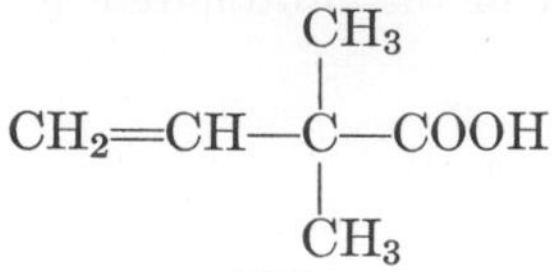   XIV

Other evidence exists [31] to indicate that the direct decarboxylation of α,β unsaturated malonic acid derivatives is, in general, quite slow. Kinetic studies on the decarboxylation of α,β and β,γ unsaturated malonic acid derivatives in pyridine have shown that the reaction takes place by way of the β,γ unsaturated acid which decarboxylates as the conjugate base. The results are consistent with the idea that the resonating anion, produced by loss of carbon dioxide, may accept a proton irreversibly at either the α- or γ-carbon atom to form the β,γ or the α,β unsaturated product. The necessary involvement of the β,γ intermediate in this process is also shown by the fact that ethyl hydrogen mesitylidenemalonate (XV) and ethyl hydrogen 2,6-dichlorobenzylidenemalonate (XVI), neither of which can undergo isomerization to the β,γ form, do not undergo ready loss of carbon dioxide in hot pyridine.

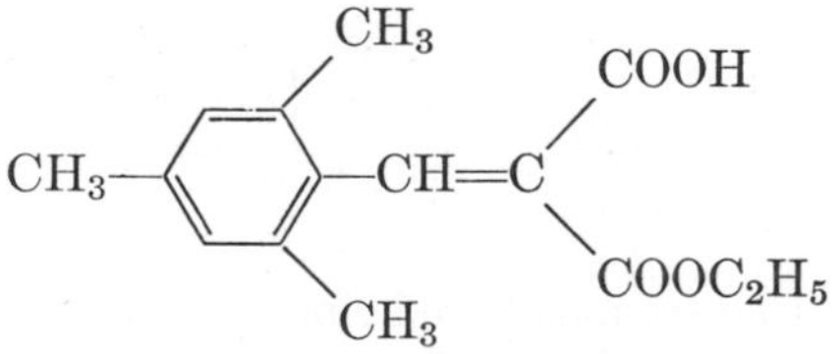

XV 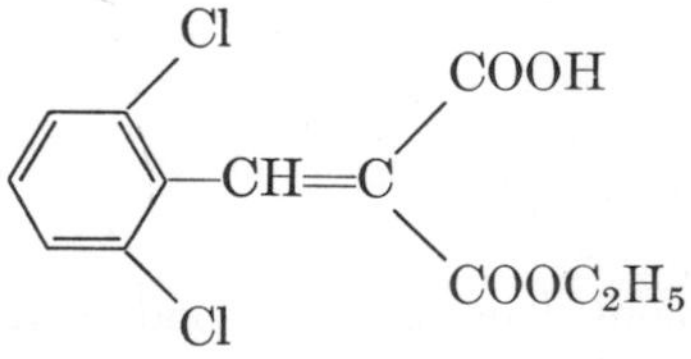   XVI

Other systems resemble β-keto acids in decarboxylating through intermediate cyclic complexes, as for example the metal-ion-catalyzed decarboxylation of oxaloacetic acids [32] via the intermediate XVII, and

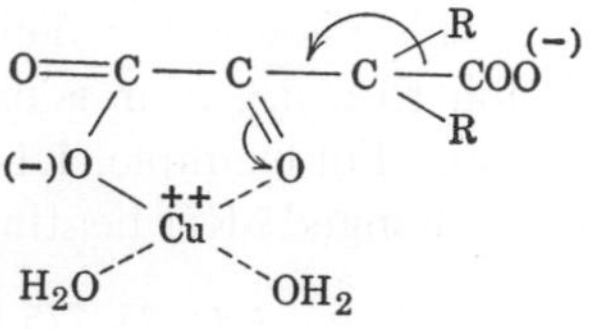

XVII

[31] E. J. Corey, *J. Am. Chem. Soc.*, *74*, 5897 (1952).

[32] R. Steinberger and F. H. Westheimer, *J. Am. Chem. Soc.*, *73*, 429 (1951).

the decarboxylation of α-pyridylacetic acid analogs [33] which may take place via the cyclic, hydrogen-bonded form.   Similarly, it has been suggested [33a] that the thermal decomposition of glycidic acids to yield

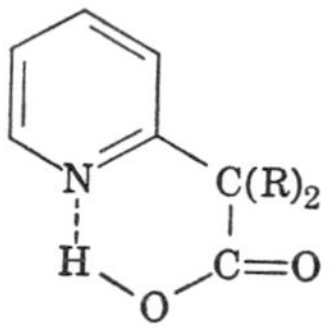

aldehydes or ketones takes place through a chelated intermediate, leading directly to the enol of the product, as shown.

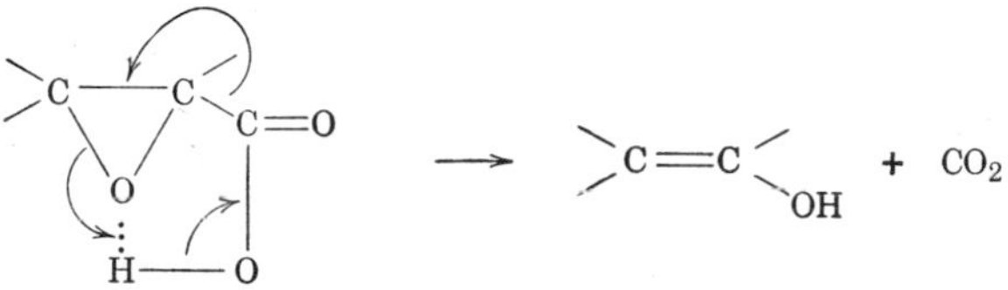

Decarboxylation of hindered aromatic acids in strong acid

The cleavage of the bond joining a carbonyl group to an aromatic nucleus in strong acids according to the scheme shown has been represented [34] as a general aromatic elimination reaction which includes

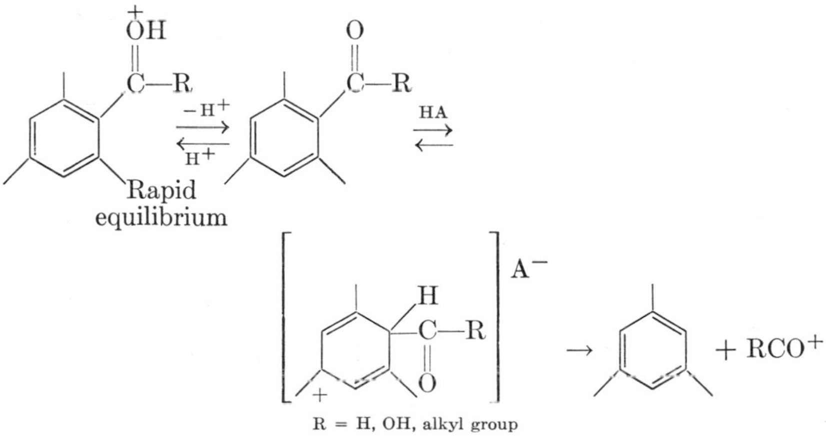

R = H, OH, alkyl group

[33] W. von E. Doering and V. Z. Pasternak, *J. Am. Chem. Soc.*, 72, 143 (1950).

[33a] R. T. Arnold, Abstracts of the Tenth National Organic Symposium, American Chemical Society, June, 1947, Boston, Massachusetts.

[34] (a) W. M. Schubert, *J. Am. Chem. Soc.*, 71, 2639 (1949); (b) W. M. Schubert and H. K. Latourette, *ibid.*, 74, 1829 (1952); (c) W. M. Schubert and R. E. Zahler, *ibid.*, 76, 1 (1954); (d) W. M. Schubert, J. Donohue, and J. D. Gardner, *ibid.*, 76, 9 (1954).

decarboxylation, decarbonylation, deacylation, the reverse Fries rearrangement, and other acid-catalyzed aromatic cleavage and rearrangement reactions. As a rule, these cleavage reactions take place most readily when bulky *ortho* substituents are present.[35] Thus, the decarboxylation of alkyl benzoic acids in boiling syrupy phosphoric acid takes place only when two alkyl substituents are substituted *ortho* to the carboxyl group, and cleavage of acyl benzenes does not occur in strong acid unless at least one *ortho* substituent is present.[35] A similar requirement appears necessary to promote the reverse Fries rearrangement [36] and to enhance the rate of the related desulfonation reaction.[37]

These reactions have been studied extensively by Schubert, who has explained the marked *ortho* effect in the following way:[34] The ground state may be considered to be the protonated acid XVIII, which is stabilized by resonance interactions between the carboxyl

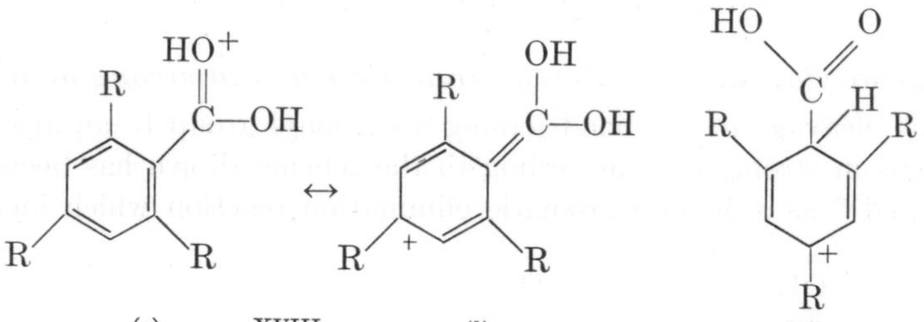

group and the ring (XVIIIa ↔ XVIIIb). Owing to the repulsive interactions between the hydroxyl groups and the bulky *ortho* substituents (methyl groups in the case of mesitoic acid), the coplanarity required by resonance contributors such as XVIIIb would be difficult to achieve. This steric effect would tend to lessen the resonance stabilization of the ground state XVIII. There would, however, be no comparable steric inhibition of resonance in the transition state, considered to be near the hybrid form XIX. In XIX, distribution of the positive charge over the dihydroaromatic ring would not involve interactions with the carboxyl group and therefore would not suffer steric interference. The van der Waals repulsion between the attached carboxyl group and the *ortho* substituents presumably also is decreased in going from XVIII to XIX. The overall effect of lowering

[35] A. Klages and G. Lickroth, *Ber.*, *32*, 1549 (1899).
[36] K. W. Rosenmund and W. Schnurr, *Ann.*, *460*, 56 (1928); R. T. Arnold and E. Rondestvedt, *J. Am. Chem. Soc.*, *68*, 2176 (1946).
[37] J. M. Crafts, *J. Am. Chem. Soc.*, *23*, 236 (1901).

the energy difference between ground and transition states for this reaction would be to weaken the bond joining the carboxyl group to the aromatic nucleus, such a bond having lessened double-bond character. This explanation accounts for the much faster rate of decarboxylation of 2,4,6-triisopropylbenzoic acid (XX, R = $CH(CH_3)_2$) compared to 2,4,6-triethylbenzoic acid (XX, R = CH_2CH_3), the latter breaking down more rapidly than mesitoic acid (XX, R = CH_3).

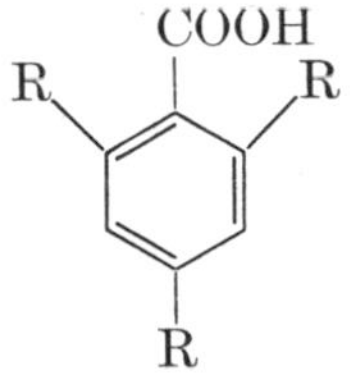

In stronger acid, where the ion XXa is formed, loss of carbon dioxide does not take place.[38]

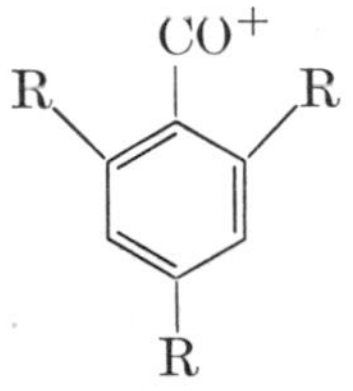

The decarbonylation reaction of aromatic aldehydes in strong sulfuric acid shows a similar dependence on *ortho* effects.[34c] The comparative rates of reaction and activation energies for the decarbonylation of aldehydes in which the *ortho* substituents are methyl, ethyl, and isopropyl are summarized in Table I.

TABLE I [34c]

	2,4,6-Trialkylbenzaldehyde		
	Methyl	Ethyl	Isopropyl
Spectrophotometric values, 85.2% H_2SO_4			
Relative k (80.0°)	1	4.5	20.6
E_A, kcal.	28.6	26.1	24.3
Gasometric values, 84.9% H_2SO_4			
Relative k (80.0°)	1	4.1	19.5
E_A, kcal.	29.1	26.9	23.8

The decrease in activation energy in progressing from the trimethyl to the triisopropyl aldehyde is explicable on the same basis as previously outlined for the decarboxylation reaction. As the bulk of the *ortho* substituents increases, the ratio of the energy of the ground state to the energy of the transition state would increase as the result

[38] M. S. Newman, *J. Am. Chem. Soc.*, **63**, 2431 (1941).

of greater steric inhibition of resonance in the ground state. Here again such an effect would weaken the bond between the carbonyl group and the aromatic ring.[38a] Related steric effects are reported to operate in the deacylation of hindered aromatic ketones [34a] and may be involved in accounting for the lower activation energy observed in the decarboxylation of 3-methylpicolinic acid compared to the decarboxylation of the 5-methyl isomer.[39]

Decarboxylation of β-halocinnamic acids

Two types of reaction are involved in the decarboxylation of the salts of β-halocinnamic acids leading to derivatives of styrene. One process is stereospecific, as in the conversion of *trans*-cinnamic acid dibromide to *cis*-ω-bromostyrene; the other process is non-stereospecific, and leads to mixtures of *cis* and *trans* olefins. Two mechanisms have been proposed [40, 41] to account for the facts. The stereospecific debrominative decarboxylation involves a concerted *trans*-elimination process (*a*) involving simultaneous loss of carbon dioxide and bromide

(*a*)

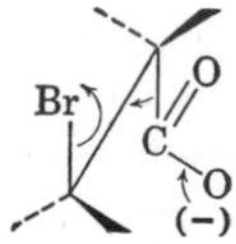

ion from the anion. The non-stereospecific elimination (*b*) is explained by postulating an initial formation of the dipolar ion XXI, resulting in the loss of stereospecific configuration at the β-carbon atom.

$$C_6H_5CHBrCHBr{-}C\begin{smallmatrix}\nearrow O \\ \searrow O^{(-)}\end{smallmatrix} \rightarrow C_6H_5\overset{+}{C}HCHBr{-}C\begin{smallmatrix}\nearrow O \\ \searrow O^{(-)}\end{smallmatrix} + Br^{(-)} \quad (b)$$

XXI

[38a] In unpublished work, W. M. Schubert and H. W. Burkett (private communication from W. M. Schubert) have shown that replacement of the aldehydic hydrogen by deuterium results in about a threefold increase in rate, even over a wide range of sulfuric acid strengths. It thus appears that, for decarbonylation, the rate-controlling step involves removal of carbonyl hydrogen, as shown.

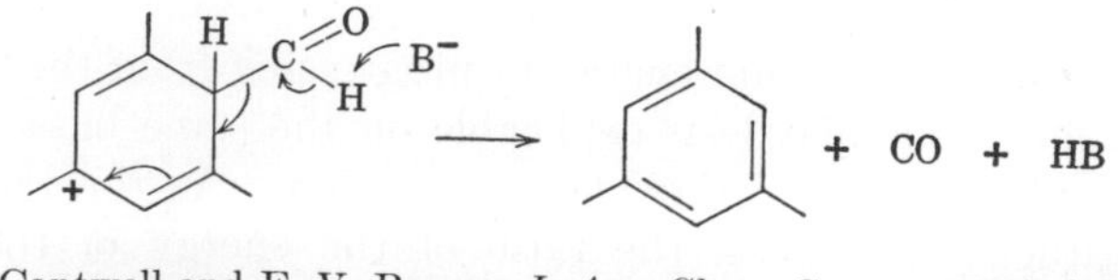

[39] N. H. Cantwell and E. V. Brown, *J. Am. Chem. Soc.*, *74*, 5967 (1952).
[40] S. J. Cristol and W. P. Norris, *J. Am. Chem. Soc.*, *75*, 632, 2645 (1953).
[41] E. Grovenstein, Jr., and D. E. Lee, *J. Am. Chem. Soc.*, *75*, 2639 (1953).

These mechanisms are supported by the following evidence.

1. The non-stereospecific elimination (*b*) is favored with respect to the stereospecific reaction (*a*) when the solvent is changed from acetone, to ethanol, to water. The process in which charge is created (dipolar ion and bromide ion) would be favored by solvents of relatively greater ionizing power, in contrast to the stereospecific process (*trans* elimination in which charge is distributed) which would be favored by non-polar solvents.

2. Electron-withdrawing substituents on the phenyl ring which do not favor solvolytic reactions [42] have been found to favor the stereospecific decarboxylation (*a*).

Support for the general picture of the stereospecific elimination process is found in studies on the decarboxylation of diastereomeric β-halocinnamic acids, where the rate and even the course of the reaction appears to be controlled by the arrangement of groups in the molecule. The *trans*-elimination process requires that the original freely rotating molecule be forced into a rigid transition state where the incipient double bond places a requirement of coplanarity on the substituents at the α- and β-carbon atoms. In systems where the requirements of this transition state would cause interactions between bulky substituents at the α and β positions, one might expect steric inhibition of the decarboxylation. Curtin [43] has discussed such cases in a general review of the "*cis*" effect. Thus, whereas *erythro*-α-phenyl-β-benzoyl-β-bromopropionic acid undergoes smooth decarboxylation in boiling pyridine, the *threo* isomer suffers only dehydrohalogenation.[44] An inspection of the preferred transition state for each of these elimination reactions shows that in the decarboxylative debromination of the *erythro* isomer by a concerted *trans* elimination, the bulky phenyl and benzoyl groups are oriented in a *trans* relationship, while in the *threo* isomer a *trans* arrangement of bulky groups coincides with a *trans* arrangement of hydrogen and bromine atoms, thus favoring the elimination of hydrogen bromide. Another example of the steric control of this decarboxylative elimination process is found in the comparative rates of decarboxylation of the diastereomeric β-phenyl-β-bromo-

[42] S. J. Cristol points out (reference 40) that electron-withdrawing groups impede the solvolysis of benzyl chloride but favor the direct displacement process with iodide ion. G. M. Bennett and B. Jones, *J. Chem. Soc.*, **1935**, 1815.

[43] D. Y. Curtin, *Abstracts* of the Thirteenth National Organic Chemistry Symposium of the American Chemical Society, June, 1953, Ann Arbor, Michigan. For an excellent discussion of the "*cis*" effect, see D. Y. Curtin, *Rec. Chem. Progr. Kresge-Hooker Sci. Lib.*, *15*, No. 3, 111 (1954).

[44] E. P. Kohler, W. D. Peterson, and C. L. Bickel, *J. Am. Chem. Soc.*, *56*, 2000 (1934).

α-phenylpropionic acids in 50% alcohol.[43]   It was found that *trans* olefin is produced in yields that are roughly 500 times greater than

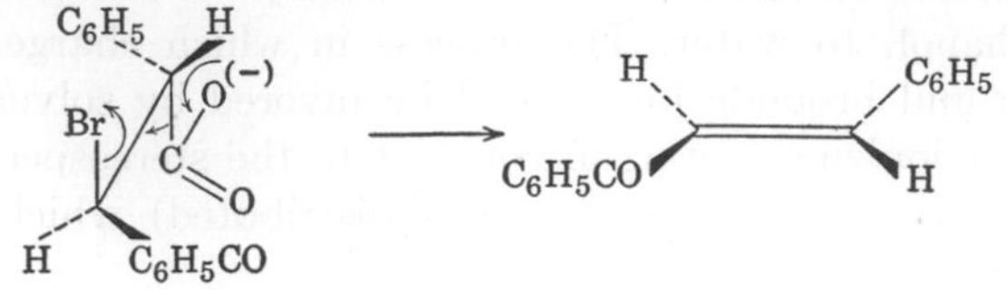

erythro

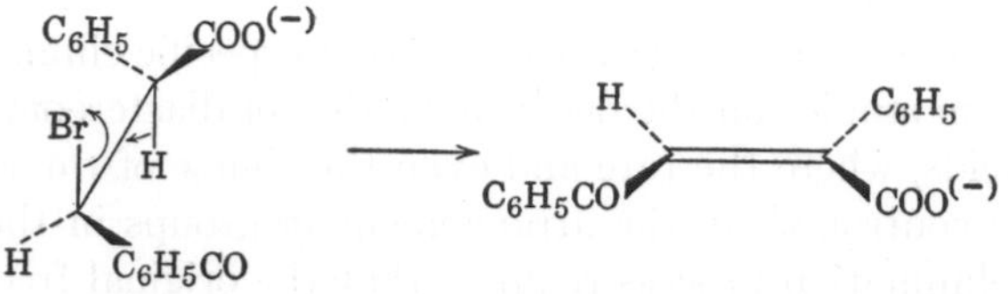

threo

the yields of *cis* product.   Here, again, a much less crowded transition state is possible during the elimination process involving the maximum separation of the bulky phenyl groups in the transition state. This may be seen by a comparison of conformation B (favored) with A (unfavored).

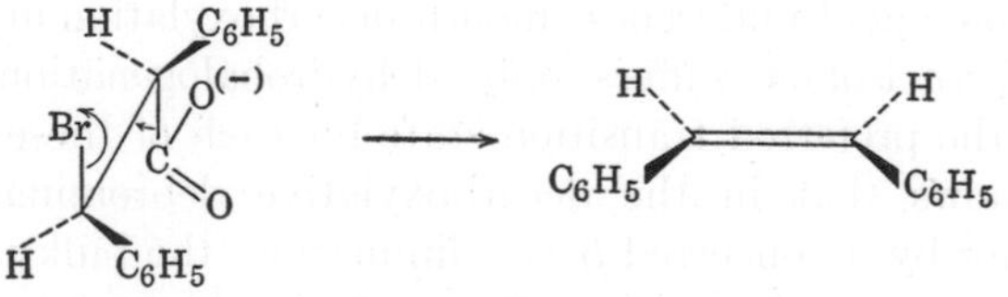

A

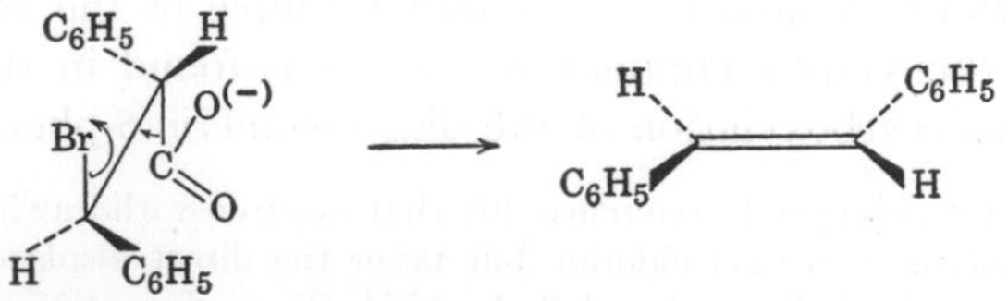

B

Decarboxylation of cinnamic acids

The acid-catalyzed decarboxylation of α,β-unsaturated acids of the cinnamic acid type has been pictured as SE_2-type interaction of the proton with the organic acid.[45, 46] Substituents at the β position which stabilize the carbonium ion D would lower the energy of the transition

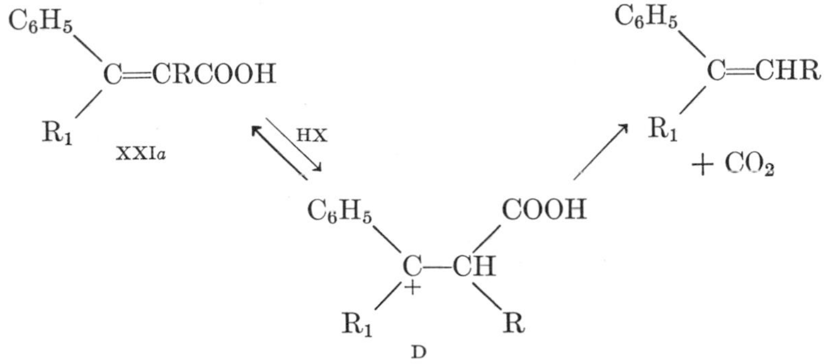

$$C_6H_5\diagdown$$
$$C=CRCOOH$$
$$R_1\diagup$$
XXIa

HX

$$C_6H_5\diagdown$$
$$C=CHR$$
$$R_1\diagup$$
$$+ CO_2$$

$$C_6H_5\diagdown \quad \diagup COOH$$
$$\overset{+}{C}-CH$$
$$R_1\diagup \quad \diagdown R$$
D

state, considered to be near D, and should thereby increase the rate of decarboxylation. In accord with the expected stabilizing effect of two β-aryl groups, it was found that β-phenylcinnamic acid decarboxylates more rapidly than other β-alkylcinnamic acids studied. When, however, a methyl group is substituted in the α position, the rate of decarboxylation decreases markedly as shown in Table II.

TABLE II

		Rate of Decarboxylation,
Acid XXIa		k, sec.$^{-1}$
$R_1 = C_6H_5$	$R = H$	0.0046
$R_1 = C_6H_5$	$R = CH_3$	0.0002
$R_1 = CH_3$	$R = H$	0.0022
$R_1 = C_2H_5$	$R = H$	0.0007

The slower rate of decarboxylation in this case might be due to a steric factor operative in the transition state, analogous to the "cis" effect [43]

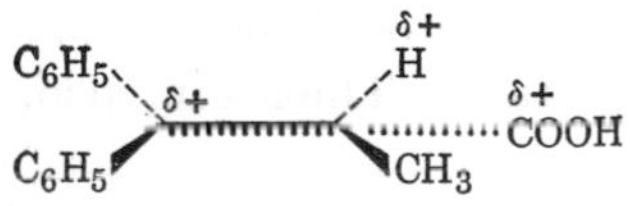

$$C_6H_5\diagdown \quad \overset{\delta+}{H}$$
$$\quad \overset{\delta+}{} \quad \overset{\delta+}{\cdots COOH}$$
$$C_6H_5\diagup \quad \diagdown CH_3$$

discussed above in connection with the decarboxylation of β-halocinnamic acids. The transition state, pictured as above,[47] would have

[45] W. S. Johnson and W. E. Heinz, *J. Am. Chem. Soc.*, **71**, 2913 (1949).

[46] A bimolecular mechanism for the decarboxylation of anthracene-9-carboxylic acid had previously been suggested by von H. Schenkel and M. Schenkel-Rudin, *Helv. Chim. Acta*, **31**, 514 (1948).

[47] E. J. Corey, private communication.

partial double bond character, and the requirements of coplanarity would be met less easily with an α-methyl substituent than with an α-hydrogen, owing to phenyl-methyl interactions.

A case where steric hindrance to the addition of a bulky fragment may reduce the rate of decarboxylation has been observed in the decarboxylation of arylidenemalonic acid derivatives of type XXII in pyridine. The presence of bulky *ortho* substituents (R = CH₃, Cl)

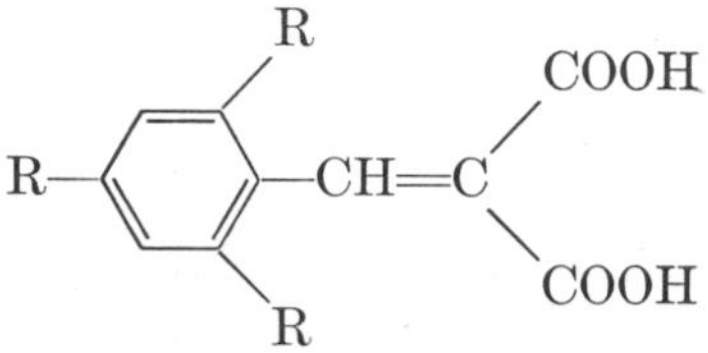

XXII

in the aromatic ring of molecules such as XXII strongly inhibits the loss of carbon dioxide, the rate of reaction in pyridine at 111° under these circumstances being too slow to measure.[48] The interpretation which is most consistent with the kinetic data, and which explains the steric effect, assumes that a solvent molecule is involved in the reaction of the acid with pyridinium ion. The combination of acid, pyridinium ion, and pyridine (solvent) leads to the intermediate XXIII as shown, in which a proton and a solvent molecule have added

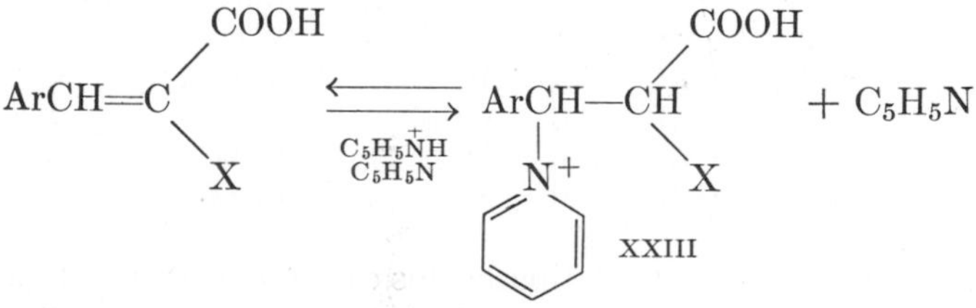

X = COOC₂H₅, C≡N, COOH

to the α,β double bond. Loss of carbon dioxide then takes place by a decarboxylative elimination. Thioacetic acid, which can substitute

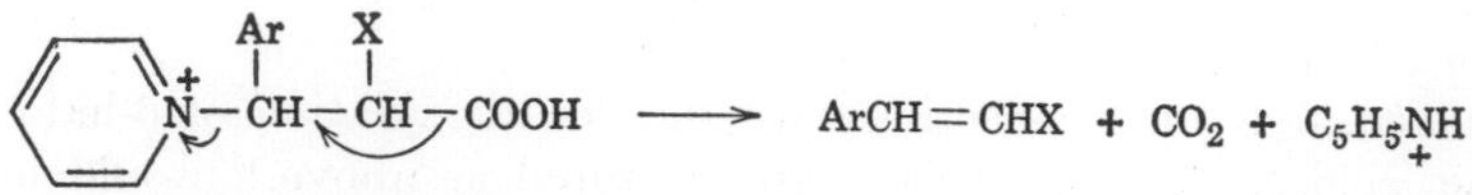

for a pyridine molecule as a nucleophilic reagent, strongly catalyzes the decarboxylation in pyridine. The probable intermediate in the

[48] E. J. Corey and G. Fraenkel, *J. Am. Chem. Soc.*, **75**, 1168 (1953).

latter reaction is shown. This mechanism features the addition of a bulky fragment to the β position, and, where the proximity of large *ortho* substituents on the adjacent aromatic ring might lead to steric

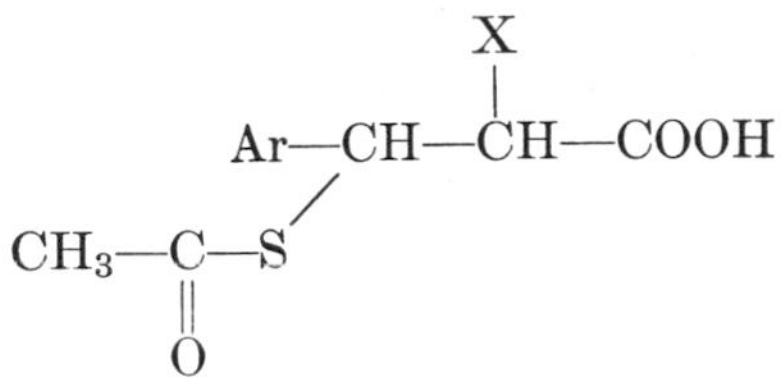

$$\begin{array}{c} \text{X} \\ | \\ \text{Ar—CH—CH—COOH} \\ \diagup \\ \text{CH}_3\text{—C—S} \\ \| \\ \text{O} \end{array}$$

repulsion, one would expect inhibition of addition, and thus resistance to decarboxylation, as is in fact observed.

Decarboxylation of optically active acids catalyzed by optically active bases

An interesting parallelism between the configuration of some optically active organic bases possessing a center of asymmetry and their catalytic effect on the decarboxylation of *dextro*-camphocarboxylic acid (XXIV) has been reported.[49] In the presence of bases with the

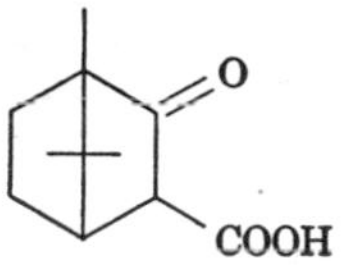

XXIV

same configuration, one antipode of the acid appears to undergo decarboxylation faster than the other. Thus, in the presence of the ethyl esters of L-alanine, L-leucine, L-tyrosine, L-proline, and other bases, *d*-camphocarboxylic acid always undergoes decarboxylation faster than the *l* acid, with differences (based on the value of the reaction constant) from 6% with proline to 44% with tyrosine. In the decarboxylation of the racemic acid, intermediate rate constants are observed.

Although no mechanism for the specific catalytic effect exerted by the optically active bases has, as yet, been established, it is possible that the "steric fit" of the base in a solvation process varies from one optical antipode to the other and may thus be responsible for the observed differences in the rates of decarboxylation.

[49] P. Pratesi, L. Arpesella, and A. La Manná, *J. Am. Chem. Soc.*, 75, 5476 (1953).

Decarboxylation of trihaloacetic acids

Although acetic acid is stable to decarboxylation, the trihalo acids lose carbon dioxide relatively easily, the ease of breakdown following the order tribromo > trichloro > trifluoroacetic acid.[50] The decarboxylation appears to take place *via* the carboxylate anion, since the activation energies for the breakdown of the acids and sodium salts in water are identical.[51]

The fact that the trifluoro acid is more stable than the trichloro acid [51] is consistent with the decreasing polarizability of the carbon-halogen bond in the order C—I > C—Br > C—Cl > C—F, and suggests that the CCl_3 group is able to withstand partial negativity in the transition state better than the CF_3 group. On the other hand, it is possible that there is greater strain in the ground state of the trihalo acid containing the bulkier halogen atoms. Decarboxylation through the transition state shown (where the carbon-carbon bond is lengthened) might provide greater relief from strain in the order tribromo > trichloro > trifluoroacetic acid.

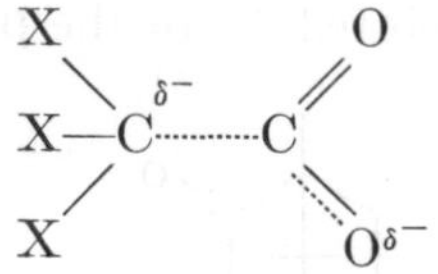

X = Br, Cl, F

CLEAVAGE OF β-DIKETONES AND RELATED COMPOUNDS

The cleavage of β-diketones by aqueous alkali to give carboxylic acids and ketones involves attack at one of the carbonyl groups of the keto form [52] according to the scheme shown below, and, in the case of an unsymmetrical diketone, can lead to two sets of products depending on whether path (a) or path (b) is taken. With aryl-substituted systems,[52a] the cleavage of unsymmetrical β-diketones takes place so as to form the stronger of the two possible resulting acids.

[50] Triiodoacetic acid and its sodium salt are both very unstable, decomposing rapidly even at room temperature to give iodine, iodoform, and carbon dioxide, R. A. Fairclough, reference 51.

[51] R. A. Fairclough, *J. Chem. Soc.*, *1938*, 1186; G. A. Hall, Jr., and F. H. Verhoek, *J. Am. Chem. Soc.*, *69*, 613 (1947); I. Auerbach, F. H. Verhoek, and A. L. Henne, *J. Am. Chem. Soc.*, *72*, 299 (1950).

[52] (a) W. Bradley and R. Robinson, *J. Chem. Soc.*, *1926*, 2356. (b) C. L. Bickel, *J. Am. Chem. Soc.*, *67*, 2204 (1945); *68*, 865 (1946). (c) C. R. Hauser, F. W. Swamer, and B. I. Ringler, *ibid.*, *70*, 4023 (1948).

There also exists a close relationship between the course of the cleavage of such aryl β-diketones and the rates of alkaline hydrolysis of the ethyl esters corresponding to the acids formed.[52c]   Thus, for each

$$R_1COOH + CH_3COR_2$$

$$(a)$$

$$R_1COCH_2COR_2 + OH^{(-)}$$

$$(b)$$

$$R_2COOH + CH_3COR_1$$

diketone studied, the acid whose ethyl ester undergoes more ready hydrolysis in base (hence the stronger acid) is obtained in greater yield. Despite a generally good correlation of the yields of acidic products with their acid strengths, there are some anomalous results which appear to involve steric effects. Thus, cleavage of o-chlorodibenzoylmethane [52b] (XXV) results in the formation of less o-chloroben-

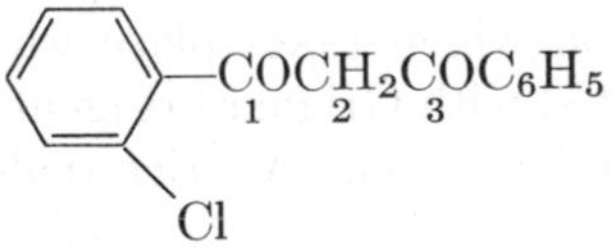

$$-COCH_2COC_6H_5$$
$$1\quad 2\quad 3$$

Cl

XXV

zoic acid [53] than benzoic acid,[52c] although o-chlorobenzoic acid is the stronger [53] acid of the two. In contrast, cleavage of p-chlorodibenzoylmethane gives results in accord with the ratio of acid strengths [53a] of p-chlorobenzoic and benzoic acids. The exceptional behavior of the o-chloro isomer demonstrates the lessened reactivity of the carbonyl group (C-1) probably caused by steric hindrance to the approach of the base.

A more striking example of steric hindrance in this cleavage reaction is the failure of highly substituted β-diketones corresponding to A to cleave after refluxing with 60% alkali for 24 hours.[53b] This behavior may be contrasted with the ready cleavage of most β-diketones under relatively mild conditions, as by gentle warming with 1% aqueous sodium hydroxide.[52a]

[53] Mole fraction of o-chlorobenzoic acid in mixture of acids, 0.442.

[53a] Ionization constants at 25°C.: benzoic acid, 6.6×10^{-5}; o-chlorobenzoic acid, 132×10^{-5}.

[53b] F. C. Whitmore and C. T. Lester, J. Am. Chem. Soc., 64, 1251 (1942).

$$
\begin{array}{c}
\text{(CH}_3\text{)}_3\text{CCH}_2 \diagdown \text{O} \text{R} \text{O} \diagup \text{CH}_2\text{C(CH}_3\text{)}_3 \\
 \text{CH} - \text{C} - \text{C} - \text{C} - \text{CH} \\
\text{(CH}_3\text{)}_3\text{CCH}_2 \diagup \text{R}' \diagdown \text{CH}_2\text{C(CH}_3\text{)}_3
\end{array}
$$

A

R = H, R' = H
R = H, R' = CH₃
R = CH₃, R' = CH₃

The somewhat less hindered β-diketones (B) cleave only after 6 hours of refluxing with 50% alkali. This hindrance effect, exerted by

$$
\text{C}_6\text{H}_5\text{COCHCOCH} \diagup \diagdown \begin{array}{l} \text{CH}_2\text{C(CH}_3\text{)}_3 \\[6pt] \text{CH}_2\text{C(CH}_3\text{)}_3 \end{array}
$$

with R below the central carbon.

B
R = H, CH₃

the dineopentylcarbinyl group, also shows up in other reactions of the diketone (A) in which normal carbonyl addition is suppressed.[54, 55]

The cleavage reaction which takes place when β-diketones and α-epoxy ketones are treated with Grignard reagents has been compared [56] to the reverse aldol condensation. A strict analogy of this sort as pic-

$$
\begin{array}{c}
\text{R}_1\text{CO} \diagdown \text{R}_3 \\
\text{C} \\
\text{R}_2\text{CO} \diagup \text{R}_4
\end{array}
\xrightarrow{\text{R'MgX}}
\left[
\begin{array}{c}
\text{R}' \text{O}^{(-)} \overset{+}{\text{MgX}} \\
\text{R}_1 \diagdown \text{C} \diagup \\
 \text{C} \diagdown \begin{array}{l}\text{R}_3 \\ \text{R}_4\end{array} \\
\text{R}_2 \diagup \text{C} = \text{O}
\end{array}
\right]
\longrightarrow
\begin{array}{c}
\text{R}' \diagdown \\
\text{C} = \text{O} \\
\text{R}_1 \diagup \\[8pt]
\text{R}_3 \diagdown \diagup \text{OMgX} \\
\text{C} = \text{C} \\
\text{R}_4 \diagup \diagdown \text{R}_2
\end{array}
$$

tured does not, however, explain certain steric aspects of these reactions,[57] particularly the markedly different behavior of straight-chain diketones compared to analogous cyclic compounds. Furthermore, in the case of oxido alcohols, strong bases other than the Grignard reagent cause rearrangement rather than cleavage.[56]

To account for the specific role of the Grignard reagent or other organometallic reagents [58] in the cleavage reaction, Geissman proposed

[54] F. C. Whitmore and C. T. Lester, J. Am. Chem. Soc., 64, 1247 (1942).

[55] For a discussion of the steric factors in carbonyl addition reactions see Chapter 4.

[56] E. P. Kohler, N. K. Richtmyer, and W. F. Hester, J. Am. Chem. Soc., 53, 205 (1931); E. P. Kohler and J. L. E. Erickson, ibid., 53, 2301 (1931).

[57] T. A. Geissman and V. Tulagin, J. Am. Chem. Soc., 63, 3352 (1941).

[58] An analogous cleavage of α-epoxy ketones takes place with phenyllithium; C. L. Bickel, J. Am. Chem. Soc., 59, 325 (1937).

that formation of chelated intermediates corresponding to A and B might be a necessary step in the reaction. Decomposition of the cyclic

intermediates as shown would lead to the observed products. In support of this hypothesis, it has been found [59] that the cyclic β-diketones XXVI and XXVII, neither of which can form cyclic complexes of

XXVI   XXVII

type A, do not undergo cleavage when treated with Grignard reagent. Instead, both substances take part in normal carbonyl addition. That tetramethylcyclobutanedione, which cannot form a cyclic intermediate, cleaves readily when treated with Grignard reagents or organolithium compounds [60] is probably a result of the strain in the four-membered ring.

Other cleavage reactions of carbonyl compounds with organometallic reagents may share features in common with the cleavage of β-diketones. It has been suggested,[61] for example, that the cleavage reaction

[59] T. A. Geissman and L. Morris, J. Am. Chem. Soc., 66, 716 (1944).

[60] T. L. E. Erickson and G. C. Kitchens, J. Am. Chem. Soc., 68, 492 (1946).

[61] S. Winstein, Colloques internationals du centre national de la recherche scientifique, XXX (Rearrangements moleculaires et inversion de Walden), Montpellier, April 24–29, 1950, p. 72.

of β-haloketones by the Grignard reagent [62] takes place via the chelated intermediate as shown.

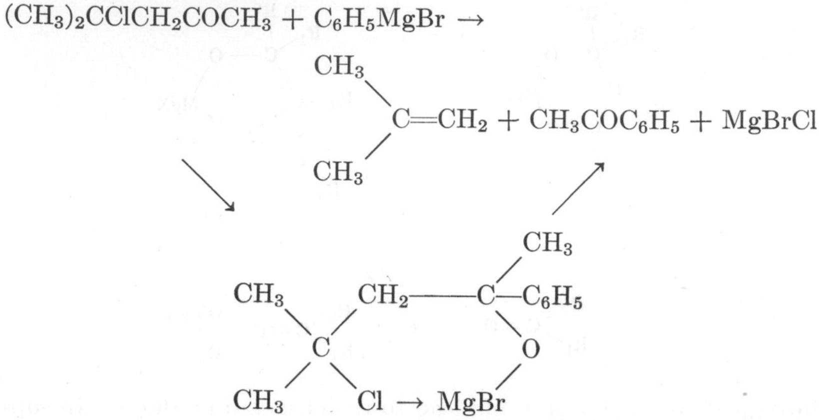

$$(CH_3)_2CClCH_2COCH_3 + C_6H_5MgBr \rightarrow$$

Grignard reagents may cause cleavage of an α,β carbon-carbon bond of a hindered ketone if the β-carbon atom is electrophilic,[63] as in the reaction of α,β-dimorpholinobenzylacetophenone (XXVIII, R = C_6H_5) with phenylmagnesium bromide. Here, normal carbonyl addition is hindered, and attack at the electrophilic β-carbon atom takes place. A cyclic mechanism is proposed by Cromwell as shown:

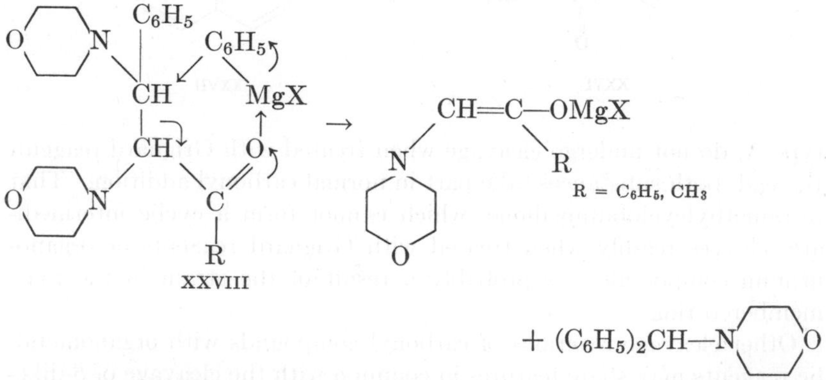

In the reactions of the less hindered α,β-dimorpholinobenzylacetone (XXVIII, R = CH_3) with Grignard reagent, normal addition takes place to give carbinols in fair yields.

[62] G. Richard and M. Mirjollet, *Compt. rend.*, 284 (1947).
[63] N. H. Cromwell, *J. Am. Chem. Soc.*, **69**, 1857 (1947).

CLEAVAGE OF SUBSTITUTED 1,3-DIOLS AND RELATED COMPOUNDS

When a substituted 1,3-diol is heated with potassium bisulfate or dilute sulfuric acid, fission of the carbon-carbon bond may occur with the formation of a ketone and an olefin.[64]   There are many recorded examples of this cleavage reaction,[65] but there has been little work on the mechanism and, in particular, on the relationship of the reaction course to the steric factors involved.[66]   Barbot [65a] was the first to suggest that a 1,3-oxide might be an intermediate step in the cleavage process, and Brown [67] pointed out that cleavage of hexamethyl-1,3-propanediol into acetone and tetramethylethylene in the presence of acids might represent relief of strain in the heavily substituted diol.

In the acid cleavage, which may take one of two paths, as shown in the diagram, the major product results by fission of the more highly substituted carbinol carbon-oxygen bond.[68]   The degree of substitu-

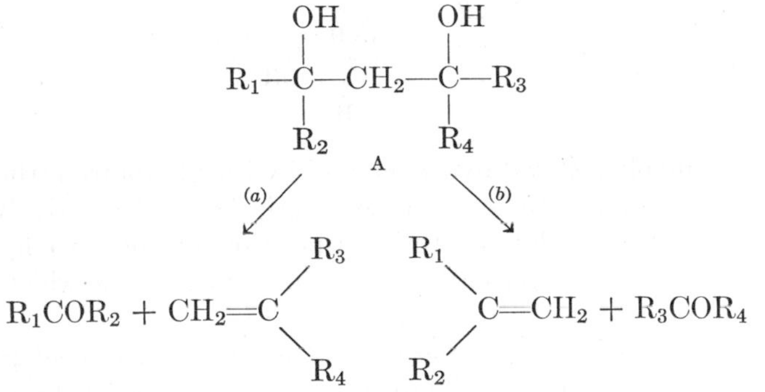

$$OH \qquad OH$$
$$R_1{-}\underset{\underset{R_2}{|}}{\overset{\overset{|}{}}{C}}{-}CH_2{-}\underset{\underset{R_4}{|}}{\overset{\overset{|}{}}{C}}{-}R_3$$

A

(a)   (b)

$$R_1COR_2 + CH_2{=}C\underset{R_4}{\overset{R_3}{\diagup}}\qquad\qquad \underset{R_2}{\overset{R_1}{\diagdown}}C{=}CH_2 + R_3COR_4$$

tion is an important factor in determining the ease of cleavage,[66] but steric factors may alter the reaction course markedly. Thus, although the open-chain diol XXIX gives 55% of cleavage products, only

---

[64] 1,3-Amino alcohols also undergo this type of cleavage; D. W. Adamson, *Nature*, *164*, 500 (1949).

[65] (a) A. Barbot, *Bull. soc. chim. France*, [5], *2*, 1438 (1935); (b) A. Kalischev, *J. Russ. Phys. Chem. Soc. 46*, 427 (1913); *Chem. Zentr.*, *85*, II, 1261 (1914); (c) K. Freudenberg and G. Wilke, *Ber.*, *85*, 78 (1953); (d) A. Franke and R. Stern, *Monatsh.*, *49*, 21 (1928).

[66] J. English, Jr., and F. V. Brutcher, Jr., *J. Am. Chem. Soc.*, *74*, 4279 (1952).

[67] H. C. Brown and R. S. Fletcher, *J. Am. Chem. Soc.*, *71*, 1845 (1949).

[68] Substitution (especially aromatic) at the site of the carbon undergoing carbon-oxygen cleavage would result in greater stabilization of the carbonium ion formed. Thus 1,1,3-triphenyl-1,3-propanediol (A, $R_1 = R_2 = R_3 = C_6H_5$; $R_4 = H$) yields over 90% of benzaldehyde (path *b*) while no carbonyl component indicative of the alternative reaction (path *a*) is found.[66]

products of dehydration appear to be formed from the analogous cyclohexanediol XXIX*a*.

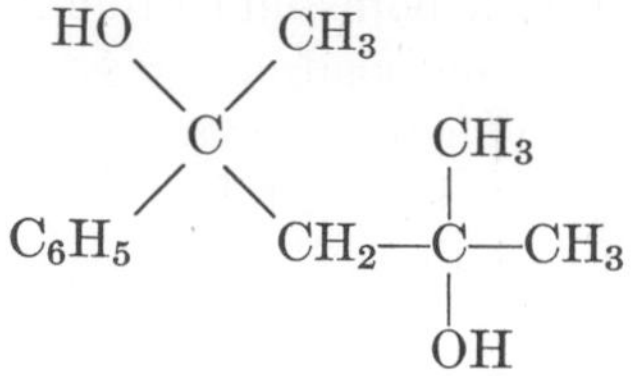

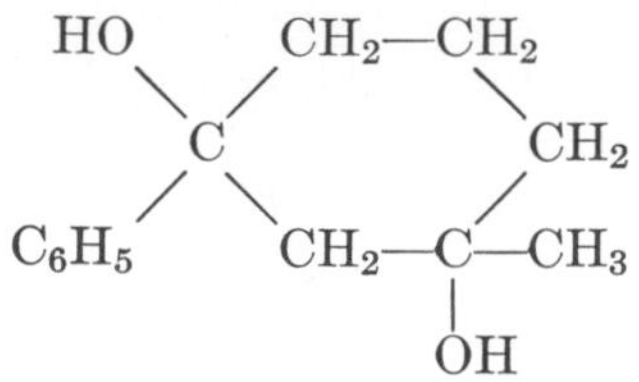

It was suggested [66] that the arrangement of substituents on the cyclohexane ring XXIX*a* (bulky phenyl group equatorial and hydroxyl group axial [69] on C-3 as shown) would favor dehydration by a *trans*

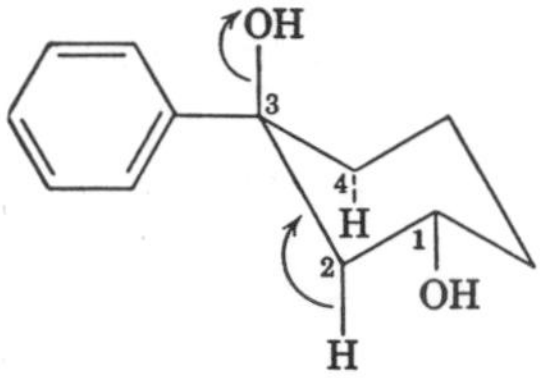

elimination involving axial hydrogen and hydroxyl groups, rather than cleavage through a path less favored sterically. Alternatively, it is possible [66] that the relative steric disposition of the two hydroxyl groups would not favor formation of a trimethylene oxide which might be an intermediate in the reaction.

When a pair of diastereomeric diols of established configuration were subjected to cleavage, differences in the speed of reaction and in the yields of products were observed.[70] It was found that, when the diastereomeric 1,1,3-triphenyl-2-methyl-1,3-propanediols XXX*a* (α) and XXX*b* (β) were refluxed with dilute ethanolic sulfuric acid, the α form cleaved faster, and in higher yield, than the β isomer. The difference in the ease of cleavage of the two isomers was explained by the following scheme in which the transition states are represented by solvated, protonated trimethylene oxide rings.

The formation of benzaldehyde from either isomer is electronically preferred, since this reaction path involves a transient carbonium ion stabilized by two phenyl groups; the alternative path leading to benzophenone affords less stabilization of the positive charge. Cleavage of the α isomer, through transition state XXXA, permits a more favored

[69] D. H. R. Barton, *Experientia*, VI/8, 316 (1950).

[70] H. E. Zimmerman and J. English, Jr., *J. Am. Chem. Soc.*, 76, 2285, 2291, 2294 (1954).

trans orientation of the phenyl and methyl groups, whereas, in the cleavage of the β isomer through XXXB, the bulky groups are in a *cis* relationship. One would therefore expect a more ready cleavage of the α isomer, as is observed.

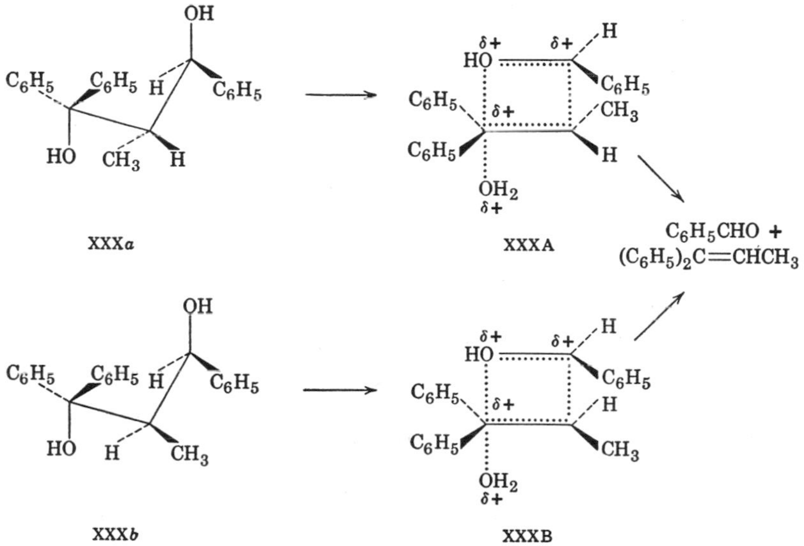

$$C_6H_5CHO + (C_6H_5)_2C{=}CHCH_3$$

XXX*a*   XXXA

XXX*b*   XXXB

In the cleavage of the diastereomeric 2-phenyl-3-methyl-4-ethyl-2,4-hexanediols, the main products from each diastereomer are different (diethyl ketone vs. acetophenone).[70] A rational explanation for these results is based on the reasoning outlined above wherein the steric factors operating in the transition states are evaluated.

Although there is no proof that a 1,3-oxide intermediate is involved in the acid cleavage of 1,3-diols, it is pertinent to note that, in the base-cleavage reactions of 1,3-diol monotosylates, the geometric requirements for fission of the carbon-carbon bond appear to parallel those for trimethylene oxide formation. Clayton and Henbest [71] observed that no compounds containing the 1,3-epoxycyclohexane system are known, although there are many examples of the corresponding 1,2- and 1,4-epoxides. They suggested that failure to obtain this fused ring system, as in the treatment of the mono-*p*-toluenesulfonate of a 1,3-diol with alkali, might be traced to an unfavorable conformation of starting material. A favorable environment for trimethylene oxide formation exists in the 3-mono-*p*-toluenesulfonates of cholestane-$3\beta,5\alpha$-diol, XXXI, and coprostane-$3\alpha,5\beta$-diol XXXII, where the *p*-

[71] R. B. Clayton and H. B. Henbest, *Chemistry & Industry, 1953*, 1315.

toluenesulfonyloxy and hydroxy groups are fixed in equatorial and axial positions respectively. In these substances, a *trans* coplanar arrangement of attacking and departing groups is possible, and these

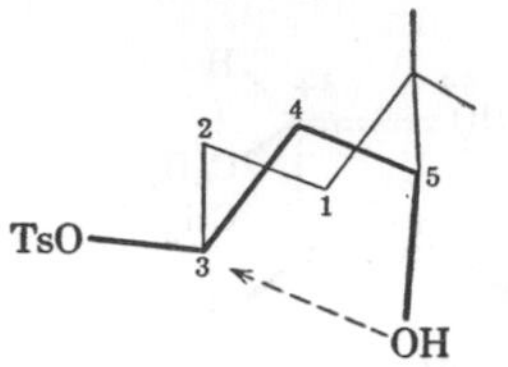

XXXI 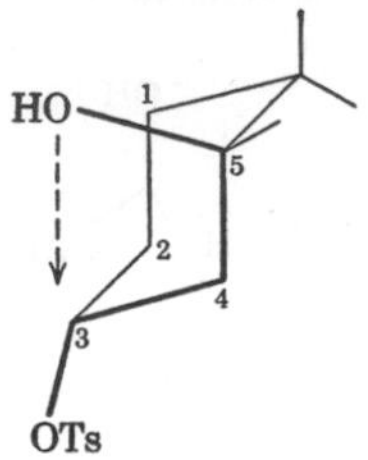   XXXII

therefore represent ideal models for studying the steric requirements for 1,3-oxide formation. Treatment of **XXXI** with sodium *tert*-butoxide in *tert*-butanol solution yields two products: the oxide, $3\alpha,5\alpha$-epoxycholestane (A), and the cleavage product, B. Under the same conditions, **XXXII** yields only the cleavage product B. The absence of

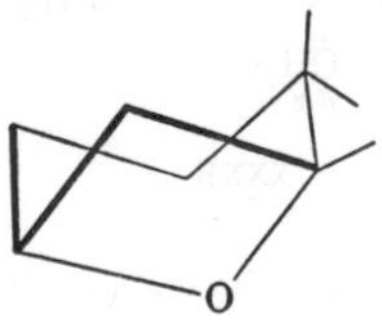

A    B

oxide formation in the latter case is ascribed to the greater steric requirements inherent in linking the 5β-oxygen with C-3 in the coprostanediol derivative.

OXIDATIVE CLEAVAGE OF 1,2-GLYCOLS AND RELATED COMPOUNDS

The oxidation of 1,2-glycols by lead tetraacetate or periodic acid effects the cleavage of carbon-carbon bonds under very mild conditions, and these reactions, which are usually quantitative, have found extensive use both for preparative purposes and also in estimating and detecting vicinal hydroxyl groupings.[72]

---

[72] Oxidative cleavage by lead tetraacetate or periodic acid also takes place with α-hydroxycarbonyl compounds and α-amino alcohols under certain conditions. For a review by R. Criegee, on this general type of reaction, and important references, see *Newer Methods of Preparative Organic Chemistry*, pp. 1–20, Interscience Publishers, New York, 1948.

In his early studies on the lead tetraacetate cleavage reaction, Criegee [73] observed that: (1) the reaction in acetic acid solution follows second-order kinetics; (2) acetic acid has a specific retarding influence; (3) the rate of the reaction varies markedly, depending on the relative steric arrangement of the vicinal hydroxyl groups. To account for these results, the following mechanism was proposed.

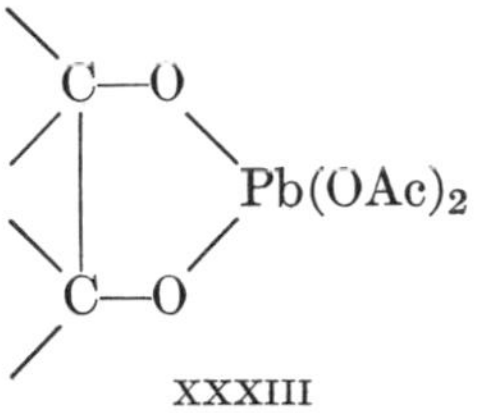

XXXIII

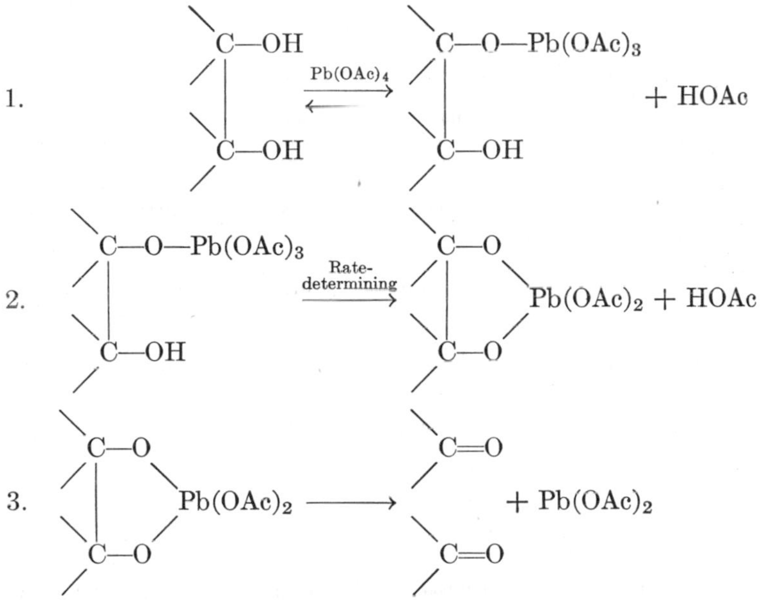

1.

2.

3.

Criegee's mechanism accounts for the marked differences in the rates of oxidation of *cis*- compared to *trans*-glycols (see Table III) since the rate-determining step is the ring closure to form the intermediate XXXIII. Formation of the cyclic intermediate [74] would de-

[73] R. Criegee, L. Kraft, and B. Rank, *Ann.*, *507*, 159 (1933–1934).

[74] The isolation of a stable osmium analog, XXXIIIa, from the reaction of aqueous potassium osmate with glycols was considered by Criegee to be supporting evidence for the existence of the intermediate XXXIII. R. Criegee, *Angew. Chem.*, *50*, 153 (1937); *Ann.*, *522*, 75 (1936). R. Criegee, B. Marchand, and H. Wannowius, *Ann.*, *550*, 99 (1942).

pend on the ease of bridging the vicinal hydroxyl groups, and would be expected to take place more readily in a *cis*-glycol than in the corresponding *trans* compound.

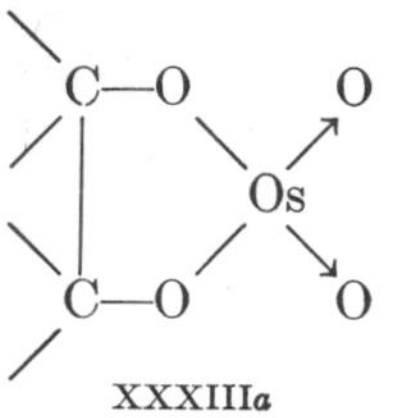

XXXIII*a*

The oxidation of 1,2-glycols by periodate was also pictured by Criegee [75] as involving a cyclic intermediate, the acidic cyclic ester

TABLE III

OXIDATION OF *cis* AND *trans* GLYCOLS

Glycol	Rate $(k_{20°})$ *cis*	Rate $(k_{20°})$ *trans*	Ratio *cis/trans*	Reference
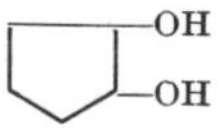 —OH —OH	40,000	12.8	3,000	78
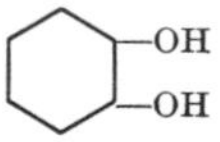 —OH —OH	5.0	0.22	23	73
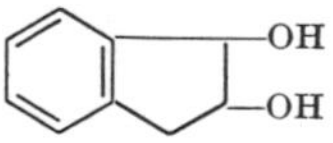 —OH —OH	27,800	0.47	60,000	73
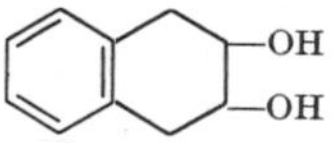 —OH —OH	40	1.9	21	73
	38	1.9	20	76
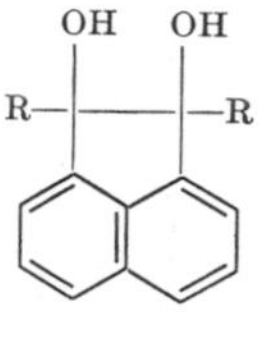 R = H	120,000	0.03	4×10^6	73
R = CH$_3$	28,600	0.06	4.8×10^5	73
R = C$_6$H$_5$	33,100	284	116	73
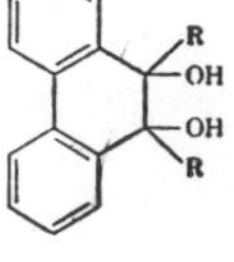 R = H	13.8	130	0.11	77
R = C$_6$H$_5$	286	25	11.5	73

[75] R. Criegee, *Ber.*, *68*, 665 (1935).

[76] J. Booth and E. Boyland, *Biochem. J.*, *44*, 361 (1949).

[77] E. Boyland and G. Wolf, *Biochem. J.*, *47*, 64 (1950).

[78] R. Criegee, E. Büchner, and W. Walther, *Ber.*, *73*, 571 (1940).

XXXIV of paraperiodic acid. Decomposition of this ester would lead

$$
\begin{array}{c}
\diagdown \\
\text{C}-\text{O} \\
\diagup \qquad \diagdown \\
\qquad\qquad \text{IO}_4\text{H}_3 \\
\diagdown \qquad \diagup \\
\text{C}-\text{O} \\
\diagup
\end{array}
$$

XXXIV

to cleavage of the carbon-carbon bond with formation of two carbonyl groups. In accord with this picture Price found [79] that the periodate oxidation follows second-order kinetics, that the reaction proceeds more rapidly in acid than in alkaline solution, and that *cis*-glycols are attacked more rapidly than the *trans* isomers.[80]

The marked differences in the rates of cleavage of *meso* versus racemic glycols [78, 81] lend further support to Criegee's cyclic mechanism. As shown in Table IV, the racemic forms of the glycols XXXV*a* and

TABLE IV

$$
\text{R}_1 - \overset{\displaystyle \text{R}_2}{\underset{\displaystyle \text{OH}}{\rule{0pt}{1em}|}} - \overset{\displaystyle \text{R}_2}{\underset{\displaystyle \text{OH}}{\rule{0pt}{1em}|}} - \text{R}_1
$$

XXXV*a, b*

Glycol		$k_{20°}$ racemic	$k_{20°}$ *meso*	Ratio
XXXV*a*	$R_1 = C_6H_5$, $R_2 = H$	2840	192	15
XXXV*b*	$R_1 = (CH_3)_3C$, $R_2 = CH_3$	26.5	3.68	7.2

[79] C. C. Price and H. Kroll, *J. Am. Chem. Soc.*, *60*, 2726 (1938); C. C. Price and M. Knell, *ibid.*, 64, 552 (1942).

[80] For a review of periodate oxidation see E. C. Jackson in *Organic Reactions*, *2*, 341 (1944); see also F. R. Duke, *J. Am. Chem. Soc.*, *69*, 3054 (1947); J. E. Taylor, *ibid.*, *75*, 3912 (1953).

Heidt, Gladding, and Purves[*Paper Trade Journal*, *121*, 81–89 (1945)] noted the similarity in the reaction kinetics and the selectivity of lead tetraacetate and periodate glycol oxidations, and they formulated certain specific requirements for the structure of an oxidizing agent capable of causing glycol fission. Among these several requirements was the specification that the central atom of the oxidant must have a diameter of 2.5 to 3 × 10^{-8} cm., which is large enough to bridge the space between hydroxyl groups in a 1,2-glycol. On the basis of their considerations of the proper size, valence, coordinating ability of the central atom, and the E_0 oxidation potential of the oxidant, they were able to predict, correctly, that both sodium bismuthate and hydrated trivalent silver ion would be effective glycol-splitting reagents.

[81] H. J. Backer, *Rec. trav. chim.*, *57*, 967 (1938).

XXXV*b* are cleaved more rapidly by lead tetraacetate than the corresponding *meso* isomers. Free rotation of the open-chain glycols would permit both *meso* and racemic forms to attain the conformations shown, which are favorable for formation of the cyclic intermediates. In the racemic glycols, such a conformation (A) permits a nearly *trans* orientation of the bulky (phenyl or *tert*-butyl) groups. On the

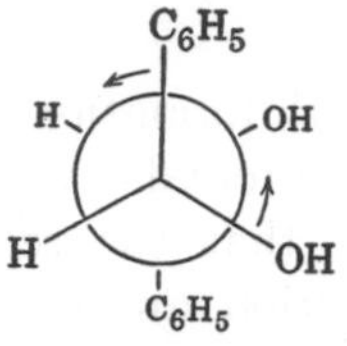

A (*d*– or *l*–glycol) 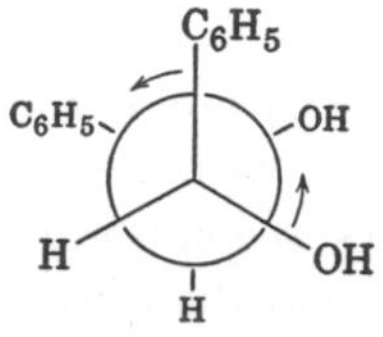   B (*meso*–glycol)

other hand, the *meso* glycols, in reacting with the glycol-bridging oxidant, must assume a conformation (B) which brings the bulky groups in close proximity. In the latter case, therefore, extra energy would be involved in forming the cyclic intermediate.

Early correlations between the rate of cleavage of glycols and the relative arrangement of hydroxyl groups in space were based on the lead tetraacetate oxidation of sugars.[82] In the case of the furanosides there appeared to be three types of 1,2-glycols: a *cis* pair substituted in the ring, a *trans* pair in the ring, and 1,2-glycol linkages outside the ring. The *cis*-hydroxyls react most rapidly, and the *trans* most slowly. For example, methyl α-D-manno-furanoside, XXXVI, rapidly con-

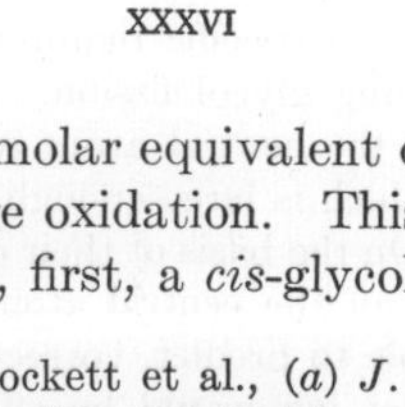

XXXVI 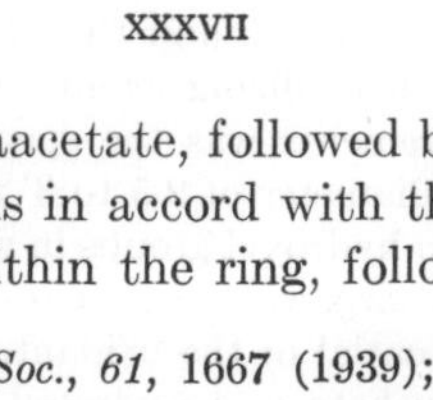   XXXVII

sumes one molar equivalent of lead tetraacetate, followed by a slower, second-stage oxidation. This behavior is in accord with the expected cleavage of, first, a *cis*-glycol linkage within the ring, followed by re-

[82] R. C. Hockett et al., (*a*) *J. Am. Chem. Soc.*, *61*, 1667 (1939); (*b*) *65*, 1474 (1943); (*c*) *66*, 472, 469 (1944).

action with the open-chain glycol whose configuration is less rigidly defined. On the other hand, ethyl β-D-galactofuranoside, XXXVII, having a *trans*-hydroxyl configuration within the ring, exhibits a completely different behavior on oxidation, consistent with the primary oxidation of the glycol linkage outside of the ring, followed by further slow oxidation of the *trans*-glycol within the ring, and then a more complex breakdown.

The marked difference between the reactivity of *cis*- versus *trans*-glycols in five-membered rings, earlier observed by Criegee (Table III), is not observed in six-membered rings, and Hockett found that in pyranose sugars [82b] it was not possible to differentiate precisely between styracitol, XXXVIII (with one "*cis*"-glycol grouping), and polygalitol, XXXIX (having only "*trans*"-glycols), based on differences in the rates of oxidation with lead tetraacetate.

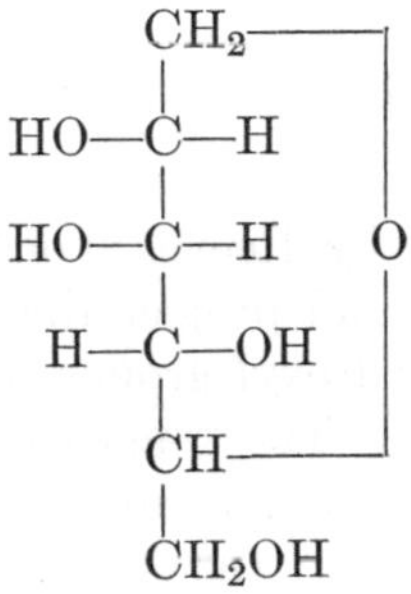

XXXVIII 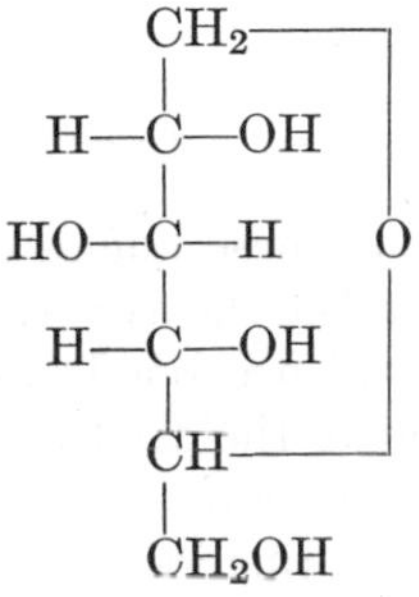   XXXIX

The most probable explanation for the different effects observed in the oxidation of five-ring compared to six-ring glycols lies in considerations of the actual shape of the five versus the six ring. In the five-membered ring, the *cis*- and *trans*-arrangements of vicinal hydroxyl groups are rigidly defined by the nearly planar nature of the ring; however, in the stable chair conformation of the six-ring, adjacent hydroxyl groups may be in a variety of axial-equational relationships none of which are truly *cis*.[83]

In discussing the spatial requirements for complexing 1,2-glycols with cuprammonium, Reeves [84] has pointed out that adjacent hydroxyl groups in five-membered planar rings or six-membered strain-

---

[83] Only when the six ring is held rigidly in the boat form, as by a bridge, is there a true *cis* pair of hydroxyls.

[84] R. E. Reeves, *Advances in Carbohydrate Chem.*, **6**, 115 (1951).

less rings must be located in one of the following orientations, a, b, c, d.

(a) 0° 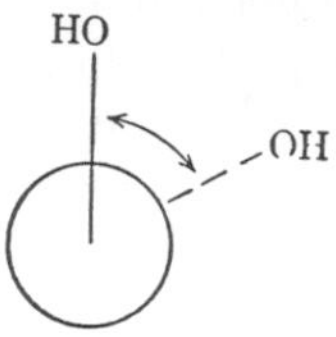   (b) 60°

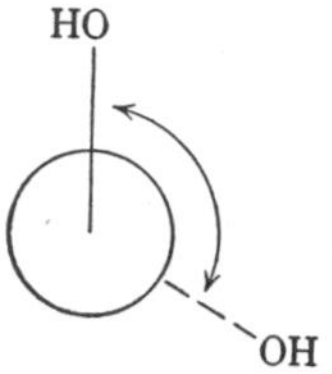

(c) 120° 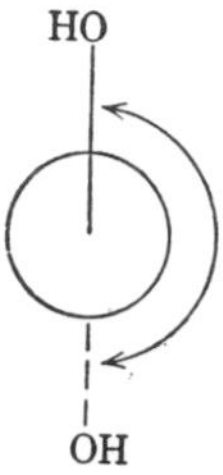   (d) 180°

(To determine these angles as suggested by Reeves [84] one must sight along the axis of the two carbon atoms and project the angle made by the two valence bonds joining the hydroxyl groups onto a plane perpendicular to the carbon-carbon bond.) The true *cis* configuration 0° (*a*) would be found in *cis*-hydroxyls on a five-membered ring, or on a six-membered ring locked in the boat form; [85] the 60° projected angle between adjacent hydroxyl groups (*b*) would result from an axial-equatorial or equatorial-equatorial relationship in a six-membered ring; [86] the 120° angle (*c*) would be found in *trans-α*-hydroxyls in a five-membered ring; [87] and axial-axial vicinal diols would be oriented at 180° (*d*) in a six-membered ring. [88]

Although the formation of complexes with cuprammonium takes place readily only with glycols having hydroxyls oriented at projected angles of 0° or 60°, [89] cleavage with periodate or lead tetraacetate may take place even when the angle between hydroxyl groups is 120°, as is observed in the slow oxidation of methyl *α*-D-arabinofuranoside (XL). [90] The difference in the cuprammonium reaction compared to the glycol cleavage is clearly due to the fact that the former is a re-

[85] R. E. Reeves, *J. Am. Chem. Soc.*, *71*, 212 (1949).

[86] R. E. Reeves, *J. Am. Chem. Soc.*, *71*, 215, 1737 (1949).

[87] E. L. Jackson and C. S. Hudson, *J. Am. Chem. Soc.*, *59*, 994 (1937).

[88] R. E. Reeves, *J. Am. Chem. Soc.*, *72*, 1499 (1950).

[89] R. E. Reeves, *J. Am. Chem. Soc.*, *71*, 212 (1949).

[90] E. L. Jackson and C. S. Hudson, *J. Am. Chem. Soc.*, *59*, 994 (1937).

versible bimolecular association, whereas the latter is an irreversible decomposition. Formation of even a small amount of cyclic intermediate during the oxidation reaction of a *trans* diol such as XL would

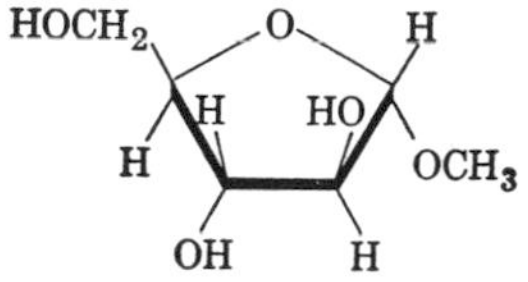

XL

thus lead eventually to complete fission of the carbon-carbon double bond.

There are cases, however, where systems containing adjacent hydroxyl groupings do not react with lead tetraacetate or other glycol-splitting reagents. In these situations, special steric factors may be present preventing formation of the required intermediate.

Outstanding examples of the resistance of 1,2-diols in a five-membered ring to cleavage by periodic acid are found in 1,6-anhydro-β-D-glucofuranose, XLI, and 1,6-anhydro-α-D-galactofuranose, XLII,[91]

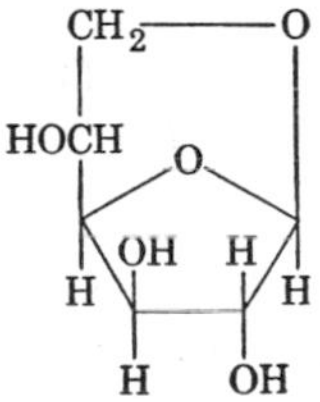

XLI 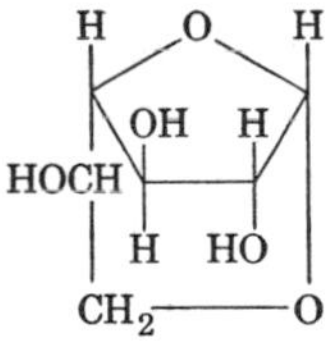   XLII

which are not cleaved even after several days of contact with sodium metaperiodate, paraperiodic acid, or lead tetraacetate.

The stability of these diols toward cleavage has been explained [92] in terms of the extra rigidity imposed on the furan ring system by the presence of a second interlocking ring. Models suggest that, in simple furan-ring diols undergoing cleavage, the "flexibility" of the ring permits movement of the hydroxyl groups closer to each other in response to the forces of complex formation. In the more rigid bicyclic systems XLI and XLII, the movement of the *trans*-hydroxyl groups

[91] R. J. Dimler, H. A. Davis, and G. E. Hilbert, *J. Am. Chem. Soc.*, *68*, 1377 (1946); B. H. Alexander, R. J. Dimler, and C. L. Mehltretter, *ibid.*, *73*, 4658 (1951).
[92] R. J. Dimler, *Advances in Carbohydrate Chem.*, *7*, 49 (1952).

might be limited sufficiently to prevent bridging by the oxidizing agent.

More recent results indicate, however, that cleavage of glycols may take place by a process which does not involve formation of a cyclic intermediate. Thus, *trans*-decalin-9,10-diol (A) and *trans*-hydrindane-8,9-diol (B) are split by lead tetraacetate, despite the fact that cyclic intermediates are impossible for these reactions.[78] Cordner and Pau-

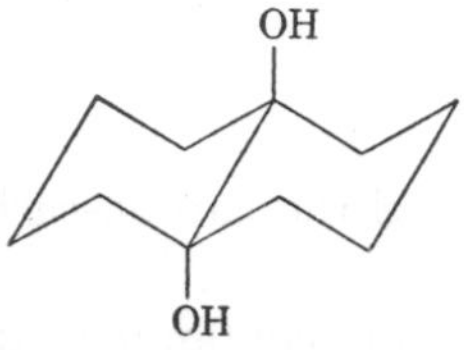

A 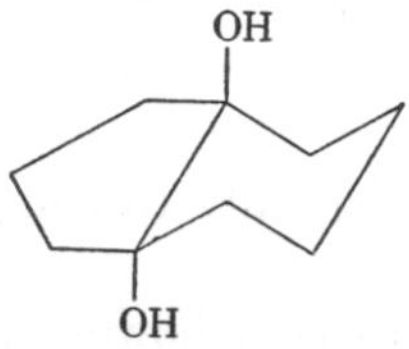   B

saker [93] propose that this anomalous oxidation of *trans*-decalin-9,10-diol can be accommodated by an alternative general cleavage mechanism applicable to all lead tetraacetate oxidations, involving a stepwise homolytic breakdown of the initially formed ester. This reac-

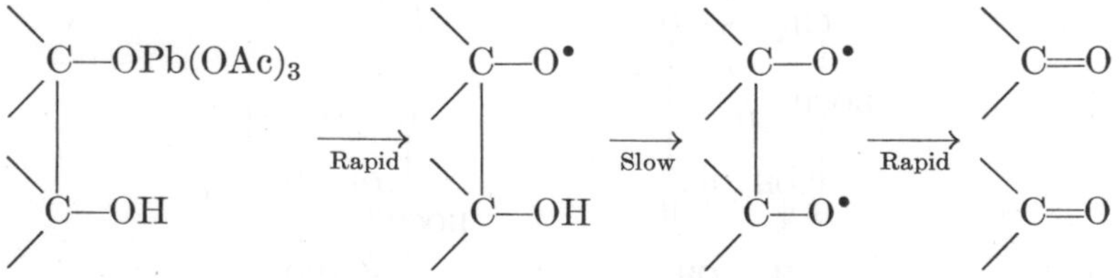

tion scheme does not, however, explain the very large differences observed in the rates of *cis*-glycol compared to *trans*-glycol oxidation (Table III).

The suggestion [93] that hydrogen bonding effects may play a role in determining the rates of glycol cleavage is given some support by studies on the reaction of aryliodosoacetate with glycols and phenols.[94] The iodoso reagent, which resembles lead tetraacetate in its selective cleavage of glycols,[95] rapidly oxidizes *meta*- and *para*-nitrophenol, but leaves the hydrogen-bonded *ortho* isomer unchanged. However, studies [96] on the intramolecular hydrogen bond in cyclic 1,2-diols by Kuhn show that there appears to be no simple correlation between the reac-

[93] J. P. Cordner and K. H. Pausaker, *J. Chem. Soc.*, *1953*, 102.

[94] K. H. Pausaker, *J. Chem. Soc.*, *1953*, 107.

[95] R. Criegee and H. Beucker, *Ann.*, *541*, 218 (1939).

[96] L. P. Kuhn, *J. Am. Chem. Soc.*, *76*, 4323 (1954).

tion rates of lead tetraacetate cleavage and the strength of the hydrogen bond.

Although Criegee's cyclic process accounts for most of the evidence in the oxidative cleavage of glycols, no single mechanism can explain all the experimental observations.

DISSOCIATION OF HEXAARYLETHANES

The dissociation of hexaarylethanes and related compounds to form triarylmethyl radicals has been one of the most extensively studied reactions involving cleavage of the carbon-carbon bond. In the years since Gomberg [97] first obtained evidence for the existence of free radicals, a great number of hexaarylethanes and analogs have been prepared, and their properties studied. These investigations, for the most part, have been directed at correlating the degree of dissociation with the nature of the substituents on the ethane. The effect of bulk, unsaturation, electronegativity, aromaticity, *ortho*, *meta*, and *para* substituents, and other structural variations has been tested, with the result that there has been accumulated a large body of data relating to the stabilities of many triarylmethyls and related free radicals. Since there exist many excellent reviews of this subject,[98-101] no attempt will be made in the following discussion to give more than a brief coverage of representative examples where steric effects seem to be important in promoting cleavage of the carbon-carbon bond.

The magnetic susceptibility measurements which have been used to a great extent in determining the degree of dissociation of substituted ethanes have been shown to contain an inherent error due to the fact that the diamagnetism of the free radical itself cannot be reliably measured or estimated. Thus, Wheland [99] has suggested that serious errors in measuring the degree of dissociation of hexaarylethanes may be inherent in estimating the diamagnetism of the free radicals, since such diamagnetism may be very large because of resonance effects. Selwood and Dobres [102] have also called attention to this error, pointing out that the discrepancy shows up when measurements are made over a range of temperatures. The above difficulties

[97] M. Gomberg, *Ber.*, *33*, 3150 (1900); *J. Am. Chem. Soc.*, *22*, 757 (1900).

[98] M. Szwarc, *Discussions Faraday Soc.*, *2*, 39 (1947).

[99] G. W. Wheland, *Advanced Organic Chemistry*, p. 685, John Wiley & Sons, New York, 1949.

[100] W. E. Bachmann, in Gilman, *Organic Chemistry*, Vol. 1, p. 593, John Wiley & Sons, New York, 1943.

[101] D. H. Hey, *Ann. Repts.*, *37*, 250 (1941).

[102] P. W. Selwood and R. M. Dobres, *J. Am. Chem. Soc.*, *72*, 3860 (1950).

can be overcome, however, by measurements of paramagnetic resonance absorption, since this resonance phenomenon is peculiar to the electrons in the paramagnetic species. By the latter method, one can essentially determine the presence of unpaired electrons without considering the diamagnetism of the undissociated fragment. For example, paramagnetic resonance absorption measurements[103] on the Chichibabin hydrocarbon (XLIIIa) have shown that it exists in the biradical state (XLIIIb) to the extent of 4–5%. These findings have

XLIIIa

XLIIIb

resolved the anomaly in the behavior of XLIIIa which, though catalyzing ortho-, para-hydrogen conversion,[104] showed negligible biradical character based on conventional magnetic susceptibility measurements.[105]

The two most important factors on which the degree of dissociation is considered to depend are resonance effects and bulk effects caused by substituents. In specific cases, either resonance or steric effects can explain the observed dissociation, but neither effect alone can account consistently for the relationship between the ease of cleavage and the nature of the substituents on the parent ethane.

The steric effect in causing dissociation has been associated with the fact that in hexasubstituted ethanes there is not enough room about the central carbon atoms to accommodate six bulky groups.[105a] The strain inherent in such a situation would favor stretching of the central carbon-carbon bond, leading to cleavage. Support for this hypothesis is found in the measurements of the carbon-carbon bond distances in hexamethylethane.[106] In this compound all the carbon-carbon bond distances with the exception of the central C—C bond

[103] C. A. Hutchison, Jr., A. Kowalsky, R. C. Pastor, and G. W. Wheland, J. Chem. Phys., 20, 1485 (1952).

[104] G. M. Schwab and N. Agliardi, Ber., 73, 95 (1940).

[105] E. Müller and I. Müller-Rodloff, Ann., 517, 134 (1935).

[105a] For a discussion of theories of the dissociation of hexaarylethanes and analogs, see W. E. Bachman, reference 100, and G. W. Wheland, reference 99.

[106] S. H. Bauer and J. Y. Beach, J. Am. Chem. Soc., 64, 1142 (1942).

are found to be 1.54 ± 0.02 A.   The central C—C bond distance is somewhat stretched (1.58 ± 0.03 A), and the central valence angles somewhat larger than tetrahedral.   If, in hexamethylethane, the methyl groups create sufficient interference to provide a measurable stretching of the central C—C bond, it is reasonable to suppose that, in the more crowded hexaarylethanes, still more stretching occurs with a correspondingly greater weakening of the ethane bond.

In analogous hexasubstituted compounds where the central pair of atoms are germanium, lead, or tin, no comparable dissociation has been observed.[107]   Even hexa-o-tolylditin, XLIV, appears to be only

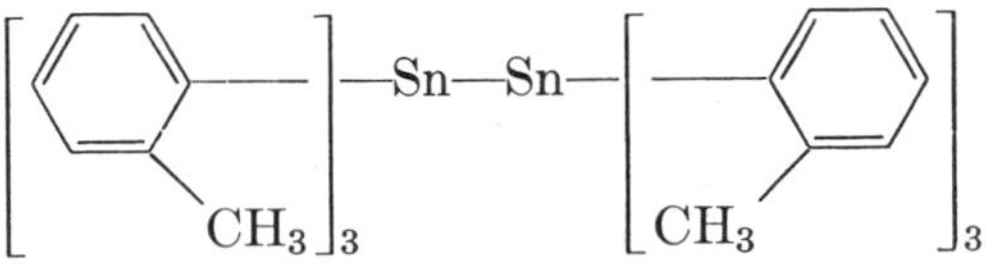

XLIV

4% dissociated at $80°C$.   In the latter type of compound, the increased size of the central (metallic) atom can more easily accommodate the bulky substituents, and thereby demand less stretching (and therefore less weakening) of the central (Sn—Sn) bond.

Other important evidence for the operation of a steric effect in the dissociation of hexaarylethanes can be derived from the studies of Bent and coworkers [108] on the heats of combustion, oxidation, and hydrogenation of hexaphenylethane.   From this work, Bent has concluded that the carbon-carbon bond in hexaphenylethane is weaker than a normal carbon-carbon bond (as in ethane) by about 30 kcal. This difference in bond strength is ascribed to steric hindrance in the hexasubstituted ethane, an effect which facilitates the cleavage of the central bond.   In the case of diphenyldibiphenylene, XLV, where two

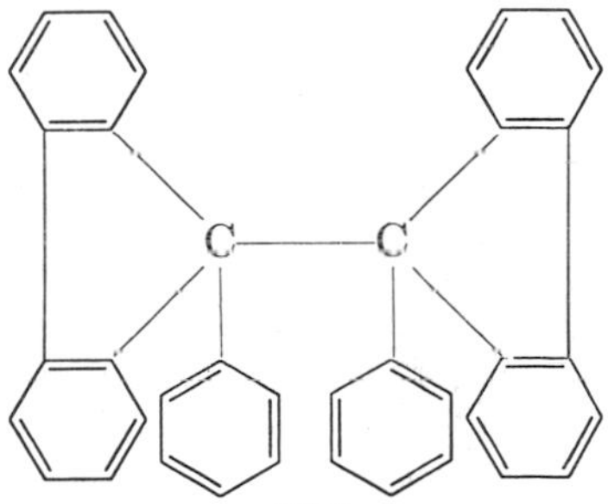

XLV

[107] H. Morris, W. Byerly, and P. W. Selwood, *J. Am. Chem. Soc., 64*, 1727 (1942).

[108] H. E. Bent, G. R. Cuthbertson, M. Dorfman, and R. E. Leary, *J. Am. Chem. Soc., 58*, 165 (1936); H. E. Bent and G. R. Cuthbertson, *ibid., 58*, 170 (1936); H. E. Bent and E. S. Ebers, *ibid., 57*, 1242 (1935).

pairs of benzene rings are tied together, models show somewhat less steric hindrance of the bulky aryl groups. The reduced hindrance here [109] shows up in the smaller degree of dissociation and smaller heat of oxidation of XLV compared to hexaphenylethane.

The resonance effect in facilitating the dissociation of hexaaryl-ethanes is explained in terms of the stabilization of the triarylmethyl radical [110] by interaction of the odd electron with the three aromatic rings, leading to forms exemplified by the contributing resonance structure A. According to this hypothesis, the resonance energy asso-

$$(C_6H_5)_3C \cdot \leftrightarrow$$

A

ciated with the variety of *ortho-* and *para*-quinoid forms similar to A compensates for the energy needed to break the carbon-carbon bond of the parent ethane. The calculations of Pauling,[111] Wheland, and others indicate that the increase in total resonance energy of the tri-phenylmethyl radicals (about 70 kcal. per mole) is approximately equal to the observed weakening of the carbon-carbon bond in hexa-phenylethane. Other calculations of the resonance effect for a variety of substituted hexaarylethanes [112] suggest that increasing free-radical resonance energies are accompanied by increasing degrees of dissocia-tion of the corresponding ethane.

As pointed out by Wheland, these calculations are based on the assumption of complete planarity of the three aromatic nuclei in the triphenylmethyl radical.[112] The interference of *ortho*-hydrogen atoms on adjacent phenyl residues would, however, make complete planarity impossible, and the twisting of the molecule out of the plane would reduce the interactions between rings somewhat, thereby lowering the resonance energy.[113]   In discussing this latter effect, Szwarc [98] points out that, because of the bulkiness of the phenyl groups, the true shape of the triphenylmethyl radical is probably propeller-like, and he esti-mates that the resonance energy of the triphenylmethyl radical is not much different from that of the benzyl radical.

[109] H. E. Bent and J. E. Cline, *J. Am. Chem. Soc.*, *58*, 1624 (1936).
[110] E. Hückel, *Trans. Faraday Soc.*, *30*, 40 (1934); C. K. Ingold, *ibid.*, p. 52.
[111] L. Pauling and G. W. Wheland, *J. Chem. Phys.*, *1*, 362 (1933).
[112] G. W. Wheland, *J. Am. Chem. Soc.*, *63*, 2025 (1941).
[113] W. Theilacker and M. L. Ewald, *Naturwiss.*, *31*, 302 (1943).

In certain cases, a resonance explanation accounts readily for the observed dissociation.[114] The complete dissociation of the parent ethane to form the pentaphenylcyclopentadienyl radical, XLVI, is explicable on the basis of the many possibilities for resonance in the symmetrical radical, where the odd electron can be distributed among the five-ring carbon atoms. Relief of steric strain in going from the ethane to the radical is probably also important. Resonance involving all five phenyl groups, implied in XLVIa, is probably sterically hindered as in the triphenylmethyl radical.

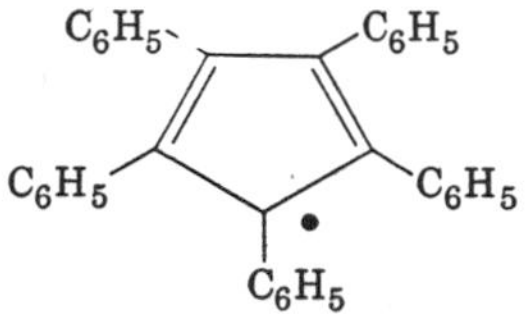

XLVI   XLVIa

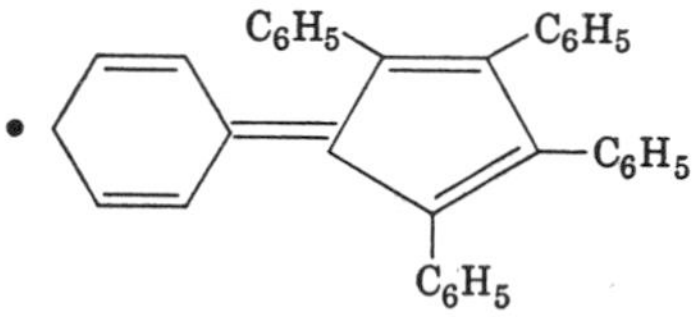

Both resonance and steric effects appear to be involved in other dissociations. For example, the fact that hexa-p-biphenylethane, XLVII, dissociates to the extent of 100% in benzene solution[115] at 20°, compared to the 2–3% dissociation of hexaphenylethane, is in agreement with expectations based on a resonance interpretation, since the odd electron can be distributed among more positions in XLVIIa, than

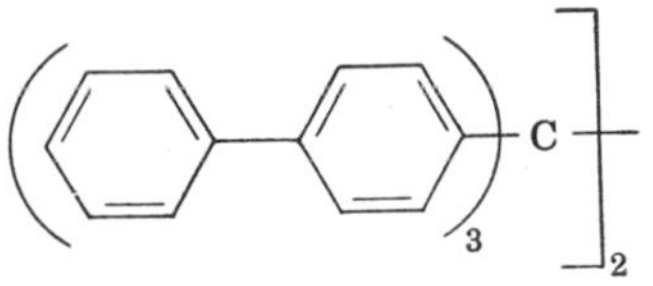

XLVII

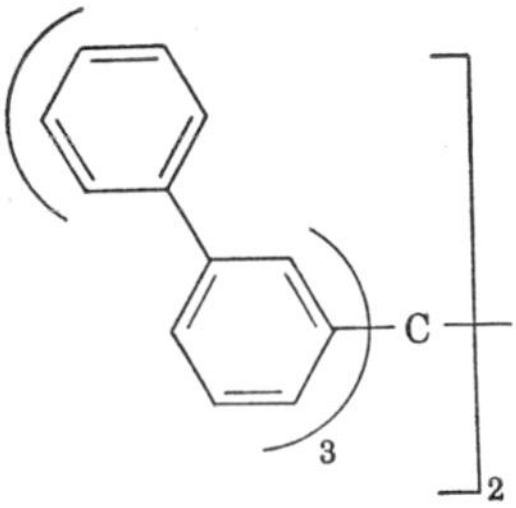

XLVIII

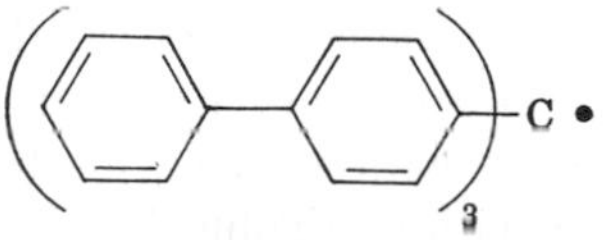

XLVIIa

in the triphenylmethyl radical. However, under the same conditions, hexa-m-biphenylethane, XLVIII, is dissociated to the extent of 60%,[116]

[114] E. Müller and I. Müller-Rodloff, *Ber.*, **69**, 665 (1936).

[115] W. Schlenk, T. Weikel, and A. Herzenstein, *Ann.*, *372*, 1 (1910); *Ber.*, *43*, 1753 (1910).

[116] C. S. Marvel, E. Ginsberg, and M. B. Mueller, *J. Am. Chem. Soc.*, **61**, 77 (1939).

although resonance stabilization of the radical should not differ markedly from that in triphenylmethyl (3% dissociation). Here, substituents in the *meta* position must help weaken the central carbon-carbon
bond by sterically interfering with normal bond formation.

Another example where resonance and steric effects may play roughly
equal roles in influencing dissociation is found in the dibiphenyltetra-
phenylethanes. Although the resonance stabilization to be expected
in the radical XLIX derived from the dissociation of di-*p*-biphenyl-

XLIX   L

tetraphenylethane should be greater than the stabilization in the radical L derived from cleavage of di-*m*-biphenyltetraphenylethane, both
ethanes dissociate to about the same extent (11–14%) in benzene
solution at 25°C.[117] (Some stabilization would, of course, be added by
higher-energy forms as shown.)

More clear-cut evidence for the role of steric effects in the dissociation of hexaarylethanes is found in the effect of alkyl substituents.[118]
Comparison of the dissociation of ethanes with varying methyl substitution at the *ortho, meta,* and *para* positions (Table V) shows the
marked influence of *ortho* substituents compared to the *meta* and *para*
analogs.

On resonance considerations alone, there should not be such a pronounced difference between an *ortho-* and a *para*-alkyl substituent.

[117] C. S. Marvel, M. B. Mueller, and E. Ginsberg, *J. Am. Chem. Soc., 61,* 2008
(1939).
[118] C. S. Marvel, J. F. Kaplan, and C. M. Himel, *J. Am. Chem. Soc., 63,* 1892
(1941).

TABLE V [118]

DISSOCIATION OF ALKYLHEXAARYLETHANES AT 25°

Alkyl Group	Disubstituted Ethane %	Tetrasubstituted Ethane %	Hexasubstituted Ethane %
p-CH$_3$	5	5.5	16
m-CH$_3$	6.5	7	40
o-CH$_3$	25	82	Highly dissociated [113]

Ortho substitution should increase the difficulty in achieving coplanarity between the three rings of the triarylmethyl and thereby decrease the resonance stabilization of the radical. This effect would lessen rather than enhance the dissociation. The marked increase in the dissociation of hexa-(o-tolyl)ethane must therefore be ascribed primarily to a steric effect whereby the bulky *ortho* substituents help to weaken the central carbon-carbon bond.

Chapter 8

by George F Wright

Steric Effects
among the Common
Organometallic Compounds

Chapter 8

This chapter deals with compounds containing metals of the first and second groups of the periodic table in which the carbon-metal bonds tend to be polar. However, the reaction media in which the widely used organometallic compounds are prepared most efficiently at convenient temperatures are electron-donating substances, like ethers, which are closely coordinated with the metal. This coordination tends to compensate the polarity of the metal. The steric requirements for this compensation account for many characteristics of reactions which such organometallic compounds undergo.

Most organometallic compounds are subject to steric influences during formation because reaction with an organic halide usually involves the corrosion of a metal surface. In some reactions (butyllithium in hexane) the surface is cleaned by sloughing-off of the lithium chloride, but usually the metal salts are adherent, so that diffusion becomes an important factor. Were it not for the solvent ether, which not only transports the newly formed organometallic compound from the metal surface but also protects it by ether-metal coordination, the outward-diffusing metallic compound would couple with the incoming halide. The relative electron-donating power (basicity) of organic ether versus halide determines the extent to which the Wurtz reaction occurs.[1]

Ether coordination is thus beneficial during formation, but it may be detrimental when the organometallic compound is used as a reagent. Experience shows[2] that the substances which react with these organometallic compounds tend to coordinate with them. But reaction in this circumstance requires coordinative exchange with the already-present ether. The ease of exchange will depend upon relative electron-donating power; reaction will not occur when the substance is weakly electron-donating or sterically hindered by contrast to the ether. In these circumstances it is frequently helpful to replace as

[1] H. L. Cohen and G. F Wright, *J. Org. Chem.*, *18*, 432 (1953).
[2] F. Straus, *Ann.*, *393*, 235 (1912).

much as possible of the solvent ether by benzene, toluene, or naphthalene. The higher reaction temperature which may thus be obtained at atmospheric pressure is beneficial, but the chief advantage accrues because the heat of solvation of organometallic compounds with hydrocarbons is negligible compared with that of the ethers. The solvation energy of diethyl ether with organomagnesium compounds has been found to be about 12.5 kcal./mole, or two-thirds that of the solvation of sulfuric acid to its monohydrate.[3] Obviously this energy is significant to the ease with which reagents coordinate with the metallic atom.

The deleterious steric effect of ethereal reaction media may be compensated by choice of metal. Although organometallic compounds containing alkali metals are more reactive than those containing alkaline-earth metals, only lithium has been employed extensively, because compounds containing the other alkali metals decompose readily available ethers much too rapidly to be useful. The ether-splitting tendency of organolithium compounds is not always onerous since the latter react more rapidly than organomagnesium compounds. Thus phenyllithium reacts more than 100 times as fast with benzonitrile as does phenylmagnesium bromide.[4] Likewise ethyl 8-benzohydryl-1-naphthoate or 2,2-diphenylacenaphthone-1 react with phenyllithium to give good yields of the expected carbinols, but neither reacts with phenylmagnesium bromide.[5] Although some have attributed this difference to greater polarization of the lithium compound, there is some evidence that organolithium compounds are less polar than organomagnesium compounds.[6] On the other hand the difference in behavior when organolithium and organomagnesium compounds are added to α,β unsaturated ketones indicates a significant steric effect. Thus Kohler[7] showed that the amounts of 1,2 and 1,4 addition to α,β unsaturated carbonyl systems of methyl, ethyl, and phenyl Grignard reagents could not be related simply to the polarity of these organic groups. Likewise a reaction which preponderantly gives 1,4 addition with phenylmagnesium bromide has been shown to react exclusively by 1,2 addition with the phenyllithium derived from bromobenzene.[8] The effect would therefore seem to be steric, but this evaluation is

[3] W. Tchelinzeff, *Ber.*, *37*, 4534 (1904); *38*, 3664 (1905); *39*, 773, 1674, 1682, 1686 (1906).

[4] C. G. Swain, *J. Am. Chem. Soc.*, *69*, 2306 (1947).

[5] G. Wittig and H. Petri, *Ber.*, *68*, 924 (1935).

[6] R. Letsinger, *J. Am. Chem. Soc.*, *72*, 4842 (1950).

[7] E. P. Kohler, *Am. Chem. J.*, *31*, 655 (1904); *38*, 511 (1907).

[8] A. Luttringhaus, *Ber.*, *67*, 1602 (1934).

more easily made after one considers the structure and composition of monovalent versus polyvalent organometallic compounds.

Grignard first defined his reagents as RMgX, but it soon was discovered that they were more complex than this symbol implies. An alternative suggestion, $R_2Mg \cdot MgX_2$, was proposed,[9] but the first convincing experimental evidence for Grignard reagent structure was offered by Schlenk and Schlenk,[10] who found that those constituents of the system that contain halomagnesium groups are precipitated as dioxanates upon addition of dioxane. Thus they established the existence of the equilibrium

$$2RMgX \rightleftarrows R_2Mg + MgX_2$$

it being understood that each constituent is solvated with two molecules of an ether. The significance of this equilibrium to practical Grignard chemistry was first suggested by Gilman and Brown,[11] who found that phenylmagnesium bromide was more reactive toward valeronitrile than was a halogen-free preparation of diphenylmagnesium. A more complete demonstration was made by Cope,[12] who found that magnesium halide reacted more rapidly, and diorganomagnesium less rapidly, than the entire Grignard reagent with dimethyl sulfate. The spatial significance of the lesser reactivity of diorganomagnesium was later suggested by its tendency to form the magnesium dienolate of benzoin rather than the addition product which normally is obtained with the whole Grignard reagent.[13]

Since the position of the Schlenk equilibrium varies markedly with respect to concentration,[14] and since this equilibrium is established quite slowly,[15] it is evident that the simple designation by Grignard of RMgX is inadequate. However, this oversimplified representation has been used, and will be used in this chapter, for reasons of graphic simplicity. Furthermore, it will now be shown that the Schlenk equilibrium is also inadequate for description of Grignard reagents.

This inadequacy has been shown by the work of Evans and Pearson [16] on electrolytic transference in Grignard reagents. Their confirmation of an earlier report [17] that magnesium migrated both to cathode

[9] P. Jolibois, Compt. rend., 155, 353 (1912); 156, 712 (1913).

[10] W. Schlenk and W. Schlenk, Ber., 62, 920 (1929).

[11] H. Gilman and Brown, J. Am. Chem. Soc., 52, 1181 (1930).

[12] A. C. Cope, J. Am. Chem. Soc., 56, 1578 (1934).

[13] G. F Wright, J. Am. Chem. Soc., 61, 1152 (1939).

[14] G. H. Coleman and J. W. Brooks, J. Am. Chem. Soc., 68, 1620 (1946).

[15] C. R. Noller and A. J. Castro, J. Am. Chem. Soc., 64, 2509 (1942).

[16] W. V. Evans and R. Pearson, J. Am. Chem. Soc., 64, 2865 (1942).

[17] L. W. Gaddum and H. E. French, J. Am. Chem. Soc., 49, 1295 (1927).

and anode prompted them to formulate the equilibrium shown herewith to represent the Grignard reagent. Earlier, Terent'ev,[18] on the basis

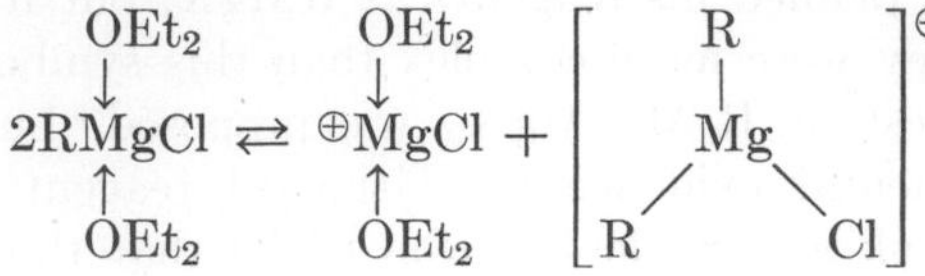

$$2\text{RMgCl} \rightleftarrows \begin{array}{c} \text{OEt}_2 \\ \downarrow \\ \oplus\text{MgCl} \\ \uparrow \\ \text{OEt}_2 \end{array} + \left[\begin{array}{c} R \\ | \\ Mg \\ \diagup \quad \diagdown \\ R \qquad Cl \end{array} \right]^{\ominus}$$

with the first term $\begin{array}{c} \text{OEt}_2 \\ \downarrow \\ \\ \uparrow \\ \text{OEt}_2 \end{array}$ on RMgCl.

I

of ebullioscopic studies in diethyl ether, had considered an equilibrium involving 2 moles of $\text{RMgX} \cdot 2\text{Et}_2\text{O}$ as displaced far toward the pair of ions shown as II and III. The solvation of II in solution may be

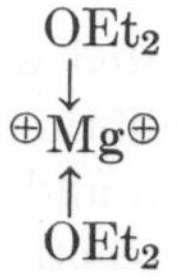

$$\begin{array}{c} \text{OEt}_2 \\ \downarrow \\ \oplus\text{Mg}\oplus \\ \uparrow \\ \text{OEt}_2 \end{array} \qquad \left[\begin{array}{c} R \quad \text{OEt}_2 \; Cl \\ \diagdown \; \downarrow \; \diagup \\ Mg \\ \diagup \; \uparrow \; \diagdown \\ Cl \quad \text{OEt}_2 \; R \end{array} \right]^{\ominus}$$

II 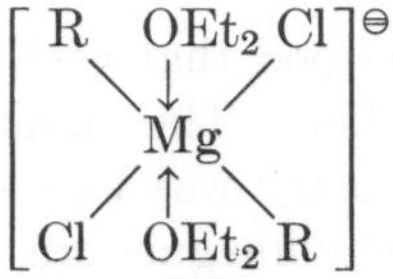   III

greater than Terent'ev suggested, but III must be more definite in conformity with the maximum hexacovalence expected for anionic magnesium. The necessity for an octahedral ion (III), if it is free for electrolytic transference, has been demonstrated [19] by a synthesis of optically active products from inactive reagents in presence of optically active 2,3-dimethoxybutane.[20]

The evidence of Décombe and Duval contributes to this concept. It is known that if zinc chloride is added to a Grignard reagent the system assumes the properties of an organozinc compound. For example, it reacts with esters and acid chlorides to give ketones under conditions wherein the organomagnesium reagent gives tertiary alcohols. This behavior is generally attributed to the following salt interchange in the ethereal medium:

$$\text{RMgCl} + \text{ZnCl}_2 \rightleftarrows \text{RZnCl} + \text{MgCl}_2$$

or in consideration of the Schlenk equilibrium:

$$\text{R}_2\text{Mg} + \text{ZnCl}_2 \rightleftarrows \text{R}_2\text{Zn} + \text{MgCl}_2$$

However, Décombe and Duval [21] electrolyzed the system (in ether or, better, in ethyl acetate) after the manner of Evans and Pearson [16]

[18] A. P. Terent'ev, Z. anorg. Chem., 156, 73 (1926).

[19] H. M. Cohen and G. F Wright, J. Org. Chem., 18, 432 (1953).

[20] Of course the postulation of III in this instance is unnecessary if the system comprises solvent-encased ion pairs.

[21] J. Décombe and C. Duval, Compt. rend., 206, 1024 (1938).

and found that, whereas magnesium migrated largely toward the cathode, the zinc was preponderant in the vicinity of the anode. According to this result the system may be formulated with anionic zinc (IV) as follows:

$$2RMgCl + ZnCl_2 \rightleftarrows \overset{OEt_2}{\underset{OEt_2}{\overset{\downarrow}{\underset{\uparrow}{\oplus Mg \oplus}}}} \quad \text{and} \quad \left[\overset{R}{\underset{Cl}{}} \overset{OEt_2}{\underset{OEt_2}{\overset{\downarrow}{\underset{\uparrow}{Zn}}}} \overset{Cl}{\underset{R}{}} \right]^{\ominus} + MgCl_2$$

$$\text{II} \qquad\qquad\qquad\qquad \text{IV}$$

The behavior of magnesium halide (itself solvated) in the several ionic systems may be quite independent of the organoanion in reactions of the type described by Cope [12] using methyl sulfate. The same direct and preferential effect of magnesium halide has been observed by Huston and Agett [22] for the reaction of the Grignard system with epoxides.

$$MgX_2 + 2CH_2\!\!-\!\!CH_2 \overset{Fast}{\longrightarrow} (X\!-\!CH_2\!-\!CH_2\!-\!O)_2Mg$$
$$\underset{O}{\diagdown\diagup}$$
$$MgX_2 + (R\!-\!CH_2\!-\!CH_2\!-\!O)_2Mg \overset{Slow}{\underset{}{\longleftarrow}} \Big| R_2Mg$$

This formulation explains the fact that reaction does not progress beyond the first stage when unreactive systems are involved. However an equally good explanation may be afforded by the solvated complex ion such as V. Actually, other evidence shows that the preferential

$$\left[\overset{CH_2\!\!-\!\!CH_2}{\underset{}{\diagdown\diagup}} \right]^{\ominus}$$

$$\overset{OEt_2}{\underset{OEt_2}{\overset{\downarrow}{\underset{\uparrow}{\oplus Mg \oplus}}}} \left[\overset{Cl \quad O \quad Cl}{\underset{Cl \quad OEt_2 \; Cl}{Mg}} \right] \overset{Et_2O}{\longrightarrow} \overset{OEt_2}{\underset{OEt_2}{\overset{\downarrow}{\underset{\uparrow}{\oplus Mg \oplus}}}} \overset{Cl^{\ominus}}{\underset{Cl^{\ominus}}{}} + Et_2O \rightarrow \overset{CH_2\!-\!CH_2}{\underset{OEt_2}{\overset{|\quad\quad|}{\underset{\uparrow}{\overset{O\quad Cl}{Mg\!-\!Cl}}}}}$$

$$\text{V}$$

action of the elements of magnesium halide may occur within anions such as II which contain R groups. Thus it has been found that treatment of methyl iodide Grignard reagent in hot tetrahydropyran with methyl 2,3-anhydro-4,6-O-benzylidene-α-D-alloside (VI) leads exclusively to methyl 4,6-O-benzylidene-3-desoxy-3-iodo-α-D-glucoside [23]

[22] R. C. Huston and A. H. Agett, *J. Org. Chem.*, *6*, 123 (1941).
[23] F. H. Newth, G. N. Richards, and L. F. Wiggins, *J. Chem. Soc.*, *1950*, 2356.

(VII). On the other hand, similar treatment with ethyl iodide Grignard reagent produces methyl 4,6-O-benzylidene-2-desoxy-2-iodo-α-D-altroside [24] (VIII).

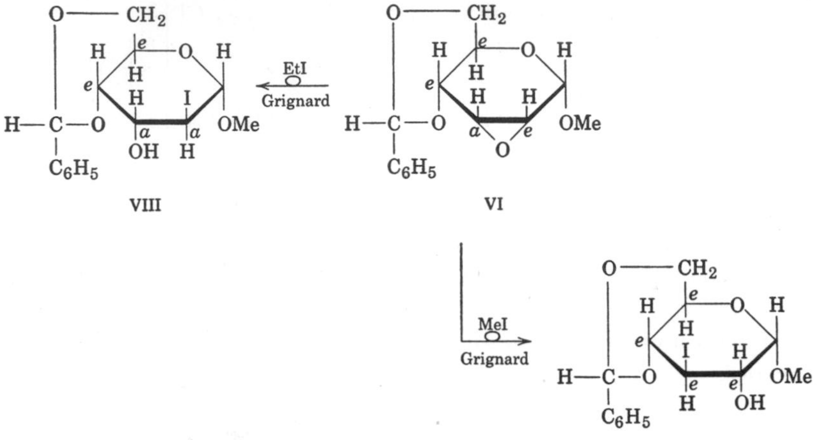

This influence of the alkyl groups on the position occupied by addition of the elements of magnesium iodide may be explained by conformational preferences within an anion such as II in which all or part of the coordinated ether is replaced by a coordinated epoxide such as VI. A similar explanation [25] may suffice to explain the observation that the ratio of addition to reduction products in the reaction

$$n\text{-}C_3H_7MgBr + (i\text{-}C_3H_7)CO(i\text{-}C_3H_7) \rightarrow$$

$$n\text{-}C_3H_7(i\text{-}C_3H_7)_2COH + (i\text{-}C_3H_7)_2CHOH + C_3H_6$$
$$\quad\quad\quad IX \quad\quad\quad\quad\quad\quad\quad X$$

may be altered from 30% of propyl diisopropyl carbinol (addition, IX) and 63% of diisopropyl carbinol (reduction, X) to 65% of IX and 26% of X by inclusion of excess magnesium halide into the system.

Of course these results may be explained otherwise. Inclusion of magnesium halide may merely shift the Schlenk equilibrium so as to reduce the concentration of the less-reactive di-n-propylmagnesium. But one is not then justified in attributing the behavior of the system to the species RMgX, the effective existence of which is questionable. Indeed an explanation based on the complex anion seems to be more

[24] G. N. Richards and L. F. Wiggins, *J. Chem. Soc.*, *1953*, 2442.
[25] C. G. Swain, *J. Am. Chem. Soc.*, **73**, 871 (1951).

satisfactory than one based on the relative reactivities of diphenylmagnesium and phenylmagnesium bromide for the addition of bromobenzene Grignard reagent to benzophenone. In this reaction equal
quantities of ketone (XI) and reagent lead to a coordination complex
from which XI is regenerated upon hydrolysis. On the other hand a
good yield of triphenylcarbinol is obtained when two equivalents of
Grignard reagent are added to benzophenone.[26]

$$\begin{bmatrix} \begin{array}{ccc} Br & XI & C_6H_5 \\ & \diagdown | \diagup & \\ & Mg & \\ & \diagup | \diagdown & \\ C_6H_5 & XI & Br \end{array} \end{bmatrix}^{\ominus} \quad \underset{\text{Grignard}}{\overset{\substack{2 \text{ moles} \\ C_6H_5Br}}{\longleftarrow}} \quad \begin{array}{c} C_6H_5 \\ | \\ C{=}O \\ | \\ C_6H_5 \end{array} \quad \underset{\text{Grignard}}{\overset{\substack{1 \text{ mole} \\ C_6H_5Br}}{\longrightarrow}} \quad \begin{array}{cc} C_6H_5 & C_6H_5 \\ | & | \\ C{=}O{\rightarrow}Mg \\ | & | \\ C_6H_5 & C_6H_5 \end{array}$$

$$\overset{+}{Mg}{}^{+}$$

Center label: XI

$$(C_6H_5)_3COMgBr \xrightarrow{\text{HOH}} \begin{array}{c} C_6H_5 \\ | \\ C_6H_5{-}C{-}OH \\ | \\ C_6H_5 \end{array} \qquad\qquad \begin{array}{c} XI \\ + \\ C_6H_6 \end{array}$$

with $\xrightarrow{H_2O}$ from the right-hand species.

    Such behavior exemplifies the concept that the right-hand side of
the Schlenk equilibrium depicts a part of the Grignard system correctly, but the left-hand side is much oversimplified.
    These evidences show that the species RMgX is inadequate to ex-
plain the behavior of the Grignard reagent, especially in its steric aspects. However, one must realize that the alternative free-ionic or
ion-pair formulation may also be erroneous. It is customary for organic chemists, properly with tongue in cheek, to employ such ionic
simplifications as a matter of convenience in expression. It is inevitable that erroneous conclusions will be drawn from these formulas if
the reader accepts them literally. Thus the evidence against $RMgX \cdot 2Et_2O$ was questioned by Meisenheimer and Schlichenmaier,[27] who
favored the idea of an associated monomer. Actually Terent'ev's re-
sults [18] indicate complex formation greater than that required for the
ion pair he proposed. Also, Evans and Pearson were cautious in de-
scribing a simple ionic species, since more than one magnesium atom
was transported per faraday. Indeed, it is probable that the Grignard
system is extremely complex and may involve colloidal agglomerates
(especially of aromatic reagents) at one extreme and diorganomagnesium with magnesium halide in high dilution at the other. Between
these limits may be expected both charged and uncharged complexes,

[26] P. Pfeiffer and H. Blank, *J. prakt. Chem.*, *153*, 242 (1939).
[27] J. Meisenheimer and W. Schlichenmaier, *Ber.*, *61*, 720 (1928).

two simple examples of which are shown as XII and XIII. The many constituents of such a system must be involved in an equilibrium the attainment of which is not yet adequately understood. For these reasons the various graphic formulations by which steric effects are

$$
\begin{array}{c}
\text{R} \\
|\\
\text{Mg}-\\
|\\
\text{R}
\end{array}
\left[
\begin{array}{ccc}
\text{OEt}_2 & & \text{R} \\
| & & | \\
\text{Cl}-\text{Mg}-\text{Cl}-\text{Mg} \\
| & & | \\
\text{OEt}_2 & & \text{R}
\end{array}
\right]_n
\begin{array}{c}
\text{OEt}_2 \\
| \\
-\text{Cl}-\text{Mg}-\text{Cl} \\
| \\
\text{OEt}_2
\end{array}
$$

XII

$$
\begin{array}{c}
\text{OEt}_2 \\
| \\
{}^{\oplus}\text{Mg}^{\oplus} \\
| \\
\text{OEt}_2
\end{array}
\left[
\begin{array}{ccccc}
& & \text{OEt}_2 & & \\
\text{R} & \text{X} & | & \text{X} & \text{R} \\
& \diagdown \diagup & \diagdown \diagup & \diagdown \diagup & \\
& \text{Mg} & \text{Mg} & \text{Mg} & \\
& \diagup \diagdown & \diagup \diagdown & \diagup \diagdown & \\
\text{R} & \text{X} & | & \text{X} & \text{R} \\
& & \text{OEt}_2 & &
\end{array}
\right]^{\ominus}
$$

XIII

described subsequently in this chapter should be considered as inadequate approximations of the true state of the system under consideration. The designation RMgX will be used subsequently in this chapter since this convenience is only a part of the approximation which must be used at the present level of comprehension.

Thus far only those Grignard reagents directly preparable from organic halides have been considered. However, complex reagents may be derived from substances which react with simple Grignard reagents, to form a hydrocarbon and a halomagnesium enolate. This removal of hydrogen occurs when the coordination complex is sterically disposed so that carbinol salt formation does not occur. When

$$
\begin{array}{ccccc}
{}^{\oplus}\text{MgX} & & \text{R}-\text{Mg}-\text{X} & & \\
& & \uparrow & & \\
{}^{\ominus}\text{O} & & \text{H} \quad \text{O} & & \text{H} \quad \text{R} \\
\| & & | \quad \| & & | \quad | \\
\text{R}'-\text{C}\cdots\text{C}-\text{R}''' & \xleftarrow[\text{RH}]{\text{Minus}} & \text{R}'-\text{C}-\text{C}-\text{R}''' & \rightarrow & \text{R}'-\text{C}-\text{C}-\text{OMgX} \\
| & & | & & | \quad | \\
\text{R}'' & & \text{R}'' & & \text{R}'' \quad \text{R}'''
\end{array}
$$

Fuson et al.[28] treated isobutyromesitylene (XIV) with ethylmagnesium bromide, ethane was evolved. The enolate, XV, reacted with benzoyl chloride to give XVI and XVII and with benzaldehyde to

    [28] R. C. Fuson, C. H. Fisher, G. E. Ullyot, and W. O. Fugate, *J. Org. Chem.*, *4*, 111 (1939).

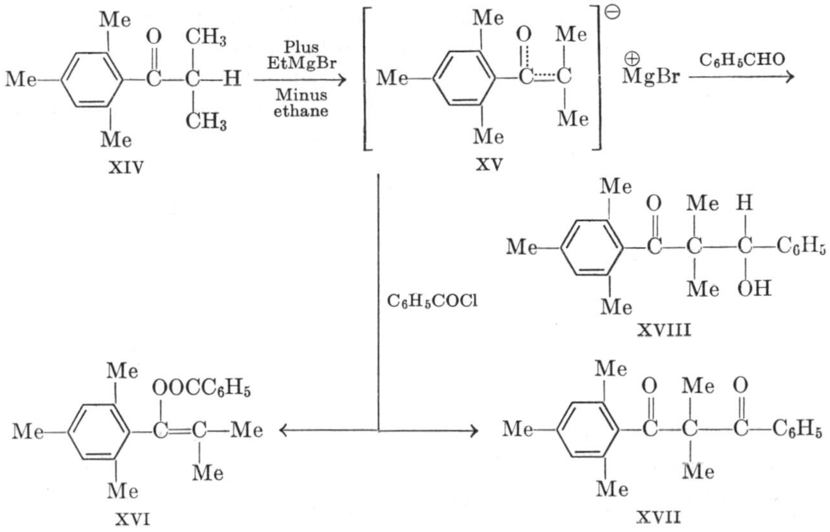

XIV → (Plus EtMgBr, Minus ethane) → [XV]$\ominus$ MgBr$\oplus$ → (C$_6$H$_5$CHO)

XV → (C$_6$H$_5$COCl) → XVII

XVIII

XVI ← → XVII

yield XVIII. Similar reactions have been observed with 2,4,6-tri-chloroacetophenone [29] and, among other hindered aliphatic ketones, with 3,3-diethyl-2-pentanone.[30] The hindrance need not necessarily exist at the unsaturated augend. Aliphatic nitriles (XIX) react with Grignard reagents in two ways.[31]

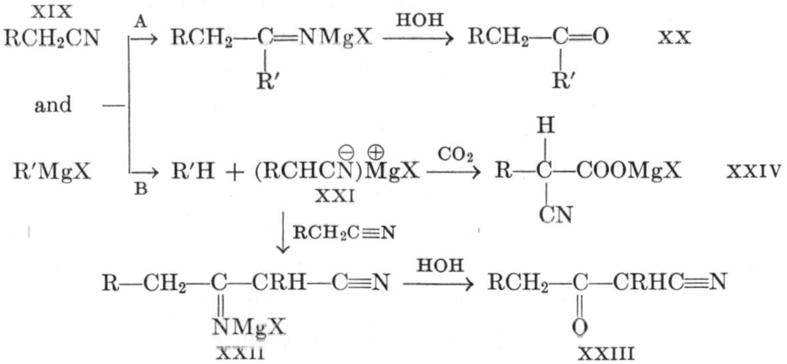

XIX
$$RCH_2CN \xrightarrow{A} RCH_2-\underset{R'}{C}=NMgX \xrightarrow{HOH} RCH_2-\underset{R'}{C}=O \quad XX$$

and —

$$R'MgX \xrightarrow{B} R'H + (RCHCN)\overset{\ominus}{\underset{\oplus}{MgX}} \xrightarrow{CO_2} R-\underset{CN}{\overset{H}{C}}-COOMgX \quad XXIV$$

XXI

$$\downarrow RCH_2C\equiv N$$

$$R-CH_2-\underset{\underset{XXII}{NMgX}}{\overset{\|}{C}}-CRH-C\equiv N \xrightarrow{HOH} RCH_2-\underset{\underset{XXIII}{O}}{\overset{\|}{C}}-CRHC\equiv N$$

The use of many aliphatic Grignard reagents leads to ketones (XX) (course A), but aromatic Grignards (notably mesitylmagnesium bromide, and also *tert*-butylmagnesium chloride) tend to give the derived Grignard reagent (XXI) (course B). Evidence for the presence of

[29] W. E. Ross and R. C. Fuson, *J. Am. Chem. Soc.*, *59*, 1508 (1937).
[30] F. C. Whitmore and C. E. Lewis, *J. Am. Chem. Soc.*, *64*, 1618 (1942).
[31] C. R. Hauser and W. J. Humphlett, *J. Org. Chem.*, *15*, 359 (1950).

XXI is found in its subsequent reaction with the parent nitrile to yield, *via* the chloromagnesium salt of the ketimine (XXII), the β-ketonitrile (XXIII). However, when the nitrile is hindered (R = mesityl) the principal reaction is by path A (since the active hydrogen is more enveloped by the shielding than is the cyano group), but 27% proceeds by path B. This small amount remains as the derived Grignard reagent (XXI) and may be converted to the α-cyanocarboxylic acid (XXIV) by treatment with carbon dioxide, which is more reactive than the hindered nitrile.

The derived Grignard reagents described above have been written in ionic form, but the original authors expressed the structures covalently. This is of interest because treatment [32] of ethyl isobutyrate with mesitylmagnesium bromide leads by Claisen condensation to ethyl isobutyrylisobutyrate, which is generally thought to proceed by a series of ionic equilibria.[33] Accordingly, the first phase of the reaction would be expressed as follows:

$$2,4,6\text{-}(CH_3)_3C_6H_2MgBr + (CH_3)_2CHCOOEt \rightarrow$$

$$2,4,6\text{-}(CH_3)_3C_6H_3 + Br\overset{\oplus}{M}g[(CH_3)_2CCOOEt]^{\ominus}$$

One is tempted to attribute abnormalities of this type to steric hindrance, but caution is advised. Because the use of Grignard reagents does not involve the traditional organic chemical discipline of stepwise isolation, the history of reagent preparation and the real composition of the systems is of great importance. But these factors generally are unknown. Thus the results shown above are difficult to correlate with the relative reactivities found when organomagnesium bromides were treated with excess benzonitrile: [34] (mesityl > *p*-tolyl > phenyl ethyl > *n*-butyl > *s*-butyl > *t*-butyl).

In one example it seems most reasonable not only to write the enolic type of Grignard reagent in ionic form but also in free-anionic form. Although Grignard reagents cannot ordinarily be prepared from α-halogenoketone and magnesium, both the chloromagnesium and the lithium derivatives have been prepared in this manner from the highly hindered 6-chloro-2,2,6-trimethylcyclohexanone (XXV).[35] Reactions with water or ethanol, carbon dioxide or oxygen show that these derivatives behave like Grignard reagents, although products character-

[32] M. A. Spielman and M. T. Schmidt, *J. Am. Chem. Soc.*, *59*, 2009 (1937).

[33] C. R. Hauser and W. B. Renfrew, *J. Am. Chem. Soc.*, *59*, 1823 (1937).

[34] H. Gilman et al., *Rec. trav. chim.*, *55*, 577, 588 (1936).

[35] A. Bell, T. Strickland, and G. F Wright, *J. Org. Chem.*, *16*, 1742 (1951).

istic of carbon as well as oxygen addition are obtained. If these reactions are carried out in d-2,3-dimethoxy butane [36] the lithium derivative (XXVI) gives inactive products (XXVII and XXVIII) as might be expected if it were freely ionic.[36a] On the other hand, oxygen

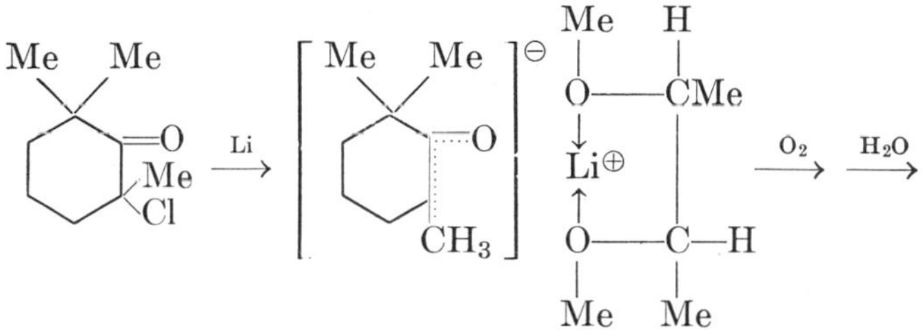

XXV   XXVI

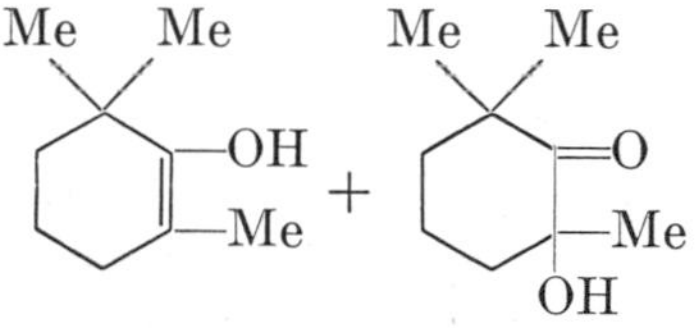

XXVII
which
ketonizes

XXVIII

treatment of the Grignard reagent from XXV in d-2,3-dimethoxybutane yields optically active 6-hydroxy-2,2,6-trimethylcyclohexanone (XXVIII).   The small amount of 2,2,6-trimethylcyclohexanone produced concurrently is inactive, as one might expect if it is formed *via* the enol XVII either by decomposition of its peroxide or by resistance toward oxidation of a salt involving XVII and magnesium.

If the Grignard reagent from XXV is freely ionic, as might be expected by analogy on the basis of evidence for II, III, IV, and XXVI, it becomes necessary to account for the optically active product by a hexacovalent anion such as XXIX. This pictured form of the anion should not be taken too literally (see structures XII and XIII), but evidently there is significance in the observation that optically active mono ethers have been ineffective in causing asymmetric Grignard syntheses.[19]

[36] K. R. Bharucha, H. M. Cohen, and G. F Wright, *J. Org. Chem.*, **19**, 1097 (1954).

[36a] It must not be implied that all organolithium compounds are freely ionic. Indeed, Evans and Pearson [16] found that neither conduction nor transference occurred with simple organolithium compounds. Furthermore, the 2-methylbutanoic acid formed from *sec*-butyllithium in d-2,3-dimethoxy butane is optically active.[31] This finding indicates that *sec*-butyllithium exists covalently or as an ion pair.

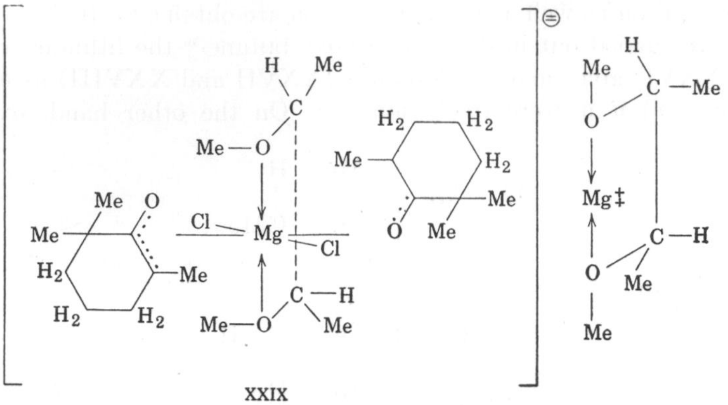

XXIX

Conversely, one cannot, of course, generalize that dual coordination by a bifunctional ether is requisite for asymmetric Grignard synthesis upon the limited evidence now available. However, dual coordination may be significant during some other Grignard reactions.[37] Although lowered temperatures do not appreciably affect the yields in reactions such as that of n-propylmagnesium bromide with diisopropyl ketone, or the ratio of 1,2 versus 1,4 addition to α,β unsaturated ketones, the yield of 2-hexanone from butylmagnesium bromide and acetic anhydride is markedly increased as the temperature is decreased.

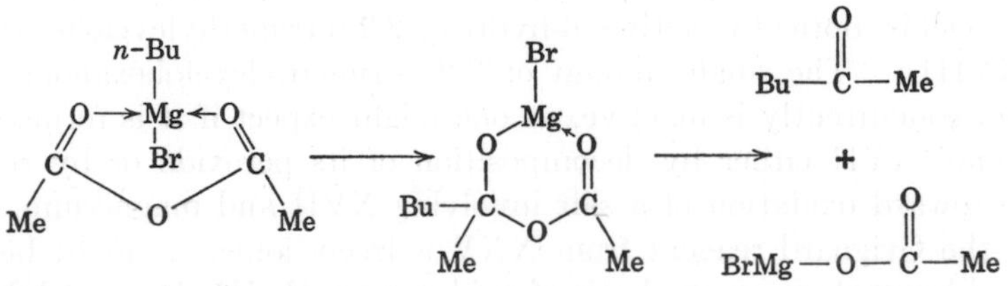

This may be expressed in terms of bifunctional coordination. The authors[37] believe that the high yield at low temperatures may be due to insolubility of the postulated cyclic 1,2 addition product.

Although one may speculate whether some of the magnesium enolates described above are free ionic or not, there seems to be little question about the covalent nature of magnesium enolates derived by 1,4 addition of Grignard reagents to hindered α,β unsaturated ketones. This covalency was first demonstrated by isolation of geometric isomers.[38] A somewhat simpler example[39] has been reported as the ad-

---

[37] M. S. Newman and A. S. Smith, *J. Org. Chem.*, *13*, 592 (1948).

[38] R. E. Lutz and C. J. Kibler, *J. Am. Chem. Soc.*, *62*, 360 (1940).

[39] A. N. Nesmeyanov, V. A. Sazonova, and E. B. Landor, *Doklady Akad. Nauk S.S.S.R.*, *63*, 395 (1948) [*C. A.*, *45*, 2902 (1951)].

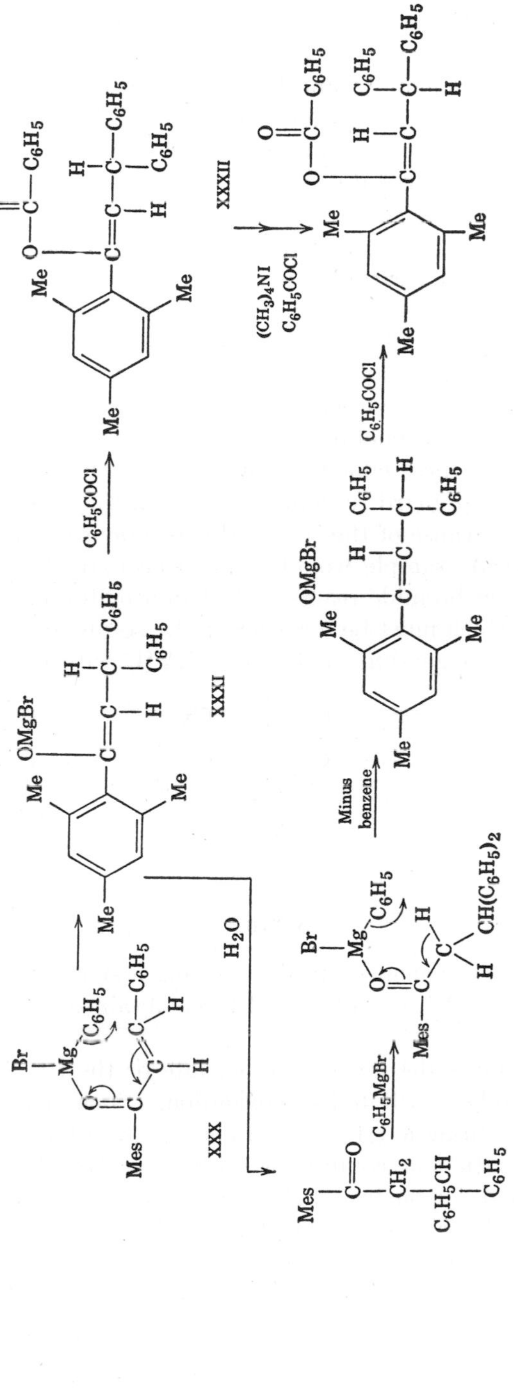
XXX
XXXI
XXXII
XXXIII
XXXIV
XXXV
XXXVI
C_6H_5COCl
H_2O
$(CH_3)_4NI$
C_6H_5COCl
Minus benzene
C_6H_5MgBr

dition of phenylmagnesium bromide to 1-mesityl-3-phenylpropen-2-one-1 (XXX, where the straight arrow signifies inductive coordination and the curved arrow the electromeric shift of electronic charge from one atomic domain to another). The single product thus obtained is evidently the geoisomeric enolate (XXXI), first because of its probable cyclic mode of formation by 1,4 addition, and second because the single enol benzoate (XXXII) obtained from it may be converted to a more stable isomer (XXXV). The latter may also be obtained from the geoisomeric bromomagnesium enolate (XXXIV), which is derived by treatment of the saturated ketone (XXXIII) with phenylmagnesium bromide. Since either α-hydrogen in the coordination complex (XXXVI) may be appropriated by the Grignard phenyl group the more stable geoisomer (XXXIV) will be formed. Presumably the hindrance afforded by the mesityl group retains these enolates in the covalent enol form.

The existence of these enolates, which are stable because of steric restriction in the Grignard reagents from which they are formed, may be evident only because of the subsequent reactions of which they are a part. A typical example would seem to be that observed [40] when mesitylmagnesium bromide reacts with 2-mesitoylfuran. The 1,6 addition product which must be formed initially seems to undergo chelation of the bromomagnesium enolate (XXXVII) with the vicinal oxy-

XXXVII   XXXVIII

gen atom, with consequent occurrence of ring fission. The final product is 1,5-dimesityl-2,4-pentadien-2-ol-1-one obtained when XXXVIII is hydrolyzed.

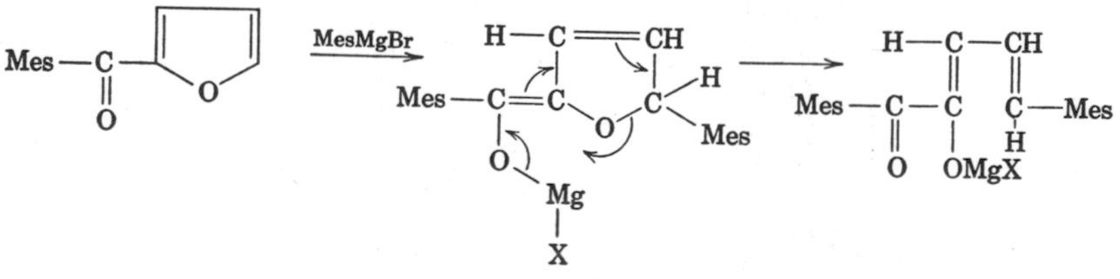

In other instances the magnesium enolate or the free enol derived from it by hydrolysis will undergo oxidation. Such an enol oxidation was observed [41] during a 1,4 addition and was attributed to peroxide (moloxide) formation in conformity with several enol peroxidations which Kohler had demonstrated rigorously. The 1,4 addition was accomplished on the highly hindered α,β-diphenylbenzalacetophenone (XXXIX). This ketone does not react with Grignard reagent in di-

[40] R. C. Fuson and H. P. Wallingford, J. Am. Chem. Soc., 75, 5950 (1953).
[41] E. P. Kohler and E. M. Nygaard, J. Am. Chem. Soc., 52, 4128 (1930).

ethyl ether, but in boiling benzene methylmagnesium iodide adds exclusively to the carbonyl group (1,2 addition) to yield 1,2,3,3-tetraphenylpropen-2-ol-1 (XL). However, phenylmagnesium bromide re-

XXXIX, XLI, XL, XLII

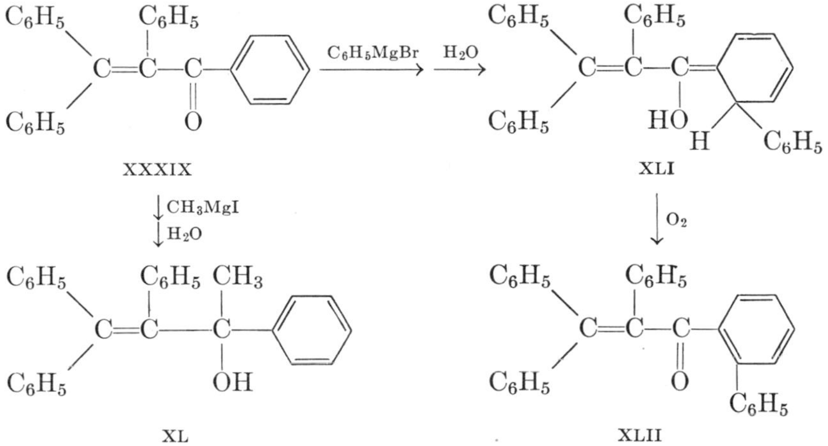

acts by 1,4 addition, though not via the hindered ethylenic conjugation. Instead, the benzenoid conjugated system reacts to give an oil, believed to be the enol XLI, which oxidizes in the air to give 2,3,3-triphenyl-1-xenylpropen-2-one-1 (XLII).

Similar examples of addition via benzenoid conjugation all are accompanied by spontaneous oxidation.[42, 43] In one instance [44] the enol (the enols are always oils) was oxidized by an alternative but not unprecedented reaction. Thus the enolic hydrolysate XLIV from phen-

XLIII, XLIV, XLV

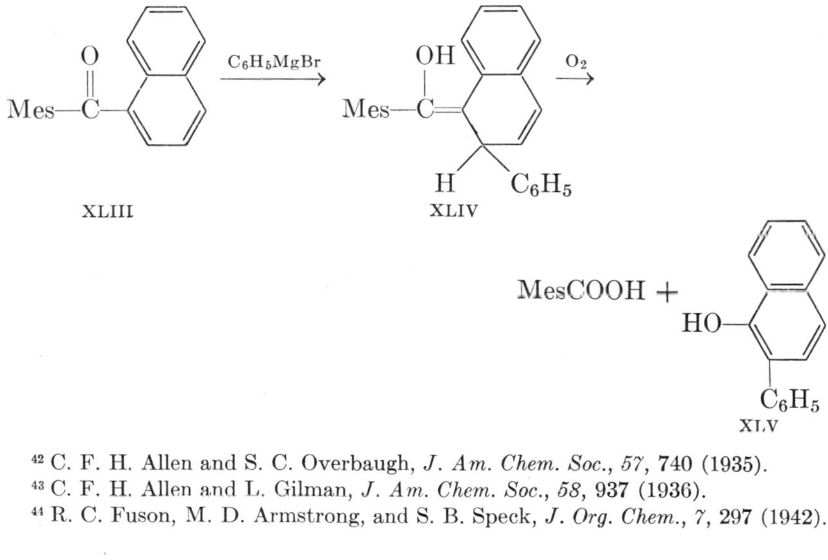

[42] C. F. H. Allen and S. C. Overbaugh, *J. Am. Chem. Soc.*, *57*, 740 (1935).
[43] C. F. H. Allen and L. Gilman, *J. Am. Chem. Soc.*, *58*, 937 (1936).
[44] R. C. Fuson, M. D. Armstrong, and S. B. Speck, *J. Org. Chem.*, *7*, 297 (1942).

ylmagnesium bromide and mesityl α-naphthyl ketone (XLIII) was oxidized by air to mesitoic acid and 2-phenyl-1-naphthol (XLV).

In only one of the preceding examples of enolate formation by 1,4 addition has the addition been expressed in terms of a six-membered cyclic intermediate containing Grignard reagent coordinated with the ketonic oxygen, but other examples might be expressed likewise. However, one hesitates to generalize in this manner in view of the reaction [45] of duryl phenyl ketone (XLVI) with sec-butylmagnesium bromide. The intermediate enol (XLVII) could not be isolated; in-

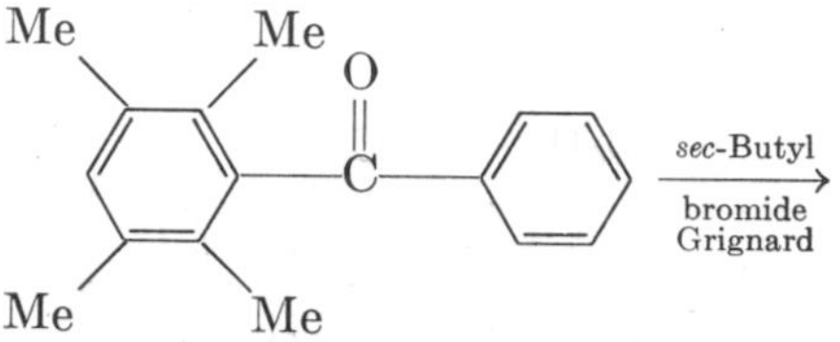

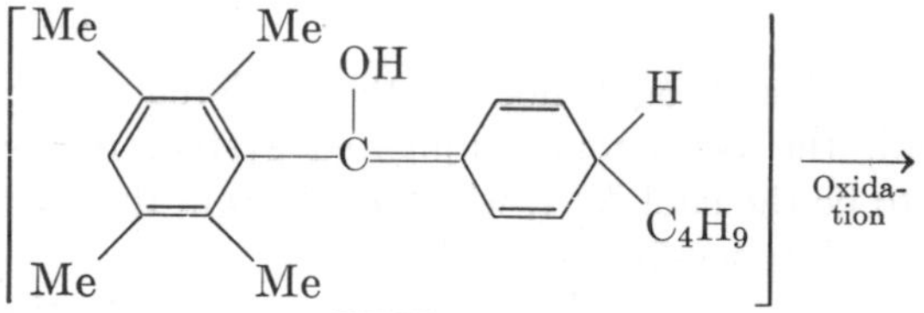

stead, duryl 4-sec-butylphenyl ketone (XLVIII) was obtained in 63% yield. Neither the 2-sec-butylphenyl derivative nor the 4-duryl derivative was detected. Obviously this addition cannot be explained in terms of the ketone-Grignard coordination depicted previously. Furthermore, a single ionization ($R^{\ominus}$ and $MgX^{\oplus}$) does not provide an adequate explanation because the use of optically active 2,3-dimethoxybutane instead of diethyl ether as the reaction medium causes the product XLVIII to be slightly enantiomeric.[19] In this and other [46] ostensible 1,6 addition reactions of Grignard reagents it is probable

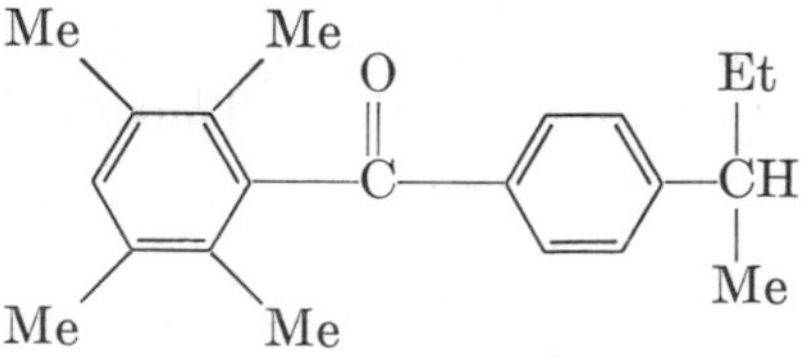

[45] R. C. Fuson and R. Tull, *J. Am. Chem. Soc.*, *71*, 2543 (1949).

[46] P. L. Julian and W. J. Gist, *J. Am. Chem. Soc.*, *57*, 2030 (1936).

that highly complex agglomerations of reagent and ketone (see p. 402) are operative. The same explanation is applicable to certain 1,4 additions.[47]

Nevertheless the cyclic intermediate provides a reasonable explanation for otherwise anomalous reactions. For example, it is known that α,β unsaturated aldehydes, in contradistinction to analogous ketones, react with Grignard reagents by 1,2 addition, to form almost exclusively the unsaturated carbinol. This result is not unexpected since the carbonyl group in aldehydes usually is thought to be more polarizable than the carbonyl group in ketones, and hence amenable to the rapid reaction which seems to favor 1,2 addition. Although Stevens [48] observed 1,2 addition when crotonaldehyde was treated with Grignard reagents from bromobenzene or ethyl, n-propyl, and isopropyl bromides, the reagents from tertiary butyl and tertiary amyl halides gave mixtures of unsaturated carbinol and saturated aldehyde. Yet these latter Grignard reagents are much more reactive toward carbonyl [49] than those which almost exclusively give 1,2 addition products. Furthermore, the yield ratio of saturated aldehyde to unsaturated alcohol is greater when the Grignard reagent is prepared from butyl chloride rather than bromide, although the bromo reagent ought to be less reactive by comparison with other examples in which the chloride reagent is more reactive than the bromide.[50] In consequence, some explanation for Stevens' results other than that of polarization or polarizability should be sought. Inspection of the graphic representation of a cyclic intermediate (XLIX) for the process shows that

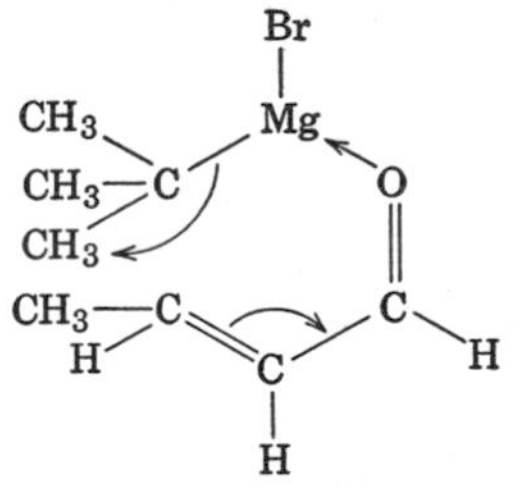

XLIX

hindrance to entry of the *tert*-butyl group at the carbonyl carbon may be compensated by entry at the penultimate carbon. Parenthetically it should be noted that crotyl alcohol but not butyraldehyde might

[47] E. R. Alexander and G. R. Coraor, *J. Am. Chem. Soc.*, *73*, 2721 (1951).

[48] P. G. Stevens, *J. Am. Chem. Soc.*, *57*, 1112 (1935).

[49] M. S. Kharasch and S. Weinhouse, *J. Org. Chem.*, *1*, 209 (1936).

[50] H. J. Shine, *J. Chem. Soc.*, *1951*, 8.

have been expected among the products.   Stevens reports neither substance.

Indeed, the steric restriction inherent in a six-atom system seems to describe in a reasonable manner many uncommon Grignard reactions. For example, ethyl cinnamate reacts with phenylmagnesium bromide by 1,4 addition to give ethyl 3,3-diphenylpropanoate.[51]   This addition may be expressed in terms of the coordination complex L (R = H).

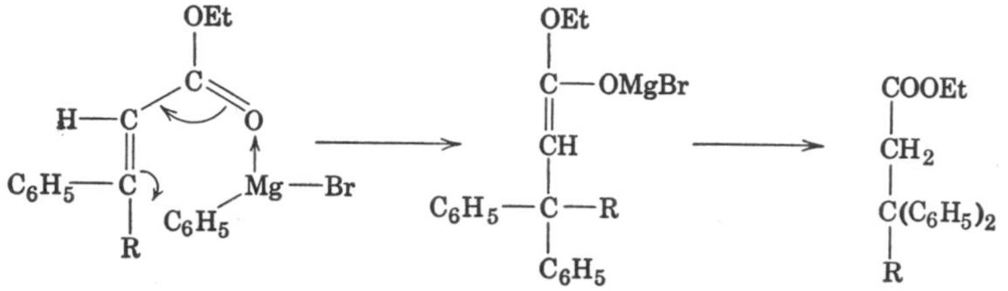

By contrast the same Grignard reagent reacts with ethyl 4,4-dimethyl-3-phenyl-2-propenoate (L, R = *tert*-butyl) entirely by 1,2 addition to give exclusively 4,4-dimethyl-1,1,3-triphenyl-2-propen-1-ol.[52]   It is evident that the tertiary butyl group has hindered 1,4 addition in the otherwise probable cyclic coordination intermediate.

These cyclic coordination intermediates explain many reactions which do not involve conjugated systems.   Hauser and his coworkers [53] have presented a series of reactions with esters which can be explained in terms of six-atom cyclic intermediates.   These are deviations from ordinary ester addition.   The latter may be described in terms of a delayed four-center reaction involving intermediate LI.   When ethyl

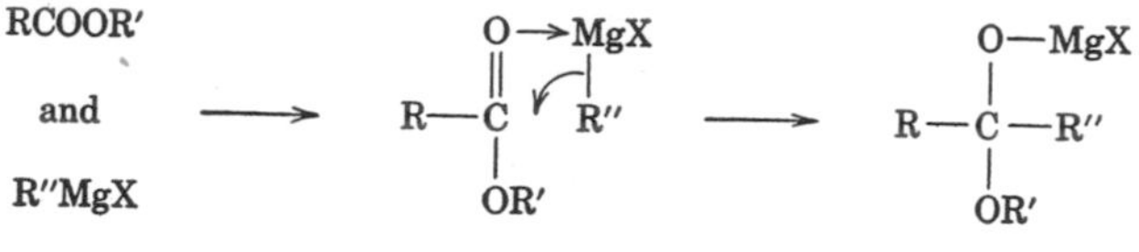

diphenylacetate is treated with isopropylmagnesium bromide this simple addition does not occur.   Instead, the reagent is reduced to propane, and the remainder behaves as a derived Grignard reagent, which reacts with benzoyl chloride to give ethyl α,α-diphenylbenzoylacetate

[51] E. P. Kohler and G. Heritage, *Am. Chem. J.*, *33*, 21 (1904).

[52] G. Tatsas, *Compt. rend.*, *234*, 2083 (1952).

[53] C. R. Hauser, P. O. Saperstein, and J. C. Shivers, *J. Am. Chem. Soc.*, *70*, 606 (1948).

in 14% yield. This transformation may be expressed in terms of intermediate LII. By contrast with this steric influence of phenyl

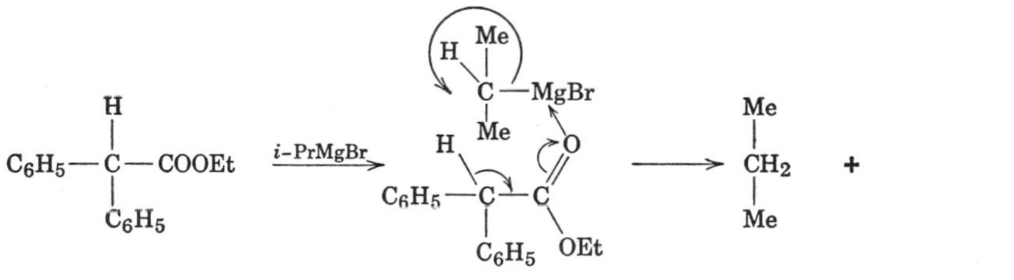

LII

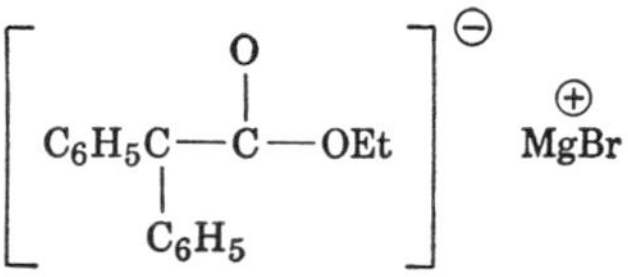

groups in the acyl part of the ester is the reaction of methylmagnesium iodide with triphenylmethyl benzoate. Here the steric hindrance resides in the alcoholic part of the ester. The intermediate LIII decom-

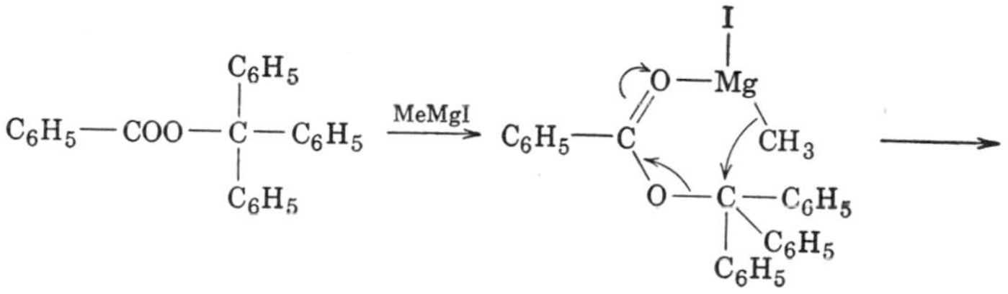

LIII

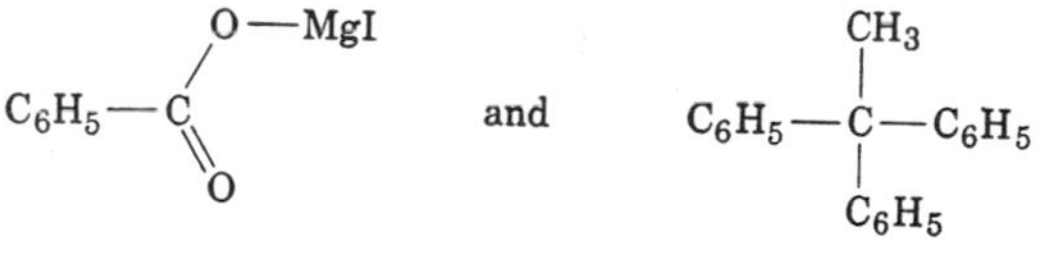

poses to yield iodomagnesium benzoate and 1,1,1-triphenylethane in 45% yield. The reaction had previously been demonstrated with 9-anthranyl acetate.[54]

Hauser's third example involves the reaction of phenylmagnesium bromide in boiling n-butyl ether with 1,2-diphenylethyl mesitoate (LIV). The carbonyl group in this ester is known from its other properties to be strongly enveloped by the hindering mesityl substituent. One might then predict the products on the basis of a cyclic inter-

[54] L. F. Fieser and H. Heymann, J. Am. Chem. Soc., 64, 376 (1942).

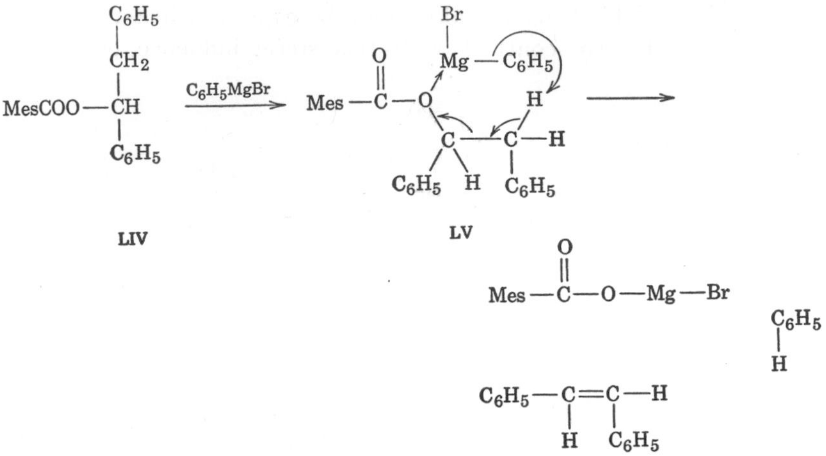

$$C_6H_5$$
$$|$$
$$CH_2$$
$$|$$
$$MesCOO-CH$$
$$|$$
$$C_6H_5$$

$$\xrightarrow{C_6H_5MgBr}$$

$$Mes-C\overset{O}{\underset{\|}{}}-O \cdots Mg-C_6H_5 \quad Br$$

(cyclic intermediate with C_6H_5, H, C, C—H, C_6H_5 H C_6H_5)

$$\longrightarrow$$

LIV   LV

$$Mes-\overset{O}{\overset{\|}{C}}-O-Mg-Br$$

$$C_6H_5-\overset{|}{\underset{|}{C}}=\overset{C_6H_5}{\underset{C_6H_5}{C}}-H$$

$$C_6H_5-\overset{}{\underset{H}{C}}=\overset{H}{\underset{C_6H_5}{C}}-H$$

mediate (LV) in which magnesium is coordinated with the alcoholic rather than the carbonyl oxygen. The products predicted from this intermediate, bromomagnesium mesitoate, benzene, and stilbene, are the principal ones, found in 80–90% yield.

Similar cyclic intermediates serve to explain the apparent anomalies that have arisen in Grignard reactions involving allylic systems where no apparent hindrance exists. The situation until 1932 has been summarized [55] and may be typified in the reaction of benzylmagnesium chloride with formaldehyde. The product is o-tolylcarbinol instead of β-phenethyl alcohol. This reaction may be described in terms of the cyclic intermediate LVI.[56] The explanation is more convincing than

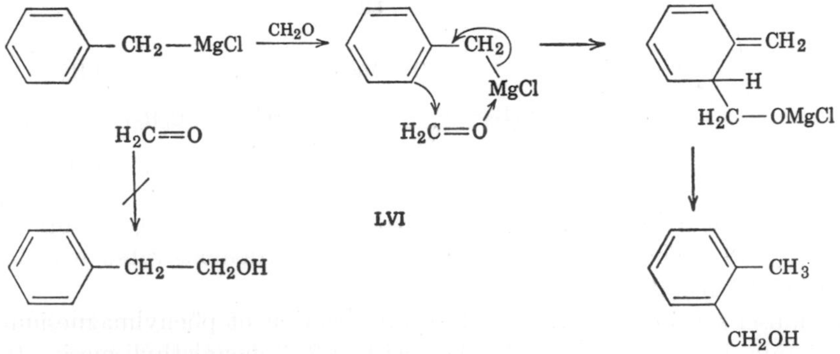

$$\text{(phenyl)}-CH_2-MgCl \xrightarrow{CH_2O} \text{(cyclic intermediate with } CH_2, MgCl, H_2C=O) \longrightarrow \text{(ring)}=CH_2, -H, H_2C-OMgCl$$

$$H_2C=O$$

LVI

$$\text{(phenyl)}-CH_2-CH_2OH$$

$$\text{(ring)}-CH_3, CH_2OH$$

others which employ ionic, tautomeric, or mesomeric structures for the reagent. It has been observed that augends other than formalde-

[55] J. R. Johnson, J. Am. Chem. Soc., 55, 3029 (1933).
[56] W. G. Young and S. Siegel, J. Am. Chem. Soc., 66, 354 (1944).

hyde react to give none or only part of the product representing rearrangement. Thus carbon dioxide, many ketones, acetals, and esters react to give only the product of direct addition, while benzaldehyde, ethyl formate, epoxyethane and others give the o-tolyl derivatives. These augends cannot be classified according to polarizability; although they have not yet been classified according to probability of the geometry of addition, a beginning seems to have been made.[57]   It is significant that minor spatial alterations in either addend or augend displace the ratio of direct versus rearranged products. The extent of this displacement is commensurate with that expected if one considers the probability of cyclic intermediate formation in respect of space and time.

This steric effect is especially apparent when the allylic system is intrinsic in the augend rather than the addend of a Grignard reaction. It has been observed by Prévost and Daujat [58] in the coupling reaction of allyl halides with Grignard reagents and also by two groups of workers [59, 60] who employ allyl and crotyl mesitoates, in which appreciable hindrance exists. When crotyl mesitoate is treated with phenylmagnesium bromide the sole product is crotylbenzene. According to the cyclic intermediate or "concerted" concept this reaction proceeds through LVII. By contrast methallyl mesitoate gives a mix-

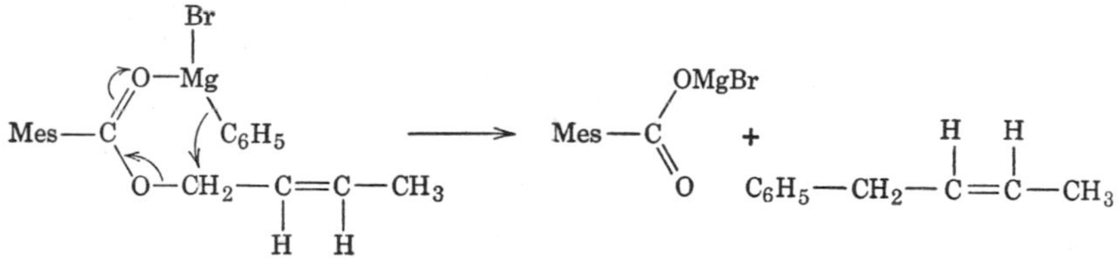

LVII

ture of 17% methylallylbenzene and 83% crotylbenzene. The workers in this field have chosen to explain the occurrence of this mixture in terms of organic ions, but an intermediate such as LVIII also explains the result.

The reactions described thus far have involved scission in the cyclic intermediate of bonds joining unlike atoms, but carbon-carbon bonds can be broken as well. The cleavage of β-diketones by Grignard re-

[57] D. J. Cram and F. D. Greene, J. Am. Chem. Soc., 75, 6005 (1953).

[58] C. Prévost and J. Daujat, Bull. soc. chim. France, [4], 47, 588 (1930).

[59] R. T. Arnold and S. Searles, J. Am. Chem. Soc., 71, 2021 (1949).

[60] K. W. Wilson, J. D. Roberts and W. G. Young, J. Am. Chem. Soc., 71, 2019 (1949).

$$Mes-\overset{\overset{O}{\|}}{C}-O-\overset{\overset{CH_3}{|}}{\underset{\underset{H}{|}}{C}}-\overset{\overset{H}{|}}{C}=CH_2 \quad \xrightarrow{C_6H_5MgBr} \quad \begin{array}{c}Type\\ LVII\end{array} \quad \longrightarrow \quad Mes-C\overset{OMgBr}{\underset{O}{\diagup}}$$

$$+$$

$$C_6H_5\overset{\overset{CH_3}{|}}{\underset{\underset{H}{|}}{C}}-\overset{\overset{H}{|}}{C}=CH_2$$

$$\Big\downarrow C_6H_5MgBr$$

$$Mes-\overset{\overset{O}{\|}}{C}-O \quad \overset{Br}{\underset{}{Mg-C_6H_5}} \quad CH_2 \longrightarrow Mes-\overset{\overset{O}{\|}}{C}\overset{OMgBr}{\diagup} \quad +$$

$$\underset{\underset{CH_3\ H}{}}{\overset{}{}}C-C$$

$$H-\overset{}{C}=\overset{}{C}-CH_2-C_6H_5$$

$$\underset{CH_3\ H}{|\quad|}$$

LVIII

agents is a case in point.[61]   The ketone and chloromagnesium enolate obtained by this scission may be thought to arise via a cyclic intermediate LIX.

$$\begin{array}{c}R-C=O\\ |\\ CH_2\\ |\\ R''-C=O\end{array} \quad + \quad \begin{array}{c}R'\\ |\\ Mg\\ |\\ X\end{array} \quad \longrightarrow \quad \begin{array}{c}O\\ \|\\ R-C\quad CH_2\\ \diagdown\quad\diagdown C-R''\\ R'\quad\quad O\\ \diagdown Mg\diagup\\ |\\ X\end{array} \quad \longrightarrow \quad R-C=O \quad + \quad \begin{array}{c}CH_2\\ \|\\ C-R''\\ |\\ OMgX\end{array}$$
$$\qquad\qquad\qquad\qquad\qquad\qquad\qquad\qquad\qquad\qquad\qquad\qquad\qquad\qquad R'$$

LIX

This explanation has been advanced to describe [62] the cleavage of α,β-dimorpholino-β-phenylpropiophenone by phenylmagnesium bromide.   The cleavage products, N-benzohydrylmorpholine and the chloromagnesium enolate of α-morpholinoacetophenone, are explained in terms of the cyclic intermediate LX; 1,1,3-triphenyl-2,3-dimorpholinopropanol-1 is a result of direct addition to the carbonyl group.

Reactions of this type are thought to occur because of the delay in rearrangement of the coordinate complex, which allows time for favorable spatial arrangement.   In consequence, esters, which react slowly with Grignard reagents, have frequently been chosen for study.   The effect of substituents in esters on the rate of reaction with methylmagnesium iodide has been studied [63] by the Zerewitinoff technique.

[61] E. P. Kohler and J. L. E. Erickson, *J. Am. Chem. Soc.*, *53*, 2301 (1931).

[62] N. Cromwell, *J. Am. Chem. Soc.*, *69*, 1857 (1947).

[63] W. Triebs, *Ann.*, *556*, 10 (1944).

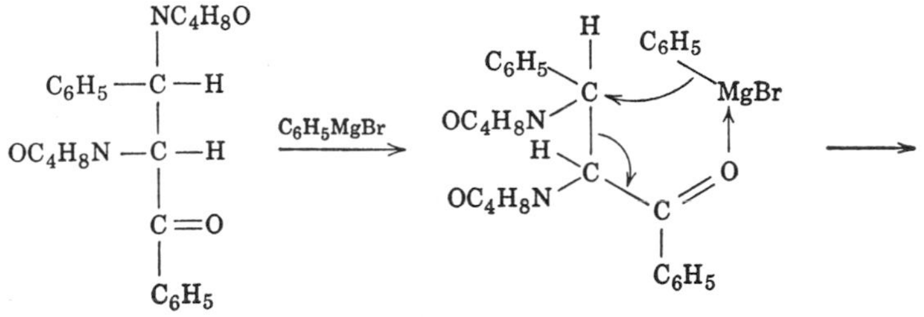

$$
\begin{array}{c}
NC_4H_8O \\
| \\
C_6H_5-C-H \\
| \\
OC_4H_8N-C-H \\
| \\
C=O \\
| \\
C_6H_5
\end{array}
\quad \xrightarrow{C_6H_5MgBr} \quad
\begin{array}{c}
H \quad C_6H_5 \\
C_6H_5\diagdown \; | \\
C \leftarrow MgBr \\
OC_4H_8N \diagup \\
H\diagdown \quad \uparrow \\
C \\
OC_4H_8N\diagup \diagdown C = O \\
| \\
C_6H_5
\end{array}
\quad \longrightarrow
$$

LX

$$
O\diagup S \diagdown N-CH\begin{array}{c} C_6H_5 \\ | \\ \\ | \\ C_6H_5 \end{array}
$$

and

$$
O\diagup S \diagdown N-CH=C-C_6H_5 \\
\qquad\qquad\qquad | \\
\qquad\qquad\qquad OMgBr
$$

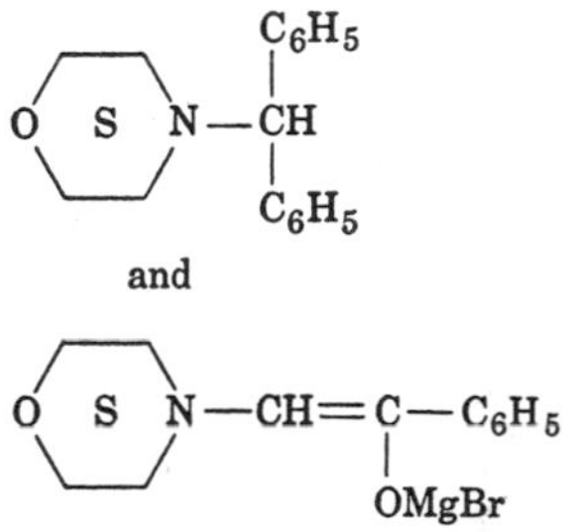

Three minutes of reaction time is allowed with each ester; then the remaining reagent is hydrolyzed. The extent of addition is thus measured by the evolution of methane from the unchanged Grignard reagent. The results are correlated in terms of polar and steric effects in the typical formula RCOOR′, and the following rules have been stated:

1. Increase in size of normal R′ up to propyl causes decrease in reactivity, negligibly thereafter (steric).

2. Benzyl esters are most reactive, but further separation of phenyl by a normal carbon chain decreases the activity (polar).

3. Branching in R′ inhibits when adjacent to COO— but accelerates when removed by at least one carbon atom (polar and steric).

4. Diastereomeric esters react at different rates (isomenthyl > neo-isomenthyl > menthyl > neomenthyl acetates) (steric).

5. Phenyl groups in R cause acceleration, but the effect is diminished by separation from —COO (polar).

6. Branching in R causes retardation in rate (steric).

Earlier studies of the same type had been made by Whitmore and Lewis [64] which confirm and elaborate Triebs' sixth rule. In Table I they show that branching by ethyl groups is more effective than methyl when either is situated on the carbon atom adjacent to the carbonyl

[64] F. C. Whitmore and C. E. Lewis, *J. Am. Chem. Soc.*, *64*, 2964 (1942).

group in esters. Similar studies have shown [65] that greatest hindrance occurs by multiplicity of groups at the fifth or, especially, the sixth atom removed from the oxygen in esters that are treated with methylmagnesium iodide. They believe that these findings are in agreement with Newman's "rule of six," [66] which is derived from a study of acid esterification.

TABLE I

CHAIN BRANCHING VERSUS REACTIVITY OF ESTERS WITH METHYL-MAGNESIUM IODIDE

Ester	$Et_3CCOOMe$	$Et_3CCOOEt$	$Me\!-\!\overset{\displaystyle Et}{\underset{\displaystyle Et}{C}}\!-\!COOEt$	$Me\!-\!\overset{\displaystyle Et}{\underset{\displaystyle Et}{C}}\!-\!COOBu$	$Et\!-\!\overset{\displaystyle Me}{\underset{\displaystyle Me}{C}}\!-\!COOEt$
Per cent addition	0	0	45	60	100

In a series of elegant studies Whitmore and his coworkers have demonstrated similar effects of hindrance in acid chlorides and ketones.[30, 67-70] Grignard reagents not only add to such substances but may cause them to be reduced or "enolized." The last term is really a misnomer, implying as it does the existence of a tautomeric equilibrium which may be shifted by cation interchange with the Grignard reagent. It seems more probable that addition, reduction, and "enolization" all proceed through coordination complexes. The so-called enolization may thus be expressed in terms of intermediate LXI.

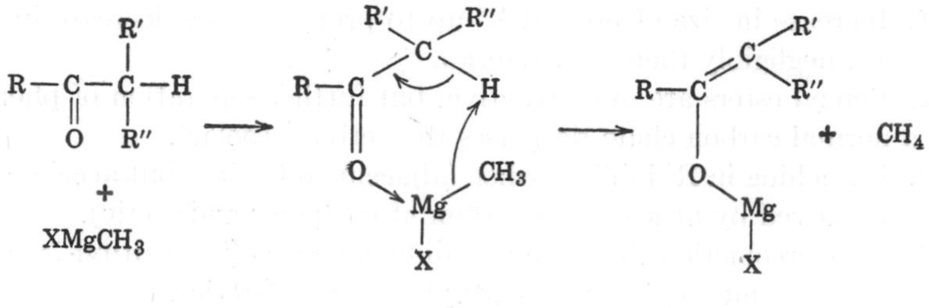

LXI

[65] O. Wichterle and F. Esterka, *Collection Czechoslov. Chem. Communs.*, *15*, 1021 (1951); *C. A.*, *46*, 8609 (1952).

[66] M. S. Newman, *J. Am. Chem. Soc.*, *72*, 4783 (1950). See Chap. 4.

[67] F. L. Greenwood, F. C. Whitmore, and H. M. Crooks, *J. Am. Chem. Soc.*, *60*, 2028 (1938).

[68] F. C. Whitmore et al., *J. Am. Chem. Soc.*, *63*, 643 (1941).

[69] F. C. Whitmore and R. S. George, *J. Am. Chem. Soc.*, *64*, 1239 (1942).

[70] F. C. Whitmore and L. P. Block, *J. Am. Chem. Soc.*, *64*, 1619 (1942).

Whitmore and Block demonstrated this dependence of "enolization" on coordination when they obtained the results of Table II by analysis of a series of ketones in the Grignard machine [71] in which both addition and enolate formation may be measured in terms of methane evolved before and after hydrolysis of a measured amount of

TABLE II

GRIGNARD MACHINE ANALYSES

Ketone	Active Hydrogen	Addition
$MeCOCH(CH_3)_2$	0	100
$EtCOCH(CH_3)_2$	0	100
$CH_3COC(CH_3)_3$	5	86
$C_2H_5COC(CH_3)_3$	9	86
$(CH_3)_2CHCOC(CH_3)_3$	0	49
$CH_3COCH(CH_3)(tBu)$	48	47
$C_2H_5COCH(CH_3)(tBu)$	62	33
$C_3H_7COCH(CH_3)(C_2H_5)$	53	40
$(C_2H_5)_2CHCOC(CH_3)_3$	5	19

methylmagnesium iodide. The last notation in this table shows that as hindrance increases both addition and enolate formation tend to decrease.

Indeed, sufficient hindrance may prevent enolate formation in favor of addition. The hindering effect of the neopentyl group was utilized [72] in this demonstration. Whereas 4-benzoyl-2,2,6,6-tetramethylheptane reacted in boiling dibutyl ether with methylmagnesium bromide to give a 61% yield of the tertiary alcohol, no evidence of enolate was found. This absence of intermediate LXI (where R = phenyl and R', R" would be neopentyl groups) must be attributed to hindrance, for, under the same conditions, 4-aceto-2,2,6,6-tetramethylheptane (where R = 2,2,6,6-tetramethyl-4-heptyl and R', R" would be hydrogens) gives a quantitative yield of the enolate, which behaves as a derived Grignard reagent. This reactivity of the enolate is characteristic of those derived from highly hindered ketones.

These derived Grignard reagents may also be prepared from highly hindered acid chlorides [30, 73] because hindrance prevents the addition of Grignard reagents beyond the stage at which the ketone (such as LXII, R = H) is formed. For this reason the addition of 2,2,6,6-tetramethyl-4-heptanoyl chloride (LXIII, R = H) to two equiva-

[71] Organic Analysis, Vol. 1, p. 155, Interscience Publishers, New York, 1953.
[72] F. C. Whitmore and C. T. Lester, J. Am. Chem. Soc., 64, 1247 (1942).
[73] F. C. Whitmore and D. I. Randall, J. Am. Chem. Soc., 64, 1242 (1942).

lents of methylmagnesium iodide provides a useful source of the derived reagent LXIV (R = H). Of course this reaction is prevented if the acid chloride is treated with a reagent that is hindered so that the ketone cannot be formed. For example, 2,2,4,6,6-pentamethyl-4-heptanoyl chloride (LXIII, R = CH$_3$) is converted by *tert*-butylmagnesium chloride to 2,2,4,6,6-pentamethyl-4-formylheptane [66, 67] (LXVI, R = CH$_3$, which is partly converted to the analogous alcohol), probably through the intermediate LXV (R = CH$_3$). Simpler hindered acid chlorides give more of the alcohol than the aldehyde when sufficient excess of Grignard reagent is available.

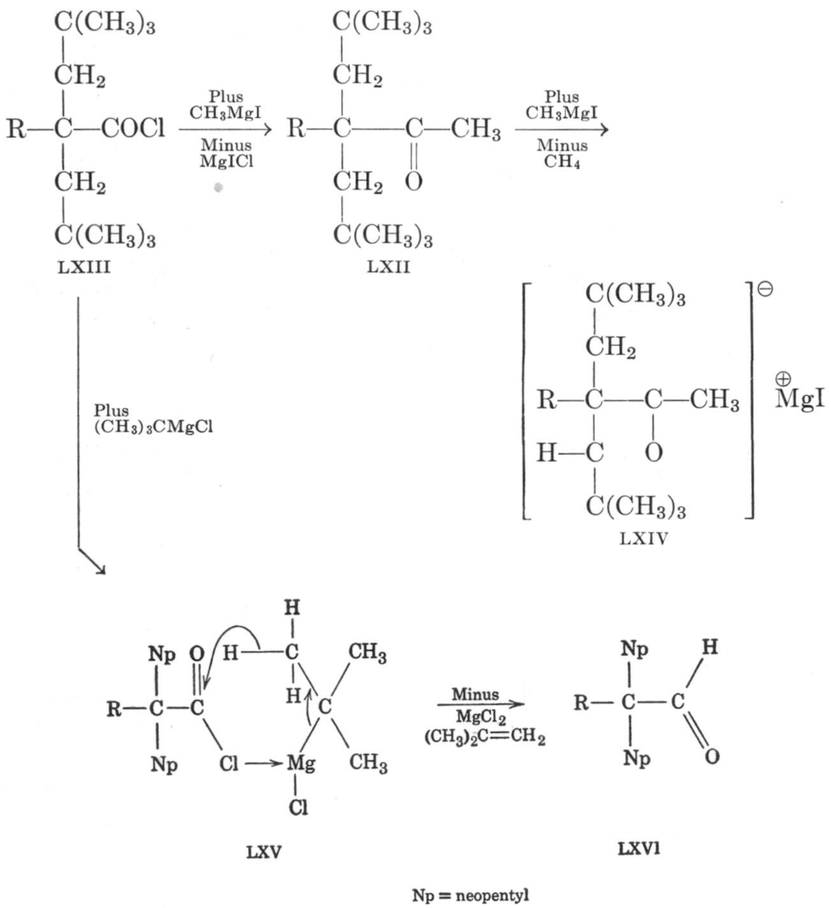

$$\text{Np = neopentyl}$$

Whereas addition and enolate formation depend largely on the nature of the ketone, reduction depends largely on the nature of the

Grignard reagent. The tendency is shown in Table III by Whitmore and George, who studied the reactions of various Grignard reagents with diisopropyl ketone.

TABLE III

PRODUCTS FROM GRIGNARD REAGENTS WITH DIISOPROPYL KETONE

Grignard Reagent	% Enolate	% Reduction	% Addition	Total
CH_3MgBr	0	0	95	95
C_2H_5MgBr	2	21	77	100
$n\text{-}C_3H_7MgBr$	2	60	36	98
iso-C_3H_7MgBr	29	65	0	94
iso-C_4H_9MgBr	11	78	8	97
tert-C_4H_9MgBr	0	65	0	65

The coordinative intermediate similar to that shown as LXV was originally suggested for ketone reactions by Whitmore and has now been substantiated by studies using enantiomers. Vavon and Riviere [74] first demonstrated the concerted nature of the reductive Grignard reaction by means of the Grignard reagent from "pinene hydrochloride." Since configuration is lost at the carbon-halogen linkage during formation of a Grignard reagent, this one evidently is a mixture of bornyl (LXVII) and isobornyl (LXVIII) magnesium chlorides. The

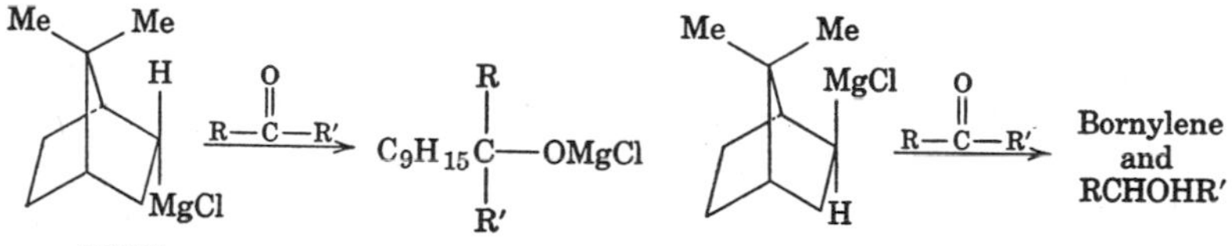

bornyl chloride reagent may be expected to add normally to unhindered ketones, but the isobornyl chloride reagent, evidently because of hindrance by the isopropylidene bridge, ought to act as a reducing agent. At any rate, the secondary alcohols formed in this way are optically active, as is shown in Table IV.

A more complete elucidation of reduction via a cyclic intermediate has been made [75] in a study of the reaction of 3,3-dimethyl-2-butanone with optically active Grignard reagents. By use of d-2-methyl-butylmagnesium chloride there was obtained, among other products, 3,3-dimethyl-2-butanol with 8–11% of the possible enantiomeric purity (the higher value at lower temperatures). This has been illus-

[74] G. Vavon and C. Riviere, *Compt. rend.*, *220*, 286 (1945); *224*, 1435 (1947).
[75] H. S. Mosher and E. La Combe, *J. Am. Chem. Soc.*, *72*, 3994 (1950).

TABLE IV

REACTION OF KETONES WITH BORNYL AND ISOBORNYL
MAGNESIUM CHLORIDES

Ketone R = C_6H_5	% Yield, Reduction Product from Isobornyl Reagent	% of Enantiomeric Alcohol from Bornyl Reagent
$RCOCH_3$	55	36
$RCOC_2H_5$	50	19
$RCOC_3H_7$	50	46
$RCOC_3H_7$ (iso)	80	55
$RCOC_4H_9$	44	52
$RCOC_4H_9$ (iso)	90	72

trated as a concerted reaction through the intermediate LXIX. This intermediate also could be written with the methyl and *tert*-butyl groups of the ketone transposed, but in the latter instance hindrance might be expected from the tertiary butyl group of the ketone and

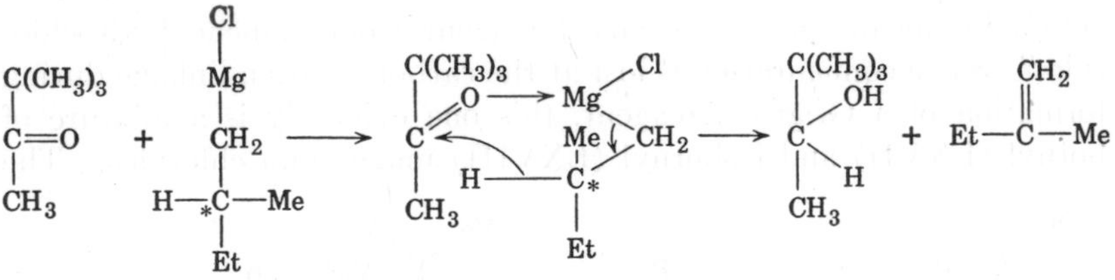

LXIX

the secondary butyl group of the Grignard reagent. Since the asymmetry in the Grignard reagent will impose a corresponding asymmetry into the six-atom coordination cycle, the secondary alcohol produced by scission of the cycle will be specifically enantiomeric. Obviously this phenomenon whereby a "dying" enantiomeric center passes its activity to a newly born molecule has a significance beyond the limits of organometallic chemistry.

These workers further demonstrated the effect of hindrance in this asymmetric induction [76] by use of the same ketone with *d*-3-methyl-pentyl chloride Grignard reagent. In this instance there is little choice, because there is no hindrance, in LXX or LXXI. Actually only a small amount of reduction product (0.2%) was obtained. Little would be expected in consequence of the open structure, which would permit direct addition via the coordination complex LXXII. How-

[76] H. S. Mosher and E. La Combe, *J. Am. Chem. Soc.*, *72*, 4991 (1950).

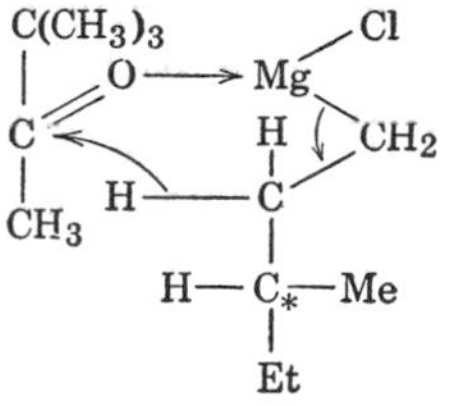

LXX 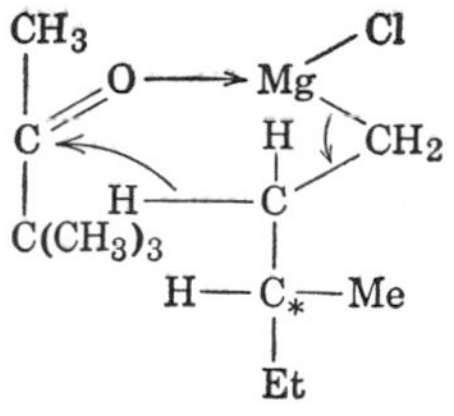   LXXI 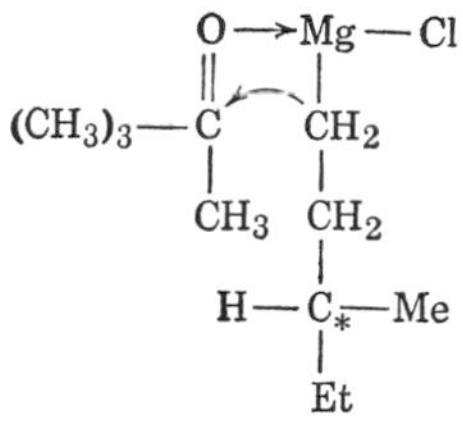   LXXII

ever, the small amount of 3,3-dimethylbutanol-2 obtained was optically inactive.

A series of organometallic reactions have now been presented in terms of concerted mechanisms involving cyclic structures which may be either intermediate structures or probable intermediate reaction paths. This presentation is recommended to the reader as a useful means of predicting steric effects, especially in lieu of explanations involving ionic carbon which never have had a sound physical basis and are gradually being shown to be untenable. However, the reader is urged not to consider the concerted mechanisms to be unequivocal. Much remains to be done before this chemistry is mature.

For example, such mechanisms as have been presented should apply in general to organolithium as well as organomagnesium compounds. Yet marked differences [77] have been found in the behavior of these two organometallic types. When isopropylmagnesium bromide (in petroleum ether) is treated with diisopropyl ketone no triisopropylcarbinol is obtained. The products, instead, are bromomagnesium enolate of diisopropyl ketone (68%) and the reduction product, diisopropylcarbinol (21%). On the other hand, isopropyllithium with diisopropyl ketone (in petroleum ether) gives about the same amount (67%) of enolate but none of the reduction product. Instead, the addition product, triisopropylcarbinol, is obtained in 19% yield. However, temperature coefficients are involved in these competing reactions, since a 17% yield of the reduction does appear when this slowly reacting system is refluxed. These results could not have been predicted on the basis of the present concerted mechanism involving cyclic coordination intermediates. The insolubility of isopropylmagnesium bromide in petroleum ether may be a factor.

In fact, reactions are known in which the basic tenet (metal coordination) of organolithium and organometallic chemistry seems not to be operative. The coupling of Grignard reagents with organic halides seems to fall into this category, since reactions of this type in d-2,3-

[77] W. G. Young and J. D. Roberts, *J. Am. Chem. Soc.*, *66*, 1444 (1944).

dimethoxybutane do not yield optically active products as do the reactions of Grignard reagents with compounds containing carbonyl groups.[19] A second instance involves the addition of organometallic compounds to dibiphenyleneethylene (LXXIII). This addition can be accomplished not only with organolithium compounds [78] but also with very reactive Grignard reagents, such as those prepared from benzyl chloride and *tert*-butyl chloride, to give the derived reagent, LXXIV.[79] While the augend (LXXIII) is atypical of alkenes (since

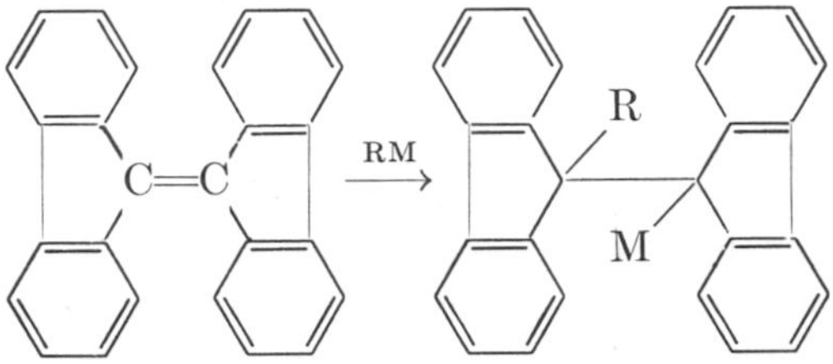

LXXIII   LXXIV

hindrance between the fluoryl groups will distort the juncture unsaturation) it is difficult to conceive of this compound (LXXIII) as unidirectionally polarized or polarizable in the sense of a carbonyl group. Of course dibiphenyleneethylene behaves toward amines and Michael addends as if it were an α,β unsaturated ketone; [80] therefore the addition of Grignard reagent is not unusual except that it cannot be expressed in terms of simple coordination interchange. But this observation may be included in paraphrasing the philosophy of the late Dean Whitmore that the only abnormality in organic chemistry is the so-called normal reaction.

[78] K. Ziegler and W. Schäfer, *Ann.*, *511*, 101 (1934).

[79] R. C. Fuson and H. D. Porter, *J. Am. Chem. Soc.*, *70*, 895 (1948).

[80] L. A. Pinck and G. E. Hilbert, *J. Am. Chem. Soc.*, *57*, 2398 (1935); *68*, 2014 (1946).

Chapter 9

by George S. Hammond

Steric Effects
on Equilibrated Systems

IONIZATION OF CARBOXYLIC ACIDS
IONIZATION OF PHENOLS AND ANILINIUM IONS
ACIDITY OF MISCELLANEOUS SECONDARY ACIDS
ENOLIZATION AND ACIDITY OF CARBONYL COMPOUNDS
LEWIS ACIDS AND BASES
RING-CHAIN TAUTOMERISM

Chapter 9

IONIZATION OF CARBOXYLIC ACIDS

The ionization constants of proton acids represent the largest body of data on equilibrium constants available anywhere in the chemical literature. As a consequence the correlation of acidity with chemical structure is usually basic to the development of new theories of chemical reactivity. For example, the σ constants of the Hammett equation [1] are defined in terms of the ionization constants of benzoic acids and its derivatives. Stereochemical problems in the correlation of ionization constants have been discussed by a number of authors. Dippy [2] has pointed out that there is frequently an acid-weakening effect observed in unsaturated carboxylic acids in which the functional group is sterically hindered. Others have noted the same effect and attempted to relate the observations with other chemical properties.[3, 4] Attempts to relate structure to acidity by means of theoretical calculations have involved the detailed analysis of steric relationships.[5]

Steric effects in ionization reactions are highly complicated. However, it seems probable that the one factor which is seldom, if ever, of major importance is the compression of other groups by the acidic hydrogen. Effects due to this small strain will nearly always be camouflaged by one or more of the following effects.

1. Steric inhibition of resonance in either the acid or its conjugate base.

2. Steric effects on the influence of polar substituents in the molecule. These may operate either by controlling the configuration of the molecule or by modifying the effective dielectric constant of the volume through which the coulombic forces are exerted.

[1] L. P. Hammett, *Physical Organic Chemistry*, p. 186, McGraw-Hill Book Co., New York, 1940.

[2] J. F. J. Dippy, *Chem. Revs.*, *25*, 151 (1939).

[3] B. Flurscheim, *J. Chem. Soc.*, *1939*, 725; *Chemistry & Industry*, *44*, 246 (1925).

[4] D. H. Hey, *J. Chem. Soc.*, *1928*, 2321.

[5] J. G. Kirkwood and F. H. Westheimer, *J. Chem. Phys.*, *6*, 506 (1938).

3. The exclusion of solvent from vicinity of the functional group in the charged form involved in the equilibrium. In addition to the dielectric effect mentioned in 2 this may prevent stabilization by oriented solvent molecules by special interactions such as hydrogen bonding.

4. Special interactions, such as *internal* hydrogen bonding, which selectively stabilize one form or the other.

Since these effects frequently overlap and cannot be separated, at least in a qualitative treatment, the following discussion will be based upon structural types as a matter of convenience to discussion. It will frequently be impossible to assign dominance to a particular effect.

The least complex of the possible steric effects is encountered in sterically hindered aliphatic acids which have only recently been investigated systematically.[6] The data in Table I show very clearly that the accumulation of bulky substituents adjacent to the carboxyl group of fatty acids has a pronounced acid-weakening effect.

TABLE I

IONIZATION CONSTANTS OF HINDERED ACIDS IN 50% BY VOLUME
METHANOL-WATER AT 40°[6]

Acid	Apparent * pK_a	Ionization Constant $\times 10^{-6}$
Acetic	5.56	2.7
Methylneopentylacetic	6.05	0.89
Methyl-*tert*-butylacetic	6.25	0.57
Ethyl-*tert*-butylacetic	6.31	0.49
Diisopropylacetic	6.40	0.40
Triethylacetic	6.44	0.36
Dimethylneopentylacetic	6.50	0.32
Dineopentylacetic	6.56	0.27
Dimethyl-*tert*-butylacetic	6.72	0.19
Methyl-*tert*-butylneopentyl-acetic	6.96	0.11

* Potentiometric titration with glass and calomel electrodes without correction for junction potential.

These data cannot be related to the electronic influences of the various alkyl groups. Since it is the acidic form which is preferentially stabilized by the bulk of the substituents it follows that any effects due to the repulsion of the acidic hydrogen are outweighed by some other effect. The ionization process must be accompanied by a

[6] G. S. Hammond and D. H. Hogle, *J. Am. Chem. Soc.*, 77, 3384 (1955).

large increase in the solvation of the organic molecule and it is probable that acid weakening is due to the exclusion of solvent molecules from the vicinity of the negatively charged carboxyl groups of the hindered anions. Since the oxygen atoms of the anion, the centers of the negative charge, are not completely shielded from the solvent these results imply that steric hindrance to solvation will assume even greater importance in acids such as *ortho*-substituted phenols and anilinium ions (see p. 436).

Contrasting effects are found in the comparison of the *cis-trans* isomers of α,β unsaturated carboxylic acids and of *ortho*-substituted benzoic acids with their *para* isomers. Relevant data are included in Tables II and III.

TABLE II

Ionization Constants of Sterically Hindered Unsaturated Acids

Carboxylic Acid	K_i^{25}(aq.) $\times 10^5$	Reference
trans-Crotonic	1.975	2, 7, 8, 9
cis-Crotonic	3.6	2
trans-Cinnamic	3.65	2, 10
cis-Cinnamic	13.2	2, 10
Fumaric	62	2, 11
Maleic	439	2, 11
Angelic	5.0	12
Tiglic	0.96	12

TABLE III

Ionization Constants of *ortho*- and *para*-Substituted Benzoic Acids [2]

Substituent	K_i^{20}(aq.) $\times 10^5$	
	ortho	*para*
H	6.27	6.27
CH$_3$	12.75	4.26
tert-C$_4$H$_9$	35.5	3.98
CH$_3$O	8.29	3.38
C$_6$H$_5$O	30.1	3.00
NO$_2$	660	37.6
F	54.0	7.22
Cl	114	10.5
Br	143	10.7
I	138	—

[7] B. Saxton and G. W. Waters, *J. Am. Chem. Soc.*, *59*, 1048 (1937).
[8] A. I. Vogel and G. H. Geffrey, *Chemistry & Industry*, 600 (1937).
[9] W. L. German, G. H. Geffrey, and A. I. Vogel, *J. Chem. Soc.*, *1937*, 1008.
[10] J. F. J. Dippy and R. H. Lewis, *J. Chem. Soc.*, *1937*, 1604.
[11] E. Cattelain and G. Couchet, *Bull. soc. chim. France*, [5], *4*, 499 (1937).
[12] W. Ostwald, *Z. physik. Chem.*, *3*, 243 (1899).

Olefinic acids in which hydrogen is *cis* to the carboxyl group are regularly stronger than their isomers. Arguments which amount to the view that this is due to the steric requirements of the proton have been advanced under the guise of kinetic discussions.[2,3] Since the kinetic description, as a discrete factor independent of the steric requirements in the resting molecules, is invalid it is not worth while to present the details. In each case the effect is due to the presence of a group of modest steric requirements attached some distance from the acid proton, and it is unlikely that the proton is "squeezed out" by these groups, in view of the results cited for saturated acids. A more likely explanation is that there is steric interaction between the *cis* group and the carboxyl group [13] which causes the carboxyl group to twist about the C—CO_2H bond, preventing the coplanar arrangement of the entire unsaturated system. This would decrease the resonance energy of both the acids and the derived anions, but the effect would be more important in the free acids since electron transfer from the double bond to the carboxyl group, indicated by structure I, would be inhibited in the anions because of the negative charge in the carboxyl group.

I

The same explanation accounts for the fact that, regardless of electronic type, nearly all *ortho* substituents are acid strengthening in the benzoic acid series [2,13] while their influence as *meta* and *para* substituents may be either acid strengthening or acid weakening, depending on the electronic character of the individual groups. It seems inevitable that an important steric effect is exerted by the *ortho* substituents. Again the data support the view that steric inhibition of resonance in the free acids is an acid-strengthening influence. It is only coincidental that the electronic influences of some of the groups do not outweigh this effect. It would be anticipated that this particular influence will be unique with conjugated unsaturated systems. The data of Dippy and Lewis for *ortho*-substituted phenylacetic acids show that this is so. Pertinent data are summarized in Table IV along with those for the related *ortho*- and *para*-substituted acids.

[13] C. K. Ingold, *Structure and Mechanism in Organic Chemistry*, p. 744, Cornell University Press, Ithaca, N. Y., 1953.

TABLE IV

IONIZATION CONSTANTS OF BENZOIC AND PHENYLACETIC ACIDS [2,14]

$$10^5 K_{thermo}$$

Substituent	CH_3	CH_3O	Cl	NO_2
Benzoic Acids				
o-	12.35	8.06	114	671
m-	5.35	8.17	14.8	32.1
p-	4.24	3.38	10.5	37.6
Phenylacetic Acids				
o-	—	—	8.60	9.90
m-	—	—	7.24	10.80
p-	4.27	4.36	6.45	14.1

A series of remarkably large effects are observed in the study of stereoisomeric dibasic acids. In general, the first ionization constants are larger than those of unsubstituted monofunctional acids and the second constants are smaller. The difference between the two constants frequently exceeds the statistical factor of 4. The acid-strengthening effect on the first dissociation is frequently attributable to the dipolar nature of carboxy groups. Thus, —CO_2H as a substituent has, qualitatively, an influence similar to that of the halogen atoms. The quantitative extent of the effect varies with orientation and with the contribution of the remainder of the molecule to the effective dielectric constant [5] of the medium separating the two functional groups. Furthermore, considerable additional direct interaction may occur between the two groups. The data in Table V provide examples of most of these effects.

Comparisons should be made on the basis of all three of the entries in Table IV. Thus, if for a given acid the ratio K_1/K_2 is abnormally large it is necessary to compare the absolute values of each of the ionization constants with those of other acids in order to determine whether one or both of the ionization processes is subject to some abnormal influence. For example, the first ionization constant of maleic

[14] J. F. J. Dippy, *J. Chem. Soc.*, *1938*, 357.

TABLE V

IONIZATION CONSTANTS OF DIBASIC ACIDS IN WATER SOLUTION *

Acid	$K_1 \times 10^5$	$K_2 \times 10^5$	K_1/K_2	Reference
Maleic	1170	0.025	45,000	15
Fumaric	93	3.2	29	15
Cyclohexene-1,2-dicarboxylic	6.5	0.596	9.5	16
cis-Cyclopropane-1,2-dicarboxylic	46.7	0.034	1,370	17
trans-Cyclopropane-1,2-dicarboxylic	22.4	0.74	30	17
cis-Cyclobutane-1,2-dicarboxylic	12.6	0.129	98	18
trans-Cyclobutane-1,2-dicarboxylic	16.6	0.245	68	18
cis-Cyclobutane-1,3-dicarboxylic	9.35	0.490	19	17
trans-Cyclobutane-1,3-dicarboxylic	15.5	0.525	29	17
cis-Cyclopentane-1,2-dicarboxylic	3.71	0.0269	138	19
trans-Cyclopentane-1,2-dicarboxylic	12.9	0.123	104	19
cis-Cyclopentane-1,3-dicarboxylic	5.5	0.31	17.7	19
trans-Cyclopentane-1,3-dicarboxylic	4.8	0.38	12.9	19

* Temperatures vary slightly but are all included in the range 19–25°.

acid is exceptionally large and the second is unusually small. One common ground for accounting for both effects is found if there is some factor which selectively stabilizes the first anion. Such an effect would almost necessarily involve hydrogen bonding between the two carboxyl groups since other effects are likely to compensate in either the free acid or in the second ion. Configuration II represents a probable arrangement of the first ion which is compatible with the interference radii of the atoms involved. That this configuration is actu-

II

ally found in maleic acid itself is shown by the determination of the structure of the solid acid by X-ray diffraction.[20] In this structure the second hydrogens are used in the formation of weak intermolecular

[15] E. E. Chandler, J. Am. Chem. Soc., 30, 694 (1938).

[16] W. Hückel, Theoretische Grundlagen der organischen Chemie, Akademische Verlagsgesellschaft, Leipzig, 2nd ed., 1934.

[17] A. Wasserman, Helv. Chim. Acta, 13, 207 (1930).

[18] R. Kuhn and A. Wasserman, Helv. Chim. Acta, 11, 600 (1928).

[19] C. K. Ingold and H. G. G. Mohrhenn, J. Chem. Soc., 1935, 1482.

[20] R. E. Rundle and M. Parasol, J. Chem. Phys., 20, 1487 (1952).

hydrogen bonds. One would expect that considerable tightening of the structure would accompany the removal of the second hydrogens. In the first ion the oxygens can approach each other without restriction to form the strongest possible bond. A study of the infrared spectrum of the bimoleate ion indicates that the hydrogen is tightly bound between the two oxygens.[21] It is also instructive to compare the products of the ionization constants for the pairs of isomeric acids since values of K_1K_2 compare the overall processes of removal of two protons from the neutral molecules.

$$H_2A \xrightarrow[\longleftarrow]{K_1K_2} 2H^+ + A^=$$

The value of K_1K_2 is 1.9×10^{-9} for maleic acid and 3.0×10^{-8} for fumaric. This variation points to the existence of some acid-weakening effect in maleic which is independent of the special stability of the bimaleate ion. At least two factors can contribute to such a phenomenon. It is possible that the weak hydrogen bond between the carboxyl groups of maleic acid persists in aqueous solution, and if it does the removal of the protons should be inhibited. The electrostatic repulsion between the negatively charged carboxyl groups in the maleate anion is probably the most important influence, since the negative oxygens are much closer together than in the fumarate ion.

The geometric relationships in cis- and trans-cyclopropane dicarboxylic acids are similar to those between maleic and fumaric. It is interesting to note that the large difference between the isomers has disappeared. The cis acid is slightly stronger than the trans in the first dissociation, a phenomenon that is repeated with the 1,2-cyclobutane diacids but not with the 1,2-cyclopentane acids. This may indicate that there is some hydrogen bonding in the first anions. In the 1,3-cyclobutane diacids, in which hydrogen bonding would be weak, the trans acid becomes the stronger in the first step. This is the behavior which would be expected if the only operative influence were the interaction of the negative carboxyl group of the first anion with the group moment of a neutral, substituent carboxyl group with the OH portion of that group directed away from the anionic portion of the molecule. This behavior is not repeated with the cyclopentane-1,3 diacids. Although the differences are small, the first ionization constant is largest for the cis acid. The contrast between the cyclobutane and cyclopentane acids probably demonstrates nothing more than the importance of the orientation of the dipole of a substituent group. In the cyclobutane acid the axis of the CO_2H group is approxi-

---

[21] H. M. E. Cardwell, J. D. Dunitz, and L. E. Orgel, *J. Chem. Soc.*, *1953*, 3740.

mately parallel to that of the CO_2^- in the *trans* acid. This orientation cannot be repeated in the cyclopentane acids, which have a different symmetry.

One factor is invariably repeated throughout the series although it is reduced to a trivial order of magnitude in the 1,3-cyclopentane acids. The value of K_1/K_2 is always smallest for the *cis* acids. *Since the other relationships undergo inversions* it is almost certain that this particular result reflects a feature, such as electrostatic repulsion, which is intrinsic to the doubly charged ions.

Because of the flexibility of cyclohexane rings it would be expected that new factors will be encountered in the isomeric diacids derived from that system. A suitable set of data was reported in a single investigation [22] and is summarized in Table VI.

TABLE VI

IONIZATION CONSTANTS OF CYCLOHEXANE DIACIDS IN WATER [*] [22]

Acid	$K_1 \times 10^5$	$K_2 \times 10^5$	K_1/K_2	$K_1K_2 \times 10^{12}$
cis-1,2	4.56	0.0182	267	8.3
trans-1,2	6.60	0.0116	56	7.6
cis-1,3	7.95	0.347	23	275
trans-1,3	4.9	0.186	26	91
cis-1,4	3.63	0.162	22	590
trans-1,4	1.58	0.38	4.2	600

[*] Temperatures varied from 16° to 20°.

The generalization that K_1K_2 is larger for the *trans* isomer of a pair of acids breaks down in this series. Furthermore, the ratio K_1K_2 undergoes an inversion as the three pairs are compared. In the 1,2 and 1,4 diacids the ratio is larger for the *cis* isomers, whereas the converse is true of the 1,3 acids. These facts indicate that some conformational adjustments (see Chapter 1) occur to give favorable electrostatic interactions between the groups.

The overall ionization constants (K_1, K_2) for the *cis* and *trans* 1,2 diacids are very nearly the same despite the fact that there is a noticeable difference in the first ionization constants. If the *trans* dianion were forced to occupy the diequatorial conformation (III) it should be relatively unstable because of electrostatic repulsion between the negative oxygens. The data indicate that the dianion has conformation IV in which the negative charges are farther apart than they are in the *cis* dianion. The ionization constants are equalized because the

[22] R. Kuhn and A. Wassermann, *Helv. Chim. Acta*, 11, 50 (1928).

minimizing of electrostatic repulsion can be accomplished only by incurring some extra strain in the diaxial conformation.

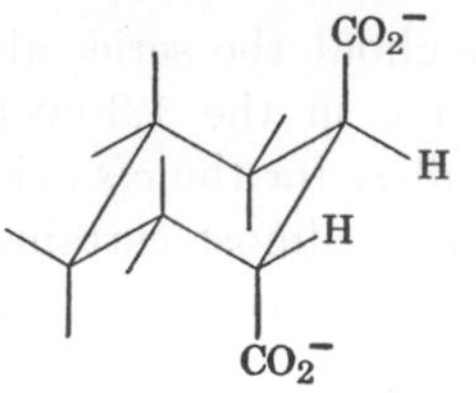

IV 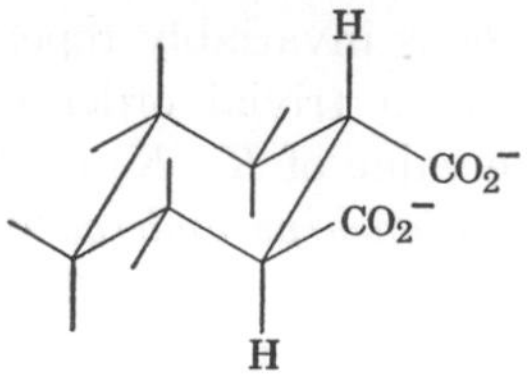   III

The *cis* 1,3 diacid can assume conformations V and VI, but there is no reason to doubt that VI, the diequatorial form, will be preferred by the acid and both of its anions. In this conformation the two negatively charged groups of the second anion are oriented at a wide angle to each other. For this reason it is easier to form this anion than its *trans* isomer, as is shown by the relative magnitudes of $K_1 K_2$ for the

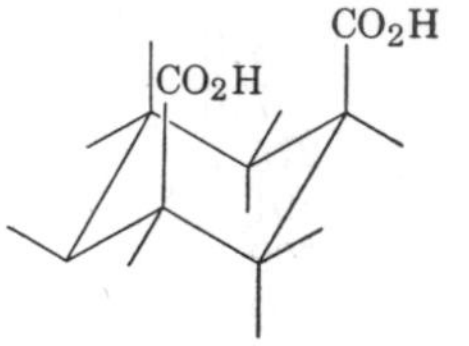

V *cis* 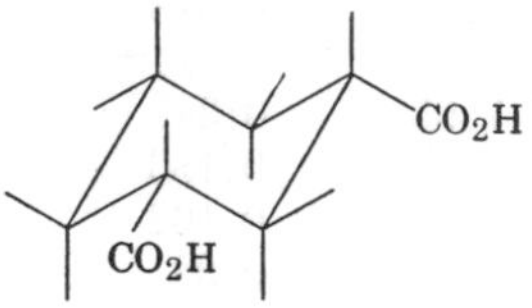   VI *cis* 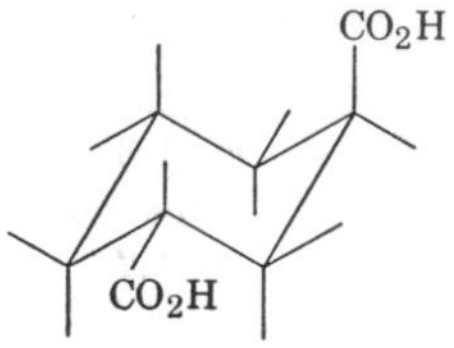   VII *trans*

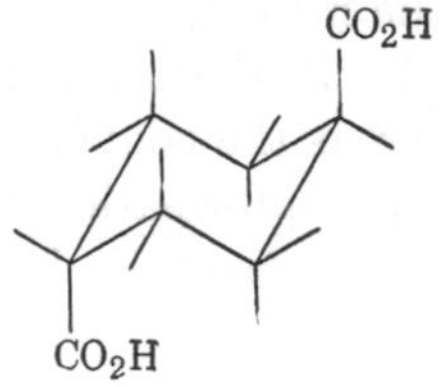

VIII   IX   X
trans   *trans*   *cis*

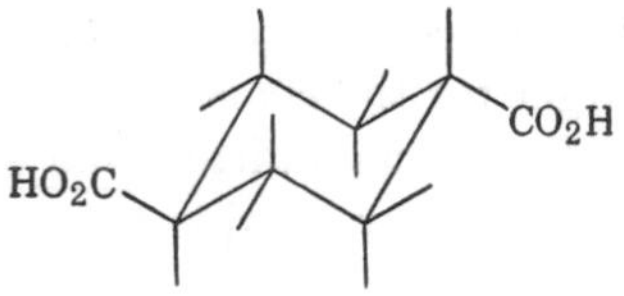

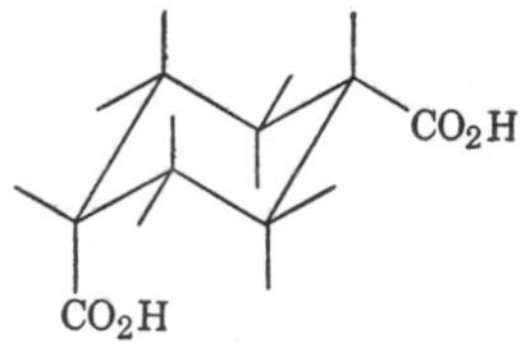

two isomers. The effect of a large separation between the negative groups in the second anion is again demonstrated by the large values of $K_1 K_2$ for both the *cis* and *trans* 1,4 diacids.

The above discussion of the six cyclohexane diacids is fortified by consideration of solvent effects on the ionization constants. Kuhn and Wassermann [22] studied the acids in 50% methanol as well as in water.

All the arguments presented are based upon long-range electrostatic interactions which should be accentuated in media of lower dielectric constant. The pattern of comparisons is repeated and exaggerated as is shown by the data in Table VII.

TABLE VII

IONIZATION CONSTANTS OF CYCLOHEXANE DIACIDS IN 50% WATER-METHANOL [22]

Acid	K_1/K_2	$K_1K_2 \times 10^{12}$
1,2-cis	885	0.347
1,2-trans	85	2.04
1,3-cis	38	8.31
1,3-trans	83	1.32
1,4-cis	36	1.82
1,4-trans	31	7.41

A set of interesting data is shown in Table VIII, which compares the ionization constants of various benzene carboxylic acids, some of which are very highly hindered.

TABLE VIII

FIRST IONIZATION CONSTANTS OF BENZENE CARBOXYLIC ACIDS IN WATER [23]

No.	Positions of Carboxyl Groups	$K_1 \times 10^4$	$K_1 \times 10^4$ Divided by Number of CO_2H Groups
XI	1	0.68	0.68
XII	1,2	10.5	5.3
XIII	1,3	3.5	1.8
XIV	1,3,5	7.5	2.5
XV	1,2,4	30.0	10.0
XVI	1,2,3	16.0	5.3
XVII	1,2,4,5	120.0	40.00
XVIII	1,2,3,4	42.0	11.1
XIX	1,2,3,5	88.0	22.0
XX	1,2,3,4,5	160.0	52.0
XXI	1,2,3,4,5,6	400.0	66.7

Acid-strengthening effects other than statistical considerations are in evidence. The comparison of phthalic acid (XII) with isophthalic (XIII) and trimesic (XIV) acids shows that a pronounced effect results from *ortho* substitution. Once again hydrogen bonding in the first anion is indicated. The fact that trimellitic (XV) is stronger than

[23] W. R. Maxwell and J. R. Partington, *Trans. Faraday Soc.*, *33*, 670 (1937).

hemimellitic (XVI) shows that the *ortho* effect is not cumulative, which is in agreement with the view that a symmetrical arrangement such as XII is unstable with respect to an unsymmetrical arrange-

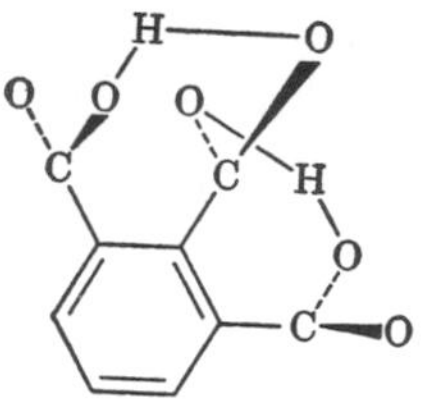

XII

ment which allows one of the O—H—O bonds to become rather short. The build-up of acid-strengthening buttressing effects is evident in prehnitic (XVIII), mellophanic (XIX), benzenepentacarboxylic (XX), and mellitic (XXI) acids but is overlain with other effects and is probably not worthy of detailed discussion.

IONIZATION OF PHENOLS AND ANILINIUM IONS

There is every reason to expect that *ortho* effects will have significant influences on the acidity of phenols and anilinium ions. However, it is generally found that such factors are not outstanding except in N-substituted anilines. Again, there is strong indication that the

TABLE IX

IONIZATION CONSTANTS OF PHENOLS IN WATER SOLUTION

Phenol	K	Reference
Phenol	1.2×10^{-10}	24
o-Nitrophenol	6.8×10^{-8}	24
m-Nitrophenol	5×10^{-9}	24
p-Nitrophenol	7×10^{-8}	24
Catechol	3.5×10^{-10}	24
Hydroquinone	4.5×10^{-11}	24
Nitrohydroquinone	1.01×10^{-6}	25
2,6-Dinitrophenol	1×10^{-4}	25
2,4-Dinitrophenol	5.6×10^{-4}	26
3-Nitrocatechol	1.88×10^{-6}	25
2-Nitroresorcinol	1.59×10^{-6}	25
4-Nitroresorcinol	1.04×10^{-6}	25

[24] G. Briegleb, *Naturwissenschaften*, *31*, 62 (1943).
[25] F. L. Gilbert, F. C. Laxton, and E. B. R. Prideaux, *J. Chem. Soc.*, *1927*, 349.
[26] H. V. Halben and G. Kortun, *Z. Electrochem.*, *40*, 502 (1934).

steric requirements of protons are so small as to be easily camouflaged by polar influences. The dissociation constants of an interesting group of phenols are listed in Table IX.

It will be noted that it makes relatively little difference whether a nitro group is placed *ortho* or *para* to a hydroxy group. This indicates two significant facts. First, it might have been expected that hydrogen bonding in the *ortho* compounds such as XX might preferentially stabilize the neutral forms of the *ortho* compounds. Secondly, one might

O—H—O$^{\ominus}$

—N$\overset{\oplus}{=}$O

XX

wonder whether or not an *ortho* nitro group will be forced out of the plane of the benzene ring and thus lose part of its potency as an acid-strengthening substituent. The results indicate that neither effect is large. This conclusion is fortified by the comparison of 2- and 4-nitroresorcinol. In the former compound both hydroxyl groups are *ortho* to the nitro function, and so distortion from planarity should be increased if it were of measurable significance.

Since the nitro group is both large and sensitive to steric arrangement it is unlikely that any remarkable effects will be observed before the *ortho* groups become so large that they exclude solvent molecules. This last effect has not been observed frequently but no doubt accounts for the fact that 2,6-di-*tert*-alkyl phenols are reported [27] to be so weakly acidic that they are insoluble in concentrated aqueous sodium hydroxide. These facts provide a clean example of steric hindrance to solvation because of the demonstrated insensitivity of phenol ionization constants to other steric effects.

Steric effects on the acidity of anilinium ions have been discussed carefully by Brown and Cahn.[28] Since their presentation is concise and complete in the original it will be treated only briefly here. The data shown in Table X and XI were gathered from the literature by Brown and Cahn.

The two variables that Brown and Cahn consider are steric inhibition of resonance in the free base, which is base strengthening, and steric strains in the conjugate acids, which are base weakening. Since the two factors oppose each other it is possible to account for the

[27] G. H. Stillson, D. W. Sawyer, and C. K. Hunt, *J. Am. Chem. Soc.*, *67*, 303 (1945).

[28] H. C. Brown and A. Cahn, *J. Am. Chem. Soc.*, *72*, 2939 (1950).

TABLE X

DISSOCIATION CONSTANTS OF ANILINIUM IONS IN WATER AT 25°

Base	pK_a	$pK_a - pK_a$(aniline)
Aniline	4.58	0
o-Toluidine	4.39	−0.19
p-Toluidine	5.12	0.54
N-Methylaniline	4.85	0.27
N-Ethylaniline	5.11	0.53
N-n-Propylaniline	5.02	0.44
N,N-Dimethylaniline	5.06	0.48
N,N-Diethylaniline	6.56	1.98
N,N-Di-n-propylaniline	5.59	1.01
N,N-Dimethyl-p-toluidine	5.50	0.92
N,N-Dimethyl-o-toluidine	5.86	1.28

TABLE XI

DISSOCIATION CONSTANTS OF ANILINIUM IONS IN 50% ETHANOL AT 25°

Base	pK_a	$pK_a - pK_a$(aniline)
Aniline	4.25	0
m-2-Xylidine	3.42	−0.83
m-4-Xylidine	4.61	0.36
N,N-Dimethylaniline	4.26	0.01
N,N-Dimethyl-o-toluidine	5.07	0.82
N,N-Dimethyl-m-2-xylidine	4.69	0.44
N,N-Dimethyl-m-4-xylidine	5.28	1.03
N,N-Dimethyl-m-5-xylidine	4.48	0.23
N,N-Dimethyl-p-xylidine	5.19	0.94

irregularities that result from the increase in the total bulk of the groups attached to the basic nitrogen or *ortho* to it. The great versatility of the method of explanation derives from the fact that a saturation effect can be achieved in the inhibition of resonance. It is unlikely that the nitrogen bond angles can be compressed beyond some lower limit which may not be much less than the tetrahedral angle. It is assumed that steric strain in the anilinium ion is felt first and accounts for the fact that o-toluidine and m-2-xylidine are weaker bases than aniline. Increasing the steric requirements somewhat more in N,N-dimethyl-o-toluidine results in a large decrease in the resonance energy of the free base and is, therefore, base strengthening. Finally, further increase in steric requirements results in another base weakening trend.

One drawback in this analysis is the flexibility of the theory. It becomes difficult to assess the importance of still other factors such as variation in solvation energy. As was previously stated, it is not common to observe major influences which can be traced to the steric requirements of a single hydrogen. Furthermore, as the hindrance to the addition of a proton is increased, the steric hindrance to solvation of the anilinium ions will also be increased. It is impossible to separate the two effects by qualitative considerations. However, there is one indication that solvation effects are of considerable importance. If the changes in basicity were due entirely to variations in the internal strain they should be independent of solvent effects. This proves not to be so. In aqueous solution dimethylaniline and dimethyl-*o*-toluidine are, respectively, 0.48 and 1.28 pK units stronger than aniline, whereas the differences are only 0.01 and 0.82 in 50% ethanol. Since solvation energies should be smaller in the latter solvent the results indicate that steric hindrance to solvation may be of considerable importance. Pearson and Williams [29] have pointed out that the variation in relative basicity constants in water and chlorobenzene show very great sensitivity to solvent effects.

Another example of the same type of ambiguity is found in a report [30] that 2,6-di-*tert*-butylpyridine is a weaker base than pyridine in water solution. While the compression of the proton in the pyridinium ions may be of some consequence it is likely that the approach of solvent molecules to the center of positive charge in the ion is a major factor.

ACIDITY OF MISCELLANEOUS SECONDARY ACIDS

The accurate estimation of the acidity of C—H bonds is usually difficult to carry out with precision. The classical acidity constants are ordinarily so small as to be unmeasurable by the usual methods or in solvents which lend themselves to treatment by conventional thermodynamic electrolyte theory. A second difficulty arises from the slow rates of most neutralization reactions.

One of the most interesting trends is found in the comparison of the apparent acidities of saturated hydrocarbons. If the results of the study of metalation reactions

$$(1) \qquad\qquad RM + R'H \rightleftarrows RH + R'M$$

can be taken as a criterion it develops that the order of acidities is methyl > primary > secondary > tertiary.[31] The same conclusion is

[29] R. G. Pearson and F. V. Williams, *J. Am. Chem. Soc.*, **76**, 258 (1954).

[30] H. C. Brown and R. B. Johannesen, *J. Am. Chem. Soc.*, **75**, 3865 (1953).

[31] H. Gilman and J. Morton, in Adams, *Organic Reactions*, Vol. 8, Chapter 6, John Wiley & Sons, New York, 1954.

reached by comparing the rates of endothermic reactions [32] such as halogen-metal interconversions.[33] In order to draw conclusions the assumption is necessary that the rates of such reactions parallel the basicities of the organometallic reagents if they are compared in the reactions with a common substrate. The basis for making such an assumption has been discussed in detail.[32] Since alkyl groups are acid weakening as substituents on benzene rings the order of acidities may be due to the electronic influence of the alkyl groups attached to the carbon atom in question.[34] However, a steric effect may be responsible for part or all of the observed effects. In a carbanion, $R_3C^{\ominus}$, the unshared pair of electrons should occupy an atomic orbital having a considerable amount of s character. If this were a pure s orbital, the R—C—R bond angles would be 90°, which might therefore be considered as the "natural" bond angle in a carbanion. Spreading of this bond angle because of repulsion between the R groups would promote the unshared pair and render the ion less stable or more basic. Therefore, B strain,[35] which increases with increased branching of the ion, should increase the basicity of the anions.

This analysis does not apply to conjugated, unsaturated carbanions. These will, of course, prefer the plan trigonal configuration in order to give maximum opportunity for the redistribution of charge to the rest of the system. The situation is illustrated nicely by cyclopropanes. Although experimental evidence to bear upon the subject has not yet been provided it would be anticipated that I strain in cyclopropane itself would be acid strengthening. However, there are indirect indications [36] that benzoyl cyclopropane is less acidic than ketones such as acetophenone. Nitrocyclopropane is insoluble in aqueous base, indicating that it is less acidic than nitroalkanes in general.[37]

[32] G. S. Hammond, *J. Am. Chem. Soc.*, 77, 334 (1955).

[33] R. G. Jones and H. Gilman, in Adams, *Organic Reactions*, Vol. 6, Chapter 7, John Wiley & Sons, New York, 1951.

[34] The commonly accepted view as to the electronic influence of alkyl groups may be erroneous. It is quite certain, for example, that the methyl group in *m*-toluic acid is acid weakening by virtue of an inductive effect. However, this can be accounted for on the basis of the polarity of the C—CH₃ bond which arises from the fact that the carbon atoms are in different states of hybridization. If this is so the inductive effect should disappear when the methyl (or other alkyl group) is attached to a saturated (tetrahedral) carbon atom. The polarity may, in fact, be reversed if the methyl group is attached to a carbanion as in $CH_3CH_2^-$.

[35] H. C. Brown, H. Batholomay, and M. D. Taylor, *J. Am. Chem. Soc.*, 66, 435 (1944).

[36] F. J. Diehl and W. G. Brown, *J. Am. Chem. Soc.*, 75, 5023 (1953).

[37] H. Shechter, personal communication.

A number of other conclusions concerning the acidity of secondary organic acids can be inferred from the literature, but two cases are particularly interesting. The data in Table XII relate to the acidity and tautomerization of nitroalkanes.

TABLE XII

ACIDITY OF ACI AND NITRO FORMS OF NITROALKANES [38]

Compound	K_a	K_{ac} *	K_i †
CH_3NO_2	6.1×10^{-11}	5.6×10^{-4}	1.1×10^{-7}
$CH_3CH_2NO_2$	2.5×10^{-9}	3.9×10^{-5}	8.9×10^{-5}
$(CH_3)_2CHNO_2$	2.1×10^{-8}	7.7×10^{-6}	2.75×10^{-3}

* $K_{ac} = [H^+][A^-]/[Aci]$.
† $K_i = [Aci]/[Nitro]$.

K_a is the overall acidity constant of the nitroalkane, which is essentially equal to the acidity constant of the nitro form since the amount of aci-nitro compound at equilibrium is very small in all cases. K_i is the isomerization constant for the reaction

$$Nitro \underset{\longleftarrow}{\overset{K_i}{\longrightarrow}} Aci\text{-}nitro$$

and K_{ac} is the specific acidity constant of the aci-nitro form. The most interesting feature is the increase of both K_a and K_i on the introduction of methyl groups. Since both ionization and tautomerization should increase the bond angles about the α-carbon atom the influence of the alkyl groups may indicate that there is appreciable strain in nitroethane and 2-nitropropane. It is reassuring to note that the usual acid-weakening electronic effect of methyl groups asserts itself in the ionization of the aci-nitro compounds since their dissociation should involve little or no change in geometry.

The bicyclic trisulfone, XXIII, is nearly as strong an acid as tri-

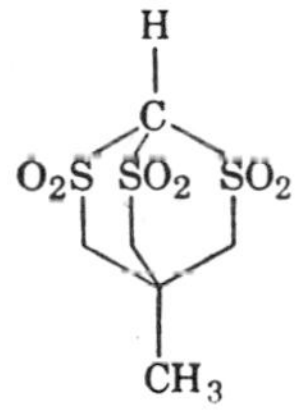

methylsulfonyl methane.[39] That the acidity is due to the bridgehead hydrogen was shown by the fact that the analogous bridgehead meth-

---

[38] D. Turnbull and S. H. Maron, J. Am. Chem. Soc., 65, 212 (1945).
[39] W. von E. Doering and L. K. Levy, J. Am. Chem. Soc., 77, 509 (1955).

ylated compound was not acidic. Conceivably the bridgehead carbon atom can become coplanar with the three sulfur atoms in this system, although such a configuration would be impossible in the corresponding all-carbon system. On the other hand, the steric requirements for redistribution of the negative charge from carbon to the adjacent sulfonyl groups may be such as to render coplanarity unnecessary. It is interesting that Bartlett and Lewis [40] have inferred that the anion, XXIV, from triptycene is a very strong base, since an at-

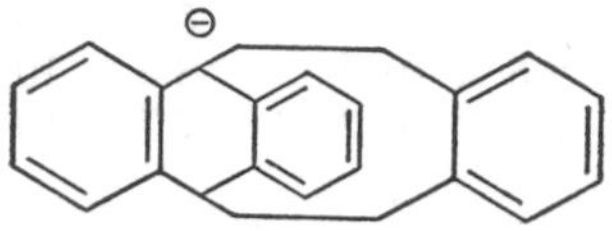

XXIV

tempt to prepare it from bromotriptycene and sodium in dry mineral oil led to the formation of triptycene and, presumably, the metalation of the saturated solvent. Since the mineral oil was in large excess the results could merely indicate that XXIV has a basicity comparable to that of saturated carbanions in general. The steric inhibition of resonance, such as renders the triphenylmethide ion a relatively weak base, is observed as expected.

ENOLIZATION AND ACIDITY OF CARBONYL COMPOUNDS

One class of pseudo acids, carbonyl compounds, was omitted from the discussion in the previous section. The reason for doing so is the convenience of discussing the acidity and the enolization of these compounds together. The stereochemical effects on both these reactions are appreciable. Much work has been devoted to the study of such reactions, and, unfortunately, many of the measurements reported in the older literature are of limited value because of the failure of the investigators to recognize the unique role of the common anion in the system. In fact, as recently as 1945, Gustafson [41] wrote of the

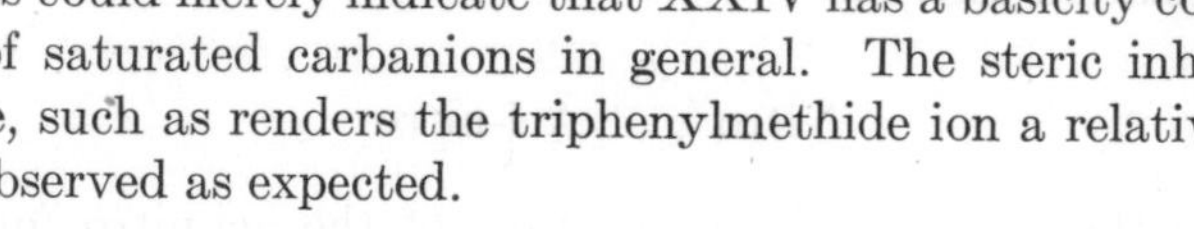

clarification which devolved from the recognition of this species and was warmly commended by Arndt,[42] one of the foremost workers in

[40] P. D. Bartlett and E. S. Lewis, J. Am. Chem. Soc., 72, 1005 (1950).
[41] C. Gustafson, Suomen Kemistilehti, 18B, 11 (1945).
[42] F. Arndt and B. Eistert, Suomen Kemistilehti, 18B, 13 (1945).

the field. However, even Gustafson remarked that it should be recalled that two other, isomeric, ions were the first products of the ionization of the keto and enol forms. Of course, some workers [43] had recognized long before that the readjustment of electron density in the system can be achieved much more rapidly than the movement of the proton away from either molecule.

Much confusion has also arisen from the unsound procedure of drawing conclusions concerning keto-enol equilibria on the basis of products derived from carbonyl compounds in various reactions. Consider, for example, the formation of an enol ester by the acid-catalyzed reaction of a carbonyl compound with an acid anhydride. The reaction may actually involve the acylation of either the enol or the keto form, as is illustrated by the equations. Since kinetic factors are completely uncontrolled, yield data have little significance in revealing the actual composition of the equilibrated mixture.

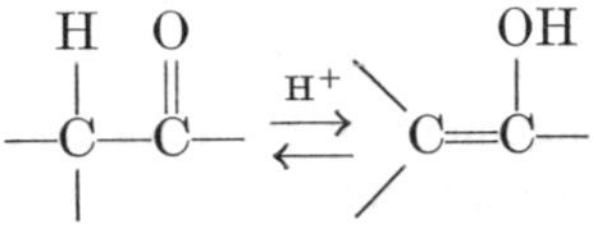

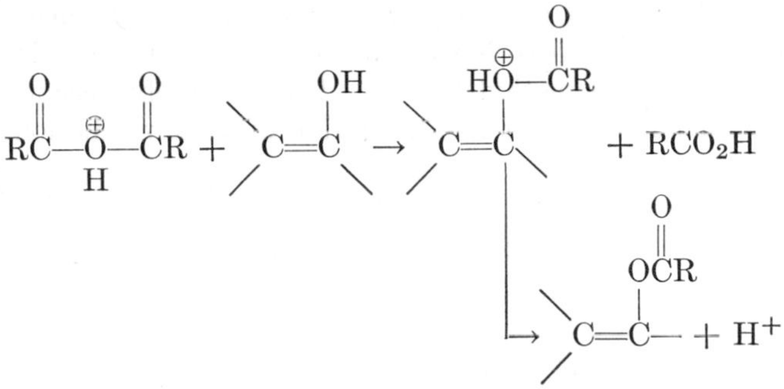

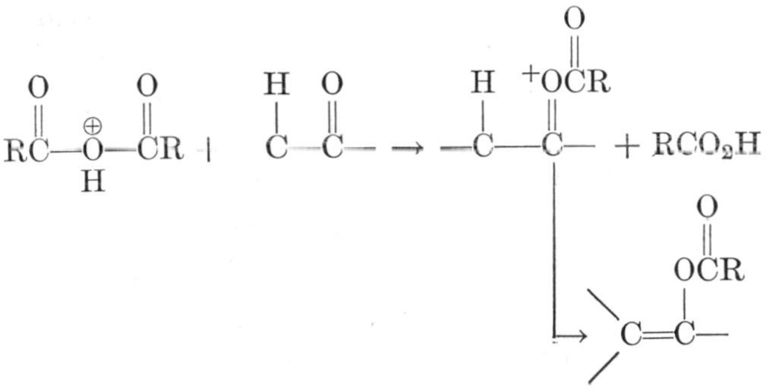

[43] L. P. Hammett, *Physical Organic Chemistry*, McGraw-Hill Book Co., New York, 1940.

In the preparation of the material discussed herein only true equilibrium measurements are considered unless otherwise stated. The most widely used method for the measurement of tautomerization constants has been the Kurt Meyer [44] titration, and nearly all the data presented were obtained by that method or by the ingenious modification of it [45] which permits the accurate estimation of very small enol contents.

In monocarbonyl compounds it is to be expected that two effects will be observed depending upon the state of unsaturation of the molecules. Among saturated compounds one should observe modest increases in enol contents as a consequence of branching at the α-carbon atom since the conversion of keto to enol spreads the bond angles between groups attached at that point. Since the introduction of alkyl groups at the α position will also increase the hyperconjugative resonance energy of the enols, data designed to bear upon this ,question should be scrutinized with great care. In conjugated, unsaturated enols the effects of branching may be quite the opposite since the coplanar arrangement of the enol and the rest of the system may be prevented. For example, one would anticipate that diisopropyl ketone would be more extensively enolized than acetone in a common solvent whereas XXV would probably have a lower enol content than benzyl methyl ketone. Unfortunately acceptable data are not available to permit the evaluation of these predictions.

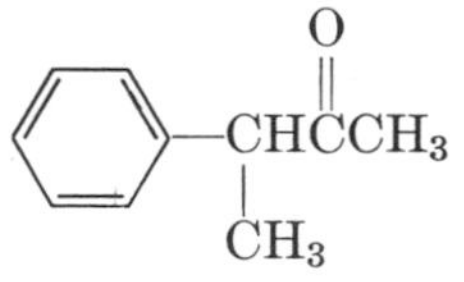

$$
\begin{array}{c}
\text{O} \\
\parallel \\
\bigcirc\text{—CHCCH}_3 \\
| \\
\text{CH}_3 \\
\text{XXV}
\end{array}
$$

The enol contents of acetone, cyclopentanone and cyclohexanone have been reported and the results shown in Table XIII.

TABLE XIII

ENOLIZATION OF MONOKETONES [45]

Ketone	Per Cent Enol in the Liquid
Acetone	2.5×10^{-4}
Cyclopentanone	4.8×10^{-3}
Cyclohexanone	2.0×10^{-2}

[44] K. H. Meyer, *Ber.*, *45*, 2843 (1912).
[45] G. Schwarzenbach and C. Wittwer, *Helv. Chim. Acta*, *30*, 669 (1947).

The extensive enolization of cyclohexanone as compared to cyclopentanone has been accounted for on a very reasonable basis.[46] A double bond exocyclic to a cyclohexane system is unstable with respect to migration into the ring,[47, 48] and the tendency is much less pronounced with cyclopentanes.[49, 50] The enolization phenomena merely represent another example of the general relationship. The explanation depends upon the fact that the introduction of a second trigonal carbon atom in the cyclopentane structure twists the methylene hydrogens on the other carbon atoms away from the eclipsed configuration whereas the converse is true of cyclohexanes. The stability difference is, therefore, related to the differences in the strain energy in the two ketones, and the assumption is made that the differences in stability of the cyclopentene and cyclohexene systems is negligible. In justification of this it is pointed out that the increment in the heats of formation between cyclopentene and cyclohexene is 9.3 kcal./mole as compared with an increment of 11 between cyclopentane and cyclohexane. These figures should be compared with the increment of 4.9 kcal. per methylene group in the alkane series. The strain which might have been expected in cyclopentenes [50a] is therefore not very significant.

It is not easy to account for the fact that cyclopentanone is more highly enolized than acetone since the above considerations would lead us to expect that aliphatic ketones should be intermediate between cyclohexanone and cyclopentanone. Possibly the difference is due to the fact that acetone loses a free rotation upon enolization whereas the cyclic compound does not.

New factors enter the picture when β-dicarbonyl systems are examined. Two features which lead to the stabilization of enol forms are sensitive to steric effects. The ultraviolet and infrared spectra of dibenzoylmethane indicate a structure such as XXVI for dibenzoylmethane, although the exact location of the hydrogen atom is uncer-

[46] H. C. Brown, J. H. Brewster, and H. Shechter, *J. Am. Chem. Soc.*, 76, 467 (1954).

[47] O. Wallach et al., *Ann.*, 360, 26 (1908), and earlier papers in the series.

[48] W. Hückel, *Theoretische Grundlagen der organischen Chemie*, 2nd ed., p. 72, 1934.

[49] W. Dieckmann, *Ber.*, 55, 2470 (1922).

[50] G. A. R. Kon and E. A. Speight, *J. Chem. Soc.*, 1926, 2727; G. A. R. Kon and J. H. Nutland, *J. Chem. Soc.*, 1926, 3101.

[50a] If the two olefinic carbon atoms in cyclopentene are given 120° bond angles the ring cannot be completed without some compression of the remaining angles below the tetrahedral value.

tain.[51]　In any event the O—O distance is short (1.44 A calculated using aromatic C—C distances), and the hydrogen bond must be rather strong. If steric factors permit, the enols of all acyclic β-dicarbonyl compounds should be planar, to maximize the resonance energy,

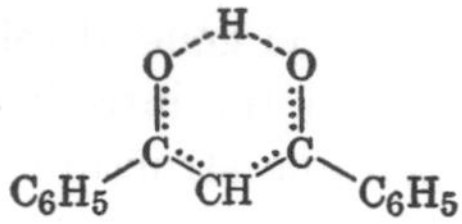

XXVI

and cyclic to permit the formation of strong hydrogen bonds. The realization of these conditions may be prevented by various steric factors as is found by inspection of the data in Table XIV.

TABLE XIV

ENOLIZATION CONSTANTS OF β-DICARBONYL COMPOUNDS [52]

Compound	K_T * Gas Phase	K_T Pure Liquid
$CH_3COCH_2CO_2CH_3$	1.19	0.062
$CH_3COCH_2CO_2C_2H_5$	0.93	0.082
$CH_3COCH(CH_3)CO_2C_2H_5$	0.16	0.043
$CH_3COCH(C_2H_5)CO_2C_2H_5$	0.11	0.031
$CH_3COCH(n\text{-}C_3H_7)CO_2C_2H_5$	0.15	0.075
$CH_3COCH(i\text{-}C_3H_7)CO_2C_2H_5$	0.066	0.051
$CH_3COCH_2COCH_3$	11	3.6
$CH_3COCH(CH_3)COCH_3$	0.79	0.44
$CH_3COCH(C_2H_5)COCH_3$	0.55	0.35

* K_T = [Enol]/[Keto].

The introduction of alkyl groups as substituents on the methylene groups of both acetylacetone and acetoacetic esters decreases the degree of enolization. That the effect is due primarily to the steric requirements of the alkyl groups is demonstrated by the comparison between the n-propyl and isopropyl derivatives of ethyl acetoacetate. The latter shows the monotonic decrease in K_T along the substituent series, H, CH_3, C_2H_5, $(CH_3)_2CH$. The n-propyl compound, on the other hand, is more highly enolized than the ethyl derivative. Examination of models shows that the methyl groups in 3-methyl acetylacetone overlap to an appreciable extent in the planar, cyclic molecules. That this results in a serious distortion of the molecule is dem-

[51] G. S. Hammond and W. G. Bordiun, unpublished observations.

[52] J. B. Conant and A. F. Thompson, *J. Am. Chem. Soc.*, *54*, 4039 (1932).

onstrated by the infrared spectrum of the enol.[53] Whereas the enol of 3-methyl acetylacetone shows an O—H stretching frequency at 3400 cm^{-1} the unsubstituted compound has only a weak band at that frequency, indicating that the strength of the hydrogen bond is much decreased in the former compound. It is probable that 3-methyl acetylacetone exists to an appreciable extent in the acyclic enol form.

A further interesting change occurs in the series of compounds XXVII in which the steric requirements of the R groups are varied by branching at the α-carbon atom.[53] In the compounds in which R

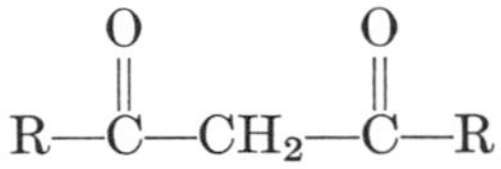

$$R-\overset{\overset{\displaystyle O}{\|}}{C}-CH_2-\overset{\overset{\displaystyle O}{\|}}{C}-R$$

XXVII

is isopropyl or *tert*-butyl the infrared spectra of the liquids reveal that the diketo content has been sharply reduced in comparison with acetylacetone. Precise determination of the enolization constants is not possible because they are exceedingly large. However, the qualitative comparisons are striking. At first it seems enigmatical that increasing the steric requirements at the ends of the chain increases the degree of enolization whereas a similar change in the middle of the chain has an opposite effect. However, molecular models show an obvious solution. In the diketo forms of diisobutyrylmethane and dipivaloylmethane, the carbonyl groups can only be rotated about 90° from the parallel, coplanar configuration XXVIII, whereas in the molecules with smaller R groups configuration XXIX, in which the

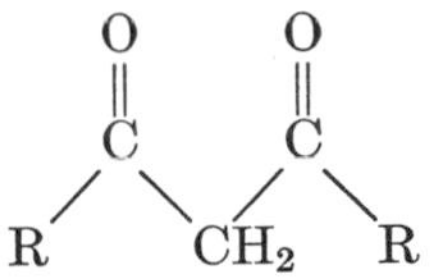

XXVIII 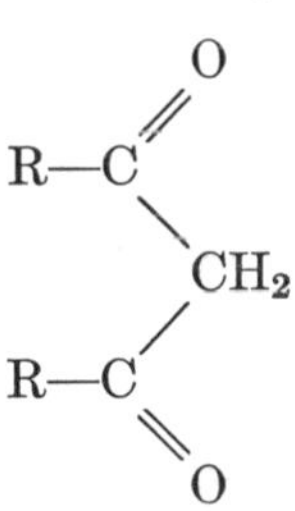   XXIX

repulsion between the carbonyl dipoles is minimized, is readily attained. There is, however, no serious interference between the hydrogen on the central carbon atom of the enol and even a pair of terminal *tert*-butyl groups in the cyclic enols.

New factors are observed when cyclic β-dicarbonyl compounds are studied. If the carbonyl groups are both included in the ring cyclic

[53] G. S. Hammond and G. Guter, unpublished observations.

hydrogen-bonded structures are not possible for geometric reasons. However, both these compounds and dicarbonyl compounds in which one of the carbonyl groups is exocyclic are in general more highly enolized than their completely acyclic analogs. Pertinent data are summarized in Tables XV and XVI.

TABLE XV

ENOL CONTENT OF CYCLIC β-KETOESTERS

	K_T * (Gas Phase)	K_T (Pure Liquid)	K_T (0.1 M in EtOH)	Reference
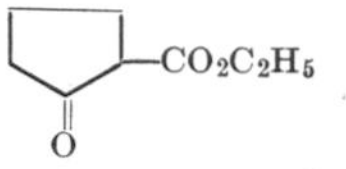 (cyclopentanone-CO$_2$C$_2$H$_5$)	0.38	0.047	0.068	54, 55
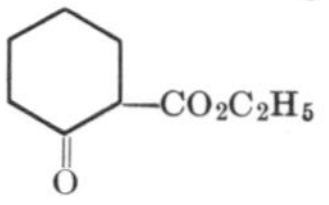 (cyclohexanone-CO$_2$C$_2$H$_5$, exocyclic)	9.9	3.2	1.5	54, 55
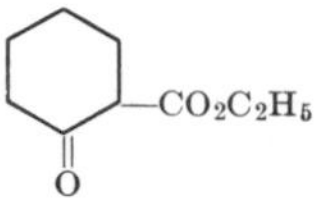 (cyclohexanone-CO$_2$C$_2$H$_5$)	—	0.22	0.16	55
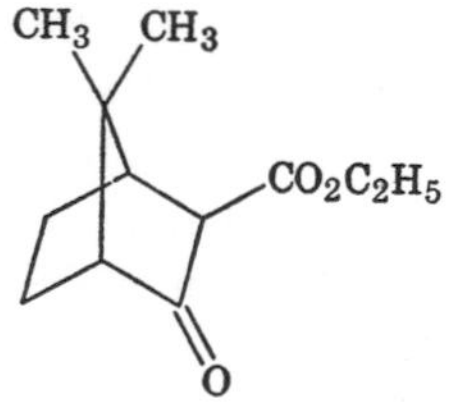 CH$_3$ CH$_3$ (camphor-CO$_2$C$_2$H$_5$)	—	0.0050	0.0050	55
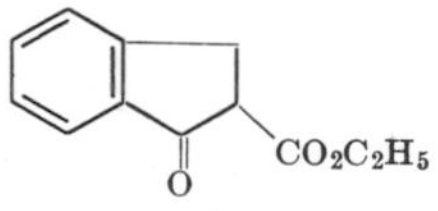 (indanone-CO$_2$C$_2$H$_5$)	—	0.33	0.31	55

* K_T = [Enol]/[Keto].

Among the β-dicarbonyl compounds two general correlations appear. The first is the comparison between the substances in which one of the carbonyl functions is exocyclic and those in which they are both included in ring. The second compares the five- and six-membered rings. In general it is found that all cyclopentanones are less highly enolized than the corresponding cyclohexanones. This appears to be a repetition of the phenomenon observed in the monoketones.

[54] R. Schreck, *J. Am. Chem. Soc.*, **71**, 1881 (1949).
[55] W. Dieckmann, *Ber.*, **55**, 2470 (1922).

TABLE XVI

Enol Content of Diketones

Compound	K_T (Water)	Reference
$CH_3COCH_2COCH_3$	0.18	56
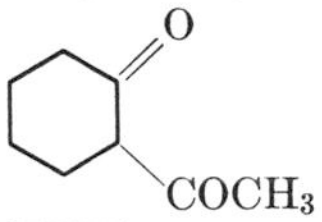 (cyclohexanone with COCH₃)	0.41	56
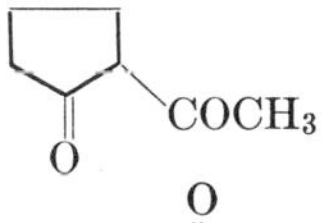 (cyclopentanone with COCH₃)	0.18	56
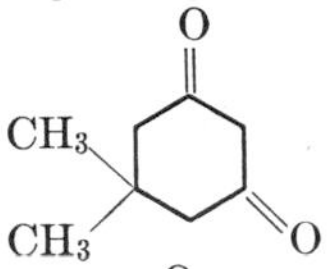 (5,5-dimethylcyclohexane-1,3-dione)	20	56
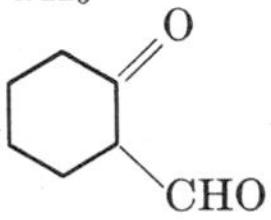 (cyclohexanone with CHO)	0.94	56
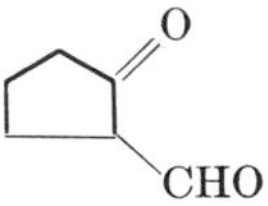 (cyclopentanone with CHO)	0.68	56
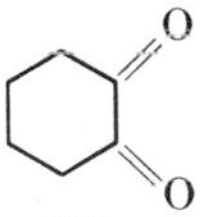 (cyclohexane-1,2-dione)	0.67	57
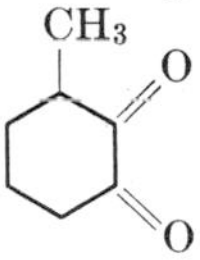 (3-methylcyclohexane-1,2-dione)	1.5	57
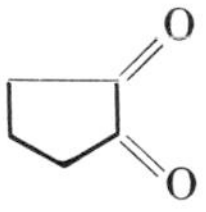 (cyclopentane-1,2-dione)	∞ *	57
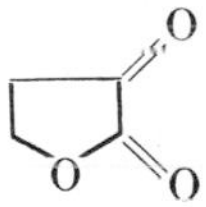 (tetrahydrofuran-2,3-dione)	∞ *	57
$CH_3COCOCH_3$	5.6×10^{-3} †	47
$C_6H_5CH_2COCO\ \phi$	1.5 †	58

* Reported as 100% enol.
† Pure liquid.

[56] G. Schwarzenback and E. Felder, *Helv. Chim. Acta*, *27*, 1044 (1944).
[57] G. Schwarzenback and C. Wittwer, *Helv. Chim. Acta*, *30*, 663 (1947).
[58] H. Moreau, *Ann. chim.*, [10], *14*, 283 (1930).

1,3-Cyclohexanediones, which are exemplified by dimedone, are close to 100% enolic [56] despite the fact that they cannot be stabilized by strong internal hydrogen bonds. This implies that the enolic structure is stabilized relative to the diketo form by as much as 10 kcal. owing to some structural feature which is either unique or of unusual importance in these substances. This is probably due to the fact that the enols are held in the *trans*, coplanar arrangement **XXX** in which

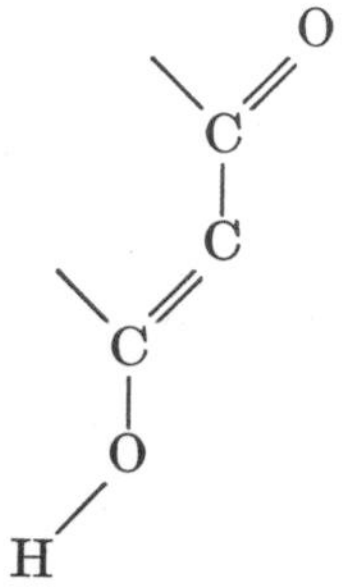

XXX

oxygen-oxygen repulsion is at a minimum and resonance stabilization is maximized. Acyclic diketones and acetyl cycloalkanones are less stable in this configuration because of the interference between groups attached to the ends of the system. As will be discussed shortly, this interpretation is further borne out by a comparison of the acidity constants of the various compounds.

The 1,2-diketones show an interesting variation from the previously established pattern of behavior. All cyclic structures should be classed together as being much more extensively enolized than their acyclic analogs. Furthermore, it now is the five-membered rings which seem most adaptable to the enolic structure. This is probably due, not to any special steric stabilization of the enols, but rather to the repulsion

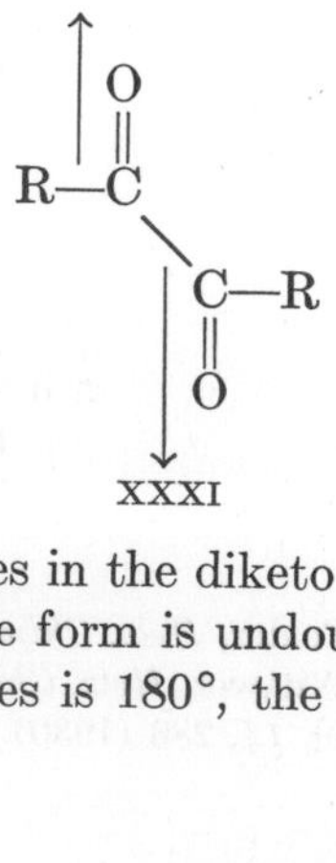

XXXI

between the carbonyl dipoles in the diketo compounds. In an acyclic 1,2-diketone the most stable form is undoubtedly **XXXI**. The angle between the carbonyl dipoles is 180°, the condition for minimum repulsion. In 1,2-cyclopentanedione the two carbonyl groups are held rigidly in a *cis*, coplanar configuration. On enolization the electrostatic repulsion is relieved by virtue of the fact that the hydroxyl hydrogen in the enol screens the electronegative oxygens from one another. The configuration is not proper for strong hydrogen bonding in the usual sense of the term, but **XXXII** may be said to be significantly stable with respect to **XXXIII** because of the high energy con-

XXXII   XXXIII

tent of the latter. In 1,2-cyclohexanedione the more flexible structure permits rotation of the carbonyl groups away from the coplanar configuration so that the electrostatic repulsion in the dicarbonyl compound is reduced relative to that in the five-membered ring. It is still sufficient, however, to make the cyclic ketone much more highly enolized than its acyclic analogs.

An interesting side issue of this discussion is the status of 1,2-cyclopentenediones. It has been shown that 1,2-diphenyl-3,4-diketocyclopentene **XXXIV** exists exclusively in the diketo form in the solid [59] and in solution.[60] This behavior has been discussed frequently,[61] since the enol, **XXXV**, would be an analog of tropolone. Since steric

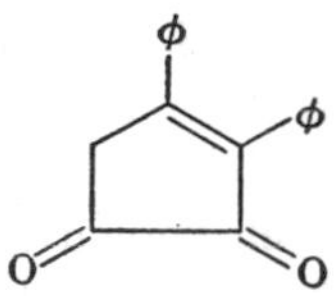

XXXIV 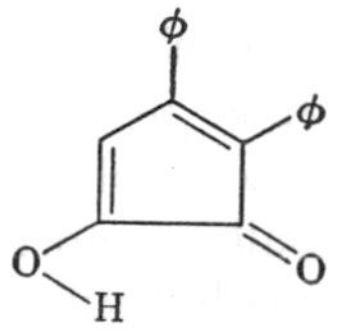   XXXV

strains should all operate in such a way as to increase the stability of the enol relative to that of the diketo form it is logical to assume that some electronic influence makes the enol structure unstable. This has been explained on the basis of the naive molecular orbital method.[62] This method indicates that the normal carbonyl polarity should be

[59] T. A. Giessman and C. F. Koelsch, *J. Org. Chem.*, *3*, 480, 489 (1938).

[60] G. S. Hammond and L. O. Raether, unpublished observations.

[61] J. W. Cook and J. D. Louden, *Quart. Revs. London*, 5, 99 (1951).

[62] J. L. Franklin and F. H. Field, *J. Am. Chem. Soc.*, *75*, 2819 (1953); W. von E. Doering, *ibid.*, *76*, 3203 (1954).

strongly opposed in the structure XXXVI since all six unsaturation electrons are demanded for utilization of three low-energy molecular orbitals associated with the ring.

XXXVI

New information is obtained by scrutiny of the acidity constants of various carbonyl compounds. In the enolate ions the preferred bond angles about the three central carbon atoms of the diketone system are again 120°. However, the hydrogen has now been removed from the system, thus destroying one major source of binding energy from those enols which can assume the cyclic structure. It is therefore safe to assume that all such ions are in the *trans* configuration unless steric strains prevent them from assuming such a configuration. A considerable body of pertinent data has been gathered by Schwarzenbach and is summarized in Table XVII.

The first point of interest is the comparison between acetylacetone and its 3-methyl derivative. It will be recalled that the decrease in the enolization aptitude of the derivative was attributed to the crowding of the three adjacent methyl groups in the cyclic enol and that furthermore it was inferred from spectroscopic evidence that the enol exists in part in the acyclic configuration. If this were so one would expect that the enol would be a stronger acid than the enol from acetylacetone since removal of the proton from the enol would not involve the breaking of a strong hydrogen bond. This steric effect should be partially compensated by the well-known acid-weakening influence of a methyl substituent. In actual fact both the enol and diketo forms of the methyl compound are weaker acids than the corresponding forms of acetylacetone. Furthermore, the change is the largest for the diketo form. However, the differences are of the same order of magnitude, 2.12 and 1.37 pK units, which is not in particularly good agreement with the simplified treatment which we have given. The results suggest that the importance of the internal hydrogen bond in acetylacetone may be greatly diminished in water solution because of hydrogen bonding to the solvent. This would imply that there may be a significant amount of the open-chain enol present in water solutions of acetylacetone. Unfortunately this possibility cannot be checked readily by the spectroscopic method. Also, the large influence on acidity of polar substituents at the central position of the

TABLE XVII

ACIDITY OF ENOLS AND RELATED COMPOUNDS IN WATER SOLUTION [56, 63]

Compound	P_K *	P_E †
$CH_3COCH_2CO_2C_2H_5$	10.49	8.09
$CH_3COCH_2COCH_3$	8.94	8.13 ‡
$CH_3COCH(CH_3)COCH_3$	11.06	9.50
$OH_3COCHBrCOCH_3$	ca. 7	ca. 5.9
$(CH_3CO)_3CH$	—	5.81

| 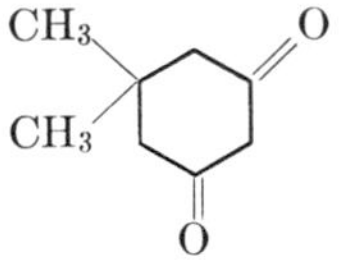 | 5.25 | 5.23 |

| 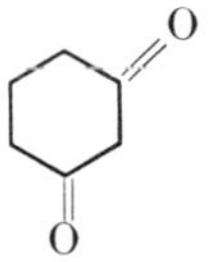 | — | 5.26 |

| 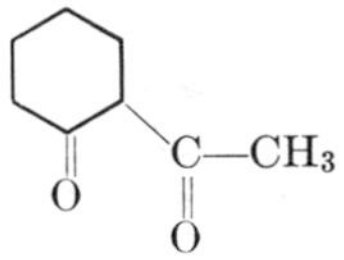 | 10.09 | 0.57 |

| 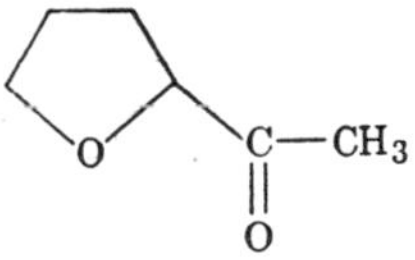 | 7.82 | 7.00 |

| 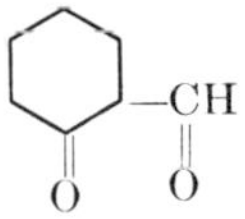 | 6.35 | 6.03 |

| 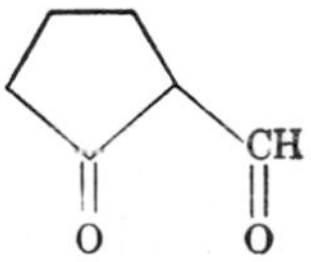 | 5.83 | 5.44 |

* $P_K = -\log \dfrac{[H^+][A^-]}{[Keto]}$.

† $P_E = -\log \dfrac{[H^+][A^-]}{[Enol]}$.

‡ Measured at 25°. All other values obtained at 20°.

[63] G. Schwarzenbach and E. Felder, *Helv. Chim. Acta*, **27**, 1701 (1944).

diketone system is clearly demonstrated by the high acidity of di-acetylbromomethane and triacetylmethane. In triacetylmethane the third acetyl group is equivalent to the other two in the anion but plays no such role in the cyclic enol.

The high acidity of the cyclohexanediones is in good agreement with the account previously given for the extensive enolization of these compounds. The resonance energy of the system should be in-creased by ionization since the two oxygens then become equivalent in the anion. Furthermore, ionization should not be opposed by any loss of binding energy due to internal hydrogen bonding. Similarly, the comparison of the acidity constants shows that the previously in-ferred similarity in structure between the enols of acetyl and formyl cyclohexanone and the enol from acetylacetone is probably proper. It is interesting that acylcyclopentanones are stronger acids than the related cyclohexanone derivatives. This suggests that the hydrogen bonds in enols of the former are stretched somewhat because of the aforementioned ring strain. This renders the bond weaker and thus accounts for the relatively easier ionization of the enol. Since the diketo form is also a stronger acid than acetylacetone one may tenta-tively assume that the 120° bond angles of the ion are fairly easily deformed to minimize strain in the five-membered ring. A 1953 study of the acidity constants of a series of 1,3-cyclohexanediones [64] in 50% ethanol shows that these compounds as a class are relatively strong acids.

LEWIS ACIDS AND BASES

The quantitative study of steric effects in the reaction of Lewis acids and bases has been developed in a thorough and imaginative manner very largely as the result of the work of H. C. Brown and his collaborators. Since most of pertinent material is available in reasonably compact form in the original literature [65] the field will not be discussed in great detail at this time.

The theoretical concepts which led to the development of the "FBI strains" as a means of classifying steric effects have guided the studies to a considerable extent and may be reviewed profitably at the outset of the discussion. F strain and B strain are defined in terms of disso-ciation reactions.[66] If we consider a reaction such as

$$A—B \rightarrow A + B$$

[64] E. G. Meek, J. H. Turnbull and W. Wilson, *J. Chem. Soc.*, *1953*, 289.

[65] H. C. Brown and R. B. Johannesen, *J. Am. Chem. Soc.*, *75*, 16 (1953), and earlier papers in the series.

[66] H. C. Brown, H. Batholomay, and M. D. Taylor, *J. Am. Chem. Soc.*, *66*, 435 (1944).

it is clear that the steric effects on such a process can be conveniently subdivided. If either A or B or both contain bulky groups as part of their structure there may be some compression of the groups in A by those in B in the compound AB. This frontal, or F, strain will be relieved to some extent by the dissociation process. In addition, the strain that arises from the crowding together of groups that remain attached to either A or B may be altered to some extent because of the reorganization of such groups during the reaction process. Strain that manifests itself by contributing to the reorganization energy is called back strain or B strain since it arises from interactions on the backside of the molecule with respect to the bond which is broken on dissociation. It is important to note that in principle it is possible for B strain either to aid or to oppose the dissociation, although the former effect is most commonly noted. The direction of the influence will be determined by the direction of change of the bond angles about the central atoms of A and B on dissociation.

I strain is actually a special-case B strain when applied to the dissociation reactions of cyclic compounds but is defined without special reference to such processes.[67] It is the strain that arises in cyclic compounds when it is necessary to deform natural bond angles in order to complete the cyclic structure or from the repulsion of nonbonded atoms or groups attached to adjacent carbon atoms.

The study of the dissociation of boron-amine complexes has been used most extensively in the development of the theory. In particular the reactions

$$R_3N: + R_3B \rightleftarrows R_3\overset{+}{N}-\overset{-}{B}R_3$$

have been studied by observing the vapor pressure of the amine and the boron compound in equilibrium with the solid addition compound. Illustrative data are presented in Table XVIII.

The concept of F strain is most clearly illustrated by comparison among the pyridine bases. Since the aromatic ring system is relatively rigid there can be no important change in bond angles or distances during the dissociation process, and one is therefore apparently safe in assigning the base-weakening effect of the 2-methyl group to F strain (see below, however). The electronic influence of the methyl group is assumed to be base strengthening, and this hypothesis is subject to a twofold control. First, the isomeric 2- and 3-methyl compounds are stronger bases than pyridine against trimethylboron, and, second, all three of the picolines are stronger bases than pyridine if compared in water solution with the proton as a reference acid.

[67] H. C. Brown and M. Gerstein, *J. Am. Chem. Soc.*, **72**, 2926 (1950).

TABLE XVIII

Dissociation of Trimethylboron-Amine Compounds

Base	K_{100}^{dis}	ΔH, cal./mole	ΔS, e.u.	Reference
NH_3	4.6	13,750	39.9	68
$MeNH_2$	0.0350	17,640	40.6	68
Me_2NH	0.0214	19,260	43.6	68
Me_3N	0.477	17,620	45.7	68
$E + NH_2$	0.0705	18,000	43.0	68
$E + {}_2NH$	1.22	16,310	44.1	68
$E + {}_3N$		No compound		68
t-$BuNH_2$	9.46	12,990	39.3	69
Quinuclidine	0.0196	19,940	45.6	70
Pyridine	0.301	17,000	43.2	71
2-Picoline		No compound		
3-Picoline	0.138	17,810	43.9	71
4-Picoline	0.105	19,400	47.5	71

If trimethylboron is used as the reference acid irregular sequences of basic strengths are observed with ammonia and the various alkyl amines. For example, the apparent basicity of ammonia is increased by the addition of the third methyl group with the consequence that trimethylamine appears as a weaker base than either methylamine or dimethylamine although it is still a stronger base than ammonia. If bulkier reference acids such as tri-*tert*-butylboron [72] are used or if larger alkyl groups are attached to the amine the relationships are further modified, with the result that the sequence of basic strengths becomes (by inference) $NH_3 > RNH_2 > R_2NH > R_3N$ with *tert*-butyl amines and trimethyl boron as a reference acid and with the ethyl amines and tri-*tert*-butylboron as the reference acid.

As a basic postulate it is assumed that the electronic influence of alkyl groups attached to nitrogen is base strengthening and that if steric strains were not important the order of basic strengths would always be $R_3N > R_2NH > RNH_2 > NH_3$. The separation of F strain from B strain is somewhat more subtle but may be indicated as follows. It is noted that there is a difference in the sensitivity of the various amines to the change from trimethylboron to tri-*tert*-butyl-boron as a reference acid. This indicates that the larger alkyl groups

[68] H. C. Brown and M. D. Taylor, *J. Am. Chem. Soc.*, *69*, 1332 (1947).

[69] H. C. Brown and G. K. Barbaras, *J. Am. Chem. Soc.*, *75*, 6 (1953).

[70] H. C. Brown and S. Sujishi, *J. Am. Chem. Soc.*, *70*, 2878 (1948).

[71] H. C. Brown and G. K. Barbaras, *J. Am. Chem. Soc.*, *66*, 1137 (1947).

[72] H. C. Brown, *J. Am. Chem. Soc.*, *67*, 374, 378 (1945).

are the most embarrassed by complex formation when they are opposed to the larger *tert*-butyl groups, which can be only a consequence of interactions between the two portions of the complex.

Brown and his group have provided many interesting special examples of F strain, but none are more intriguing than the special effects of ethyl groups when they are introduced into the ammonia structure. There is first an increase in the basicity in ethylamine, followed by a modest decrease in diethylamine and then a large decrease in triethylamine. However, quinuclidine, **XXXVII**, is a stronger base

XXXVII

than even ethylamine. It is held that these data indicate that at least one of the methyl groups of triethyl amine is held in a rotational configuration such as **XXXIX** in which it protrudes in front of the nitrogen. Since compound formation was not observed it is trivial to speculate as to whether the methyl group would remain in this configuration in the adduct, giving rise to F strain, or whether it would be forced back close to the other methyl groups as in **XL**, giving rise

XXXIX   **XL**

to B strain. It is interesting that these two possibilities do serve to illustrate the conceptual difference between the two types of strain.

Explicit demonstrations of B strain are much more difficult to find. It has been suggested that the failure to observe a variation in the base strengths of the methyl amines against protons in water solution is such a demonstration.[72] The observed order of basicity is NH_3 < CH_3CN_2 < $(CH_3)_2NH$ > $(CH_3)_3N$. It is maintained that the process

$$(CH_3)_3\overset{+}{N}H \rightarrow (CH_3)_3N + H^+$$

is accompanied by a spreading of the C—N—C bond angles, which decreases the mutual compression of the methyl groups. That this explanation is neither entirely satisfactory nor unambiguous has been pointed out by several authors. Spitzer and Pitzer [73] showed that, if reasonable values were taken for the force constants for bending the bond angles in trimethylamine and if the usual harmonic approximation was assumed, it was not possible to account for the observed changes in the free energy of ionization in terms of angle bending alone. This approach is not entirely satisfying since the B-strain explanation is based upon the hypothesis that, as the bond angles of trimethylamine are decreased toward the tetrahedral value, compression of the methyl groups occurs. If this is actually true the harmonic approximation would be invalid.[73a] Trotman-Dickenson [74] has raised another very significant objection. He points out that the positive entropy change in the reaction

$$B + H_3 \overset{+}{O} \rightarrow BH^+ + H_2O$$

increases in the methylamine series as the number of methyl groups is increased. This indicates that the number of rigidly oriented solvent molecules about the ammonium ions is decreased as the number of methyl groups increases. If this is so the steric effect of the methyl groups is not entirely manifested by increases in internal strain but is responsible for a decrease in the heat of solvation in the methylammonium ions.

This brings up a related problem which bears upon the quantitative significance of the data for dissociation of alkylboronamine compounds. Such compounds do not ordinarily show a stable liquid phase at ordinary pressures. This behavior leads to their description as saltlike, which of course implies that there are strong electrostatic forces which hold the molecules in rigid orientations in the crystals. This is entirely consistent with the assignment of very large dipole moments to the molecules because of the formal charge separation in XLI. As

$$R_3 \overset{+}{N} - \overset{-}{B} R_3'$$
XLI

the size of the R and R' groups is increased, the separation of the dipoles in the crystals must be increased if the same packing arrangement is maintained. This would decrease the crystal energies in the compounds containing large groups and would contribute to the ease

[73] R. Spitzer and K. S. Pitzer, *J. Am. Chem. Soc.*, **70**, 1261 (1948).

[73a] We should note that the assumption that the bond angles of trimethylamine are larger than tetrahedral is itself arbitrary and perhaps not entirely justified. See footnote 3a in reference 73.

[74] A. F. Trotman-Dickenson, *J. Chem. Soc.*, *1949*, 1293.

of their dissociation. This factor is inseparable from internal strains as long as molecules of a given charge distribution are compared. A separation could be approximated by comparing the stabilities of the dipolar addition compounds with those of neutral molecules. It is not likely that dipole interactions have any measurable influence on gaseous dissociation constants. The variation in the latter is sufficient to guarantee that internal strains are of considerable importance. However, quantitative conclusions concerning very highly hindered adducts are based upon sublimation data or on the solubility of a boron compound in the liquid amine. The use of such data for the purpose of estimating the internal strain in "homomorphic" hydrocarbons [75] is questionable. Similarly, the measured or inferred stabilities of highly hindered quarternary ammonium ions should be corrected for solvation or crystal energies before they can be said to measure internal strain quantitatively.

The principle of I strain has been utilized to aid in accounting for the irregularities that occur in the behavior of cyclic compounds. Table XIX contains the data for the dissociation of the trimethylboron adducts of cyclic amines. The increase in basicity observed in going from the six- to the four-membered ring is attributed to a decrease in F strain associated with the decreasing ring size. The argument is not entirely unequivocal, as one might expect to find more strain in the adduct from tetramethyleneimine in which the N—B bond is eclipsed by C—H bonds to two adjacent carbon atoms. In the six-membered ring the most stable conformation should be XLII,

XLII

in which the equatorial location of the trimethylboron residue should minimize its compression by other atoms. It seems that the assumption of a planar configuration about nitrogen in the free bases is implicit in the discussion of the problem by Brown and Gerstein.[67] On the other hand, the explanation for the weak basicity of ethyleneimine is found in the assumption that the distortion of the internal bond

[75] H. C. Brown, G. K. Barbaras, H. L. Berneis, W. H. Bonner, R. B. Johannesen, M. Grayson, and L. K. Nelson, J. Am. Chem. Soc., 75, 1 (1953).

angle is increased by complex formation. This is eminently reasonable, as there would be no apparent reason for the amine bond angles to exceed $90°$ [75a] if it were not for repulsion between attached groups (i.e., B strain).

TABLE XIX

DISSOCIATION OF TRIMETHYLBORON ADDUCTS OF POLYMETHYLENEIMMINES [67]

Compound	K_{100}	H, cal./mole	S, e.u.
$(CH_2)_2NH:B(CH_3)_3$	0.0284	17,590	40.1
$(CH_2)_3NH:B(CH_3)_3$	0.000322	22,480	44.3
$(CH_2)_4NH:B(CH_3)_3$	0.00350	20,430	43.5
$(CH_2)_5NH:B(CH_3)_3$	0.0210	19,650	43.6

Another approach to the study of saturated, heterocyclic bases is by study of the shift in the C—H stretching frequency in chloroform on becoming hydrogen bonded to various ethers.[76] The results parallel those of Brown and coworkers as far as the apparent variation of basicity with ring size is concerned. However, the authors disagree in interpretation since they doubt that any appreciable change in bond angle accompanies the formation of hydrogen-bonded complexes. Again, the adoption of a particular point of view makes the conclusion that low basicity of ethylene oxide is due to the use of the "unshared" oxygen electrons to contribute to the binding between oxygen and carbon seem inescapable. However, the basic assumption is equivocal, and so the results *can* be construed as supporting the I-strain hypothesis.

RING-CHAIN TAUTOMERISM

A most inviting area for the study of steric effects on equilibria is found in the field of ring-chain tautomerism. The term is used loosely to cover a number of systems in which equilibrium can be established under any circumstances between open-chain compounds and various cyclic isomers. Among the systems of this type which have been examined are the following.

[75a] This conclusion is based upon the assignment of the non-bonding pair to the nitrogen 2s atomic orbital. Such an assignment is rather arbitrary and may be incorrect because of the polarity of the C—N bonds. However, the configuration should, in any event, be easily attained if it minimizes strains.

[76] S. Searles and M. Tamres, *J. Am. Chem. Soc.*, *73*, 3704 (1951).

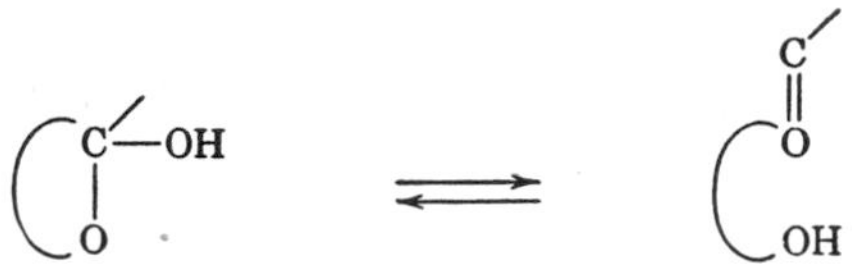

Hemiacetal

Hydroxy ketone or aldehyde

Pseudo acid

Keto or aldehydo acid

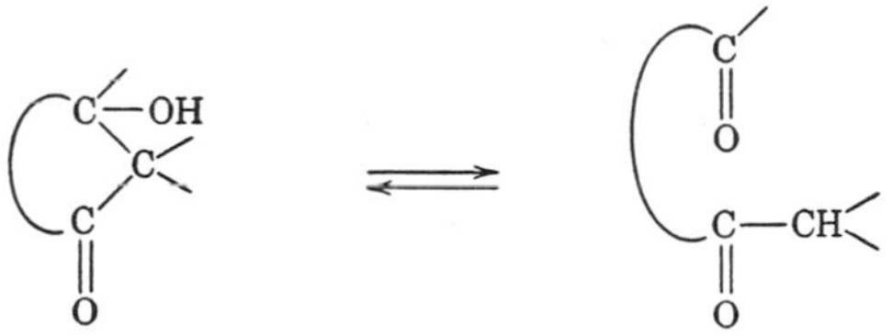

Cyclic aldol or ketol

Dicarbonyl compound

Pseudo acid chloride

Diacid chloride

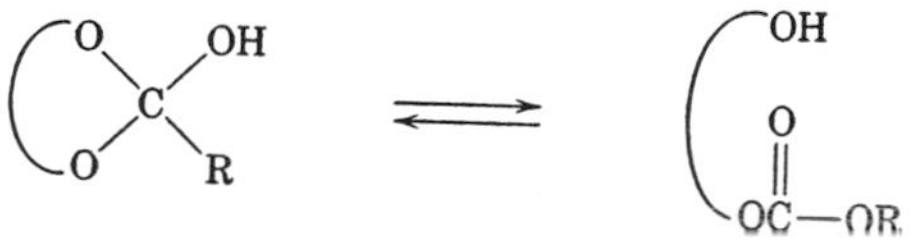

Cyclic *ortho* ester

Hydroxy ester

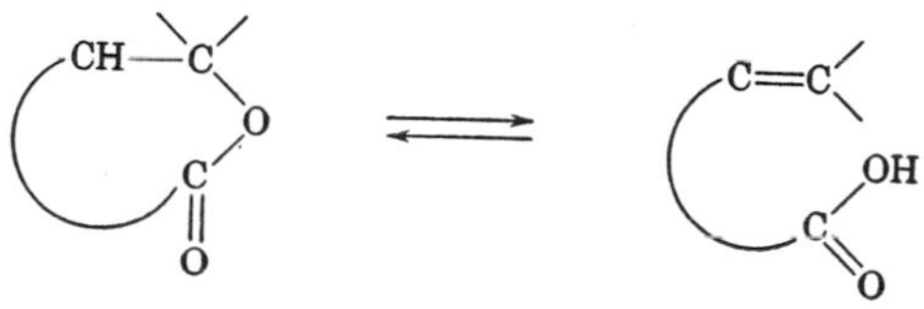

Lactone

Eneoic acid

It is disappointing to discover the paucity of data available on the equilibration of such systems. In many cases both the cyclic and acyclic members of an isomeric pair have been isolated. However, the fact that such isolations of the individuals can be carried out serves as a warning against any but the most casual interpretation of qualitative evidence concerning stability relationships. Since interconversions can be made immeasurably slow, the isolation of a particular form may merely indicate that it is the less soluble (or more volatile) of the pair.

In order to study the problem properly it is necessary to analyze equilibrated systems, preferably without isolation or analytical procedures which involve the hazard of disturbing the equilibrium condition. In many instances it is quite feasible to expect to be able to develop chemical methods of analysis comparable to the familiar bromimetric method for the analysis of keto-enol systems. Such a scheme has in fact been developed for the study of "lacto-enoic" tautomerism.[77]

$$\gamma,\delta\text{-Unsaturated acid} \rightleftarrows \delta\text{-Lactone}$$

However, the most powerful and generally applicable tool for the study of such problems is infrared and ultraviolet spectroscopy. Since the development of these methods has postdated the era of most vigorous study of this type of tautomeric relationship it is reasonable to expect that there will be extensive reinvestigation of these problems in the near future. For this reason the present discussion is appropriately kept brief as it could become badly outdated with the completion of a single thorough study.

Two important steric factors have been noted. These relate to the effect of ring size on stability and to the influence of substituents. The latter effect is generally referred to as "the *gem*-dimethyl effect," although the observations are unique neither to methyl groups nor to the geminal structure.

The only commonly encountered systems in which ring-chain tautomers seem to be readily interconvertible involve either five- or six-membered rings. The best-known examples are found in carbohydrates.[78] Among compounds that can exist in both furanose and pyranose forms there seems to be a general, but not complete, preference for the larger ring size. Furanose rings, when they are encountered, are usually found in stable glycosides, so that there is no assur-

[77] R. P. Linstead and H. H. Rydone, *J. Chem. Soc.*, *1933*, 580.
[78] W. W. Pigman and R. M. Goepp, Jr., *Chemistry of the Carbohydrates*, Academic Press, New York, 1948.

ance that they are actually thermodynamically stable with respect to six-membered rings. It is significant that no compelling evidence has yet been presented for the occurrence of either four- or seven-membered rings.

Similar conclusions concerning the preferential stabilization of five- and six-membered rings are reached by the study of less highly functional systems. The only recurrent reference to rings of other sizes is found in a series of studies [79, 80-82] in which it is claimed that equilibration in the sense of the following equation is established in the presence of concentrated alkali. Since the various stereoisomeric

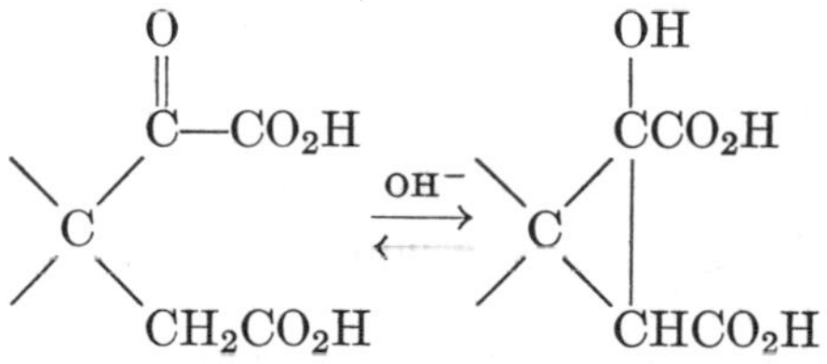

modifications of the corresponding hydroxylactones are known these are certainly not involved in this system. However, it is also true that the structures of the hydroxy acids have not been established in a rigorous fashion.

The influence of substituents on the stability of the position of cyclization equilibria in general is apparently dramatic if qualitative observations and inferences based upon chemical behavior are to be trusted. It would appear that the replacement of hydrogen by almost any hydrocarbon substituent increases the stability of the cyclic isomers. Kinetic effects of substituents upon the ease of ring closure have been reported frequently. For example, the amount of cyclopropane formed in the reaction of α-bromoglutaric acids with strong base increases in the following sequence.[83]

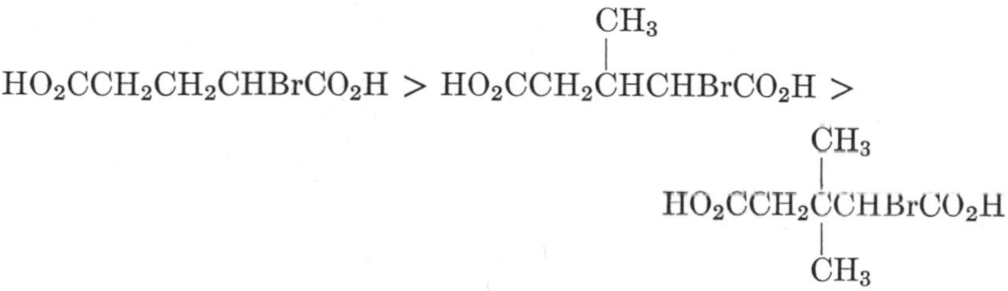

$$HO_2CCH_2CH_2CHBrCO_2H > HO_2CCH_2\overset{\overset{\displaystyle CH_3}{|}}{C}HCHBrCO_2H >$$

$$HO_2CCH_2\overset{\overset{\displaystyle CH_3}{|}}{\underset{\underset{\displaystyle CH_3}{|}}{C}}CHBrCO_2H$$

[79] C. K. Ingold, J. Chem. Soc., 119, 305 (1923).
[80] E. W. Lanfear and J. F. Thorpe, J. Chem. Soc., 123, 1683 (1923).
[81] S. S. Deshapanda and J. F. Thorpe, J. Chem. Soc., 121, 1430 (1922).
[82] L. Bains and J. F. Thorpe, J. Chem. Soc., 123, 1206 (1923).
[83] C. K. Ingold, J. Chem. Soc., 121, 2676 (1922).

This and similar observations have led to the inference that the substituents stabilize the small ring. However, entirely different explanations could be given for most of the results. For example, in the case cited it is noteworthy that direct displacement of bromide by an S_N2 reaction should become increasingly more difficult as the substituent methyl groups are added. In fact, it is rather remarkable that α-bromo-β,β-dimethylglutaric acid gives any substitution product at all since it is constitutionally similar to neopentyl bromide. It is, of course, possible that the displacement product is formed by way of an α-lactone [84] even under highly alkaline conditions. As a further example of the hazard in inferring stability relationships from isolated kinetic evidence it may be mentioned that 1,1-dimethylcyclopropane undergoes ring opening with hydrogen bromide more rapidly than does cyclopropane.[85] From this observation it might be inferred that the *gem*-dimethyl group preferentially stabilizes the open-chain compound. On the other hand, if one assumes that the ring-opening reaction is mechanistically similar to the addition of hydrogen bromide to olefins it is immediately realized that the observed effect is probably due to the stabilizing influence of the methyl groups on intermediates (possibly the tertiary carbonium ion) involved in the reaction.

One of the few cases in which equilibration studies have been carried out is that previously mentioned involving hydroxycyclopropane $\rightleftarrows$ α-keto acid interconversion. While the method of analysis was by

TABLE XX

EQUILIBRATION [77] OF THE SYSTEM

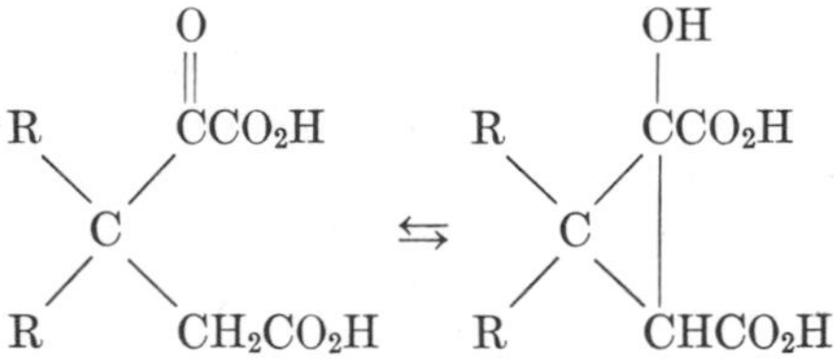

R	R'	Per Cent Hydroxy-cyclopropane at Equilibrium
H	H	0
CH_3	CH_3	0
CH_3	C_2H_5	0
C_2H_5	C_2H_5	62
n-C_3H_7	n-C_3H_7	71
— $(CH_2)_5$	—	100

[84] L. P. Hammett, *Physical Organic Chemistry*, p. 175, McGraw-Hill Book Co., New York, 1941.

[85] A. Kötz, *J. prakt. Chem.*, **68**, 156 (1903).

product isolation, equilibration was observed by carrying out the conversion in both directions. Therefore, if the hydroxycyclopropane structure is correct the results in Table XX are certainly significant because of the wide variation in values observed.

Other examples are reported from which similar stabilizing effects of substituents on cyclic molecules can be inferred although most are subject to the above-mentioned reservations to a certain extent. The 1,6-diketone prepared by the reduction of mesityl oxide by metals shows none of the properties expected on the basis of the dicarbonyl structure XLIII but behaves chemically as a monoketone XLIV.[86]

$$CH_3COCH_2C(CH_3)_2C(CH_3)_2CH_2COCH_3 \rightleftarrows$$

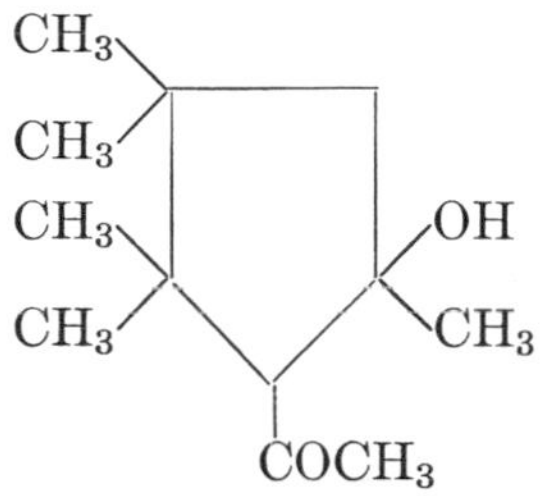

XLIII   XLIV

Two products are obtained which apparently are the expected stereoisomeric modifications of XLIV since both show the rather clean-cut monofunctional behavior. The two isomers are readily interconverted, and a reasonable mechanism for the interconversion involves equilibration via the dicarbonyl system. If this is so (and other acceptable mechanisms can be formulated) it assures that *at equilibrium* the cyclic forms are stable with respect to the acyclic. On the other hand, XLV [87] and XLVI [88] are normal diketones.

$$CH_3CO(CH_2)_4COCH_3 \qquad C_6H_5CO(CH_2)_4COC_6H_5$$
XLV   XLVI

Another example of a system in which equilibration may be inferred is found in the aldehyde diacid XLVII. The substance is evidently a dilactone, XLVIII, but it may be titrated in water solution as

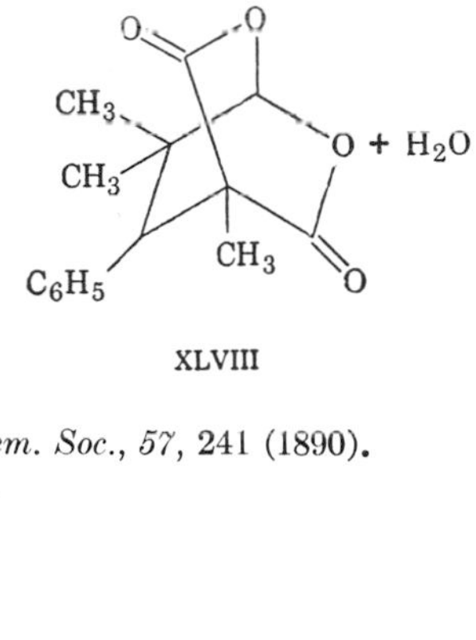

XLVII

XLVIII

[86] I. Vogel, *J. Chem. Soc.*, *1927*, 594.
[87] T. R. Marshall and W. H. Perkin, Jr., *J. Chem. Soc.*, *57*, 241 (1890).
[88] J. Wollemann, Dissertation, Göttingen, 1913.

a weak acid with a first ionization constant of 4.4×10^{-6}.[89]   Compound XLIX, which lacks one of the methyl groups, has an ionization

$$OHCC(CH_3)_2CH(C_6H_5)CH(CO_2H)_2$$
XLIX

constant of 2.18×10^{-5}, which is considerably larger although it is a little weak in comparison with the ionization constants of most malonic acids.[90]   It is doubtful that the presence of the methyl group alone could account for such an effect by its influence on the solvation of the carboxylate ion (see p. 428).   It is also unlikely that there is a cyclic anion of any appreciable stability.   Ionization must produce the anion with an open structure.   The fact that titration could be carried out in a normal fashion implies that acid-base equilibrium and, therefore, equilibrium between open and closed forms is achieved under the conditions of the titration.   One mould therefore infer that the "cyclization constant," K_c, for XLVII is about ten times as large as that for XLIX and that appreciable amounts of the latter may be cyclized in water solution.   There is ample evidence to indicate that the monoacids L, LI, and LII are equilibrated with small amounts of cyclic isomers, but there is no way of inferring, from published data, the relative magnitudes of the cyclization constants.

$$OCHC(CH_3)_2CH(C_6H_5)CH_2CO_2H$$
L

$$OCHC(CH_3)_2CH(C_6H_5)CH(CH_3)CO_2H$$
LI

$$OCHC(CH_3)_2CH(C_6H_5)CH(C_2H_5)CO_2H$$
LII

It has been claimed that equilibrium relations in the δ-keto malonic acid systems may be estimated by the yield of monobasic acid formed by pyrolytic decarboxylation.[91]   By this method it was estimated that LIII contained 68–70% dilactone whereas the cyclopentane analog LIV was 47–48% lactonic.   Such data have very limited significance,

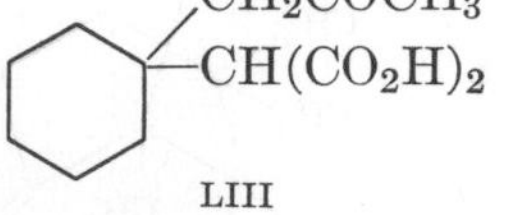

LIII 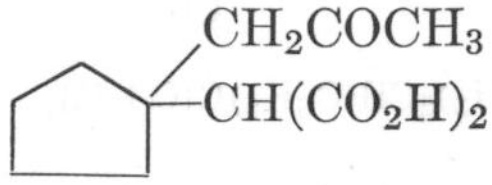   LIV

[89] H. Meerwein, H. Broke, W. Komont, and H. Morschel, *J. prakt. Chem.*, *116*, 229 (1927).

[90] G. H. Jeffrey and A. I. Vogel, *J. Chem. Soc.*, *1936*, 1756.

[91] A. M. Qudrat-I-Khuda, *J. Chem. Soc.*, *201*, 713 (1929).

but to the writer it seems remarkable that the yields in the two instances are as close as they are. The original authors chose to interpret the differences between the yields, but it seems safer to limit oneself to the more approximate conclusion that the stabilities of the two spiro dilactones LV and LVI, with respect to the corresponding open keto acids, are rather comparable.

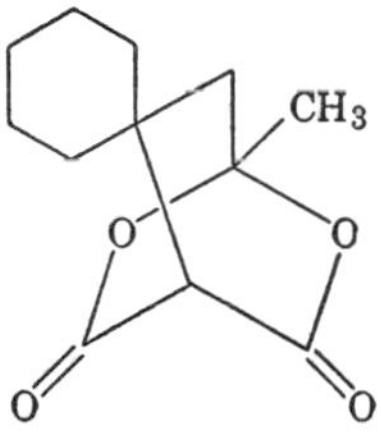

LV 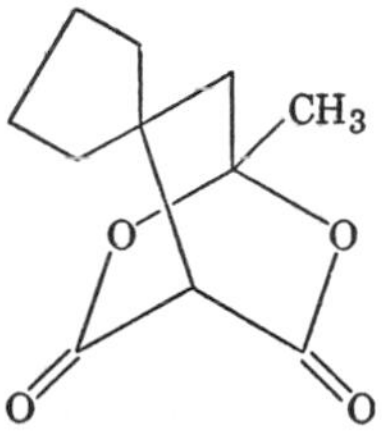   LVI

Hydroxylactones derived from keto diacids have also been studied. It has been shown that Balbiano's acid LVII is isolated as a mixture of open-chain and cyclic modifications.[92] The addition of a second

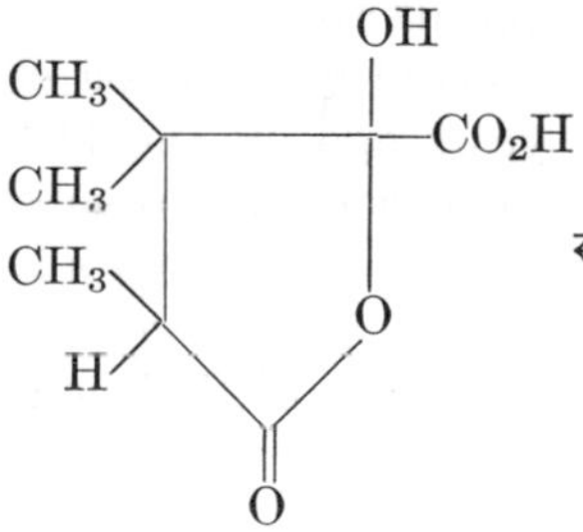

$\rightleftarrows$ HO$_2$CCH(CH$_3$)C(CH$_3$)$_2$COCO$_2$H

LVII

methyl group to give LVIII yields a compound that titrates cleanly

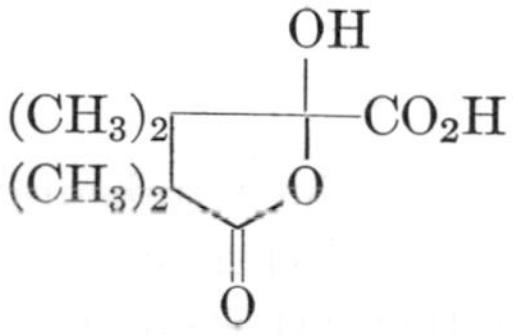

LVIII

as a monobasic acid. Boiling with 0.1 N base effects *partial* ring opening. It is conceivable that the effects are due entirely to the steric effect of the additional methyl group on the rate of nucleophilic attack at the carbonyl group of LVII. However, the incomplete con-

[92] G. A. R. Kon, A. Stevenson, and J. F. Thorpe, *J. Chem. Soc.*, **121**, 650 (1922).

version to an open chain makes it seem probable that a considerable amount of the cyclic monoanion LIX exists in the alkaline solution in

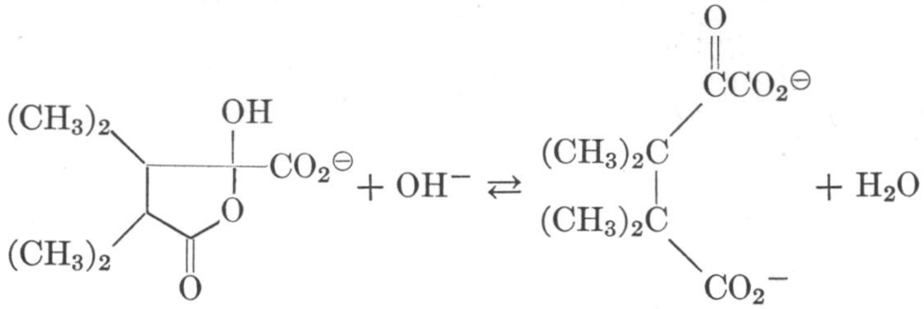

LIX

equilibrium with the open, second conjugate base. The equilibration of this system with hydroxycyclopropane is only claimed under much more drastic conditions (see p. 464).

The foregoing observation and a wealth of kinetic information concerning the ease of ring closure in substituted systems prompted the development of the concept of the *gem*-dimethyl effect. This can be expanded to the observation that the accumulation of substituents along the chain of a bifunctional system appears to selectively stabilize the corresponding cyclic forms. A theoretical explanation of the phenomenon was presented a number of years ago by Ingold.[93] It was pointed out that if the bond angle, Θ, external to two substituents, R and R', was a function of the size of those substituents it was possible to give a consistent account of the behavior observed to that time. If it was assumed that the angle external to a methylene group

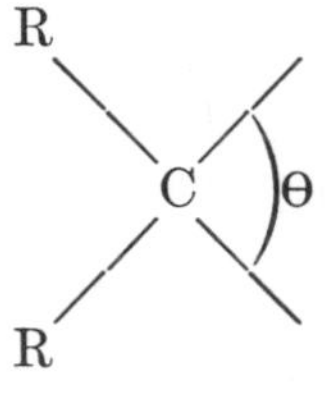

was considerably larger than the tetrahedral angle it would follow that the cyclization of polymethylene compounds would be energetically less favorable than the corresponding reactions of substituted compounds. Although it is now apparent that bond-angle variations were probably overestimated this effect may remain a significant one. Another possible effect relates to the possible restriction of free rotation in substituted acyclic molecules. Thus if rotation about bonds *a* and *b* in LX is restricted by the R groups the entropy of formation

[93] C. K. Ingold, *J. Chem. Soc.*, *119*, 305 (1921).

of a cyclic isomer would be less negative than with the corresponding methylene compound. No estimate of the importance of entropy

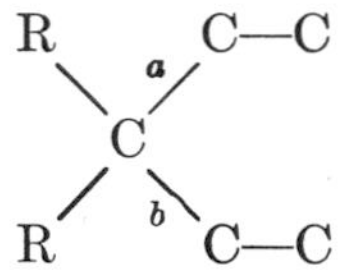

LX

variations in cyclization reactions can be made at present, although such information should be easily obtained from quantitative measurement of cyclization constants as a function of temperature.

One interesting investigation [94] seems to foreshadow the systematic study of substituent effects in unsaturated systems and their comparison with saturated systems. On the basis of ultraviolet spectra, it is concluded that at equilibrium the *cis* isomers of β- aroyl-α and β-methacrylic acids are largely cyclic whereas both the saturated analogs and β-aroyl-α-methylenepropionic acids are primarily acyclic under the same conditions. The unsaturated hydroxylactones, LXI,

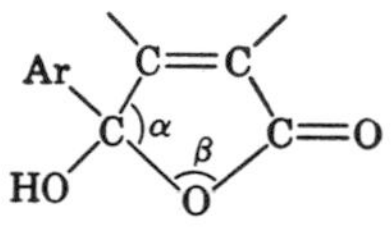

LXI

should suffer somewhat from classical ring strain, since, if the molecules are planar, the sum of the angles α and β is only 180° if each of the trigonal carbon atoms has its natural 120° angle. This strain, which could be avoided by puckering in the saturated analog, must be compensated by an increase in the resonance energy of LXI since steric hindrance probably prevents attainment of coplanarity in the open keto acids.

In another study ultraviolet spectra were used to estimate the amounts of cyclic isomers present in methanol solutions of 2-benzoyl-

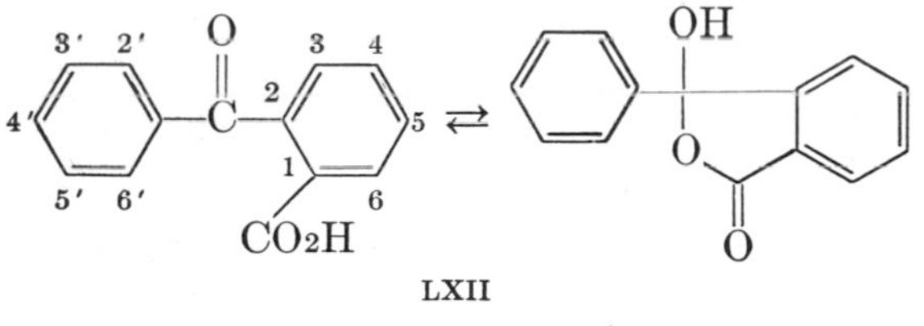

LXII

[94] R. E. Lutz, P. S. Bailey, C. Dien, and J. W. Rinker, *J. Am. Chem. Soc.*, **76**, 5039 (1954).

benzoic acid, LXII, and certain of its methyl derivatives.[95] The absorption spectra of the derived normal and pseudo esters were measured, and the assumption was made that these spectra were the same as those of the keto and pseudo acids. Using this estimate it was possible to calculate the values shown in Table XXI.

TABLE XXI

CYCLIZATION OF 2-BENZOYLBENZOIC ACIDS IN METHANOL SOLUTION [95]

Substituents	Per Cent Keto Acid
None	100
6-Methyl	35
3-Methyl	80
4,4'-Dimethyl	97
3,6-Dimethyl	14
2',4',6-Trimethyl	88
2',3,4'-Trimethyl	102
2',3,4',6-Tetramethyl	22

The results give a consistent and reasonable picture. Methyl groups in the ring bearing the carboxyl group force the molecule into the cyclic structure. Substitution in the 6 position, adjacent to the carboxyl group, is particularly effective because the steric strain between the methyl and carboxyl groups is partially relieved by cyclization.

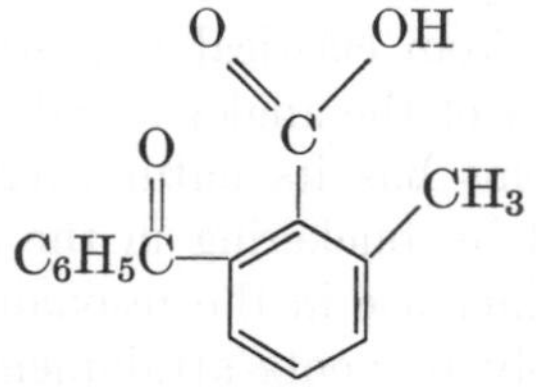

XLIII

A 3-methyl group will tend to force the benzoyl group out of the plane of other benzene rings so that less resonance energy is lost in the formation of the cyclic structure. Methyl groups in the second ring *ortho* to the carbonyl group inhibit cyclization, as would be expected in any change in which the adjacent substituent undergoes an addition reaction.

[95] M. S. Newman and C. W. Muth, *J. Am. Chem. Soc.*, *73*, 4627 (1951).

Chapter 10

by Melvin S. Newman

Molecular Complexes
and Molecular Asymmetry

Chapter 10

The field of molecular complexes is so vast that a complete survey is out of the question for a book of limited size. Accordingly this discussion is to be limited to polynitro compound–aromatic hydrocarbon complexes and to clathrate (inclusion) compounds.

Complexes between polynitro compounds and aromatic hydrocarbons

After a survey of the literature pertaining to molecular complex formation (especially with regard to picric acid), Orchin [1] concluded: (a) Picrate formation (with hydrocarbons) results from interaction of acceptor centers on one or more nitro groups with one or more donor centers on the hydrocarbon. (b) The melting point of the complex can generally be used to estimate stability of the complex. (c) The donor centers on the hydrocarbon must be suitably spaced for effective complexing with the nitrogen acceptor centers. (d) If the hydrocarbon is non-planar, complex formation is decreased.

Later a comprehensive study of molecular complexes of 2,4,7-trinitrofluorenone (TNF) with each of the monomethyl derivatives of 1,2-benzanthracene, I, and of benzo[c]phenanthrene, II,[2] showed that

I   II

[1] (a) M. Orchin, *J. Org. Chem.*, **16**, 1165 (1951); (b) see also G. M. Badger, *The Structures and Reactions of the Aromatic Compounds*, pp. 79ff, Cambridge University Press, London, England, 1954.

[2] K. H. Takemura, M. D. Cameron, and M. S. Newman, *J. Am. Chem. Soc.*, **75**, 3280 (1953).

generalization (*b*) above does not hold in the 1,2-benzanthracene series since the complex formed from 9-methyl-1,2-benzanthracene is the lowest melting (m.p. 209°) but the second most stable (K_{diss} 0.019 mole/l.) whereas the 1′-methyl complex is the second highest melting (m.p. 241°) but next to the least stable (K_{diss} 0.040). However, in the benzo[c]phenanthrene series the 1-methyl complex is both the lowest melting and the least stable.[3] Furthermore, 1-methylbenzo[c]phenanthrene does not form a complex with picric acid.[4] These observations lend further support to generalization (*d*) above.

In the author's experience an additional generalization may be stated: (*e*) If any nitro group (or groups) is prevented from assuming a coplanar arrangement with the attached ring, then the polynitro compound will be a less effective complexing agent.

For example, trinitrobenzene forms more stable complexes with hydrocarbons than does either picric acid or trinitrotoluene. Both polar and steric factors may be responsible for this decrease in complexing ability, but in the following examples the steric factors are undoubtedly responsible. In an attempt to prepare an optically active polynitro reagent [5] for the purpose of resolving hydrocarbons, 2,2′,4,4′,6-penta-nitro-3-methylbiphenyl,[6] III*a* and 2,2′,4,4′,6-pentanitro-3-carboxybiphenyl,[5] III*b*, were prepared. However, neither of these compounds

III*a*, R = CH₃   III*b*, R = COOH

would readily form a crystalline complex with anthracene.[5] Although there are five nitro groups in each of these molecules, only two in each are capable of coplanarity with the rings. Accordingly the low complexing ability is not surprising.

[3] The melting points of the hydrocarbons in the benzo[c]phenanthrene series (see reference 2) are of interest. The parent, II, melts at 68°, and the 2-, 3-, 4-, 5-, and 6-methyl derivatives melt in the range 54–81°. However, the 1-methyl derivative melts at 141°. This behavior is supplemented by the fact that the heat of fusion of the 1-methyl compound is 26 cal./gram whereas that for all the others, including II, are in the range 18–20 cal./gram. (Unpublished experiments by D. D. Tunnicliff of the Shell Development Co. See D. D. Tunnicliff and H. Stone, *Anal. Chem.*, *27*, **73** (1955), for a description of the apparatus used.)

[4] M. S. Newman and W. B. Wheatley, *J. Am. Chem. Soc.*, *70*, 1913 (1948).

[5] See M.S. thesis of B. Bennett, Ohio State University, 1948.

[6] H. A. Stearns and R. Adams, *J. Am. Chem. Soc.*, *52*, 2070 (1930).

The problem of the preparation of a polynitro compound suitable for resolution by means of complex formation has been solved by the synthesis and resolution of α-(2,4,5,7-tetranitrofluorenidylaminoöxy)-propionic acid, IV. 1-Naphthyl sec-butyl ether and methyl α-(1-anthracene)propionate have been resolved by preferential complex formation with the enantiomorphic forms of IV.[7]

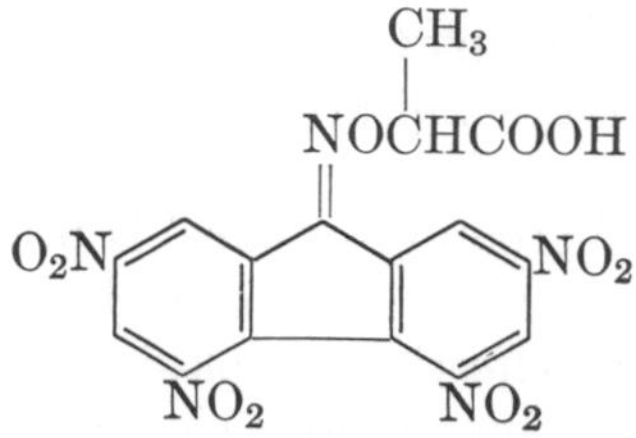

$$CH_3$$
$$|$$
$$NOCHCOOH$$

IV

Clathrate (inclusion) compounds

These complexes are distinguished from more conventional molecular complexes by the fact that they may be composed of integral or non-integral combinations of molecules. An excellent review of such (intermolecular) compounds is given by Powell,[8] who has originated much work in this field. Steric factors are of the greatest importance in determining which combinations of molecules will form clathrate (inclusion) complexes and which will not. A characteristic of clathrates is that one component crystallizes in such a way that a hole exists in which other molecules may fit. The size of the molecule that is to fit in the hole is all-important; its chemical nature is of little importance.

These compounds have been used to obtain substances in optically active form without the use of any optically active starting material. For example, tri-o-thymotide,[9] V, is a molecule that can assume forms similar to three-bladed propellers of opposite pitch.[8] Thus mirror images whose interconversion is sterically hindered (half-life about 3.5 minutes) are present in solution. When crystallization occurs, large enantiomorphic crystals are formed. The discovery that the crystals are enantiomorphic stems from X-ray diffraction studies and not from hand sorting and microscopic examination for enantiomorphic crystal faces as in Pasteur's work. Solutions of single crystals of V which include benzene or chloroform rotate the plane of polarized light, some

[7] M. S. Newman, W. B. Lutz, and D. Lednicer, J. Am. Chem. Soc., 77, 3420 (1955).

[8] H. M. Powell, J. Chem. Soc., 1954, 2658; 1948, 61.

[9] W. Baker, B. Gilbert, and W. D. Ollis, J. Chem. Soc., 1952, 1443.

to the right, some to the left. Rates of racemization of the benzene compound have been measured, and the energy of activation is estimated to be 16 kcal./mole.[10]

This drawing does not do justice to the model. Actually, the oxygen atoms that form the carboxy groups are not in the same plane as the ring attached to the carbonyl carbon.

V

When 2-butyl bromide was the compound included in the crystalline lattice it was possible to obtain a homogeneous crystallizate by seeding with crystals of a single type. When this crystallizate was dissolved in chloroform a negative rotation was observed which rapidly diminished until a constant negative rotation remained. These facts indicate that the original crystals included only l-2-butyl bromide. After the l-tri-o-thymotide, V, which had included the bromide, had racemized in solution, the remaining bromide was optically active. A similar resolution of 2-chlorooctane by means of the urea clathrate compound has been reported.[11] The use of this type of compound for resolution of asymmetric molecules can be expected to contribute greatly in future research on optically active compounds which hitherto have not been readily resolvable.

Molecular asymmetry

Steric factors within molecules play an important role in determining many properties of compounds. Steric inhibition of resonance [12] and optical activity due to restricted rotation about single bonds [12b, 13]

[10] A. C. D. Newman and H. M. Powell, *J. Chem. Soc., 1952*, 3747.

[11] W. Schlenk, Jr., *Experientia, 8*, 337 (1952).

[12] (a) G. W. Wheland, *The Theory of Resonance*, Chapters 4 and 6, John Wiley & Sons, New York, 1954. (b) A. E. Remick, *Electronic Interpretations of Organic Chemistry*, Chapter 9, John Wiley & Sons, New York, 1949.

[13] (a) H. Gilman, *Organic Chemistry, an Advanced Treatise*, Vol. 1, 2nd ed., pp. 347–382. John Wiley & Sons, New York, 1943. (b) G. M. Badger, *The Structures and Reactions of the Aromatic Compounds*, pp. 411ff, Cambridge University Press, London, England, 1954.

represent two well-known fields in which steric factors play important roles in determining properties of molecules.

Optical activity which arises from out-of-plane distortions of aromatic polycyclic compounds represents a newer development in the field of molecular asymmetry. The possibility that optical activity might be found in compounds of this type was first pointed out in 1940 [14] and has been demonstrated by the partial resolution of VI,[15]

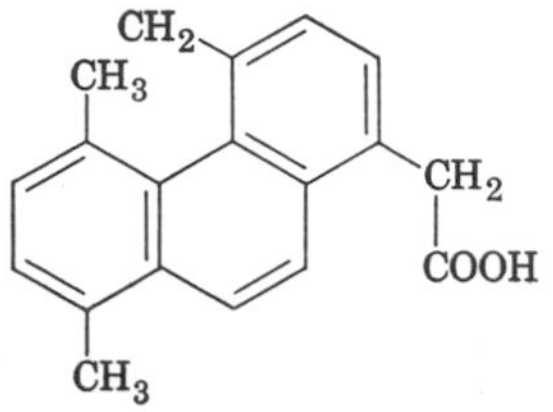

VI

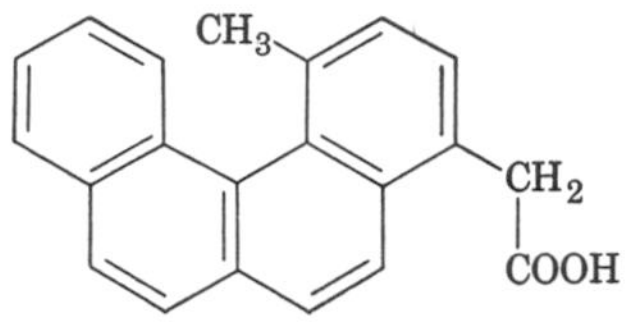

VII

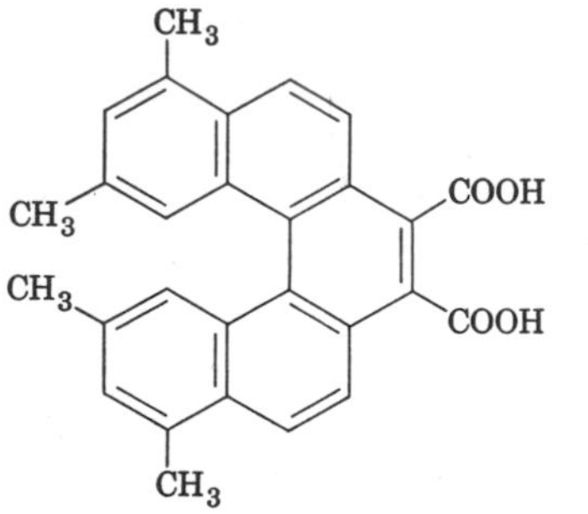

VIII

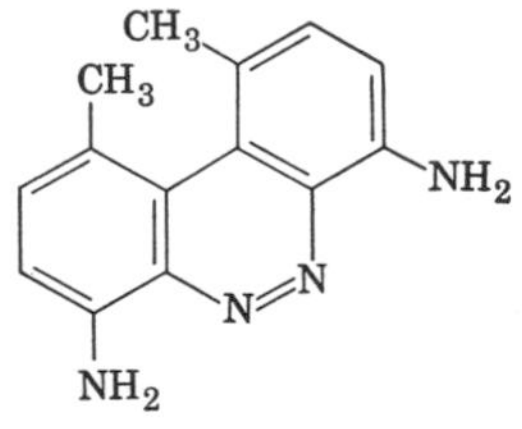

IX

VII,[16] VIII,[17] and IX,[18] although in each instance the optical stability was low. The compound 9,10-dihydro-3,4,5,6-dibenzophenanthrene has also been prepared in optically active form,[19] $[\alpha]_D$ 1496°. This represents a borderline case between optical activity of the biphenyl type and that of the intramolecular overcrowding type. In this example the optical stability was greater than that of any of the compounds VI–IX.

[14] M. S. Newman, *J. Am. Chem. Soc.*, *62*, 2295 (1940).

[15] M. S. Newman and A. S. Hussey, *J. Am. Chem. Soc.*, *69*, 3023 (1947).

[16] M. S. Newman and W. B. Wheatley, *J. Am. Chem. Soc.*, *70*, 1913 (1948).

[17] F. Bell and D. H. Waring, *J. Chem. Soc.*, *1949*, 2689. These authors proposed the term optical activity due to intramolecular overcrowding for this type of stereoisomerism.

[18] W. Theilacker and F. Baxmann, *Ann.*, *581*, 117 (1953).

[19] D. M. Hall and E. E. Turner, *J. Chem. Soc.*, *1955*, 1242.

A characteristic of compounds of this type is that strain is produced by the crowding of two groups, such as the methyl groups in the 4 and 5 position of a substituted phenanthrene, VI. This strain is relieved by a bending of the aromatic rings, by bending of the substituents out of the plane of the rings, or by a combination of these two types of distortion. Since the distortion in each of the compounds VI, VII, VIII, and IX may take place in such a way that enantiomers can be formed, optical activity results.

The structure of benzo[c]phenanthrene, X, in which aromatic rings are rendered non-planar because of internal strain, has been established by X-ray diffraction analysis.[20]

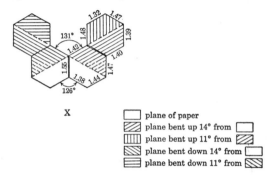

X

☐ plane of paper
▨ plane bent up 14° from ☐
▥ plane bent up 11° from ▨
◺ plane bent down 14° from ☐
▤ plane bent down 11° from ◺

A few of the points of interest are shown in formula X, but the original article should be consulted for details. The structures of a number of other strained compounds have also been determined [21] by X-ray analysis.

The most stable (from the optical activity point of view) compounds of this type are 1,12-dimethylbenzo[c]phenanthrene-5-acetic acid,[22] XI, and phenanthro-[3,4; c]phenanthrene,[23] XII (hexahelicene).

The former, $[\alpha]_D$ ±360°, maintains optical stability at temperatures well over 200°. When racemization commences near 250°, decomposition also sets in. Decomposition near 250° is also characteristic of the methyl ester of XI. The low temperature at which thermal decomposition begins is undoubtedly due to the high internal strain.

[20] F. H. Herbstein and G. M. J. Schmidt, *J. Chem. Soc.*, *1954*, 3302. In a recent communication, Dr. Schmidt has stated that certain changes in bond lengths in X are required because of recent work at low temperature; in particular, the bond length of 1.55 for the central bond is shorter.

[21] G. M. J. Schmidt et al., *J. Chem. Soc.*, *1954*, 3288, 3295, and 3314. A. D. McIntosh, J. M. Robertson, and V. Vand, *ibid.*, *1954*, 1661.

[22] M. S. Newman and R. M. Wise, *J. Am. Chem. Soc.*, *78*, 450 (1956).

[23] M. S. Newman and D. Lednicer, unpublished experiments. See Ph.D. thesis of D. L., Ohio State University, 1955.

Two features of XII are of interest. One is the high rotation, $[\alpha]_D$ $-3640°$, and the other is the fact that the resolution of XII was accomplished by a new method.[7] Although XII complexes with IV, as evidenced by formation of a dark color when solutions of the two

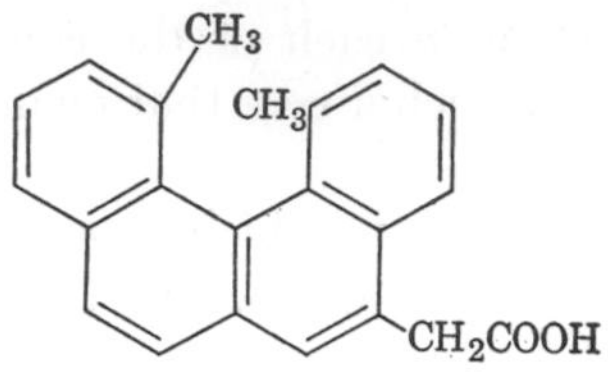

XI 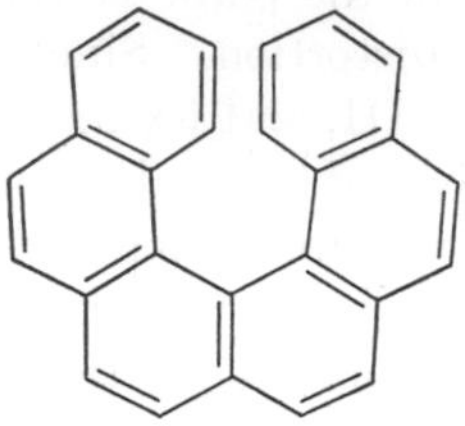   XII

were mixed, no crystalline complex was isolated. However, on suitable manipulation of solvents the hydrocarbon crystallized in active form. Maximum rotation was then obtained by recrystallization.

Many interesting problems relating to the energy of activation of the racemization of appropriate derivatives of this type of compounds and to the reactivities and properties of aromatic substituents in this field await solution.

Chapter 11

by Lloyd L. Ingraham

Steric Effects on Certain Physical Properties

INTRODUCTION

ELECTRONIC SPECTRA

The Effect of Twisting a "Single" Bond in a Conjugated System
The Effect of Twisting an Essential Double Bond in a Conjugated System
Steric Effects That Cause Increased Electronic Interactions
The Effect of Bending a Benzene Ring

VIBRATIONAL SPECTRA

Interaction Terms
Repulsion Terms
The Effect of Twisting a Single Bond in a Conjugated System
Strain in Cyclic Ketones

DIPOLE MOMENTS

Twisting a Single Bond in a Conjugated System
Structures of Hindered Molecules

REFRACTIVE INDEX AND MOLECULAR REFRACTION

MISCELLANEOUS PROPERTIES

    Thermochromism
    Paramagnetism
    Fluorescence
    Polarographic Reduction Potential
    Elasticity
    Melting Point

STRAIN IN THREE-MEMBERED RINGS

    Structures
    Electronic Spectra
    Vibrational Spectra
    Dipole Moments

SUMMARY

Chapter 11

INTRODUCTION

This discussion will proceed from the point of view of the physical property affected by the steric effect. An attempt is made to discuss these effects in terms of molecular orbitals wherever possible. "Strain in three-membered rings" is treated separately at the end of the chapter because this subject bears so little relationship to other types of strain. Electronic spectra will be discussed first, then vibrational spectra, dipole moments, and various physical properties of lesser importance in the study of steric effects.

Several reviews [1-3] have discussed the electronic spectra of sterically hindered molecules. In the following section the accent will be on developments since these reviews have appeared.

ELECTRONIC SPECTRA

The effect of twisting a "single" bond in a conjugated system

THEORETICAL CONSIDERATIONS. The steric effects most studied by electronic spectra are those involving a "single" bond in a conjugated system. Such a bond will have some double-bond character, which will affect the spectrum of the molecule.

We shall discuss first how the energy of a double bond is affected by this twist caused by steric effects and later the relationship this effect on energy bears to the electronic spectrum. If only electronic energy is considered, the strength of a double bond or any bond with some double-bond character will be maximal when all atoms attached to the two atoms of the bond lie in the same plane. This structure allows for maximum overlap of the p orbitals across the bond. In a molecule

[1] R. N. Jones, *Chem. Revs.*, *32*, 1 (1943).

[2] L. G. S. Brooker, F. L. White, R. H. Sprague, S. G. Dent, Jr., and G. Van Zandt, *Chem. Revs.*, *41*, 325 (1947).

[3] L. N. Ferguson, *Chem. Revs.*, *43*, 385 (1948).

such as biphenyl where the resonance energy [4] depends upon the double-bond character between the rings, the most stable configuration would be a coplanar configuration if there were no steric effects. However, fairly large deviations from coplanarity will not reduce greatly the stability of the molecule or destroy all of the inter-ring resonance energy. Considerable overlap of p orbitals involved in the double-bond character may exist even though they are twisted far from coplanarity (Fig. 1).

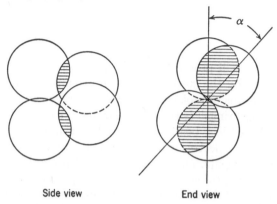

Side view   End view

Fig. 1.   The overlap between p orbitals when a double bond ($2p\pi$) is twisted by an angle α.

The resonance energy varies with the $\cos^2$ of the angle of twist.[5] This function plotted in Fig. 2 shows that there is considerable resonance energy even though the twist may be quite large. Steric effects may therefore cause relatively large twists and not destroy all of the resonance energy.[6]

The problem then arises as to what effects will appear in the electronic spectrum because of substituents that cause large twists in bonds with partial double-bond character. If the angle of twist is quite large, there is no p-electron interaction across the bond and the spectrum is similar to the additive spectra of the component parts of the molecule.

[4] We are considering here only the extra resonance energy biphenyl has over that of two isolated benzene rings.

[5] M. J. S. Dewar, *J. Am. Chem. Soc.*, *74*, 3341 (1952). See also C. A. Coulson, *Conference on Quantum Mechanical Methods in Valence Theory*, 1951, p. 42. (Printed 1952 by U. S. Government Printing Office.)

[6] G. H. Beavan, D. M. Hall, M. S. Lesslie, and E. E. Turner, *J. Chem. Soc.*, *1952*, 854.

To understand the effects of smaller twists it is helpful to look at the C—N bond orders,[7] for example, in the ground and first excited state of aniline. In the ground state the C—N bond order is 1.30,[8] whereas in the excited state the bond order is 1.39. These bond orders show that to twist the C—N bond in aniline by *ortho* groups and consequently to reduce the amount of double-bond character would raise (reduce stability) the upper level more than the ground state. The transition occurring between these two states would then occur

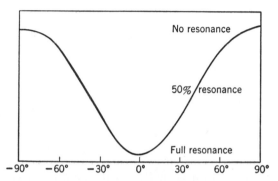

FIG. 2.   The excess resonance energy of biphenyl over two benzene rings as a function of the angle of twist between the phenyl groups. At even as large twists as 45° there is still 50% resonance energy.

at higher energies and shorter wavelengths. This is experimentally found to be true with aniline and most substituted benzene derivatives.

Another effect of twisting a bond with partial double-bond character is to reduce the absorption intensity, for example in benzene derivatives, of the band near 260 mμ. This effect not only occurs concurrently with shifts in wavelength but also occurs at smaller twists where there is relatively little change in wavelength. In benzene the 260-mμ band is forbidden on symmetry arguments [9] but does occur with a low intensity. In monosubstituted benzenes where the symmetry of the electronic wave functions is perturbed by the substituent, the symmetry arguments no longer hold and the absorption is much greater. This increase in absorption intensity depends upon the amount of perturbation and is proportional to the square of a constant

[7] The bond order is a quantitative measure of bond character. The bond order is 1.00 for a single bond and 2.00 for a double bond. See C. A. Coulson and H. C. Longuet-Higgins, *Proc. Roy. Soc. London, A191*, 39 (1947) for a more quantitative definition.

[8] C. A. Coulson and J. Jacobs, *J. Chem. Soc., 1949*, 1983.

[9] A. L. Sklar, *Revs. Mod. Phys., 14*, 232 (1942).

called the "spectroscopic moment," [10] which has been shown to be related to $\Delta\sigma$ values.[11] However, if the interaction of the substituent with the π electrons of the benzene is decreased by twisting the bond involved in this perturbation, the perturbation is decreased and the absorption intensity is decreased.[12]

In biphenyl derivatives similar experimental results are found; i.e., the intensity of the 250-mμ band is decreased with *ortho* substitution. However, the perturbations in this case are probably on the 210-mμ band of benzene. Because the 250-mμ ($\sim$5.2 V.) band of biphenyl is a superposition of two transitions corresponding to the 210-mμ ($\sim$5.8 V.) and 260-mμ ($\sim$5.0 V.) transitions of benzene,[13] it is difficult to know which one is affected by *ortho* substitution although it is probably the transition that corresponds to the 210-mμ transition of benzene.[14]

Twisting a single bond in a conjugated system away from coplanarity may therefore affect the spectrum in any of three ways: [15] (1) No change in wavelength of the maximum but a decrease in the absorption intensity. This effect is caused by relatively small twists. (2) Absorption maximum shifts to shorter wavelengths in addition to decreased absorption intensity. This effect is caused by larger twists than the first effect. (3) Spectrum is similar to the sum of the spectra of the component parts of the molecule on either side of the twisted bond. This effect occurs when the twist is large enough to almost completely eliminate interaction between the two portions of the molecule.

There are also examples in which the intensity is decreased by steric effects and the absorption maximum shifts slightly to longer wavelengths.[16, 17, 18] These wavelength shifts are small, and it is difficult to decide whether they are actually the result of steric effects or other factors.

EXPERIMENTAL EVIDENCE FOR RELATIVELY SMALL TWISTS. We shall now discuss the experimental absorption spectra for the above three

[10] J. R. Platt, *J. Chem. Phys.*, *19*, 263 (1951).

[11] C. C. Price, *Chem. Revs.*, *29*, 37 (1941).

[12] H. B. Klevens and J. R. Platt, *J. Am. Chem. Soc.*, *71*, 1714 (1949).

[13] A. London, *J. Chem. Phys.*, *13*, 396 (1945); J. R. Platt, *ibid.*, *19*, 101 (1951).

[14] A. Wenzel, *J. Chem. Phys.*, *21*, 403 (1953).

[15] R. B. Turner and D. M. Voitle, *J. Am. Chem. Soc.*, *73*, 1403 (1951). See also E. A. Braude, E. R. H. Jones, H. P. Koch, R. W. Richardson, F. Sondheimer, and J. B. Toogood, *J. Chem. Soc.*, *1949*, 1890, for a similar classification.

[16] R. Van Heldin, P. E. Verkade, and B. M. Wepster, *Rec. trav. chim.*, *73*, 39 (1954).

[17] B. M. Wepster, *Rec. trav. chim.*, *72*, 661 (1953).

[18] R. T. Arnold, V. J. Webers, and R. M. Dodson, *J. Am. Chem. Soc.*, *74*, 368 (1952).

general classes of steric effects.   There are many borderline examples, and they have been arbitrarily included in one or the other class.

Numerous investigators [19] have studied the decreases in absorption intensity caused by *ortho* substituents.   We have chosen only a few typical studies to discuss here.

O'Shaughnessy and Rodebush [20] found that 2,4-dimethylacetophenone has an absorption intensity comparable to that of acetophenone. However, two *ortho* methyls do greatly lower the intensity.   The E_{max} is reduced from $\sim$13,000 in acetophenone to $\sim$4000 in 2,4,6-trimethylacetophenone.   Other physical properties that will be discussed later also indicate that two, but not one, methyl groups are required to force the acetyl group out of the benzene plane.

Studies [21] with *ortho*-substituted anilines and dimethylanilines have shown similar effects in these series.   The absorption intensity for the 400-mμ band of *o*-nitroaniline and *o*-nitrodimethylaniline is much less than for the *para* derivatives.   There is also some change in absorption maximum.   Similar studies giving comparable results have been made for the nitrotoluenes, nitrocumenes,[22] and derivatives of anisole. It is interesting that the decrease in absorption intensity varies not only with the amount of twist in the bond with partial double-bond character [23] but also with the amount of double-bond character.   The bonds with more double-bond character are shorter and hence more susceptible to steric effects.   The compounds 4-amino-4'-nitrobiphenyl and 4,4'-dinitrobiphenyl seem to have enough variation in the double-bond character of the 1,1' bond to show this effect.[24]   The compound 4-amino-4'-nitrobiphenyl shows a large decrease in absorption intensity with 2,2'-dimethyl substitution, but the less conjugated compound 4,4'-dinitrobiphenyl shows comparatively little.

Arnold and coworkers showed that the hindrance decreases in the order CH_3, six-membered ring, five-membered ring by studying the

[19] See, for example, M. J. Murray and W. S. Gallaway, *J. Am. Chem. Soc.*, 70, 3867 (1948); S. D. Ross, *ibid.*, 70, 4039 (1948); L. W. Pickett, M. Groth, S. Duckworth, and J. Cunliffe, *ibid.*, 72, 44 (1950); E. A. Braude and J. A. Coles, *J. Chem. Soc.*, 1951, 2085; P. Ramart-Lucas, M. J. Hock, and Vial, *Bull. soc. chim. France*, 1952, 220; G. D. Hedden and W. G. Brown, *J. Am. Chem. Soc.*, 75, 3744 (1953); B. M. Wepster, *Rec. trav. chim.*, 72, 661 (1953); L. H. Schwartzman and B. B. Corson, *J. Am. Chem. Soc.*, 76, 781 (1954); W. M. Schubert, W. A. Sweeney, and H. K. Latourette, *ibid.*, 76, 5462 (1954).

[20] M. T. O'Shaughnessy and W. H. Rodebush, *J. Am. Chem. Soc.*, 62, 2906 (1940).

[21] W. R. Remington, *J. Am. Chem. Soc.*, 67, 1838 (1945).

[22] W. G. Brown and H. Reagan, *J. Am. Chem. Soc.*, 69, 1032 (1947).

[23] A. Burawoy and J. T. Chamberlain, *J. Chem. Soc.*, 1952, 2310.

[24] D. W. Sherwood and M. Calvin, *J. Am. Chem. Soc.*, 64, 1350 (1942).

spectra of the *p*-nitroaniline derivatives shown in Fig. 3.[25] Van Heldin, Verkade, and Wepster [26] found that the order observed by Arnold and coworkers is dependent upon the presence of two methyl groups *ortho* to each other. For example, the absorption intensity decreases in the series 2,5-dimethyl-4-nitroaniline > 1-amino-4-nitro-5,6,7,8-tetrahydronaphthalene > 2,3-dimethyl-4-nitroaniline. Arnold's series of the

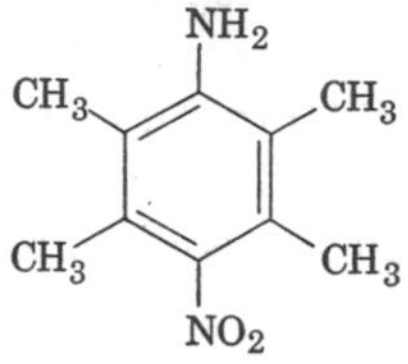

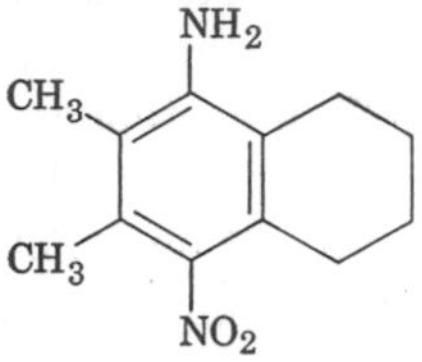

FIG. 3.

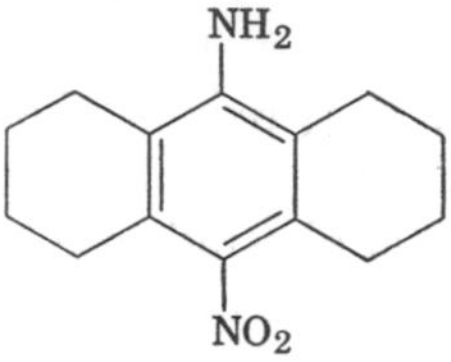

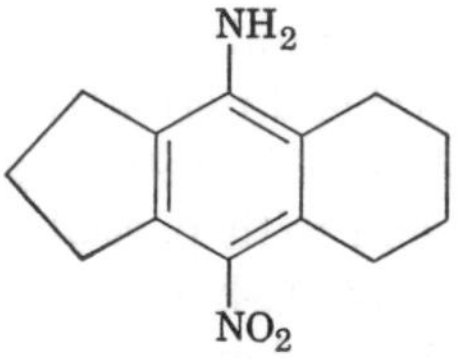

I. λ_{max} 395 mμ, ϵ_{max} 1.57 $\times$ 10^3.
II. λ_{max} 393 mμ, ϵ_{max} 1.97 $\times$ 10^3.
III. λ_{max} 397 mμ, ϵ_{max} 2.24 $\times$ 10^3.
IV. λ_{max} 387 mμ, ϵ_{max} 7.3 $\times$ 10^3.
V. λ_{max} 372 mμ, ϵ_{max} 12.8 $\times$ 10^3.

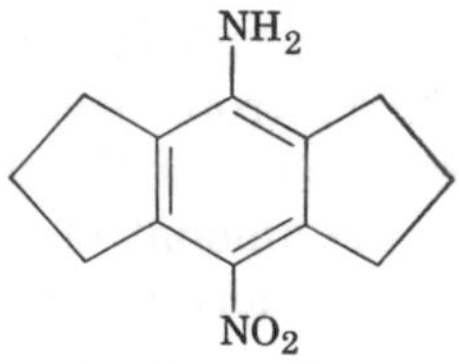

relative steric effect of groups should therefore by modified to read CH$_3$ (*o*-xylyl) > six-membered ring > CH$_3$ (tolyl) > ? five-membered ring. The greater effect of two *ortho* methyl groups can be called a "buttressing effect."

One of the most informative studies of the effect on absorption intensity is that of Klevens and Platt,[27] who studied the spectra of some *ortho*-substituted dimethylanilines. There was sufficient perturbation in the parent compound to make the 260-mμ forbidden band of ben-

[25] R. T. Arnold and J. Richter, *J. Am. Chem. Soc.*, *70*, 3505 (1948); R. T. Arnold and P. N. Craig, *ibid.*, *72*, 2728 (1950); R. T. Arnold, V. J. Webers, and R. M. Dodson, *ibid.*, *74*, 368 (1952).

[26] R. Van Heldin, P. E. Verkade, and B. M. Wepster, *Rec. trav. chim.*, *73*, 39.

[27] H. B. Klevens and J. R. Platt, *J. Am. Chem. Soc.*, *71*, 1714 (1949).

zene quite intense. However, by adding bulky *ortho* groups the absorption intensity was decreased, and it was shown that this decrease could be related to the size of the *ortho* substituent. The oscillator strength [28] is linearly related to the van der Waals radii of the interfering group and to the $\cos^2$ of the calculated angle of the C—N bond twists. Beale and Roe [29] found that the changes in oscillator strength for substitution with methyl groups in stilbene are additive. Note in Table I that the non-hindering methyl groups increase the oscillator strength, whereas the hindering methyl groups decrease it.

TABLE I

CHANGES IN OSCILLATOR STRENGTH, DUE TO METHYL SUBSTITUTION
IN STILBENE

	F (Change in Oscillator Strength)
Non-hindering methyl (4 or 4')	0.05
Non-hindering methyl (3 or 3')	0.005
Single hindering methyl	−0.04
Second hindering methyl in the same ring	−0.100
Second hindering methyl in the other ring	−0.075
Fourth hindering methyl	−0.135

The decrease in absorption frequency of certain hindered substituted nitroanilines can be related to the absolute configuration of the hindering groups.[30] This may be valuable in determining absolute configurations.

EXPERIMENTAL EVIDENCE FOR INTERMEDIATE TWISTS. Molecules with steric effects great enough to cause larger twists than those mentioned previously show a shift in the absorption maximum to shorter wavelengths in addition to a decrease in absorption intensity.[31]

The absorption spectra at around 288 mμ has been studied for a series of substituted benzoic acids.[32] The *ortho*-substituted benzoic

---

[28] Oscillator strength, a measure of the absorption intensity, is equal to the area under the absorption curve. See Herzberg, *Spectra of Diatomic Molecules*, 2nd ed., p. 383.

[29] R. N. Beale and E. M. F. Roe, *J. Am. Chem. Soc.*, *74*, 2302 (1952).

[30] F. Hawthorne and D. J. Cram, *J. Am. Chem. Soc.*, *74*, 5859 (1952).

[31] Ramart-Lucas, *Bull. soc. chim. France*, [5], *3*, 738 (1936); J. S. P. Blumberger, *Rec. trav. chim.*, *63*, 127–33 (1944); A. J. Bilbo and G. M. Wyman, *J. Am. Chem. Soc.*, *75*, 5312 (1953).

[32] C. M. Moser and A. I. Kohlenberg, *J. Chem. Soc.*, *1951*, 804.

acids were found to have an absorption maximum at lower wavelengths than the corresponding *para* isomer.

EXPERIMENTAL EVIDENCE FOR LARGE TWISTS. If steric hindrance is large enough there is practically no interaction between the two portions of the molecule, and the spectrum approaches the spectrum of a

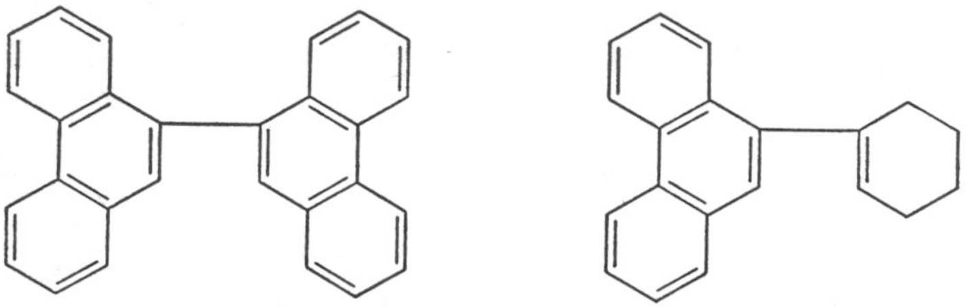

FIG. 4. The structure of two non-planar phenanthrene derivatives that have the same spectrum as phenanthrene.

mixture of the component parts.[33-41] This effect was first found by Pickett, Walter, and France,[42] who compared the spectrum of bimesityl with mesitylene and 2,2′,4,4′,6,6′-hexachlorobiphenyl with *sym*-trichlorobenzene. This effect was also found with the two phenanthrene derivatives [43] shown in Fig. 4 and the naphthalene derivative [44]

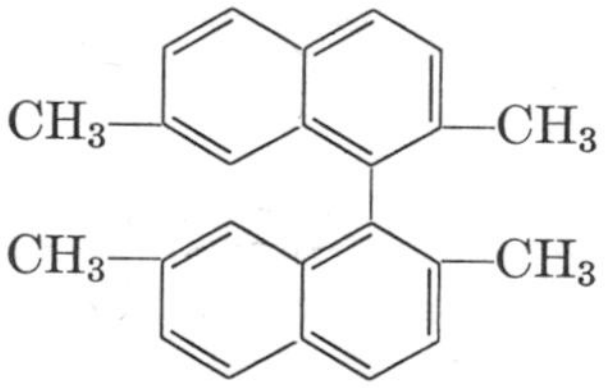

FIG. 5. The structure of a hindered binaphthyl that has a spectrum similar to that of naphthalene.

in Fig. 5, which have spectra quite similar to those of phenanthrene and naphthalene, respectively. Although smaller 2,2′ derivatives of bi-

[33] M. Calvin, *J. Org. Chem.*, *4*, 256 (1939).

[34] R. N. Jones, *J. Am. Chem. Soc.*, *63*, 1658 (1941).

[35] R. N. Jones, *J. Am. Chem. Soc.*, *65*, 1815 (1943).

[36] R. N. Jones, *J. Am. Chem. Soc.*, *67*, 2127 (1945).

[37] L. F. Fieser and M. Pechet, *J. Am. Chem. Soc.*, *68*, 2577 (1946).

[38] R. J. Morris and W. R. Brode, *J. Am. Chem. Soc.*, *70*, 2485 (1948).

[39] W. R. Brode and R. J. Morris, *J. Org. Chem.*, *13*, 200 (1948).

[40] F. Bell and D. H. Waring, *J. Chem. Soc.*, *1949*, 2689.

[41] Y. Hirschberg, *J. Am. Chem. Soc.*, *71*, 3241 (1949).

[42] L. W. Pickett, G. F. Walter, and H. France, *J. Am. Chem. Soc.*, *58*, 2296 (1936).

[43] V. Henri and E. Bergmann, *Nature*, *143*, 278 (1939).

[44] R. A. Friedel, M. Orchin, and L. Reggel, *J. Am. Chem. Soc.*, *70*, 199 (1948).

phenyl showed the effects mentioned previously, 2,2′-dicarboxybiphenyl has an absorption spectrum like that of benzoic acid and 2,2′-dinitrobiphenyl has a spectrum like that of nitrobenzene.[45] Similarly the absorption spectra of substituted benzils are close to those for the corresponding benzaldehydes.[46] The results are interpreted in terms of a skew structure for benzil, in which there is no interaction between the carbonyl groups.

QUESTION OF UNSYMMETRICAL TWISTS. The spectra of large molecules containing four aryl groups, like tetraphenylethylene,[47] are not different from those of similar molecules containing fewer phenyl groups, even though all the phenyl groups are in positions where conjugation is possible. Thus the spectra of triphenylethylene and tetraphenylethylene are similar to the spectrum of *trans*-stilbene. This effect is commonly attributed to the fact that two of the phenyl groups are non-coplanar in tetraphenylethylene and the remaining two give the spectrum of *trans*-stilbene. From a comparison of the energies involved in a model 1 where one or more phenyl groups are "non-coplanar and therefore unconjugated" with a model 2 where each phenyl group is twisted by the same angle, we will show that the latter model is to be preferred.

As mentioned previously the extra stability of a molecule with a bond having partial double-bond character is proportional to the $\cos^2$ of the angle of twist in the bond. Let us compare then the energy of a structure 1 with two phenyl groups each twisted θ with structure 2 where one phenyl group is coplanar and the other is twisted $2\theta°$.[48] The extra resonance energy for the first structure is $(R/2)$ $(2 \cos^2 \theta)$ and for the second structure $(R/2)$ $(1 + \cos^2 2\theta)$, where R would be the extra resonance energy if both phenyl rings were coplanar. For values of θ between $0°$ and $45°$, it can be seen from Fig. 6 that the structure 1 is more stable. Extending this curve above $45°$ would be meaningless, since structure 2 cannot reduce the steric hindrance further after the $90°$ ($2\theta = 90°$) structure is obtained. As might be expected, structure 1 where the strain is taken up in as many ways as possible is more stable than structure 2 where the strain is taken up by only one or two phenyl groups.

[45] E. C. Dunlop, B. Williamson, W. H. Rodebush, and A. M. Buswell, *J. Am. Chem. Soc.*, *63*, 1167 (1941); B. Williamson and W. H. Rodebush, *ibid.*, *63*, 3018 (1941).

[46] N. J. Leonard, R. T. Rapala, H. L. Herzog, and E. R. Blout, *J. Am. Chem. Soc.*, *71*, 2997 (1949).

[47] R. N. Jones, *J. Am. Chem. Soc.*, *65*, 1818 (1943).

[48] Actually there is a little more steric hindrance in the example where both phenyl groups are twisted $\theta°$.

There are compounds, however, where unsymmetrical twists probably occur. If the groups are not both phenyl groups but one is a benzoyl group and the other is a phenyl group as in the α-phenylchalcones, the arguments above no longer apply and unsymmetrical twists are possible. The similarity of the spectra of *cis*-α-phenylchalcone and *trans*-stilbene [49] is probably, in this example, due to the fact that

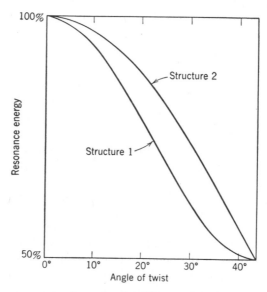

Fig. 6. Resonance energy of a molecule with two phenyl groups conjugated with the rest of the molecule. In structure 1, one phenyl group is twisted $2\theta°$ and the other phenyl group is planar with the rest of the molecule. In structure 2, both phenyl groups are twisted by $\theta°$. It is evident that structure 2 has more resonance energy and hence is more stable.

the more easily twisted benzoyl group is twisted more than the phenyl group. Unsymmetrical twists are also possible when one aryl group experiences more repulsion than the other. For example, in trimesitylvinyl alcohol [50] one mesityl group is in the same plane as a hydroxy group, whereas the other mesityl group competes with the third mesityl group for space. Similar arguments apply for triphenylethylene. [51]

A set of a symmetrically and an unsymmetrically twisted isomer is possible when three aryl groups are attached to the same carbon atom.

[49] W. B. Black and R. E. Lutz, *J. Am. Chem. Soc.*, *75*, 5990 (1953).
[50] W. H. Rodebush and I. Feldman, *J. Am. Chem. Soc.*, *68*, 896 (1946).
[51] R. N. Jones, *J. Am. Chem. Soc.*, *65*, 1818 (1943).

One isomer has a symmetrical propeller-like structure, and the other isomer has a propeller-like structure with one blade bent backwards.[52] This type of isomerism was later found in crystal violet by Lewis, Magel, and Lipkin.[53] The absorption peak maximum at around 590 mμ was attributed to the main isomer, A, and a shoulder at 550 mμ to the other isomer, B. It was shown that these absorption peaks were due to different isomers by varying the temperature and thereby varying the proportions of the isomers present.   These studies revealed that the A isomer is more stable in the ground state by 580 cal., and the spectra showed that the A isomer is more stable in the excited state by 3300 cal. Isomer A was postulated to be the symmetrical one.

Newman and Deno [54] have proposed that the aromatic groups in tri-p-chlorophenylcarbonium ion in 100% sulfuric acid are also unsymmetrically twisted. Only one isomer was detected in these studies.

NON-STERIC EFFECTS OF ORTHO GROUPS. We would like to point out that *ortho* substituents may affect the spectrum in ways other than sterically. First is the obvious fact that *ortho* substituents may affect the spectrum of aromatic compounds because of additional conjugation or electronegativity differences.[55] Certain *ortho* substituents may shift the absorption to longer wavelengths by increasing the conjugation between the two parts of the molecule [56] as shown in Fig. 7.

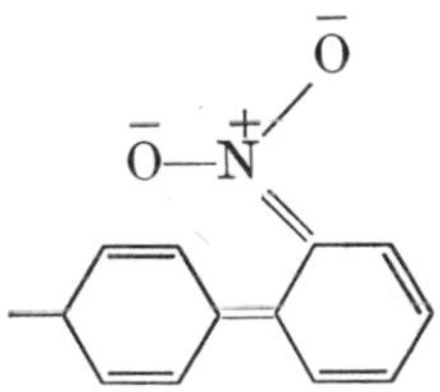

FIG. 7.   The way in which *ortho* groups can increase the conjugation between the rings in biphenyl.

On the other hand it is claimed that, in certain *ortho* groups, opposed electron-releasing tendencies decrease conjugation between the two parts of the molecule. The spectrum of 5,7-dihydrodibenz[c,e]oxepin shown in Fig. 8 has been determined and compared with the spectrum

[52] G. N. Lewis and M. Calvin, *Chem. Revs.*, *25*, 273 (1939).

[53] G. N. Lewis, T. T. Magel, and D. Lipkin, *J. Am. Chem. Soc.*, *64*, 1774 (1942).

[54] M. S. Newman and N. C. Deno, *J. Am. Chem. Soc.*, *73*, 3644 (1951).

[55] W. W. Robertson and F. A. Matsen, *J. Am. Chem. Soc.*, *72*, 5252 (1950).

[56] B. Williamson and W. H. Rodebush, *J. Am. Chem. Soc.*, *63*, 3018 (1941); L. W. Pickett, M. Groth, S. Duckworth, and J. Cunliffe, *ibid.*, *72*, 44 (1950).

of the 1,11-dimethoxy derivative.[6]　The parent oxepin was found to have an absorption maximum at 250 mμ.　The dimethoxy derivative was found to have an absorption at 250 mμ also, but of lower intensity, in addition to an absorption at 293.5 mμ.　Since the phenyl groups are held ~50° from coplanarity by the oxepin ring in both compounds, the reduction in intensity of the 250 mμ was explained not by steric effects of the methoxy groups but by less interaction between the

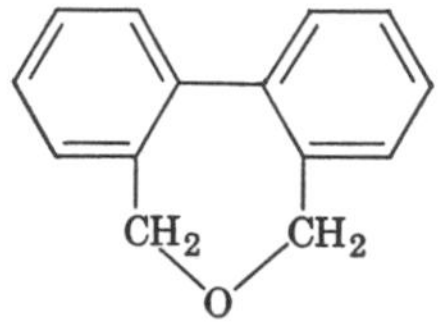

FIG. 8.

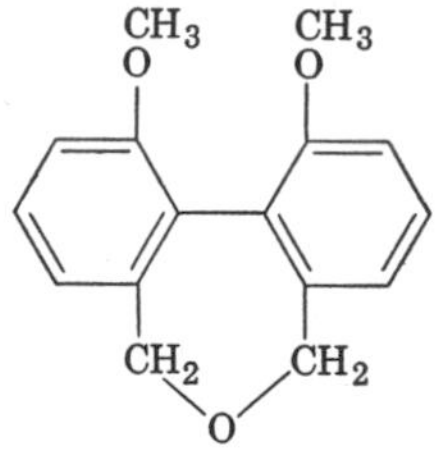

I. 5,7-Dihydrodibenz[c,e]oxepin.
II. 1,11-Dimethoxy-5,7-dihydrodibenz[c,e]oxepin.

phenyl rings in the dimethoxy derivative.　It was assumed that the opposed electron-releasing abilities of the methoxy groups in 2,2'-dimethoxybiphenyl can reduce the interaction between the rings from that in biphenyl.　It is interesting that the biphenyl portion of the molecule shows normal absorption even though the rings are twisted ~50° from coplanarity.

The absorption intensity varies not only with the amount of twist in the bond with partial double-bond character but also with another effect that should be kept in mind.　That effect is variation in the relative absorption intensity with length of the conjugated system. This has been particularly important in the study of *S-cis* and *S-trans* isomers.　*S-cis* and *S-trans* isomerization refers to *cis-trans* isomerization about a bond normally written as a single bond but containing sufficient double-bond character to permit the existence of *cis-trans* isomers. Such isomerization was first described by Mulliken [57] for the center bond of butadiene. The absorption spectrum has a lower intensity for the *S-cis* form than the *S-trans*, but otherwise the spectra are similar.[58] The *S-trans* form is slightly more stable (2.3 kcal.) than the *S-cis* form.[59]

The molecule 2-methyl-1-acetyl-1-cyclohexene shown in Fig. 9 may exist as *S-cis* and *S-trans* isomers about the bond marked *S*. It was formerly believed to exist as the *S-trans* isomer because the low absorption maximum indicated steric hindrance between the methyl

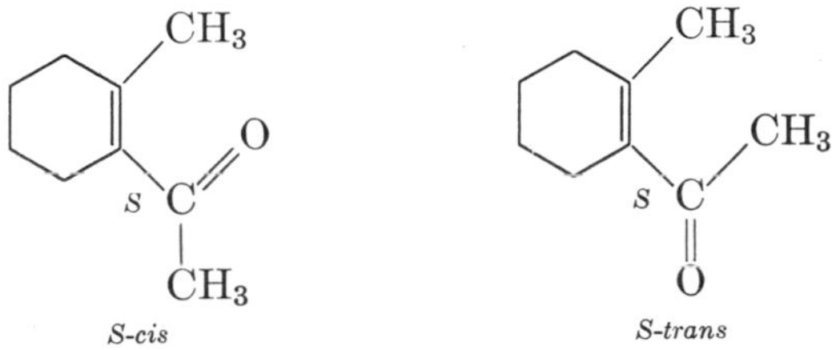

FIG. 9.   *S-cis* and *S-trans* forms of 2-methyl-1-acetyl-1-cyclohexene.

groups. Turner and Voitle [15] have shown that, by assuming absorption intensity proportional to the distance between the ends of the conjugated system, the low absorption intensity can be explained on the basis of an *S-cis* structure. The *S-cis* structure is evidently more stable in this molecule because of the interference between the methyl groups in the *S-trans* structure.

The effect of twisting an essential double bond in a conjugated system

At first it is difficult to decide what distinguishes a single bond with double-bond character discussed in the previous section from the double bonds to be discussed in this section. In this section the double bonds will be considered to be "essential" [60] as defined by Longuet-Higgins.[61] An essential double bond is one which is double in all Kekule

[57] R. S. Mulliken, *Revs. Mod. Phys.*, *14*, 265 (1942).

[58] R. S. Mulliken, *J. Chem. Phys.*, *7*, 121 (1939).

[59] A. D. Walsh, *Nature*, *157*, 768 (1946); J. G. Aston, G. Szasz, H. W. Woolley, and F. G. Brickwedde, *J. Chem. Phys.*, *14*, 67 (1946).

[60] I wish to thank Professor John R. Platt of the Physics Department of the University of Chicago for pointing out the usefulness of Longuet-Higgins' definition in this discussion.

[61] H. C. Longuet-Higgins, *J. Chem. Phys.*, *18*, 265 (1950).

structures.   The double bonds in benzene, for example, are not essential, whereas the double bonds in butadiene are essential.

In these molecules twisting will shift the absorption spectra to longer wavelengths, since there is more double-bond character in the ground state than in the excited state.*   For example, the central "double bond" of the stilbene has an order of 1.82 in the ground state but only 1.44 in the first excited state.[62]   Twisting, therefore, will now increase the energy of the ground state more than that of the excited state, and the maximum will shift to longer wavelengths.

This fact can be seen more clearly in the energy-level diagram for ethylene [63] shown in Fig. 10.   It is evident that $N \rightarrow V$ transitions

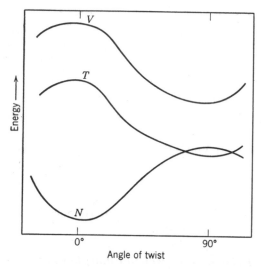

Fig. 10.   Variation of the ground level N, the first triplet level T, and the excited level V of ethylene with a twist θ, about the double bond.   Notice that $N \rightarrow V$ transitions will occur with less energy and at longer wavelengths as the angle is increased from 0° to 90°.

will be at longer wavelengths (less energy) as the double bond is twisted.

Molecular orbital treatment of the planar models for dibiphenylene-ethylene (I), dibiphenylene-butadiene (II), and dibiphenylene-hexa-

---

* The same effect for the same reason is observed when a conjugated cation is twisted.   This effect, commonly called the Brunings-Corwin effect, has been thoroughly reviewed by L. G. S. Brooker, F. L. White, R. H. Sprague, S. G. Dent, and G. van Zandt [*Chem. Revs.*, *41*, 325 (1947)].

[62] C. A. Coulson and J. Jacobs, *J. Chem. Soc.*, *1949*, 1983.

[63] R. S. Mulliken and C. C. J. Roothaan, *Chem. Revs.*, *41*, 219 (1947).

triene (III) (cf. Fig. 11) have shown that there should be a shift to longer wavelengths in the series I, II, and III.[64] It was found, however, that the wavelength of the maximum increases in the order II,

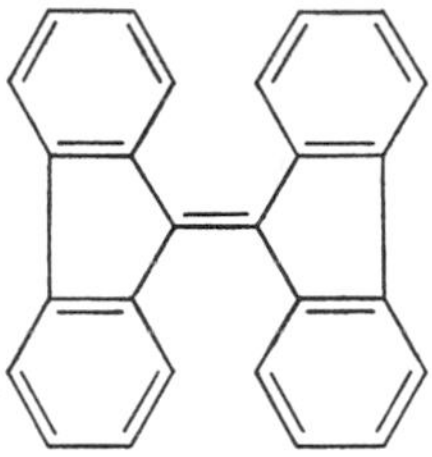

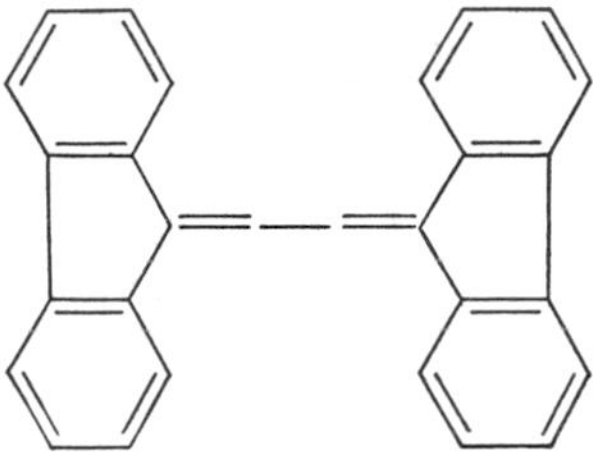

FIG. 11.

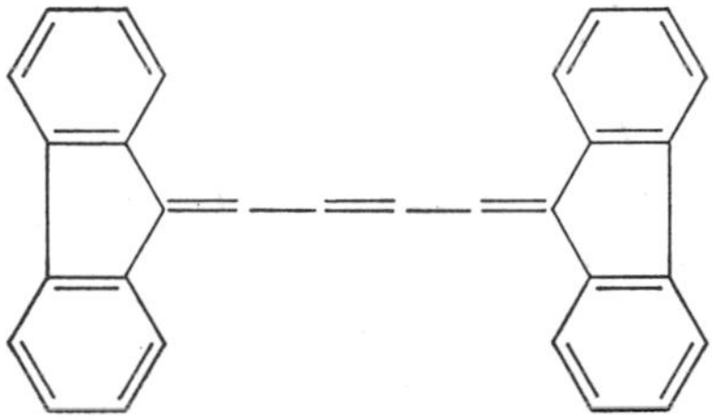

I. Dibiphenylene-ethylene.
II. Dibiphenylene-butadiene.
III. Dibiphenylene-hexatriene.

I, III. This series was interpreted as meaning that I absorbs at unusually long wavelengths because of steric effects that twist the central double bond.

Steric effects that cause increased electronic interactions

In the previous sections we have discussed examples where electronic interaction is decreased by steric effects. In the first section it was shown that twisting a single bond in a conjugated system resulted in a decreased interaction in the excited state, and in the second section it was shown that twisting a double bond in a conjugated system resulted in a decreased interaction in the ground state. In this sec-

[64] E. D. Bergmann, G. Berthier, A. Pullman, and M. B. Pullman, *Bull. soc. chim. France*, *17*, 1079 (1950).

tion we shall discuss examples in which steric effects either increase electronic interactions or cause new electronic interactions between normally "non-bonded atoms."

TYPES OF p-ORBITAL OVERLAP. Since electronic interactions occur through p-orbital overlap we shall first review the various types of

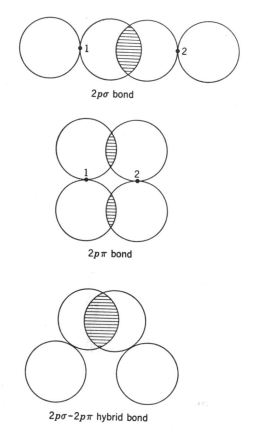

2$p\sigma$ bond

2$p\pi$ bond

2$p\sigma$-2$p\pi$ hybrid bond

FIG. 12. Types of p-orbital overlap possible. Shaded area indicates overlap of orbitals.

p-orbital overlap that are possible. As shown in Fig. 12, p-orbitals may overlap either endwise to form a 2$p\sigma$ bond,[65] in a parallel fashion to form a 2$p\pi$ bond, or at angles to form many types of hybrid bonds. Since the overlap integral [66] is an approximate measure of the binding

[65] The number 2 refers to the principal quantum number. Carbon is a second-row element, and its valence electrons are in the second shell.

[66] R. S. Mulliken, *J. Am. Chem. Soc.*, *72*, 4493 (1950).

power of two p orbitals,[67] it is instructive to notice how the overlap integral varies with distance, as is shown in Fig. 13. The $2p\sigma$ overlap integral is negative (antibonding) at low values of bond distance because the positive and negative lobes begin to interact. Note also that the $2p\sigma$ bonds are much stronger at large distances than the $2p\pi$ bonds. One might expect, therefore, to find interaction between relatively distant non-bonded atoms only when $2p\sigma$ bonds are possible.

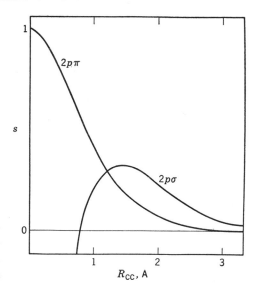

FIG. 13.   The variation of overlap integral with bond distance for $2p\sigma$ and $2p\pi$ bonds. At short distances $2p\sigma$ bonds are stronger, but at large distances $2p\pi$ bonds are stronger.

STERIC EFFECTS THAT CAUSE NEW INTERACTIONS BETWEEN ATOMS. Hybrid $2p\sigma$-$2p\pi$ bonds (cf. Fig. 14) were postulated by Bartlett and Lewis [68] to explain the increased intensity and shift to longer wavelengths in the spectrum of triptycene compared with triphenylmethane.

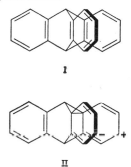

FIG. 14.

I. Triptycene.

II. One of the resonance forms of triptycene involving a $2p\sigma$-$2p\pi$ hybrid bond between the benzene rings.

[67] $B = KS/(1 + S)$, where B is bond energy, K is a constant, and S is the overlap integral. See previous reference for more details.

[68] P. D. Bartlett and E. S. Lewis, *J. Am. Chem. Soc.*, **72**, 1005 (1950).

Cram and Steinberg have prepared the unusual compound di-*p*-xylylene [69] shown in Fig. 15. The unexpected spectrum of this com-

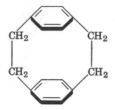

FIG. 15.   The structure of di-*p*-xylylene. The benzene rings are perpendicular to the plane of the paper.

pound containing shoulders both above and below the normal benzene absorption was explained in terms of strain and $2p\sigma$ bonds between the rings.

Although there are sixteen resonance forms involving these $2p\sigma$ bonds, it is interesting that they do not increase the stability of the compound over two isolated benzene rings.[70] This is because the double electronic levels (one electron level for each benzene ring) of di-*p*-xylylene are repelled by the interactions between them and to a first approximation lie one above and the other an equal distance below the levels of benzene where they would normally lie without interaction. The resultant electronic energy for the whole molecule is therefore the same as for two benzene rings infinitely separated. Electronic transitions between the levels as shown in Fig. 16 will give, in

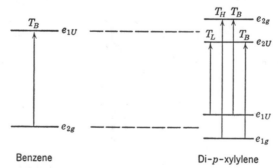

FIG. 16.   The 260-mμ transition of benzene and the corresponding transitions in di-*p*-xylylene occurring at 240 mμ, 260 mμ, and 300 mμ.

addition to the normal benzene transition T_B, a low-frequency shoulder T_L and a high-frequency shoulder T_H.

[69] D. J. Cram and H. Steinberg, *J. Am. Chem. Soc.*, *73*, 5691 (1951).

[70] L. L. Ingraham, *J. Chem. Phys.*, *18*, 988 (1950).

The $2p\sigma$ interactions have been estimated from overlap integrals to be about $\frac{1}{6}\beta$, where β is the interaction in a $2p\pi$ benzene bond. It can be shown that this would predict a long-wavelength absorption band at 300 mμ and a short-wavelength band at 220 mμ for di-p-xylylene.

p-Orbital overlap between carbons 1 and 3 of 1-acetyl-1,4-cyclohexadiene was considered as a possible explanation of the absorption at longer wavelengths and higher intensities than that in 1-acetyl-1-cyclohexene.[71] It was decided, however, that a $2p\pi$ bond would be too weak to have any effect at this great distance ($\sim$2.5 A; cf. Fig. 13) and the enhanced spectra must be due to hyperconjugation.[72]

It has been found with the benzils that although the carbonyls are far from planar in the unsubstituted compound they can be crowded into planarity by ortho groups to allow for $2p\pi$ interaction across the C—C single bond between the carbonyl groups.[73] The absorption maximum is at 370 mμ for benzil, but increases to 400 mμ for mesitylphenyldiketone and finally to two peaks at 467 and 493 mμ in mesitil. It should be pointed out that only the spectra of the last two compounds are due to interaction between the carbonyl groups. The benzil spectrum is a result of phenylcarbonyl interactions.

In the series of diketones shown in Fig. 17, as the angle between the

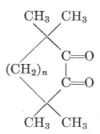

Fig. 17. The structure of the diketones synthesized by N. L. Leonard and co-workers to vary the angle between the carbonyl groups. The methyl groups were added to prevent enolization. Compounds were synthesized with n equal to 1, 2, 3, 4, and 14.

groups increases from 0° to 180°, the wavelength of spectral absorption maximum decreases to a minimum at 90° and increases again at larger angles [74] (cf. Table II).

[71] K. Bowden and E. R. H. Jones, *J. Chem. Soc.*, *1946*, 52.

[72] E. A. Braude, E. R. H. Jones, F. Sondheimer, and J. B. Toogood, *J. Chem. Soc.*, *1949*, 607.

[73] N. J. Leonard and E. R. Blout, *J. Am. Chem. Soc.*, *72*, 484 (1950).

[74] N. J. Leonard and P. M. Mader, *J. Am. Chem. Soc.*, *72*, 5388 (1950).

TABLE II

THE ABSORPTION MAXIMUM OF DIKETONES AS A FUNCTION OF THE ANGLE
BETWEEN THE CARBONYL GROUPS

n	Angle between C=O	λ_{max}
1	0–10	466
2	0–60	380
3	90–110	337
4	100–140	343
14	100–180	384

The spectra of thioctic acid, shown in Fig. 18, and similar compounds containing a dithio group have been examined by Calvin and Barltrop. Although open-chain dithio compounds absorb at 250 mμ, a dithio group in a six-membered ring absorbs at 280 mμ and at 330 mμ in a five-membered ring.[75] Calvin [76] offers the following interesting explanation of this phenomenon. A sulfur atom in a thio or dithio ether is bonded by p orbitals leaving a non-bonded s and p orbital.

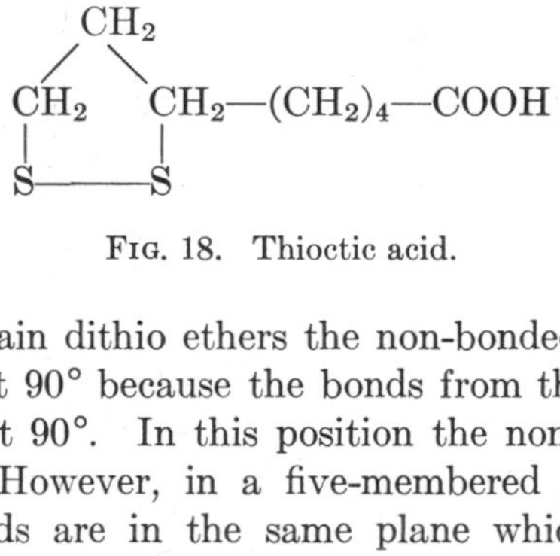

$$\begin{array}{c} CH_2 \\ \diagup \quad \diagdown \\ CH_2 \qquad CH_2-(CH_2)_4-COOH \\ | \qquad\qquad | \\ S\text{------}S \end{array}$$

FIG. 18.   Thioctic acid.

In normal open-chain dithio ethers the non-bonded p orbitals on the sulfur atoms are at 90° because the bonds from the sulfurs to the organic groups are at 90°. In this position the non-bonded p orbitals cannot interact. However, in a five-membered ring the sulfur-to-organic-group bonds are in the same plane which forces the non-bonded p orbitals also into the same plane. In this position the non-bonded p orbitals may interact, causing a change in the absorption spectra.

The effect of bending a benzene ring

A lack of fine structure is characteristic of the spectra of aromatic rings that are warped out of a planar configuration.[77] This effect may

[75] M. Calvin and J. A. Barltrop, *J. Am. Chem. Soc.*, *74*, 6153 (1952).

[76] M. Calvin, Federation Proc., *13*, 697 (1954).

[77] This lack of fine structure should not be confused with the lack of fine structure in the "loose bolt" molecules discussed by G. N. Lewis and M. Calvin, *Chem. Revs.*, *25*, 273 (1939).

be because the vibrational and electronic wave functions are not separable;[78] i.e., when the rings are badly warped vibrations will vary the warping and thus also vary the electronic energy.* This effect will cause a loss of fine structure. Examples of this effect have been found in the spectrum of 4,5-dimethylchrysene,[79] 4,5-dimethylphenanthrene,[80] 1,12-dimethylbenzo[c]phenanthrene,[81] and 1-methyl-3,4-benzo[c]phenanthrene.[82] The spectrum of di-p-xylylene[83] also shows this fine-structure effect in addition to the previously mentioned effects of $2p\sigma$ interaction between the rings. In order to test the hypothesis that the loss of fine structure in di-p-xylylene was a result of warping the benzene rings, Cram, Allinger, and Steinberg prepared compounds with the benzene ring warped by bridges connecting the *para* positions of the benzene ring. These compounds, shown in Fig. 19, also lacked

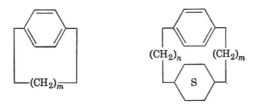

FIG. 19. Model compounds prepared by Cram, Allinger, and Steinberg to study the lack of fine structure in the spectra of warped benzene rings.

fine structure in their spectra as compared with the benzene spectrum.

Another characteristic of the spectra of bent benzene rings, evident in the above examples, is a slight shift to longer wavelengths. The first excited state of benzene by necessity must have more antibonding interactions and less bonding interactions than the ground state. When a benzene ring is bent, all interactions are affected about the same so that the ground state and excited states become closer in energy and the band moves to longer wavelengths.

* The steric strains tend to counteract the planar constraints of resonance, thus making the rings more flexible.

[78] I wish to thank Dr. F. Stitt for suggesting this possibility.

[79] R. N. Jones, *J. Am. Chem. Soc.*, *63*, 313 (1941).

[80] G. M. Badger, J. E. Campbell, J. W. Cook, R. A. Raphael, and A. I. Scott, *J. Chem. Soc.*, *1950*, 2326.

[81] M. S. Newman and M. Wolf, *J. Am. Chem. Soc.*, *74*, 3225 (1952).

[82] G. M. Badger and I. S. Walker, *J. Chem. Soc.*, *1954*, 3238.

[83] D. J. Cram, N. L. Allinger, and H. Steinberg, *J. Am. Chem. Soc.*, *76*, 6132 (1954).

VIBRATIONAL SPECTRA

From a thorough study of the vibrational spectra of small molecules we can obtain much information concerning the interactions of non-bonded atoms that may some day be applied to organic chemistry. Interactions between atoms can be studied from imperfections in the gas laws. However, the intermolecular forces found in this way may not be the same as the intramolecular forces involved in steric effects. The latter forces act between atoms in a very specific electronic environment, i.e., when the atoms are bonded to another atom and carry a partial charge. A study of the vibrational spectra enables one to estimate intramolecular repulsion forces between non-bonded atoms under these special conditions of electronic environment. The repulsion forces can be estimated from either interaction terms or repulsion force constants.

Interaction terms

Hooke's law states that the stress in a stretched spring is proportional to the strain. This may be expressed as shown in equation 1,

$$F = KX \qquad (1)$$

where F is the force necessary to exert on a stretched spring of Hooke's law constant, K, to give a displacement X. It follows therefore that the potential energy, V, of a stretched spring is expressible as

$$V = \tfrac{1}{2}KX^2 \qquad (2)$$

By analogy with this equation the simplest potential-energy function for a polyatomic molecule can be written as

$$V = \tfrac{1}{2}k_a\,\Delta r_a{}^2 + \tfrac{1}{2}k_b\,\Delta r_b{}^2 + \tfrac{1}{2}k_c\,\Delta r_c{}^2 \qquad (3)$$

where V is the potential energy, Δr_n is the change in distance on vibration of bond n, and k_n is the Hooke's law constant or stretching force constant for the bond.

From this potential-energy function can be calculated the normal modes [84] of vibration of the molecule, and these are correlated with the vibrational spectra. A better approximation to the potential energy resulting in a better correlation with the vibrational spectra will be obtained if additional terms called interaction terms, $k_{nm}\,\Delta r_n\,\Delta r_m$, are added to the potential function. These additional constants, k_{nm},

[84] G. Herzberg, *Molecular Spectra and Molecular Structure*, II, *Infrared and Raman Spectra of Polyatomic Molecules*, pp. 61–76, D. Van Nostrand Co., New York, 1945.

called interaction constants, are not analogous to Hooke's Law Constants, and their interpretation has led to much interesting discussion. The values of k_{nm} can be either positive or negative.

The cause of these terms [85] is not simple but depends upon at least three factors: (1) resonance involving other atoms; (2) interactions between non-bonded atoms; (3) changes in hydribization at the central atom. The second factor is the only one that is of interest here. Steric hindrance in a molecule is related to a positive interaction term.[86] Duchesne and Monfils [87] have calculated the interaction terms in a series of triatomic molecules from a Lennard-Jones potential [88] with the assumption that interactions between non-bonded atoms are the only cause of the interaction terms. The calculated values shown in Table III are in reasonably good agreement with the experimental values.

TABLE III

VIBRATIONAL INTERACTION TERMS

Compound	Observed	Calculated
CO_2	1.32	— *
COS	0.90	— *
COSe	0.76	0.79
CS_2	0.59	0.59
HCN	−0.30	— *
ClCN	1.01	— *
BrCN	0.95	0.90
ICN	1.07	0.74

* The first two compounds in each series were used to determine the parameters in the Lennard-Jones potential.

Repulsion terms

Another approach to the problem of interactions between non-bonded atoms is to add specific repulsion terms to the potential-energy function to take care of these interactions. Urey and Bradley [89] have

---

[85] C. A. Coulson, J. Duchesne, and C. Manneback, *Nature*, *160*, 793–794 (1947); C. A. Coulson, J. Duchesne, and C. Manneback, *Contribution a, étude de la structure moléculaire*, p. 33, Maison Desoer, Liège, 1947–1948.

[86] D. F. Heath and J. W. Linnett, *Trans. Faraday Soc.*, *44*, 556 (1948).

[87] J. Duchesne and A. Monfils, *J. Chem. Phys.*, *17*, 586 (1949).

$$ ^{88} V = A \left[6 \left(\frac{a}{r} \right)^{12} - 12 \left(\frac{a}{r} \right)^{6} \right] $$

V is the potential energy at a distance r between two non-bonded atoms. A and a are constants.

[89] H. C. Urey and C. A. Bradley, Jr., *Phys. Rev.*, *Ser. 2*, *38*, 1969 (1931).

proposed a potential function containing repulsion terms between non-bonded atoms.[90] The repulsion terms contain the constants B and A, defined by the first and second derivatives of the potential with change in distance between the non-bonded atoms, respectively. The terms containing the B's assume that there is a constant repulsive force, B_{ij}, between the non-bonded atoms i and j, whereas the terms containing the A's are comparable to the interaction terms discussed above with the exception that these terms now involve non-bonded atoms. The values of B (the repulsive force) for interactions between halide atoms in several tetrahalides have been compared with the corresponding values for the next inert gas (Br with Kr and Cl with A) at the proper distance for the molecule concerned. These values are shown in Table IV. Although we should not expect agreement,

TABLE IV

Repulsion Forces (B)

Compound	Source	
	Vibrational Spectra	Imperfections in Inert Gas
CCl_4	21.3×10^{-5} dyne	24.2×10^{-5} dyne
$SiCl_4$	9.7	9.9
$SnCl_4$	4.8	2.7
CBr_4	14.7	28.1
$SnBr_4$	4.3	2.6

the correspondence is good enough to support the theory that they are the result of a common cause, i.e., that steric effects measured in this manner by vibrational spectroscopy and deviations from the ideal gas laws are both due to repulsions between non-bonded atoms.

Notice that the values for interactions in the compounds $SnCl_4$ and $SnBr_4$ are higher than those predicted for the corresponding inert gases. This is usually true when the non-bonded atoms are attached to an electropositive atom like tin. In these cases the non-bonded atoms tend to carry a partial negative charge which increases the repulsion between them. This effect is shown quite clearly in the work of Heath and Linnett summarized in Table V, where the ratio of A

$$^{90} \sum_{ij} [B_{ij} \Delta q_{ij} + \tfrac{1}{2} A_{ij}(\Delta q_{ij})^2]$$

In these terms B_{ij} and A_{ij} are the repulsive force constants and q_{ij} is the distance between the non-bonded atoms i and j. These terms represent the increase in potential energy when the distance between the non-bonded atoms is changed by Δq_{ij}.

from the vibrational spectra to the A from argon gas law imperfections increases with the electropositiveness of the central atom.[91]

The corresponding ratio compared to neon has been calculated for a series of oxyanions (e.g., $SO_4^=$, $CO_3^=$, ClO_4^-, etc.). It was found that the ratio increased with the charge on the anion and was directly proportional to n/N, where n is the charge carried by the ion

TABLE V

REPULSION CONSTANTS, $A \times 10^5$ dynes/cm., FOR VARIOUS TETRACHLORIDES

	A (argon)	A (vibrational spectra)	A (vibrational spectra)/A (argon)
CCl_4	0.494	0.31	0.63
$SiCl_4$	0.079	0.15	1.9
$GeCl_4$	0.046	0.10	2.2
$SnCl_4$	0.011	0.06	5.5

and N is the number of oxygen atoms.[92] Many repulsion constants will be found summarized by Simanouti,[93] and others will be found scattered through the papers of Linnett and Heath.

Although it should be possible to directly measure steric interactions between atoms in organic compounds by the methods indicated above, the author is not aware of any such study. The reason of course is that these methods require a complete vibrational analysis, which is a very difficult task in complex organic molecules. In the succeeding sections on vibrational spectra we shall discuss not direct measurements of steric interactions but the effect that these steric interactions have on the vibrational frequencies of other bonds.

The effect of twisting a single bond in a conjugated system

As an example of a single bond in a conjugated system we might consider the single bond between the phenyl and carbonyl groups in acetophenone. The stretching frequency of the carbonyl bond is directly related to the amount of double-bond character,[94] as exemplified by the higher frequency in phenylacetone than in the acetophenone shown in Table VI. However, ortho methyl groups twist the aromatic

[91] D. F. Heath and J. W. Linnett, Trans. Faraday Soc., 44, 873 (1948).

[92] D. F. Heath and J. W. Linnett, Trans. Faraday Soc., 44, 884 (1948); J. W. Linnett and D. F. Heath, ibid., 48, 592 (1952).

[93] T. Simanouti, Bull. Inst. Phys. Chem. Research Tokyo, Ser. Phys., 23, 314 (1944) [C. A., 42, 5345 (1948)]. T. Simanouti, J. Chem. Phys., 17, 848 (1949).

[94] M. L. Josien, N. Fuson, J. M. Lebas, and T. M. Gregory, J. Chem. Phys., 21, 331 (1953).

carbonyl bond in acetophenone, and thereby they decrease the resonance and increase the carbonyl bond order.

Thus the carbonyl frequencies of 2,4,6-trimethylacetophenone and 2,3,5,6-tetramethylacetophenone are higher than those for acetophenone. The hydrogen atom on benzaldehyde is not large enough to give this effect (cf. section on dipole moments).

TABLE VI*

CARBONYL STRETCHING FREQUENCIES, cm.$^{-1}$

Acetophenone	1684
Phenylacetone	1697
2,4,6-Trimethylacetophenone	1699
2,3,5,6-Tetramethylacetophenone	1699
Benzaldehyde	1700
Phenylacetaldehyde	1718
o-Tolualdehyde	1688
Mesitaldehyde	1687

* R. H. Saunders, M. J. Murray, and F. F. Cleveland J. Am. Chem. Soc., 63, 3121 (1941).

Similar results were found for the frequency of the nitro group in benzyl nitrite (1367 cm.$^{-1}$), nitrobenzene (1341 cm.$^{-1}$), o-nitrotoluene (1345 cm.$^{-1}$), and nitromesitylene (1363 cm.$^{-1}$).

In the styrene series *ortho* substitution also raises the double-bond deformation frequency. Thus, *ortho*-methyl substitution increases the frequency from 889 cm.$^{-1}$ in p-methylisopropenylbenzene to 898 cm.$^{-1}$ in o-methylisopropenylbenzene.[95] *Ortho*-chloro groups show effects similar to those of o-methyl groups. The carbonyl stretching frequency is 1707 cm.$^{-1}$ in 2,4-dichlorobenzoic acid but 1724 cm.$^{-1}$ in 2,6-dichlorobenzoic acid.[96]

Strain in cyclic ketones

For the most stable configuration of a ketone the angle between the two bonds attached to the carbonyl group is 120°. In cyclopentanone and cyclobutanone this angle is reduced, and the molecule is strained. This strain causes a rehybridization in the orbitals of the carbonyl carbon. A smaller angle than 120° gives the ring bonds more p character (more like sp^3 bonds at 109°) and consequently the σ bond in the carbonyl group more s character. Because s character in a bond will increase the stretching frequency (this will be discussed later un-

[95] M. J. Murray and W. S. Gallaway, J. Am. Chem. Soc., 70, 3867 (1948).
[96] S. D. Ross, J. Am. Chem. Soc., 70, 4039 (1948).

der strain in three-membered rings), cyclobutanone and cyclopentanone should have a higher carbonyl stretching frequency than cyclohexanone. This has experimentally been found to be true. The carbonyl stretching frequency for cyclohexanone shown in Table VII is

TABLE VII

CARBONYL STRETCHING FREQUENCIES OF CYCLIC KETONES, cm.$^{-1}$

	D. Biquard	J. Lecomte
Cyclobutanone	1774	
Cyclopentanone	1727, 1744	1742
Cyclohexanone	1714, 1698, 1697	1718
Methyl ethyl ketone	1714	
Cycloheptanone		1709
Cyclooctanone		1709
Cyclopentadecanone		1708

the same as that for a strainless acyclic ketone, but the frequency of
cyclopentanone is high, and that for cyclobutanone is higher yet.[97]
For cyclic ketones larger than cyclohexanone the frequency is slightly
lower.[98] However, the assumption of a one-to-one correspondence
between frequency and force constant is only an approximation when
the atoms are as heavy as oxygen.

DIPOLE MOMENTS

Twisting a single bond in a conjugated system

The mesomeric moments of conjugated systems depend upon the
amount of double-bond character in a bond normally written single,
as for example the C—N bond in aniline shown in Fig. 20. As dis-

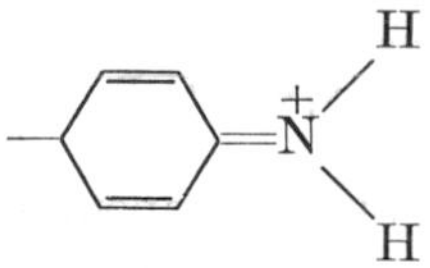

FIG. 20. Resonance structure for aniline, showing how the mesomeric moment
depends upon the double-bond character between the ring and the nitrogen.

cussed under "electronic spectra," twisting the bond will reduce its
double-bond character and, in this case, its mesomeric moment. It

[97] K. W. F. Kohlrausch and R. Skrabal, Z. Elektrochem., 43, 282 (1937); D.
Biquard, Compt. rend., 204, 1721 (1937); D. Biquard, Bull. soc. chim. France, [5]
7, 894 (1940); E. J. Hartwell, R. E. Richards, and H. W. Thompson, J. Chem. Soc.,
1948, 1436.
[98] J. Lecomte, J. phys., Ser. 8, 6, 257 (1945).

can be shown quite simply from the equation of Matsen [99] for the mesomeric moment of a monosubstituted benzene that twisting affects the mesomeric moment by the $\cos^2$ of the angle of twist.[100] If the mesomeric moment is completely eliminated by twisting the bond to 90° there will still be the usual inductive moment found in aliphatic compounds due to the differences in electronegativities of the atoms. The total moment of the molecule may increase or decrease on twisting, depending upon the relative direction and magnitude of the two moments.

Hampson and coworkers [101] have compared the dipole moments of several o-methyl derivatives of anilines, phenols, and anisole with the unsubstituted compounds. In Table VIII we see that the dipoles of

TABLE VIII

DIPOLE MOMENTS OF VARIOUS COMPOUNDS *

Hindered		Unhindered	
Nitrodurene	3.62 †	Nitrobenzene	3.95
Nitromesitylene	3.67 ‡	Nitrobenzene	3.95
Aminodurene	1.39	Aniline	1.53
Pentamethylaniline	1.10	p-Toluidine	1.36
Mesidine	1.40	Aniline	1.53
Dimethylmesidine	1.03	Dimethylaniline	1.58
Durenol	1.68	Phenol	1.61
Nitrodimethyl-		p-Nitrodimethyl-	
aminodurene	4.11	aniline	6.87
Nitrodurenol	4.08	p-Nitrophenol	5.04

* Data of R. H. Birtles and G. C. Hampson, *J. Chem. Soc.*, *1937*, 10, and C. E. Ingham and G. C. Hampson, *ibid.*, *1939*, 981, except where noted.

† Data of H. Kofod, L. E. Sutton, W. A. DeJong, P. E. Verkade, and B. M. Wepster, *Rec. trav. chim.*, *71*, 521 (1952). The "nitrodurene" measured by Birtles and Hampson was actually nitroethoxydurene.

‡ D. L. Hammick, R. G. A. New, and R. B. Williams, *J. Chem. Soc.*, *1934*, 29.

the aromatic amines and nitro compounds are greatly reduced by *ortho* substitution but that of phenol is increased. In the amines the mesomeric and normal moments are opposed, and since the meso-

[99] F. A. Matsen, *J. Am. Chem. Soc.*, *72*, 5243 (1950).

[100] By using perturbation theory for the λ_{ij} and substituting the proper wave functions in the resulting equation, the mesomeric moment becomes proportional to β^2, where β is the exchange integral between an orbital on the substituent and an orbital on carbon atom 1. Since β varies with the cos of the angle of twist, we obtain the result that the mesomeric moment varies with the $\cos^2$ of the angle of twist.

[101] R. H. Birtles and G. C. Hampson, *J. Chem. Soc.*, *1937*, 10; C. E. Ingham and G. C. Hampson, *ibid.*, *1939*, 981.

meric moment is the largest the resultant moment is in the direction of the mesomeric moment. Steric effects will therefore decrease the moment. Phenols also have their normal and mesomeric moments opposed, but the resultant moment here is in the direction of the inductive moment and so *ortho* substitution should increase the moment. The dipole of benzyl alcohol ($\mu = 1.70D$) is similar to that of durenol. In nitrobenzene the two moments add, and *ortho* substitution decreases the moment.

Ortho substitution decreases the moment in acetophenones.[102] For example, changing a methyl group from a *meta* position in 2,4,5-trimethylacetophenone to an *ortho* position in 2,4,6-trimethylacetophenone reduces the dipole moment from $3.22D$ to $2.81D$.[103] However, in spite of the increased twist of the acetyl group in 2,4,6-trimethylacetophenone, it has been shown by heats of combustion that 2,4,6-trimethylacetophenone is more stable than 2,4,5-trimethylacetophenone by 3.9 kcal. The extra stability in the 2,4,6 derivative is best explained by an instability in the 2,4,5 derivative because of *o*-dimethyl interactions.

Aldehydes are not similarly affected by *ortho* methyl substitution. The dipole moment of benzaldehyde is $2.92D$, and that of 2,4,6-trimethylbenzaldehyde is $2.96D$.

Hindrances to mesomeric moments have been found also where nitro groups are hindered by *ortho*-chloro groups,[104] 4-dimethylaminostilbenes hindered by 2-methyl and 2-ethyl groups,[105] and stilbene hindered by a 2-dimethylamino group.[106]

It has been shown that in 1-phenylpyrrole the mesomeric moment is opposed to the normal moment, since *ortho* substitution increases the dipole. The compound 2,5,2',4',6'-pentamethyl-1-phenylpyrrole has a moment of $2.06 \pm 0.04D$, whereas the moment predicted from 1-phenylpyrrole and toluene is $1.54 \pm 0.04D$.[107] The mesomeric moment is therefore about $-0.52D$. This value is close to the difference in dipoles ($-0.60D$) of 1-methylpyrrole and 1-phenylpyrrole.

An interesting study of the variation in dipole moment with solvent changes [108] has revealed (as shown in Table IX) that in molecules

[102] R. G. Kadesch and S. W. Weller, *J. Am. Chem. Soc.*, *63*, 1310 (1941); J. B. Bentley, K. B. Everard, R. J. B. Marsden, and L. E. Sutton, *J. Chem. Soc.*, *1949*, 2957.

[103] J. W. Baker and W. T. Tweed, *J. Chem. Soc.*, *1941*, 796.

[104] G. Thomson, *J. Chem. Soc.*, *1944*, 404.

[105] K. B. Everard and L. E. Sutton, *J. Chem. Soc.*, *1951*, 2816.

[106] K. B. Everard and L. E. Sutton, *J. Chem. Soc.*, *1951*, 2817.

[107] H. Kofod, L. E. Sutton and J. Jackson, *J. Chem. Soc.*, *1952*, 1467.

[108] J. W. Smith, *J. Chem. Soc.*, *1953*, 109.

with mesomeric moment the dipole is $0.18D$ to $0.24D$ larger in dioxane than in the less polar solvent benzene. In compounds with little or no mesomeric moment the difference is much less. This method of testing for a mesomeric moment is not encumbered by having to de-

TABLE IX

DIPOLE MOMENTS OF VARIOUS AMINES IN BENZENE AND DIOXANE

Compound	Dipole in Benzene	Dipole in Dioxane	Increase in Dipole
Little steric hindrance			
Aniline	1.53	1.77	0.24
Methylaniline	1.68	1.86	0.18
More steric hindrance			
Mesidine	1.45	1.57	0.12
Aminodurene	1.45	1.57	0.12
Methylmesidine	1.22	1.26	0.04
Aliphatic amine			
Butylamine	1.34	1.33	−0.01

cide what model compound to compare with the compound in question. Smith discusses an anomaly of the dipoles of 2,4,6-tribromoaniline in benzene and dioxane.

Structures of hindered molecules

In hindered molecules with no mesomeric moment it is possible to determine the structure of the molecule by comparing the moment with the vectorial addition of the moments of its component parts. This information has been combined with X-ray and electron diffraction data in Table X to make a more complete discussion of the structures of hindered molecules.

The most surprising fact in Table X is that all the angles are below 90°, indicating structures more *cis* than *trans*. Bastiansen has attributed [109] these structures to quantum-mechanical attractive forces (London forces) between the halogen atoms. These forces are balanced out by the actual impenetrability of the halogen atoms to give the resultant structures found. It is interesting to note that the 2,2'-dinitro- and dicarboxybiphenyls, in which the central bond is twisted almost 90°, also showed large steric effects in the electronic spectra.

From molecular refraction data, as will be discussed later, it can be shown that *cis*-4-bromo-4'-nitrostilbene is greatly hindered, and the structure can be determined by comparing its dipole moment with the dipoles of bromobenzene and nitrobenzene.[110]

[109] O. Bastiansen, *Acta Chem. Scand.*, 4, 926 (1950).
[110] K. B. Everard and L. E. Sutton, *J. Chem. Soc.*, *1951*, 2826.

TABLE X

Compound	Angle *
Biphenyl	45° ± 10° †
3,3',5,5'-Tetrabromobiphenyl	49° ‡
3,3'-Dichlorobenzidine	52° ‡
3,3'-Dibromobiphenyl	54° ± 5° †
2,2'-Dichlorobiphenyl	62°,§ 74° ‡
2,2'-Dimethylbenzidine hydrochloride	70.6° ‖
2,2'-Dichlorobenzidine	72° ¶
2,2'-Dibromobiphenyl	75° ‡
2,2'-Diiodobiphenyl	79° ‡
2,2'-Dinitrobiphenyl	90° **
2,2'-Dicarboxybiphenyl	90° **

* An angle of 0° means a *cis* structure; an angle of 180° means a *trans* structure.

† O. Bastiansen, *Acta Chem. Scand.*, *3*, 408 (1949). Electron diffraction in gas phase.

‡ O. Bastiansen, *Acta Chem. Scand.*, *4*, 926 (1950). Electron diffraction in gas phase.

§ G. C. Hampson and A. Weissberger, *J. Am. Chem. Soc.*, *58*, 2111 (1936).

‖ F. Fowweather and A. Hargreaves, *Acta Cryst.*, *3*, 81 (1951). X-rays on crystals.

¶ D. L. Smare, *Acta Cryst.*, *1*, 150 (1948). X-rays on crystals.

** R. J. W. LeFévre and H. Vine, *J. Chem. Soc.*, *1938*, 967.

From this comparison, it is found that 1:4 and 1':4' diagonals are at 82° to each other and the C—C= angle is 131° in *cis*-4-bromo-4'-nitrostilbene.

The dipole of 2,4-di-*tert*-butylphenol is perpendicular to the ring.[111] H. G. Walker has suggested that 2,6-di-*tert*-butyl-3-methylphenol or any similarly labeled 2,6-di-*tert*-butylphenol should possess optical isomerism.[112]

The half-amplitude of free rotation, $\pm\theta$, of a hindered methoxy group on a benzene ring can be calculated from the dipole moment of the compound. These values suggest that two methoxyls on the same benzene ring tend to loosen the π bonding between the ring and oxygen because of the build-up of negative charges in the ring. This effect allows a larger value of θ where there are two methoxyl groups on the same ring. For example, dipole-moment measurements show that

[111] P. Rumpf and H. Lumbroso, *Bull. soc. chim. France*, *1950*, 283. For similar effects with methoxy groups, see K. B. Everard and L. E. Sutton, *J. Chem. Soc.*, *1949*, 2312.

[112] Howard G. Walker, Western Regional Research Laboratory, U. S. Department of Agriculture, private communication.

θ is 40° in 1,5-dimethoxynaphthalene but increases to 83° in 1,4-dimethoxynaphthalene. Larger separation, as occurs in 1,5-dimethoxyanthracene,[113] reduces the θ value to 37°.

REFRACTIVE INDEX AND MOLECULAR REFRACTION

The refractive index and molecular refraction are measures of electron polarizability. Compounds containing a conjugated system are usually more polarizable and therefore have higher refractive indices or molecular refractions. If the conjugation is decreased by steric effects, the refractive index and molecular refraction will also be decreased. For example, the refractive indices of ortho-chloro or ortho-methyl substituted α-methyl styrenes are $274 - 352 \times 10^{-4}$ unit lower than for the corresponding ortho substituted styrene where there is much less steric hindrance. The differences for the corresponding meta and para substituted compounds are $80 - 110 \times 10^{-4}$ unit.[114]

Decreases of molecular refraction with ortho substitution are shown in Table XI for the dichloronitrobenzenes.[115] The group of compounds

TABLE XI

MOLECULAR REFRACTIONS OF DICHLORONITROBENZENES

Position of Chlorine	R 5461	$\Delta R \times 10^2$ *
No ortho Chlorine		
3,4	43.15	4
3,5	43.19	0
One ortho Chlorine		
2,3	42.79	40
2,4	42.62	57
2,5	42.50	69
Two ortho Chlorines		
2,6	42.32	87

* Differences refer to 3,5-dichloronitrobenzene.

with one ortho chlorine have molecular refractions lower than those with no ortho chlorines, and the compound with two ortho chlorines has a still smaller molecular refraction. Similar results were found

[113] K. B. Everard and L. E. Sutton, J. Chem. Soc., 1951, 16.

[114] G. H. Stempel, Jr., C. Greene, R. Rongone, B. Sobel, and R. Odioso, J. Am. Chem. Soc., 73, 455 (1951).

[115] G. Thomson, J. Chem. Soc., 1944, 404.

for the molecular refraction of the *ortho*-methyl derivatives of aniline and dimethylaniline.[116]

The decrease in molecular exaltation [117] relative to stilbene produced by *ortho* substitution in the 4-dimethylaminostilbene series [118] is shown in Table XII.

TABLE XII

MOLECULAR EXALTATIONS IN 4-DIMETHYLAMINOSTILBENE DERIVATIVES

Substituent	Molecular Exaltation *
None	7.5
2'-Ethyl	3.3
2',4',6'-Trimethyl	1.6

* Relative to stilbene.

Large differences were also found for the molecular refraction of the *cis* and *trans* isomers of 4-bromo-4'-nitrostilbene. For the *trans* isomer the exaltation was 7.4, but in the highly hindered *cis* isomer it was lowered to 1.8.[110]

MISCELLANEOUS PROPERTIES

Thermochromism

Grubb and Kistiakowsky [119] have shown that thermochromism in bianthrone is due to steric effects. Repulsions between the hydrogens at points marked X in Fig. 21 twist the central double bond. This

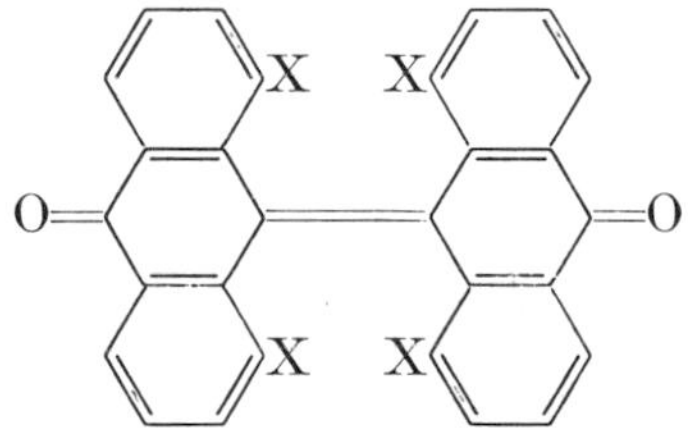

FIG. 21. Bianthrone; positions of interfering hydrogens are marked by X.

causes a change in the energy levels as shown in the much simplified diagram in Fig. 22, where θ is the angle of twist. The ground (singlet, labeled S_1) state will approximately vary as the $\cos^2 \theta$ with the energy

[116] G. Thomson, *J. Chem. Soc.*, *1944*, 408.

[117] Molecular exaltation is the increase in molecular refraction due to mesomerism over the value for a reference compound or that calculated for the compound without mesomerism.

[118] K. B. Everard and L. E. Sutton, *J. Chem. Soc.*, *1951*, 2816.

[119] W. T. Grubb and G. B. Kistiakowsky, *J. Am. Chem. Soc.*, *72*, 419 (1950).

maximum (least stability) at 90°. However, the excited states (S_2, singlet, and T_2, triplet) will be slightly more stable [120] at 90° because the interaction across the double bond is now antibonding and less interaction will make the molecule more stable. The diradical triplet state, T_1, dips below the singlet state, S_1, at 90° by the amount of resonance energy of the two unpaired electrons.

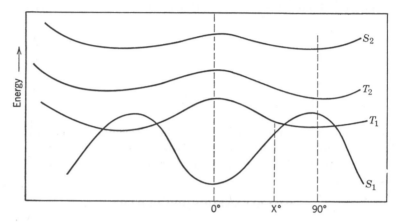

FIG. 22. The electronic levels of bianthrone as a function of the angle of twist of the central bond.

If the molecule were planar ($\theta = o$), S_1 and T_1 would have a large separation, but if the molecule were twisted by steric effects to $\theta = X$ the levels S_1 and T_1 would be close. The actual separation was found experimentally to be only 3.5 kcal., and this makes it possible for molecules in level S_1 to be excited thermally to level T_1. Since electronic transitions by absorption of light between singlet and triplet states are forbidden, the molecules in level T_1 can be excited only to T_2. This transition will occur at longer wavelengths than the transition S_1 to S_2. An increase in temperature will therefore shift the spectra to longer wavelengths and in the case of bianthrone from the ultraviolet to the visible. Grubb and Kistiakowsky have pointed out that this is only one of the reasons for thermochromism.

Since this work was finished it has been shown that bianthrone is paramagnetic and this paramagnetism is higher at higher temperatures.[121] This helps to confirm the theory of Grubb and Kistiakowsky that a triplet state (paramagnetic) is involved.

[120] R. S. Mulliken and C. C. J. Roothaan, *Chem. Revs.*, *41*, 219 (1947). See also Sheldon L. Matlow, *J. Chem. Phys.*, *23*, 152 (1955).
[121] W. G. Nielsen and G. K. Fraenkel, *J. Chem. Phys.*, *21*, 1619 (1953).

Hirshberg, Loewenthal, and Bergmann [122] have studied the spectra of 4,4' disubstituted bianthrones. The compounds are not thermochromic, and the spectra have no long-wave transition corresponding to a triplet transition. They offer the untenable explanation that bianthrone is twisted at lower temperatures but the central double bond stretches at higher temperatures to allow the molecule to be planar. The planar form absorbs at longer wavelengths to exhibit thermochromism. The 4,4' disubstituents prevent the molecule from being planar even at higher temperatures, and so these derivatives do not exhibit thermochromism.

If this explanation for thermochromism in bianthrone were true the long-wavelength transition would gradually move to longer wavelengths as the angle of twist became less at higher temperature. Grubb and Kistiakowsky showed that there is no moving of the long-wavelength band. It gradually increases in intensity, but its wavelength does not vary with temperature. There seems to be no explanation why these 4,4' derivatives do not exhibit thermochromism or at least have a long-wavelength absorption.

In a study of spiropyrans, Koelsch [123] has found another cause of thermochromism related to steric effects. The thermochromism in

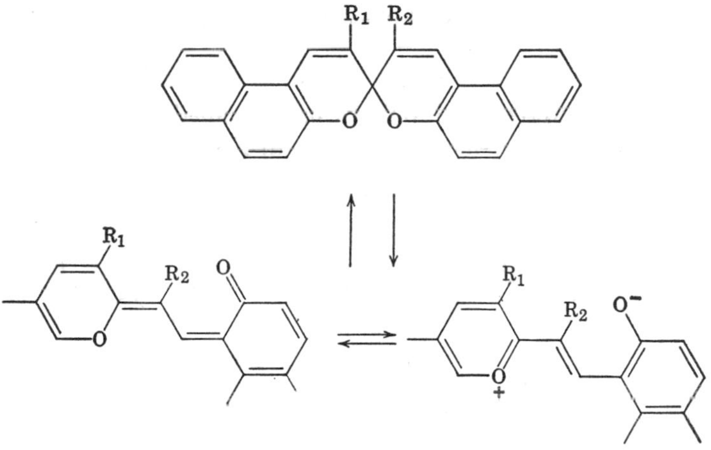

FIG. 23. The equilibrium involved in thermochromism of one of the spirans.

spiropyrans is due to their ability to open to the colored form shown in Fig. 23. If R_1 and R_2 are hydrogens the compound is thermo-

[122] Y. Hirschberg, F. Loewenthal, and E. D. Bergmann, *Bull. Research Council Israel*, **1**, 139 (1951) (*C. A.*, *46*, 1169).

[123] C. F. Koelsch, *J. Org. Chem.*, *16*, 1362 (1951).

chromic; if R_1 and R_2 are methyls there is more steric hindrance in the open than in the spiro form (the rings in a spiro compound are perpendicular to each other) and the compound does not open enough to exhibit thermochromism.

Similar studies have been made by Knott,[124] who also found that steric hindrance is an important factor in the thermochromism of spiropyrans.

Paramagnetism

The paramagnetism of bianthrone has been discussed above under "thermochromism."

The compound shown in Fig. 24 is also paramagnetic.[125]　Again, the

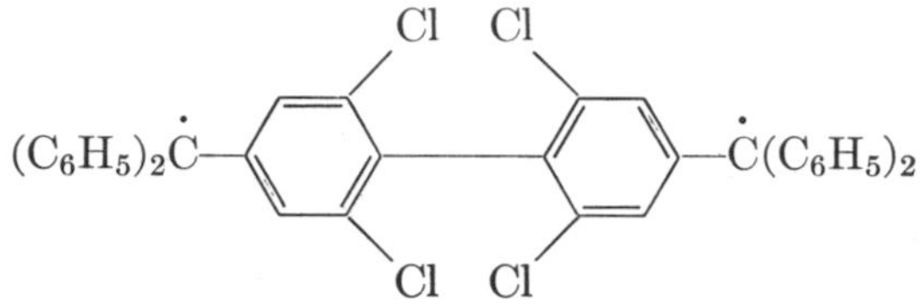

FIG. 24.　A strained molecule that has a triplet (diradical) ground state.

singlet ground state is so strained by the repulsion of the chlorine atoms that the diradical triplet state is more stable (cf. Fig. 22). The triplet state is further stabilized by resonance.

Fluorescence

Hofer, Grabenstetter, and Wiig [126] have studied the fluorescence of several series of cyanine-like dyes shown in Fig. 25.　The initial mem-

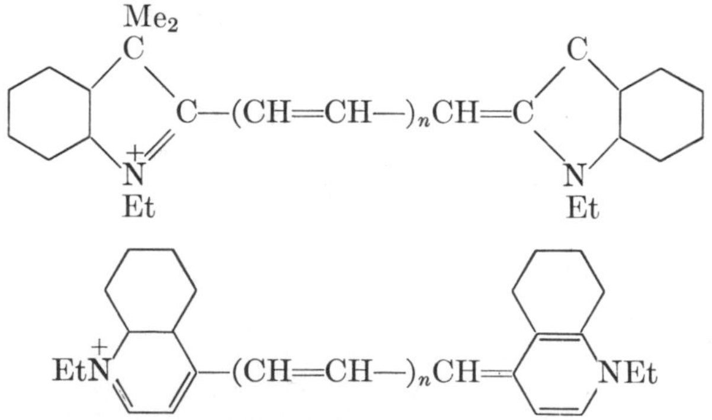

FIG. 25.　The cyanine-like dyes studied by Hofer, Grabenstetter, and Wiig.[126]

[124] E. B. Knott, *J. Chem. Soc.*, *1951*, 3038.
[125] E. Müller and H. Neuhoff, *Ber.*, *72*, 2063 (1939).
[126] L. J. E. Hofer, R. I. Grabenstetter, and E. O. Wiig, *J. Am. Chem. Soc.*, *72*, 203 (1950).

bers ($n = 1$) of some series are not fluorescent, whereas larger members of the same series are fluorescent. This effect was explained as being due to steric hindrance. Steric hindrance across the central double bond tends to counteract the planar constraint of resonance. With less constraint the excited molecules lose electronic energy by conversion to vibrational energy instead of by fluorescence.

Polarographic reduction potential

The polarographic reduction potential of a conjugated unsaturated hydrocarbon can be calculated by a clever molecular orbital method proposed by Maccoll.[127]

The experimental reduction potential for dibiphenylene ethylene lies between the value calculated for the planar model and a model where the two portions of the molecule are rotated at 90° to each other.[64] This indicates that the central bond is twisted but not twisted as far as 90°.

The electronic spectra of dibiphenylene ethylene also indicates that the central double bond is twisted. (Cf. "twisting a double bond in a conjugated system" in the section on electronic spectra.)

Elasticity

Polyisobutylene is a highly elastic material at room temperature, whereas polyethylene becomes elastic only at around 120°. Mizushima and Simanouti [128] have pointed out that the elasticity in polyisobutylene may be due to steric effects. They took 2,2-dimethyl butane as a model for a unit of polyisobutylene and n-butane as a model for a unit of polyethylene. All conformations of 2,2-dimethyl butane have the same energy, but the *trans* form of the n-butane is more stable than the *gauche* (cf. Chapter 1) forms of n-butane. If elasticity were due to an easy transformation between the *trans* and *gauche* forms this would explain a difference in elasticity. A probable energy difference of only 1 kcal. betweeen the *trans* and *gauche* forms of n-butane would allow this transformation to occur easily at higher temperatures. This would explain the elasticity of polyethylene at higher temperatures.

[127] A. Maccoll, *Nature*, *163*, 178 (1949); A. Pullman, B. Pullman, and G. Berthier, *Bull. soc. chim. France*, *17*, 591 (1950). For an interesting similar type of correlation of reduction potential with electronic spectra, see A. T. Watson and F. A. Matsen, *J. Chem. Phys.*, *18*, 1305 (1950).

[128] S. Mizushima and T. Simanouti, *J. Am. Chem. Soc.*, *71*, 1320 (1949).

Melting point

As we have seen from the previous discussion, steric effects may lower the dipole moment by eliminating the mesomeric moment. Because dipole moments affect melting points, the melting point is lowered with increasing steric hindrance in the compounds listed in Table XIII. It should be pointed out,[129] however, that melting point is

TABLE XIII

EFFECT OF STERIC HINDRANCE ON THE MELTING POINT

Compound	Melting Point
Nitroaminodurene	161°
Nitrodimethylaminodurene	90°
Derivatives of 4-nitronaphthalene	
1-Amino	190°
1-Methylamino	184°
1-Ethylamino	176°
1-Benzylamino	156°
1-Dimethylamino	65°
1-Diethylamino	Liquid

a very complex property and depends upon many variables other than dipole moment, such as crystal structure, van der Waals forces, and hydrogen bonding. Although the series in Table XIII is interesting, melting points should never be used as a test of steric effects.

STRAIN IN THREE-MEMBERED RINGS

Structures

Theoretical studies [130] of three-membered rings have shown that the strain can best be accommodated by bending (rehydridizing) the endo ring orbitals to only 106° and not to the angle between the carbons, 60°. The smaller overlap between the bonds at 106° than at 60° is offset by the less damage done to the orbitals in a smaller bend. These ring orbitals are now $sp^{4.12}$ orbitals [131] instead of the usual tetrahedral

[129] R. T. Arnold, G. Peirce, and R. A. Barnes, *J. Am. Chem. Soc.*, *62*, 1627 (1950).

[130] J. E. Kilpatrick and R. Spitzer, *J. Chem. Phys.*, *14*, 463 (1946); C. A. Coulson and W. E. Moffitt, *ibid.*, *15*, 151 (1947).

[131] One of the orbitals in the ring, ψR, may be written as

$$\psi R = 0.442[\psi(2S) + 2.03\psi(2p\sigma R)]$$

where $\psi(2p\sigma R)$ is a $2p$ orbital in the ring. Since $(2.03)^2 = 4.12$, the ring orbitals are $sp^{4.12}$. Similarly, the orbital to hydrogen may be written as

$$\psi C\!-\!H = 0.552[\psi(2S) + 1.51\psi(2p\sigma C\!-\!H)]$$

and these orbitals are $sp^{2.28}$.

sp^3 orbitals formed at 109° 18′. The $sp^{4.12}$ bonds formed are shorter than normal; the carbon-carbon bond distance [132] is 1.526 A in cyclopropane. The high p character in the endo orbitals results in high s character $sp^{2.28}$ exo bonds. These bonds are at 116° to each other. This strained structure affects the properties of three-membered ring compounds in several ways. The most important effects are a result of the fact that these $sp^{4.12}$ bonds are in a good position for overlap with adjacent p orbitals of a double bond as might occur for example in vinyl cyclopropane shown in Fig. 26. This effect of conjugation be-

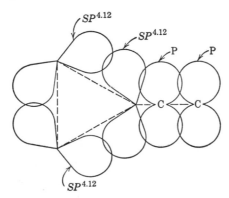

FIG. 26.   The orbitals in vinyl cyclopropane, showing conjugation between the vinyl and cyclopropyl groups.

tween adjacent p orbitals and three-membered rings exhibits itself in several physical properties which will be discussed below.

Electronic spectra

The ability of a three-membered ring to conjugate with a double bond tends to make cyclopropyl and ethylene oxide derivatives absorb at wavelengths intermediate to the corresponding alkyl and vinyl compounds. For example,[133] Rogers [134] has shown (cf. Table XIV) that the short-wavelength absorption of methylcyclopropyl ketone and of phenylcyclopropane occur at wavelengths intermediate to the corresponding compounds where the cyclopropyl ring is replaced by an alkyl group and by a double bond. Robertson, Music, and Matsen [135]

[132] L. Pauling and L. O. Brockway, *J. Am. Chem. Soc.*, *59*, 1223 (1937).

[133] E. P. Carr and C. P. Burt, *J. Am. Chem. Soc.*, *40*, 1590 (1918); I. M. Klotz, *ibid.*, *66*, 88 (1944); J. D. Roberts and C. Green, *ibid.*, *68*, 214 (1946); N. H. Cromwell, N. G. Barker, R. A. Wankel, P. J. Vanderhorst, F. W. Olson, and J. H. Anglin, Jr., *ibid.*, *73*, 1044 (1951).

[134] M. T. Rogers, *J. Am. Chem. Soc.*, *69*, 2544 (1947).

[135] W. W. Robertson, J. F. Music, and F. A. Matsen, *J. Am. Chem. Soc.*, *72*, 5260 (1950).

have calculated the spectral shift of phenylcyclopropane relative to benzene by assuming orbital overlap between the cyclopropane and benzene rings. It is interesting that in this case the maximum overlap occurs when the rings are mutually perpendicular instead of coplanar as in the biphenyl case.

TABLE XIV

Comparison of Short-Wave Absorption Band of Cyclopropyl Compounds with Conjugated and Non-Conjugated Compounds

	A
Methylisopropyl ketone	1930
Methylcyclopropyl ketone	2080
Methylvinyl ketone	2190
Ethyl benzene	2060
Phenylcyclopropane	2200
Styrene	2455

Vibrational spectra

Linnett has pointed out [136] that the high C—H stretching force constant 5.0×10^5 dynes/cm. in the three compounds cyclopropane, ethylene oxide, and ethylene sulfide indicates a large amount of s character in the C—H bonds. The C—H force constant is 4.56 in a normal methylene group [137] and an α oxygen or sulfur atom tends to lower the force constant slightly as shown in Table XV. Since s character in a

TABLE XV

Effect of O or S Atom on C—H Force Constant

C—CH$_3$	4.75 * $\times 10^5$ dynes/cm.
O—CH$_3$	4.68 †
S—CH$_3$	4.73 †

* J. J. Fox and A. E. Martin, *Proc. Roy. Soc. London, 175A*, 208 (1940).
† J. Duchesne, *Nature, 159*, 62 (1947).

TABLE XVI

Effect of Bond Type on C—H Force Constant *

CH	p	4.09×10^5
CH^4	sp^3	4.79
C$_2$H$_4$	sp^2	5.1
C$_2$H$_2$	sp	5.85

* A. D. Walsh, *Discussions Faraday Soc., 2*, 18 (1947).

[136] J. W. Linnett, *Nature, 160*, 162 (1947).
[137] J. J. Fox and A. E. Martin, *Proc. Roy. Soc. London, 175A*, 208 (1940).

bond will raise the force constant as shown in Table XVI, the high C—H force constant in the three-membered ring compounds can be explained as having a lot of *s* character.

Dipole moments

The dipole moments of cyclopropyl derivatives also show that the three-membered ring can conjugate with p orbitals. Thus the dipole moment of cyclopropyl chloride,[138] $1.76D$, is lower than that of cyclopentyl chloride, $2.08D$, and in the direction of chlorobenzene, $1.60D$. Conjugation with the ring gives rise to some of the character shown in Fig. 27.

$$\begin{array}{cc} \text{CH}_2 & {}^-\text{CH}_2 \\ \Big| \diagdown & \Big| \\ \Big| \quad \text{CH}={}^+\!\!\text{Cl} & \Big| \quad \text{CH}={}^+\!\!\text{Cl} \\ \Big| & \diagup \\ {}^-\text{CH}_2 & \text{CH}_2 \end{array}$$

Fig. 27. Resonance in cyclopropyl chloride that tends to lower the dipole moment.

Methylcyclopropyl ketone [134] has a dipole moment ($\mu = 2.84D$) larger than that of methyl *n*-propyl ketone ($\mu = 2.70D$), where there is no mesomeric moment, but not as large as methyl vinyl ketone ($\mu = 2.98D$), where there is a large mesomeric moment. Phenylcyclopropane has a mesomeric moment ($\mu = 0.49D$) even larger than that of toluene ($\mu = 0.40D$). It would be interesting to know whether the moments of toluene and phenylcyclopropane are in the same direction.

SUMMARY

Certain physical properties of compounds are affected by steric effects. Steric effects may cause twists in bonds, but there may still be some double-bond character in these twisted bonds if the twist is not as large as 90°. Coplanarity is therefore not a necessary condition for resonance. Twisting a single bond in a conjugated system will reduce the absorption intensity of the ultraviolet spectra and will shift certain bonds to shorter wavelengths. If the twist is quite large (~90°) the ultraviolet spectra will be similar to the additive spectra of the components on either side of the twist. Unsymmetrical twists, where one group is twisted more than another group, are possible only under certain conditions. If a double bond is twisted, the reverse of the effect found in the single-bond example is true; the ultraviolet spectrum is shifted to longer wavelengths. There are examples of

[138] B. I. Spinrad, *J. Am. Chem. Soc.*, *68*, 617 (1946); M. T. Rogers and J. D. Roberts, *ibid.*, *68*, 843 (1946).

steric effects that cause increased interaction or new interactions between atoms. These interactions may occur through $2p\sigma$ bonds. The ultraviolet spectra of molecules with warped aromatic rings have little fine structure because the vibrational and electronic states interact. The steric repulsions between atoms can be estimated from the infrared spectra if the molecules are small. In larger molecules, infrared spectroscopy detects only the secondary effects of these repulsions. The higher stretching frequency of the carbonyl group in cyclobutanone and cyclopentanone than in aliphatic ketone is explained by a larger amount of s character in the σ bonds of the carbonyl group of small cyclic ketones. Twisting a bond will decrease the mesomeric moment of the compound but may either increase or decrease the total dipole moment. Steric effects also change the refractive index and various other minor properties of the compound. One of the types of thermochromism is due to the fact that steric effects cause the ground (singlet) state of the molecule to be raised to within thermal excitation range of the triplet state. Strain in three-membered rings causes a change in the hybridization of the bonds involved, and the abnormal physical properties of three-membered rings can be attributed to this change in hybridization.

ACKNOWLEDGMENTS

The author wishes to thank Professor Melvin Calvin, Professor Donald J. Cram, Dr. Joseph Corse, Dr. Benjamin Makower, Professor Melvin S. Newman, Professor Joseph R. Platt, Dr. Fred Stitt, and Dr. Howard G. Walker for helpful criticisms and suggestions.

Chapter 12

by Frank H. Westheimer

Calculation of the Magnitude of Steric Effects

INTRODUCTION

FORCE CONSTANTS

VAN DER WAALS POTENTIAL FUNCTIONS

ESTIMATES OF STERIC STRAIN
    Cyclobutane
    Dichloroöctadiene
    The Apocamphyl Cation
    The Displacement Reaction

GENERAL THEORY
    Racemization of Optically Active Biphenyls
    Mathematical Method
    cis- and *trans*-Butene-2

Chapter 12

INTRODUCTION

The steric requirements of molecules dominate the rates and equilibria of many reactions in organic and inorganic chemistry, and strongly modify the course of many others. Our understanding of these reactions will not be complete until fairly precise calculations of steric effects can be made for all chemical processes. Admittedly, steric effects are not the only ones which influence reaction rates and equilibria; electrostatic effects and resonance effects must also be taken into account. Furthermore, the three effects mentioned above often interact. If the quantum-mechanical problem connected with any particular reaction could be accurately solved, a division of chemical effects into three or more categories would be unnecessary; since, however, such solutions are unlikely in the immediate future, an attack upon chemical problems in piecemeal fashion is still required. Fortunately, the calculations required to determine steric effects are relatively simple, at least in principle, and have been carried to completion in a few of those cases where the steric effect is the dominating one (i.e., where uncertainties caused by the resonance and electrostatic effects, although real, are relatively small). The qualitative principles controlling steric effects then become clear, and the quantitative methods can perhaps be applied even where other influences are of comparable importance with steric ones. The general principles on which quantitative calculations of steric effects can be performed are outlined in this chapter.

The most important qualitative conclusions that can be obtained from this study can be stated in advance. Whenever there is a severe steric interference between two atoms in the same molecule, the strain is always partially relieved by the deformation of valence angles within the molecule, to allow the interfering atoms to move further apart. Of course, such bending introduces some strain energy into the molecule. However, the energy required to deform bond angles always proves to be less that the energy "saved" by allowing the interfering atoms to move farther apart. In a few favorable cases, the amount of bending and stretching of valence bonds which must occur in a particular strained conformation of a molecule has been calcu- lated. Furthermore, the theory for the calculation of steric effects is now better than the fundamental data which must go into the calcu- lation. In particular, the van der Waals potential curves (energy vs. distance of separation) for various non-bonded atoms are essential, but they are now known only in the crudest way. In addition to these potentials, bond lengths and angles, and force constants for bending and stretching various bonds, are required. Bond lengths and angles are known with precision; the uncertainties in force con- stants, although real, are small compared to the uncertainties in van der Waals potentials. Since both force constants and van der Waals potentials are required for calculations of steric effects, short sections dealing with these quantities have been introduced at this point.

FORCE CONSTANTS

The energy needed to bend and stretch valence bonds can be calcu- lated, at least approximately, from a knowledge of the "force con- stants" for molecules. The concept of force constants is based on the assumption that valence bonds are essentially springs which obey Hooke's law; in other words, when the ith particle in a molecule is displaced from equilibrium by a distance q_i, it is acted upon by a re- storing force F such that

$$F = -k_i q_i \tag{1}$$

where k_i is the force constant for the motion in question. In classical mechanics, the potential energy, V, of the particle is

$$V = \tfrac{1}{2} k_i q_i^2 \tag{2}$$

and

$$\nu = (1/2\pi)\sqrt{k_i/m_i} \tag{3}$$

where ν is the vibration frequency and m_i the mass of the ith particle. When two or more particles are connected by valence bonds, equation 3 often (but not always) relates frequency and force constant provided that the mass, m_i, is replaced by the "reduced mass," m, for the sys- tem. For two particles, $1/m = 1/m_1 + 1/m_2$; for several particles the relationship between force constants, masses, and frequencies can be calculated by straightforward (but usually very complex) methods of classical mechanics. A complicated molecule with n particles has of course $3n$ degrees of freedom, including three degrees of translational motion and two degrees (for linear molecules) or three degrees (for non-linear molecules) of rotational motion; there must then be $3n - 5$ vibrations (for linear molecules) or $3n - 6$ vibrations (for non-linear molecules). If the atoms strictly obeyed Hooke's law, it would be possible to separate the vibrations into $3n - 5$ (or $3n - 6$) completely independent harmonic oscillations (the "normal" vibrations) such that

$$V = \frac{1}{2} \sum^{\substack{3n - 5 \text{ or} \\ 3n - 6}} k_i q_i^2 \tag{4}$$

Since in fact Hooke's law is not strictly obeyed, such a separation is only approximately valid. For simple molecules, those displacements of the atoms which correspond to the "normal" (independent) motions can be found. For example, CO_2 is a linear triatomic molecule with $3n - 5 = 4$ "normal" vibrations. These consist of two stretching and two (degenerate) bending modes as shown.

For more complicated molecules, more elaborate sets of "normal" vibrations can be formulated. Subject to certain selection rules, these vibrations can be found experimentally in infrared and Raman spectra; with sufficient effort the observed vibrations can be identified with particular modes of atomic motion.[1a] (A comparison of the vibrations of isotopically substituted molecules with those for the corresponding unsubstituted molecules constitutes an important tool for these identifications.) For example, three vibrations are known for carbon dioxide, and they have been identified as $\nu_1 = 1337$ cm.$^{-1}$, $\nu_2 = 667$ cm.$^{-1}$, and $\nu_3 = 2349$ cm.$^{-1}$

A complete description of the potential fields in any molecule will suffice for the calculation of all the vibration frequencies. Unfortunately, it is rather difficult to go the other way, and to calculate the potential energy function from the vibration frequencies. However, a useful potential function can often be found by the "valence bond" approximation, where it is assumed that forces between atoms operate only along valence bonds and that a force constant may be assigned to the stretching (or compression) of each valence bond and to the bending of each valence angle in the molecule. For example, two force constants are needed for carbon dioxide: one (k_1) for stretching the

[1] (a) G. Herzberg, *Infra-Red and Raman Spectra*, Van Nostrand, New York, 1945; (b) *ibid.*, p. 173.

C=O bond and one (k_δ) for bending the O=C=O bond angle. Since three frequencies are known (see above), from which only two force constants can be obtained, the calculations automatically provide a test of internal consistency. The agreement actually obtained from this model for carbon dioxide is fair: [1b] $k_\delta = 0.77 \times 10^{-11}$ erg/radian², and $k_1 = 15.5 \pm 1.3 \times 10^5$ dynes/cm. The uncertainty in k_1 means, of course, that the assumptions put into the calculation are not entirely correct: The vibrations are not strictly harmonic or independent of one another, and the forces in the molecule are not exclusively those which operate along valence bonds. The approximation is, however, satisfactory for estimate of steric strain.[2]

[2] The calculation of force constants from vibration frequencies (Raman and infrared data) can be illustrated by a simplified example: a hypothetical molecule of CO_2 constrained to vibrate only along the O=C=O line. Since these vibrations are independent of the out-of-plane bending vibrations, the calculation constitutes a real part of the solution of the problem for carbon dioxide. Define x_1, x_2, and x_3 as the displacements in the positive directions of the atoms marked 1, 2, and 3 in the diagram; let m_O be the mass of an oxygen and m_C the mass of the carbon atom, and k_s the stretching force constant for the C=O bond.

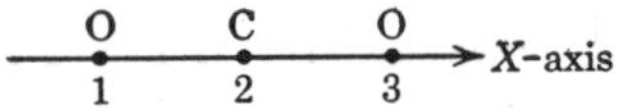

$$\begin{array}{ccc} \text{O} & \text{C} & \text{O} \\ \bullet & \bullet & \bullet \longrightarrow X\text{-axis} \\ 1 & 2 & 3 \end{array}$$

Then (if Hooke's law is obeyed) the potential energy of the system is expressed by the equation

$$V = \tfrac{1}{2}k_s(x_2 - x_1)^2 + \tfrac{1}{2}k_s(x_3 - x_2)^2 \tag{1'}$$

The force on atom 1 can be calculated from the potential energy:

$$F_1 = \frac{-\partial V}{\partial x_1} = k_s(x_2 - x_1) \tag{2'}$$

The resulting expression is simply Hooke's law for stretching the C=O bond to which atom 1 is attached. Similarly,

$$F_2 = \frac{-\partial V}{\partial x_2} = -k_s(x_2 - x_1) + k_s(x_3 - x_2) \tag{3'}$$

$$F_3 = \frac{-\partial V}{\partial x_3} = -k_s(x_3 - x_2) \tag{4'}$$

Newton's second law states that $F_i = m_i a_i$ (where m_i is the mass of any atom and a_i its acceleration), and so

$$k_s(x_2 - x_1) = m_O \frac{d^2 x_1}{dt^2} \tag{5'}$$

$$k_s(x_2 - x_1) - k_s(x_3 - x_2) = m_C \frac{d^2 x_2}{dt^2} \tag{6'}$$

$$-k_s(x_3 - x_2) = m_O \frac{d^2 x_3}{dt^2} \tag{7'}$$

With more complicated molecules the assignment of particular vibrational modes to particular frequencies is less positive than for carbon dioxide, and the calculation of force constants from the valence-bond model much more difficult. Force constants for the bending and stretching of particular valence bonds are, therefore, known only with considerable uncertainty. In fact, the values calculated for the force constants may even depend upon the way in which the potential system is set up. The remarkable point, under the circumstances, is

---

Now, each of the three atoms of carbon dioxide is assumed to carry out harmonic vibrations, so that

$$x_1 = A_1 \sin 2\pi\nu t + B_1 \cos 2\pi\nu t \tag{8'}$$

and

$$\frac{d^2x_1}{dt^2} = -4\pi^2\nu^2 A_1 \sin 2\pi\nu t - 4\pi^2\nu^2 B_1 \cos 2\pi\nu t = -4\pi^2\nu^2 x_1 \tag{9'}$$

Since all three atoms of carbon dioxide must vibrate with the same frequency, ν,

$$\frac{d^2x_2}{dt^2} = -4\pi^2\nu^2 x_2 \quad \text{and} \quad \frac{d^2x_3}{dt^2} = -4\pi^2\nu^2 x_3 \tag{10'}$$

Substitution of 9' and 10' in 5', 6', and 7' leads to 11', 12', and 13'.

$$-4\pi^2 m_O\nu^2 x_1 + k_s x_1 - k_s x_2 = 0 \tag{11'}$$

$$-k_s x_1 + 2k_s x_2 - 4\pi^2 m_C\nu^2 x_2 - k_s x_3 = 0 \tag{12'}$$

$$-k_s x_2 + k_s x_3 - 4\pi^2 m_O\nu^2 x_3 = 0 \tag{13'}$$

These three equations can be simultaneously valid only if the determinant below (equation 14') vanishes.

$$\begin{vmatrix} k_s - 4\pi^2 m_O\nu^2 & -k_s & 0 \\ -k_s & 2k_s - 4\pi^2 m_C\nu^2 & -k_s \\ 0 & -k_s & k_s - 4\pi^2 m_O\nu^2 \end{vmatrix} = 0 \tag{14'}$$

Expansion of this determinant yields

$$4\pi^2\nu^2(k_s - 4\pi^2\nu^2 m_O)(4\pi^2\nu^2 m_O m_C - k_s m_C - 2k_s m_O) = 0 \tag{15'}$$

The solutions of this equation which correspond to molecular vibrations are

$$\nu_1 = \frac{1}{2\pi}\sqrt{\frac{k_s}{m_O}} \quad \text{and} \quad \nu_3 = \frac{1}{2\pi}\sqrt{\frac{k_s(m_C + 2m_O)}{m_C m_O}} \tag{16'}$$

The reduced mass of CO_2 for ν_1 is then m_O; that for ν_3 is $m_C m_O/(m_C + 2m_O)$. The observed value for the frequency ν_1 is 1337 cm.$^{-1}$, or 4.008×10^{13} sec.$^{-1}$; the mass of an oxygen atom is $16/6.03 \times 10^{23}$ grams. When these figures are substituted in the equation for ν_1 above, the value for k_s is found to be 16.8×10^5 dynes/cm. Since ν_3 is 2349 cm.$^{-1}$, similar substitution leads to $k_s = 14.2 \times 10^5$ dynes/cm.; the average is then $(15.5 \pm 1.3) \times 10^5$ dynes/cm.

More elegant methods have been developed for handling more complex calculations, and force constants have been obtained from vibration frequencies of many molecules.

that reasonable values for force "constants" have been obtained. Calculations for a number of molecules has led to approximate constants for stretching a C—H bond, for stretching a C—C bond, for bending a C—C—H bond angle, and for many others. The fact that force constants for particular bonds are (roughly) independent of the details of the molecule in which they occur is of course related to the approximate constancy of group frequencies in infrared spectra. Some (approximate) force constants are listed in Table I.

TABLE I

FORCE CONSTANTS

Bond	Stretching Force Constant	Bond Angle	Bending Force Constant
C—H *	4.8 × 10⁵ dynes/cm.	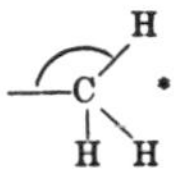 (H)—C—(H, H) *	0.55 × 10⁻¹¹ erg/radian²
C—C *	4.5 × 10⁵ dynes/cm.		
C=O *	12.1 × 10⁵ dynes/cm.	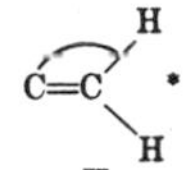 C=C (H, H) *	0.68 × 10⁻¹¹ erg/radian²
C=C *	9.6 × 10⁵ dynes/cm.	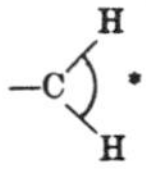 —C (H, H) *	0.32 × 10⁻¹¹ erg/radian²
C—Br *	3.1 × 10⁵ dynes/cm.		
C—H (aromatic) †	5.0 × 10⁵ dynes/cm.	 —H (aromatic) †	0.86 × 10⁻¹¹ erg/radian²

* G. Herzberg, *loc. cit.*
† K. W. F. Kohlrausch, *Z. physik. Chem.*, B30, 305 (1935).

Rather constant differences obtain between force constants for single and double bonds, for aromatic and aliphatic bonds, etc.; and therefore reasonable estimates can often be made for force constants even where they have not been determined directly. Although in principle the force constants needed for any particular calculation should be determined from the infrared and Raman spectra of the molecule or molecules under consideration, such a complete analysis is at present impossible, and calculations of bending and stretching energies can be made only on the basis of the assumption that the force constants for particular bonds or angles are at least approximately constant from molecule to molecule.

VAN DER WAALS POTENTIAL FUNCTIONS

The attractive and repulsive forces between molecules are qualitatively apparent from the existence of liquids and solids on the one hand, and from their relative incompressibility on the other. Many attempts have been made to derive a potential function for the interaction between two atoms (or molecules) where these atoms (or molecules) are not connected by valence forces. In principle, the potential curve (here called van der Waals potential) for any particular pair of atoms can be calculated from a consideration of the deviation of the corresponding gas from ideal behavior.

A series of van der Waals potential curves for the interactions of various pairs of "non-bonded" atoms show considerable similarity as to shape. Apparently non-bonded atoms (atoms not bonded to each other) interact very much less specifically than bonded atoms; the attraction and repulsion of closed electronic shells is more or less independent of the electronic kernels and nuclei they enclose. The considerable similarity among van der Waals potential functions expresses mathematically the qualitative fact, discovered by Bridgman, that there is not much variation, at high pressures, in the compressibility of a wide variety of liquids.[3]

A crude but moderately satisfactory van der Waals potential function, suggested by Lennard-Jones,[4] has the form

$$V = -\mu/d^7 + \lambda/d^{11} \tag{5}$$

where d is the distance between the two interacting atoms. This function has a gentle minimum at $d_0 = \sqrt[4]{1.57\lambda/\mu}$, and then rises steeply as the distance between the non-bonded atoms is diminished. The parameters μ and λ must be selected for each individual pair of atoms that interact. When these parameters for rare-gas atoms are correctly chosen, calculations based on the Lennard-Jones potential (and on more refined potential functions) approximate the deviations of the gas from ideal behavior.

However, a severe difficulty arises in the evaluation of these potential functions. Even at fairly high pressures, gas molecules are well separated, and the deviations from the gas laws measure the interactions of atoms that have not been pushed very close together. The best calculations based on the behavior of the rare gases [5] at high pressures leads to the evaluation of the van der Waals potential function only near the minimum, where the energy of interaction is less than 500 cal./mole and the actual compression less than 0.5 A. But steric effects are often large, and the calculations (see below) that have been made suggest that it is necessary to know the potential function where

[3] P. W. Bridgman, *International Critical Tables, 3*, 40, McGraw-Hill Book Co., 1928.

[4] J. E. Lennard-Jones, *Proc. Phys. Soc. London, 43*, 461 (1931).

[5] O. K. Rice, *J. Am. Chem. Soc., 63*, 3 (1941).

the compression energy is at least 3–4 kcal./mole, and the actual compression is of the order of 0.5–1.0 A. This difficulty can be overcome in several ways. An extrapolation can be made from the region of low to the region of high energy, and this extrapolation can be made somewhat less risky by the aid of quantum-theory calculations.[6] Further, some information about the interactions of atoms in the region of high potential energy can be obtained from the compressibility of solids; Born and Mayer [7] have used this method to obtain the van der Waals function for the mutual interaction of halide ions. The best data for neutral atoms at high potential are those of Amdur.[8-11] Rare-gas atoms are raised to a high velocity in a molecular beam and then allowed to penetrate another sample of the same gas. The observed scattering of the beam can then be correlated with the van der Waals potential function; the greater the interaction between the atoms, the greater the scattering will be. (Experimentally, the energy of the molecular beam is controlled and the beam collimated by forming, collimating, and accelerating a beam of gaseous cations which then are allowed to pick up electrons to become neutral atoms.) Amdur has approximated his potential functions at small interatomic distances for helium, neon, and argon by the following expressions:

For helium

$$V(r) = 6.18 \times 10^{-10}e^{-4.55d} \text{ ergs/molecule} \quad 1.27 \text{ A} < d < 2.30 \text{ A}$$

For neon

$$V(r) = 5.00 \times 10^{-10}/d^{9.99} \text{ ergs/molecule} \quad 1.96 \text{ A} < d < 2.2 \text{ A}$$

For argon

$$V(r) = 1.36 \times 10^{-9}/d^{8.33} \text{ ergs/molecule} \quad 2.18 \text{ A} < d < 2.69 \text{ A}$$

These potentials fit smoothly into those obtained, at larger values of d, from the behavior of the gases under pressure.

Although the van der Waals potential functions for the rare gases are known with at least moderate precision, other van der Waals interactions are less precisely defined. For example, only very crude estimates can be made for the energy of interaction of non-bonded

[6] W. E. Bleick and J. E. Mayer, *J. Chem. Phys.*, **2**, 252 (1934).

[7] M. Born and J. E. Mayer, *Z. Physik*, **75**, 1 (1932).

[8] I. Amdur, C. F. Glick, and H. Pearlman, *Proc. Am. Acad. Arts Sci.*, **76**, 101 (1948).

[9] I. Amdur and A. L. Harkness, *J. Chem. Phys.*, **22**, 664 (1954).

[10] I. Amdur and E. A. Mason, *J. Chem. Phys.*, **22**, 670 (1954).

[11] I. Amdur, private communication.

iodine and hydrogen atoms. These estimates are made the more uncertain by the fact that in particular steric problems the atoms may (and probably do) interact in some more or less fixed orientation. The rare-gas atoms are spherically symmetrical; however, a hydrogen atom, bound to carbon, is only conically symmetrical, and the interaction potential of this hydrogen atom with another atom will depend (among other parameters) on the particular point on the carbon-hydrogen bond to which the other atom approaches, and on the angle at which it approaches the C—H bond. Some preliminary calculations of the energy when a hydrogen atom approaches a hydrogen molecule suggest that the directional factor is an important one; [12,13] certainly this problem has not yet been solved for complicated interatomic relationships.

The solution of actual problems in organic chemistry will require van der Waals potential functions for the interaction between methyl groups in different molecules, or between methyl groups in different parts of the same molecule, or between a hydrogen atom in one molecule and a free halide ion, or between a halogen atom in a molecule and a hydrogen atom in a different part of the same molecule, etc. The correct van der Waals potential function for these interactions will probably be worked out during the next few decades. Meanwhile, it is possible to make semiquantitative evaluations of steric strain by using crude estimates for the appropriate van der Waals functions. Occasionally it is possible (vide infra) to estimate the van der Waals potential function in several different ways and so acquire at least a rough idea of the errors introduced into the calculations because of uncertainties in the potential functions. Occasionally steric strain arises largely from angular deformations, and the calculations are not strongly dependent on the van der Waals functions.

Fortunately, the van der Waals radii of atoms are well known, usually from X-ray data in crystals. A crude approximation to the van der Waals potential functions can, therefore, be made by assuming that the shape of the van der Waals curve for any two atoms will approximate that for the rare gas with about the same interatomic separation at the energy minimum (i.e., where the van der Waals radius of the rare gas is nearest to the average of the van der Waals radii of the interacting atoms). This approximation is unfortunately the best now available.

[12] H. Margenau, *Phys. Rev.*, *63*, 385 (1943); *64*, 131 (1943); *66*, 303 (1944).
[13] L. Pauling, *The Nature of the Chemical Bond*, Cornell University Press, 1940.

ESTIMATES OF STERIC STRAIN

Although a quantitative (or, more precisely, a semiquantitative) calculation of the magnitude of steric strain has been carried out for only a few examples, some useful estimates of strain have been made and applied to problems of organic chemistry. Some of these estimates are based on the correct principle (see below) that stretching of valence bonds contributes little to the relief of steric strain; the major effects are those of bond bending.

Cyclobutane

A useful estimate of the limit of applicability of the methods here outlined can be obtained by a consideration of the strain in cyclobutane. The C—C—C bond angle in this ring has here been diminished from the normal tetrahedral angle by an amount so large (almost 20°) that the energy can no longer be expected to be a quadratic function of the displacement (i.e., equation 4 cannot be expected to hold). However, the deviation of theory from experiment here serves to place an upper limit on the errors to be anticipated when the bending is not so severe.

The strain energy in cyclobutane can be roughly estimated from force constant data. Both Kaarsemaker and Coops [14] and Dunitz and Schomaker [15] estimated about 0.8×10^{-11} erg/radian^2 for the force constant [16] for bending the C—C—C angle, so that $E = 17.5\theta^2$ cal./mole for each angle, where θ is the angular deflection in degrees (cf. equation 4). Since each bond angle has been bent by 19.5°, the total strain energy in cyclobutane can, in first approximation, be estimated as $4 \times 19.5^2 \times 17.5 = 26,600$ cal./mole. This value is in almost precise agreement with the experimental [14] (thermochemical) value of 26,200 cal./mole.

The calculation shown above is, however, much too simple and must be corrected; the corrections all increase the calculated value of the strain energy so that it exceeds the experimental by a sizable amount. First and foremost, a pair of hydrogen atoms in the eclipsed position [17,18] on adjacent carbon atoms may increase the energy of the system (see Chapter 2) by as much as 0.9–1.0 kcal./mole. If cyclo-

[14] S. Kaarsemaker and J. Coops, *Rec. trav. chim.*, *71*, 261 (1952).

[15] J. D. Dunitz and V. Schomaker, *J. Chem. Phys.*, *20*, 1703 (1952).

[16] T. P. Wilson, *J. Chem. Phys.*, *11*, 369 (1943).

[17] K. S. Pitzer, *Science*, *101*, 672 (1945).

[18] J. E. Kilpatrick, K. S. Pitzer and R. Spitzer, *J. Am. Chem. Soc.*, *69*, 2483 (1947).

butane were a rigid square, all the hydrogen atoms would be in the eclipsed position, and the energy of the compound would be increased by perhaps as much as 7–8 kcal./mole. However, in fact, the compound is probably somewhat twisted;[15] comparison with the data for cyclopentane suggests that 5 kcal./mole would be a better estimate for the net effect of the hydrogen-hydrogen repulsions. (Since the eclipsed hydrogen atoms in cyclobutane are relatively far apart, the energy of interaction may be even lower here.) This brings the calculated value for strain in cyclobutane to about 31–32 kcal./mole. Further, the carbon atoms at opposite corners in cyclobutane are less than 2.2 A apart. Although it is difficult to estimate the magnitude of the strain that arises because these carbon atoms are so close, the van der Waals repulsions must certainly add several kilocalories to the total strain energy. It is, therefore, clear that a crude calculation for the strain energy in cyclobutane yields a value 20–50% too high. Considering the very large angle of bending, the agreement between the estimate and experiment is satisfactory.

A further point should be made about this crude calculation of the strain energy in cyclobutane. The equation for the energy of a cyclobutane molecule contains quadratic terms for all the independent bending and stretching motions; even a simplified potential functon includes terms for bending of the C—C—C, the C—C—H, and the H—C—H bonds. Of course, it is impossible to change one of these bond angles without simultaneously changing others.

For example, when the C—C—C bond angles are diminished from 109° 28′ to 90°, some of the other bond angles must be changed; if the H—C—H bond angles could remain unchanged, the C—C—H bond angles would be increased to about 114°. Of course all the bond angles must be adjusted so as to minimize the strain; there is a shallow energy minimum when the H—C—H bond angle has been increased to around 112°. The changes in the C—C—H and in the H—C—H bond angles are so small, relative to the large change in the C—C—C bond angle, that the correction to the total strain energy of the cyclobutane molecule is insignificant. However, the increase in the H—C—H bond angle has been (approximately) verified by experiment.[15]

A similar calculation for the strain energy of the cyclopropane ring yields a value about four times that observed experimentally. Apparently the calculation of strain as bond bending alone yields a crude but useful approximation when the change in bond angles is 20° (as in cyclobutane) and fails completely when the change is 50° (as in cyclopropane).   Several quantum-mechanical calculations [15,19,20] of the energy of cyclopropane (and of cyclobutane) take into account the change in the hybridization of the bond orbitals which must accompany a large deflection from the tetrahedral angle.   Such calculations are very crude but do show that the estimate of strain, based on equation 4, is too large.   However, when the angular deflection is small (i.e., small compared to that in cyclobutane), the simple classical calculation is the best now available.

Dichloroöctadiene

An example of a reasonably simple calculation of steric strain has been presented by Roberts.[21]   He considered three models for 1,6-dichlorocyclooctadiene-1,5, corresponding to three strainless conformations: boat, chair, and skew forms.   Dipole moment measurements

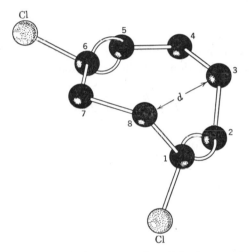

FIG. 1.   Transition state for the interconversion of the boat to the chair conformation of dichlorocyclooctadiene.

showed that the known compound has the boat conformation; in order to decide whether the chair and skew conformations corresponded to compounds which could be isolated, Roberts made approximate calculations of the strain energies for the transition states between the three conformations.   In particular, he decided from an inspection of the models that the transition state for the conversion of the boat to the chair conformation has the geometry shown in Fig. 1.   Here atoms

[19] C. A. Coulson and W. E. Moffitt, *J. Chem. Phys.*, *15*, 151 (1947).
[20] J. E. Kilpatrick and R. Spitzer, *J. Chem. Phys.*, *14*, 463 (1946).
[21] J. D. Roberts, *J. Am. Chem. Soc.*, *72*, 3300 (1950).

3, 4, 5, 6, 7, and 8 lie in a single plane; atoms 1, 2, 3, and 8 lie in a second plane at 109.5° to the first. The model suggests that the angles about atoms 3 and 8 are not greatly distorted. The effects of stretching (or compressing) the valence bonds were (properly) ignored. Roberts designated by θ the increase in the bond angles at 4, 5, 6, and 7; for convenience in calculation, the increase in each of these angles was assumed to be the same. Similarly, the decrease in the bond angles at 1 and 2 was designated by ϕ. (The small errors introduced by these assumptions are considered later.) The angles θ and ϕ are related to the distance, d, between atoms 3 and 8 of Fig. 1 by the equations

$$d = 1.34 + 3.08[\sin (30° + \theta) - \sin (40.5° - 2\theta)] \qquad (6)$$

and

$$d = 1.34 + 3.08 \sin (30° + \phi) \qquad (7)$$

(The distance, d, is a mathematical parameter and of course does not represent any sort of chemical bond.) For each value of d, a definite value of θ and a definite value of ϕ can be calculated. The strain energy (in first approximation) for the transition state can be expressed by the equation

$$E = \frac{k}{2} [4\theta^2 + 2\phi^2] \qquad (8)$$

where k is the average force constant for bending the various C—C—C bonds in the molecule. In his publication, Roberts assigned [22] to k

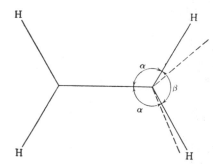

FIG. 2.   Distortion of the bond angles in ethylene.

the value 0.57×10^{-11} erg/radian^2, the bending constant for the C=C—H angle, α, in ethylene (see Fig. 2). This value is probably somewhat low;[23] the treatment [21] ignores the fact that bending the

[22] G. Herzberg, *Infra-Red and Raman Spectra*, p. 184.
[23] J. D. Roberts, private communication.

C—C—H bond of ethylene automatically involves changes in other angles. A composite constant is the correct one for this problem. When the angle α is increased, the angle β is decreased. However, the system as a whole can achieve minimum energy if the decrease in angle is shared between β and α' as shown in dotted lines in Fig. 2; the principles and methods involved are discussed later.

The corrected force constant is close to the value of 0.8×10^{-11} erg/radian^2 which was chosen for the cyclobutane calculation. With this force constant, the energy, E, of equation 8 can be calculated as a function of the parameter, d. The minimum energy corresponds to around 12 kcal./mole where the distance, d, is about 2.5 A; the increase in the bond angles at atoms 4, 5, 6, and 7 is about 12°, and the decrease in the angles at atoms 1 and 2 is about 7°. These angular changes are then within the range where the vibrations are approximately harmonic. Of course this calculation rests on the assumed geometry of the activated complex. It should be pointed out, however, that the activation energy is the minimum energy for a transition state. If any error has, therefore, been made by assuming a poor geometry for the activated complex, the error is in the direction of overestimating the activation energy.

There is, however, one possible error in this calculation in the opposite direction. The model for the transition state shows that two hydrogen atoms (one attached to atom 3 and one to 8) are so close as to cause considerable van der Waals repulsion. This repulsion can be avoided by twisting the ring, but such twist will introduce additional strain energy and will also bring four pairs of hydrogen atoms into eclipsed positions.

The magnitude of this extra energy is very difficult to calculate. However, the repulsion probably will not exceed a few kilocalories. If this be so, then the total activation energy for the interconversion will scarcely exceed 15 kcal./mole. Roberts argued that these two conformations (boat and chair), although both thermodynamically possible, will be interconverted too rapidly to permit the isolation of the less stable one. (He presented a similar argument for the interconversion of the skew and boat conformations.) Since the estimated energy for the transition state is of moderate size and since the uncertainty in the force constant is considerable, the argument is not completely convincing, but the conclusion still appears the most probable one. Whether it will prove possible to detect the less stable conformations spectroscopically (or by some other means) is not yet known.

The apocamphyl cation

Bartlett and Knox [24] made one of the first estimates of steric strain. They discovered that 1-chloroapocamphane does not undergo solvolysis, and they attributed this fact to the strain that would necessarily be present in the (hypothetical) apocamphyl cation. They summarized the evidence [25, 26] that carbonium ions have their minimum energy in the planar conformation and noted that such a planar ion could not be formed in the apocamphyl system unless three C—C—C bond angles were each decreased by 19° 28′, or unless some equivalent distortion was introduced into the ion. Since each of the bond angles in cyclobutane is decreased from the tetrahedral value by this same amount, and since the strain energy in a mole of cyclobutane amounts to about 6.5 kcal./angle, the total strain in the (hypothetical) apocamphyl cation may approximate 3 × 6.5 or about 20 kcal./mole. Such a large strain energy can easily account for the fact that, even under drastic experimental conditions, no appreciable quantity of the cation is formed, and the solvolysis therefore does not occur. (A more refined calculation would allow some distortion of the planar structure of the carbonium ion, with the result that the total calculated strain energy, although still large, would certainly be less than originally estimated. The method of minimizing strain energy with respect to distortion of bond angles is treated below under the section General Theory.)

The displacement reaction

Another early attempt to make a complete calculation of steric effects was carried out by Dostrovsky, Hughes, and Ingold.[27] Their experimental data are reproduced in part in Table II. Bartlett and Rosen [28]

TABLE II

RELATIVE RATES AND ARRHENIUS ACTIVATION ENERGIES, E^*, FOR THE
REACTION $RBr + \overline{OC_2H_5} \rightarrow ROC_2H_5 + Br^-$

R =	Methyl	Ethyl	n-Propyl	Isobutyl	Neopentyl
Relative rates at 55°	17.6	1	0.028	0.030	0.0000042
E^*, kcal./mole	20.0	21.0		22.8	26.2
Steric strain, kcal./mole	0.0	1.0		2.8	6.2

[24] P. D. Bartlett and L. H. Knox, J. Am. Chem. Soc., 61, 3184 (1939).

[25] P. D. Bartlett, in H. Gilman, Organic Chemistry, Vol. III, p. 57, John Wiley & Sons, 1953.

[26] Cf. P. D. Bartlett and S. G. Cohen, J. Am. Chem. Soc., 62, 1183 (1940).

[27] I. Dostrovsky, E. D. Hughes, and C. K. Ingold, J. Chem. Soc., 1946, 173.

[28] P. D. Bartlett and L. J. Rosen, J. Am. Chem. Soc., 64, 543 (1942).

had previously demonstrated that the effect of the β-t-butyl group is not electrical and is, therefore, presumably steric. The observed differences in energy of activation were assumed [27] to be steric in origin. Previous work [29-33] had established with very high probability that the activated complex for the displacement of alkyl halides has a configuration where the reactive carbon atom and the entering and leaving groups lie in a straight line, and the three substituents on the carbon atom at which reaction takes place are arranged at least roughly in a plane at right angles to the line joining the leaving and entering substituents. Such a model for the activated complex in the reaction between an alkyl bromide and ethoxide ion is shown schematically in Fig. 3.

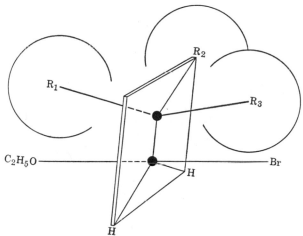

Fig. 3.   The activated complex in a displacement reaction.

When R_1, R_2, and R_3 are hydrogen atoms (i.e., when the halide is ethyl bromide), these atoms provide only minimal steric interferences with the entering ethoxide ion and the leaving bromide ion; but scale models show that, when R_1, R_2, and R_3 are methyl groups (i.e., when the halide is neopentyl bromide), they interfere severely with the leaving and entering ions.

In order to estimate the magnitude of these steric interferences, the usual covalent bond radii were chosen [27] except for the groups (e.g.,

[29] H. Phillips, *J. Chem. Soc.*, *123*, 44 (1923).

[30] J. Kenyon, H. Phillips, and V. Pittman, *J. Chem. Soc.*, *1935*, 1072.

[31] A. R. Olson and F. A. Long, *J. Am. Chem. Soc.*, *56*, 1294 (1934).

[32] E. Hughes, F. Juliusburger, S. Masterman, B. Topley, and J. Weiss, *J. Chem. Soc.*, *1935*, 1525.

[33] E. Hughes, F. Juliusburger, A. Scott, B. Topley, and J. Weiss, *J. Chem. Soc.*, *1936*, 1173.

$^-OC_2H_5$ and Br^-) involved in the reaction.   In the activated state each of these groups has acquired (approximately) half a charge, and so the average of their ionic and covalent radii was employed.   The bond angles used were those implied by Fig. 3.   A special problem arose with respect to the van der Waals radii, since these radii depend upon the angle of approach [12, 13] as well as upon the atoms involved; Dostrovsky, Hughes, and Ingold assumed that the van der Waals radius is substantially diminished whenever the angle between a va- lence bond and the line drawn between two interfering but non-bonded atoms falls below 90°.   In a first approximation to the quantitative problem, the only steric forces they considered were the van der Waals repulsions between the non-bonded atoms.   Unfortunately, the van der Waals potential function appropriate for the interaction of the halogen substituent and the hydrogen atoms of the methyl groups is not known.   The minimum distance of approach, or the sum of the van der Waals radii, is known (at least for large angles) and the po- tential function near the minimum is approximately known, but the part of the potential function that is important in steric problems, the potential between non-bonded atoms at relatively small distances, has not been determined in any unambiguous way.   The potential function chosen by Dostrovsky, Hughes, and Ingold is shown in Fig. 4.   It is altogether possible (see below) that this potential function is

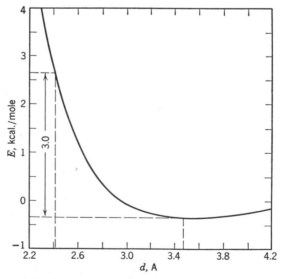

Fig. 4.   Van der Waals potential function for carbon-bromine interaction (Dos- trovsky, Hughes, and Ingold).

too "soft" (i.e., the energy at small distances is probably greater than that shown in the graph). Yet, even with this potential function, the overlap of the methyl groups and the bromine atoms is so great as to produce a calculated repulsion about twice that observed experimentally. (See Table III.)

TABLE III

CALCULATED AND OBSERVED STERIC CONTRIBUTION TO THE ENERGY OF ACTIVATION IN SECOND-ORDER DISPLACEMENT REACTIONS

Steric Strain	Me	Et	s-Pr	t-Bu	n-Pr	Isobutyl	Neopentyl
Observed (see Table II)	0.0	1.0			2.8	2.8	6.2
Calculated, rigid model	0.0	0.9	1.9	2.7	0.9	2.3	12.6
Calculated, with C—Br stretching	0.0	0.7	1.4	2.2	0.7		11.7

The rigid model here described necessarily exaggerates the amount of steric strain. Only a small relief of strain can be obtained by allowing the C—Br (or C—O) bonds in the activated state to stretch slightly. The force constants for the stretching are unknown, since the bromine and oxygen atoms are only partially bonded to carbon in the transition state. Nevertheless, it is possible to choose a reasonable force constant and then to calculate the increase in the C—Br bond lengths that will minimize the total strain energy.

As a second approximation,[27] the C—Br bonds in the activated complex were allowed to stretch (about 0.1 A for the neopentyl case), but this stretching, although it diminished the calculated repulsions (see Table III), did not bring the calculated and observed values into good agreement. If the English workers had used a "harder" van der Waals potential function or had diminished the van der Waals radii less sharply with decreasing angle, the calculated values would have exceeded the experimental ones by an even larger margin. But the direction of the discrepancy should be noted. The steric theory does not fail to account for the facts; it accounts for them twice over, or more.

The University College (London) investigators have improved[34] their earlier calculations[27] of the activation energy for the displacement reaction. The crucial role of bending in steric effects was demonstrated in 1946–1947 by Westheimer and Mayer (see section on p. 543, Racemization of Optically Active Biphenyls); the new work[34] takes the bending of valence bonds into account. The calculations are necessarily very complex, since the minimization of the energy for the

[34] P. de la Mare, L. Fowden, E. D. Hughes, C. K. Ingold, and J. Mackie, J. Chem. Soc., 1955, 3200.

transition state (see Mathematical Method) requires the adjustment of many bond lengths and angles, and the selection of preferred rotational conformations for substituent groups. Further, the calculations are necessarily somewhat uncertain, since they involve not only van der Waals potentials but also such difficultly accessible quantities as the force constants for bending and stretching "half-bonds" and the energy of solvent interaction with ionic species of various shapes. Nevertheless, the introduction of bond-angle deflections (i.e., bending) materially improves the agreement between calculation and experiment.

The examples of steric strain so far considered have largely been concerned with angular deflections and with van der Waals repulsions (which can be relieved by angular deflection). Only brief account has been taken of the strain introduced by placing hydrogen atoms in eclipsed positions on adjacent carbon atoms. (Of course, this latter type of strain can also be relieved, in part, by changes in bond angle.) Many successful calculations of steric strain have been concerned largely, if not exclusively, with this special hydrogen-hydrogen (or more properly bond-bond) interaction. These examples have been omitted here despite their obvious importance; they are considered in detail in Chapter 1.

GENERAL THEORY

In the foregoing sections the importance of bond bending relative to stretching (or compression) has repeatedly been stressed; in some instances the energy of the strained molecule (or transition state) has been minimized with respect to various parameters, but the detailed mathematical processes were not illustrated. Actually, a general theory for steric effects, formulated by Hill [35] early in 1946, predated some of the examples of semiquantitative estimates which have so far been presented. Hill showed that the energy of any molecule (or activated complex) can be expressed in terms of the van der Waals potential function for the interactions of the interfering but non-bonded atoms, and in terms of the energy necessary to distort the various bond lengths and angles in the molecule. Naturally such bending and stretching of the valence bonds change the distance between the interfering atoms and, therefore, change the van der Waals repulsion. For any particular arrangement of the atoms in space, a perfectly definite amount of strain energy and a perfectly definite amount of van der Waals energy of repulsion are associated with the

[35] T. L. Hill, *J. Chem. Phys.*, *14*, 465 (1946).

system. In order to find the energy and preferred conformation of the real system, the atomic positions corresponding to the minimum energy must be found. The problem of determining the strain energy in a molecule is then solved by setting up an energy function for the molecule in question and minimizing this energy. Mathematically, the problem has many of the aspects and many of the advantages of the variation principle of quantum mechanics.

Racemization of optically active biphenyls

Almost simultaneously with Hill, and independently, Westheimer and Mayer [36] developed the mathematical theory for a similar minimization principle and showed how the method could be applied to the calculation of the activation energy for the racemization of optically active derivatives of biphenyl. Their method and calculations are here presented in detail. A generalized theory for steric effects and the justification for many statements in the earlier sections can conveniently be presented in terms of this example. This choice is a fortunate one: (a) The reaction is one where no chemical bonds are made or broken. Further, (b) there is no doubt that the reaction is really controlled by steric interactions.[37] (c) The activation energy, in typical cases, amounts to about 20–40 kcal./mole. Even if small energies of the order of a kilocalorie (which may arise from resonance effects, etc.) are neglected, the calculation will be essentially correct. (d) The activated state for the racemization of an optically active derivative of biphenyl is assumed to be planar. This fact enormously simplifies the numerical calculations.

Mathematical method

The general lines of the mathematical argument will here be outlined; the details can be found in the original publications.[36, 38, 39] Inspection of a scale model for 2,2'-dibromo-4,4'-dicarboxybiphenyl shows that the two bromine atoms cannot possibly pass one another; in other words, for the racemization of this compound, bromine interferes with hydrogen, not bromine (Fig. 5). In this conformation there are two (presumably equal) bromine-hydrogen interactions. The distance between one of the hydrogen atoms and the interfering bromine atom is called d_1; the corresponding distance between the other non-bonded

[36] F. H. Westheimer and J. E. Mayer, *J. Chem. Phys.*, *14*, 733 (1946).

[37] R. Adams and H. C. Yuan, *Chem. Revs.*, *12*, 261 (1933).

[38] F. H. Westheimer, *J. Chem. Phys.*, *15*, 252 (1947).

[39] M. Rieger and F. H. Westheimer, *J. Am. Chem. Soc.*, *72*, 19 (1950).

bromine and hydrogen atoms is called d_2. The van der Waals curve gives the energy of repulsion as a function of the distances of separation (i.e., d_1 and d_2) of the non-bonded atoms. Of course, any change of bond lengths or of bond angles will affect the distances d_1 and d_2 and, therefore, the magnitude of the van der Waals energy.

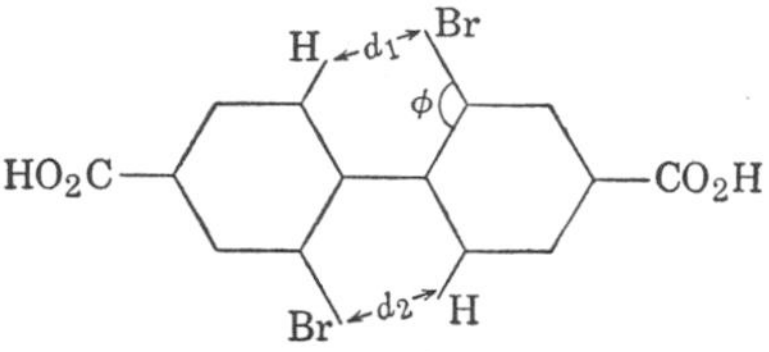

FIG. 5.   Planar conformation of 2,2′-dibromo-4,4′-dicarboxybiphenyl.

For any biphenyl molecule, it is possible to choose a set of coordinates with which to express the motion of every atom in the system. These coordinates will be labeled q_1, q_2, $\cdots$, q_n; they do not represent the absolute location of atoms in the molecule but rather the *displacements* of these atoms caused by changes from the normal bond lengths and bond angles. A force constant will be associated with each of these displacements. For example, one of the possible modes of motion is the stretching of the interannular bond. Such stretching is associated with a force constant (obtained from infrared and Raman data) of 5.5×10^5 dynes/cm. Another (and very important) coordinate, which can be considered q_2, is the bending of the carbon-carbon-bromine bond angle, ϕ; the corresponding force constant is approximately 1.1×10^{-11} dyne cm./radian.[2] Similarly, every other distortion of the molecule is associated with its force constant. The overall energy of the molecule can be obtained, then, from the expression

$$E = \Sigma \tfrac{1}{2} k_i q_i{}^2 + V(d_1) + V(d_2) \qquad (9)$$

where the various terms, $\tfrac{1}{2} k_1 q_1{}^2$, $\tfrac{1}{2} k_2 q_2{}^2$, etc., are the energies for the harmonic oscillations associated with various bending and stretching modes in the molecule, and $V(d_1)$ and $V(d_2)$ are the van der Waals energies of repulsion for the two pairs of non-bonded bromine-hydrogen atoms. Now, if the van der Waals potential curve for the particular interaction is known, it can be approximated by an exponential function:

$$V = Ae^{-d/\rho} \qquad (10)$$

where the values of A and ρ can be found by fitting the exponential function (curve B, Fig. 6) to the known potential curve (curve A). Of course, the exponential will not fit well at large distances, since the

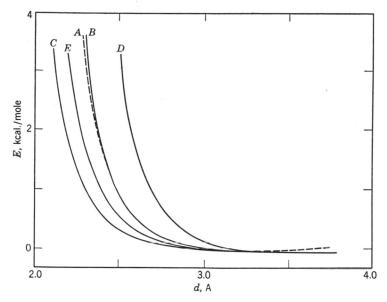

FIG. 6.   Van der Waals potential functions for bromine-hydrogen interaction.

true potential curve shows a definite minimum whereas the exponential approximation asymptotically approaches zero with increasing values of d.   But in the region of interest (i.e., where there is a substantial repulsion between the non-bonded atoms), the approximation is quite good.

Further, to solve the problem, a connection must be established between the distances d_1 and d_2 and the various coordinates (increase in the interannular bond length, increase in the C—C—Br bond angle, etc.) represented by the coordinates q_1, q_2, q_3, $\cdots$, etc.   For small displacements of the coordinates from equilibrium, the distances d_1 and d_2 can be expressed by the equations

$$d_1 = d_0 + \sum_i b_i q_i \quad \text{and} \quad d_2 = d_0 + \sum_i b_i' q_i \tag{11}$$

where d_0 is the value of the distance (d_1 or d_2) in the planar, undistorted rigid molecule, and the various b's and b''s are constants which can be calculated from the geometry of the molecule.   For small displacements of the atoms in the biphenyl molecule, the increase in d is approximately linear in the displacement (i.e., equation 11) is valid. For example, when the interannular bond in the biphenyl molecule is stretched 0.01 A, the distances d_1 and d_2 are each increased 0.0091 A. The increase is less than 0.01 A because the bromine atom sticks out further from the ring than the hydrogen atom.[40] Of course, the factor b, for this particular stretching mode, is $0.0091/0.01$, or 0.91. Combining equations 9, 10, and 11

$$E = \sum_i \tfrac{1}{2}k_iq_i^2 + A \exp\left(-d_0/\rho\right) \exp\left(-\sum_i b_iq_i/\rho\right)$$
$$+ A \exp\left(-d_0/\rho\right) \exp\left(-\sum_i b_i'q_i/\rho\right) \quad (12)$$

Since the reaction will occur by the easiest possible pathway, the activation energy is the smallest value of E, and can be found by minimizing E with respect to every possible variation of every coordinate. For the coordinate q_j, and provided that the various coordinates q_1, q_2, q_3, etc., are independent, this leads to the expression

$$\frac{\partial E}{\partial q_j} = 0 = k_jq_j - \frac{b_j}{\rho} A \exp\left(-d_0/\rho\right) \exp\left(-\sum_i b_iq_i/\rho\right)$$
$$- \frac{b_j'}{\rho} A \exp\left(-d_0/\rho\right) \exp\left(-\sum_i b_i'q_i/\rho\right) \quad (13)$$

[40] This calculation is carried out as follows: The geometry of the biphenyl, in the

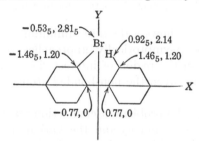

Fig. 7.   Coordinates for some of the atoms in bromobiphenyl.

absence of any stretching or bending, is that shown in Fig. 7. Then

$$d_0 = \sqrt{1.46^2 + 0.67_5^2} = 1.61 \text{ A} \quad (1'')$$

When the interannular bond has been stretched by an amount q_1, the distance d_1 is equal to

$$d_1 = \sqrt{(1.46 + q_1)^2 + 0.67_5^2} = \sqrt{d_0^2 + 2.92q_1 + q_1^2} \quad (2'')$$

Since q_1 is assumed to be small, q_1^2 is negligible and binomial expansion of the radical leads to the expression

$$d_1 \doteq d_0 + \frac{2.92q_1}{2d_0} = d_0 + 0.91q_1 \quad (3'')$$

Hence $b_1 = 0.91$, and equation 11 is accurate (at least for this particular coordinate) with only a very small error, and an error that can be estimated by comparing the approximate and exact square roots for the radicals in equation $2''$.

Now, since the energy E must be minimized with respect to every coordinate, and not just with respect to q_j, it is clear that there will be a set of equations similar to 13. In fact, if there are n coordinates q_1, q_2, q_3, etc., there will be a set of n such equations. In principle, a set of n equations in n unknowns can always be solved, even if the equations are non-linear. In the particular case under discussion, the solution has, in fact, been achieved.[41]

NUMERICAL RESULTS. Actual numerical calculations will depend on the values chosen for the force constants, k_i, for bending and stretching the various bonds in the molecule and will depend on the shape of the van der Waals potential curve for the interaction of the two non-bonded groups or atoms (e.g., bromine and hydrogen) which interfere in the activated complex. It has already been shown that, at the present state of the development of chemistry, accurate values for the force constants or for van der Waals potential functions cannot be assigned, so that a completely accurate computation for the activa-

---

[41] The solution depends upon the fact that, for the activated complex, the term

$$\exp\left(-\sum_i b_i q_i/\rho\right)$$

which appears in each equation 13 is a constant since in the activated state the values of q_1, q_2, q_3, etc., are definite and are not variable. Further, the symmetry of the problem shows that in the activated complex

$$\exp\left(-\sum_i b_i q_i/\rho\right) = \exp\left(-\sum_i b_i' q_i/\rho\right)$$

The problem can then be solved by introducing a mathematical parameter, Z, such that

$$A \exp\left(-d_0/\rho\right) \exp\left(-\sum_i b_i q_i/\rho\right) = A \exp\left(-d_0/\rho\right) \exp\left(-\sum_i b_i' q_i/\rho\right) = Z \quad (1''')$$

Z is, in fact, the van der Waals repulsive energy for each bromine-hydrogen interaction in the transition state (i.e., its value is determined and cannot be arbitrarily chosen). With the aid of equation $1'''$, equation 13 can be reduced to a linear equation ($2'''$), which can then be solved for q_j in terms of b_j, b_j', k_j, ρ, and Z.

$$k_j q_j - \frac{b_j}{\rho} Z - \frac{b_j'}{\rho} Z = 0 \qquad (2''')$$

Similar solutions can be obtained for each of the other equations (in q_1, q_2, etc.) of the set of equations 13. When the values of q_1, q_2, q_3, etc., in terms of Z (from equations $2'''$) are substituted into equation $1'''$, a single equation is obtained in the known quantities k_i, b_i, b_i', A, and d_0, and the one unknown, Z. This equation can then be solved numerically for Z. When a definite numerical value for Z is known, then the equations of the set $2'''$ can be solved for definite numerical values of q_1, q_2, q_3, $\cdots$, q_j, $\cdots$, q_n. Once the values for the coordinates, q_i, are known, the minimum value for the energy E_0, for the planar biphenyl (i.e., the activation energy) can easily be calculated from equation 12. The details of the calculation are given in the original publications.

tion energy cannot now be made. However, an approximate calculation can be made, and this approximate calculation is probably as good as is now warranted, for the simple theory, as presented above, neglects several small effects (such as resonance between the rings) which certainly affect the numerical accuracy of the result. When and if accurate van der Waals potential functions are available, and precise force constants are known, it will still be necessary to reconsider the details of the problem in order to calculate a really accurate activation energy.

Most of the important force constants needed for this calculation are known with moderate accuracy. However, the bending force constant for a bromine atom attached to an aromatic ring has not yet been determined. It was, therefore, estimated by starting, as a first approximation, with the bending constant for hydrogen attached to an aromatic ring. This constant was then increased in the ratio of the force constant for the bending of an aliphatic C—C—Br bond to that for bending an aliphatic C—C—H bond. This second approximation to the desired force constant was then slightly increased (10%) to account for resonance stiffening of the bond. Clearly, this estimate can be subject to considerable error. The van der Waals potential for the interference of two neon atoms was used as an approximation to the potential for the interference of a bromine with a hydrogen atom. The sum of the van der Waals radii for hydrogen (1.2 A) and bromine (1.95 A) is the same as the sum of the van der Waals radii for two neon atoms (3.15 A). The calculations were based on curve B in Fig. 6; more modern work [11] suggests that curve E would have been preferable. However, both curves lie between the pair (C and D) from which estimates of probable error were made. The difficulties inherent in these estimates of force constants and van der Waals potentials have already been discussed.

AGREEMENT BETWEEN THEORY AND EXPERIMENT. Calculations based on the theory presented above have been carried out for 2,2'-dibromo-4,4'-dicarboxybiphenyl (the "dibromo acid"), for 2,2'-diiodo-5,5'-dicarboxybiphenyl (the "diiodo acid"), and for 2,2',3,3'-tetraiodo-5,5'-dicarboxybiphenyl (the "tetraiodo acid"). These calculations, of course, required the selection of approximate values for the force constants, k_i, and approximate van der Waals potential curves, $V(d)$. The reasons for the choices that were made and the probable limits of error in the calculations are presented in a later section. The data obtained are presented in Table IV. The agreement between the calculated and the experimental values of the activation energy is remarkably good.

TABLE IV

OBSERVED AND CALCULATED ACTIVATION ENERGIES, kcal./mole, FOR THE RACEMIZATION OF SOME OPTICALLY ACTIVE DERIVATIVES OF BIPHENYL

Biphenyl	$\Delta F_{obs}^{\ddagger}$	$\Delta S_{obs}^{\ddagger}$	$\Delta H_{obs}^{\ddagger}$	$\Delta H,^{\ddagger}$ calc
Dibromo acid	19.5	(8) *	(17.3) *	18.2
Diiodo acid	23.4	8.1 †	21.0 †	21.4–23.6
Tetraiodo acid	30.4	8.8 †	27.3 †	28.6–33.1

* Estimated on the basis of the assumption that the entropy of activation will not differ appreciably among these acids.

† These values differ a little from those previously published. The earlier values were for Arrhenius activation energies; these are heats of formation of an (Eyring) activated complex.

THE ACTIVATED COMPLEX. The numerical calculations lead to the values for the activation energy shown in Table IV; they lead as well to values shown in Table V for all the coordinates q_1, q_2, $\cdots$ in the

TABLE V

DISPLACEMENTS AND ENERGY IN THE ACTIVATED COMPLEX

Vibration	Displacement (for each bond or angle)	Energy, kcal./mole (for all bonds of a given type)
Stretching interannular bond	+0.040 A	0.65
Deformation of angle β	−3.9°	0.78
Deformation of C—C—H angle	+5.0°	0.96
Compressing C—H bond	−0.020 A	0.30
Stretching C—Br bond	+0.004 A	0.00
Deformation of C—C—Br angle	+12.3°	7.22
All deformations of benzene ring		2.46

activated complex. Figure 8 pictures the activated complex for the racemization of 2,2'-dibromo-4,4'-dicarboxybiphenyl. Qualitatively,

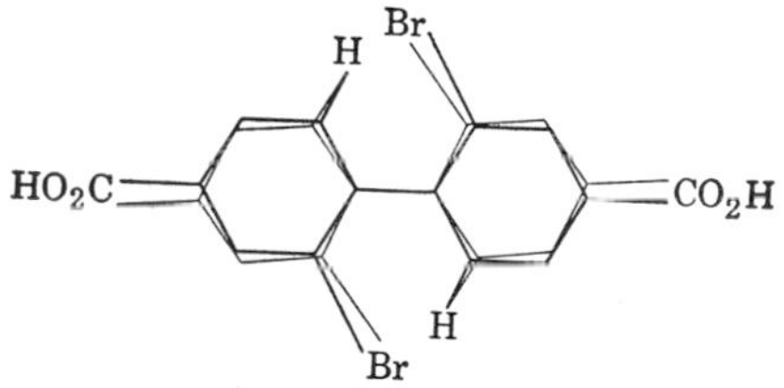

FIG. 8. The activated complex (heavy lines) in the racemization of 2,2'-dibromo-4,4'-dicarboxybiphenyl. (The rigid planar conformation is shown in light lines.)

the following features are observed: the C—C—Br bonds bend considerably (more than 10°), and the C—C—H bonds and the C—C—C bonds also bend but to a lesser degree. The benzene rings are not collinear in the activated complex, but the rings themselves are so stiff that they are only slightly deformed. In total, bending accounts for more than half of the activation energy for the racemization and is the most important feature of the process. About a third of the activation energy arises from climbing the potential energy (van der Waals) curve; the remainder arises from stretching deformations.

This conclusion is a general one. Whenever two groups are forced into close proximity, the valence angles are considerably modified. This bending cannot be said to cause steric strain; rather, the bending occurs to mitigate or relieve the steric strain. But the major result of steric strain is the deformation of bond angles.

LIMITS OF ERROR. Any approximate calculation such as that here outlined must be subject to very considerable errors. By far the largest errors arise because of the uncertainties in the van der Waals potential functions. In order to evaluate the quantitative significance of these uncertainties, several different van der Waals functions were tried; the numerical results suggest that the calculations here made could be in error by 3 or even 5 kcal./mole.

There are numerous other errors and uncertainties in the calculation as presented. The most important (and the least certain) force constant is that for bending the carbon-carbon-bromine bond angle; but, if this constant is in error by as much as 20%, the calculated activation energy will be in error by only about 1 kcal./mole. Although, from some points of view, a kilocalorie is a large energy value, it is small compared to the errors that can arise from the uncertainties in the van der Waals potential functions.

Some other sources of error are these: (a) There is undoubtedly some resonance stabilization of the planar form of the biphenyl molecule. This resonance interaction may amount to 3 kcal./mole in biphenyl itself; it must be less in a hindered biphenyl. However, whatever the magnitude of the resonance interaction, in the biphenyl, it will of course operate to lower the energy of the planar structure and, therefore, to lower the energy of activation.[42]   (b) T. L. Hill [43] has pointed

---

[42] M. Calvin [J. Org. Chem., 4, 256 (1939)] suggested that interannular resonance will decrease rather than increase the rate of racemization. Specifically, 2,2'-dibromo-4,4'-diaminobiphenyl, (a), has not been resolved, whereas 2,2'-dibromo-4,4'-dicarboxybiphenyl, (b), has been resolved. Calvin attributed this difference to interannular resonance between the carboxyl groups in (b) and predicted that 2,2'-dibromo-4-amino-4'-nitrobiphenyl, (c), would racemize very slowly. This prediction has not yet been tested experimentally. His argument was based on the contention that resonance between the two rings of a biphenyl would shorten the interannular bond, and thereby increase the interference of the groups in the

out that the problem has been treated as a classical rather than as a quantum-mechanical one. Every quantized vibration has associated with it a zero-point energy equal to $\frac{1}{2}h\nu_0$, where ν_0 is the fundamental vibration frequency for the motion in question. If a molecule is in an unstable (strained) conformation, the vibration frequencies must certainly be somewhat different from (and greater than) those for the unstrained molecule; the zero-point energy of the activated complex therefore exceeds that for the normal biphenyl. This effect is probably not large and operates in the opposite direction to the resonance effect. It could, in fact, be calculated, but such calculation has not yet been carried out. (c) There are, in addition, a large number of other small effects such as dipole-dipole interactions which have been neglected.

Clearly, the calculation for the activation energy in the racemization of an optically active derivative of biphenyl is merely a first approximation. Only because the activation energy is large can several small errors be neglected.

However, the general method of minimizing energy with respect to all possible molecular adjustments is a powerful one. The calculated energy of a hypothetical planar but rigid model for 2,2'-dibromo-4,4'-dicarboxybiphenyl (i.e., one for which no bending or stretching is per-

---

ortho positions. Such increased interference should then make racemization more difficult. This argument is, however, faulty. Resonance always decreases the energy of a molecule, never increases it. The interannular bond in a planar biphenyl can be shortened by resonance if and only if resonance lowers the energy of the

(a)   (b)

(c)

planar conformation. If the planar conformation (which is the transition state for racemization) has less energy, the reaction will proceed more rapidly. Conversely, if resonance cannot lower the energy of the planar conformation of the biphenyl, it cannot shorten the interannular bond either. The conclusions presented above are predicated on the assumption that neither interannular resonance nor steric repulsion is large in the twisted (normal) biphenyl molecule; this assumption, although unproved, seems reasonable.

[43] T. L. Hill, *J. Chem. Phys.*, *16*, 938 (1948).

mitted) exceeds 200 kcal./mole. Similarly, the calculated energy for a planar biphenyl made up of hard spheres (i.e., one for which no penetration of the van der Waals radii is allowed) exceeds 70 kcal./mole. Only where the energy is minimized both with respect to bond deformation and with respect to van der Waals interaction does the calculated value for the activation energy approach the experimental value.

THE "BUTTRESSING" EFFECT. The most important *qualitative* conclusion which stems from the mathematical theory is this: the bending of valence bonds is vitally important to steric strain. This principle was recognized, at least partially, by Kistiakowsky and his collaborators [44] long before the quantitative theory had been developed.

The clearest demonstration of the importance of bond bending can be obtained in the biphenyl series. A hint of the importance of bond bending is contained in the data of Adams and his students,[45, 46, 37] who measured the rates of racemization of a series of optically active biphenyls derived from 2-nitro-6-carboxy-2'-methoxybiphenyl. These

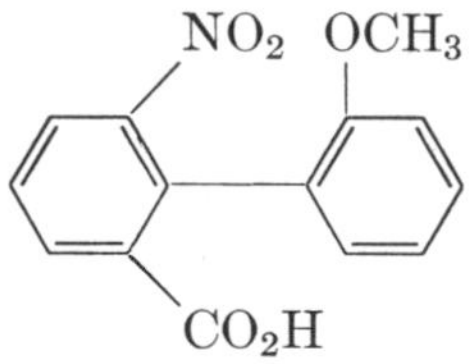

biphenyls were substituted in the 3' position, the 4' position, or the 5' position with a single substituent. The pertinent data are contained in Table VI.

TABLE VI

HALF-TIME, minutes, about 25°C., FOR THE RACEMIZATION OF BIPHENYLS

Substituent	3'	4'	5'
H	9.4	9.4	9.4
OCH_3	98.1	2.6	10.8
CH_3	332	3.6	11.5
Cl	711	12	31.0
Br	827	25	32.0
NO_2	1905	115	35.4

These data show that substituents in the 5' position exert only a small effect on the rate, whereas substituents in the 3' position exert a very large effect on the rate; the effects are always retarding. Substituents in the 4' position exert a small effect on the rate which may

[44] G. B. Kistiakowsky and W. R. Smith, *J. Am. Chem. Soc., 58,* 1043 (1936).
[45] S. L. Chien and R. Adams, *J. Am. Chem. Soc., 56,* 1787 (1934).
[46] W. E. Hanford and R. Adams, *J. Am. Chem. Soc., 57,* 1592 (1935).

either accelerate or retard the racemization. When these data are considered in the light of the importance of bond bending, it is clear that the 3' substituents "buttress" the methoxyl group, and so raise the energy needed to push this group out of the way in the activated state. In the 5' position, these same groups do not interact very much with the adjacent (6') hydrogen atom; the small retarding effect may also be a buttressing effect. Substituents in the 4' position sometimes accelerate and sometimes retard; the effect is (generally) smaller than that observed in the 3' position. These data suggest buttressing. Adams stated that "the greater stability of the 3' series may, perhaps, be related to the proximity of the 3' substituents to the methoxyl group in the 2' position."

In order to provide data on which the buttressing effect could better be judged, Rieger and Westheimer synthesized and resolved 2,2'-diiodo-5,5'-dicarboxybiphenyl (A) and 2,2',3,3'-tetraiodo-5,5'-dicarboxybiphenyl (B). The relative rates for the racemization of A and B

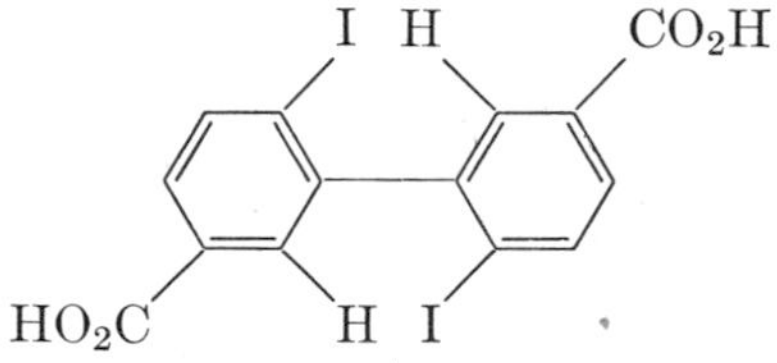

are 30,000 to 1; the difference in activation energy (calculated and observed) is presented in Table IV. There can be very little doubt in this instance that the iodine atoms in the 3 and 3' positions buttress those in the 2 and 2' positions. The importance of the deformation of bond angles has, therefore, been established.

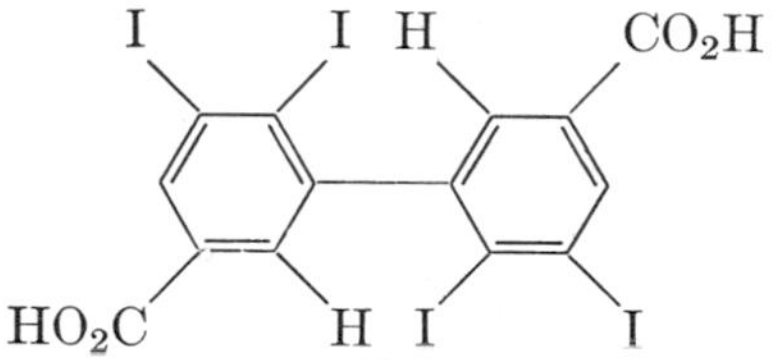

4' SUBSTITUENTS. For the sake of completeness, the effects of substituents in the 4' position of optically active biphenyls are worth noting. The largest effect, that of the nitro group, decreases the racemization rate tenfold. A similar but smaller effect of a 4'-nitro group had previously been observed by Kuhn and Albrecht,[47] who measured the rates of racemization at 98° of the sodium salts of two acids of the formula

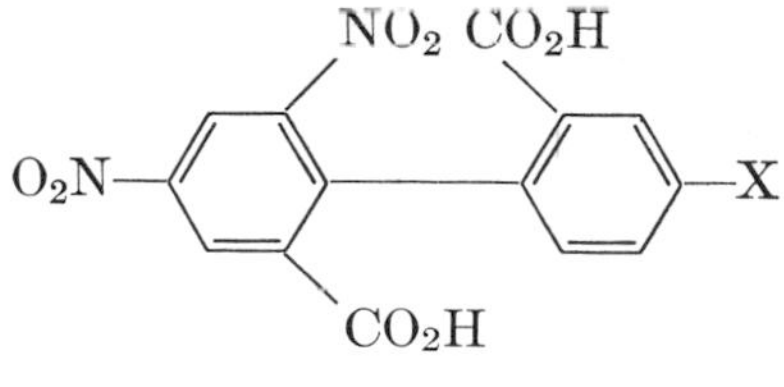

[47] R. Kuhn and O. Albrecht, *Ann.*, *458*, 221 (1927).

When X was H, the half-time was 18 minutes; when X was NO_2, the half-time was 50 minutes. The reason for stabilizing effect of the 4'-nitro group is not yet clear.

ADAMS' RULE. Adams has formulated a useful empirical rule with which he can predict whether a given biphenyl can be resolved. According to this rule, a substituted biphenyl of formula F can be resolved

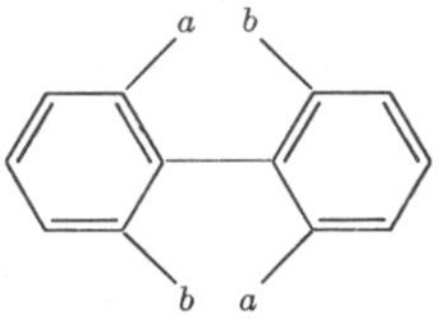

F

if, but only if, the sum of the bond lengths of C—a and C—b exceeds 2.90 A. The critical distance is that separating the *ortho*-carbon atoms. Of course the question of whether a biphenyl can be resolved depends upon the temperature at which the resolution is attempted, on the technique of the investigator, and upon such additional factors as the presence or absence of a large buttressing effect. Nevertheless, it is true that, for simple compounds of structure F and at temperatures around 0–25°C., the rule is a useful guide. The lengths used in the rule are bond lengths, not van der Waals radii. Why then should the rule hold? It holds (approximately) because it neglects both van der Waals radii and activation energy. A biphenyl can be resolved by ordinary technique only if it has a half-time for racemization at room temperature (or at least at 0°) of several minutes. This requires that the activation energy for racemization be 17 kcal./mole or greater. Apparently, when the shorter bond radii, rather than the longer van der Waals radii, are used in a calculation, the sum exceeds 2.90 A when the activation energy for racemization (approximately) exceeds 17 kcal./mole.

cis- and trans-butene-2

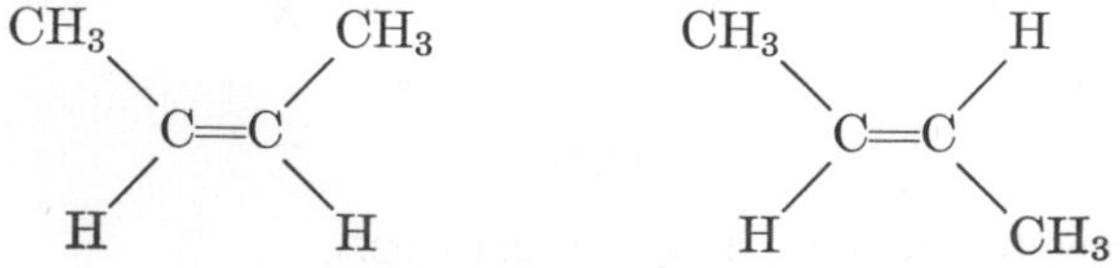

trans-Butene-2 is more stable than the corresponding *cis* isomer, and the energy difference for this and for other *cis-trans* pairs has usually been ascribed to steric interactions in the *cis* isomer. Hill has calculated the steric interaction between the methyl groups in the *cis* isomer.[43] He worked out a reasonable van der Waals function [48] for the interaction of the methyl groups and extended the methods which Westheimer and Mayer had developed. His calculated value for the excess steric energy in the *cis* isomer is 1.85 kcal./mole; the experimental value, from Kistiakowsky's [49] heats of hydrogenation, is 1.29 kcal./mole. The agreement is good.

The calculation for the butenes, however, is less certain just because of the smaller magnitude of the steric effect. Unfortunately, the energy barrier for rotation in ethane is 3 kcal./mole, and even hyperconjugation effects may account for 1 kcal./mole. Until the small effects then can be carefully calculated, the result for *cis*-butene-2 must remain somewhat in doubt. Nevertheless, the calculation (perhaps fortuitously) does give a result close to the experimental one; the method here outlined has therefore proved useful both in a thermodynamic problem where the strain energy is less than 2 kcal./mole and in a kinetic problem where the strain energy exceeds 20 kcal./mole.

ACKNOWLEDGMENT

The author wishes to express his gratitude to Professor J. D. Roberts for his trenchant and constructive criticism of this chapter.

[48] T. L. Hill, *J. Chem. Phys.*, *16*, 399 (1948).

[49] G. B. Kistiakowsky, J. R. Ruhoff, H. A. Smith, and W. E. Vaughan, *J. Am. Chem. Soc.*, *57*, 876 (1935).

Chapter 13

by Robert W. Taft, Jr.

Separation of Polar, Steric, and Resonance Effects in Reactivity

PART A.   Principles and Methods

I. INTRODUCTION

II. SOME BASIC PRINCIPLES FROM THERMODYNAMICS AND THE TRANSITION-STATE THEORY OF RATES

III. PRINCIPLES OF THE EFFECT OF STRUCTURE ON EQUI-LIBRIA AND RATES
1. Equilibria
2. Rates
3. Meaning of Thermodynamic Equations and Limitations
4. Factors Contributing to the Potential-Energy Term
5. Definitions

IV. REACTIONS OF *m*- AND *p*-SUBSTITUTED BENZENE DERIVATIVES
1. The Hammett Equation
2. Use of the Hammett Equation in Mechanism Studies
3. Additive Nature of Polar Effects
4. The Effect of Resonance of the Functional Group

5. The Effect of Resonance of the Substituent

6. The Effect of Steric Inhibition of Resonance

7. Reactivity as a Mathematical Function of Structure

8. Failure of the Hammett Equation

V. THE SEPARATION OF POLAR, STERIC, AND RESONANCE EFFECTS IN RATES OF NORMAL ESTER HYDROLYSIS

1. Historical

2. Polar Substituent Constants for Groups Directly Adjoining the Reaction Center

3. Steric Effects of Unconjugated Groups

4. Resonance Effects of α,β-Unsaturated Groups

5. Comparison of the Magnitude of Polar, Steric, and Resonance Effects

VI. THE GENERAL NATURE OF THE PROPORTIONALITY OF POLAR EFFECTS

1. A Quantitative Relationship

2. Use of Linear Free-Energy–Polar-Energy Relationships for Prediction and Mechanism Purposes

3. Correlation of Physical Properties by Equation 16. Electronegativity and Electron Withdrawing Power

4. Tabulation of Polar Substituent Constants

5. Equation 16 as a Criterion of Constant Steric and Resonance Effects. Comments on Precision

6. The Failure of Equation 16 and Its Meaning. Linear Polar-Energy Relationship

7. A Further Criterion of Polar Effects

8. Concerning a General Theory of the Effect of Structure on Reactivity

9. Requirements and Limitations in Use of Equation 16

10. Use of Equations 16 and 17 to Quantitatively Evaluate Other Effects

VII. GENERAL AND SPECIFIC STERIC EFFECTS IN REACTIVITY

1. Linear Steric Energy Relationships

2. Discussion of Equation 19

3. The *ortho* Effect

4. Kinetic-Energy Steric Effects

VIII. GENERAL RESONANCE EFFECTS OF α,β-UNSATURATED GROUPS

IX. SUMMARY

PART B. More Detailed Considerations

X. ENTROPY EFFECTS AND THE HAMMETT EQUATION.
RIGOR OF THE DEFINITION OF POLAR EFFECTS

XI. $\Delta\Delta F^{\ddagger}$ OR $\Delta\Delta H^{\ddagger}$ AS THE BETTER MEASURE OF $\Delta\Delta E_p{}^{\ddagger}$

XII. THE SEPARATION OF STERIC EFFECTS IN ESTER HYDROLYSIS
RATES TO THE CONTRIBUTING POTENTIAL- AND KINETIC-
ENERGY TERMS

XIII. THE EVALUATION OF RESONANCE EFFECTS AND RESO-
NANCE ENERGIES FROM ESTER HYDROLYSIS RATE
DATA

XIV. LINEAR STRAIN ENERGY RELATIONSHIPS

Chapter 13

PART A. PRINCIPLES AND METHODS

I. INTRODUCTION

Additive relationships between bond energies and between bond distances have made possible the assignment of numerical values of electronegativities, ionic and covalent radii, and bond energies as fundamental empirical constants of the elements and their chemical bonds. Use of these parameters has contributed much in relatively recent years to both practical and theoretical chemistry.

An increasing amount of critical evidence within the past few years indicates that the effect of structure on the free energy of activation (or the logarithm of a rate constant) may be frequently treated, approximately, as the sum of independent contributions of polar, resonance, and steric effects. That is, these three effects combine additively to determine the free energy of activation. Such a relationship makes possible the assignment of numerical values to elements or groups as empirical constants associated their effects on reaction rates and equilibria. These constants may be used to distinguish between, and to evaluate the polar, resonance, and steric effects of, substituent groups.

An approximately quantitative separation of reactivity to these contributing factors, if achieved, permits the unambiguous study of the effect of structure on each. In turn, quantitative correlations and predictions of rates are made possible.

It is the purpose of the present chapter to collect the principal arguments and accomplishments of this new approach to structure and reactivity, to show the internal consistency of the treatment, and, where possible, to show the agreement between the results of this treatment and other independent evidence. Because of the complexity of reactivity problems it should not be surprising to the reader to find that a number of the conclusions reached in the chapter are at some variance with ideas that have been expressed by other investigators. No attempt has been made to review critically or to compare all other treatments and points of view. Instead it is only the purpose of this chapter to collect the basic principles, methods, and conclusions of this particular approach to reactivity problems so that they may be readily available for application and testing against other theories by workers in the field.

It is yet too early to state the general applicability of some of the numerical rate parameters. Detailed theoretical treatment of these quantities has yet to be accomplished. The empirical correlations discussed in this chapter, however, do suggest a general usefulness. In particular, the separation of the polar effects from resonance and steric effects of substituents R in the rates of hydrolysis of esters of the general formula $RCO_2C_2H_5$ has provided a quantitative scale of the electron-attracting powers (polarities) of organic groups. These parameters show much promise of having a wide range of application. With quantitative control over one variable contributing to reactivity (the polar effect), the investigator is in a favorable position to identify and evaluate the other contributing variables.

Given below are two examples of the effect of structure on the rates of hydrolysis of esters in organic or mixed aqueous solvents at room temperature. Accompanying conclusions illustrate the type of decisions (cf. section V) that have been made possible by the evaluation of the polar and steric contributions to these rates.

In the alkaline hydrolysis of ethyl esters, the trichloroacetate reacts about 8 million times faster than the trimethylacetate. Thus the change from a t-butyl group to a trichloromethyl group at the carbonyl reaction center increases rate by 6.9 powers of 10. This very large effect is almost entirely the result of the greater electron-withdrawing power of the latter group.

In the acid-catalyzed hydrolysis of ethyl esters, the formate reacts 100,000 times faster than the ester of β-Butlerow's acid (methyl neopentyl t-butyl acetic acid). Replacing the methyl neopentyl t-butyl carbinyl group by a hydrogen atom thus increases rate by 5.0 powers of 10, an effect almost entirely steric in origin.

One of the most powerful of all the numerical constants is the thermodynamic property. These quantities make possible the quantitative prediction of the extent of chemical reactions.

The connection between the thermodynamic properties and the empirical rate parameters is not completely trivial. Although no thermodynamic proofs may be offered for the relationships and the methods to be discussed, thermodynamic reasoning provides the background of this discussion of reactivity.

Any macroscopic system of organic substances above the absolute zero of temperature consists of an enormous number of molecules constantly undergoing many complex kinds of nuclear motions. Yet the extent of a reaction at equilibrium may be exactly predicted from free energies of formation, the experimental measurement of which does not require this knowledge of the nature of matter.[1] Analogously, the empirical rate parameters for one reaction may be used in the correlation and prediction of rate in other reactions without a detailed knowledge of the modes of nuclear motion or the types of collision necessary to produce reaction. However, the molecular motions are all important in determining the value of a thermodynamic property, and, indeed, for simple molecules, calculation of the property is possible by theoretical means which take these motions into account. Similarly, complete understanding of the effect of structure on reactivity cannot be expected until the statistical contributions of molecular motions and collisions to the empirical rate parameters are known. The complexity of organic molecules makes this task very difficult, and little has been accomplished on this detailed level. Further quantitative development may be possible from the type of qualitative considerations of the effect of molecular motions on reactivity which are discussed in this chapter.

II. SOME BASIC PRINCIPLES FROM THERMODYNAMICS AND THE TRANSITION-STATE THEORY OF RATES

The great power of the thermodynamic method results from the fact that differences in thermodynamic quantities depend only upon the initial and final states of the process under consideration. In no way are these quantities dependent upon the manner in which the change from the fixed initial to the fixed final state is carried out.[1] Thus, for example, thermodynamic properties, in contrast to rate properties, are independent of the variable time. Experience has shown that the change between most initial and final states of chemical interest does not take place instantaneously, and, very frequently, there is no direct relationship between the rate of approach to, and the extent of, reaction at equilibrium.

It might appear, therefore, that studies of the effect of structure on equilibrium and on rate would have little in common. This is not so;

[1] G. N. Lewis and M. Randall, *Thermodynamics and the Free Energy of Chemical Substances*, McGraw-Hill Book Co., New York, 1923.

indeed, the two involve the same principles. The transition-state theory of reaction rates makes this point clear.

According to the transition-state theory, the rate of most reactions is given by the product of the concentration of activated complexes $(C^{\ddagger})$ and a universal decomposition rate for all such complexes, RT/Nh. The concentration of activated complexes is determined by an "equilibrium" with the reactant molecules. The "equilibrium constant" for this process is represented by the symbol $K^{\ddagger}$. The activated complexes are molecules sufficiently activated and properly oriented to possess free energy in excess of a critical amount which specifies the transition state for the given reaction.[2]

$$k = \text{Rate at unit concentration of reactants}$$

$$= (RT/Nh)K^{\ddagger} = (RT/Nh) \exp\left(-\Delta F^{\ddagger}/RT\right) \qquad (1)$$

The important variable (other than temperature) which determines reaction rate is the free energy of activation, $\Delta F^{\ddagger}$. This free-energy term, as a true thermodynamic quantity, depends only upon the nature of two fixed states. In this case the fixed states are the reactant and the transition states. The manner in which the reaction proceeds from a given reactant state to a given transition state in no way affects the rate.[3] Thus, if adequate information about the structure of the reactant and transition states is available, reaction rates can in principle be predicted.

The difference between the free energy of the reaction transition state and the sum of the free energies of the reactants (i.e., the free energy of activation) is the requisite quantity for the rate problem. In an equilibrium problem it is the difference in free energies of the products and the reactants that is required. With neither rate nor equilibrium is it necessary to be concerned with such matters as the existence of unstable intermediates, or the kinds and frequency of collisions between molecules.

Organic chemists have frequently considered the order of increasing reactivity in a series of similar aliphatic compounds to be governed by the order of decreasing hindrance of the approach of the reagent to the reactant molecule. Although this reasoning is frequently helpful, these ideas can be expressed at least as adequately in terms of the difference between the free energies of the transition state and the reactants. The development of concepts of structural factors which

---

[2] H. Eyring, *J. Chem. Phys.*, *3*, 107 (1935); M. Polanyi and M. G. Evans, *Trans. Faraday Soc.*, *31*, 875 (1935).

[3] S. Glasstone, K. Laidler, and H. Eyring, *The Theory of Rate Processes*, McGraw-Hill Book Co., New York, 1941.

affect the free energy of activation (or reaction) is one of the important purposes of this chapter. These concepts are readily associated with quantitative correlations of the effect of structure on reactivity.

In combination with carefully conducted mechanism studies, the theories of chemical bonding [4] make it possible to draw conclusions about the structures of the reactant and transition states for a chemical reaction.[5] With only qualitative concepts about the structure of these two states useful conclusions can be made concerning the importance of polar, steric, and resonance effects, and, in turn, quantitative correlations of reactivity. The existence of these correlations provides strong experimental support for the transition-state theory.

III. PRINCIPLES OF THE EFFECT OF STRUCTURE ON EQUILIBRIA AND RATES

1. EQUILIBRIA

Most reactions can be represented on the following general basis. RY represents a reactant (R is a substituent group and Y is a functional group); Z, a reagent; and P, the products, in a general reaction

$$RY + Z \rightleftarrows P \tag{2}$$

The equilibrium constant for this reaction is given by K. For the same type of reaction involving the specific reactant R_0Y, and products P_0, the corresponding equilibrium constant is given as K_0.

For a series of reactions involving a common functional group, reagent, and set of experimental conditions (called a reaction series), the quantitative measure of the effect on equilibrium 2 of altering the structure of the reactant from R_0, an arbitrary standard, to R, a general substituent, is the equilibrium constant (K/K_0) of reaction 3.[6]

$$RY + P_0 \rightleftarrows R_0Y + P \tag{3}$$

The thermodynamic quantities in terms of which the effect of structure on equilibria may properly be discussed are the relative standard

[4] (a) L. Pauling, *The Nature of the Chemical Bond*, Cornell University Press, 1944; (b) C. A. Coulson, *Valence*, Oxford, The Clarendon Press, 1952.

[5] Cf. A. A. Frost and R. G. Pearson, *Kinetics and Mechanism*, John Wiley & Sons, New York, 1953.

[6] (a) L. P. Hammett, *Physical Organic Chemistry*, p. 78, McGraw-Hill Book Co., New York, 1940; (b) G. E. K. Branch and M. Calvin, *The Theory of Organic Chemistry*, p. 185, Prentice-Hall, New York, 1941.

free-energy, enthalpy, and entropy changes for the reaction of equation 2, or simply the standard free-energy, enthalpy, and entropy changes for the reaction of equation 3. According to basic relations of statistical thermodynamics,[7] the following equations apply:

$$\Delta\Delta F^\circ = \Delta F^\circ - \Delta F_0{}^\circ = \Delta\Delta E_p{}^\circ - RT \ln (\Pi Q) \qquad (4a)$$

$$\Delta\Delta F^\circ = -RT \ln (K/K_0) \qquad (4b)$$

where $\Delta\Delta F_0{}^\circ$ = the standard free-energy change accompanying reaction 3.

$\Delta\Delta E_p{}^\circ$ = the standard energy change accompanying reaction 3 when both reactant and product states are completely deprived of all their energies of molecular motion. This energy may be regarded as the potential-energy change accompanying reaction 3. In principle, $\Delta\Delta E_p{}^\circ$ is predictable by quantum mechanics.

$$(\Pi Q) = \frac{q_P q_{R_0Y}}{q_{P_0} q_{RY}}$$

where q's are partition functions involving temperature-dependent kinetic energies of motion. These partition functions may be based upon the energy levels of all forms of motions, including solvent molecules involved in solvation and the motions at the absolute zero (zero-point vibrations). It is not yet possible, for reactions in solution, to calculate (ΠQ) from statistical theory. However, this quantity may be determined at least crudely by experiment (cf. sections XI and XII). Basically, (ΠQ) is determined by the changes in molecular motions accompanying reaction 3. Inasmuch as reaction 3 involves the same number of moles of reactants as products, translational motions make little contribution to (ΠQ). The exception is the system for which reaction 3 is accompanied by substantial changes in the translational degrees of freedom of the solvent. Neglecting solvation changes (which may be quite important in some reactions, cf. sections X and XI), the translational contribution to (ΠQ) is given by $\left[\dfrac{M_P M_{R_0Y}}{M_{P_0} M_{RY}}\right]^{3/2}$, where M's are molecular weights. If the mass of the reagent is small compared to that of the reactant, the translational contribution is negligible for all practical purposes. The principal forms of motion of

[7] (a) W. F. Giauque, *J. Am. Chem. Soc.*, *52*, 4816 (1930); (b) reference 6a, p. 74.

reactant and product molecules which contribute to (ΠQ) are thus rotations, and bending and stretching motions of the atoms.

$$\Delta\Delta H^\circ = \Delta H^\circ - \Delta H_0{}^\circ = \Delta\Delta E_p{}^\circ + RT^2\frac{d(\ln \Pi Q)}{dt} \tag{5a}$$

$$\Delta\Delta H^\circ = \frac{-R[\ln (K/K_0)_{T_2} - \ln (K/K_0)_{T_1}]}{1/T_2 - 1/T_1} \tag{5b}$$

$$\Delta\Delta S^\circ = \Delta S^\circ - \Delta S_0{}^\circ = R \ln \Pi Q + RT\frac{d(\ln \Pi Q)}{dt} \tag{6a}$$

$$\Delta\Delta S^\circ = \frac{RT_2 \ln (K/K_0)_{T_2} - RT_1 \ln (K/K_0)_{T_1}}{T_2 - T_1} \tag{6b}$$

In equations 4–6 the (a) equations give the statistical relationships. The (b) equations give the thermodynamic properties in terms of experimental quantities. In particular, it is essential to remember (equation 4b) that log (K/K_0) is proportional to $\Delta\Delta F^\circ$ and is therefore a measure of the free-energy change accompanying reaction 3.

2. RATES

The transition-state theory of reaction rates leads to the result that relative rates are simply a special case of relative equilibria; i.e., $(k/k_0) = (K^{\ddagger}/K_0{}^{\ddagger})$. It follows that the above formulations (equations 4–6) apply to the effect of structure on reaction rates. To maintain a formal distinction between reaction equilibria and rates a superscript $\ddagger$ is employed when reference is made to the thermodynamic quantities for the latter and a small k in place of a large K is used to denote a rate instead of an equilibrium constant. We now write a set of equations 4′–6′ analogous to equations 4–6 by making these changes in symbolism. This new set of equations applies to the change that takes place between the reactant and the transition states, rather than reactant and product states. The difference in the two sets of equations may be illustrated by considering the transition and product states for a given reaction series. If a certain structural change affects the free energy of the transition state in the same direction as that of the product state, rate parallels equilibrium. That is, the fastest reaction also goes to the greatest extent. If the effect on the free energies of the transition and product states is in opposite directions, the slowest reaction goes to the greatest extent.

The basic equilibrium for discussion of the effect of structure on reactivity (analogous to equation 3) is the hypothetical one [8]

$$RY + P_0^{\ddagger} \rightleftarrows R_0Y + P^{\ddagger} \qquad (3')$$

($P^{\ddagger}$ is the general and $P_0^{\ddagger}$ the standard transition state.)

The so-called thermodynamic rate quantities are given by

$$\Delta\Delta F^{\ddagger} = \Delta\Delta E_p^{\ddagger} - RT \ln (\Pi Q^{\ddagger}) \qquad (\Pi Q^{\ddagger}) = \left(\frac{q_{\mathrm{P}^{\ddagger}}q_{\mathrm{R}_0\mathrm{Y}}}{q_{\mathrm{P}_0^{\ddagger}}q_{\mathrm{RY}}}\right) \qquad (4'a)$$

$$\Delta\Delta F^{\ddagger} = -RT \ln (k/k_0) \qquad (4'b)$$

$$\Delta\Delta H^{\ddagger} = \Delta\Delta E_p^{\ddagger} + RT^2 \frac{d(\ln \Pi Q^{\ddagger})}{dt} \qquad (5'a)$$

$$\Delta\Delta H^{\ddagger} = \frac{-R[\ln (k/k_0)_{T_2} - \ln (k/k_0)_{T_1}}{1/T_2 - 1/T_1} \qquad (5'b)$$

$$\Delta\Delta S^{\ddagger} = R \ln (\Pi Q^{\ddagger}) + RT \frac{d(\ln \Pi Q^{\ddagger})}{dt} \qquad (6'a)$$

$$\Delta\Delta S^{\ddagger} = \frac{RT_2 \ln (k/k_0)_{T_2} - RT_1 \ln (k/k_0)_{T_1}}{T_2 - T_1} \qquad (6'b)$$

$\Delta\Delta F^{\ddagger}$, $\Delta\Delta H^{\ddagger}$, and $\Delta\Delta S^{\ddagger}$ are the relative free energy, enthalpy, and entropy of activation, respectively, or the standard changes in these thermodynamic properties accompanying the hypothetical equilibrium 3'.

$\Delta\Delta E_p^{\ddagger}$ is the relative potential energy of activation. The $(\Pi Q^{\ddagger})$ term gives the relative change in kinetic energies of motion accompanying the activation process. These motions, including those at absolute zero, may be associated either with reactants, with the transition state, or with the solvent.

The same factors affect $\Delta\Delta F^{\ddagger}$, $\Delta\Delta H^{\ddagger}$, and $\Delta\Delta S^{\ddagger}$ as discussed in section III-1, for only a different change in states is involved. For this reason all general discussions and equations in this chapter are given in terms of k, $\Delta\Delta F^{\ddagger}$, $\Delta\Delta H^{\ddagger}$, and $\Delta\Delta S^{\ddagger}$ with the understanding that K, $\Delta\Delta F°$, $\Delta\Delta H°$, and $\Delta\Delta S°$ may apply as well. Only in discussions of specific reaction rates or equilibria are the distinguishing symbols used.

[8] F. P. Price, Jr., and L. P. Hammett, *J. Am. Chem. Soc.*, *63*, 2387 (1941).

3. MEANING OF THE THERMODYNAMIC EQUATIONS AND LIMITATIONS

According to equation 4, the relative free-energy change, $\Delta\Delta F°$, at any temperature above the absolute zero is a composite of a temperature-independent potential-energy term and a temperature-dependent term associated with changes in the kinetic energies of motions of the molecules.

If the heat capacities of products and reactants from the absolute zero to the desired temperature, and a measured value of $\Delta\Delta H°$ or $\Delta\Delta F°$ at any intervening temperature, are known, $\Delta\Delta F°$ may be separated to two terms. The first of these terms gives the $\Delta\Delta F°$ (or $\Delta\Delta H°$) for reaction 3 at the absolute zero, usually given by the symbol $\Delta\Delta E_0°$ (cf. section XI). The second term, $-RT \ln (\Pi Q')$, is a kinetic-energy term, analogous to $-RT \ln (\Pi Q)$, but the partition functions are based upon $\Delta\Delta E_0°$ rather than $\Delta\Delta E_p°$ as the zero-point energy. The $\Delta\Delta E_0°$ term exceeds the $\Delta\Delta E_p°$ term by an amount equal to the difference in the zero-point vibrational energies of the products and the reactants, $\Delta\Delta E_Z°$. To achieve the separation of $\Delta\Delta F°$ indicated in equation 4, $\Delta\Delta E_Z°$ must be obtained from spectroscopic data, i.e., $\Delta\Delta E_p° = \Delta\Delta E_0° - \Delta\Delta E_Z°$ and $-RT \ln (\Pi Q) = \Delta\Delta E_Z° - RT \ln (\Pi Q')$. The only considerable number of organic substances for which data are available to obtain even the $\Delta E_0°$ values are the hydrocarbons.[9]

In principle, it should be possible to make, in the same manner, the separation of $\Delta\Delta F^{\ddagger}$ indicated in equation 4'a. In practice, the situation is hopeless. It has not been possible to determine the rate of any reaction from the absolute zero to near room temperature, not to mention the measurement of heat capacities of reaction transition states.

Extrathermodynamic methods must always be employed to obtain the separation of $\Delta\Delta F^{\ddagger}$ indicated in equation 4'. The same methods provide the only means presently practical for achieving the separation of $\Delta\Delta F°$ given in equation 4. However, one should not confuse the difficulty in achieving the separation of $\Delta\Delta F^{\ddagger}$ values to potential- and kinetic-energy terms with the realization that log (k/k_0) values are usually determined by both these factors.

4. FACTORS CONTRIBUTING TO THE POTENTIAL-ENERGY TERM

The qualitative theories of reactivity that have been developed through the years indicate that three basic effects may contribute to the potential-energy term, $\Delta\Delta E_p^{\ddagger}$: (a) polar, (b) resonance, and (c)

[9] *Selected Values of Physical and Thermodynamic Properties of Hydrocarbons and Related Compounds*, F. D. Rossini et al., Carnegie Press, Pittsburgh, 1953.

steric.[10] Thermodynamics does not provide a means of separating the potential-energy terms into these contributing effects. Thus, even in the equilibrium case if all the thermodynamic data discussed above were available, extrathermodynamic methods would be necessary to accomplish this purpose.

Polar interactions between a substituent R and a functional group Y are associated with coulombic forces which result from charge separations within the groups R and Y. Polar interactions require for transmission only a σ bond (internal inductive and bond polarization interactions [11]) or space (field interaction [11]). The charge separations may arise from differences in electronegativities of the atoms involved, resonance interactions, or poles (unit electronic charges) within R or Y.[4, 12]

Resonance interaction between R and Y is the type of interaction requiring quantum-mechanical description.[4, 12] An interaction that requires at least two valence bond structures (canonical forms) for the bond R—Y may be regarded as a resonance interaction.

Steric interaction between R—Y results from van der Waals type forces.[13, 14] Although this interaction may be one of either attraction or repulsion, the latter is usually involved in considerations of reactivity. That is, repulsion between non-bonded atoms in R and Y (strain energy) is of particular concern. Angle strain energies are usually classified as steric interactions. This type of energy is associated with the decrease in the R—Y binding energy that results from the distortion from normal of bond angles within the group, R.

For reactions in solution, potential energies of solvation must also be considered.[15] These solvent interactions may be directly related to the three basic interactions listed above (steric inhibition of solvation,[16]

[10] (a) Reference 6a, p. 77; (b) reference 6b, p. 193.

[11] Lapworth, *Mem. Manchester Phil. Soc.*, *64*, 13 (1921); G. N. Lewis, *Valence and the Structure of Atoms and Molecules*, p. 84, Chemical Catalog Co., New York, 1923; H. J. Lucas, *J. Am. Chem. Soc.*, *46*, 2475 (1924); C. K. Ingold, *J. Chem. Soc.*, *1926*, 1307; see discussion by W. A. Waters, *Physical Aspects of Organic Chemistry*, Chapter 11, D. Van Nostrand, New York, 1950; R. P. Smith and H. Eyring, *J. Am. Chem. Soc.*, *75*, 5183 (1953), and earlier references; see A. E. Remick, *Electronic Interpretations of Organic Chemistry*, Chapter 2, John Wiley & Sons, New York, 1949, for review of earlier contributions to the theory.

[12] Cf. G. W. Wheland, *The Theory of Resonance*, John Wiley & Sons, New York, 1944.

[13] Reference 6b, p. 62.

[14] H. C. Brown et al., *J. Am. Chem. Soc.*, *75*, 1 (1953), and previous references.

[15] J. G. Kirkwood and F. H. Westheimer, *J. Chem. Phys.*, *6*, 506 (1938).

[16] A. G. Evans, *The Reactions of Organic Halides in Solution*, p. 14, Manchester University Press, Manchester, 1946.

electrostriction of solvent,[17] dipole solvation [18]) or may be more specific solvation interactions.

5. DEFINITIONS

All the factors that contribute to the potential-energy term $\Delta\Delta E_p^{\ddagger}$ are basically electrical interactions, either of attraction or of repulsion. The term $\Delta\Delta E_p^{\ddagger}$ may be regarded as the change in the net binding energies (solvation included) accompanying the reaction of equation 3'.[19] There has been some tendency in the past to consider that only polar interactions lead to electrical effects on reactivity. Clearly, however, repulsions between non-bonded atoms are also electronic in origin.

The following definitions have been adopted in this chapter.

Any factor that affects the $\Delta\Delta E_p^{\ddagger}$ term is regarded as an electrical effect.

A change in polar, resonance, or steric interactions between the reactant state $(R{-}Y + P_0^{\ddagger})$ *of equation 3' and the final state* $(P^{\ddagger} + R_0Y)$ *leads to a polar, resonance, or steric effect, respectively, on the* $\Delta\Delta E_p^{\ddagger}$ *term, and in turn on the rate* (cf. section VI-8).

It is also highly useful and rigorous (cf. section X) to regard as a polar effect any kinetic-energy term, $-RT \ln (\Pi Q^{\ddagger})$ or $RT^2 \, d[\ln (\Pi Q^{\ddagger}) /dt]$, which is directly related to a potential-energy polar effect. Thus, if a series of kinetic-energy terms quantitatively parallel a series of corresponding polar potential-energy terms, the former are also regarded as polar effects.

A steric effect may include both potential-energy and kinetic-energy factors; i.e., both $\Delta\Delta E_p^{\ddagger}$ and $-RT \ln (\Pi Q^{\ddagger})$ $\left(\text{or } RT^2 \dfrac{d(\ln \Pi Q^{\ddagger})}{dt} \right)$ terms may contribute. Any $-RT \ln (\Pi Q^{\ddagger})$ or $RT^2 \dfrac{d(\ln \Pi Q^{\ddagger})}{dt}$ term is necessarily regarded as a steric effect, except in the instance (noted above) in which this term (or any factor in it) is directly related to a potential-energy polar effect. Kinetic-energy terms of this kind are particularly likely to arise as the result of nuclear motions of solvent molecules which are associated with the solvation of poles or dipoles (cf. section X).

Resonance within the substituent R may lead to a resonance contribution to the polar effect of R on rates. It is convenient to regard

[17] R. G. Pearson, *J. Am. Chem. Soc.*, 70, 207 (1948).

[18] Reference 5, p. 137.

[19] Cf. reference 4b for the distinction between binding and bond energy.

the polar effect of R as an inductive effect if it arises from a polar inter-action referred to a given site in R. For example, in an *m*- or *p*-substituted benzene derivative, RY, may be represented by X—C_6H_4—Y. The polar effect of X on the reactivity of RY may be regarded as the sum of effects resulting from charge separation within the aromatic ring induced by resonance and by polar interactions of X (cf. section IV-5). The former will be referred to as a resonance polar effect, and the latter as an inductive polar effect. It should be recognized that by this convention resonance within the substituent X may make a contribution to the so-called inductive effect of X.

It is important to remember that by the present convention polar and steric effects transcend the separation of free-energy terms to potential- and kinetic-energy terms; i.e., both types of energy may contribute to either of these effects.

It is in fact doubtful that the separation of potential and kinetic energy effects (if it could be accomplished easily and precisely) would be a generally useful way of factoring reactivity. From a consideration of the origin of polar, steric, and resonance effects on reaction rates, it is to be expected that these effects generally have both potential- and kinetic-energy contributions.

IV. REACTIONS OF *m*- AND *p*-SUBSTITUTED BENZENE DERIVATIVES

1. THE HAMMETT EQUATION

Within reaction series of the *m*- and *p*-substituted side-chain derivatives of benzene, the effect of structure on rates and equilibria is nearly always determined by a single basic factor, the polar effect of the substituent. Substituents are held rigidly at such large distances from the reaction center that no change in steric interactions occurs between the reactant and the transition state (in the rate case), or the product state (in the equilibrium case). This situation is generally further characterized by the absence of neighboring group participation [20] and by no change in reaction mechanism within a reaction series. The substituents thus produce free-energy changes which are one, or any combination of, the inductive, resonance, or kinetic-energy type polar effects.

The result of this simplification is the most general relationship

---

[20] (a) S. Winstein and E. Grunwald, *J. Am. Chem. Soc.*, 70, 828 (1948); (b) M Simmonetta and S. Winstein, *ibid.*, 76, 18 (1954); (c) earlier papers cited in these references.

known for the effect of substituents on rates or equilibria, the Hammett equation [21, 22]

$$\log (k/k_0) = \sigma\rho \tag{7}$$

σ is a substituent constant independent of the nature of the reaction. It is a quantitative measure of the polar effect in any reaction of a given m or p substituent relative to a hydrogen atom. Hammett selected as the standard reaction for obtaining this constant the ionization of substituted benzoic acids in water at 25°C., i.e., $\sigma \equiv \log (K/K_0)$, for this reaction. Some typical σ values are listed in Table I. Jaffé has given a summary of available σ values.[22]

TABLE I

TYPICAL σ VALUES

Substituent	σ_{para}	σ_{meta}	Substituent	σ_{para}	σ_{meta}
NH_2	−0.660	−0.161	Br	+0.232	+0.391
$N(CH_3)_2$	−0.600	−0.211	I	+0.276	+0.352
OH	−0.357	−0.002	$COCH_3$	+0.516	+0.306
OCH_3	−0.268	+0.115	$CO_2C_2H_5$	+0.522	+0.398
OC_6H_5	−0.028	—	CF_3	+0.551	+0.415
CH_3	−0.170	−0.069	CN	+0.628	+0.678
t-C_4H_9	−0.197	−0.120	SO_2CH_3	+0.728	+0.647
H	0.000	0.000	NO_2	+0.778	+0.710
F	+0.062	+0.337	$N(CH_3)_3{}^+$	+0.859	+0.904
Cl	+0.227	+0.373			

ρ is a proportionality constant, dependent upon the nature of the reaction and the conditions. It is a measure of the susceptibility of a given reaction series to polar substituents.

The subscript zero in equation 7 refers to the unsubstituted benzene derivative.

Jaffé has found that about 42,000 rate and equilibrium constants are encompassed by this equation and the available σ and ρ values. The equation is followed with a median precision of $\pm 15\%$ by experimentally measured rate and equilibrium constants for 3180 reactions.[22] The relationship, though not an exact one, is thus a very useful and generally reliable first approximation.

Equation 7 demonstrates that the corresponding polar effects of substituents on free-energy differences are proportional from one reaction series to another—a relationship which is independent of reac-

[21] (a) L. P. Hammett, *Chem. Revs.*, *17*, 125 (1935); (b) *Physical Organic Chemistry*, p. 184, McGraw-Hill Book Co., New York, 1940.

[22] H. H. Jaffé, *Chem. Revs.*, *53*, 191 (1953).

tion mechanism, attacking reagent, solvent, temperature, or nature of the functional groups involved in the initial, transition, or final states. Although these variables determine the value of the reaction constant ρ, the fit of the data to the equation 7 is independent of them.

The substituent constant σ is not always independent of the nature of the reaction. Hammett found that the σ value for the p-NO$_2$ group obtained from the ionization of p-nitrobenzoic acid does not fit equation 7 when reactions of derivatives of aniline and phenol are considered. However, if a σ value for the p-NO$_2$ group based upon the relative ionization constant for p-nitroanilinium ion in water at 25° was used all the reactions of aniline and phenol derivatives for which data were available were found to fit equation 7 satisfactorily. Duality of σ values for other substituents has been proposed.[22] The role of resonance in affecting an apparent dependence of σ on reaction type is discussed in section IV-4.

The Hammett equation can be illustrated by giving an example of its use for prediction purposes. Suppose that it is desirable to know the stability of 0.1 molar p-nitrobenzenesulfonyl chloride in benzene containing 0.1 molar aluminum chloride at 30°. This mixture undergoes the Friedel-Crafts reaction, but the rate of this reaction has not been determined. The rate of reaction of the unsubstituted benzenesulfonyl chloride and five m- or p-substituted derivatives has been determined by Olivier.[23] From this work, we have log $k_0 = -4.31$ and $\rho = -1.80$.[21b] Taking the value of σ for the p-NO$_2$ group, $+0.778$,[21b] we get

$$\log k = (-1.80)(+0.778) - 4.31 = -5.71$$

This rate constant is given in sec.$^{-1}$ (the reaction is first order), and thus the half-life of the p-nitrobenzenesulfonyl chloride in the benzene solution is about 6000 minutes. This value may be used with confidence.

In using the Hammett equation for prediction purposes it is more likely that a value of σ for the desired substituent will be available than the reaction constant ρ for the chosen reaction at the desired conditions. It is not yet possible to generally predict even crudely the value of ρ from a theoretical or empirical consideration of the nature of the reaction and the experimental conditions, but some progress in this direction is being made.[24]

[23] S. C. J. Olivier, *Rec. trav. chim.*, *33*, 244 (1914).

[24] Cf. discussion in review by H. H. Jaffé, reference 152, including work by G. A Gallop, W. R. Gilkerson, and M. M. Jones, *Trans. Kansas Acad. Sci.*, *55*, J. 232 (1952); H. H. Jaffé, *J. Chem. Phys.*, *21*, 415 (1953); L. P. Hammett, *J. Am. Chem. Soc.*, *59*, 96 (1937); H. H. Jaffé, L. D. Freedman, and G. O. Doak, *ibid.*, *75*, 2209 (1953); B. Gutbezahl and E. Grunwald, *ibid.*, *75*, 559 (1953).

The value of ρ may be determined with a relatively small number of experimental measurements if a wise selection of substituents is made. Thus four or more substituted and the unsubstituted benzene derivative chosen to cover as wide a range of σ values as practical, to avoid possible reaction of the substituent, and to avoid the duality of σ values (particularly where the appropriate σ value is uncertain) will lead to a reliable value of ρ. The experimental values of log k, or log (k/k_0), are plotted against the corresponding values of σ. The determination of the best straight line (unless a non-linear relationship results) gives the value of ρ (cf. Fig. 1). It is well to determine and re-

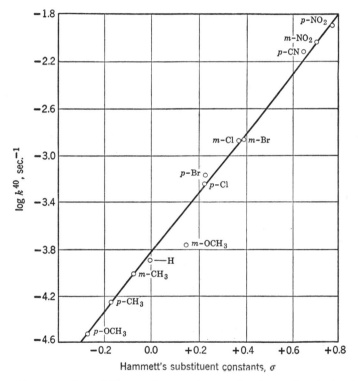

FIG. 1. Determination of the reaction constant, ρ, for the methanolysis of *meta*- and *para*-substituted *l*-menthyl benzoates at 40°C. Slope $= \rho = +2.552$. Intercept $= \log k_0 = -3.859$.

port the probable error of this slope (or the correlation coefficient [22]) and the probable error of a single point by the correlation. From the value of ρ so determined, the rate or equilibrium constant for any other substituent for which a value of σ is available may be readily calculated by equation 7.

If it is desirable to determine a new substituent constant, this may be obtained from the experimental values of k for the given substituted and the unsubstituted benzene derivative, and the slope of the correlation line ρ obtained from the data for other substituents; i.e.,

$$\sigma = (1/\rho)[\log (k/k_0)]$$

The value of σ so derived must be used with caution until it has been established that it generally fits equation 7 for other reactions.

2. USE OF THE HAMMETT EQUATION IN MECHANISM STUDIES

The sign and magnitude of the reaction constant ρ have been used as important tools in the study of reaction mechanisms. Since groups which are electron withdrawing relative to hydrogen are defined so as to have positive σ values, a reaction series in which rates or equilibria are facilitated by electron withdrawal will have a positive ρ value. A negative value of ρ indicates facilitation by electron-releasing substituents, etc.

Hammett has indicated that the following general considerations apply to any reaction which can be formulated as follows: [21b]

$$A + BC \rightarrow AB + C$$

If A contains an m- or p-substituted benzene ring and is electron rich relative to B (i.e., a nucleophilic displacement is involved), electron-attracting m or p substituents will hinder the formation of the new A—B bond, and thus a negative ρ value is implied. Similarly electron-attracting substituents in the A component in an electrophilic displacement (i.e., A is electron poor relative to B) will stabilize the resulting A—B bond so that ρ will have a positive value if the reaction is of this type. In a similar fashion the type of displacement reactions leading to positive and negative values of ρ can be predicted for substituents in the C component.

When substituents are in the B component, the formation of the new AB and the breaking of the old BC bonds are effected in opposite directions by electron release. Thus, for example, in a nucleophilic displacement on B the former is retarded and the latter facilitated. Since we do not at present have ways of deciding from the nature of the reaction which process is the more important, the sign of ρ cannot be predicted with certainty. The experimentally determined values of ρ provide the answer, indicating a further use to which the Hammett equation may be put.

The solvolysis of benzyl and benzoyl halides is an example of reactions in which substituents are introduced in the B component. Swain and Langsdorf consider all these reactions to involve concerted displacements.[25] The sign of ρ in these reactions under given conditions tells whether the nucleophilic $(+\rho)$ or the electrophilic $(-\rho)$ participation provides the greater driving force.[25b]

A specific example of the use of the Hammett relationship in a mechanism study is given as follows. Bartlett and Kice have determined the rates of rearrangement of substituted benzoates of 9-decalyl hydroperoxide to 1-benzoyloxy-1,6-epoxycyclodecanes in methanol at 24.6°.[26] A Hammett plot is followed with the usual precision and gives a ρ value of $+1.34$. Criegee, who discovered this type of rearrangement, has proposed on the basis of subsequent studies that the rearrangement involves an ionic scission of the O—O bond.[27, 28] Bartlett and Kice believe that the value of ρ they have determined confirms the essentially ionic nature of the rearrangement. Rates respond to substituents in the benzoate group in the same direction and with similar magnitude as in the ionization of benzoic acids ($\rho = +1.54$), which involves ionic scission in the same position with respect to the substituents.

Leffler has pointed out an important limitation of the above discussion.[29] The sign of ρ may actually be inverted by temperature (presumably without change in mechanism) for a reaction series involving variable entropies of activation (cf. section X). For this type of reaction series, it is therefore unsound to use the sign of ρ for conclusions concerning mechanism unless the magnitude of ρ is quite large.

3. ADDITIVE NATURE OF POLAR EFFECTS

The polar effects of m or p substituents are additive. Most polysubstituted (in 3, 4, or 5 position) benzene derivatives follow, with the same precision as equation 7, the equation [21, 22]

$$\log (k/k_0) = \rho\Sigma\sigma \qquad (8)$$

where $\Sigma\sigma$ = sum of the σ values of the substituents present.

[25] (a) C. G. Swain and W. P. Langsdorf, Jr., J. Am. Chem. Soc., 73, 2813 (1951); (b) for interesting applications see C. G. Swain and C. B. Scott, ibid., 75, 141 (1953), and M. F. Hawthorne and D. J. Cram, ibid., 76, 3451 (1954).

[26] P. D. Bartlett and J. L. Kice, J. Am. Chem. Soc., 75, 5591 (1953).

[27] R. Criegee, Ber., 77B, 722 (1944); R. Criegee and R. Kasper, Ann., 560, 127 (1948).

[28] See also S. L. Friess, J. Am. Chem. Soc., 71, 2571 (1949); W. von E. Doering and E. Dorfman, ibid., 75, 5595 (1953); H. L. Goering and A. C. Olson, ibid., 75, 5853 (1953).

[29] J. E. Leffler, J. Org. Chem., 20, 1202 (1955).

Compounds that contain more than one benzene ring (e.g., Ar_2CHY) follow the equation [22] (if both rings are equally substituted).

$$\log (k/k_0) = n\sigma\rho \qquad (9)$$

where n = number of equally substituted rings.

If the compounds contain unequally substituted benzene rings symmetrically located with respect to the reaction center, the Hammett equation may be used in the form [22]

$$\log (k/k_0) = \rho(\sigma_1 + \sigma_2) \qquad (10)$$

Jaffé has contributed much to the investigation of the additive nature of polar effects associated with the Hammett equation.[22] His review article should be consulted for a more detailed discussion.

4. THE EFFECT OF RESONANCE OF THE FUNCTIONAL GROUP

The fact that the Hammett equation holds regardless of the extent of resonance of the functional group with the benzene ring in the reactant, transition, or product states must mean that the polar effect of the substituent and the resonance effect of the functional group are independent variables. The latter resonance effect is essentially the same for any substituted derivative as for the unsubstituted derivative. Within a given reaction series of m- and p-substituted benzene derivatives, only the polar effects on rate, which are proportional from one reaction series to another, vary with the substituent.

When resonance is possible across the aromatic system, between substituent and functional center, any change in this interaction between initial and transition states of a process produces a resonance effect.[30] That is, the substituent effect on rate or equilibrium is a composite of polar and resonance effects. Further, the resonance effect will be specific for the type of substituent, functional group, and reaction involved. Resonance effects of this kind are one of the principal causes of failure of the Hammett equation, or, in the more fortunate cases, of the duality of substituent constants.[31]

The σ value for the p-NO_2 substituent obtained from the ionization of p-nitrobenzoic acid does not apply in the ionization of p-nitro-

[30] G. E. K. Branch, and M. Calvin, *The Theory of Organic Chemistry*, p. 250, Prentice-Hall, New York, 1941.

[31] Cf. reference 22, p. 227, for a discussion of other factors affecting σ values and departures from the Hammett equation.

anilinium ion because of resonance between the substituent and the reaction center (in p-nitroaniline):

$$H_2N \overset{O}{\underset{O}{\diagdown}} N \diagup \quad \leftrightarrow \quad H_2N^+ = \overset{O^-}{\underset{O^-}{\diagdown}} N \diagup$$

In a number of very similar reactions [21, 32, 33] the resonance effects appear to contribute a constant fraction to the total substituent effect. In this event it becomes possible to define a new substituent constant which may be applied to several different reaction series. Evidently dual substituent constants are more frequently applicable for electron-withdrawing groups than electron-releasing ones.[32] Unless the above relation between resonance and polar effects holds, the Hammett equation simply fails when there is a resonance effect resulting from the delocalization interaction between a *para* substituent and the reaction center.[34]

It appears more sound theoretically to apply the following equation, rather than to attempt to calculate a new substituent constant for each reaction or reaction type:

$$\log (k/k_0) = \sigma\rho + \psi \tag{11}$$

Equation 11 attributes the effect of the substituent on rates to the sum of both polar and resonance effects. ψ is the resonance effect, and $\sigma\rho$ is the polar effect. Once evaluated, the relationship between ψ for various *para* substituents and reaction types can be investigated and correlations established (cf. section IV-6).

The resonance parameter ψ may be evaluated by plotting $\log (k/k_0)$ as ordinate and σ as abscissa for normal substituents (those which do not resonate with functional center). The vertical displacement of the experimental point for the resonating *para* substituent from the correlation line at the position of the polar σ value gives the value of ψ. In adopting this approach, note should be made of the fact that the *para* NH$_2$ and $-$ N(CH$_3$)$_2$ groups, for example, are not normal substituents in the ionization of benzoic acids (or the rate of saponification of benzoates, etc.), just as *para* $-$NO$_2$ or CO$_2$Et groups are

[32] Cf. reference 22, p. 225.

[33] N. C. Deno, J. J. Jaruzelski, and A. Schriescheim, *J. Am. Chem. Soc.*, *77*, 3044 (1955).

[34] Cf., for example, J. K. Kochi and G. S. Hammond, *J. Am. Chem. Soc.*, *75*, 3445 (1953); reference 33; D. E. Pearson, J. F. Baxter, and J. C. Martin, *J. Org. Chem.*, *17*, 1511 (1952).

not normal in reactions of anilines or phenols. That is, resonance effects are produced from the following type of resonance:

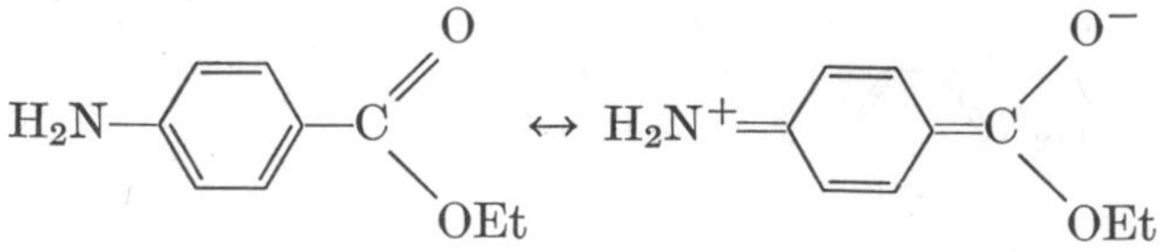

The Hammett σ values are obviously not the polar σ values required to evaluate ψ in a circumstance such as this (cf. section IV-6).

5. THE EFFECT OF RESONANCE OF THE SUBSTITUENT

Although the resonance of the *functional center* with the benzene ring does not generally produce resonance effects on rates within a given reaction series of *m*- and *p*-substituted benzene derivatives, the polar effects of the *substituents* are best interpreted on the basis that they are the *net* effect of inductive and resonance polar effects. That is, resonance of the *substituent* with the benzene ring contributes indirectly (i.e., by induction) to determining the net electron density at the side-chain reaction center. This type of resonance (in contrast to that involving both the substituent and the reaction center *directly*) will produce effects (called resonance polar effects) which follow the Hammett equation. Hammett pointed out that a substantial resonance contribution to the net electron-releasing effect of the *p*-OCH$_3$ group is indicated by the fact that the σ value for this group is negative whereas that for the *m*-OCH$_3$ group is positive.[35] A similar explanation readily accounts for the more positive σ values for *m*- than *p*-halogens, particularly fluorine (cf. section V-2*c*).

One might assume that the difference in the σ values for a given substituent in the *p* and *m* positions ($\sigma_p - \sigma_m$) should be a measure of the resonance polar effect. Although this difference generally gives the right qualitative order of resonance polar effects, the method does not give a quantitative separation, for two reasons. The inductive effect of a given substituent is somewhat larger in the *m* than in the *p* position because of the shorter distance involved.[36] Much more important, the effect of resonance of an *m* substituent on the charge distribution at the positions *ortho* to the side-chain reaction center is in turn transmitted to the reaction center.[37, 38]

[35] Reference 21*b*, p. 196.
[36] J. D. Roberts, R. A. Clement, and J. J. Drysdale, *J. Am. Chem. Soc.*, *73*, 2181 (1951).
[37] C. C. Price and D. C. Lincoln, *J. Am. Chem. Soc.*, *73*, 5841 (1951).
[38] J. D. Roberts and W. T. Moreland, Jr., *J. Am. Chem. Soc.*, *75*, 2167 (1953).

The work of Roberts and Moreland provides a particularly convincing demonstration of the importance of the latter effect. This work also has provided a quantitative type separation of inductive and resonance polar effects of m and p substituents. A close geometrical model of the benzene system, but one completely saturated, was ingeniously devised in the form of 4-substituted bicyclo-[2.2.2]-octane-1-carboxylic acids and esters.[38] The relative reactivities of these compounds are of nearly the same order of magnitude as those for the corresponding reactions involving the same substituents in the m and p positions of benzene derivatives.

A linear free-energy relationship similar to the Hammett equation is followed by reactions of these bicyclic compounds,[38]

$$\log (k/k_0) = \sigma'\rho' \tag{12}$$

where σ' = polar substituent constant.

ρ' = reaction series constant.

By virtue of the same argument that was applied to the reactions of m- and p-substituted benzene derivatives, the effects of substituents on the free-energy changes for these reactions should also be entirely polar. Indeed, because the bicyclic system is saturated, the effects of the 4-substituents are strictly inductive. By equating ρ' for the ionization of these acids with the Hammett ρ for the ionization of benzoic acids, Roberts and Moreland calculated σ' values for the several 4-substituents investigated. In this manner it is expected that the inductive effects for the 4-bicyclic substituents and corresponding p-benzoate substituents will be placed upon the same scale. The difference, $(\sigma - \sigma')$, should then be a measure of the resonance contribution to σ values, i.e., the resonance polar effect. Table II lists values of $(\sigma_{para} - \sigma')$ and $(\sigma_{meta} - \sigma')$ for the substituents studied.

TABLE II

COMPARISON OF σ' AND σ VALUES; RESONANCE POLAR EFFECTS OF m AND p SUBSTITUENTS

Substituent	$(\sigma_{para} - \sigma')$	$(\sigma_{meta} - \sigma')$
H	(0.00)	(0.00)
OH	−0.62	−0.27
CO_2Et	+0.11	+0.04
Br	−0.22	−0.06
CN	+0.08	+0.03

The substituents CO_2Et and CN, which by resonance theory are expected to be electron-withdrawing,[39] give positive values of $(\sigma_p - \sigma')$. The larger value for CO_2Et than CN is in accord with other evidence indicating that the former group is generally a better conjugating group.[40] In turn, substituents which resonance theory indicates to be electron-releasing give negative values of $(\sigma_p - \sigma')$, with bromine less negative than hydroxyl. The resonance effect of m substituents on the positions *ortho* to the functional group is shown to have an appreciable effect at the reaction center by the fact that $(\sigma_m - \sigma')$ is in each case of the same sign as $(\sigma_p - \sigma')$, but about one-third as large. For the substituents m-CO_2Et, m-Br, and m-CN, the near-zero values for $(\sigma_m - \sigma')$ indicate that essentially inductive effects alone determine σ values.

A more extensive separation of inductive and resonance contributions to σ values is considered in section V-2c.

6. THE EFFECT OF STERIC INHIBITION OF RESONANCE

Studies of dipole moments indicate that adjacent methyl groups (2,6-disubstituted) substantially inhibit the resonance of dimethylamino, carboxylate, and nitro groups with the benzene ring.[41] The steric interaction of the methyls is so great that the latter groups cannot assume the coplanarity with the benzene ring required for substantial resonance interaction. Only a few systematic quantitative studies have been made of the effect of steric inhibition of resonance on the reactivity of m- and p-substituted benzene derivatives.[42] The results obtained, however, have been striking, and confirm the conclusions reached in section IV-4. More work in this area is of interest and offers considerable promise of useful results.

a. Steric inhibition of the resonance of the functional center

Goering, Rubin, and Newman [43] and Roberts and Regan [44] have measured the ionization constants of a series of 4-substituted-2,6-dimethylbenzoic acids, the former in 20% (by volume) aqueous dioxane

[39] G. W. Wheland, *The Theory of Resonance*, Chapter 7, John Wiley & Sons, New York, 1944.

[40] R. G. Pearson and R. L. Dillon, *J. Am. Chem. Soc.*, **75**, 2439 (1953).

[41] Cf. reference 39, p. 136.

[42] Cf. reference 39, p. 185.

[43] H. L. Goering, T. Rubin, and M. S. Newman, *J. Am. Chem. Soc.*, **76**, 787 (1954).

[44] (a) J. D. Roberts and C. M. Regan, *J. Am. Chem. Soc.*, **76**, 939 (1954); (b) cf. also J. D. Roberts and J. A. Yancey, *ibid.*, **73**, 1011 (1951).

and the latter in 50% (by volume) aqueous ethanol. In both, the polar effects of the 4-substituents are essentially equal to the corresponding effects in the ionization of p-substituted benzoic acids under the same conditions. That is, both the ionizations of 4-substituted-2,6-dimethylbenzoic acids and p-substituted benzoic acids follow the Hammett equation with essentially equal ρ values. This result is in excellent accord with the conclusion that the resonance effect of the functional center and the polar effects of m and p substituents are independent variables. Further, the effect accompanying the steric inhibition of resonance of the functional group may be evaluated as follows.

Both investigations show that 2,6-dimethylbenzoic acid is 0.6 log unit stronger than benzoic acid, even though methyl substituents normally retard the acidity slightly. Applying equation 11 and allowing -0.2 log unit for the polar effect of the two methyl groups (i.e., setting $(\Sigma\sigma)\rho = -0.2$), we obtain for ψ, the steric inhibition of resonance effect on the ionization, the value $+0.8$ log unit. This result indicates that the resonance of the carbonyl group with the benzene ring is approximately 1 kcal. greater in benzoic acid than in the resulting benzoate ion. Independent evidence discussed in section VIII is in good accord with this assignment. For the ionization of a "normal" series of 4-substituted-2,6-dimethylbenzoic acids, ψ remains constant and thus the simple Hammett equation 7 applies.[44b]

b. Steric inhibition of resonance of the substituent

Westheimer and Metcalf found the rate of saponification of ethyl 3,5-dimethylbenzoate to be 0.26 log unit greater than that for ethyl 3,5-dimethyl-4-dimethylaminobenzoate in 87.83% (by weight) aqueous ethanol at 55°.[45] The value of ρ for this reaction at 55° has not been directly determined, but it may be estimated with confidence from the value at 30° ($+2.498$ [21]) and the relatively precise inverse relationship between ρ and the absolute temperature shown by the rates of saponification of benzoates.[46] That is, ρ at 55° $= +2.498(303/328)$ $= +2.31$. Applying the Hammett equation to calculate a σ value for the resonance-inhibited 4-dimethylamino substituent, we obtain

$$\sigma = \frac{1}{(+2.31)} (-0.26) = -0.11$$

In a similar fashion the sigma value for the resonance-inhibited p-NO$_2$ group is found to be $+0.68$.

[45] F. H. Westheimer and R. P. Metcalf, J. Am. Chem. Soc., 63, 1339 (1941).
[46] Cf. ρ values listed by Jaffé, reference 22, pp. 201–202.

Assuming that nearly complete steric inhibition of resonance of the dimethylamino group occurs in ethyl 3,5-dimethyl-4-dimethylamino-benzoate,[47] this value of σ represents crudely the normal inductive effect of the $(CH_3)_2N$ group. The Hammett σ for this group, which includes both the resonance effect with the ring and with the carboxyl group, is -0.600. The fact that σ values calculated on the assumption of the applicability of the Hammett equation have been found to range from -1.05 to -0.21 indicates that the resonance effect of this group is quite variable.[48]

Let us now apply the crude inductive σ value for the $p\text{-}(CH_3)_2N$ group to equation 11 and estimate the total resonance effects, ψ, of this substituent in several reactions. The results for three reaction series are listed in Table III.

TABLE III

APPROXIMATE RESONANCE EFFECTS OF p-DIMETHYLAMINO GROUP IN
SEVERAL REACTIONS

Reactions	ψ, log units
1. Rate of saponification of ethyl p-dimethylamino-benzoate 87.03% (wt.) aqueous ethanol, 30° [45] (k_0 = ethyl benzoate)	-1.81
2. Rate of saponification of ethyl 3-methyl-4-di-methylaminobenzoate, 56% (wt.) aqueous acetone [37] (k_0 = ethyl 3-methyl benzoate)	-0.87
3. Rate of reaction of p-dimethylamino dimethyl-aniline with trinitrophenol methyl ether, acetone, 35° [49] (k_0 = dimethylaniline)	-0.45

The resonance effects, ψ, calculated in this manner for reactions 1 and 2 of Table III undoubtedly result from the resonance of the p-dimethylamino group both with the ring alone (the resonance polar effect) and with the functional center (the resonance effect). In reaction 3 the latter effect cannot operate (cf. description of the reaction), so that ψ approximates only the resonance polar effect in this reaction. It is thus reasonable that ψ for reaction 3 is less than that for 1 and 2 (in spite of the large ρ value for the former). It is also reasonable that ψ in the saponification reaction is reduced by the adjacent 3-methyl group which partially inhibits the resonance of the 4-dimethylamino group.[37]

[47] The fact that the σ value obtained is not the expected small positive value (cf. reference 37) indicates that the steric inhibition of resonance, though very substantial, is not quite complete.

[48] Cf. reference 22, p. 224.

[49] Cf. reference 21b, pp. 188, 189.

Since the transition state in the saponification reaction is saturated, resonance between p substituent and functional center is not possible in this state.[45] Consequently, the change in resonance energy accompanying the activation process becomes equal to a resonance energy associated with the reactant state alone. That is, neglecting the small resonance polar effect, ψ for reaction 1 gives roughly the resonance energy (2.5 kcal.) of the following interaction in the ester.[45]

It is important to recognize that this is not the total resonance energy of the dimethylamino group in the ester (approximately 8 kcal.),[50] but only the part of it (as indicated) that changes in going from the ester to the saponification transition state (cf. section VI-8c).

7. REACTIVITY AS A MATHEMATICAL FUNCTION OF STRUCTURE

The Hammett equation serves several important purposes from the standpoint of the theory of reactivity. It shows that the proportional nature of polar effects is completely general for reaction series in the benzene system which involve no steric or resonance effects. It establishes an important relationship between polar effects and structure, namely the additive relationship. The Hammett equation serves also the important purpose of demonstrating that the effect of changing structure on reactivity (in practice a discontinuous operation) can be described in a quantitative fashion in terms of a continuous mathematical function.[21b] For this reason we may speak of the polar effects of substituents as definite and characteristic functions of structure. There is the implication that steric and resonance effects are also definite functions of structure.

8. FAILURE OF THE HAMMETT EQUATION

Reactivity is greatly complicated in reaction series in which substituents are introduced close to the reaction center. This situation prevails in reactions of *ortho*-substituted benzene derivatives and most aliphatic derivatives. One, part, or all of the effects listed in sections IV-3, 4, and 5 may be involved in rates or equilibria of reactions of this type. Immediate testimony to this conclusion is furnished by

[50] Cf. reference 39, p. 69.

the fact that the Hammett-type equation 7 very generally fails completely in this class of reactions.[21b, 51] That is, the effects of substituents on the ionization of carboxylic acids, RCOOH, do not generally parallel in a quantitative fashion the corresponding effects of substituents in other reactions (R—Y + Z $\rightleftarrows$ P). Figure 2 gives a quite typical example, in which the latter reaction involves the rates of alkaline saponification of ethyl esters, $RCO_2C_2H_5$.

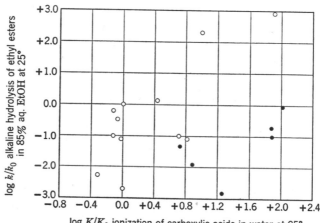

FIG. 2. Failure of Hammett-type equation for o-substituted benzene and aliphatic derivatives. Aliphatic and o-substituted derivatives are denoted by o and •, respectively.

The Hammett-type equation does not always fail for reactions in which substituents are varied near the reaction center.[52] The Brönsted catalysis law holds frequently for such cases.[52a] This law is usually expressed in the form

$$\log (k) = \alpha \log (K) + G \tag{13}$$

where k is the catalytic constant for the rate of an acid- or base-catalyzed reaction and K is the corresponding ionization constant of the acid or base. α and G are characteristic constants for the given reaction. This equation is really a Hammett-type equation, as may be seen by expressing it in the form

$$\log (k/k_0) = \alpha \log (K/K_0) = (\text{“}\rho\sigma\text{”})$$

[51] L. P. Hammett, *Physical Organic Chemistry*, pp. 204–208, McGraw-Hill Book Co., New York, 1940.

[52] Cf. (a) reference 51, pp. 215–228; (b) R. G. Pearson and R. L. Dillon, *J. Am. Chem. Soc.*, **75**, 2439 (1953); (c) G. L. O'Connor and H. R. Nace, *ibid.*, **75**, 2118 (1953).

The Brönsted equation has certain noteworthy limitations. Thus, serious departures are noted when the electronic structure of the anion differs considerably (e.g., saturated, unsaturated, unsaturated and conjugated) from that of the acid.[53] Most of these deviations are probably associated with resonance effects.

Other types of linear free-energy relationships have been noticed, but all have narrow ranges of applicability.[52, 54] Indeed, the existence of linear free relationships by no means indicates that only the polar effects of substituents are involved within a reaction series. In section VII-1, linear free-energy relationships are discussed for cases involving only the steric effects of substituents.

Let us consider Fig. 2 again. The relationship of log (K/K_0) values for the ionization of carboxylic acids, RCOOH, to the structure of R, together with the existence of the Brönsted relationship, has led most authors to conclude that the ionization is generally only a function of polar effects.[55] This conclusion is further reasonable on the basis that little if any change in structure (bond angles and distances) occurs at the carboxyl carbon in the ionization, and steric repulsions between the leaving proton and the substituents R are negligible.

Following this line of argument, the great disorder in Fig. 2 must be ascribed to variable steric and resonance effects on the ester hydrolysis rates. Basically, however, the type of results obtained in plots like Fig. 2 leave unanswered these questions:

1. Are the relative ionization constants of aliphatic or o-substituted benzene carboxylic acids (or any other reaction series that might be proposed) generally determined only by the polar effects of substituents?

2. Are polar and steric factors in a reaction series such as the alkaline hydrolysis of esters separable?

3. If so, would the resulting polar effects show any direct relationship to those in the ionization of the carboxylic acids? That is, would the variable steric effects in the ester hydrolysis reaction alter the nature of the polar effects so that no simple relationship would exist between corresponding polar effects for these two reaction series?

Very convincing answers to these questions are provided by the results of the method (discussed in the next section) of separating polar, steric, and resonance effects in the rates of hydrolysis of esters.

[53] Cf., for example, A. A. Frost and R. G. Pearson, *Kinetics and Mechanism*, p. 213, John Wiley & Sons, New York, 1953.

[54] (a) Reference 53, pp. 216–218; (b) F. W. Fitzpatrick and J. D. Gettler, *J. Am. Chem. Soc.*, *78*, 530 (1956); (c) R. L. Hill and T. I. Crowell, abstracts of papers, American Chemical Society Meeting, Cincinnati, April, 1955, p. 36N.

[55] Cf., for example, reference 30, pp. 218, 221.

V. THE SEPARATION OF POLAR, STERIC, AND RESONANCE EFFECTS IN RATES OF NORMAL ESTER HYDROLYSIS

1. HISTORICAL

In no other reaction has the effect of structure on rates been so widely and systematically investigated as in the hydrolysis of esters or acid esterifications. There is very little effect of structure on equilibrium in this reaction,[56] but both forward and reverse rates show very wide variations with structure. Qualitative comparisons of the effect of structure lead various investigators to conclude that steric hindrance,[57] polarity,[58] and resonance contribute [45] to the rates of this reaction. Generally, an observed effect has been ascribed to one or the other of these factors. A quantitative theory of reactivity must take into account the fact that polar, steric, and resonance effects may vary simultaneously as structure is varied. Apparently Kindler made the earliest attempt at a quantitative separation of steric and polar effects from rates.[59]

Kindler observed an empirical relationship between the relative rates k'/k_H' (k_H = unsubstituted) for the alkaline hydrolysis of m- and p-substituted ethyl cinnamates and the corresponding relative rates k/k_H for the similar reaction of m- and p-substituted ethyl benzoates, i.e., $\sqrt{k/k_H} = k'/k_H'$. He assumed that the failure of the relationship to hold for o substituents was the result of an "*ortho* effect" operating only in the benzoate hydrolysis. Using his empirical relationship he calculated a hypothetical "rate constant without *ortho* effect" for the o-substituted benzoates. The ratio of the hypothetical to the observed rate constant was taken as a measure of the *ortho* effect. In this manner he obtained the values: F = 1, Cl = 2, Br = 5, I = 7.5, and NO_2 = 11. This order of values corresponds to that of increasing substituent size (with NO_2 and ring coplanar). It is an order very much different from that for the o-substituted benzoate

[56] (a) Cf. reference 51, p. 213; (b) M. H. Palomaa, *Ber.*, *71B*, 480 (1938).

[57] (a) V. Meyer, *Ber.*, *27*, 510 (1894); (b) J. J. Sudborough, *J. Indian Inst. Sci.*, *8*, 89 (1925); and earlier paper in *J. Chem. Soc.*; (c) C. N. Hinshelwood and A. R. Legard, *J. Chem. Soc.*, *1935*, 587, 1588; (d) H. A. Smith and J. Burn, *J. Am. Chem. Soc.*, *66*, 1494 (1944); (e) M. S. Newman, *ibid.*, *72*, 4783 (1950).

[58] (a) C. K. Ingold, *J. Chem. Soc.*, *1931*, 2170; (b) M. Ritchie, *ibid.*, *1931*, 3112; (c) H. S. Levenson and H. A. Smith, *J. Am. Chem. Soc.*, *62*, 2324 (1940); L. P. Hammett, reference 51, p. 213.

[59] K. Kindler, *Ann.*, *464*, 278 (1928).

rate constants, i.e., $I < Br < Cl < F < NO_2$. The same order of *ortho* effect values is obtained from the ratio k_p/k_o of the rate constants for corresponding p- and o-substituted benzoates [60] (cf. section VII-3).

A short time later a more general method of separating polar and steric effects in ester hydrolysis rates was proposed by Ingold.[61] According to this proposal the ratio of rate constants (k_B/k_A), of alkaline to acidic hydrolysis of an ester is a function only of the "polarity" of substituent groups, even though both k_B and k_A are affected by "steric hindrance." The rate constants k_B and k_A refer to a given ester in a reaction series in which the structure of one component of the ester is held constant and the other varied. Solvent and temperature are the same for both k_B and k_A. Ingold's hypothesis received little test at the time, but it appears on the basis of more recent work (discussed in the following section) to be an important near-quantitative relationship which will lead to much progress in the study of structural factors determining reactivity.

2. POLAR SUBSTITUENT CONSTANTS FOR GROUPS DIRECTLY ADJOINING THE REACTION CENTER

a. Ingold-Taft equation

Following along the lines of Ingold's proposal, Taft gave the following equation for evaluating the polar effects of substituents R in the rates of normal hydrolysis of esters, RCOOR': [62]

$$\sigma^* \equiv \frac{1}{2.48} [\log (k/k_0)_B - \log (k/k_0)_A] \tag{14}$$

σ^* is a substituent constant dependent only upon the net polar effect of the substituent (corresponding to the rate constant k) relative to that for the standard of comparison (k_0, R = CH_3). σ^* is analogous to the Hammett substituent constant but expressed with an asterisk to denote its different nature and origin (i.e., $\sigma^* \neq \log$ (K/K_0) for the ionization of carboxylic acids; cf. section VI-1). B and A (subscripts) refer to otherwise identical alkaline and acidic reactions respectively, i.e., both involving the same ester, solvent, and temperature. The factor 2.48 is a constant introduced in an attempt to put the polar effects obtained in this manner on about the same scale as for the Hammett σ values.[60]

[60] R. W. Taft, Jr., M. S. Newman, and F. H. Verhoek, *J. Am. Chem. Soc.*, *72*, 4511 (1950).

[61] C. K. Ingold, *J. Chem. Soc.*, *1930*, 1032.

[62] (a) R. W. Taft, Jr., *J. Am. Chem. Soc.*, *74*, 3120 (1952); (b) *75*, 4231 (1953).

The basic assumptions of the above relationship are: (1) the relative free energy of activation ($\therefore$ log k/k_0) for those reactions may be treated as the sum of independent contributions from polar, resonance, and steric effects; (2) in corresponding acidic and alkaline reactions, the steric and resonance effects are the same; (3) the polar effects of substituents are markedly greater in the alkaline than in the acidic series.

The assumption that steric and resonance effects are the same in the otherwise identical acidic and alkaline hydrolysis rates is the heart of equation 14. This assumption appears quite reasonable on the basis of the normal ester hydrolysis mechanisms. The oxygen exchange work of Bender offers compelling evidence for the existence of a carbonyl addition intermediate in both the acidic and alkaline reactions.[63] Thus the transition state for the former differs from that for the latter by the presence of two protons. The small size of these protons and their positions with respect to the substituents make the following conclusion reasonable. The difference in the steric interactions of the substituent, R, in the corresponding transition states for the acidic and alkaline reactions is essentially a constant, independent of R.

Acidic transition state   Alkaline transition state

Since both reactions involve the same reactant, the substituent steric effects in both must therefore be very nearly equal (cf. section VI-8).

The equality of resonance effects in corresponding acidic and alkaline ester hydrolysis rates may be accounted for on the basis that the effect arises from the conjugation between the substituent and the ester function in the reactant state, both transition states being saturated with respect to such conjugation.

The Hammett reaction constants ρ for the reaction of m- or p-substituted benzoates support assumption 3. For alkaline saponifications, ρ values are in the range +2.2 to +2.8.[46] For acid-catalyzed ester hydrolysis or benzoic acid esterifications, ρ values fall in the region −0.2 to +0.5.[46] Within the precision with which these latter reactions follow the Hammett equation, ρ may generally be taken as zero.

Although the foregoing arguments stand in apparent support of this method for obtaining polar substituent constants, the nature of

[63] M. L. Bender, *J. Am. Chem. Soc.*, **73**, 1626 (1951).

the results obtained must serve as the final basis for judging the validity of the method. Before a discussion of the results is begun it is necessary to give some details of the procedure.

In the absence of complete rate data for acidic and alkaline reaction series under identical conditions, Taft was aided in evaluating σ^* values by the fact that a number of reaction series of either the acidic or alkaline type involving a different solvent, attacking reagent, or the fixed structural component R' have, wherever comparison is possible, closely equivalent log (k/k_0) values.[64] Accordingly, the average values of log (k/k_0) for these reaction series were used, a treatment which tends to reduce small specific effects and experimental errors. For the acidic reactions the rate data used were: (1) hydrolysis of ethyl esters in 70% (by volume) aqueous acetone, 25°; [65-67] (2) esterification of carboxylic acids in methanol, 25°; [68-70] (3) esterification of carboxylic acids with ethanol, 25°; [71] (4) hydrolysis of ethyl esters in 60% (by volume) aqueous acetone, 25°; [72] (5) esterification of benzoic acids in cyclohexanol.[73] For the alkaline reactions, the rate data used were: (1) hydrolysis of ethyl esters in 70% (by volume) aqueous acetone, 25°; [66] (2) hydrolysis of ethyl esters in 85% (by volume) aqueous ethanol, 25°; [74-77] (3) hydrolysis of benzyl and ethyl esters in 60%

---

[64] (a) R. W. Taft, Jr., J. Am. Chem. Soc., 74, 2729 (1952). (b) This rule appears to hold to good approximation in solvents such as those listed above. It does not hold well for the change from such solvents to pure water. Compare, for example, reference 64a and the more recent results of S. A. Bernhard and L. P. Hammett, J. Am. Chem. Soc., 75, 1798, 5834 (1953).

[65] H. A. Smith and R. R. Myers, J. Am. Chem. Soc., 64, 2362 (1942).

[66] G. Davies and D. P. Evans, J. Chem. Soc., 1940, 339.

[67] V. C. Haskell and L. P. Hammett, J. Am. Chem. Soc., 71, 1284 (1949).

[68] H. A. Smith and J. Burn, J. Am. Chem. Soc., 66, 1491 (1944); H. A. Smith, ibid., 61, 254 (1939).

[69] H. A. Smith and R. B. Hurley, J. Am. Chem. Soc., 72, 112 (1950).

[70] (a) R. J. Hartman and A. G. Gassmann, J. Am. Chem. Soc., 62, 1559 (1940); (b) R. J. Hartman and A. M. Borders, ibid., 59, 2107 (1937).

[71] B. V. Bhide and J. J. Sudborough, J. Indian Inst. Sci., 8, 89 (1925); Chem. Zentr., 97, I, 80 (1926); see also J. J. Sudborough and L. L. Lloyd, J. Chem. Soc., 75, 467 (1899); J. J. Sudborough and M. K. Turner, ibid., 101, 237 (1912).

[72] W. B. S. Newling and C. N. Hinshelwood, J. Chem. Soc., 1936, 1357.

[73] R. J. Hartman, H. M. Hoogsteen, and J. A. Moede, J. Am. Chem. Soc., 66, 1714 (1944).

[74] D. P. Evans, J. J. Gordon, and H. B. Watson, J. Chem. Soc., 1938, 1439; ibid., 1937, 1430.

[75] H. S. Levenson and H. A. Smith, J. Am. Chem. Soc., 62, 2324 (1940).

[76] C. K. Ingold and W. S. Nathan, J. Chem. Soc., 1936, 222.

[77] K. Kindler, Ann., 464, 278 (1928).

(by volume) aqueous acetone, 25°;[78] (4) methanolysis of *l*-menthyl benzoates in methanol, 30°.[60] The procedure originally used for *o*-substituted benzoates differed in detail from that (above) used for aliphatic derivatives, but the results obtained either way are essentially the same.[62a] In this chapter the results given for both the *o*-substituted benzoates and the aliphatic esters have been obtained as described above.

b. σ* values and structure

Listed in Table IV are several series of σ* values which serve particularly well to illustrate that these parameters are true measures of the polar effects of substituent groups. Given also are the corresponding values of log (k/k_0) for both the alkaline and acidic reactions. A more complete list of σ* values is given in section VI-4, Table XII.

Each of the series 1-1 to 1-4 shows results in complete accord with the qualitative English school theory of the polarities of aliphatic derivatives.[79, 80] It is quite striking that the orders of increasing σ* values are never the same as the orders of either of the log (k/k_0) values from which they are derived. In series 1-1, the order of increasing σ* values is that expected on the basis of the effect of greater electron withdrawal by a phenyl group than a methyl group or a hydrogen atom.[81] Series 1-2 shows the effect of increasing the branching on the α-carbon atom. The order of the effect of increasing electron release is $CH_3 < C_2H_5 < i\text{-}C_4H_9 < t\text{-}C_4H_9$ as shown by the increasingly more negative values of σ*. Series 1-3 shows, as anticipated by the English school theories, that increased branching on the β-carbon atom does not materially increase the electron-releasing effect. Series 1-4 shows the same order of polar effects for *o* substituents as for *p* substituents.

It is important to consider the quantitative aspects of the σ* values. Series 1-1 provides an illustration (cf. Table XII and section VI-7 for

[78] E. Tommila, *Ann. Acad. Sci. Fennicae*, Ser. *A57*, No. 13, 3 (1941); *A59*, No. 3, 3 (1942); *A59*, No. 4, 3 (1942); *C. A.*, *38*, 6171 (1944).

[79] Cf. W. A. Waters, *Physical Aspects of Organic Chemistry*, Chapter 11, D. Van Nostrand, New York, 1950.

[80] An electronegativity series for organic groups was proposed by Kharasch and coworkers [M. S. Kharasch and R. E. Marker, *J. Am. Chem. Soc.*, *48*, 3130 (1926); M. S. Kharasch and A. L. Flenner, *ibid.*, *54*, 674 (1932)] based upon the direction of splitting of unsymmetrical mercury alkyls with hydrogen chloride. Although there are a number of glaring exceptions, restricted to the phenyl and alkyl groups, the Kharasch series is in the same order as the quantitative σ* values.

[81] For a theoretical explanation of this result see A. D. Walsh, *Discussions Faraday Soc.*, *2*, 18 (1947); P. D. Bartlett, *J. Chem. Educ.*, *30*, 29 (1953); and section VI-3.

TABLE IV

σ^* VALUES AND STRUCTURE

Series 1-1

Substituent, R	σ^*	$(\log k/k_0)_B$	$(\log k/k_0)_A$
1. C_6H_5	+0.600	−1.06	−2.55
2. $(C_6H_5)_2CH$	+0.405	(−0.76)	−1.76
3. $C_6H_5CH_2$	+0.215	+0.15	−0.38
4. $C_6H_5(CH_3)CH$	+0.105	−0.93	−1.19
5. $C_6H_5CH_2CH_2$	+0.080	−0.18	−0.38
6. CH_3	0.000	0.00	0.00
7. C_2H_5	−0.100	−0.31	−0.07

Series 1-2

Substituent, R	σ^*	$(\log k/k_0)_B$	$(\log k/k_0)_A$
1. H	+0.490	+2.46	+1.24
2. CH_3	0.000	0.00	0.00
3. C_2H_5	−0.100	−0.31	−0.07
4. $i\text{-}C_3H_7$	−0.190	−0.94	−0.47
5. $(C_2H_5)_2CH$	−0.225	−2.70	−1.98
6. $t\text{-}C_4H_9$	−0.300	−2.28	−1.54

Series 1-3

Substituent, R	σ^*	$(\log k/k_0)_B$	$(\log k/k_0)_A$
1. C_2H_5	−0.100	−0.31	−0.07
2. $n\text{-}C_3H_7$	−0.115	−0.64	−0.36
3. $n\text{-}C_4H_9$	−0.130	−0.71	−0.39
4. $i\text{-}C_4H_9$	−0.125	−1.24	−0.93
5. $neo\text{-}C_5H_{11}$	−0.165	(−2.04)	−1.63
6. $i\text{-}C_3H_7$	−0.190	−0.94	−0.47
7. $s\text{-}C_4H_9$	−0.210	(−1.65)	−1.13

Series 1-4 †

o Substituent, X	σ_o^*	σ_n	$\log (k/k_0)_B$	$\log (k/k_0)_A$
1. OCH_3	−0.22	−0.10	+0.45	+0.99
2. OC_2H_5	−0.18	−0.08	+0.45	+0.90
3. CH_3	0.00	0.00	0.00	0.00
4. F	+0.41	+0.06	+1.51	+0.49
5. Cl	+0.37	+0.40	+1.10	+0.18
6. Br	+0.38	+0.40	+0.95	0.00
7. I	+0.38	+0.45	+0.75	−0.20
8. NO_2	+0.97	+0.95	+1.65	−0.75

† σ_o^* and σ values are given relative to the methyl group.

further examples) of the additive nature of σ^* values. Thus on an additive basis one obtains, from the substituents numbered 3, 6, and 7, σ^* values of $+0.430$ for the $(C_6H_5)_2CH$ group and $+0.115$ for the $(C_6H_5)(CH_3)CH$ group. The observed values of σ^* are $+0.405$ and $+0.105$, respectively. Considering the precision of the σ^* values (median deviations ±0.020 to ±0.040), the agreement is quite satisfactory.

Series 1-1 gives another illustration of the behavior expected of polar effects. The ratio of the σ^* value for the C_6H_5 group to that for the $C_6H_5CH_2$ group is $+2.7$. The ratio of the σ^* values for the $C_6H_5CH_2$ and $C_6H_5CH_2CH_2$ groups is $+2.8$. The factor of approximately 2.8 for the reduction of the inductive effect of a substituent resulting from the interposition of a methylene group is also obtained

$$\overset{O}{\underset{\|}{}} \qquad \overset{O}{\underset{\|}{}}$$

for other series, e.g., $-CH_2Cl$, $-CH_2CH_2Cl$, and CH_3C-, CH_3C-CH_2- (Table XII).[82] The fact that this ratio is obtained with the phenyl and benzyl groups confirms the assumption that the effect of the resonance of the benzene ring with the adjoining carbalkoxy group is the same on both acidic and alkaline benzoate hydrolysis rates. That is, this result indicates that a resonance-independent value of the polar effect of the C_6H_5 group is obtained by equation 14.

In series 1-2, σ^* values decrease regularly (within their precision) by about -0.10 for each successive methyl group introduced on the α-carbon atom. This result is a further illustration of the additive relationship between the σ^* values and structure. It has previously been proposed that the polar effects in the series Me, Et, i-Pr, t-Bu should bear this quantitative relationship based upon the relative ionization constants of the alkyl carboxylic acids in water at $25°$.[83] However, in the latter reaction series the polar effects are relatively small [log (K/K_0) values are 0.00, -0.12, -0.11, -0.30, respectively], and the argument is not nearly so convincing as with the σ^* values.

According to the σ^* values of series 1-2, a hydrogen atom has a very appreciably greater electron-withdrawing effect than the methyl group. This effect is about five times greater than that between a methyl and an ethyl group. A factor of about 5 also holds consistently for the effect on σ^* of interposing a methylene group between a hydrogen atom or an alkyl group and the functional center (in contrast to the

[82] (a) A factor of approximately 3 was previously proposed for the reduction of the polar effect of a substituent resulting from the interposition of a methylene group: C. G. Derick, J. Am. Chem. Soc., 33, 1181 (1911); (b) cf. also G. E. K. Branch and M. Calvin, The Theory of Organic Chemistry, p. 218, Prentice-Hall, New York, 1941.

[83] Reference 82b, p. 221.

factor of 2.8 for Cl, C_6H_5, etc., groups).   This result is most readily seen by placing the σ^* values of series 1-2 and 1-3 relative to the hydrogen atom as the standard of comparison (i.e., with $\sigma^*_{(H)} = 0.000$, $\sigma^*_{(CH_3)} = -0.490$, etc.).   The decrease in σ^* values with successive substitution of a methyl group on the β-carbon atom is regular but scarcely outside of the uncertainty of these values.

Finally, series 1-4 gives the convincing result that the polar effects of most substituents are nearly the same in the o and p positions, i.e., $\sigma_p \cong \sigma_o^*$.   The resonance polar effect of a benzoate substituent has long been considered to be equivalent in the o and p positions.   The inductive effect is also apparently similar in these two positions.   The larger value of σ_o^* than σ_p for the very electronegative fluorine atom is in accord with the closer proximity of the o position to the reaction center (cf. section V-2c).

The available ester rate data do not permit nearly so extensive an evaluation of the polar effects of substituents in the alkyl component

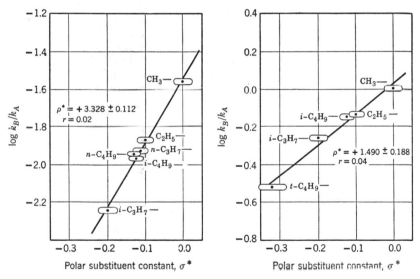

Fig. 3.   Correlation of $\log(k_B/k_A)$ values for structure variation in the alkyl component of an ester with σ^* values for acyl substituents.   Left, plot for hydrolysis of glycerate esters; right, hydrolysis of thiolacetates.

of esters (i.e., R' of RCOOR').   Where comparison can be made, however, $\log (k_B/k_A)$ terms for substituents in the alkyl component R' of a given reaction series quantitatively parallel the σ^* values for the corresponding acyl component substituents R.   This relationship is illustrated in Fig. 3 for the hydrolysis of a series of glycerate esters,

CH$_2$OHCHOHCOOR', in water at 25° [84] and for a series of thiolace-tates, CH$_3$COSR', in 43% (by weight) aqueous acetone at 30°.[85]

Although σ^* values are empirical, their approximate additive and proportional nature is typical of the behavior shown by the Hammett polar substituents constants σ and frequently by bond energies.[86] Taken as a whole it is exceedingly difficult to imagine how the kind of log (k/k_0) values involved in equation 14 could yield the results discussed in this section if the basic assumptions used to obtain σ^* values were not essentially correct. The correlations of rates and equilibria of numerous other reactions with σ^* values (discussed in section VI-1) make the conclusion that σ^* values are true measures of substituent polar effects yet more certain.

c. Comparison of σ^* and σ'.   A separation of inductive and resonance contributions to σ values

The aliphatic series polar substituent constants σ^* should be measures of the inductive effects of groups, since the effects of resonance interaction between the substituents and the reaction center have been eliminated. This conclusion is shown to be sound by a quantitative parallel (of acceptable precision) between the σ' values of Roberts and Moreland for 4-X-bicyclo-[2.2.2]-octane-1-derivatives [87] and corresponding σ^* values for X-CH$_2$ groups. The comparison of XCH$_2$ rather than X groups is dictated by the availability of data. The best value of the σ'/σ^* ratio is $+0.450$. The precision of this relationship is illustrated in Table V.

The relationship between σ' and σ^* values is very useful. It permits the calculation of many new σ' values, which in turn may be used (as discussed in section IV-5) to separate the resonance and inductive contributions to the Hammett σ values for m- and p-substituted benzene derivatives. Table V summarizes the results that have been obtained (but not previously reported).

Substituents are listed in Table V according to increasing values of $(\sigma_p - \sigma')$, the resonance polar effect. It is readily apparent that there is no relationship between the order of these values and that of the σ and σ^* values. In every case $(\sigma_p - \sigma')$ has the same sign as $(\sigma_m - \sigma')$, and the former is on the average about three times larger than the

[84] C. M. Groocock, C. K. Ingold, and A. Jackson, *J. Chem. Soc.*, *1930*, 1039.

[85] R. N. Rylander and D. S. Tarbell, *J. Am. Chem. Soc.*, *72*, 3021 (1950); J. R. Schaefgen, *ibid.*, *70*, 1308 (1948).

[86] L. Pauling, *The Nature of the Chemical Bond*, p. 47, Cornell University Press, 1944.

[87] J. D. Roberts and W. T. Moreland, Jr., *J. Am. Chem. Soc.*, *75*, 2167 (1953).

TABLE V

COMPARISON OF σ' AND σ^* VALUES. SEPARATION OF INDUCTIVE AND RESONANCE CONTRIBUTIONS TO σ VALUES

Substituent X	σ_p	σ_m	σ^* (for XCH_2—)	σ' (Calculated for X—)	$(\sigma_p - \sigma')$	$(\sigma_m - \sigma')$
OH	−0.36	0.00	+0.555	+0.25(+0.28) †	−0.61	−0.25
OCH_3	−0.27	+0.12	+0.52	+0.23	−0.50	−0.11
F	+0.06	+0.34	+1.10	+0.50	−0.44	−0.16
OC_6H_5	−0.03		+0.850	+0.38	−0.41	—
Cl	+0.23	+0.37	+1.050	+0.47	−0.24	−0.10
Br	+0.23	+0.39	+1.00	+0.45(+0.45) †	−0.22	−0.06
CH_3	−0.17	−0.07	−0.100	−0.05	−0.13	−0.02
$(CH_3)_3C$	−0.20	−0.12	−0.165	−0.07	−0.12	−0.05
I	+0.28	+0.35	+0.85	+0.38	−0.10	−0.03
C_6H_5	+0.01	+0.06 ‡	+0.215	+0.10	−0.09	−0.04
H	0.00	0.00	(0.000)	(0.00)(0.00) †	(0.00)	(0.00)
CH_2Cl	+0.18		+0.385	+0.17	+0.01	—
$N(CH_3)_3^+$	+0.86	+0.90	+1.90	+0.86	+0.00	+0.04
CN	+0.66	+0.62	+1.300	+0.59(+0.58) †	+0.07	+0.03
$(CH_3)_3Si$ ¶	−0.01 ¶	+0.08 ¶	−0.26	−0.12	+0.11	+0.04
CF_3	+0.55	+0.42	+0.92	+0.41	+0.14	0.00
CH_3SO_2	+0.73	+0.65	+1.32	+0.59	+0.14	+0.06
NO_2	+0.78	+0.71	+1.40 §	+0.63	+0.15	+0.08
$C_2H_5O_2C$	+0.52	+0.40	+0.71 ‖	+0.32(+0.30) †	+0.20	+0.08
CH_3CO	+0.52	+0.31	+0.60	+0.27	+0.25	+0.04

† σ' values given by Roberts and Moreland.

‡ The σ_m value obtained by N. N. Lichtin and H. P. Leftin, *J. Am. Chem. Soc.*, *74*, 4207 (1952), has been used.

§ Estimated as $2.8\sigma^*$ for the $NO_2(CH_2)_2$ group.

‖ Estimated as $\sigma^*/2.8$ for the CH_3O_2C group.

¶ σ values given by J. D. Roberts and C. M. Regan, *J. Am. Chem. Soc.*, *75*, 4102 (1953).

latter [the $N(CH_3)_3^+$ group is the only significant exception]. Each substituent which is electron-releasing by resonance theory (*ortho-para* directing for electrophilic aromatic substitution) has a negative value of $(\sigma_p - \sigma')$. Likewise, the groups that are electron-releasing by resonance theory have positive values of $(\sigma_p - \sigma')$. The $N(CH_3)_3^+$ group has a $(\sigma_p - \sigma')$ value that is not significantly different from zero in accord with its saturated and charged structure. The abnormal $(\sigma_m - \sigma')$ value for this substituent may be explained in terms of the very strong electron-withdrawing power of this substituent, and the nearer proximity of the m than the p position to the reaction center.[88] That is, $(\sigma_m - \sigma')$ does not represent a resonance polar effect for this substituent. The $N(CH_3)_3^+$ group is apparently the only group included in Table V for which equating the inductive effects of a substituent in the m and p positions introduces a noticeable error in the evaluation of the resonance polar effect.

[88] J. D. Roberts, R. A. Clement, and J. J. Drysdale, *J. Am. Chem. Soc.*, *73*, 2181 (1951).

Values of $(\sigma_p - \sigma')$ show that the electron-releasing conjugation of the halogens with the aromatic system decreases in the order F > Cl, Br > I. Values of $(\sigma_p - \sigma')$ are in accord with qualitative evidence obtained by Pearson and Dillon indicating that acetyl and nitro groups are better conjugating groups in the anions of pseudo acids than are methyl sulfone and nitrile groups.[89]

The more positive values of $(\sigma_p - \sigma')$ for the phenoxy group than the methoxy group, and for the acetyl group than the carbethoxy group, are results in accord with cross-conjugation theory.[90] The small positive value of $(\sigma_p - \sigma')$ for the trifluoromethyl group supports the conclusion of Roberts et al. that the following type of hyperconjugation contributes to its σ_p value.[91]

The small negative values of $(\sigma - \sigma')$ for alkyl groups are in accord with hyperconjugation theory.[92] The nearly equivalent values for methyl and t-butyl groups may be accounted for on the basis that C—C hyperconjugation and C—H hyperconjugation make nearly equivalent contributions to the Hammett σ values for these groups.[93]

The positive values of $(\sigma - \sigma')$ for the $(CH_3)_3Si$ group provide evidence of a small resonance interaction as follows:[94]

The results given in Table V present strong evidence not only that $(\sigma - \sigma')$ is a measure of the resonance polar effect but that resonance and inductive contributions to σ values are independent and separable

[89] R. G. Pearson and R. L. Dillon, *J. Am. Chem. Soc.*, 75, 2439 (1953).

[90] Reference 83, pp. 235, 268.

[91] J. D. Roberts, R. L. Webb, and E. A. McElhill, *J. Am. Chem. Soc.*, 72, 408 (1950).

[92] J. W. Baker, *Hyperconjugation*, Chapter 1, Oxford University Press, London, 1952.

[93] Cf. discussions of C—C hyperconjugation by E. Berliner and F. J. Bondhus, *J. Am. Chem. Soc.*, 68, 2355 (1946); and E. S. Lewis and E. B. Miller, *ibid.*, 75, 429 (1953).

[94] For other evidence of this interaction cf. (a) H. Soffer and T. De Vries, *J. Am. Chem. Soc.*, 73, 5817 (1951); (b) R. A. Benkeser and H. R. Krysiak, *ibid.*, 75, 2421 (1953); (c) R. A. Benkeser et al., *ibid.*, 78, 682 (1956); (d) C. Eaborn and S. H. Parker, *J. Chem. Soc.*, 1954, 939.

variables. The results also support the conclusion of Roberts and Moreland that the inductive effects on ionization are alike in kind and essentially equivalent for p substituents in benzoic acids and for corresponding 4-substituents in the bicyclooctane carboxylic acids. These conclusions are dictated by the narrow range of possible σ' values which will lead to $(\sigma_p - \sigma')$ and $(\sigma_m - \sigma')$ values which bear the relationships discussed above.

The usefulness of the separation of resonance and inductive polar effects is indicated by the σ value obtained in section IV-6b for the resonance-inhibited p-NO_2 group $(+0.68)$. It is reasonably expected that inhibition of resonance in the limit would reduce the σ value of a substituent to σ'. The difference between σ' for the NO_2 group $(+0.63)$ and the value given above is within the combined errors of the two values.

3. STERIC EFFECTS OF UNCONJUGATED GROUPS

a. Basis for steric effects

The polar effects of groups on ester hydrolysis rates having been evaluated, it is possible to use this information to obtain the substituent steric effects. It is instructive to consider first the basis on which steric effects of substituents are expected in rates of this type of reaction.

The transition state for the alkaline or the acid-catalyzed hydrolysis or esterification of normal esters is probably near tetrahedral in structure at the carbonyl carbon. Hybrid sp^2 bonding in the ester or acid requires a planar structure with bond angles of about 120°. Consequently in the activation process the coordination number of the carbonyl carbon is increased from three to four by addition of the relatively large water molecule, and the atoms or groups bonded to this carbon atom are forced from positions of approximately 120° to 109° apart. In the presence of adjacent groups of increasing steric requirements this may result in (1) increasing steric strain (potential energy) in the transition state because of repulsions between non-bonded atoms;[95a, b] (2) increasing interference of adjacent groups or atoms with the internal motions of one another (kinetic energy).[95c] Both these factors act to increase the free energy of activation. The steric effects evaluated in the following section are probably generally the composite effects of both these kinetic- and potential-energy factors.

[95] (a) H. C. Brown and G. K. Barbaras, *J. Am. Chem. Soc.*, *69*, 1137 (1947); (b) H. C. Brown, R. S. Fletcher, and R. B. Johannesen, *ibid.*, *73*, 217 (1951); (c) F. P. Price and L. P. Hammett, *ibid.*, *63*, 2387 (1941).

b. Steric substituent constants

The log (k/k_0) value for the acidic hydrolysis of ethyl chloroacetate in aqueous acetone at 25° is -0.16, and that for ethyl propionate is -0.08. In view of the similar size but very marked difference in σ^* values for the chloromethyl and ethyl groups ($+1.05$ and -0.100, respectively), the small difference in the log (k/k_0) values shows that the susceptibility of the acidic hydrolysis to polar effects is virtually zero. This same conclusion was reached in section V-2a upon the

TABLE VI

STERIC SUBSTITUENT CONSTANTS, E_s, FOR o-SUBSTITUTED BENZOATE AND ALIPHATIC SUBSTITUENTS AT 25°

o-Substituted Benzoates

Substituent	E_s	Substituent	E_s
OCH_3	$+0.99$	CH_3	0.00
OC_2H_5	$+0.90$	I	-0.20
F	$+0.49$	NO_2	-0.75
Cl	$+0.18$	C_6H_5	-0.90
Br	$+0.00$		

Aliphatic Series, RCOOR′

Substituent	Acyl Component R E_s	Substituent	Acyl Component R E_s
$H(C_6H_5*)$	$+1.24$	$i\text{-}C_4H_9$	-0.93
CH_3	0.00	$Cyclo\text{-}C_6H_{11}CH_2$	-0.98
C_2H_5	-0.07	$(CH_3)(C_2H_5)CH$	-1.13
$Cyclo\text{-}C_4H_7$	-0.06	F_3C	-1.16
CH_3OCH_2	-0.19	$Cyclo\text{-}C_7H_{13}$	-1.10
$ClCH_2,FCH_2$	-0.24	$(CH_3)(C_6H_5)CH$	-1.19
$BrCH_2$	-0.27	$t\text{-}C_4H_9$	-1.54
CH_3SCH_2	-0.34	$(C_6H_5)(C_2H_5)CH$	-1.50
ICH_2	-0.37	Cl_2CH	-1.54
$n\text{-}C_3H_7$	-0.36	$t\text{-}C_4H_9CH_2$	-1.74
$n\text{-}C_4H_9$	-0.39	$(C_6H_5)_2CH$	-1.76
$n\text{-}C_5H_{11}$	-0.40	$(CH_3)(neopentyl)CH$	-1.85
$i\text{-}C_5H_{11}$	-0.35	Br_2CH	-1.86
$n\text{-}C_8H_{17}$	-0.33	$(C_2H_5)_2CH$	-1.98
$t\text{-}C_4H_9CH_2CH_2$	-0.34	Cl_3C	-2.06
$C_6H_5OCH_2$	-0.33	$(n\text{-}C_3H_7)_2CH$	-2.11
$C_6H_5CH_2$	-0.38	$(i\text{-}C_4H_9)_2CH$	-2.47
$C_6H_5CH_2CH_2$	-0.38	$(Br)_3C$	-2.43
$C_6H_5CH_2CH_2CH_2$	-0.45	$(CH_3)_2(neopentyl)C$	-2.57
$i\text{-}C_3H_7$	-0.47	$(neopentyl)_2CH$	-3.18
$Cyclo\text{-}C_5H_9$	-0.51	$(CH_3)(t\text{-}C_4H_9)CH$	-3.33
F_2CH	-0.67	$(CH_3)_2(t\text{-}C_4H_9)C$	-3.9
$Cyclo\text{-}C_6H_{11}$	-0.79	$(C_2H_5)_3C$	-3.8
$CH_3OCH_2CH_2$	-0.77	$(CH_3)(t\text{-}C_4H_9)$	
$ClCH_2CH_2$	-0.90	(neopentyl)	-4.0

* Cf. section XIII.

basis of the Hammett ρ values for the acidic hydrolysis of m- and p-substituted benzoates. To a good approximation, therefore, relative rates in these reactions are independent of polar effects.

Except for unsaturated substituents conjugated with the carbonyl group, or for substituents which give rise to changes in attractive interaction between reactant and transition states, e.g., internal hydrogen bonding, it has been assumed that the non-polar (log k/k_0)$_A$ values are near-quantitative measures of the net potential- and kinetic-energy steric effects [96] (cf., however, section XIII). Again, the most impressive argument in favor of this assumption is the nature of the results obtained from its use. In equation form, this assumption (limited as indicated above) is given by [96]

$$\log \ (k/k_0)_A \equiv E_s \tag{15}$$

and

$$\log \ (k/k_0)_B \equiv E_s + 2.48\sigma^* \tag{15'}$$

E_s is a near-quantitative measure of the total steric effect associated with a given substituent relative to the standard of comparison. Table VI lists a number of E_s values that have been obtained in this manner. The standard of comparison in each case is the CH_3 group.

c. E_s values and structure

Qualitatively, the order of decreasing E_s values (decreasing reactivity) conforms to the order of increasing approach or overlap between the substituent and the adjacent carbalkoxy group as shown by Fisher-Hirshfelder-Taylor atom models. Thus in this reaction the order of steric interactions in the reactant molecule gives an indication of the expected order of *increase* in steric interactions accompanying the formation of the reaction transition state. This relationship does not apply to all reactions (cf. section VI-8) but follows in the present reaction from the consideration (section V-3a) of the effects produced by addition to the carbonyl carbon.

An increasing number of substitutions of alkyl, phenyl, or halogen groups on the α- or β-carbon atom leads to decreasing reactivity because of steric influences, as shown by the decreasing values of F_a. For cyclic substituents the total steric effect increases with the size of the ring (from four to seven atoms), and is markedly less than for corresponding open-chain substituents (for example, cyclopentyl compared to 3-pentyl). Similar orders of steric effects have been observed

[96] R. W. Taft, Jr., *J. Am. Chem. Soc.*, *74*, 3120 (1952).

by a number of investigators in a variety of reactions. For example, H. C. Brown and coworkers have noted the indicated order of steric effects in comparisons of the enthalpies of dissociation of the addition compounds of boron trimethyl with N-alkyl substituted amines and cyclic imines [97] (cf. section VI-10a). Arnold and coworkers from the results of a number of carbonyl reactions and of Raman frequencies have shown the steric effect of a methylene group in a five-membered ring fused to acetophenone is smaller than that of a corresponding six-membered ring.[98]

Let us investigate the quantitative aspects of the E_s values. Listed in Table VII are several series of E_s values, each illustrating the effect of a certain type of substitution. Corresponding σ^* values are included in several cases for comparison.

Series 2-1 lists E_s values for symmetrical orthobenzoate substituents with the values given relative to the fluorine atom. The quantitative parallel of these values with corresponding van der Waals radii given by Pauling [99] shows conclusively that these E_s values depend upon (and are a measure of) the effective size of substituents.

In series 2-2, the total steric effect resulting from a single substitution on the α-carbon atom increases (E_s decreases) in an order which also appears to be that of increasing effective size of the substituent. Since the substituents involved are asymmetrical XCH_2 groups, E_s values cannot strictly be compared with van der Waals radii. However, the order of decreasing E_s values is not greatly different from that of increasing van der Waals radii of X. The σ^* values bear no relation whatever to corresponding E_s values.

Series 2-3, 2-4, and 2-5 show the effect of successive methyl substitutions on the α, β, and γ positions. In both the α and β positions the E_s values indicate that the increasing total steric effect is far from additive but instead tends to telescope. In each case methyl substitution is more effective in the β than in the α position. However, in the γ position the result of a second or third methyl substitution is essentially equivalent to that for the first in either the β or the γ position.

Although series 2-3, 2-4, and 2-6 (the last shows the effect of successive α-ethyl substitution) all show the telescoping effect, series 2-7, 2-8, and 2-9 show that this result is not general. In these series the first methyl (or bromo) substitution produces over twice as large a decrease in E_s as the second one. The important conclusion to be drawn from all these results is that the regular decrease accompanying

[97] H. C. Brown and M. Gerstein, *J. Am. Chem. Soc.*, **72**, 2926 (1950).

[98] R. T. Arnold et al., *J. Am. Chem. Soc.*, **68**, 2176 (1946); **70**, 2791, 3505 (1948).

[99] Reference 86, p. 189.

TABLE VII

E_s VALUES AND STRUCTURE

Series 2-1. Steric Substituent Constants for Symmetrical Orthobenzoate Substituent and van der Waals Radii

Substituent	$E_s - E_{s(F)}$	Van der Waals Radii, A (relative to F = 1.35 A)	$\sigma^* - \sigma^*_{(F)}$
F	(0.00)	(0.00)	(0.00)
Cl	−0.31	0.45	−0.04
Br	−0.49	0.60	−0.03
CH₃	−0.49	0.65	−0.41
I	−0.69	0.80	−0.04

Series 2-2. Effect of Single α-Substitution of Group X; i.e., R = XCH₂

X	E_s for R	σ^* for R
H	(0.00)	(0.000)
CH₃	−0.07	−0.100
Cl	−0.24	+1.050
Br	−0.27	+1.000
I	−0.37	+0.85
C₂H₅	−0.36	−0.115
C₆H₅	−0.38	+0.215
i-C₃H₇	−0.93	−0.125
t-C₄H₉	−1.74	−0.165

Series 2-3. Effect of α-Methyl Substitution

R	E_s	σ^*
CH₃	0.00	0.00
C₂H₅	−0.07	−0.100
i-C₃H₇	−0.47	−0.190
t-C₄H₉	−1.54	−0.300

Series 2-4. Effect of β-Methyl Substitution

R	E_s	σ^*
C₂H₅	−0.07	−0.100
CH₃(CH₂)₂	−0.36	−0.115
(CH₃)₂CHCH₂	−0.93	−0.125
(CH₃)₃CCH₂	−1.74	−0.165

Series 2-5. Effect of γ-Methyl Substitution

R	E_s	σ^*
n-C₃H₇	−0.36	−0.115
CH₃(CH₂)C—	−0.39	−0.130
(CH₃)₂CH(CH₂)₂	−0.35	(−0.13)
(CH₃)₃C(CH₂)₂	−0.34	(−0.13)

TABLE VII (*Continued*)

E_s VALUES AND STRUCTURE

Series 2-6.   Effect of α-Ethyl Substitution

R	E_s
$C_2H_5CH_2$	-0.36
$(C_2H_5)_2CH$	-1.98
$(C_2H_5)_3C$	-3.8

Series 2-7.   Effect of α-Methyl Substitution on 3,3,3-Trimethyl Propyl Group

R	E_s
$(neo\text{-}C_5H_{11})CH_2$	-0.34
$(neo\text{-}C_5H_{11})(CH_3)CH$	-1.85
$(neo\text{-}C_5H_{11})(CH_3)_2C$	-2.57

Series 2-8.   Effect of α-Methyl Substitution on Neopentyl Group

R	E_s
$t\text{-}C_4H_9CH_2$	-1.74
$t\text{-}C_4H_9(CH_3)CH$	-3.33
$t\text{-}C_4H_9(CH_3)_2C$	-3.9

Series 2-9.   Effect of α-Bromo Substitution on Bromomethyl Group

R	E_s
$BrCH_2$	-0.27
Br_2CH	-1.85
Br_3C	-2.43

Series 2-10.   Series Substituent Constants for Cyclic Groups

R	E_s	R	E_s
$C_2H_5(CH_3)CH$	-1.13	Cyclo-C_4H_7	-0.06
$(C_2H_5)_2CH$	-1.98	Cyclo-C_5H_9	-0.51
$C_2H_5(n\text{-}C_3H_7)CH$	—	Cyclo-C_6H_{11}	-0.79
$(n\text{-}C_3H_7)_2CH$	-2.15	Cyclo-C_7H_{13}	-1.10

successive substitutions on a given carbon atom, which is characteristic of the polar substituent constants σ^*, does not hold for the steric substituent constants E_s.

Series 2-10 shows the decrease in the total steric effect produced when the end atoms of a branched alkyl group are tied down in a cyclic structure. Adjacent substituents in this table are corresponding open-chain and cyclic structures. The right-hand vertical column of this series shows the nearly regular increase in total steric effect which results with successively increasing ring size.

In section XII, the separation of the composite E_s steric effects to contributing potential- and kinetic-energy steric effects is considered. From the cases for which data are available for carrying out this separation, it has been possible to reach a number of additional conclusions concerning the relationship between structure and steric effects.

d. Conclusions resulting from the separation of polar and steric effects

A comparison of corresponding σ^* and E_s values permits the following important conclusions which arise from the separation of polar and steric effects in ester hydrolysis (or esterification) reactivity.

Polar and steric factors may be distinguished qualitatively when comparisons involve a variety of substituents such as those given in series 2-2. Here σ^* and E_s values are of completely different orders and, frequently, are of opposite sign. However, if one is confined to very similar groups (such as the alkyls), σ^* and E_s values are of the same sign and frequently the same qualitative orders (cf. series 2-3 and 2-4). Nevertheless, on the basis of quantitative values, the polar and steric effects are distinguishable. One is limited in this approach only if too narrow a range of structures is considered (cf., for example, series 2-5).

The body of the σ^* and E_s values shows that, when wide ranges of substituent polar and steric requirements are considered, the polar and steric effects in the ester hydrolysis rates are distinguishable, often qualitatively and nearly always quantitatively, as completely different functions of structure. The application of this result to the problem of structure and reactivity in other reactions forms the basis for the discussions of sections VI and VII.

4. RESONANCE EFFECTS OF α,β-UNSATURATED GROUPS

According to resonance theory, α,β-unsaturated substituents adjacent to a carbonyl group give rise to unusual stability.[100] For the phenyl substituent this resonance stabilization has been estimated to be 4–6 kcal.[101,102] Westheimer and Metcalf have pointed out that, since the transition state in the alkaline hydrolysis of an ester (by the normal mechanism) is saturated, an important factor determining the

[100] G. W. Wheland, *The Theory of Resonance*, pp. 60, 69, and 278, John Wiley & Sons, New York, 1944.

[101] G. E. K. Branch and M. Calvin, *The Theory of Organic Chemistry*, p. 284, Prentice-Hall, New York.

[102] D. M. Coulson and W. R. Crowell, *J. Am. Chem. Soc.*, *74*, 1297 (1952).

free energy of activation of a benzoate relative to a corresponding aliphatic ester is resonance.[103]

The resonance concept provides a convincing explanation of the fact that at room temperatures the rates of both alkaline and acidic hydrolysis of normal benzoate, furoate, cinnamate, crotonate, etc., esters are very appreciably slower than corresponding acetates (see Table VIII). This inertia holds in spite of the fact that the substitu-

TABLE VIII

The Effect of α,β-Unsaturated Substituents, R and R'. Rates of Hydrolysis of Esters, RCOOR'

Substituent, R	Alkaline log $(k/k_0)_B$	Acidic log $(k/k_0)_A$
CH_3	(0.00)	(0.00)
$C_6H_5CH_2$	+0.17 *	−0.38 *
C_6H_5	−1.06 *	−2.55 *
2-C_4H_3O		−2.85 [104]
3-C_4H_3O		−2.48 [104]
$C_6H_5CH=CH$	−0.86 *	−1.89 *
$CH_3CH=CH$	−1.20 *	−1.63 *
Substituent, R'		
CH_3	(0.00) *	(0.00) *
C_6H_5	+0.62 *	−0.30 *

* Data are for the reaction series taken as the standards for obtaining σ^* and E_s values; cf. section V-2.

ents involved are, relative to the methyl group, moderately strong electron-withdrawing groups. The σ^* values for phenyl, cinnamyl, and crotonyl substituents are +0.600, +0.410, and +0.360, respectively. Further, these substituents normally produce only small steric effects (cf. E_s values of Table VI) so that the substantially slower rates may not be attributed to this cause (cf. also section XIII).

When resonance between an unsaturated substituent and the carbonyl group of the ester is not possible, as in the case of a phenyl or a phenyl acetate ester, the alkaline hydrolysis is more rapid than for a corresponding methyl or acetate ester, respectively (cf. Table VIII). This is the result expected from the greater electron-withdrawing power of the phenyl group.

Using data on enthalpies and entropies of activation, it has been

[103] F. H. Westheimer and R. P. Metcalf, *J. Am. Chem. Soc.*, **63**, 1339 (1941).

[104] H. A. Smith, J. B. Conley, and W. H. King, *J. Am. Chem. Soc.*, **73**, 4633 (1951).

possible to make good estimates of the resonance effects in benzoate, cinnamate, etc., ester hydrolysis rates.   Discussion of this work is postponed until section XIII.   The results provide quantitative support for the idea that the transition states in both acidic and alkaline ester hydrolysis are saturated and that no important resonance of the functional group with α,β-unsaturated substituents is possible in this state.

5. COMPARISON OF THE MAGNITUDE OF POLAR, STERIC, AND RESONANCE EFFECTS

The powers of 10 in rates associated with a given substituent R (relative to the CH_3 group) in the alkaline hydrolysis of esters, RCOOR', are given by $2.48\sigma^*$ for the polar effect, and by E_s for the total steric effect.   In the Introduction, examples are given of the magnitude of the larger polar and steric effects.   The results discussed in section XIII permit the conclusion that the 3.8 powers of 10 decrease in the rate of acid-catalyzed hydrolysis of a benzoate relative to the corresponding formate ester results from the resonance between the phenyl and the carbalkoxy groups in the former.   Clearly, if this reaction is even crudely representative of other reactions in the aliphatic series, a theory of general reactivity that ignores either polar, steric, or resonance effects is completely inadequate.

VI. THE GENERAL NATURE OF THE PROPORTIONALITY OF POLAR EFFECTS

1. A QUANTITATIVE RELATIONSHIP

The simple qualitative generalization that like substances tend to react similarly and that similar changes in structure produce similar changes in reactivity generally becomes quantitative within reaction series of most m- and p-substituted benzene derivatives.   The fact that only the polar effects of substituents affect rate or equilibrium is responsible.

In section IV-8 the question was raised whether a simple relationship of this kind holds for the polar effects within a reaction series in which steric and resonance effects are also variable.   Linear free-energy relationships do not generally hold between two such reaction series, but what relationship exists between the corresponding polar effects [separated by a suitable means from log (k/k_0) values]?   Do the variable steric and resonance effects destroy the simple approximate proportionality between corresponding polar effects? The results of section V may be used to provide an answer to this question. The answer is, quite convincingly, no! A simpler result could not have been hoped for.

Rates and equilibria for reactants R—Y in a wide variety of reaction types fit with relatively good precision an equation, analogous to that of Hammett with respect to the proportionality of polar effects, namely,[105]

$$\log (k/k_0) = \sigma^* \rho^* \tag{16}$$

where σ^* is the polar substituent constant for the group R relative to the standard CH_3 group. ρ^* is a constant giving the susceptibility of a given reaction series to polar substituents. Its value depends upon the nature of the reaction center Y, the attacking reagent, etc.

Certain reactions of o-substituted benzene derivatives, o-X–C_6H_4–Y, also follow equation 16. For o substituents, σ^* and k values are relative to the unsubstituted (X = H) derivative (unless otherwise noted in Table IX).

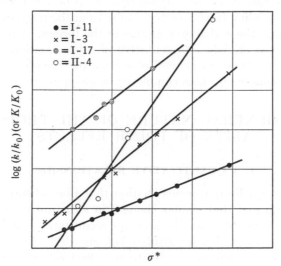

FIG. 4. Typical examples of reactions following equation 16. Numbers following symbols refer to reactions as listed in Table IX. The positions of both ordinate and abscissa are arbitrary. Unit scale of the former is 1 log unit, and of the latter is 0.5 polarity unit.

Table IX summarizes the reactions following equation 16. Figure 4 illustrates several typical examples. Given in Table IX are descrip-

[105] R. W. Taft, Jr., J. Am. Chem. Soc., 75, 4231 (1953).

TABLE IX

REACTION CONSTANTS ρ^* FROM EQUATION 16

I. Aliphatic Derivatives, RY

Reaction	ρ^*	r	$\log k_0$ (in sec.$^{-1}$)	Substituents
1. R. [log $(k/k_0)_B$ − log $(k/k_0)_A$] for the hydrolysis of esters, $RCO_2C_2H_5$ [1]	(+2.480)	—	—	Cf. Table XII
2. R. log (k_B/k_A) for the methanolysis of *l*-menthyl esters, $RCO_2C_{10}H_{19}$, methanol, 30° [2]	+2.186 ± 0.115	0.23	—	3; 7; 10; 14; 21; 25; 34; 36; 39
3. E. Ionization of carboxylic acids, RCOOH, water, 25° [3]	+1.721 ± 0.025	0.06	−4.65	5a; 10; 14; 18; 21; 24; 27; 31; 34; 36; 37; 38; 39; 42; 45a; 47 [4,5]
4. R. Hydrolysis of diethyl monosubstituted acetals, $RCH(OC_2H_5)_2$, acid-catalyzed, 50% (wt.) aq. dioxane, 25° [6]	−3.652 ± 0.085	0.08	−0.733 $R_0 = CH_3CH_2$	10; 18; 19; 27; 31; 36; 38
5. R. Hydrolysis of diethyl monosubstituted acetonals, $RCCH_3(OC_2H_5)_2$, conditions same as in 4 [6]	−3.541 ± 0.176	0.19	+3.081 $R_0 = CH_3CH_2$	10; 11; 14; 18; 27; 36
6. R. Reaction of diphenyldiazomethane with carboxylic acids, RCOOH, ethanol, 25° [7]	+1.175 ± 0.043	0.06	−1.937	7; 10; 15; 18; 21; 23; 24; 27; 31; 34; 39; 47 [4]
7. R. Alkaline hydrolysis of acetatopentammine cobalt (III) ions, $[Co(NH_3)_5X]^{+2}$, where $X = RCO_2^-$, water, 25° [8]	+0.786 ± 0.023	0.08	−3.213	1; 3; 10; 18; 34; 36; 42; 47
8. E. Acidities of alcohols, RCH_2OH, isopropyl alcohol, 27° [9]	+1.364 ± 0.027	0.09	−0.07	14; 17; 19; 21; 34; 36; 37; 42 [10]
9. R. Alkaline hydrolysis of ethyl 4-X-bicyclo-[2.2.2]-octane-1-carboxylates, $XC_8H_{12}CO_2C_2H_5$, 87.83% (wt.) aq. ethanol, 30° [11]	+0.975 ± 0.042	0.04	−4.536	7; 11; 18; 34 [12]
10. R. Sulfation of alcohols, ROH, equimolar sulfuric acid, initial $H_2O/H_2SO_4 = 1.290$, 25° [13]	+4.600 ± 0.149	0.03	−6.139	34; 36; 38; 39; 42
11. R. Catalysis of dehydration of acetaldehyde hydrate by carboxylic acids, RCOOH, acetone, 25° [14]	+0.801 ± 0.015	0.02	−0.108	3; 7; 10; 11; 17; 21; 22; 23; 24; 27; 31; 34; 36 [15]
12. R. Catalysis of iodination of acetone by carboxylic acids, RCOOH, water, 25° [16]	+1.143 ± 0.022	0.02	−7.65	10; 18; 24; 34; 36
13 R. Catalysis of decomposition of nitramide by carboxylate ions, $RCOO^-$, water, 15° [17]	−1.426 ± 0.035	0.07	−0.373	3; 10; 21; 27; 34; 36; 47 [4]

TABLE IX (*Continued*)

REACTION CONSTANTS ρ^* FROM EQUATION 16

Reaction	ρ^*	r	$\log k_0$ (in sec.$^{-1}$)	Substituents
14. *R.* Catalysis of depolymerization of dimeric dihydroxyacetone by carboxylate ions, RCOO$^-$, water, 25° [18]	-1.362 ± 0.069	0.07	-2.180	10; 21; 27; 34; 47
15. *R.* Thermal decomposition of cholesteryl xanthates, RSCSOC$_{27}$H$_{45}$, 176° [19]	$+1.438 \pm 0.092$	0.05	-3.634	23; 27; 34; 36 [20]
16. *R.* Hydrolysis of formals, H$_2$C(OR)$_2$, acid-catalyzed, water, 25° [21]	-4.173 ± 0.150 [22b]	0.05	-4.570	34; 36; 37; 38; 39; 42; 44
17. *R.* Bromination of ketones, C$_6$H$_5$COCHR$_1$R$_2$, base-catalyzed, water, 25° [22a]	$+1.590 \pm 0.079$	0.06	-4.628	34, 34; 21, 42; 21, 36; 21, 34; 21, 21
18. *R.* Vapor phase reaction of alkyl chlorides, RCl, with sodium [23]	-2.480 ± 0.174	0.05	—	34; 36; 37; 42; 47 [24]
19. *R.* $\log (k_B/k_A)$ for hydrolysis of glycerate esters, CH$_2$OHCHOHCO$_2$R, water, 25° [25]	$+3.328 \pm 0.112$	0.02	—	34; 36; 37; 38; 39; 42
20. *R.* $\log (k_B/k_A)$ for hydrolysis of thiolacetates, CH$_3$COSR, 43% (wt.) aq. acetone, 30° [26]	$+1.490 \pm 0.188$	0.04	—	34; 36; 38; 42; 47
21. *E.* [$\log (K/K_0)$ + 0.393 (n-6)] for hydrogenation of aldehydes and ketones, R$_1$R$_2$C=O + H$_2$ ⇌ R$_1$R$_2$HCOH, toluene, 60° (K_0, acetone, $n = 6$) [27]	$+4.681 \pm 0.065$	0.35	3.96	21, 34; 18, 34; 23, 34; 21, 38; 21, 47; 27, 34; 34, 34; 34, 36; 34, 42; 34, 40; 36, 36; 27, 27; 38, 38; 34, 47; 37, 37; 42, 42 [4]
22. *E.* $\Delta\Delta H_d$, dissociation of trimethylboron addition compounds with straight-chain primary amines, RNH$_2$, in kcal. [28]	-7.26 ± 0.21	0.10 kcal.	17.4 kcal.	21; 34; 36; 37; 39
23. *E.½.* Polarographic reduction of α-bromoacetic acids, R$_1$R$_2$C(Br)CO$_2$H 9.5% (vol.) aq. ethanol, pH = 1.1, 0° [29]	-0.397 ± 0.012	0.012 volt	-0.300 volt	21, 21; 21, 34; 21, 26; 34, 34; 34, 36; 36, 36
24. *R.* [$\log (k/k_0)_B$ − $\log (k/k_0)_A$] for the hydrolysis of lactate or acetate esters, R'CO$_2$R, H$_2$O or aq. acetone, 25° [34]	$+1.465 \pm 0.129$	0.11		13; 17; 24; 34 [35]
25. *R.* Acid-catalyzed hydrolysis of monosubstituted ethylene oxides, RHC——CH$_2$, \\O aq. HClO$_4$ at $H_0 = 0,0$°C [36]	-1.827 ± 0.079	0.07	-2.521	10; 11; 18; 21; 34
26. *R.* Solvolysis of secondary carbinyl p-Br-toluene sulfonates, *cis*-2-R-cyclohexyl-OBs, and R$_1$R$_2$CHOBs, acetic acid, 70–75° [37]	-3.49	0.17		10; 11; 34; 47. 34, 34; 34, 36; 34, 42; 34, 47; 34, 41; 34, 37; 34, 38 [38,39]

TABLE IX (Continued)

REACTION CONSTANTS ρ^* FROM EQUATION 16

Reaction	ρ^*	r	$\log k_0$ (in sec.$^{-1}$)	Substituents
27. R. Solvolysis of tertiary alkyl halides, $R_1R_2R_3CCl$ (and a few bromides), 80% aq. ethanol, 25° [37]	−3.29	0.22		10, 34, 34; 10, 34, 36; 18, 34, 34; 18, 36, 36; 34, 34, 34; 34, 34, 36; 34, 36; 34, 36, 36; 36, 36, 36; 34, 34, 37; 34, 34, 42; 34, 34, 39; 34, 34, 47; 34, 42, 42 [39,40]
28. R. Solvolysis of primary alkyl toluene sulfonates, RCH_2OTs, ethanol, 100° [37]	−0.742	0.03		7; 19; 27; 36; 37; 39 [41]
29. R. Displacement of primary alkyl bromides, RCH_2Br, by thiophenolate ion, methanol, 20° [37]	−0.606	0.02		8; 10; 11; 36; 37 [42]

II. o-Substituted Benzene Derivatives

Reaction	ρ^*	r	$\log k_0$ (in sec.$^{-1}$)	Substituents
1. R. [$\log (k/k_0)_B$ − $\log (k/k_0)_A$] for hydrolysis and esterification of esters [1]	(+2.480)	—	—	Cf. Table XII
2. E. Ionization of benzoic acids, water, 25° [3]	+1.787 ± 0.13	0.15	−3.69	1; 3; 5; 6; 7; 8; 9 [30]
3. R. Catalysis of dehydration of acetaldehyde hydrate by benzoic acids, acetone, 25° [14]	+0.771 ± 0.019	0.02	+0.336	1; 3; 4; 6; 9
4. E. Ionization of anilinium ions, water, 25° [31]	+2.898 ± 0.15	0.19	+0.61 $X_0 = CH_3$	1; 3; 6; 7; 10 [30,32]
5. R. Benzanilide formation, anilines with benzoyl chloride, benzene, 25° [33]	+2.660 ± 0.22	0.28	−1.861 $X_0 = CH_3$	1; 3; 6; 9 [30]

REFERENCES FOR TABLE IX

[1] Cf. section V-2a for conditions and literature references.
[2] W. A. Pavelich and R. W. Taft, Jr., unpublished data.
[3] (a) Landolt-Börnstein, *Physikalisch-Chemische Tabellen*, Springer Verlag, Berlin, 1936, Vol. III, p. 2120; (b) J. F. J. Dippy, *Chem. Revs.*, 25, 151 (1939); (c) reference 14; (d) reference 83, p. 224; (e) A. L. Henne and C. J. Fox, *J. Am. Chem. Soc.*, 76, 479 (1954); (f) M. Kilpatrick and J. G. Morse, *ibid.*, 75, 1854 (1953); (g) E. Gelles, *ibid.*, 75, 6201 (1953); (h) L. Sommer et al, *ibid.*, 71, 1509 (1949).
[4] Equation 16 fails for α,β-unsaturated substituents. For the criterion of failure cf. section VI-5.
[5] Equation 16 fails for substituents of the type $(C_2H_5)_2CX$, where X is H or CO_2H.
[6] M. M. Kreevoy and R. W. Taft, Jr., *J. Am. Chem. Soc.*, 77, 5590 (1955).
[7] R. W. Taft, Jr., and D. J. Smith, *J. Am. Chem. Soc.*, 76, 305 (1954).
[8] F. Basolo, J. G. Bergmann, and R. G. Pearson, *J. Phys. Chem.*, 56, 22 (1952).
[9] J. Hine and M. Hine, *J. Am. Chem. Soc.*, 74, 5266 (1952).
[10] Dihydroxyalcohols do not follow equation 16.
[11] J. D. Roberts and W. T. Moreland, Jr., *J. Am. Chem. Soc.*, 75, 2167 (1953).
[12] σ^* values used are for XCH_2 groups.
[13] N. C. Deno and M. S. Newman, *J. Am. Chem. Soc.*, 72, 3852 (1950).
[14] R. P. Bell and W. C. E. Higginson, *Proc. Roy. Soc. London*, 197A, 141 (1949).
[15] Equation 16 fails for substituent 47.
[16] H. M. Dawson, G. V. Hall, and A. Key, *J. Chem. Soc.*, 1928, 2849.
[17] See A. A. Frost and R. G. Pearson, *Kinetics and Mechanism*, p. 222, John Wiley & Sons, New York, 1953.

REFERENCES FOR TABLE IX (Continued)

[18] R. P. Bell and E. C. Baughan, J. Chem. Soc., 1937, 1947.

[19] G. L. O'Connor and H. R. Nace, J. Am. Chem. Soc., 75, 2118 (1953).

[20] The $(C_6H_5)_3C$ group has been included using a σ^* value of $+0.65$ based upon the additive relationship of σ^* values.

[21] A. Skrabal and H. H. Eger, Z. physik. Chem., 122, 349 (1926).

[22] (a) D. P. Evans and J. J. Gordon, J. Chem. Soc., 1938, 1434. (b) A statistical factor of 2 has been used in evaluating the value of ρ^*.

[23] H. V. Hartel, N. Meer, and M. Polanyi, Z. physik. Chem., B19, 139 (1932).

[24] Equation 16 fails for substituents 37 and 38.

[25] C. M. Groocock, C. K. Ingold, and A. Jackson, J. Chem. Soc., 1930, 1057.

[26] P. N. Rylander and D. S. Tarbell, J. Am. Chem. Soc., 72, 3021 (1950); J. R. Schaefgen, ibid., 70, 1308 (1948).

[27] H. Adkins, R. M. Elofson, A. G. Rossow, and C. C. Robinson, J. Am. Chem. Soc., 71, 3622 (1949).

[28] H. C. Brown, M. D. Taylor, and S. Sujishi, J. Am. Chem. Soc., 73, 2464 (1951).

[29] J. M. Markowitz, M.S. thesis, Pennsylvania State University, June, 1952; unpublished data of P. J. Elving and J. M. Markowitz.

[30] Equation 16 fails for the unsubstituted benzene derivative, i.e., substituent 4. This result indicates that there is a substantial resonance or steric effect between the unsubstituted benzene derivative and any of the o-substituted derivatives listed. Within the series of o substituents indicated, however, steric or resonance effects must be nearly constant (cf. section VI-5).

[31] M. Kilpatrick and C. A. Arenberg, J. Am. Chem. Soc., 75, 3812 (1953).

[32] The σ^* value used for the NO_2 group is the Hammett value for p-NO_2 used for phenol and aniline derivatives.

[33] F. J. Stubbs and C. Hinshelwood, J. Chem. Soc., 1949, S71.

[34] (a) K. H. Vogel and J. C. Warner, J. Am. Chem. Soc., 75, 6072 (1953); (b) A. A. Colon, K. H. Vogel, and J. C. Warner, ibid., 75, 6074 (1953); (c) A. L. Henne and R. L. Pelley, ibid., 74, 1426 (1952).

[35] Substituents $CH_3OCH_2CH_2$, $HOCH_2CH_2$, and $CF_3C(CH_3)H$ were also included in the correlation. The σ^* values for the first two were taken as $(1/2.8)$ σ^* for substituents 19 and 18, respectively. σ^* ($+0.820$) for the latter was obtained by the additivity rule. This correlation is not followed by ordinary alkyl groups (substituents 36, 37, 38, 39, 42, 44). These substituents define a line of good precision but with $\rho^* \cong +4.1$. Although no explanation can be offered, it is striking that the ratio of these ρ^* values is 2.8, and that the ρ^* value for the former groups is essentially the same as that for alkyl groups in reaction 20.

[36] F. A. Long and J. G. Pritchard, abstracts of papers, American Chemical Society Meeting, Minneapolis, September 14, 1955; the author is indebted to Professor Long for permission to report this correlation.

[37] I am indebted to Dr. A. Streitwieser, Jr., for permission to report the correlations of reactions 26, 27, 28, 29, in advance of his publication, J. Am. Chem. Soc., forthcoming. Reference to the original data will be found in this journal.

[38] Correlation fails for most trans-2-substituted cyclohexyl brosylates and secondary alkyl brosylates with neighboring phenyls. Deviations may be attributed to anchimeric assistance (cf. section VI-10c).

[39] These correlations neglect hyperconjugation effects which are apparently relatively small compared to the polar effects.

[40] Correlation generally fails for substituents with neighboring bromine or iodine, or for substituents with very large steric requirements. Deviations may be attributed to anchimeric assistance or steric facilitation (cf. section VI-10c).

[41] σ^* for substituent $CH_3OCH_2CH_2$ obtained as in footnote 35. Correlation fails for substituent 34, indicating that steric requirements of substituents must be very similar for correlation to hold.

[42] Correlation expected to fail for substituents of widely varying steric requirements.

tions of the reactions, a notation as to whether data are for rates or equilibria (R or E, respectively), the reaction constant ρ^* and its probable error (obtained by methods of least squares), the probable error of the fit of a single observation r, and a listing of the substituents that fit the correlation. The last is given by numbers referring to those assigned the substituents in Table XII. The median probable error of Table IX is 0.09 in the logarithm or 12% in the value of the rate constant. The correlations cover maximum variation in the constants, k or K, of six powers of 10.

Reaction series I-3 and II-2 and the Brönsted catalysis law require reaction series I-11, 12, 13, 14, and II-3 to follow equation 16. No attempt has been made to include in Table IX all reactions following the Brönsted relation. Two reaction series of each the acid and the base type have been included in Table IX.

Although analogous to the Hammett equation 7 in respect to the proportionality of polar effects, equation 16 is a distinctly different kind of relationship, and provides an additional result of theoretical importance (cf. section VI-6). The Hammett equation is a linear free-energy relationship; i.e., it involves linear log-log relationships between rates and equilibria for reaction series within which steric factors are essentially constant. Equation 16 is not a linear free-energy relationship, for σ^* values are not free-energy measures but rather polar-energy measures (cf. section XII) which have been separated from free energies. Equation 16 is, therefore, properly termed a linear free-energy-polar-energy relationship.

It must be emphasized that equation 16 is implied to fail (cf. section VI-5) for those reaction series within which there are substantial steric and resonance effects on the rate constants. Since this situation frequently prevails for reaction series involving bulky and unsaturated substituents at the reaction center, equation 16 has much greater limitations than the Hammett equation.

2. USE OF LINEAR FREE-ENERGY-POLAR-ENERGY RELATIONSHIPS FOR PREDICTION AND MECHANISM PURPOSES

a. Prediction of rates and equilibria

Equation 16 can be used to predict rate and equilibrium constants in the same fashion and to about the same precision that equation 7 can (as illustrated in section IV-1). The available values of σ^* and ρ^* imply that over a thousand rate and equilibrium constants are encompassed at the present writing by this relationship. Since the reactions involved are those in which substituents directly adjoin the reaction center, there is an important uncertainty in the use of equation 16 for prediction purposes.

The condition under which equation 16 holds is that all effects other than polar must remain nearly constant within the given reaction series (this condition is discussed fully in section VI-5). The fact that certain substituents in a reaction series are found to follow equation 16 does not imply that all substituent effects will be correlated by the equation. In using equation 16 one must do more than investigate a few substituents of sufficiently differing polarities to establish an accurate value of ρ^*. In addition, substituents of wide enough ranges of steric and resonance requirements to establish the complete generality of equation 16 must be investigated. If the $\sigma^*\rho^*$ correlation holds for certain types of substituents but fails for others, its use should be judiciously restricted to the former cases (cf. section VI-10).

b. Reaction mechanism

The same uses of ρ^* values as those discussed previously for ρ values are implied. Thus, for example, the ρ^* value of $+4.60$ for the rate of sulfation of alcohols (reaction 1 of Table IX) excludes a mechanism for which the rate-determining step is carbonium-ion formation.[95] Further, the larger value of ρ^* (nearer to that for the ionization of carboxylic acids) for the rates of reaction of diphenyldiazomethane with carboxylic acids in ethanol at $25°$ than for the catalysis of the dehydration of acetaldehyde hydrate by carboxylic acids in acetone at $25°$ (cf. Table IX) suggests that the transition state in the latter reaction has appreciably less anion character than the former.[106]

The quantitative prediction of ρ^* from theory has not been considered and remains an endeavor for the future.

The required condition of only variable polar effects within a reaction series gives equation 16 an additional valuable use for investigating mechanisms. This special condition for reactions involving substituents adjacent to the reaction center is permitted by only certain types of reaction mechanisms (see discussion in section VI-8). To take an extreme example, the fact that the ionization of carboxylic acids in water (reactions I-3 and II-2 of Table IX) follows equation 16 immediately excludes the possibility that these substances are present in solution as hydrates (a water molecule added across the carboxyl group) which lose both H_2O and H^+ on ionization. If this were the case, steric interactions of substituents would be variable between the reactant and product states and there would be important steric effects on the ionizations. Following a similar line of reasoning, the fact that the rates of alkaline hydrolysis of acetatopentammine cobalt (III) ions (reaction I-7 of Table IX) follow equation 16 shows that hydroxide ion attacks cobalt (III) directly and does not add to the carbonyl group of the acetate groups in the complex.[107]

The failure of equation 16 for a particular substituent (or type of substituent) may result from a change in reaction mechanism. It has been noted [108] that the departure from equation 16 of the polar param-

[106] Cf. J. E. Leffler, *Science, 117*, 340 (1953).
[107] F. Basolo, J. G. Bergmann, and R. G. Pearson, *J. Phys. Chem., 56*, 22 (1952).
[108] R. W. Taft, Jr., *J. Am. Chem. Soc., 75*, 4237 (1953).

eter, log (k_B/k_A), for the t-butyl group in the hydrolysis of acetate esters is consistent with the evidence for a carbonium-ion type mechanism in the acid-catalyzed hydrolysis of t-butyl esters.[109, 110] Similarly, the fact that equation 16 is followed by reaction I-20 (Table IX) is in accord with the evidence that the normal mechanism is involved in the acid-catalyzed hydrolysis of t-butyl thiolacetate.[110]

3. CORRELATION OF PHYSICAL PROPERTIES BY EQUATION 16. ELECTRONEGATIVITY AND ELECTRON WITHDRAWING POWER

A number of physical properties are correlated by equation 16. These correlations support σ^* values as quantitative polarity measures. Table X summarizes the correlations that have been noted.

Calculated and observed values for the dipole moments of hydrogen and alkyl iodides in carbon tetrachloride at 20° and of aliphatic amines in benzene at 25° are given in Table XIa to illustrate the nature of these correlations. Deviations of the experimental values and those calculated by the correlation are not on the average outside of uncertainties of the former. The correlations of series 7 of Table X are better described as qualitative than quantitative.

Mulliken has pointed out that the intrinsic power of an atom in a molecule to attract electrons is obtained from the average of the ionization potential (I) and the electron affinity (A).[111] He has also stated that this *intrinsic electronegativity*, as we shall refer to it, depends strongly upon the valence state of the atom.[111] The electronegativities obtained by Pauling from bond energies by the additivity principle [112] were shown in a practical sense to be measures of the intrinsic electronegativity for monovalent atoms in their ground electronic state. This

is the quantity $\dfrac{I + A}{130}$ that gives approximately Pauling's electronegativity. An important difference in the intrinsic electronegativity and the electronegativity depends upon the degree of hybridization of the bonding orbital of the atom in a molecule.

[109] S. G. Cohen and A. Schneider, *J. Am. Chem. Soc.*, *63*, 3382 (1941); A. A. Colon, K. H. Vogel, and J. C. Warner, *ibid.*, *75*, 6074 (1953).

[110] P. N. Rylander and D. S. Tarbell, *J. Am. Chem. Soc.*, *72*, 3021 (1950).

[111] R. S. Mulliken, *J. Chem. Phys.*, *2*, 782 (1934); *ibid.*, *3*, 573 (1935); *ibid.*, *J. Phys. Chem.*, *41*, 318 (1937); also cf. W. Moffitt, *Proc. Royal Soc. London*, *202A*, 548 (1950), for calculations of intrinsic electronegativities for valence states other than the ground state of the atom.

[112] L. Pauling, *The Nature of the Chemical Bond*, p. 64, Cornell University Press, Ithaca, N. Y., 1944.

TABLE X

Physical Parameters Correlated by Equation 16

Description	Equation	r	Substituent
1. Dipole moments (debyes) of RCl, vapor state, 290 to 400°K. [1]	$\mu = (-1.416 \pm 0.069)\sigma^* + 1.823$	0.05 debye	21; 34; 36; 37; 38; 39; 42; 44; 47
2. Dipole moments (debyes) of RI, carbon tetrachloride, 20° [1]	$\mu = (-2.200 \pm 0.067)\sigma^* + 1.611$	0.05 debye	21; 34; 36; 37; 38; 42; 44; 45; 47
3. Dipole moments (debyes) of amines $R_1R_2R_3N$, benzene, 25° [1]	$\mu = (+0.530 \pm 0.019)\Sigma\sigma^* + 0.920$	0.02 debye	21, 21, 34; 21, 21, 36; 21, 21, 39; 21, 21, 44; 21, 21, 47; 21, 34, 34; 21, 36, 36; 34, 34, 34; 36, 36, 36
4. Dipole moments (debyes) of alkyl cyanides, RCN, benzene, 25° [1]	$\mu = (-0.444 \pm 0.024)\sigma^* + 3.51$	0.01 debye	34; 36; 37; 39; 42; 47
5. Bond energy (e.v./molecule) of alkyl-hydrogen bonds (D_{R-H}) [2]	$D = (+1.800 \pm 0.166)\sigma^* + 4.43$	0.04 e.v.	34; 36; 37; 42; 47
6. Quadrupole coupling constants of alkyl-chlorine bonds RCl, (eq. Q) av., 20°K., mc.[3]	(eq. Q) = $(+20.32 \pm 1.08)\sigma^* + 68.3$	0.2 mc.	34; 36; 37; 42; 47
7. Carbon-oxygen stretching spectra for alcohols, ROH (8–10), in wave no.[4a,5]	$\sigma = (-229 \pm 35)\sigma^* + 1049$	22 cm.$^{-1}$	27; 34; 36; 37; 38; 39; 41; 42; 44; 45; 46; 47 [4b]

References for Table X

[1] Taken from L. G. Wasson, *Tables of Electric Dipole Moments*, The Technology Press, M.I.T., 1948.

[2] D. P. Stevenson, unpublished.

[3] R. Livingston, *J. Chem. Phys.*, 19, 1434 (1951); 20, 1170 (1952).

[4] (a) H. H. Zeiss and M. Tsutsui, *J. Am. Chem. Soc.*, 75, 897 (1953); (b) in obtaining this correlation, the substituents Me(i-Pr)CH, (i-Pr)$_2$CH, (t-Bu)$_2$CH, and Me(Et)(i-Bu) were also included. The σ^* values were estimated for these groups on the basis of the additivity principle. The precision of the fit for this correlation is not as good as others. The correlation is generally good qualitatively but leaves much to be desired quantitatively. There appear to be trends in certain cases opposite to the predicted. For example, for the class of substituents $C_6H_5(R)CH$, where R is 23, 25, 30, and 34, cm.$^{-1}$ fits with reasonably good precision a correlation of opposite sign to that given above.

[5] R. T. Blickenstaff and E. C. Coolidge, Abstracts of Papers Presented before the Division of Organic Chemistry, American Chemical Society Meeting, Minneapolis, Minn., Sept. 11–16, 1955, p. 38–0, have reported a correlation between the infra absorption frequencies of diethylphosphonates and σ^* values.

Dailey and Shoolery have recently proposed a scale of electronegativities of substituent groups obtained from shifts in the proton nuclear magnetic resonance spectra of ethyl and methyl derivatives.[113] It was strikingly demonstrated that the electronegativities obtained in

[113] B. P. Dailey and J. N. Shoolery, *J. Am. Chem. Soc.*, 77, 3977 (1955).

TABLE XIa

CORRELATION OF DIPOLE MOMENTS BY σ^* VALUES

RI	μ Calculated, debyes	μ Experimental, debyes	d	Amine	μ Calculated, debyes	μ Experimental, debyes	d
H	0.53	0.50	0.03	CH_3NH_2	1.47	1.46	0.01
CH_3	1.61	1.56	0.05	$C_2H_5NH_2$	1.39	1.37	0.02
C_2H_5	1.82	1.89	0.07	$n\text{-}C_4H_9NH_2$	1.37	1.40	0.03
$i\text{-}C_3H_7$	2.02	2.08	0.06	$s\text{-}C_4H_8NH_2$	1.33	1.28	0.05
$n\text{-}C_3H_7$	1.86	1.92	0.06	$t\text{-}C_4H_9NH_2$	1.26	1.29	0.03
$i\text{-}C_4H_9$	1.88	1.92	0.04	$(CH_3)_2NH$	1.18	1.17	0.01
$s\text{-}C_4H_9$	2.07	2.10	0.03	$(C_2H_5)_2NH$	1.08	1.13	0.05
$(C_2H_5)_2CH-$	2.11	2.09	0.02	$(CH_3)_3N$	0.86	0.92	0.06
$t\text{-}C_4H_9$	2.27	2.20	0.07	$(C_2H_5)_3N$	0.77	0.79	0.02
			Av. 0.05				Av. 0.03

this manner are generally essentially equal to the electronegativity (of the Pauling scale) of the first atom in the group, irrespective of its degree of hybridization. However, their scale bears little relationship to the σ^* values for corresponding groups (cf. Table XIb).

TABLE XIb

CONTRAST BETWEEN ELECTRON-WITHDRAWING POWER OF GROUPS (σ^*) AND THEIR ELECTRONEGATIVITY

Group	Electron-Withdrawing Power, σ^*	Electronegativity of D and S
CN	+3.64 [a]	2.52
COOH	+2.94 [a]	2.57
I	+2.38 [a]	2.68
C_6H_5	+0.60	2.70
Br	+2.80 [a]	2.94
Cl	+2.94 [a]	3.19
OH	+1.55 [a]	3.51
F	+3.08 [a]	3.93

[a] Obtained from σ^* values of XCH_2 groups by multiplying by 2.8 (cf. section V-2b).

On the basis of the correlations of σ^* values with dipole moments, which imply a relationship to the charge distribution in the molecule, the σ^* values are defined as measures of the inductive electron-withdrawing power of an atom or group of atoms in a molecule. It appears, as will be established by examples in the discussion to follow, that the environmental factors listed contribute appreciably to the electron-withdrawing power: (a) the *intrinsic electronegativities* of the atoms in the group, especially of the first atom of the group; (b) resonance within the group; (c) field effects, especially those from unit electronic charges within the group; (d) hybridization involving relatively low-lying available orbitals (e.g., d orbitals of the valence shell) and an essentially constant source of electrons; (e) the electron density on the first atom of the group.

The very appreciably smaller dipole moment of HI than CH_3I (cf. Table XIa) and the more positive σ^* values of both H and I than CH_3 (cf. Table XIc) indicate that the electron-withdrawing power of hydrogen (and iodine) is greater than CH_3. Indeed it has been shown that, in spite of the greater electronegativity of carbon than hydrogen, the sp^3 hybridization leads to the following net bond moment in methane: $\mu_{C^+H^-} \cong 0.3$ debye.[114-116] The direction of the dipole is in accord with the order of σ^* values and the *intrinsic electronegativities* in methane.

Further evidence of the effect of orbital hybridization on σ^* is apparent in the values for the following substituents: $C_6H_5CH_2CH_2$, $\sigma^* = +0.080$; $C_6H_5CH{=}CH$, $\sigma^* = +0.410$; $C_6H_5C{\equiv}C$, $\sigma^* = +1.35$. The hybridization of the bonding orbital of the α-carbon atom of these substituents is sp^3, sp^2 and sp, respectively. With increasing s character the intrinsic electronegativity of C and the electron-withdrawing power of the substituent markedly increase.

An important factor (and remarkably so!) governing the discrepancies between the electron-withdrawing power as measured by σ^* and Dailey and Shoolery's electronegativities appears to be the hybridization factor. For example, the σ^* values for the groups C_6H_5, CO_2H, and CN increase markedly (Table XIb) in the order given, whereas the group electronegativities are essentially constant in accord with the electronegativity of the first atom (C) in its ground electronic state. The increase in σ^* between C_6H_5 and CO_2H undoubtedly results in part from the greater intrinsic electronegativities of the atoms (of the latter) bonded to the first carbon atom. The σ^* value for CN is larger yet because of the greater intrinsic electronegativity of the first carbon atom (sp instead of sp^2 of the former groups). The fact that σ^* for CN is greater than that of F is striking. For the same valence state of the atom, the electronegativity of fluorine greatly exceeds that of carbon. For roughly the same degree of hybridization of the first atom, σ^* increases with increasing electronegativity, as indicated by the order of values for the halogens.

[114] W. L. G. Gent, *Quart. Rev.*, *2*, 383 (1948).
[115] C. A. Coulson, *Valence*, pp. 207–208, Clarendon Press, Oxford, 1952.
[116] C. R. Mueller and H. Eyring, *J. Chem. Phys.*, *19*, 193 (1951).

The contributions of factors (b) and (c) to σ^* (and σ') has been discussed in earlier sections. For example, resonance involving structures with positive charges on the first carbon atom contribute to the large σ^* values for COOH and CN groups. The very positive σ^* value for the $(CH_3)_3N^+CH_2$ group must in part be due to factor (c).

The importance of factor (d) is illustrated by comparing electronegativities on the Pauling scale for C, H, and the halogens with corresponding σ^* values for a second independent measure of the electron-withdrawing power. A crude measure of the latter may be estimated from the bond charge separation, q_{AB}, obtained by dividing the bond moment, μ_{AB}, by the interatomic distance, r_{AB}, i.e., $q_{AB} = \mu_{AB}/r_{AB}$. Table XIc lists values of q_{C-X}, σ^* and $X_X - X_C$, Pauling's electronegativities relative to carbon.

It is apparent from Table XIc that there is a close parallel between σ^* values and the electron-withdrawing power as measured by the quantity q_{C-X}. On the other hand the electronegativity values generally do not even qualitatively parallel corresponding q_{C-X} or σ^* values. However, the charge separations, q_{H-X}, obtained in a similar manner for hydrogen halide bonds, parallel quite closely Pauling's electronegativities (Table XIc).

TABLE XIc

COMPARISON OF CHARGE SEPARATIONS OBTAINED FROM DIPOLE MOMENTS, σ^* VALUES, AND PAULING'S ELECTRONEGATIVITIES

Element, X	Bond Moment,[117 a] debyes		Interatomic Distance,[117 b] A		Charge Separation, e.s.u.		Polar Substituent Constant	Pauling's Electronegativity[112]
	μ_{C-X}	μ_{H-X}	r_{C-X}	r_{H-X}	q_{C-X}	q_{H-X}	σ^*	$(X_X - X_C)$
C(CH₃)	0.0		1.54		(0.00)		(0.0)	(0.0)
H	0.3		1.07		0.28		+0.5	−0.4
I	1.91	0.38	2.10	1.62	0.91	0.23	+2.4	0.0
Br	2.08	0.79	1.91	1.42	1.09	0.56	+2.8	+0.3
Cl	2.16	1.08	1.77	1.28	1.22	0.85	+2.9	+0.5
F	2.11	1.91	1.41	0.92	1.53	2.08	+3.1	+1.5

The contrast in the relationship of q_{C-X} and q_{H-X} values to electronegativity may be explained as follows. In the hydrogen halides there is but a single important factor, the relative intrinsic electronegativities of the halogens in the atomic ground state, which can determine electron-withdrawing power (the H atom has no additional

[117] (a) Obtained by the method described by Pauling, reference 112, p. 68, using the vapor state dipole moments of reference 1 of Table X. The calculations for μ_{C-X} are based upon $\mu_{C^+-H^-} = 0.3$ debye. (b) The interatomic distances are from reference 112, p. 164.

electrons). In the case of C—X bonds, the electron-withdrawing powers of I, Br, and Cl relative to F are much greater than expected on the basis of the relative electronegativities. It appears very likely that the ability of the former three halogens to use the d orbitals of the valence shell to accept electrons from the other bonds of the carbon atom contributes to their increased electron-withdrawing power.[118] By the definitions of section III-4 this factor is strictly a resonance effect, but since it appears to be essentially constant for halogen bonds to any carbon atom it is convenient to include the factor within the inductive electron-withdrawing power.

The fact that σ^* values have general application, i.e., are essentially independent of the functional group Y of R—Y, indicates that factor (e) is not of great importance in determining the electron-withdrawing power of a group. An interesting illustration is provided by

values for the groups C_6H_5, $\sigma^* = +0.600$; CH_3, $\sigma^* = 0.00$; $C_6H_5\overset{\displaystyle H}{\underset{\displaystyle |}{C}}\!=\!\overset{\displaystyle H}{\underset{\displaystyle |}{C}}$,

$\sigma^* = +0.410$; and $CH_3\!-\!\overset{\displaystyle H}{\underset{\displaystyle |}{C}}\!=\!\overset{\displaystyle H}{\underset{\displaystyle |}{C}}$, $\sigma^* = +0.360$. The difference in σ^* values for the last two groups $(+0.050)$ is equal (within the combined errors) to the difference between the first two divided by $(2.8)^2$, which allows for the effect of the two interposed carbon atoms, i.e., $\dfrac{0.600 - 0.000}{(2.8)^2} + 0.077$ (cf. also the additive relationships of section V-2b).

4. TABULATION OF POLAR SUBSTITUENT CONSTANTS

The correlations obtained by equation 16 permit the assignment of σ^* values to a number of substituents for which ester rate data are not available. Table XII gives a summary of available σ^* values, rounded off to the nearest 0.005. Included in Table XII are notations to the reaction series in Table IX used as a source of the σ^* value, the number of correlations n for which data are available for each substituent, and the median deviation r of the value of σ^*. Where the needed ester rate data were unavailable, the reaction series chosen (if a choice was available) to obtain a value of σ^* was that giving the best fit to equation 16 of the data for the other reactions series. The σ^* values

[118] R. S. Mulliken, *J. Am. Chem. Soc.*, 77, 884 (1955), has shown the importance of an interaction of this type in the halogen molecules.

given to two decimal places are those that are based on data for a single reaction series, or are otherwise uncertain. For two substituents (indicated in Table XII under source by an asterisk), the σ^* value obtained from the indicated reactions series gives appreciably better fit with other reactions than that obtained from ester rate

TABLE XII

POLAR SUBSTITUENT CONSTANTS

I. Aliphatic Series R—Y (where R is substituent, Y is functional group)

Substituent R	σ^*	r	n	Source	Substituent R	σ^*	r	n	Source
1. Cl_3C	+2.65		2	1	24. $Cl(CH_2)_2$	+0.385	0.01	5	13
1a. F_2CH	+2.05		1	3	25. $CH_3CH=CH$	+0.360	0.02	2	1
2. CH_3O_2C	+2.00		1	1	26. $CF_3(CH_2)_2$	+0.32		1	3
3. Cl_2CH	+1.940	0.02	5	3-1 †	27. $C_6H_5CH_2$	+0.215	0.04	14	1
4. $(CH_3)_3N^+CH_2$	+1.90		1	1	28. $CH_3CH=CHCH_2$	+0.13		1	3
5. CH_3CO	+1.65		1	1	29. $CF_3(CH_2)_3$	+0.12		1	3
5a. $C_6H_5C\equiv C$	+1.35		2	1	30. $C_6H_5(CH_3)CH$	+0.11		1	1
6. $CH_3SO_2CH_2$	+1.32		1	3	31. $C_6H_5(CH_2)_2$	+0.080		5	1
7. $CNCH_2$	+1.300	0.03	5	3-1 †	32. $C_6H_5(C_2H_5)CH$	+0.04		1	1
8. FCH_2	+1.10		1	3	33. $C_6H_5(CH_2)_3$	+0.02		1	1
9. HO_2CCH_2	+1.05		1	3	34. CH_3	0.000	0.03	63	1
10. $ClCH_2$	+1.050	0.03	15	1	35. $Cyclo-C_6H_{11}CH_2$	−0.06		1	1
11. $BrCH_2$	+1.000	0.03	6	3	36. C_2H_5	−0.100	0.02	40	1
12. ICH_2	+0.85		1	3	37. $n-C_3H_7$	−0.115	0.02	15	1
13. CF_3CH_2	+0.92		2	3	38. $i-C_4H_9$	−0.125	0.02	14	1
14. $C_6H_5OCH_2$	+0.850	0.05	4	11-1 †	39. $n-C_4H_9$	−0.130	0.02	16	1
15. $C_6H_5(OH)CH$	+0.765	0.03	2	3	40. $Cyclo-C_6H_{11}$	−0.15		2	3
16. CH_3COCH_2	+0.60		1	1	41. $t-C_4H_9CH_2$	−0.165	0.04	4	10
17. C_6H_5	+0.600	0.06	5	1	42. $i-C_3H_7$	−0.190	0.03	23	1
18. $HOCH_2$	+0.555	0.07	11	11	43. $Cyclo-C_5H_9$	−0.20		1	3
19. CH_3OCH_2	+0.520	0.05	5	1	44. $s-C_4H_9$	−0.210	0.01	6	10
20. $NO_2(CH_2)_2$	+0.50		1	3	45. $(C_2H_5)_2CH$	−0.225	0.04	4	10*
21. H	+0.490	0.03	19	1	45a. $(CH_3)_3SiCH_2$	−0.26		2	1
22. $C_6H_5CH=CH$	+0.410	0.03	2	11	46. $(t-C_4H_9)(CH_3)CH$	−0.28	0.04	2	10
23. $(C_6H_5)_2CH$	+0.405	0.04	6	3*	47. $t-C_4H_9$	−0.300	0.04	20	1

II. o-Substituted, X, Benzene Derivatives

	σ^*	r	n	Source		σ^*	r	n	Source
1. OCH_3	−0.39	0.03	5	1,3	6. Cl	+0.20	0.05	5	1,3
2. OC_2H_5	−0.35		1	1,3	7. Br	+0.21	0.07	3	1,3
3. CH_3	−0.17	0.09	5	1,3	8. I	+0.21	0.07	2	1,3
4. H	0.00		1	1,3	9. NO_2 ‡	+0.80 †	0.05	4	1,3
5. F	+0.24	0.05	2	1,3	10. NO_2 §	+1.22 ‡		1	4

† Originally defined σ^* value has been subsequently found to follow equation 14 with acceptable precision.
‡ To be used for benzene derivatives other than anilines, phenols, or like.
§ To be used for derivatives of anilines, phenols, or like.

data. Ultimately a statistical evaluation of σ^* values based upon the entire body of data correlated by equation 16 may be desirable, but this is not worth while until equation 16 has received more test.

Reaction series II-3 of Table IX has made it possible to give σ^* values for o-substituted benzene derivatives relative to the unsubstituted derivative. The phenyl as well as o-substituted phenyl groups follow equation 16 for this reaction series. The polar substituent constants for o-substituted benzoates were previously given relative to the CH_3 group.[119]

5. EQUATION 16 AS A CRITERION OF CONSTANT STERIC AND RESONANCE EFFECTS. COMMENTS ON PRECISION

Equation 16 provides an important new criterion for determining (approximately) that polar effects alone determine rates or equilibria within a reaction series involving substituents directly adjoining the reaction center.

The separation of polar and steric effects in rates of ester hydrolysis and esterification has shown that there is no relationship between corresponding polar, steric, and resonance effects of substituents, except possibly in limited coincidental cases. Polar and steric effects in these reactions are completely different functions of structure, frequently qualitatively, and nearly always quantitatively. Although there is rather limited tendency for steric effects in reactions of widely different types to quantitatively parallel one another, the qualitative (or semiquantitative) orders are in general quite distinct from polar and resonance effects (cf. section VII). For this reason it seems safe to conclude that very generally (i.e., for any type of reaction) polar, steric, and resonance effects are completely different quantitative functions of structure.

On this basis the demonstration of a simple proportionality between a series of $\log (k/k_0)$ values and corresponding polar substituent constants σ^* requires that a single variable, the polar effect, is operating. Steric and resonance effects must be nearly constant. This will be true only if the correlation has been established over a wide enough range of structure to avoid coincidental fits. That is, variable steric and resonance effects will lead to plots similar to Fig. 2 when $\log (k/k_0)$ is plotted vs. σ^*, but nearly constant steric and resonance effects will lead to plots like Fig. 4.

The above conclusion is perhaps made clearer by the use of a simple A, B, C mathematical proposition. If A is proportional to B but not to C, then B plus C cannot be proportional to A (unless C is very small). In the demonstrative, A corresponds to the σ^* value for a substituent; B corresponds to the polar effect of a substituent in a given reaction series; and C is the corresponding steric effect. B plus C gives the total effect of the substituent on the logarithm of the rate constant.

[119] R. W. Taft, Jr., *J. Am. Chem. Soc.*, *74*, 3120 (1952).

The use of equation 16 for the expressed purpose of demonstrating the constancy of resonance and steric effects within a reaction series is subject to the following limitation. The method cannot detect resonance or steric effects which are of the same order of magnitude as the usual precision of equations 7 and 16. That is, resonance or steric effects which are less than 10% of the log (k/k_0) values are not likely to be detected by this method.

The mean percentage probable error of the ρ^* values of Tables IX and X is $4.5 \pm 1.7\%$. The mean value of r/ρ^* $(= 0.04 \pm 0.01)$, the ratio of the probable error of a single point to ρ^* for a given reaction series, appears to provide the best criterion of failure of equation 16. That is, this value gives the precision to be expected for the proportionality of strictly polar effects. On this basis (admittedly arbitrary) it was decided to regard a vertical deviation from the correlation line which exceeds $(4)(0.04\rho^*)$, or $0.16\rho^*$ log units, as outside the precision of the linear polar-energy relationship, and therefore attributable to another variable.

6. THE FAILURE OF EQUATION 16 AND ITS MEANING. LINEAR POLAR-ENERGY RELATIONSHIP

The fact that the proportionality of polar effects of substituents is not destroyed by variable and quite substantial steric and resonance effects in rates of hydrolysis of esters does not mean, of course, that there cannot be reaction series in which this does happen. The simplicity of equation 16 arising as it does from complicated rate quantities is sufficiently striking, however, that the burden of proof now rests with the demonstration of any such case.

According to the hypothesis evolved above, a non-linear relationship between log (k/k_0) values for any reaction and corresponding σ^* values, instead of demonstrating against the proportional nature of polar effects, shows that these rates or equilibria are determined by factors other than polar effects (cf. sections VI-10, VII-2, and VIII). A possible exception to this conclusion is the displacement reaction A | BC $\rightarrow$ AB + C, in which substituents are varied in the component B. If there is a delicate balance between bond making and bond breaking, the polar effects of the substituents on rates over wide ranges of polarity are not expected to be linearly related to σ^* values. Instead a plot of the polar effects on rate vs. σ^* values should lead to a smooth curve.[120]

[120] Cf. C. G. Swain and W. P. Langsdorf, Jr., J. Am. Chem. Soc., 73, 2813 (1951).

The condition of variable steric effects in an aliphatic reaction series is probably the most frequent cause of non-parallelism between free energies (or enthalpies) and corresponding polar substituent constants. Thus plots of log (k/k_0) vs. σ^* show much the same high degree of scatter as in Fig. 2 for the following reactions: aliphatic alcohols ROH with phenyl isocyanate in benzene at 26°,[121] and with p-nitrobenzoyl chloride in ether at 25°;[122] aliphatic acid chlorides RCOCl with β-chloroethanol in dioxane at 25°;[123] the ammonolysis of methyl esters RCO_2CH_3 and acetate esters CH_3CO_2R in anhydrous ethylene glycol at 30°;[124] and all the reactions considered in section VII. These results indicate that the rate constants within these reaction series are dependent upon important steric effects of the substituents R.

This theory predicts that, if the polar and steric effects are separated from log (k/k_0) values for the above reactions, a plot of the resulting polar effects vs. σ^* will probably be linear (cf. above qualification). The problem of separating reactivity is sufficiently difficult that it has not yet been possible to confirm this prediction for the above reactions. However, Table IX does contain a number of reaction series for which polar effects separated from free-energy differences are correlated by σ^* values (reactions I-2, I-19, I-20, I-21, I-22, and I-24).

The above discussion amounts to the proposal of a linear polar-energy relationship of very great generality, namely,

$$P_\sigma = \sigma^* \rho^* \quad (\text{or } \sigma\rho) \tag{17}$$

P_σ is the polar effect on rate of a substituent in a given reaction series relative to the standard of comparison (H for benzene derivatives and CH_3 for aliphatic derivatives). The symbols σ^*, σ, ρ^*, and ρ are as previously defined. The Hammett equation 7 is a special case of equation 17, for, in a reaction series of m- and p-substituted benzoates, steric and resonance effects are usually constant so that log (k/k_0) becomes equal to P_σ. Therefore, it follows that

$$\log (k/k_0) = P_\sigma = \sigma\rho$$

Taft's equation 16 is also a special case of equation 17. A reaction series which follows equation 16 is one in which resonance and steric effects are nearly constant, and again log (k/k_0) becomes equal to P_σ. This conclusion is supported by the wide variety of functional groups,

[121] T. L. Davis and J. McFarnum, *J. Am. Chem. Soc.*, **56**, 883 (1934).

[122] J. F. Norris and A. A. Ashdown, *J. Am. Chem. Soc.*, **47**, 837 (1925).

[123] R. Leimu, *Ber.*, **70B**, 1040 (1937).

[124] M. Gordon, J. G. Miller, and A. A. Day, *J. Am. Chem. Soc.*, **71**, 1245 (1949).

reaction mechanisms, attacking reagents, experimental conditions, etc., involved in the reaction series which follow equation 16; i.e.,

$$\log (k/k_0) = P_\sigma = \sigma^* \rho^*$$

In other reaction series, P_σ cannot be obtained directly from a rate or equilibrium measurement, i.e., $P_\sigma \neq \log (k/k_0)$. Instead, P_σ, the polar effect contribution to $\log (k/k_0)$, must be quantitatively separated by some suitable means from the other effects contributing to these free-energy terms. When this separation is accomplished, the resulting polar effects should follow equation 17.

Equation 17 is simply an expression of the great generality of the near quantitative proportionality of corresponding polar effects between one reaction series and another. In fact, equation 17 serves as the best definition of a polar effect on rate or equilibrium. The σ^* values are "yardsticks" for identifying polar effects by equation 17.

Equation 17 requires two sets of sigma values, σ and σ^*. This situation results from the fact that polar effects in the substituted benzene side-chain series are generally the sum of inductive and resonance polar effects. In the aliphatic series, polar effects are generally inductive only. It is therefore expected that the polar effects in other types of substituted aromatic systems, e.g., derivatives of thiophene, in which the relative contributions of inductive and resonance polar effects may differ appreciably from the benzene series, will require a new set of polar substituent constants. The results discussed in section V-2c provide evidence that the inductive effect constants σ' (or σ^* in the aliphatic series) have potentially much greater generality than the polar substituent constants σ (or σ^* for o-substituted benzene derivatives). Even here there is the unanswered question whether the internal inductive and the field effects require different sets of σ' values.

7. A FURTHER CRITERION OF POLAR EFFECTS

The additive nature of the polar substituent constants σ^* was pointed out in section IV-3. This additive behavior is supported by two additional facts. The σ^* values used in correlating reactions I-16, I-17, I-21, I-26, and I-27 of Table IX by equation 16 are the sum of the σ^* values for the R groups involved at the reaction center, that is to say, $\Sigma \sigma^*$. Figure 5 shows a plot of the ionization constants of polysubstituted acetic acids RCOOH in water at 25° vs. corresponding calculated values of σ^*. The value of σ^* for the group R has been estimated from the σ^* values for monosubstituted methyl groups on an additive basis. The full line shown in Fig. 5 is the "best" straight

624   STERIC EFFECTS IN ORGANIC CHEMISTRY

line obtained in a plot of the logarithm of the ionization constant vs. σ^* for the substituents where σ^* has been obtained from the ester rate data (i.e., for reaction I-3 of Table IX).

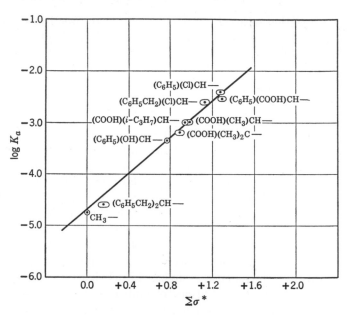

Fig. 5.   Demonstration of additive polar effects in the ionization of carboxylic acids.

For groups with σ^* values between -0.3 and $+1.5$ the precision of these correlations makes it apparent that the additive relationship of σ^* values is exact within their precision measures. For larger values of σ^*, a precise additive relationship is questionable. A "saturation" effect for polar effects in the aliphatic series has frequently been mentioned,[125, 126] but the evidence is likewise not very convincing. Listed below are σ^* values for chloromethyl groups, and pK_a's for corresponding chloroacetic acids in water at 25°.

Group	σ^*	pK_a
CH_3	0.000	4.75
CH_2Cl	$+1.050$	2.86
$CHCl_2$	$+1.940$	1.30
CCl_3	$(+2.65)$	0.7

[125] G. E. K. Branch and M. Calvin, *The Theory of Organic Chemistry*, pp. 202, 218, Prentice-Hall, New York, 1941.
[126] R. P. Smith and H. Eyring, *J. Am. Chem. Soc.*, **75**, 5183 (1953).

On the basis of these values one would conclude that a saturation effect exists. However, because of the very rapid rate of alkaline ester hydrolysis, the σ^* value for the CCl_3 group is based upon questionable data. Also the pK_a value of 0.7 for CCl_3COOH cannot be trusted because of the experimental difficulty of the measurement. There is further the possibility associated with the pK_a values that the apparent acidities of the highly halogenated acids are lowered by partial hydrate formation.

Data which at least surmount the latter difficulty favor the additivity principle. Thus there is a nearly regular increase in the Cl^{35} quadrupole spectra of solid chloroacetic acids and chloromethanes with increasing halogenation.[127] A regular increase in the half-wave potential for the polarographic reduction of the three ethyl chloroacetates has also been reported.[128]

Pearson and Dillon have given the following list of pK_a values for pseudo acids as evidence that there is a saturation effect which sets in with increasing electron-withdrawing power of the substituent groups.[129] However, these comparisons do not involve exclusively the effects of electron-withdrawing power of substituents, for the anions of the pseudo acids have variable specific conjugation and cross-conjugation possibilities.[130, 131] For example, the enolate ion of acetylacetone is more favored by resonance than that of acetone.[130] Indeed, if account is taken of resonance, Pearson and Dillon's data tend towards support of the additive relationship. The poorer conjugating groups, cyano and sulfone (section V-2c), follow the additive relationship more closely.

pK_a's OF POLYSUBSTITUTED METHANES

CH_4	40						
CH_3NO_2	11	CH_3COCH_3	20	$CH_3SO_2CH_3$	23	CH_3CN	25
$CH_2(NO_2)_2$	4	$CH_2(COCH_3)_2$	9	$CH_2(SO_2CH_3)_2$	14	$CH_2(CN)_2$	12
$CH(NO_2)_3$	0	$CH(COCH_3)_3$	6	$CH(SO_2CH_3)_3$	0	$CH(CN)_3$	0

The range over which the additive nature of polar effects remains of good precision is therefore in doubt. Even for very wide ranges of polar effects, however, this relationship is at least a useful first approximation.

[127] (a) H. C. Allen, Jr., J. Am. Chem. Soc., 74, 6074 (1952); (b) R. Livingston, J. Phys. Chem., 57, 496 (1953).

[128] P. J. Elving and C. S. Tang, J. Am. Chem. Soc., 74, 6109 (1952).

[129] R. G. Pearson and R. L. Dillon, J. Am. Chem. Soc., 75, 2439 (1953).

[130] G. W. Wheland, The Theory of Resonance, p. 170, John Wiley & Sons, New York, 1944.

[131] G. E. K. Branch and M. Calvin, The Theory of Organic Chemistry, p. 268, Prentice-Hall, New York, 1941.

8. CONCERNING A GENERAL THEORY OF THE EFFECT OF STRUCTURE ON REACTIVITY

Relative rates are not governed solely by the changes produced by substituents in the free energy of the reactant state. Instead, the changes in the free-energy difference between the reactant and transition states, i.e., the $\Delta\Delta F^{\ddagger}$ of equation 4', determine rate. The nature of the transition state is just as important in reactivity considerations as the initial state. This situation is well expressed by the following equation:

$$\Delta\Delta F^{\ddagger} \quad = \quad (F^{\ddagger} - F_0{}^{\ddagger}) \quad - \quad (F - F_0)$$

That is,

$$\left\{\begin{array}{l}\text{The effect of substituent}\\ \text{on the free energy of ac-}\\ \text{tivation}\end{array}\right\} \quad \text{equals} \quad \left\{\begin{array}{l}\text{The effect of substituent}\\ \text{on the free energy of the}\\ \text{transition state}\end{array}\right\} \quad \text{minus} \quad \left\{\begin{array}{l}\text{The effect of substituent}\\ \text{on the free energy of the}\\ \text{reactant state}\end{array}\right\}$$

Most of the early qualitative theories of reactivity have in effect placed emphasis only on the free energy of the reactant (or product). This has led to successful interpretations in some areas, but in others this line of approach has badly confused the factors governing reactivity.[132]

Since the rate constant is determined by a difference in the free energies between two states, it is completely unaffected by those factors that change the free energy of the reactant ($F - F_0$, above) by the same amount as the free energy of the transition state ($F^{\ddagger} - F_0{}^{\ddagger}$, above). Our concern in reactivity considerations is therefore not *all* the factors that change the free energies of these two states but *only* *those* factors that do not change the free energies of these states by the same amount. The other factors simply cancel in the free-energy difference, and make no contribution to the rate constant. This cancellation is actually very fortunate, for it means that the free-energy change $\Delta\Delta F^{\ddagger}$ (and therefore the rate constant) may be governed by fewer factors than the free energies of either the reactant or the transition states alone. In fact, if the investigator is sufficiently clever in the choice of a reaction series, the rate constants will be a delicate measure of a single variable.

Given below are several examples of how this cancellation of factors "operates" as it relates to polar, steric, and resonance effects on rate constants.

[132] Cf. discussion by G. S. Hammond, *J. Am. Chem. Soc.*, **77**, 334 (1955).

a. Polar effects

There have been some successful correlations of polar effects on rate and equilibrium with calculations of electron density at the reaction center.[133] The notion that reactivity depends upon the electron distribution in the reactant molecule has thus received support. This hypothesis, however, must be used with caution and understanding. The free energy of the reactant molecule presumably varies with the electron density at the reaction center. But only the change in electron density produced by the substituent between the reactant and the transition states will affect the rate constant. Apparently, the differences in the electron-density change between two states are frequently proportional to corresponding differences in the electron density associated with a single state. This relationship accounts not only for the correlations mentioned above but also for the correlations of σ and σ^* values with physical properties of single states, e.g., nuclear magnetic resonance absorptions.[134] Some of the limitations of the physical-property correlations (section VI-3) must be due to the failure of this relationship to be completely general, however.[135]

There have also been made several promising theoretical calculations (based on localization energies) of the energy differences between reactant and transition states.[136]

It is instructive to consider how it is possible for rates and equilibria of a series of m- and p-substituted benzene derivatives, for example, to be influenced only by the polar effects of substituents. For a reaction series including a wide variety of substituents, the internal motions of the reactant molecules vary markedly. The free energies of the reactants thus are variable for this reason as well as for reasons of polarity. It is because the contributions of molecular motions to the free energies cancel in the difference between the reactant and the transition states that these rates are affected only by polar effects.

This type of cancellation is nicely illustrated by the following two linear free-energy relationships. Plotted as ordinate in Fig. 6a are $\log (k/k_0)$ values for the second-order rates of reaction of diphenyldiazomethane (DDM) with the bicyclooctane acids of Roberts and

[133] (a) H. H. Jaffé, J. Chem. Phys., 20, 279, 778, 1554 (1952); J. Am. Chem. Soc., 76, 5843 (1954); (b) R. P. Smith and H. Eyring, J. Am. Chem. Soc., 74, 229 (1952); 75, 5183 (1953).

[134] (a) Cf. H. H. Jaffé, Chem. Revs., 53, 214 (1953); (b) cf. Table X.

[135] Cf. discussion by H. S. Gutowsky et al., J. Am. Chem. Soc., 74, 4809 (1952).

[136] (a) R. D. Brown, Quart. Rev., 6, 63 (1952); (b) F. L. J. Sixma, Rec. trav. chim., 72, 673 (1953); (c) H. H. Jaffé, J. Am. Chem. Soc., 76, 5843 (1954).

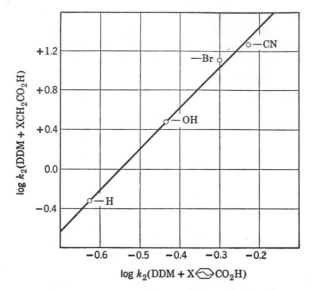

FIG. 6a.   Linear free-energy relationship for diphenyldiazomethane reactivities.

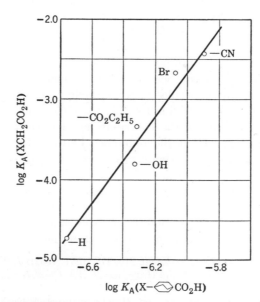

FIG. 6b.   Linear free-energy relationship for carboxylic acid ionization.

Moreland [137] in ethanol at 30°. As abscissa in Fig. 6a are plotted the corresponding values for the DDM reaction with aliphatic carboxylic acids XCH_2COOH in ethanol at 25°.[138] Figure 6b gives the corresponding plot for the ionization constants (log (K/K_0) values) for these acids. The former series of acid ionization constants apply for 50% (by volume) aqueous ethanol at 25°, and the latter series for water at 25°. All these reaction series follow equation 16.

In the series of bicyclooctane derivatives the X groups are held firmly at essentially a fixed distance from the carboxyl group. In the aliphatic derivatives, the XCH_2 groups rotate differently about the carboxyl group as H is replaced by OH, Br, or CN because of the variable potential barriers to rotation. This rotation factor causes both variable rotational entropies and effective distances between the reaction center and the C—X bond dipole. Thus, if reactant states alone were involved in determining rates or equilibria, the rotation factor would be sufficient to upset the simple type of relationship illustrated in Fig. 6.

The existence of these relationships must therefore mean that the variable rotation factor for the XCH_2COOH acids very nearly cancels between the reaction transition (or product) and the reactant states. It is this type of cancellation of the factors associated with kinetic energies of motions which results in the relative rate constants (for reactions following equations 7 and 16) being essentially quantitative measures of polar effects.

b. Steric effect

We have seen that variable degrees of molecular motions within a series of reactant molecules is not a sufficient condition for steric effects on rate or equilibrium constants. The same is true of potential energies of repulsion between the substituent and the rest of the reactant molecule. Equation 16 serves as strong confirmation of this conclusion. The reactions involve substituents directly adjoining the reaction center, so there are large variations in the steric interactions between the substituents and the functional group. Again, the fortunate cancellation of these interactions between reactant and transition states leads to rates that are functions of polar effects alone. *We are led to the important conclusion that the presence of compressed groups in a reactant molecule is a necessary but by no means a sufficient condition for the existence of important substituent steric effects in reactivity.*

[137] J. D. Roberts and W. T. Moreland, Jr., *J. Am. Chem. Soc.*, 75, 2167 (1953).
[138] R. W. Taft, Jr., and D. J. Smith, *J. Am. Chem. Soc.*, 76, 305 (1954).

It is apparent from the above discussion that it is meaningless and deceptive to say that a molecule is "sterically hindered" from a general reactivity standpoint. Changes in steric interactions between reactant and transition states are the only steric factors that affect rates. These changes are dependent upon the nature of the process involved. The term "steric hindrance" in reactivity must therefore be applied with respect to both the reactant molecule and a particular rate or equilibrium process.

The changes in steric interactions accompanying various processes may be predicted qualitatively from the change in structure which takes place between the two states. Three categories of steric effects will result from the introduction of a very large substituent in place of a small one at the reaction center under the following three conditions: (1) the increase in steric interaction (between the substituent and the rest of the molecule) is greater in the transition state than in the reactant state; (2) the increase in steric interaction is less in the former state than the latter; and (3) the change in steric interaction is the same in both states. The first condition produces an unfavorable effect on rate; the second, a favorable effect;[139] and the third, no effect. The first condition may be referred to as "steric hindrance," and the second as "steric facilitation."

Structural changes which lead (with a common carbonyl reactant) to each of these conditions are illustrated, for example, by the following three processes:

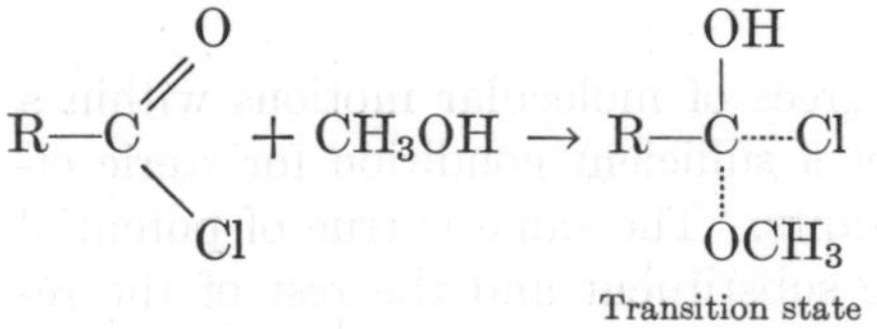

$$
R-\underset{\underset{Cl}{}}{\overset{O}{\underset{\|}{C}}} + CH_3OH \rightarrow R-\underset{\underset{OCH_3}{}}{\overset{OH}{\underset{|}{C}}}\cdots Cl \qquad\qquad \text{rate} \quad (1)
$$

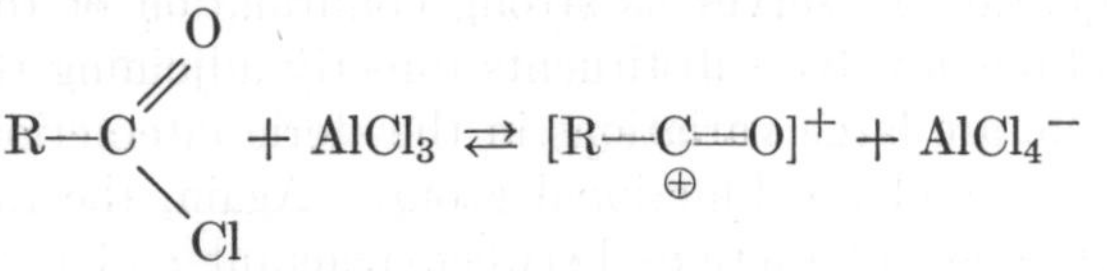

Transition state

$$
R-\underset{\underset{Cl}{}}{\overset{O}{\underset{\|}{C}}} + AlCl_3 \rightleftarrows [R-\underset{\oplus}{C}{=}O]^+ + AlCl_4^- \qquad \text{equilibrium} \quad (2)
$$

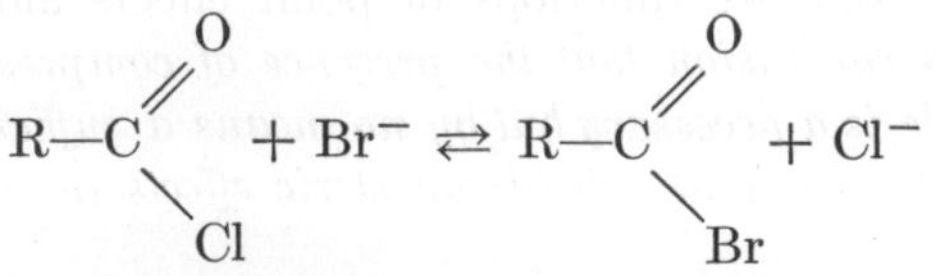

$$
R-\underset{\underset{Cl}{}}{\overset{O}{\underset{\|}{C}}} + Br^- \rightleftarrows R-\underset{\underset{Br}{}}{\overset{O}{\underset{\|}{C}}} + Cl^- \qquad \text{equilibrium} \quad (3)
$$

[139] Cf. discussions by H. C. Brown, *Science*, *103*, 385 (1946), and P. D. Bartlett *Bull. soc. chim. France*, *1951*, C100.

Example 1 is typical of a rate process involving a transition state formed by addition of a large reagent across an unsaturated function. The normal ester hydrolysis rate involves the same type of structural change, and this has been discussed in detail in section V-3a.

Example 2 is an ionization process in which the coordination number of the central carbon atom is decreased and the bond angles increased (presumably from 120° to 180°). This change may alleviate strains and hindrances to molecular motions. Hill has apparently made qualitative use of this type of structural change to synthesize esters which are prepared with great difficulty by direct esterification of the carbinols and carboxylic acids.[140]

In example 3 there is no change in bond angles or coordination number and the group replaced has nearly the same steric requirements as the one added. This particular equilibrium has not been studied, but the prediction of little if any steric effects may be used with confidence from the principles involved.

The condition of nearly constant steric effects required of the reaction series correlated by equation 16 is consistent with the above principles and the nature of the reactions involved. An inspection of the reactions given in Table IX indicates that the following type of structural changes are involved: (1) No change in bond angles at the reaction center with addition or loss of a reagent at a center removed from the substituent—rates of formal, acetal, and ketal hydrolysis, ionization of carboxylic acids and carbinols, rates of sulfation of carbinols; (2) a change in bond angles and coordination number at the reaction center, but the substituent is sufficiently far removed so that no change in steric interactions is produced—rates of alkaline hydrolysis of ethyl 4-X-bicyclo-[2.2.2]-octane-1-carboxylates, rates of alkaline hydrolysis of acetatopentammine cobalt (III) ions; (3) a change in bond angles and coordination number at the reaction center with addition or loss of a very small reagent (e.g., hydrogen atom) and no substantial change in steric interactions of substituents—the hydrogenation of aldehydes and ketones.

c. Resonance effects

In section IV-6 it was pointed out that the resonance energy for the interaction of the dimethylamino and the p-carbethoxyphenyl groups is about 8 kcal./mole. Yet the activation energy for the alkaline saponification rate is decreased by only about 2.5 kcal./mole when this resonance is nearly completely destroyed by steric inhibition. In view of the evidence for the saturated nature of the transition state

[140] M. E. Hill, J. Am. Chem. Soc., 75, 3020 (1953); 76, 2329 (1954).

(sections V-2 and XIII), the difference in these two figures may at first appear anomalous. The difference, however, represents that part of the total resonance energy which is the same in the transition state for the saponification of ethyl p-dimethylaminobenzoate as in the reactant state. This energy cancels in the free energy of activation, and thus has no effect on reactivity. As far as this part of the resonance energy is concerned it makes no difference in the saponification rate whether or not the resonance is sterically inhibited.

9. REQUIREMENTS AND LIMITATIONS IN USE OF EQUATION 16

Several of the reaction series listed in Tables IX and X do not provide a critical test of equation 16 over a wide range of substituent electrical properties. In most cases the correlations cover a sufficient variety of groups to make coincidental fits very unlikely. This possibility remains, however, wherever the range of the polar and steric requirements of the substituent is relatively narrow.

The successful use of equation 16 to demonstrate the near constancy of steric and resonance effects within a reaction series (or the uses discussed in section VI-10) depends upon quantitative data. But even with quantitative data much depends upon a wise selection of a variety of substituents. Coincidental fits (see section IV-4, for example) can be avoided with certainty if a set of substituents is chosen within which polar and steric requirements run both in the same and in opposite directions. Much of the past quantitative work on the effect of structure on reactivity in the aliphatic series for this reason has not been suited to these purposes.

10. USE OF EQUATIONS 16 AND 17 TO QUANTITATIVELY EVALUATE OTHER EFFECTS

In a given reaction series, certain types of substituents may follow equation 16 and others not (cf. footnotes to Table IX, for example). The former may be, for example, a series of substituents of closely the same steric requirements, whereas the latter are groups for which these requirements vary widely. Another possibility is that the former are substituents of such a nature that resonance effects are constant, but the latter are such as to involve variable effects of this kind.

The correlation of the limited series of log (k/k_0) values, or of $\Delta\Delta H^{\ddagger}$ values if desirable (cf. section XI), with corresponding σ^* values is indeed very valuable. The deviations of the other substituents from the correlation predicted by equation 16 may be, according to equation 17, quantitative measures of other effects. The type of effect is indicated by the nature of the reaction, the substituents, and their deviations. That is, for example, if the first group of reactants follow the equation $\log (k/k_0) = \sigma^*\rho^*$, and the second group follow the relationship $\log (k/k_0) = \sigma^*\rho^* + \psi$ = "polar + resonance effects," then, of course,

$$\psi = \log (k/k_0) - \sigma^*\rho^*$$

This use of equation 16 is perhaps its most valuable one, for it permits the quantitative evaluation of steric and resonance effects. In turn the unambiguous study of the relationship of these effects to structure and reaction type may be carried out. Three examples (one of each type) are cited below for which this procedure has given particularly encouraging results in the evaluation of steric, resonance, and anchimeric assistance effects.

a. Steric strain energies

The enthalpies of dissociation for ammonia and straight-chain primary amine-trimethyl boron addition compounds follow equation 16 as shown in Fig. 7. Specifically, ΔH_d (kcal./mole) = (-7.26 ± 0.21) $(\Sigma\sigma^*) + 24.54$, where $\Sigma\sigma^*$ is the sum of σ^* values for the R's of $R_1R_2R_3N$.[141] The median deviation of the predicted from experimental values of ΔH_d is 0.1 kcal. (about experimental uncertainty) and covers a range of 4.7 kcal. If trimethylenimine is included, the range covered is 8.7 kcal. Taking the $\Sigma\sigma^*$ value for trimethylenimine to be the sum of σ^* values for H, Me, and Et groups (the latter two are here tied together), the above equation predicts a ΔH_d value of 21.7 kcal. The experimental value is 22.5 ± 0.5 kcal.[142] The agreement is satisfactory considering the approximation made for $\Sigma\sigma^*$.

The enthalpies of dissociation predicted from the above equation are appreciably greater than the measured values when branched-chain primary, secondary, or tertiary amines are considered. The difference between the two values has been taken as a measure of the increase in steric strain in the addition compounds. That is, the steric strain is taken as the vertical deviation from the best straight line defined by the straight-chain primary amines in the plot of ΔH_d vs. $\Sigma\sigma^*$ [141] (cf. Fig. 7).

This method assumes that $\Delta\Delta H_d$ is determined by polar and strain potential energies (other effects being negligible) and that the polar potential energy may be evaluated and removed by the $\Sigma\sigma^*\rho^*$ corre-

[141] R. W. Taft, Jr., J. Am. Chem. Soc., 75, 4231 (1953).
[142] H. C. Brown and M. Gerstein, J. Am. Chem. Soc., 72, 2926 (1950).

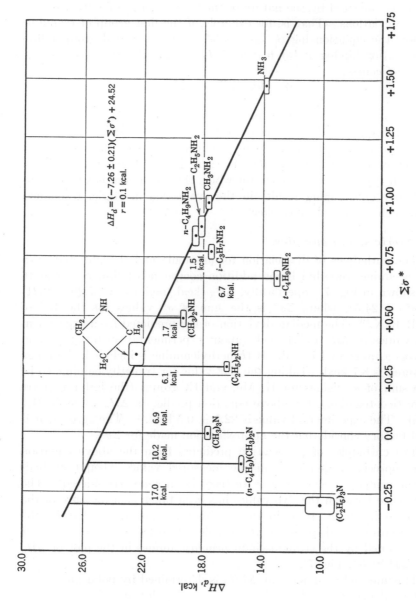

FIG. 7. Evaluation of steric strains from heats of dissociation: $(CH_3)_3B - NR_1R_2R_3 \rightarrow (CH_3)_3B + R_1R_2R_3N$.

lation.   In support of these assumptions are the following facts (in addition to those given above).   These equilibria have been determined in the absence of a solvent; i.e., these are gas-phase equilibria. Both reactant and product states involve saturated aliphatic compounds, eliminating the possibility of resonance effects.   Plots of log K_d vs. $1/T$ are linear within experimental error over temperature ranges of at least 40°, typically from about 350 to 390°K. (suggesting that $RT^2 \dfrac{d(\ln \Pi Q)}{dt}$ terms in equation 5 are small; i.e., $\Delta\Delta H \cong \Delta\Delta E_p$; cf. section XI).   Molecular models suggest that there is an increased compression of groups in the formation of the addition compounds of the branched-chain amines.[143]

Table XIII lists the steric strains evaluated in this manner.   The values given are relative to those for the ammonia addition compound.

TABLE XIII

STRAIN ENERGIES FOR THE FORMATION OF AMINE-BORONTRIMETHYL ADDITION COMPOUNDS

Amine	σ^*	ΔH_d (calculated), kcal.	ΔH_d (observed), kcal.	Steric Strain, kcal.	Estimated Strain of Homomorphic Hydrocarbons, kcal.[148]
NH_3	+1.470	13.9	13.8 [145]	(0)	0.0
CH_3NH_2	+0.980	17.4	17.6 [145]	0	0.2
$C_2H_5NH_2$	+0.880	18.1	18.0 [145]	0	0.2
$n\text{-}C_3H_7NH_2$	+0.865	18.2	18.1 [145]	0	0.7
$n\text{-}C_4H_9NH_2$	+0.850	18.4	18.4 [145]	0	—
$i\text{-}C_3H_7NH_2$	+0.790	18.8	17.4 [146]	1.4	2.5
$s\text{-}C_4H_9NH_2$	+0.770	18.9	17.3 [146]	1.6	—
$t\text{-}C_4H_9NH_2$	+0.680	19.6	13.0 [146]	6.6	5.2
$(CH_3)_2NH$	+0.490	21.0	19.3 [147]	1.7	2.2
$(C_2H_5)_2NH$	+0.290	22.4	16.3 [147]	6.1	—
$(CH_3)_3N$	+0.000	24.5	17.6 [148]	6.9	5.0
$(n\text{-}C_4H_9)(CH_3)_2N$	−0.130	25.5	15.3 [148]	10.2	—
$(C_2H_5)_3N$	−0.300	26.4	(10) [149]	(17)	—

The results are (wherever comparison is possible) within the limits that were estimated earlier by Spitzer and Pitzer,[144] and, in general, are in reasonable accord with the steric strains which those authors estimated for the corresponding homomorphic hydrocarbons.[143]   How-

[143] H. C. Brown et al., *J. Am. Chem. Soc.*, **75**, 1 (1953), and previous references.

[144] R. Spitzer and K. S. Pitzer, *J. Am. Chem. Soc.*, **70**, 1261 (1948).

[145] H. C. Brown, M. D. Taylor, and S. Sujishi, *J. Am. Chem. Soc.*, **73**, 2464 (1951).

[146] H. C. Brown and G. K. Barbaras, *J. Am. Chem. Soc.*, **75**, 6 (1953).

[147] H. C. Brown, H. Bartholomay, Jr., and M. D. Taylor, *J. Am. Chem. Soc.*, **66**, 435 (1944).

[148] H. C. Brown and R. B. Johannesen, *J. Am. Chem. Soc.*, **75**, 16 (1953).

[149] H. C. Brown and S. Sujishi, *J. Am. Chem. Soc.*, **70**, 2878 (1948).

ever, extensive comparisons are not available for the two sets of strain energies. One set actually represents the strain energy of formation of the addition compound from the amines and the boron trimethyl whereas the other gives the strain energies of formation of the homomorphic hydrocarbons from their elements. The apparent agreement may therefore be fortuitous.

It is important to notice that the steric strains are not additive, but telescope (in a fashion similar to that noted in section V-3c for E_s values) with an increasing number of methyl or ethyl substitutions on the nitrogen atom. This result indicates that the principal cause of the increased strain in the addition compounds is not a *simple* F strain. This conclusion is based upon the fact that the symmetry of the $B(CH_3)_3$ group in the addition compound should lead to nearly regular increases in F strain (assuming fixed C—N—B and N—B—C bond angles and B—N interatomic distance) with each successive substitution of a methyl (or ethyl) group on the nitrogen atom.

b. Resonance effects

Mechanism work [150] on the acid-catalyzed hydrolysis of acetals, together with bond theory, indicates that the transition state for this reaction probably has nearly the same bond angles and distances about the central carbon atom as in the reactant acetal molecule. On the basis of the principles discussed in section VI-8, few if any steric effects on the hydrolysis rate are thus expected with structure variation in the acetal. This conclusion, as well as the fact noticed earlier by Skrabal [151] that substituents produce large effects on the rates, led Kreevoy and Taft to investigate the effect of structure on the hydrolysis rates of twenty-four diethyl acetals and ketals of the general formula $R_1R_2C(OC_2H_5)_2$.[152a] The substituents R_1 and R_2 were varied over wide limits of polar and steric requirements with the result that the rate constants cover a range of nine powers of 10.

The hydrolysis rates for two series of compounds, monosubstituted acetals, $(XCH_2)(H)C(OC_2H_5)_2$, and monosubstituted ketals, $(XCH_2)(CH_3)C(OC_2H_5)_2$, were found to follow equation 16 with acceptable precision (reactions I-4 and I-5 of Table IX); cf. Fig. 8. The ρ^* values

[150] (a) J. M. O'Gorman and H. J. Lucas, *J. Am. Chem. Soc.*, 72, 5489 (1950); (b) C. K. Ingold, *Structure and Mechanism in Organic Chemistry*, p. 334, Cornell University Press, Ithaca, 1953.

[151] A. Skrabal et al., *Z. physik. Chem.*, 111, 98–109 (1924); 122, 349 (1926); 130, 29 (1927).

[152] (a) M. M. Kreevoy and R. W. Taft, Jr., *J. Am. Chem. Soc.*, 77, 5590 (1955); (b) R. W. Taft, Jr., and M. M. Kreevoy, unpublished results; (c) C. R. Morgan, and M. M. Kreevoy, unpublished results.

for the two reaction series are essentially identical. However, the entire body of rate data is definitely not correlated by equation 16 in the form $\log (k/k_0) = (\Sigma\sigma^*)\rho^*$, where $\Sigma\sigma^*$ is the sum of σ^* values for the groups R_1 and R_2.

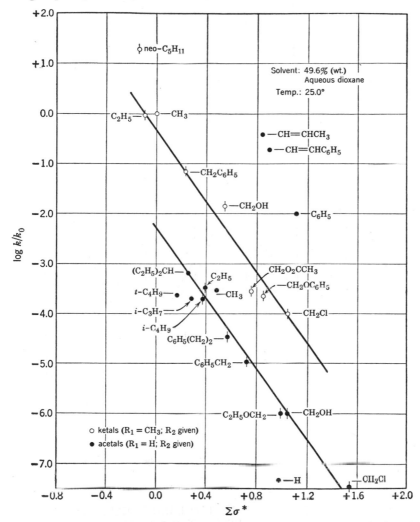

FIG. 8.   Relationship between diethyl acetal and ketal, $R_1R_2C(OC_2H_5)_2$, hydrolysis rates and sum of polar substituent constants, σ^*, for R_1 and R_2.

The deviations from a single straight line in a plot of $\log (k/k_0)$ vs. $\Sigma\sigma^*$, Fig. 8, are strongly implied to be measures of hyperconjugation effects by the following considerations. If a correlation line of the same slope as ρ^* for the monosubstituted acetals or ketals is drawn through the point for acetonal (the standard of comparison), the vertical deviation for each acetal or ketal point from this line correlates

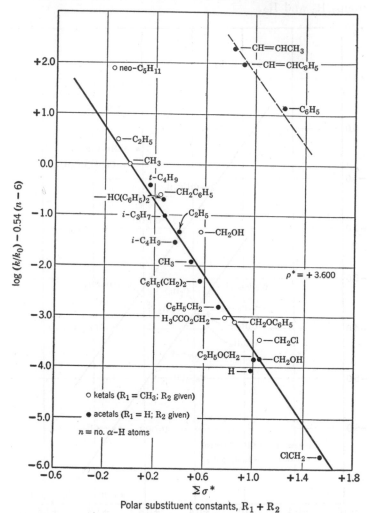

FIG. 9. Correlation of diethyl acetal and ketal, $R_1R_2C(OC_2H_5)_2$, hydrolysis rates by the equation $\log(k/k_0) = (\Sigma\sigma^*)\rho^* + 0.54(n-6)$.

with the number of α-hydrogen atoms in the substituents. In fact, these deviations divided by $n-6$, the decrease in the number of α-hydrogen atoms in R_1 and R_2 compared to the six in acetonal, gives a constant h of acceptable precision. Included, for example, are formal and trimethylacetal, both of which have no α-hydrogen atoms, but involve the groups H and t-C_4H_9 of widely different steric requirements. The above findings are equivalent to stating that the hydrolysis rates follow an equation that relates the free energies of activation to the sum of independent contributions from the polar $(\Sigma\sigma^*\rho^*)$ and hyperconjugation $[(n-6)h]$ effects of the substituents R_1 and R_2. This relationship is represented by the equation [152a]

$$\log (k/k_0) = (\Sigma\sigma^*)\rho^* + (n-6)h \qquad (18)$$

The value of ρ^* used is the average $(+3.600)$ of those found for the monosubstituted acetals and ketals. The average value of h, the only adjustable parameter in equation 18, was found to be 0.54 ± 0.06. This empirical constant is attributed to the rate-facilitating hyperconjugation effect of a single α-hydrogen atom in the transition state. Equation 18 is followed by the reaction rates of twenty acetals and ketals with a mean deviation of 0.22 log unit and covers a range of eight orders of magnitude in the hydrolysis rates (cf. Fig. 9).

The generally accepted mechanism for this reaction (below), due to

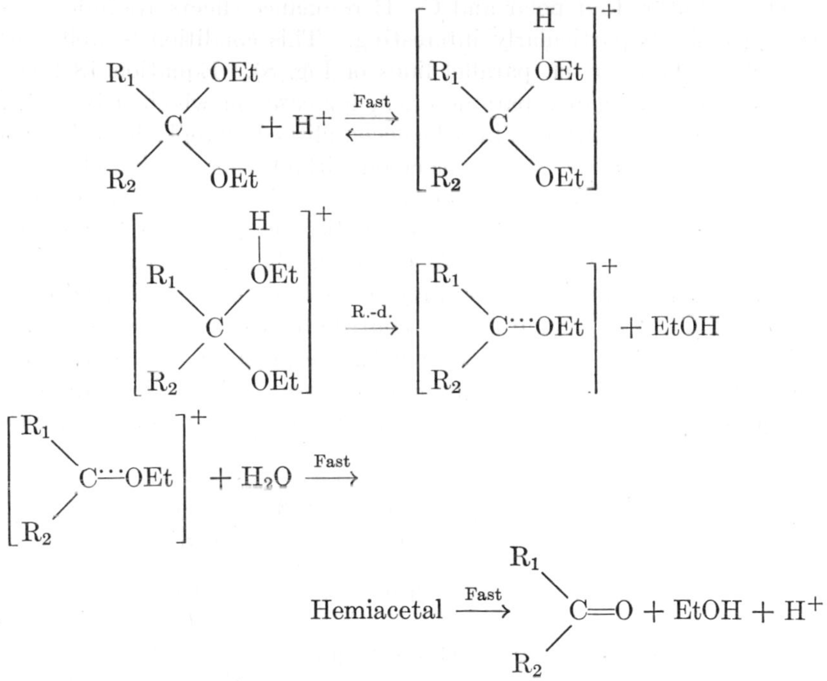

O'Gorman and Lucas,[150] readily accommodates the finding of hyperconjugation resonance effects. The transition state is reasonably pic-

tured as having some oxocarbonium ion character whereas the reactant state is saturated. The former state but not the latter should
permit hyperconjugation. This situation, therefore, produces hyperconjugation effects on the rates.

Substituents with α,β unsaturation show large deviations from equation 18. The points for cinnamyl acetal, crotonal, and benzal apparently form a line of parallel slope but 5.2 log units above that defined
by the unconjugated substituents. The rate-facilitating effect of α,β
unsaturation is expected on the basis of the above discussion by virtue of a resonance interaction with the central carbon atom (conjugation stabilization) in the acetal transition state.

The success of equation 18 in correlating the hydrolysis rates may
be interpreted as providing evidence that the following conditions
apply (approximately) to reactivity within this reaction series: (a)
polar effects are proportional to the polar substituents constants, σ^*;
(b) polar and C—H resonance effects are separate and independent
variables; (c) polar and C—H resonance effects are additive; (d) steric
effects are second order in comparison to polar and resonance effects.

The condition that polar and C—H resonance effects are independent variables is particularly interesting. This condition is well supported by the data (cf. parallel lines of Fig. 8). Equation 18 holds
with a single resonance parameter, h, for cases in which n is varied
from 0 to 6. This variation may be accomplished by replacing α-hydro-
gen atoms either by strong electron-withdrawing or by electron-
releasing groups. Thus pronounced variation in the intrinsic acidities
of the α-hydrogen atoms is without noticeable effect on the hyperconjugation parameter h. Further, an α-carbon atom with its substituents (α-H atoms or others) may be replaced by a single hydrogen
atom. If C—C hyperconjugation contributes to the hydrolysis rates
the effects are so small as to be within the precision of equation 18.
Summarized herewith are the number of cases which follow equation
18 for various values of n, together with the powers of 10 in reactivity
covered by each series.

n	0–1	2–3	5–6
No. of cases	4	8	8
Powers of 10 in reactivity	3.9	4.3	4.0

The ketals of methylneopentyl ketone and pinacolone [152c] deviate by
$+1.0$ and $+2.0$ log units, respectively, from equation 18. The failure
of condition (d) is indicated, i.e., the very large steric requirements of
the substituent groups increase reactivity. There are therefore structural limits beyond which condition (d) does not hold.

The conclusions concerning reactivity in the acetal and ketal hydrolysis reaction receive additional support from the fact that the equilibrium constants for the hydrogenation of aldehydes and ketones (reaction I-21 of Table IX) follow equation 18 with acceptable precision.[152b] Adkins and his students determined a large number of equilibrium constants for the following reaction:

$$
\underset{\substack{\|\\O}}{R_1-\overset{O}{C}-R_2} + \underset{\substack{|\\H}}{CH_3-\overset{OH}{\underset{|}{C}}-CH_3} \rightleftarrows \underset{\substack{|\\H}}{R_1-\overset{OH}{\underset{|}{C}}-R_2} + \underset{\substack{\|\\O}}{CH_3-\overset{O}{C}-CH_3}
$$

The data for unconjugated R groups follow equation 18 over a range of equilibrium constants of better than four powers of 10 with a probable error of 0.35 log unit. The value of the reaction constant ρ^* is $+4.681 \pm 0.065$, and the value of the parameter h is -0.393 ± 0.043. The resonance parameter h for this reaction indicates that the hyperconjugation resonance energy of a single α-hydrogen atom in an aldehyde or a ketone is about 0.5 kcal. The fit of the data to equation 18 implies that this hyperconjugation energy is essentially independent of the intrinsic acidity of the α-hydrogen atom. That is, the value 0.5 kcal. holds regardless of the other substituents present on the α-carbon atom.

As in the acetal hydrolysis rates, α,β-unsaturated substituents do not follow equation 18 in the hydrogenation equilibria. However, in a plot of $[\log (k/k_0) + (n - 6)h]$ vs. the $\Sigma\sigma^*$, the points for benzaldehyde, crotonaldehyde, cinnamaldehyde, and straight-chain alkyl phenyl ketones form a line of essentially the same slope as for the unconjugated substituents. The vertical displacement of these two lines gives roughly the resonance energy (5.5 kcal.) of the phenyl group (and the $C_6H_5CH=CH$ and $CH_3CH=CH$ groups) with the adjacent carbonyl group in the aldehydes or ketones.

c. Anchimeric assistance effects

Winstein and his students through extensive studies have developed a comprehensive theory of neighboring group reactivity.[153a] Streitwieser has recently used equation 16 to correlate the solvolysis rates of secondary alkyl toluene sulfonate esters and tertiary alkyl halides (reactions I-26 and I-27 of Table IX).[153b] The positive vertical deviations from equation 16 of trans-2-substituted cyclohexyl brosylates, α-phenylcarbinyl brosylates, and α-bromo- and iodo-tertiary-carbinyl halides may be attributed to anchimeric assistance effects (L'). Sev-

[153] (a) Cf. reference 20; (b) cf. reference 37 of Table IX,

eral typical values obtained in this manner are listed below. The relationship of the L' values to structure is in accord with the earlier discussions of Winstein et al.

ANCHIMERIC ASSISTANCE PARAMETERS

Trans-2-X-Cyclohexyl Brosylates		Secondary Carbinyl Brosylates		Tertiary Carbinyl Halides	
X	L', log units	Substituents	L', log units	Substituents	L', log units
Cl	0.0	1-Phenyl-2-propyl	+0.3	Dimethyl-α-phenylethyl	0.0
OCH$_3$	+0.7	1-p-Anisyl-2-propyl	+1.4	Dimethyl chloromethyl	0.0
O$_2$CCH$_3$	+2.5	1,1-Diphenyl-2-propyl	+1.8	Dimethyl-α-bromoethyl	+0.8
Br	+2.7	3-Phenyl-2-butyl	+0.6	Dimethyliodomethyl	+2.9
					Steric Facilitation Effects, log units
I	+6.2	3-Methyl-3-phenyl-2-butyl	+2.0	Dimethylneopentyl	+1.2
				Methyldineopentyl	+2.1

VII. GENERAL AND SPECIFIC STERIC EFFECTS IN REACTIVITY

1. LINEAR STERIC ENERGY RELATIONSHIPS

The general nature of the quantitative parallel of corresponding polar effects in various reaction series naturally raises the question whether a similar relationship exists for steric effects. It is conceivable that the failure of linear free-energy relationships (e.g., Fig. 2) results from different susceptibilities of each reaction series to polar and steric effects (resonance effects excluded) even though a simple parallel exists between both effects separately. However, nature apparently does exceed generally to this degree of simplicity. Although there is evidence (which will be a special concern of this section) that the above idealized behavior is approached under certain conditions of structure, there is also evidence that it is not general. Many pertinent data must be collected before clear-cut conclusions are possible, however, for there is a serious lack of information in this area.

A convenient starting point in an investigation of general relationships between structure and steric effects is the comparison of the steric substituent constants E_s from ester hydrolysis rates with corresponding log (k/k_0) values for reaction series in which polar effects are small or negligible. The latter decision can be made with useful approximation (see section V-3b) if the Hammett ρ value for the corresponding reaction of m- and p-substituted benzene derivatives is very small

$(<\pm0.4)$ or the range of σ^* values (but not of E_s values) of the substituents is quite small.

The logarithms of the relative rates of the acid-catalyzed hydrolysis of o-substituted benzamides in water at 100° parallel with acceptable precision corresponding E_s values [154] (cf. Fig. 10). Since this re-

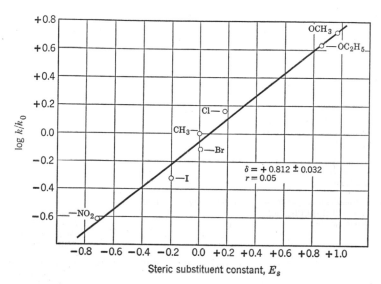

FIG. 10.   Linear steric energy relationship for the acid-catalyzed hydrolysis of o-substituted benzamides.

action series is one for which polar effects of substituents are quite small in even the most favorable case, log (k/k_0) measures nearly quantitatively the steric effect of a given substituent relative to the standard of comparison (the CH_3 group).

The relationship followed by the rates of hydrolysis of o-substituted benzamides may be called a linear steric energy relationship and is represented by the equation [154]

$$\log (k/k_0) = \delta E_s \qquad (19)$$

δ is a reaction constant, independent of the nature of the substituent groups. The value of δ gives a measure of the relative susceptibility of the reaction series to the steric requirements of the substituents.

Table XIV lists the above and other reactions (of the specified type) which follow equation 19, the corresponding steric susceptibility

[154] R. W. Taft, Jr., J. Am. Chem. Soc., 75, 4538 (1953).

TABLE XIV

Steric Reaction Constants δ from Equation 19

Reaction	δ	r	$-\log k_0$, in sec.$^{-1}$	Substituent
1. Acid-catalyzed hydrolysis of o-substituted benzamides, water, 100° [1]	$+0.812 \pm 0.032$ [2]	0.10	4.485	OCH_3, OC_2H_5, Cl, CH_3, Br, I, NO_2
2. Acid-catalyzed methanolysis of β-naphthyl esters, $RCO_2\ \beta$-$C_{10}H_7$, methanol, 25° [3]	$+1.376 \pm 0.057$ [4]	0.07	2.240	Me, Et, n-Pr, i-Pr, n-Bu, t-Bu
3. Acid-catalyzed n-propanolysis of β-naphthyl esters, $RCO_2\ \beta$-$C_{10}H_7$, n-propyl alcohol, 25° [3]	$+1.704 \pm 0.093$ [4]	0.11	2.860	Me, n-Pr, i-Pr, n-Bu, t-Bu
4. Acid-catalyzed i-propanolysis of β-naphthyl esters, $RCO_2\ \beta$-$C_{10}H_7$, i-propyl alcohol, 25° [3]	$+1.882 \pm 0.106$ [4]	0.13	4.114	Me, Et, n-Pr, i-Pr, n-Bu, t-Bu
5. Rate of reaction of methyl iodide with 2-monoalkyl pyridines, nitrobenzene, 30° [5]	$+2.065 \pm 0.096$ [4]	0.12	3.643	Me, Et, i-Pr, t-Bu
6. Rate of alkaline hydrolysis of acetate esters, $RCH_2O_2CCH_3$, 70% aq. dioxane, 30° [6a]	$+0.301 \pm 0.018$ [4]	0.07	1.594	Cyclo-C_4H_7, cyclo-C_5H_9, cyclo-C_6H_{11}, s-C_4H_9, t-C_4H_9, $(C_2H_5)_2CH$—, $(t$-$C_4H_9)(C_2H_5)CH$, $(C_2H_5)_3C$ [6b]
7. Acid-catalyzed methanolysis of l-menthyl esters, $RCO_2C_{10}H_{16}$, methanol, 30° [7]	$+1.687 \pm 0.064$ [4]	0.18	3.236	H, CH_3, C_2H_5, n-C_5H_{11}, $ClCH_2CH_2$, t-C_4H_9, $(C_2H_5)_2CH$
8. Activation energy for reaction of methyl iodide with 2-monoalkylpyridines, nitrobenzene [5]	$+2.235 \pm 0.089$ [4]	0.11	14.0	Me, Et, i-Pr, t-Bu
9. Enthalpy of reaction of 2-monoalkyl pyridines with diborane [8]	$+3.322 \pm 0.365$ [4]	0.45	17.5	Me, Et, i-Pr, i-Bu
10. Enthalpy of reaction of 2-monoalkyl pyridines with boron trifluoride in nitrobenzene [9]	$+5.49 \pm 0.36$ [4]	0.45	23.6	Me, Et, i-Pr, t-Bu
11. Enthalpy of reaction of 2-monoalkyl pyridines with trimethylboron in nitrobenzene [10]	$+6.36 \pm 0.34$ [4]	0.42	10.0	Me, Et, i-Pr, t-Bu

References for Table XIV

[1] E. E. Reid, *Am. Chem. J.*, *24*, 397 (1900).

[2] E_s values used are those for o-substituted benzoates.

[3] M. Harfenist and R. Baltzly, *J. Am. Chem. Soc.*, *69*, 362 (1947).

[4] E_s values used are for the substituent R in the acyl component of the ester RCOOR′.

[5] H. C. Brown and A. Cahn, *J. Am. Chem. Soc.*, 77, 1715 (1955).

[6] (a) M. S. Newman and S. Sarel, unpublished results; the author is indebted to Professor Newman for permission to use these data; (b) equation 19 fails for the substituents t-$C_4H_9CH_2$— and t-$C_4H_9(CH_2)CH$—.

[7] W. A. Pavelich and R. W. Taft, Jr., unpublished results.

[8] H. C. Brown and L. Domash, *J. Am. Chem. Soc.*, forthcoming.

[9] H. C. Brown and R. H. Horowitz, *J. Am. Chem. Soc.* 77, 1733 (1955).

[10] H. C. Brown and D. Gintes, *J. Am. Chem. Soc.*, forthcoming.

constant δ, and its probable error (obtained by methods of least squares), the probable error of the fit of a single observation r, and a list of the substituents that fit the correlation. The median probable error of Table XIV is 0.10 in the logarithm, or 13% in the value of the relative rate constant. The correlations cover maximum variation in rates of 100,000.

Enthalpies of reaction or activation for several reactions series (also of the specified type) have been found to fit equation 19, i.e., $\Delta\Delta H$ (or $\Delta\Delta H^{\ddagger}$) $= \delta E_s$. These correlations are also listed in Table XIV (reactions 8–11). The correlations cover a maximum variation in relative enthalpies of 10.0 kcal. with a median probable error of 0.4 kcal.

However, a linear relationship of good precision does not exist between the log (k/k_0) values for the acid-catalyzed hydrolysis of a series of thiolacetates at $30°$ [155] and E_s values for corresponding substituents in the alkyl component of an ordinary ester. The two sets of data show much the same trends as the tabulated data show.

	Steric Effect	
Substituent	Alkyl Component, Thiolacetate Hydrolysis log (k/k_0)	Acyl Component, Normal Ester E_s
CH_3	0.00	0.00
C_2H_5	−0.16	−0.07
i-C_3H_7	−0.27	−0.47
t-C_4H_9	−0.40	−1.54
i-C_4H_9	−0.34	−0.93

The steric effects of substituents in the acyl and alkyl components of an ester apparently do not always run quantitatively parallel, as the few available comparisons of E_s values below indicate. Reaction series 6 of Table XIV indicates that steric factors of substituents in the two components of the ordinary ester may, on the other hand, frequently have a quantitative type parallel.

Substituent	Acyl Component R E_s	Alkyl Component R' E_s
CH_3	0.00	0.00
C_2H_5	−0.07	−0.09
i-C_3H_7	−0.47	−0.42
i-C_4H_9	−0.93	−0.22

[155] (a) P. N. Rylander and D. S. Tarbell, J. Am. Chem. Soc., 72, 3021 (1950); (b) J. R. Schaefgen, ibid., 70, 1308 (1948); log (k/k_0) values given here are averages of those obtained for 43% (by weight) aqueous acetone and 62% (by weight) aqueous acetone (maximum deviation from average = 0.05).

2. DISCUSSION OF EQUATION 19

Not only is there a lack of data on various reaction series to test equation 19, but most of the reactions listed in Table XIV involve a small number of substituents. Thus only limited conclusions concerning equation 19 are justified.

Reactions 1, 2, 3, 4, and 7 of Table XIV very likely proceed by similar mechanisms involving reactant and transition states in which all the atoms adjoining the carbonyl carbon are of closely the same diameters.

The hydrolysis of thiolacetates probably proceeds also by an analogous mechanism, but the geometry of the ester and the reaction transition state is altered compared to the first set of reactions because of the larger diameter of sulfur than oxygen. It is thus apparent that equation 19 is sensitive to structure, and there are definite limits to its applicability.

On the other hand, reaction series 5, 8, 9, 10, and 11 of Table XIV bear little apparent resemblance to esterifications or ester or amide hydrolysis. Yet the precision of the fit of these data to equation 19 is in acceptable agreement with the others. In reaction series 6 the polar effect of substituents is virtually constant, owing to the nature of the substituents involved (even though the ρ^* value for this reaction is relatively large). A satisfactory number of substituents covering a moderate range of steric requirements is included in this reaction series. However, two substituents, t-$C_4H_9CH_2$— and t-C_4H_9-$(CH_3)CH$—, fit this correlation so poorly that they have been excluded. This provides further evidence that equation 19 fails beyond certain limits of structure variation. This limitation appears reasonable on the basis that the surroundings offered the substituents by the remainder of the molecule (in both reactant and transition states) are not completely similar in the acyl and alkyl components of the esters.

There is as yet no theoretical basis for equation 19, and it is not readily apparent that steric effects of substituents even within the range of structure variations in reactions 1, 2, 3, 4, and 7 of Table XIV should be so simply related.

Since E_s values come from log $(k/k_0)_A$ values (cf. section V-3b), equation 19 may be considered a linear free-energy relationship. Equation 19 shows very definitely that the proportionality of corresponding log (k/k_0) values between a few reaction series (linear free-energy relationships) provides no basis for the conclusion that these parameters are quantitative measures of polar effects.[156]   Instead this decision must be based upon a very general demonstration of the proportionality and additivity of substituent effects, coupled with a consideration of the nature of the substituent effects and the reaction processes.

Again, emphasis must be placed on the necessity of varying substituents widely in the use of equation 19 as well as of equation 16. Sommer and Barie have found a very interesting example (cf. further discussion of this reaction in section VII-4) of certain additive steric effects (instead of polar effects) of alkyl groups on the rates of alkaline Si—H cleavage of silanes.[157]   Over wider ranges of structure the effects on rate are far from additive.

The most important conclusion to be drawn from the correlations of equation 19 is that it now is of the utmost importance to establish the limits of structure variation permitted by this equation. There are several goals in this objective. First, the possibility of predicting many new reaction rates or enthalpies from the δ values of Table XIV and the E_s values of Table IV is implied. There can be no guarantee of the validity of these predictions, however, until equation 19 has had sufficient test to provide some definite conclusions as to the types of reactions and substituents for which it becomes invalid. Second, equation 19 has an important bearing on the problem of the quantitative correlation and prediction of general reactivity. Equation 19 is expected to fail in any reaction series in which polar effects are important. Both equation 19 and equation 16 of section VI-1 are to be applied under limiting conditions. That is, the former may apply when polar effects approach zero, and the latter when steric effects approach zero. These two limiting equations have definite implications.

Certainly a great many of the rates and equilibria for reactions involving substituents adjacent to the reaction center are governed by both polar (P) and steric (S) effects. This situation may be represented by the equation

$$\log k = f(P, S)$$

From the basic equation of partial differential equations and the condition that P and S are independent functions (section V-3d) we obtain

$$d \log k = \left(\frac{\partial \log k}{\partial P}\right)_S dP + \left(\frac{\partial \log k}{\partial S}\right)_P dS$$

[156] For a similar conclusion see A. A. Frost and R. G. Pearson, *Kinetics and Mechanisms*, p. 216, John Wiley & Sons, New York, 1953.

[157] L. H. Sommer and W. P. Barie, Jr., unpublished data, cf. reference 171.

By the arguments of section V,

$$\left(\frac{\partial \log k}{\partial P}\right)_S \quad \text{is equivalent to} \quad \left(\frac{\partial \log k}{\partial \sigma^*}\right)_S = \rho^*$$

and, to the extent that equation 19 is valid,

$$\left(\frac{\partial \log k}{\partial S}\right)_P = \left(\frac{\partial \log k}{\partial E_s}\right)_P = \delta$$

An equation results which is applicable to a reaction series for which both polar and steric effects vary simultaneously with structure:

$$\log (k/k_0) = \sigma^* \rho^* + \delta E_s \tag{20}$$

Equation 20 attributes the relative free energy of activation to the sum of independent polar and steric effects. The former terms for a given reaction series quantitatively parallel corresponding σ^* values, and the latter terms bear a similar relationship to the steric substituents E_s.

The limitations placed on this equation are that resonance and effects other than polar and steric are excepted, and that steric factors must follow equation 19. Pavelich and Taft have found equation 20 to correlate with relatively good precision the acid- and the base-catalyzed rates of methanolysis of l-menthyl esters $RCO_2C_{10}H_{19}$ in methanol at $30.0°$.[158] Both reaction series cover a range of five powers of 10 in rate and include substituents R of widely varying polar and steric requirements. Equation 20 is expected to be a useful relationship in correlating the effect of structure on reactivity in other reaction series.

3. THE *ortho* EFFECT

The reaction rates for several series of o-substituted benzene derivatives provide some support (at least qualitative) for equation 20. Complicated interactions of a variety of kinds have frequently been assumed in discussions of the *ortho* effect. A re-examination of the relatively meager data indicates that the effects of o substituents on rates and equilibria for a number of reactions can be explained on the basis of a combination of steric and polar effects. Cases where hydrogen bonding between the o substituent and the functional group have been well established are not considered.

[158] W. A. Pavelich and R. W. Taft, Jr., abstracts of papers presented before Division of Organic Chemistry, American Chemical Society Meeting, Minneapolis, Minn., Sept. 11–16, 1955, p. 54–O.

The ratio of the rate constant for an o- to that of a corresponding p-substituted benzene derivative, k_o/k_p, may frequently be taken as an approximate measure of the steric effect of the o substituent.[159] The total polar effect relative to the unsubstituted benzene derivative is given by $\sigma_p\rho$ for the p substituent and $\sigma_o^*\rho^*$ for the o substituent. We have seen (section V-2b) that corresponding values of σ_p and σ_o^* are approximately equivalent. Thus the polar effect will be nearly the same for corresponding o and p substituents and will cancel in the ratio k_o/k_p *if* the susceptibility constants ρ^* and ρ are identical. Unfortunately, these reaction constants are not always the same, and in fact may be seriously different.[160] Values of ρ^* and ρ for corresponding reactions are summarized in Table XV. It is interesting in

TABLE XV

COMPARISON OF ρ^* AND ρ FOR CORRESPONDING REACTIONS

Reaction	Reaction Constant ρ^* for o Substituents	Reaction Constant ρ for m or p Substituents
1. Alkaline saponification of benzoates, 25°	+2.5	+2.2 to +2.8
2. Ionization of benzoic acids, H$_2$O, 25°	+1.787	+1.000
3. Benzoic acid catalyzed dehydration of acetaldehyde hydrate, acetone, 25°	+0.771	+0.574
4. Ionization of anilinium ions, H$_2$O, 25°	+2.898	+2.767
5. Anilines with benzoyl chloride, benzene, 25°	−2.660	−2.781

this connection that ρ^* values for reactions of o-substituted benzene derivatives and for the corresponding reactions of aliphatic derivatives (R—Y) are the same within their precision measures wherever comparison is possible (cf. Table IX).

Comparison of the (k_o/k_p) ratio for various substituents in a given reaction is nevertheless valuable. In Table XVI are listed log (k_o/k_p) values for a variety of reactions and substituents. The results may be classified according to three catagories: (i) reactions in which the polar contributions are small, and log (k_o/k_p) values closely parallel corresponding steric substituent constants E_s for the hydrolysis rates of o-substituted benzoates; (ii) reactions in which log (k_o/k_p) values correspond to an order intermediate between those of σ^* and E_s values,

[159] R. W. Taft, Jr., M. S. Newman and F. H. Verhoek, *J. Am. Chem. Soc.*, **72**, 4511 (1950).

[160] Roberts and Moreland (reference 137) have noted a similar situation with respect to ρ' and ρ values for corresponding reactions.

TABLE XVI

Log (k_o/k_p) Values for Several Reaction Series

Type i

Reaction	Benzoate Hydrolysis	Acid-Catalyzed Hydrolysis Benzamides, H_2O, 100° [1]	Aryl Sulfuric Acid Hydrolysis, H_2O, 48.6° [2]	Basic Dehydrochlorination of Benzaldchlorimines, aq. EtOH, 0° [3]	Hydrolysis of Diphenyl Ketimines, H_2O, 0° [4]
Substituents	E_s	log (k_o/k_p)	log (k_o/k_p)	log (k_o/k_p)	log (k_o/k_p)
OH	—				+0.23
OCH₃	+0.99	−0.03	+0.60	−0.22	−0.12
F	+0.45				
Cl	+0.18	−0.80	+0.08	+0.44	−0.65
Br	+0.00	−1.06			
CH₃	0.00	−0.91	+0.05	+0.71	−0.91
I	−0.20	−1.17			
NO₂	−0.75	−1.64	−0.10	+0.84	

		Type ii		Type iii Diacyl Peroxides, Initiation Rates for Polymerization of Styrene [7]
Reaction	Benzoate Hydrolysis	Deacylation of 2′-Substituted Benzoylamino-4-Nitrobenzenes [5]	Dimethylanilines with Methyl Iodide, MeOH, 65° [6]	
Substituents	E_s	log (k_o/k_p)	log (k_o/k_p)	log (k_o/k_p)
OCH₃	+0.99	−0.46	−0.25	+0.87
F	+0.49	+0.67	−0.49	+0.28
Cl	+0.18	−0.25	−0.92	+0.72
Br	+0.00	−0.54		+1.21
CH₃	0.00	−0.49	−1.79	+0.43
I	−0.20	−0.66		+3.0
NO₂	−0.75	−0.43	−1.25	+0.60
C₆H₅	−0.90		−1.54	

REFERENCES FOR TABLE XVI

[1] E. E. Reid, *Am. Chem. J.*, *24*, 397 (1900).

[2] G. N. Burkhardt, W. G. Ford, and E. Singleton, *J. Chem. Soc.*, *1936*, 17.

[3] C. R. Hauser, J. W. Le Maistre, and A. E. Rainsford, *J. Am. Chem. Soc.*, *57*, 1056 (1935).

[4] J. B. Culbertson, *J. Am. Chem. Soc.*, *73*, 4818 (1951).

[5] (a) P. E. Verkade, B. M. Wepster, and P. H. Witjens, *Rec. trav. chim.*, *70*, 127 (1951); I am indebted to these authors for this reference. (b) These authors have pointed out the close parallel of rates of the o-substituted derivatives (methyl and halogens) and corresponding van der Waals radii (cf. section V-3c).

[6] D. P. Evans, H. B. Watson, and R. Williams, *J. Chem. Soc.*, *1939*, 1345.

[7] W. Cooper, *J. Chem. Soc.*, *1951*, 3106.

indicating appreciable contributions of both polar and steric effects; (iii) reactions in which the order of log (k_o/k_p) values does not correspond to that of either σ^* or E_s values, and cannot be represented by any possible combination of the two. To these categories may be added the fourth discussed in section VI-1, namely, reactions in which steric and resonance effects are essentially constant for a series of o substituents. For these cases, log (k_o/k_p) values are either nearly constant for the series or parallel in a quantitative manner corresponding σ^* values.   In benzyl halide solvolysis log (k_o/k_p) values are also nearly constant (see Chapter 2).

Among the reactions classified in type i are examples of both steric hindrance and steric facilitation.   The log (k_o/k_p) values for the alkaline dehydrochlorination of benzaldchlorimines are particularly interesting.   The increase of these values with increasing steric requirements of the o substituents provides strong evidence for the concerted $E2$ type mechanism for this reaction.   That is, this result is reasonable on the basis that there is a considerable stretching of the C—Cl bond in the reaction transition state.   In other words, the transition state possesses some of the properties of the reaction product, the nitrile, in which the steric interactions of o substituents are less than in the reactant chlorimine.

A particularly distinguishing feature between the orders of polar and steric effects of o substituents is the position of the methyl group with respect to the methoxy group and the halogens.   The order of increasing σ^* values is $OCH_3 < CH_3 < F$, Cl, Br, I $< NO_2$, whereas the order of $(-E_s)$ values is $OCH_3 < F < Cl < Br$, $CH_3 < I < NO_2$.

The position of the nitro group in the order of steric effects is also worthy of comment.   If the nitro group lies in the plane of the benzene ring as resonance interaction favors, its effective size is quite large, appreciably greater than that of the iodine atom.   If, on the other hand, the nitro group is approximately perpendicular to the benzene ring, its steric interaction with a group in the o position to it is relatively small.

The order of E'_s values indicates that the nitro group in o-substituted benzoates is coplanar (or nearly so) with the ring.   The order of increasing buttressing effects of substituents X in the rates of racemization of 2-nitro-6-carboxy-2'-methoxy-3'-X-biphenyls [161] is essentially the same as the order of decreasing E_s values.   The 3'-nitro group must therefore remain essentially coplanar during this racemization process.   However, the order of increasing effectiveness of substituents in retarding the rates of racemization of 2-X-2'-nitro-6'-carboxybiphenyls is $OCH_3 < NO_2 < Cl < CH_3 < Br$.[161]   The position of the nitro group in this series indicates that it becomes nearly perpendicular to the plane of the benzene ring in the racemization transition state for this reaction.

Holleman has obtained from isomer distributions the following order of increasing steric effects of electrophilic reagents for substitution in

[161] R. Adams in Gilman, *Organic Chemistry*, Vol. 1, pp. 362, 368, John Wiley & Sons, New York, 1943.

the o position of aromatic derivatives: $Cl < NO_2 < Br < SO_3H$.[162] This order indicates that the entering nitronium ion is far from co-planar with the aromatic ring in the transition states of aromatic ni-trations. Such a structure for the transition state is supported by the evidence indicating that there is no significant loosening of the proton to be displaced.[163] Because of the saturated central carbon atom in the transition state there can be no significant resonance interaction leading to coplanarity of the nitro group and the aromatic system.

4. KINETIC-ENERGY STERIC EFFECTS

The kinetic-energy steric effects (or the changes in steric hindrance of motions) have been assumed small and disregarded as a first ap-proximation in some discussions of reactivity. Such an assumption, however, is frequently a very bad one. Hammett has carefully pointed out the necessity of considering the extent to which reactivity is gov-erned by these entropy factors.[164a] Price and Hammett have shown that the entropy of activation in both the rates of formation and the hydrolysis of semicarbazones is a dominant factor and bears no rela-tionship to polar effects [164b] (cf. Table XVII). These authors proposed a qualitative rule which is in good general accord with their results. In a solvent of high dielectric constant and for a reaction having a highly polar transition state, it is expected that the more complex (entropy-containing) molecule will lose more entropy in the formation of the transition state; i.e., its entropy of activation will be less (more negative).[165] This rule has found subsequent general confirmation in the reaction of benzaldehyde with acetone and methyl ethyl ketone; [165b] in the acid-catalyzed hydration of isobutene, trimethylethylene, as-methylethylethylene, and 1-methylcyclopentene-1 by aqueous acid; [166]

[162] A. F. Holleman, *Die direkt Einführung von Substituenten in der Benzolkern*, Veit, Leipzig, 1910; *Chem. Revs.*, *1*, 187 (1925).

[163] L. Melander, *Arkiv Kemi*, *2*, 213 (1950).

[164] (a) L. P. Hammett, *Physical Organic Chemistry*, p. 119, McGraw-Hill Book Co., New York, 1940; (b) F. P. Price, Jr., and L. P. Hammett, *J. Am. Chem. Soc.*, *63*, 2387 (1941).

[165] (a) See discussion by A. E. Remick, *Electronic Interpretations of Organic Chemistry*, p. 211, John Wiley & Sons, New York, 1949; (b) Gettler and L. P. Hammett, *J. Am. Chem. Soc.*, *65*, 1824 (1943); (c) compare, however, the results of F. W. Fitzpatrick and J. D. Gettler, *J. Am. Chem. Soc.*, *78*, 530 (1956).

[166] R. W. Taft, Jr., J. B. Levy, D. Aaron, and L. P. Hammett, *J. Am. Chem. Soc.*, *74*, 4735 (1952); *75*, 3955 (1953); E. L. Purlee, R. W. Taft, Jr., and C. A. DeFazio, *ibid.*, *77*, 837 (1955).

TABLE XVII

RELATIVE ENTROPIES AND FREE ENERGIES OF ACTIVATION FOR
SEMICARBAZONE FORMATION AT 12.5° [164b]

	$T\Delta\Delta S^{\ddagger}$, kcal.	$\Delta\Delta H^{\ddagger}$, kcal.	$\Delta\Delta F^{\ddagger}$ (calculated), kcal.
Acetone	(0.0)	(0.0)	(0.0)
Diethyl ketone	−1.9	−0.6	+1.3
Pinacolone	−2.8	−0.2	+2.6
Cyclopentanone	+0.9	+2.0	+1.1
Cyclohexanone	+0.1	−0.9	−1.0
Furfural	+0.9	+2.1	+1.2
Acetophenone	−0.6	+2.6	+3.2

FOR SEMICARBAZONE HYDROLYSIS AT 12.5°

Acetone	(0.0)	(0.0)	(0.0)
Diethyl ketone	−2.4	−2.4	0.0
Cyclopentanone	−0.9	+0.6	+1.5
Cyclohexanone	−0.1	−0.9	−0.8

and in the hydrolysis of esters catalyzed by ion-exchange resins.[167]

Price and Hammett's rule appears subject to the following modifications. The entropy-bearing substituent apparently must be introduced close to the reaction center (cf. section XII), and the reaction process must be of such nature that there is an increase in steric interactions in going from reactant to transition state (cf. section VI-8). The condition of high dielectric of the solvent does not appear necessary.

The entropies of activation for the reaction of methyl iodide with certain amines in nitrobenzene show a close correlation with the rule of Price and Hammett (cf. Table XVIII). As more entropy is introduced via the substituent in the 2 position of pyridine, the more negative becomes the entropy of activation. Further, the nearly one hundred fold greater rate of reaction of quinuclidene than of triethylamine is (within experimental error) entirely a matter of a more favorable entropy of activation. Quinuclidene may be considered to be triethylamine with the three ethyl groups tied at their ends to a bridgehead carbon atom. Accordingly quinuclidene has many less internal

[167] V. C. Haskell and L. P. Hammett, *J. Am. Chem. Soc.*, 71, 1284 (1949); S. A. Bernhard and L. P. Hammett, *ibid.*, 75, 1798, 5834 (1953); S. A. Bernhard, E. Garfield, and L. P. Hammett, *ibid.*, 76, 991 (1954); P. Riesz and L. P. Hammett, *ibid.*, 76, 992 (1954); H. Samelson and L. P. Hammett, *ibid.*, 78, 524 (1956).

degrees of freedom than triethylamine.   The latter loses 8 e.u. more entropy in the formation of the transition state.

The methyl iodide-amine reaction is also of interest from the standpoint of a relationship between the effect of structure on activation energies and on entropies of activation.   From the results of separating the potential- and kinetic-energy steric effects on ester hydrolysis rates (cf. section XII), Taft was led to the following rule: "If a group such as H (or CH_3) be replaced by a group with many more internal degrees of freedom, and if the activation process is such that these groups are compressed into positions resulting in greater repulsions for the latter than the former substituent, then the activation process will also be accompanied by a greater loss of internal motions." [168] The converse does not necessarily hold.   The increasing values of $\Delta\Delta E_a$ and corresponding decreasing values of $\Delta\Delta S^{\ddagger}$ for the reactions of the 2-alkyl pyridines shown in Table XVIII are therefore nicely consistent with this rule.   Brown and Cahn originally proposed that the $\Delta\Delta E_a$ values in these reactions are measures of increased strain in the transition states.[169]

TABLE XVIII

RELATIVE ENERGIES AND ENTROPIES OF ACTIVATION IN THE REACTION OF METHYL IODIDE WITH AMINES IN NITROBENZENE [169,170]

Substituent	$\Delta\Delta E_a$, kcal.	$\Delta\Delta S^{\ddagger}$, e.u.
Pyridine	(0.0)	(0.0)
2-Methyl pyridine	+0.1	−1.3
2-Ethyl pyridine	+0.3	−1.9
2-i-Propyl pyridine	+0.9	−2.1
2,6-Dimethyl pyridine	+1.0	−2.8
2-t-Butyl pyridine	+3.6	−4.6
Triethylamine	−4.2	−5.9
Quinuclidene	−4.4	+2.3

Sommer and Barie [171] and Price [172] have determined rates, enthalpies, and entropies of activation for the alkaline Si—H cleavage of a series of alkyl silanes in 95% aqueous ethanol.   The rates are not correlated by equation 16, indicating that there are important steric effects in operation.   The entropies of activation show substantially wider

[168] R. W. Taft, Jr., *J. Am. Chem. Soc.*, **75**, 4534 (1953).

[169] H. C. Brown and A. Cahn, *J. Am. Chem. Soc.*, **77**, 1715 (1955).

[170] H. C. Brown and N. R. Eldred, *J. Am. Chem. Soc.*, **71**, 445 (1949).

[171] L. H. Sommer and W. P. Barie, Jr., unpublished results.   The author is indebted to Professor Sommer for permission to quote these data.

[172] F. Price, *J. Am. Chem. Soc.*, **69**, 2600 (1947).

variation with structure than do the enthalpies. The entropies of activation are in good general accord with the Price and Hammett rule. This series has the particular value that the increase in entropy of the silane probably can be estimated closely from the known absolute entropies of the corresponding hydrocarbons.

Table XIX lists the values of $\Delta\Delta S^{\ddagger}$ and $\Delta\Delta H^{\ddagger}$ relative to ethyldimethylsilane as the standard of comparison. Included are the corresponding entropy increments, $\Delta\Delta S^{\circ}_{298}$, for the homomorphic hydrocarbons (using ethyldimethylmethane as the standard of comparison).

TABLE XIX

Comparison of the Relative Entropies of Activation in the Alkaline
Si—H Cleavage of Silanes with the Entropy Increments of
Corresponding Hydrocarbons

Silane	$\Delta\Delta H^{\ddagger,*}$ kcal.	$\Delta\Delta S^{\ddagger,\dagger}$ e.u.	Hydrocarbon	$\Delta\Delta S^{\circ}_{298,}[173]$ e.u.
$C_2H_5(CH_3)_2SiH$	(0.0) §	0	2-Methylbutane	(0.0)
i-$C_3H_7(CH_3)_2SiH$	-0.5 §	-4 §	2,3-Dimethylbutane	$+5.3$
n-$C_3H_7(CH_3)_2SiH$	-1.5 ‖	-5 ‖	2-Methylpentane	$+8.9$
t-$C_4H_9(CH_3)_2SiH$	-0.5 §	-13 §	2,2,3-Trimethylbutane	$+9.5$
$(i$-$C_3H_7)_2(Me)SiH$	-1.0 §	-12 §	2,3,4-Trimethylpentane	$+20.2$
$C_6H_5(CH_3)_2SiH$	-1.0 §	$+1$ §	i-Propylbenzene	$+10.8$

* Given to nearest 0.5 kcal.
† Given to nearest 1.0 e.u.
§ Reference 171.
‖ Reference 172.

Phenyl dimethylsilane does not follow the Price and Hammett rule. Apparently the entropy increase associated with the change from an ethyl group to a phenyl group is not the kind that is frozen out in the transition state. For the alkylsilanes, the decrease in $\Delta\Delta S^{\ddagger}$ values accompanying increasing $\Delta\Delta S^{\circ}_{298}$ values is readily accounted for on the basis that the internal motions of the alkyl groups are increasingly more hindered in the ionic transition state than in the hydrocarbon-like reactant state. There is no indication from the $\Delta\Delta H^{\ddagger}$ values that changes in steric strain play an important role in the rates of these reactions.

VIII. GENERAL RESONANCE EFFECTS OF α,β-UNSATURATED GROUPS

The ionization constants of benzoic, cinnamic, and crotonic acids do not follow equation 16. Instead these unsaturated acids are weaker than the $\sigma^*\rho^*$ correlation (reaction I-3 of Table IX) predicts. These

[173] F. D. Rossini et al., *Selected Values of Physical and Thermodynamic Properties of Hydrocarbons and Related Compounds*, Carnegie Press, Pittsburgh, 1953.

deviations from equation 16 have been ascribed to a decrease in conjugation between the unsaturated substituents and the adjacent carbonyl group in the resulting carboxylate ion compared to that in the free acid.[174] According to cross-conjugation theory, the increase in resonance energy of the carboxylate group (COO^-) compared to the carboxyl group (COOH) leads on the formation of the former to a decrease in resonance energy between the carbonyl carbon and a conjugated unsaturated substituent ($\overset{\frown}{R—C}\overset{\frown}{=O}$).[175]

In the case of benzoic acid (cinnamic and crotonic acids, as well) the deviation from equation 16 indicates that the decreased conjugation (and accompanying solvent effect) is equal to about 0.7 kcal. This value is in very acceptable agreement with the figure of 1 kcal. reached in section IV-4 from a consideration of the ionization constants of benzoic and 2,6-dimethylbenzoic acids. In other words, when resonance between the benzene ring and the adjacent carbonyl group is sterically inhibited in both the acid and the anion, there is no resonance effect (only the polar effect) on the ionization equilibrium. The 2,6-dimethylbenzoic acid follows equation 16 with much better precision than does benzoic acid.

The phenyl and cinnamyl groups follow equation 16 in the rates of dehydration of acetaldehyde hydrate as catalyzed by carboxylic acids (reaction I-11 of Table IX). On the other hand, these groups do not follow equation 16 in the rates of reaction of the carboxylic acids with diphenyldiazomethane (reaction I-6), just as in the ionization of the acids. These results indicate that only in the dehydration reaction is there sufficiently little change in the $\overset{\frown}{R—C}\overset{\frown}{=O}$ resonance between the acid and the reaction transition state so that essentially no resonance effects are associated with these α,β-unsaturated groups. This conclusion is supported by the appreciably lower ρ^* value for the dehydration reaction than the diphenyldiazomethane reaction (cf. discussion in section VI-2).

Rates or equilibria for all kinds of carbonyl addition processes at room temperatures are retarded by α,β-unsaturated groups conjugated (in the reactant state) with the functional center.[176] A number of examples of this kind are collected in Table XX. Listed are $\Delta\Delta F^{\ddagger}$ (or $\Delta\Delta F^{\circ}$) and $\Delta\Delta H^{\ddagger}$ (if available) values for the phenyl group rela-

[174] R. W. Taft, Jr., *J. Am. Chem. Soc.*, *74*, 3127 (1952); *75*, 4237 (1953).

[175] G. E. K. Branch and M. Calvin, *The Theory of Organic Chemistry*, p. 235, Prentice-Hall, New York, 1941.

[176] G. W. Wheland, *The Theory of Resonance*, Chapters **7** and **8**, John Wiley & Sons, New York, 1944.

tive to the methyl group. The phenyl group was chosen because of the greater abundance of data, but it is at least qualitatively typical of other α,β-unsaturated substituents.

TABLE XX

EFFECTS OF α,β-UNSATURATED SUBSTITUENTS ON THE THERMODYNAMIC PROPERTIES OF CARBONYL ADDITION PROCESSES

Reaction [1]	Reference	Solvent	Temperature, °C.	$\Delta\Delta F°$ (or $\Delta\Delta F^{\ddagger}$), kcal.	$\Delta\Delta H°$ (or $\Delta\Delta H^{\ddagger}$), kcal.
1. E. $(R)(n\text{-}C_3H_7)C{=}O + HCN \rightleftarrows$ $R(n\text{-}C_3H_7)C(OH)(CN)$	2	96% aq. C_2H_5OH	20	$+1.9$	
2. E. $(R)(H)C{=}O + 2C_2H_5OH \rightleftarrows$ $(R)(H)C(OC_2H_5)_2 + H_2O$	3	Reaction mixture	25	$+2.3$	
3. E. $(R)(H)C{=}O + H_2 \rightleftarrows R(H)CHOH$	4	Toluene	60	$+1.3$	
4. R. $(R)(H)C{=}O + H_2NNHCONH_2 \rightarrow$ $(R)(H)C{=}NNHCONH_2 + H_2O$	5	H_2O	25	$+3.1$	
5. R. $(R)(CH_3)C{=}O + H_2NNHCONH_2 \rightarrow$ $(R)(CH_3)C{=}NNHCONH_2 + H_2O$	6	H_2O	25	$+3.2$	$+2.6$
6. R. $(R)(H)C{=}NNHCONH_2 + H_2O \rightarrow$ $(R)(H)C{=}O + NH_2NHCONH_2$	5	H_2O	25	$+4.4$	
7. R. $RCOCl + C_2H_5OH \rightarrow$ $RCO_2C_2H_5 + HCl$	7	60% $(C_2H_5)_2O$– 40% C_2H_5OH	25	$+3.1$	$+1.9$
8. R. $RCONHC_6H_5 + C_2H_5OH_2^+ \rightarrow$ $RCO_2C_2H_5 + C_6H_5NH_3^+$	8	C_2H_5OH	65	$+0.6$	

REFERENCES TO TABLE XX

[1] E indicates that data refers to an equilibrium process; R, to a rate process.
[2] A. Lapworth and R. H. F. Manske, *J. Chem. Soc.*, *1928*, 2533.
[3] W. H. Hartung and H. Adkins, *J. Am. Chem. Soc.*, *49*, 2517 (1927).
[4] H. Adkins et al., *J. Am. Chem. Soc.*, *71*, 3622 (1949).
[5] J. B. Conant and P. D. Bartlett, *J. Am. Chem. Soc.*, *54*, 2881 (1932).
[6] F. P. Price, Jr., and L. P. Hammett, *J. Am. Chem. Soc.*, *63*, 2387 (1941).
[7] G. E. K. Branch and A. C. Nixon, *J. Am. Chem. Soc.*, *58*, 2499 (1936).
[8] D. D. Karve and B. W. Kelkar, *Proc. Indian Acad. Sci.*, *24A*, 254 (1946).

Probably none of the $\Delta\Delta F$ or $\Delta\Delta H$ values of Table XX are quantitative measures of resonance effects (for this evaluation in rates of ester hydrolysis cf. section XIII, and in the hydrogenation of aldehydes and ketones cf. section VI-10*b*). In addition to resonance contributions, these values may contain steric and polar effects. The polar effect is particularly likely in view of the greater electron-withdrawing property of the phenyl than the methyl group. There are insufficient data on the effects of other substituents on the rates and equilibria of the reactions of Table XX (except reaction 3) to permit attempts at quantitative separation of polar, steric, and resonance effects.

IX. SUMMARY

The principles of the effect of structure on rates and equilibria have been considered in detail. Polar and steric effects on rates and equilibria have been defined so as to transcend the separation of free energies to potential- and kinetic-energy terms.

Evidence has been presented supporting the following general principles.

1. The effect of structure on free energies of activation can frequently be treated in a quantitative fashion as the sum of independent contributions from polar (P), steric (S), and resonance (R) effects; i.e.,

$$\Delta\Delta F^{\ddagger} \doteq P + S + R$$

(a) For reactions of p-substituted benzene derivatives in which there is no resonance interaction between substituent and functional center in either the reactant or transition states

$$\log (k/k_0) = \sigma_p \rho = [(\sigma_p - \sigma') + \sigma']\rho$$

$$= \text{"Resonance polar effect + Inductive polar effect"}$$

(b) For reactions of p-substituted benzene derivatives in which there is a change in resonance interaction of the substituent with the reaction center between the initial and the transition state

$$\log (k/k_0) = \sigma_p \rho + \psi = \text{Polar effect + Resonance effect}$$

(c) For the rate of hydrolysis of the ester $RCO_2C_2H_5$

$$\log (k/k_0) = \sigma^*\rho^* + E_s + \psi = \text{Polar + Steric + Resonance effects}$$

2. For otherwise equivalent alkaline (B) and the acidic (A) normal ester hydrolysis rates ($RCO_2C_2H_5$), steric and resonance effects (E_s and ψ, respectively) of the R group are essentially the same. Therefore,

(a) $\log (k/k_0)_B - \log (k/k_0)_A = [\sigma^*\rho^*_B + (E_s)_B + (\psi)_B]$

$$- [\sigma^*\rho^*_A + (E_s)_A + (\psi)_A] \equiv (+2.48)\sigma^*$$

3. Corresponding polar and steric effects of a substituent on the logarithm of rates are generally completely different quantitative functions of structure. (a) Polar effects are approximately additive. (b) Steric effects are generally far from additive.

4. The proportionality between the corresponding polar effect contributions to the free energies of activation of one reaction series com-

pared to another (the linear polar-energy relationship) is much more general than the proportionality of the total substituent effects on free energies of activation (the linear free-energy relationship).

(a) Even though there are important steric and resonance as well as polar effects of substituents on rates (causing failure of linear free-energy relationships), corresponding polar effects of substituents P_σ (separated by a suitable means from log (k/k_0) values) are frequently proportional between one reaction series (1) and another (2); i.e.,

$$\log (k/k_0)_1 \neq \rho \log (k/k_0)_2$$

but

$$(P_\sigma)_1 = \sigma^*\rho^*_1 \quad \text{and} \quad (P_\sigma)_2 = \sigma^*\rho^*_2$$

5. For reactions involving substituents adjacent to the reaction center, the criterion of near constancy of all but polar effects within a reaction series is the equation

$$\log (k/k_0) = \sigma^*\rho^* \quad \text{or} \quad (\Sigma\sigma^*)\rho^*$$

6. The direction of steric and resonance effects of substituents on rates or equilibria can be predicted from a knowledge of the structural change at the reaction center.

7. There is probably no quantitative proportionality of wide generality between the corresponding steric effects of substituents on one reaction series compared to another (i.e., linear steric energy relationships). Such a relationship does exist in some cases, however.

(a) In limited reaction series within which polar and resonance effects are nearly constant,

$$\log (k/k_0) = \delta E_s$$

8. The deviations from the equation log $(k/k_0) = (\Sigma\sigma^*)\rho^*$ may sometimes be used to evaluate quantitatively the resonance (ψ) and steric (E_s') effects of substituents; i.e.,

$$\log (k/k_0) - (\Sigma\sigma^*)\rho^* = \psi \text{ (and/or } E_s')$$

9. The successful use of all the previous relationships for the correlation and prediction of rates and equilibria, or the study of structural relationships and reaction mechanisms, *must be based upon a reaction series in which the polar, steric, and resonance requirements of the substituents are varied widely.*

PART B.   MORE DETAILED CONSIDERATIONS

X. ENTROPY EFFECTS AND THE HAMMETT EQUATION.   RIGOR OF THE DEFINITION OF POLAR EFFECTS

Let us reconsider the basic equation 4'.   If $RT \ln (\Pi Q^{\ddagger})$ is zero, then

$$\Delta\Delta F^{\ddagger} = \Delta\Delta E_p{}^{\ddagger} \qquad (21)$$

That is, under this special circumstance the relative free-energy change is independent of temperature and is equal to the relative potential-energy change.

Since the partition function term $\ln (\Pi Q^{\ddagger})$ cannot be directly measured, we must resort to the measurable term $\Delta\Delta S^{\ddagger}$ to provide an indication of whether $RT \ln (\Pi Q^{\ddagger})$ is essentially zero within a particular reaction series.   One of the conditions (cf. eq. 6') under which $\Delta\Delta S^{\ddagger}$ becomes zero is that $-R \ln (\Pi Q^{\ddagger}) = 0$ and $-RT \dfrac{d \ln (\Pi Q^{\ddagger})}{dt} = 0.$[177]

There is a considerable probability (although it is not a rigid requirement) that this condition holds when $\Delta\Delta S^{\ddagger}$ is shown to approach zero.

To choose a specific example, the saponifications of m- and p-substituted benzoates have nearly constant entropies of activation.[178] The logarithms of the relative rates in this reaction series, therefore, are apparently equal to potential-energy effects; i.e., equation 21 holds.   On the other hand, in the ionization of m- and p-substituted benzoic acids (H_2O, 25°) the relative entropies of reaction are much more important than relative enthalpies.[179]   Beyond question, $RT \ln (\Pi Q)$ terms do not reduce to zero in this second reaction series.

Yet there is a precise parallel between $\log (k/k_0)$ values for the former reaction series and corresponding $\log (K/K_0)$ values for the latter (the Hammett equation 7).   This relationship requires the following condition.

$$(\Delta\Delta E_p{}^{\ddagger})_{BS}\rho = [(\Delta\Delta E_p{}^{\circ})_{BI} - (RT \ln (\Pi Q))_{BI}] \qquad (22)$$

The subscript BS refers to the rates of the benzoate saponifications and BI refers to the benzoic acid ionizations.   The potential-energy effects in the one series must quantitatively parallel the *sum* of po-

[177] L. P. Hammett, *Physical Organic Chemistry*, p. 78, McGraw-Hill Book Co., New York, 1940.

[178] Cf. reference 167, p. 121.

[179] Reference 167, p. 84.

tential-energy and kinetic-energy effects in the second.   Considering the wide variety of substituent sizes, entropy contents, and solvating powers involved, such a relationship is beyond reason except under the following circumstance.   The kinetic-energy terms parallel in a quantitative fashion the corresponding potential-energy terms in the benzoic acid ionizations.   Further, a similar relationship must exist between the potential-energy effects in the saponification rates and corresponding potential-energy effects in the benzoic acid ionizations. That is, when

$$(\Delta\Delta E_p{}^{\ddagger})_{BS} = \alpha(\Delta\Delta E_p)_{BI} \tag{23}$$

and

$$(\Delta\Delta E_p{}^{\circ})_{BI} = \beta(-RT \ln (\Pi Q)_{BI}) \tag{24}$$

with α and β characteristic proportionality constants, then equation 22 follows; i.e.,

$$(\Delta\Delta E_p{}^{\ddagger})_{BS} \left(\frac{\beta + 1}{\alpha\beta}\right) = (\Delta\Delta E_p{}^{\ddagger})_{BS}\, \rho = [(\Delta\Delta E_p{}^{\circ})_{BI} - (RT \ln (\Pi Q))_{BI}]$$

$$\left(\frac{\beta + 1}{\alpha\beta}\right) = \rho = \text{a characteristic proportionality constant.}$$

We see, then, that $\Delta\Delta F^{\circ}$ in the ionization of m- and p-substituted benzoic acids is *not equal* to a potential-energy term, but it is *proportional* to one.   In this respect $\Delta\Delta F^{\circ}$ for this reaction is *a measure* of potential-energy effects.   Since our concern in reactivity correlations is only the proportionality of the potential-energy effects of substituents, the $\Delta\Delta F^{\circ}$ values for the benzoic acid ionizations are just as good measures of polar potential-energy effects as are the $\Delta\Delta F^{\ddagger}$ values for the benzoate saponifications.

The situation which has been illustrated by the above two reaction series prevails generally in the reactions of m- and p-substituted benzene derivatives.   Some reaction series have essentially constant entropies of activation or reaction; others have widely varying entropy terms.[180]

The basic criterion of polar effects of substituents in the reaction of m- and p-substituted benzene derivatives is not that $\Delta\Delta S^{\ddagger}$ be zero, but simply that the Hammett equation be followed.   The definition that a substituent effect on rate is a polar effect if equation 7 or 16 is

[180] See for example reference 22; G. E. K. Branch and A. C. Nixon, *J. Am. Chem. Soc.*, *58*, 2499 (1936); I. Meloche, K. J. Laidler, *ibid.*, *73*, 1712 (1951); E. Berliner and L. H. Altschul, *ibid.*, *74*, 4110 (1952); S. J. Cristol et al., *ibid.*, *74*, 3333 (1952); E. W. Timm and C. N. Hinshelwood, *J. Chem. Soc.*, *1938*, 862; G. N. Burkhardt, C. Horrex, and D. I. Jenkins, *ibid.*, *1936*, 1649; W. C. Davies, *ibid.*, *1938*, 1865.

followed, even though both kinetic- and potential-energy terms are involved, is perfectly rigorous for the correlation of potential-energy effects of substituents. The kinetic-energy terms (if any), in effect, go into the empirical susceptibility constant ρ.

The above discussion is aimed at clearing the wide confusion which has prevailed concerning the Hammett equation and the effects of substituents on entropies of activation and reaction. Prominent workers have incorrectly concluded that linear free-energy relationships such as equation 7 strongly imply that entropy terms remain constant within a reaction series. Others have considered that the effects of m and p substituents on reactions of benzene derivatives do not measure polar effects unless the entropies of activation are constant. The latter conclusion is correct only if the Hammett equation fails. Variable entropies of activation serve as a useful warning that substantial changes in steric hindrances of internal motions or steric hindrances of solvation may be involved within a reaction series. This possibility is eliminated, however, by demonstrating that for a wide variety of substituents equation 7 or 16 is followed with usual precision.

It is of interest to consider the kind of kinetic-energy terms (polar kinetic-energy effects) which quantitatively parallel corresponding potential-energy terms. Hammett has shown that $\Delta\Delta S°$ values in the ionization of m- and p-substituted benzoic acids parallel $\Delta\Delta F°$ values precisely, and the proportionality constant is that predicted by considering the effect of the substituents on the electrostatic energy of the benzoate ion.[181] This result indicates that the internal motions of the substituents do not contribute to $\Delta\Delta F°$ but that kinetic-energy terms resulting from "external" solvent interactions (which are directly related to the internal electron distributions) do contribute.[181] In this connection it should be remembered that the equating of the free-energy change with electrical work is the basis of all electrostatic theories (e.g., the Debye-Hückel theory) of electrolytes. Entropy changes are always associated with these $\Delta F°$ values.[182]

Kinetic-energy terms arising from solvent interaction with poles and dipoles are probably the principal cause of variable entropy terms in the reactions of m- and p-substituted benzene derivatives. The fact that infrared absorption frequencies, for example, are correlated by the Hammett equation [183] suggests, however, that certain types of in-

[181] Reference 167, pp. 83, 84, 122.

[182] A. A. Frost and R. G. Pearson, *Kinetic and Mechanisms*, Chapter 7, John Wiley & Sons, New York, 1953.

[183] H. H. Jaffé, *Chem. Revs.*, *53*, 214 (1953).

ternal motions may produce kinetic-energy terms which parallel the potential-energy effects of m and p substituents.

It is not known whether the σ^* values obtained by equation 14 contain contributions from kinetic-energy terms. The same information is also lacking for an extensive series of the log (k/k_0) values for the reactions (cf. Table IX) which follow equation 16. By analogy with the above discussion of the Hammett equation, it is immaterial to the correlation of the polar effects whether or not polar kinetic-energy terms are involved. The argument that the σ^* values are measures of potential-energy polar effects would be strengthened, however, by the demonstration of constant entropies of activation *for at least one* reaction series that follows equation 16.

The relationship between $\Delta\Delta S^\circ$ and $\Delta\Delta F^\circ$ mentioned above for the ionization of m- and p-substituted benzene derivatives is a necessary one for linear free-energy relationships in which the entropy terms do not remain constant.[184] By the well-known relationship between the thermodynamic quantities, a quantitative parallel between $\Delta\Delta H^\circ$ and $\Delta\Delta S^\circ$ is also required. Leffler has discussed this connection between the Hammett equation and linear entropy-enthalpy relationships.[185]

XI. $\Delta\Delta F^\ddagger$ OR $\Delta\Delta H^\ddagger$ AS THE BETTER MEASURE OF $\Delta\Delta E_p^{\ddagger}$

In the quest for experimental quantities which are approximately equal to the potential-energy terms $\Delta\Delta E_p^{\ddagger}$ of equation 4′, the question naturally arises as to which is the better measure of this term, $\Delta\Delta F^\ddagger$ or $\Delta\Delta H^\ddagger$? From equations 4′ and 5′ it is readily apparent that this is equivalent to asking which kinetic-energy term, $RT \ln (\Pi Q^\ddagger)$ or $RT^2 \dfrac{\ln (\Pi Q^\ddagger)}{dt}$, is nearer to zero. No general answer to this question can be given in the absence of the necessary partition functions. From the principles involved, it appears that in certain reactions $\Delta\Delta H^\ddagger$ is the more appropriate quantity, whereas in others it is $\Delta\Delta F^\ddagger$ that is wanted.[186]

The first condition (that $\Delta\Delta H^\ddagger$ is the better estimator of $\Delta\Delta E_p^{\ddagger}$) appears to be more commonly associated with reaction series carried out in the absence of a solvent (e.g., the one discussed in section VI-10a) or ones for which it appears that there is no large change in solvation accompanying the reaction of equation 3′. Probably this condition is

[184] Reference 173, p. 193.

[185] J. E. Leffler, *J. Org. Chem.*, **20**, 1202 (1955).

[186] L. P. Hammett, *Introduction to the Study of Physical Chemistry*, pp. 161–163, McGraw-Hill Book Co., New York, 1952.

of more general occurrence than the second, and is generally assumed in the absence of evidence to the contrary. However, the relative ionizations of carboxylic acids, for one, appear to fall in the second category; i.e., for this reaction $\Delta\Delta F°$ is in a practical sense a much better measure of $\Delta\Delta E_p°$ than is $\Delta\Delta H°$.[186]

It is instructive to consider the relationship between $\Delta\Delta E_0°$, $\Delta\Delta H°_{298}$, and $\Delta\Delta F°_{298}$ for two hypothetical hydrocarbon equilibria for which the necessary data are available. The distinction between $\Delta\Delta E_p°$ and $\Delta\Delta E_0°$ is that the former is obtained from the latter by removing the

TABLE XXI

EFFECT OF STRUCTURE ON STANDARD ENERGIES (°K.), ENTHALPIES (298°K.), AND FREE ENERGIES (298°K.) OF REACTION [187]

Reaction: $R\text{—}H + H_3C\text{—}CH_3 \rightleftarrows R\text{—}CH_3 + CH_4$

Substituents R	$\Delta\Delta E_0°$	$\Delta\Delta H°_{298}$	$\Delta\Delta F°_{298}$
H	−15.5	−15.5	−16.4
CH_3	(0.0)	(0.0)	(0.0)
C_2H_5	−2.4	−2.2	−2.0
$n\text{-}C_4H_9$	−3.4	−2.8	−2.5
$neo\text{-}C_5H_{11}$	−2.8	−2.3	−3.0
$i\text{-}C_3H_7$	−4.6	−4.3	−3.0
$t\text{-}C_4H_9$	−6.2	−5.9	−3.6
$(CH_3)_2(t\text{-}C_4H_9)C\text{—}$	−3.0	−2.7	−0.2
Cyclo-C_6H_{11}	−5.8	−5.2	−5.4
C_6H_5	−6.0	−5.3	−6.0
$CH_2\text{=}CH\text{—}$	−5.5	−5.3	−5.6
$C_6H_5CH_2$	−3.1	−2.5	−2.3
$C_6H_5(CH_3)CH\text{—}$	−4.1	−3.8	−2.8

Reaction: $R\text{—}\overset{\displaystyle H}{\underset{}{C}}\text{=}\overset{\displaystyle H}{\underset{}{C}}\text{—}H + CH_4 \rightleftarrows R\text{—}\overset{\displaystyle H}{\underset{\displaystyle CH_3}{C}}\text{——}\overset{\displaystyle H}{\underset{\displaystyle H}{C}}H$

Substituents R			
H	−1.0	−1.0	−2.6
CH_3	0.0	0.0	0.0
$C_2H_5\text{—}$	−0.8	−0.9	−1.4
$n\text{-}C_4H_9$	0.0	−0.3	−0.5
$i\text{-}C_3H_7$	+0.7	+0.8	+0.5
$t\text{-}C_4H_9$	+1.7	+1.6	+1.0

[187] (a) Values in this table were calculated from the data of *Selected Values of Physical and Thermodynamic Properties of Hydrocarbons and Related Compounds,* reference 173. (b) The values given for the upper reaction of Table XXI are also those for the effect of structure on such reactions as $R\text{—}H + CH_3 \rightleftarrows R\text{—}CH_3 + H$ and $R\text{—}H + CH_2 \rightleftarrows R\text{—}CH_3$.

changes in zero-point vibrational energies, $\Delta \Delta E_z°$, associated with the equilibrium 3; cf. section III-3. The results are presented in Table XXI. The $\Delta \Delta H_{298}°$ values rarely differ from $\Delta \Delta E_0°$ values by more than 0.5 kcal., whereas $\Delta \Delta F_{298}°$ values may be different by as much as 2.8 kcal. It is interesting to note that, for the relatively rigid substituents, e.g., cyclo-C_6H_{11}, C_6H_5, and CH_2=CH—, $\Delta \Delta F_{298}°$ values are very close (better than $\Delta \Delta H_{298}°$) to corresponding $\Delta \Delta E_0°$ values. These results also indicate the qualitative relationships between $\Delta \Delta F_p°$, $\Delta \Delta H_{298}°$ and $\Delta \Delta F_{298}°$. This conclusion follows from the fact that $\Delta \Delta H_0° = \Delta \Delta F_0° = \Delta \Delta E_0° = \Delta \Delta E_p° + \Delta \Delta E_z°$.

In terms of rate data, information is scarce, but some evidence that kinetic-energy terms may be relatively unimportant in an enthalpy of activation comes from the results of Caldin, Long, and Trouse.[188] The activation energy for the reaction of ethylate ion with trinitrotoluene in ethanol has been found to be constant (within the experimental error of 2.5%) from 193 to 293°K.

XII. THE SEPARATION OF STERIC EFFECTS IN ESTER HYDROLYSIS RATES TO THE CONTRIBUTING POTENTIAL- AND KINETIC-ENERGY TERMS

The separation of relative rates to polar and steric substituent constants discussed in section V may be expressed in terms of the relative free energy of activation by the following equation: [189]

$$\Delta \Delta F^{\ddagger} = \Delta \Delta E_{\sigma}^{\ddagger} + \Delta \Delta E_{s}^{\ddagger} \tag{25}$$

$\Delta \Delta E_{\sigma}^{\ddagger}$ is the relative energy of activation associated with a polar effect, i.e., the polar activation energy. $\Delta \Delta E_{s}^{\ddagger}$ may be called the total steric energy of activation. To the approximation used in obtaining steric substituent constants (section V-3b), these quantities are defined as

$$\Delta \Delta E_{\sigma}^{\ddagger} = -2.303RT(\sigma^*\rho^*) \text{ [190]} \tag{26}$$

and

$$\Delta \Delta E_{s}^{\ddagger} = -2.303RT(E_s) \tag{27}$$

[188] E. F. Caldin, G. Long, and F. W. Trouse, *Nature, 171*, 1124 (1953).

[189] R. W. Taft, Jr., *J. Am. Chem. Soc., 74*, 4534 (1953).

[190] (a) If σ^* values contain kinetic-energy contributions, these contributions may be removed in the empirical ρ^* value, so this possibility is not inconsistent with $\Delta \Delta E_p^{\ddagger}$ as a *measure* of a potential-energy effect (cf. section X); (b) in using equations 26 and 27 to obtain the results given in Tables XXII and XXIII, σ^* and E_s values have been adjusted so that the substituent H, rather than CH_3, is the standard of comparison.

where the reaction constant ρ^* is equal to $+2.48$ in the alkaline saponi-fication and zero in the acid-catalyzed hydrolysis. Equation 27 is, of course, valid only at the temperature for which E_s has been deter-mined.

The $\Delta\Delta E_\sigma^\ddagger$ term is only one of the potential-energy factors that may contribute to the $\Delta\Delta E_p^\ddagger$ term of the basic equation 4'. Neglect-ing cases where changes in attractive interactions between substitu-ent and reaction center may occur between transition and reactant states, the effects that may contribute to $\Delta\Delta E_p^\ddagger$ terms according to the discussion of section III-4 are represented by the equation

$$\Delta\Delta E_p^\ddagger = \Delta\Delta E_\sigma^\ddagger + \Delta\Delta E_\psi^\ddagger + \Delta\Delta E_R^\ddagger \qquad (28)$$

The terms on the right-hand side of this equation are the potential-energy contributions of polar, resonance, and steric repulsion or strain effects, respectively.

Substituting equation 28 in equation 4' gives

$$\Delta\Delta F^\ddagger = \Delta\Delta E_\sigma^\ddagger + \Delta\Delta E_R^\ddagger + \Delta\Delta E_\psi^\ddagger - RT \ln (\Pi Q^\ddagger) \qquad (29)$$

This equation summarizes most of the effects that may generally con-tribute to reactivity. Comparing equations 29 and 25, and remem-bering that for unconjugated substituents the term $\Delta\Delta E_\psi^\ddagger$ has been taken as zero (section V-3b), the following relationship results

$$\Delta\Delta E_s^\ddagger = \Delta\Delta E_R^\ddagger - RT \ln (\Pi Q^\ddagger) \qquad (30)$$

Equations 27 and 30 show that the steric substituent constants E_s are determined by both potential-energy (strain) and kinetic-energy (hindrances to motions) steric effects.

The separation of the total steric energy of activation into the two terms on the right-hand side of equation 30 is important theoretically, for a determination of the effect of structure on $\Delta\Delta E_R^\ddagger$ and $-RT \ln (\Pi Q^\ddagger)$ terms leads to a more complete understanding of the structural factors affecting chemical reactivity. The separation has a very prac-tical significance, for from it we learn the part $(\Delta\Delta E_R^\ddagger)$ of the total $(\Delta\Delta E_s^\ddagger)$ steric effect observed in the neighborhood of room tempera-ture that may be effectively overcome at high temperatures.

Enthalpies and entropies of activation (from temperature coeffi-cients of rates) in combination with equations 25 and 30 permit an approximate separation of $\Delta\Delta F^\ddagger$ to $\Delta\Delta E_\sigma^\ddagger$, $\Delta\Delta E_R^\ddagger$, and $-RT \ln (\Pi Q^\ddagger)$ terms. This follows from the basic equations 5' and 6', given below with the substitutions indicated above; i.e.,

$$\Delta\Delta H^{\ddagger} = \Delta\Delta E_{\sigma}{}^{\ddagger} + \Delta\Delta E_{R}{}^{\ddagger} + RT^2 \frac{d \ln (\Pi Q^{\ddagger})}{dt} \qquad (31)$$

$$\Delta\Delta S^{\ddagger} = R \ln (\Pi Q^{\ddagger}) + RT \frac{d(\ln \Pi Q^{\ddagger})}{dt} \qquad (32)$$

If, as a first approximation, the $RT^2 \dfrac{d \ln (\Pi Q^{\ddagger})}{dt}$ terms are taken as negligible (section XI), equations 31 and 32 reduce to

$$\Delta\Delta H^{\ddagger} = \Delta\Delta E_{\sigma}{}^{\ddagger} + \Delta\Delta E_{R}{}^{\ddagger} \qquad (31')$$

$$\Delta\Delta S^{\ddagger} = R \ln (\Pi Q^{\ddagger}) \qquad (32')$$

The fact that plots of log k vs. $1/T$ are linear within experimental uncertainty over 30–40° temperature intervals (which are admittedly small compared to 300°, however) is evidence consistent with the assumption that $RT^2 \dfrac{d \ln (\Pi Q^{\ddagger})}{dt}$ terms are small.[191, 192]

From equations 31', 32', and 26, expressions are obtained for each of the desired rate effects in terms of experimentally determinable quantities.

$$\Delta\Delta E_{R}{}^{\ddagger} = \Delta\Delta H^{\ddagger} - \Delta\Delta E_{\sigma}{}^{\ddagger} = \Delta\Delta H^{\ddagger} + 2.303RT(\sigma^*\rho^*) \qquad (33)$$

$$-RT \ln (\Pi Q^{\ddagger}) = -T\Delta\Delta S^{\ddagger} \qquad (34)$$

Making use (according to equation 5') of the reliable temperature coefficients of rates from the literature (largely from the excellent studies of Hilton Smith and coworkers), the steric strains $\Delta\Delta E_R{}^{\ddagger}$ associated with various unconjugated substituents R have been calculated for hydrolysis rates of esters, RCO_2R'. The results are listed in Table XXII. The corresponding total steric energies of activation $\Delta\Delta E_s{}^{\ddagger}$ and steric hindrances of internal motions $-RT \ln (\Pi Q^{\ddagger})$ at 30°C. are also listed. The values of $\Delta\Delta E_R{}^{\ddagger}$ and $-RT \ln (\Pi Q^{\ddagger})$ given in Table XXII are, wherever possible, averages obtained from $\Delta\Delta H^{\ddagger}$ and $\Delta\Delta S^{\ddagger}$ values for both the alkaline and the acid-catalyzed reactions. Deviations from the average in no case exceed 0.3 kcal. $\Delta\Delta E_R{}^{\ddagger}$ was taken as zero if a value between ±0.2 kcal. was obtained. The total steric energies of activation $\Delta\Delta E_s{}^{\ddagger}$ were obtained by equation 27 using H (rather than CH_3) as the standard substituent of comparison.

[191] H. A. Smith, *J. Am. Chem. Soc.*, **61**, 254 (1939).
[192] H. A. Smith and J. Burn, *J. Am. Chem. Soc.*, **66**, 1494 (1944).

TABLE XXII

Contributions of Steric Strain and Steric Hindrance of Motions to the Total Steric Effect of Aliphatic Groups, R, in Rates of Esterification and Ester Hydrolysis (RCOOR′) at 30°C.[188]

Substituent R	Total Steric Energy of Activation, $\Delta\Delta E_s^{\ddagger}$, at 30°C., kcal.	Increased Steric Strain, $\Delta\Delta E_R^{\ddagger}$, kcal.	Increased Steric Hindrance of Motions, $RT \ln (\Pi Q^{\ddagger})$, at 30°C., kcal.
H	(0.0)	(0.0)	(0.0)
CH₃—	+1.7	0.0	+1.6
C₂H₅	+1.8	0.0	+1.8
n-C₃H₇, n-C₄H₉, n-C₅H₁₁	+2.2	0.0	+2.1
C₆H₅CH₂—	+2.2	0.0	+2.2
C₆H₅CH₂CH₂—	+2.3	0.0	+2.2
i-C₃H₇—	+2.4	0.0	+2.5
i-C₄H₉—	+3.0	0.0	+2.8
Cyclo-C₆H₁₁CH₂—	+3.0	+0.7	+2.4
s-C₄H₉—	+3.1	+0.5	+2.6
s-C₄H₉CH₂—	+3.1	+0.4	+2.7
t-C₄H₉—	+3.8	+1.4	+2.2
neo-C₅H₁₁	+4.1	+1.8	+2.3
(C₆H₅)(C₂H₅)CH—	+3.8	+1.2	+2.6
(C₆H₅)₂CH—	+4.2	+1.8	+2.3
(C₂H₅)₂CH—	+4.4	+2.0	+2.4
(i-C₄H₉)₂CH—	+5.1	+2.6	+2.4
(neo-C₅H₁₁)(CH₃)₂C—	+5.3	+2.7	+2.5
(neo-C₅H₁₁)₂CH—	+6.0	+3.5	+2.4
(t-C₄H₉)(CH₃)CH—	6.2	+3.6	+2.5
(C₂H₅)₃C—	+6.8	+4.3 *	+2.5 *
(t-C₄H₉)(CH₃)₂C—	+6.9	+4.4 *	+2.5 *
(t-C₄H₉)(neo-C₅H₁₁)(CH₃)C—	+7.1	+4.6 *	+2.5 *

* Steric strains have been estimated from the total steric energy of activation, $\Delta\Delta E_s^{\ddagger}$, using the apparent limiting value of $-RT \ln (\Pi Q^{\ddagger})$ of approximately 2.5 kcal.

Because of the methods employed, the sum of $\Delta\Delta E_R^{\ddagger}$ and $-RT \ln (\Pi Q^{\ddagger})$ does not in every case total exactly (as it should) to $\Delta\Delta E_s^{\ddagger}$. The sources of data used are the following: (1) the acid-catalyzed esterification of carboxylic acids with methanol; [191-193] (2) the acid-catalyzed hydrolysis of ethyl esters in 70% (by volume) aqueous acetone; [194a] (3) the alkaline hydrolysis of ethyl esters in 85% (by volume) aqueous ethanol; [194b] and (4) the alkaline hydrolysis of benzyl esters in 60% (by volume) aqueous acetone.[195]

Insufficient data are available to permit the same type of analysis

[193] K. Loening, A. B. Garrett, and M. S. Newman, J. Am. Chem. Soc., 74, 3929 (1952).

[194] (a) H. A. Smith and R. R. Myers, J. Am. Chem. Soc., 64, 2362 (1942); (b) H. S. Levenson and H. A. Smith, J. Am. Chem. Soc., 62, 2324 (1940).

[195] E. Tommila, Ann. Acad. Sci. Fennicae, Ser. A59, No. 4, 3 (1942); C. A., 42, 4031 (1948).

to be carried out for structure variation in R' of RCOOR', or for o-substituted benzoates.

The fact that $\Delta\Delta F^{\ddagger}$ values (or log (k/k_0) values; cf. section V-2a) are very nearly independent of wide ranges of solvent composition [196] indicates that the $-RT \ln (\Pi Q^{\ddagger})$ terms of Table XXII are associated with increased steric hindrance of the internal motions of the substituents groups (as expressed in section V-3a). If steric inhibition of solvation were involved, for example, $-RT \ln (\Pi Q^{\ddagger})$ terms (and thus $\Delta\Delta F^{\ddagger}$ values) would vary with the size and nature of the solvent molecules. Further, the $-RT \ln (\Pi Q^{\ddagger})$ terms would decrease rather than increase with increasing steric requirements of the substituent R, because of increased "freezing out" of the solvent in the charged transition state.

A number of important conclusions are to be drawn from the results given in Table XXII. The introduction of a straight-chain alkyl group in place of the standard hydrogen substituent results in an increase in activation energy due to increased steric hindrance of motions.[197] For the lower members of the homologous series, this hindrance increases with the number of carbon atoms introduced. This is a result in accord with the principle of Price and Hammett (cf. section VII-4). The more entropy that is introduced into the system via the substituent group R, the more is frozen out in the transition state. It is to be noted, however, that the entropy which is frozen out is that introduced close to the reaction center. The introduction of alkyl groups beyond the γ position leads to no further increase in the $-RT \ln (\Pi Q^{\ddagger})$ term.

The introduction of any aliphatic derivative in place of hydrogen leads to increased steric hindrance of motions, but not necessarily to increased steric strain. The former is the only steric effect involved in a number of cases and is accordingly more sensitive to such a structural change than the latter. It is further important to notice that, for the highly branched groups, the change in steric hindrance of motions appears to reach a limiting value of about 2.5 kcal. Thus the introduction of alkyl groups into a sufficiently branched aliphatic derivative leads to no further freezing-out of entropy in the transition state. This result implies that such groups have considerably restricted motions in the reactant state.

Increased steric strain becomes increasingly greater with branched-chain substituents the larger the number and the greater the steric

[196] R. W. Taft, Jr., *J. Am. Chem. Soc.*, *74*, 2739 (1952).

[197] Cf., however, H. M. Humphreys and L. P. Hammett, *J. Am. Chem. Soc.*, *78*, 521 (1956).

requirements of the branched groups. In a number of cases the steric strain term makes much the larger contribution to the total steric effect. However, no substituent leads to increased steric strain without an accompanying increased steric hindrance of motions.

This last result may be stated in the following more general manner: "If a group such as H of CH$_3$ be replaced by a group with many more internal degrees of freedom, and if the activation process is such that these groups are compressed into positions resulting in greater repulsions for the latter than the former substituent, then the activation process will also be accompanied by a greater loss of internal motions." This statement has been referred to as the strain-entropy (*SE*) principle, and it is proposed as a working hypothesis to account for the parallel retarding effects sometimes observed in relative enthalpies and entropies of activation resulting from structure variation.[188] This principle is not intended to apply to those reaction processes in which bulky groups lead to a freezing-out of solvent, but only to those (like the present) where steric hindrance of solvation makes little contribution to $\Delta\Delta E_R^{\ddagger}$ and $-RT \ln (\Pi Q^{\ddagger})$ terms.

In view of the large number and variety of groups for which the *SE* principle holds without exception, there is the strong implication that the absence of the increased steric hindrance of motions term requires the absence of a corresponding increased steric strain term. That is, an appreciable steric hindrance of motions term for the type of substitution specified by the *SE* principle is a necessary but not a sufficient condition for an appreciable steric strain term. Accordingly, the absence of the increased steric hindrance of motions term may be used to demonstrate the absence of increased steric strain (cf. following section).

XIII. THE EVALUATION OF RESONANCE EFFECTS AND RESONANCE ENERGIES FROM ESTER HYDROLYSIS RATE DATA

In accord with the discussion of section V-4, equations 25, 31, and 33 must be invalid in the case of α,β-unsaturated substituents. The more general equations 28 and 29 involving the resonance factor $\Delta\Delta E_\psi^{\ddagger}$ must be used. In fact, ester rate data may be employed to obtain reasonable estimates of the $\Delta\Delta E_\psi^{\ddagger}$ term.[198, 199] From equations

[198] H. A. Smith, J. B. Conley, and W. H. King, *J. Am. Chem. Soc.*, *73*, 4633 (1951).
[199] R. W. Taft, Jr., *J. Am. Chem. Soc.*, *74*, 3120 (1952); *75*, 4537 (1953).

5' and 28 and the assumption that $RT^2 \dfrac{d \ln (\Pi Q^{\ddagger})}{dt}$ is small, we have, approximately,

$$\Delta\Delta H^{\ddagger} = \Delta\Delta E_{\sigma}^{\ddagger} + \Delta\Delta E_R^{\ddagger} + \Delta\Delta E_{\psi}^{\ddagger} \tag{35}$$

Further, application of the strain-entropy (SE) principle indicates that $\Delta\Delta E_R^{\ddagger}$ for a number of α,β-unsaturated substituents is close to zero. Listed in Table XXIII are $-RT \ln (\Pi Q^{\ddagger})$ terms (obtained by

TABLE XXIII

RESONANCE ENERGIES FROM AN APPLICATION OF THE *SE* PRINCIPLE

Substituent	$-RT \ln (\Pi Q^{\ddagger})$[198, 199] (300°K.), kcal.	$\Delta\Delta H_A^{\ddagger}$,[198, 200] kcal.	$\Delta\Delta H_B^{\ddagger} + 2.303$ $RT(\sigma^*\rho^*{}_B)$,[201] kcal.	$\Delta\Delta E_{\psi}^{\ddagger}$(ave.), kcal.
Hydrogen	(0.0)	(0.0)	(0.0)	(0.0)
Phenyl	+0.3	4.6	5.0	4.8
2-Furyl	−0.6	6.1	—	6.1
3-Furyl	−0.3	5.2	—	5.2
Cinnamyl	−0.5	—	5.1	5.1

methods discussed in section XII) for several α,β-unsaturated substituents. There is no case involving the α,β-unsaturated substituents in which the $-RT \ln (\Pi Q^{\ddagger})$ term is a positive quantity (outside of experimental error), and thus by the *SE* principle it follows that $\Delta\Delta E_R^{\ddagger}$ is negligible; i.e.,

$$\Delta\Delta H^{\ddagger} = \Delta\Delta E_{\sigma}^{\ddagger} + \Delta\Delta E_{\psi}^{\ddagger} \tag{36}$$

By the methods of section XII, one then obtains

$$\Delta\Delta E_{\psi}^{\ddagger} = (\Delta\Delta H^{\ddagger})_B + 2.303RT(\sigma^*\rho^*{}_B) \tag{36'}$$

or

$$\Delta\Delta E_{\psi}^{\ddagger} = (\Delta\Delta H^{\ddagger})_A \tag{36''}$$

Table XXIII lists values of $(\Delta\Delta H^{\ddagger})_A$ and of the quantity $(\Delta\Delta H_A^{\ddagger} + 2.303RT(\sigma^*\rho^*{}_B)$ for the α,β-unsaturated substituents. The average value is taken as $\Delta\Delta E_{\psi}^{\ddagger}$. The $\Delta\Delta E_{\psi}^{\ddagger}$ values are within the limits estimated by other means for the resonance stabilization resulting

[200] H. A. Smith and R. B. Hurley, *J. Am. Chem. Soc.*, *72*, 112 (1950).

[201] Obtained from data of the following: D. P. Evans, J. J. Gordon, and H. B. Watson, *J. Chem. Soc.*, *1937*, 1430; H. A. Smith and H. S. Levenson, *J. Am. Chem. Soc.*, *61*, 1172 (1939); E. Tommila, and C. N. Hinshelwood, *J. Chem. Soc.*, *1938*, 1801; W. B. S. Newling and C. N. Hinshelwood, *J. Chem. Soc.*, *1936*, 1357; E. Tommila, *Suomen Kemistilehti*, *16B*, *26* (1943); *C. A.*, *40*, 6956 (1946).

from the conjugation of these substituents with the carbonyl group in the esters.[202, 203] The agreement between these resonance energies and the $\Delta\Delta E_v^{\ddagger}$ values calculated by either equation 36′ or equation 36″ indicates that in both acidic and alkaline esterification or ester hydrolysis the resonance of the α,β-unsaturated substituents with the carbonyl group is essentially completely frozen out in the reaction transition state. That is, the free energy of activation of the benzoate ester, for example, is greater than that of the formate ester by the amount of $\overset{\frown}{R}—\overset{\frown}{C}{=}O$ resonance stabilization in the former ester (cf. section V-5).

The E_s values for unconjugated substituents have been obtained upon the assumption (section V-3b) that there is little or no resonance interaction between this type of substituent and the carbalkoxy group of the esters. For substituents with α-hydrogen atoms this assumption is probably not strictly valid because of hyperconjugation. The general relationship between E_s values and structure of the substituents (Table VI) indicates, however, that hyperconjugation effects must generally be quite small in comparison to the steric effects.

XIV. LINEAR STRAIN ENERGY RELATIONSHIPS

The general importance of steric strain in determining reactivity has been well demonstrated by excellent work of H. C. Brown and coworkers.[204] Two cases of linear strain energy relationships have been reported.

To a good precision the increased strains accompanying the formation of the ester hydrolysis transition states (Table XXII) are one-fourth that for the formation of corresponding homomorphic amine addition compounds (Table XIII).[205] Table XXIV lists the strain energies for the latter in the second column as $\Delta\Delta E_R$, and for the former in the fourth column as $\Delta\Delta E_R^{\ddagger}$. The fifth column of Table XXIV gives values of $\Delta\Delta E_R/4.0$. The differences between the corresponding values of the fourth and fifth columns of Table XXIV in no case exceed the combined uncertainties of the data upon which these values are based, not to mention the approximations made by present methods.

[202] G. W. Wheland, *The Theory of Resonance*, pp. 60, 69, and 278, John Wiley & Sons, New York, 1944.

[203] G. E. K. Branch and M. Calvin, *The Theory of Organic Chemistry*, p. 284, Prentice-Hall, New York.

[204] H. C. Brown et al., *J. Am. Chem. Soc.*, 75, 1 (1953), and previous references.

[205] R. W. Taft, Jr., *J. Am. Chem. Soc.*, 75, 4534 (1953).

TABLE XXIV

COMPARISON OF STERIC STRAINS IN THE FORMATION OF ESTER TRANSITION STATES WITH CORRESPONDING QUANTITIES FOR THE FORMATION HOMOMORPHIC AMINE-BORONTRIMETHYL ADDITION COMPOUNDS [205]

Amine $R_1R_2R_3N$	Addition Compound Steric Strain, $\Delta\Delta E_R$, kcal./mole	Aliphatic Groups $R_1R_2R_3C$	$\Delta\Delta E_R^{\ddagger}$ (obsd.)	Transition State Steric Strain, kcal./mole $\Delta\Delta E_R^{\ddagger}$ (calcd.)	d
NH_3	0.0	CH_3	0.0	0.0	0.0
CH_3NH_2	0.0	CH_3CH_2	0.0	0.0	0.0
$C_2H_5NH_2$	0.0	$C_2H_5CH_2$	0.0	0.0	0.0
$n\text{-}C_3H_7NH_2$	0.0	$n\text{-}C_3H_7CH_2$	0.0	0.0	0.0
$n\text{-}C_4H_9NH_2$	0.0	$n\text{-}C_4H_9CH_2$	0.0	0.0	0.0
$i\text{-}C_3H_7NH_2$	1.4	$i\text{-}C_3H_7CH_2$	0.0	0.3	0.3
$s\text{-}C_4H_9NH_2$	1.6	$s\text{-}C_4H_9CH_2$	0.4	0.4	0.0
$t\text{-}C_4H_9NH_2$	6.6	$t\text{-}C_4H_9CH_2$	1.8	1.7	0.1
$(CH_3)_2NH$	1.7	$(CH_3)_2CH$	0.0	0.4	0.4
$(CH_3)_3N$	6.9	$(CH_3)_3C-$	1.4	1.7	0.3
$n\text{-}C_4H_9(CH_3)_2N$	10.2	$neo\text{-}C_5H_{11}(CH_3)_2C-$	2.7	2.5	0.2
$(C_2H_5)_2NH$	6.1	$(C_2H_5)_2CH$	2.0	1.5	0.5
$(C_2H_5)_3N$	(17)	$(C_2H_5)_3C$	4.3	(4.2)	0.1
					Ave. 0.2

$$
\begin{matrix}
& R_2 & CH_3 \\
& | & | \\
R_1 & -N-B- & CH_3 \\
& | & | \\
& R_3 & CH_3
\end{matrix}
$$

Addition compound

$$
\begin{matrix}
& R_2 & OH \\
& | & | \\
R_1 & -C-C- & OR' \\
& | & | \\
& R_3 & OH
\end{matrix}
$$

Ester transition state (minus or plus proton)
$R' = CH_3, C_2H_5,$ or $CH_2C_6H_5$

The direct proportionality between the two series of steric strains (i.e., $\Delta\Delta E_R = \alpha\Delta\Delta E_R^{\ddagger}$) indicates that such a relationship is not highly specific to the kind of atoms present. The two series of strain energies apparently are directly related because the geometries of two systems are closely the same. The structural formulas listed at the bottom of Table XXIV illustrate how the transition-state geometry is probably related to that of the addition compound. Although all the substituents for which the correlation has been obtained are aliphatic, they are of sufficient number and variety to establish the validity of the correlation.

The value of separating reactivity according to equation 29 is well demonstrated by the steric strain correlation. By so doing a relationship has been established which does not exist between corresponding free energy or total steric energy differences. It should also be remembered that this strain-energy correlation establishes that structure affects analogous rate and equilibrium quantities in a parallel manner. Such correlations are well known for quantities determined by polar effects (equations 7 and 16) but only recently have been indicated for strain energies. It is worthy of note that the presence of solvent in the one reaction series has not prevented the determination of basic molecular parameters which are simply related to corresponding quantities determined for a second reaction series in the absence of solvent (i.e., in the gas phase).

The first reported case of a linear strain energy relationship is due to Brown and Horowitz.[206] A linear relationship was found between the enthalpy of dissociation of boron trifluoride-2-monoalkyl pyridine addition compounds in nitrobenzene solution and the activation energy for the reaction of the corresponding 2-monoalkyl pyridines with methyl iodide in the same solvent. The equation is $\Delta E_{act.} = (-0.368) \Delta H_d + 22.8$. A comparison of experimental and predicted values is given in Table XXV.

TABLE XXV

LINEAR STRAIN-ENERGY RELATIONSHIP FROM REACTIONS OF
2-ALKYL PYRIDINES [206]

Alkyl Pyridine R	ΔH_d, kcal. $RC_5H_4N + BF_3$	$\Delta E_{act.}$, kcal. $RC_5H_4N + CH_3I$	$\Delta E_{act.}$, kcal. (calculated)
H	25.0	13.9	13.6
3-Me	25.3	13.6	—
4-Me	25.5	13.6	—
2-Me	23.3	14.0	14.2
2-Et	22.7	14.2	14.5
2-i-Pr	21.7	14.8	14.8
2-t-Bu	14.8	17.5	17.4

It is assumed that both $\Delta\Delta H_d$ and $\Delta\Delta E_{act.}$ are measures (to a good approximation) of the increased strain in the addition compound and the halide reaction transition state, respectively. The polar energy is taken to be negligible for these reactions, since the introduction of a methyl (or other alkyl groups) in the 3 or 4 position has very little effect.

The linear strain-energy relationships imply some limitations of the linear steric energy relationships (equation 19, discussed in section VII-1). The E_s values are composite terms, consisting of contributions from both potential- and kinetic-energy steric effects. It seems likely, therefore, that equation 19 is less fundamental than linear relationships between strain energies alone. Particular weight is given this conclusion by the fact that only the latter relationship holds in the appropriate comparisons for the formation of ester hydrolysis transition states and the formation of the corresponding homomorphic

[206] H. C. Brown and R. H. Horowitz, J. Am. Chem. Soc., 77, 1733 (1955).

amine-trimethylboron addition compounds. That is, although the linear free-energy and linear steric energy relationships fail, the linear strain-energy relationship holds.

Acknowledgment. I wish to express my thanks to the Office of Naval Research for the financial support (Project NR055-328) which has made possible a number of the studies reported herein. Particular thanks are also due Professors M. M. Kreevoy and Lionel Goodman for numerous stimulating discussions which have in no small way contributed to this chapter. The helpful comments of Professors H. H. Jaffé, J. E. Leffler, L. P. Hammett, J. D. Roberts, and many of my associates and students at Penn State are also acknowledged with gratitude. I dedicate this work to my teachers (including my father) with the hope that it carries on in their tradition.

Author Index

Aaland, S. E., 160
Aaron, D., 652
Abell, P. I., 243
Abbott, D. C., 355
Acree, F., 237
Adams, F. H., 141, 153
Adams, R., 64, 66, 91, 140, 215, 473, 543, 552, 651
Adams, R. M., 109
Adamson, D. W., 375
Adkins, H., 610, 657
Afanas'ev, N. M., 101
Agett, A. H., 399
Agliardi, N., 388
Albrecht, H., 153
Alder, K., 147
Alexander, B. H., 385
Alexander, D. S., 109
Alexander, E. R., 49, 143, 162, 250, 297, 398, 411
Alexander, H. E., 84
Allen, C. F. H., 409
Allen, H. C., Jr., 625
Allen, P. W., 119
Allinger, J., 153, 227
Allinger, M. L., 501
Altschul, L. H., 661
Amdur, I., 530
Amundsen, L. H., 96
Andrews, L. J., 84
Anglin, J. H., 519
Angyal, S. J., 28, 37, 44, 91, 125, 126
Anschütz, R., 145
Anziani, P., 128
Appel, H., 211
Applequist, D. F., 134
Archibald, F. R., 109
Arcus, C. L., 120, 252, 355
Arenberg, C. A., 610
Armstrong, M. D., 409
Arndt, F., 442
Arnold, H., 126

Arnold, R. T., 159, 240, 309, 358, 361, 362, 415, 484, 486, 518, 600
Arpesella, L., 369
Aschan, O., 352
Ash, A. B., 147, 151
Ash, L. B., 227
Ashdown, A. A., 622
Aspinall, G. O., 234
Aston, J. G., 35, 122, 493
Attenburrow, J., 292
Auerbach, I., 370
Austin, P. R., 414
Auwers, K. von, 119
Aycock, B. F., 243

Babcock, S. H., 104, 240
Bachmann, W. E., 31, 227, 264, 387, 388
Backer, H. J., 118, 381
Baddeley, G., 88, 102, 175
Badger, G. M., 472, 475, 501
Baeyer, A., 3
Bailey, P. S., 83, 469
Bailey, W. J., 151, 313
Bains, L., 463
Baker, B. R., 295
Baker, J. W., 88, 90, 104, 118, 157, 596
Baker, R. H., 78
Baker, W., 234, 474
Baltzly, R., 644
Bamberger, R., 288
Bamford, W. R., 281
Banigan, T. F., 247
Banta, C., 89
Barbaras, G. K., 456, 459, 597, 635
Barbier, M., 322
Barbot, A., 375
Barie, W. P., Jr., 647, 654
Barkemeyer, H. R., 232
Barker, N. G., 114, 519
Barltrop, J. A., 500
Barman, P., 42, 353
Barnes, R. A., 356, 518

Bartels, R., 115
Barthel, R., 225
Bartholomay, H., Jr., 440, 454, 635
Bartlett, P. D., 65, 71, 72, 76, 81, 103, 105, 109, 135, 142, 149, 235, 244, 250, 253, 254, 276, 286, 333, 353, 442, 497, 538, 575, 599, 630, 657
Barton, D. H. R., 9, 15, 17, 28, 39, 44, 48, 49, 135, 152, 156, 222, 309, 321, 326, 358, 376
Basolo, F., 609, 612
Bastiansen, O., 23, 119, 510
Basyrin, M., 120
Bauer, E., 236
Bauer, S. H., 388
Baughan, E. C., 74, 148, 610
Baxmann, F., 476
Baxter, J. F., 577
Baxter, W. N., 44
Bayer, E., 242
Beach, J. Y., 9, 388
Beal, P. F., 286
Beale, R. N., 487
Beckett, C. W., 14, 16, 39, 326
Beckmann, S., 288
Beesley, R. M., 119
Beilstein, F., 188
Bell, A., 404
Bell, F., 252, 355, 476, 488
Bell, J., 144
Bell, R. P., 609, 610
Bello, J., 151
Bender, M. L., 204, 224, 588
Benjamin, B., 268
Benkeser, R. A., 596
Bennett, B., 473
Bennett, G. M., 88, 90, 102, 115, 116, 280, 365
Benneville, P. de, 69
Benoit, G., 113
Bent, H. E., 300, 389
Bentley, J. B., 509
Berenbaum, M. B., 148
Bergmann, E., 488
Bergmann, E. D., 495, 515
Bergmann, J. G., 609, 612
Bergstrom, C. G., 279
Berliner, E., 182, 187, 229, 231, 596, 661
Berneis, H. L., 70, 333, 459
Bernhard, S. A., 589, 653
Bernstein, H. I., 253
Bernstein, H. J., 52, 53
Bernstein, S., 10
Berst, N. W., 109
Berthier, G., 495, 517
Berti, G., 314

Beucker, H., 386
Bevan, C. W. L., 77
Bevan, G. H., 482
Beyaert, M., 118
Bharucha, K. R., 405
Bhattacharyya, A. K., 132
Bhide, B. V., 207, 209, 210, 211, 589
Bickel, A. F., 151
Bickel, C. L., 342, 365, 370, 372
Bilbo, A. J., 487
Biletch, H., 148
Billen, G. N., 109
Binovic, K., 109
Biquard, D., 507
Birch, S. F., 36
Bird, M. L., 66
Birtles, R. H., 508
Bishop, G., 253
Bissinger, W. E., 81
Black, W. B., 490
Blackwood, R. K., 161
Blake, J. T., 89
Blank, H., 401
Blankman, H. D., 78
Blatt, A. H., 235
Bleick, W. E., 531
Blicke, F. F., 126, 230
Blickenstaff, R. T., 614
Bloch, L. P., 235, 418
Blout, E. R., 489, 499
Blumberger, J. S. P., 487
Blunck, F. H., 307
Bobko, E., 348
Bock, L., 69
Böckemuller, W., 354
Bockhacker, E., 190
Bohnert, E., 153
Bokadi, M. M., 162
Bolle, J., 91
Bondar, L. S., 126
Bone, W. A., 120
Bondhus, F. J., 596
Bonner, W. A., 143
Bonner, W. H., 160, 169, 459
Boord, C. E., 117, 155, 246
Booth, J., 380
Boozer, C. E., 81, 167, 200
Borders, A. M., 211, 215, 589
Bordian, W. G., 446
Bordwell, F. G., 77, 96, 103
Borkowski, M., 123
Born, M., 531
Boschan, R., 292
Bose, A. K., 51, 128, 132
Bourgeois, L., 91
Bouveault, L., 228

Bowden, K., 499
Boyd, G. V., 355
Boyland, E., 380
Brader, W. H., 102
Bradley, C. A., 503
Bradley, W., 370
Brady, O. L., 195, 253
Brain, D. K., 109
Branch, G. E. K., 179, 225, 563, 576, 592, 603, 624, 625, 656, 657, 661, 672
Brändström, A., 161
Bransen, W. R., 282
Braude, E. A., 155, 484, 485, 499
Braun, J. von, 64, 126, 174, 251
Braye, E., 162
Brebner, D. L., 104
Bredt, J., 353
Brenner, J., 252
Bretschneider, H., 110
Brewster, J. H., 64, 68, 234, 239, 281, 359, 445
Brewster, P., 83
Brickwedde, F. G., 493
Bridgeman, P. W., 530
Briegleb, G., 436
Brill, W. F., 77, 87, 96
Britton, E. C., 109
Brockway, L. O., 120, 519
Brode, W. R., 488
Broke, H., 466
Brooker, L. G. S., 481, 494
Brooks, C. J. W., 358
Brooks, J. W., 397
Brous, J. B., 134
Brown, D. A., 91, 226
Brown, D. E., 157
Brown, E. V., 364
Brown, F., 71, 72, 262, 277
Brown, H. C., 42, 62, 70, 73, 75, 102, 121, 122, 123, 141, 145, 146, 147, 148, 151, 157, 158, 159, 160, 168, 169, 234, 237, 238, 239, 248, 276, 278, 333, 338, 359, 375, 437, 439, 440, 445, 454, 455, 456, 459, 568, 596, 600, 610, 630, 633, 635, 644, 654, 672, 674
Brown, J., 397
Brown, M., 262
Brown, R. D., 627
Brown, R. F., 113, 117, 254, 267
Brown, W. G., 109, 158, 172, 216, 440, 485
Brown, C. L., 109
Bruckner, V., 293
Brutcher, F. V., Jr., 375
Bruylants, A., 151, 162
Bruun, T., 135

Bryce-Smith, D., 356
Bruchkremmer, J., 237
Büchner, E., 380
Buckles, R. E., 155, 272, 291, 292
Buijs, J. B., 235
Bunnett, J. F., 166, 189, 193, 196, 225
Bunton, C. A., 226
Burawoy, A., 86, 485
Burgstahler, A. W., 78, 110
Burkhardt, G. N., 650, 661
Burn, J., 207, 586, 589, 667
Burr, J. G., 83, 268
Burt, C. P., 519
Burton, H., 88
Butler, E. T., 148
Buu-Hoi, N. P., 151, 160
Byerly, W., 389
Byers, A., 245
Byrne, F. P., 20

Cadogan, J. I. G., 199
Cahn, A., 159, 437, 654
Caldin, F. F., 665
Calvin, M., 179, 485, 488, 491, 500, 550, 563, 576, 592, 603, 624, 625, 656, 672
Cameron, M. D., 472
Campbell, A., 252, 281, 355
Campbell, D. H., 103
Campbell, J. E., 501
Campbell, K. N., 246
Cantwell, N. H., 364
Cardwell, H. M. E., 162, 432
Carlisle, C. H., 39
Carr, E. P., 519
Carré, E. P., 81
Carter, J. M., 341
Casaletto, G. A., 143
Caserio, F. F., 99
Cason, J., 207, 227, 228, 233, 355
Castro, A. J., 109, 397
Cattelain, E., 428
Caunt, D., 104
Cavell, E. A. S., 182
Chadwick, J., 88
Chamberlain, J. T., 485
Chambers, V. C., 123, 209, 278
Chandler, E. E., 431
Chanley, J., 111, 237
Chao, T. H., 102, 141
Chapman, A. W., 280
Chapman, N. B., 130, 182
Charalambous, G., 134
Charlesworth, E. H., 109
Charlton, J. C., 262
Chase, B. H., 228
Chaudhuri, D. K. R., 132

Chavanne, G., 316
Chien, S. L., 552
Chiola, V., 86
Chitwood, H. C., 109
Choppin, A. R., 224
Christoffel, I., 109
Chu, Y., 155
Ciereszko, L. S., 268
Clark, D., 143
Clark, R. C., 292
Clarke, H. T., 106
Clayton, R. B., 377
Clement, R. A., 96, 578, 595
Cline, J. E., 390
Clippinger, E., 127, 259
Cogdell, J. F., 237
Cohen, H. L., 395
Cohen, H. M., 398, 405
Cohen, M., 48
Cohen, S. G., 149, 219, 538, 613
Cole, A. R. H., 51
Cole, W. E., 267
Coleman, G. H., 397
Coles, J. A., 155, 485
Collett, A. R., 220
Collins, C. J., 268
Colon, A. A., 610, 613
Conant, J. B., 4, 46, 74, 84, 139, 235, 657
Conley, J. B., 604, 670
Connor, H. E., 248
Conrad, W. E., 109
Conroy, H., 300
Cook, J. W., 451, 501
Cook, P. L., 109
Cookson, R. C., 39, 132
Coolidge, E. C., 614
Cooper, G. D., 103
Cooper, K. A., 73
Cooper, W., 650
Coops, J., 4, 533
Cope, A. C., 44, 109, 245, 246, 288, 310, 354, 397
Coraor, G. R., 411
Cordner, J. P., 386
Corey, E. J., 40, 41, 218, 360, 367, 368
Cormack, J. F., 189
Cornubert, R., 128
Corse, J., 123, 217, 262, 325, 327
Corson, B. B., 485
Coryell, C. D., 10, 271, 316
Cotman, J. D., 286
Couchet, G., 428
Coulson, C. A., 482, 483, 494, 518, 535, 563, 616
Coulson, D. M., 603

Couvreur, P., 151
Cowdrey, W. A., 66, 80
Cox, J. C., 287
Crafts, J. M., 362
Craig, P. N., 240, 486
Cram, D. J., 12, 66, 80, 81, 92, 139, 153, 195, 229, 239, 256, 257, 258, 261, 264, 272, 275, 308, 310, 319, 324, 341, 343, 344, 415, 487, 498, 501, 575
Cramer, P. L., 307
Creighton, E. M., 280
Cremlyn, R. J., 128
Crew, M., 273
Criegee, R., 378, 379, 380, 386, 575
Cristol, C. S., 317, 319, 321, 364, 365
Cristol, S. J., 109, 661
Cromwell, N. H., 110, 114, 157, 374, 416, 519
Crooks, H. M., 418
Cropper, F. R., 195
Crow, W. D., 104
Crowell, T. I., 76, 585
Crowell, W. R., 603
Crowfoot, D., 39
Culbertson, J. B., 650
Cunliffe, J., 485, 491
Curtin, D. Y., 10, 111, 154, 155, 271, 273, 283, 301, 313, 339, 341, 365
Cuthbertson, G. R., 389

Dailey, B. P., 120, 614
D'Amico, J. J., 96
Dasent, W. E., 247
Daub, G. H., 224
Dauben, W. G., 13, 28, 38, 51, 78, 83, 128
Daujat, J., 415
Davies, G., 589
Davies, G. F., 26
Davies, M. J. P., 212
Davies, S. H., 241
Davies, T. D., 71, 277
Davies, W. C., 661
Davis, H. A., 385
Davis, S. B., 247
Davis, T. L., 622
Dawent, B. de B., 148
Dawson, H. M., 609
Day, A. A., 622
Dean, R. A., 36
Décombe, J., 398
DeFazio, C. A., 652
De la Mare, P. B. D., 87, 96, 98, 243, 541
DeMooy, M. W. J., 190
Denney, D. B., 20, 47

Dennis, G. E., 99
Dennison, D. M., 55
Dennler, W. S., 272
Deno, N. C., 491, 494, 577, 609
Dent, S. G., Jr., 481
Denton, J. J., 91
DePuy, C. H., 343
Derfer, J. M., 117
Derick, C. G., 592
Deshapanda, S. S., 463
Detar, D. F., 155, 199
Deuticke, F., 66
De Vries, T., 596
Dewar, M. J. S., 63, 86, 179, 250, 269, 482
Dewey, R. S., 224
DeWolfe, R. H., 99
Dhar, M. L., 314
Dickel, D. F., 13
Dieckmann, W., 445, 448
Diederichsen, J., 297
Diehl, F. J., 440
Dien, C., 469
Dienske, J. W., 90
Dillon, R. L., 580, 584, 596, 625
Dillon, R. T., 316
Dimler, R. J., 385
Dippy, J. F. J., 205, 426, 428, 430, 609
Ditmer, D. C., 157
Doak, G. O., 572
Dobres, R. M., 387
Dobriner, K., 51
Dodson, R. M., 159, 309, 358, 484, 486
Doering, W. von E., 67, 101, 137, 163, 247, 259, 288, 361, 441, 451, 575
Doll, W., 128
Domash, L., 644
Dominguez, X. A., 40
Donahue, J., 119, 361
Dorfman, E., 575
Dorfman, M., 389
Dorlencourt, 266
Dostrovsky, I., 15, 71, 74, 76, 262, 277
Doty, P. M., 35, 122
Douglass, J. R., 109
Douglass, K. J., 182
Douslin, D. R., 35
Dowell, A. M., 100
Drake, W. V., 160
Dreiding, A. S., 31, 78, 155
Drikos, G., 140
Dripps, R. D., 250
Drysdale, J. J., 578, 595
Duckworth, S., 485, 491
Duke, F. R., 381
Dunitz, J. D., 432, 533

Dunlop, E. C., 489
Dunn, J. L., 280
Dutt, P. N., 230
Duval, C. P., 398

Eaborn, C., 596
Ebers, E. S., 389
Eby, L. T., 246
Edgerton, P. J., 182, 187
Edwards, J. O., 157
Eger, H. H., 610
Egerer, G., 232
Ehrenson, S. J., 101
Eistert, B., 442
Eldred, N. R., 75, 654
Eleuterio, H. S., 80, 298
Elhafez, F. A. A., 12, 92, 229, 239, 261, 264, 275, 308, 319, 344
Eliel, E. L., 47, 64, 68, 95, 96, 126, 143, 144, 227, 250
Elliot, D. F., 292
Elmer, O. C., 358
Elofson, R. M., 610
Elving, P. J., 610, 625
Emerson, W., 109
Emster, K. van, 255
England, B. O., 96
Englemann, F., 149
English, J., Jr., 375, 376
Erickson, J. L. E., 372, 373, 416
Eschenmoser, A., 152
Esterka, F., 418
Evans, A. G., 64, 77, 85, 89, 148, 568
Evans, D. P., 160, 589, 610, 650, 671
Evans, E. B., 145
Evans, M. G., 148, 562
Evans, O. J., 71, 277
Evans, W. V., 397
Evenhuis, N., 118
Everard, K. B., 509, 510, 511, 512, 513
Ewald, M. L., 390
Eyring, H., 562, 568, 616, 624, 627

Fainberg, A. H., 127, 259
Fairclough, R. A., 370
Farber, M., 51
Farmer, E. H., 245
Farmer, H. H., 229
Fasce, E. V., 226
Faust, W., 20
Favini, G., 102
Fawcett, F. S., 137, 352
Fedorov, B. P., 77
Feith, E., 241
Felder, E., 449, 453
Feldman, I., 490

Feldstein, A., 112
Felkin, H., 80
Felletschin, G., 280
Fenton, S. W., 44, 245, 288
Ferguson, J. W., 264
Ferguson, L. N., 481
Feurer, M., 130, 131
Ficini, J., 109
Field, F. H., 451
Fierens, P. J. C., 87, 123
Fieser, L. F., 40, 97, 214, 228, 413, 488
Filbert, W. F., 296
Finestone, A. B., 148
Fink, A. L., 35
Finck, H. L., 122
Firestone, R. A., 300
Fischer, C. H., 240
Fischer, W., 240
Fisher, H. D., 109
Fittig, R., 144, 145
Fitzpatrick, F. W., 585, 652
Fix, D. D., 319
Flenner, A. L., 590
Fletcher, R. S., 70, 121, 237, 239, 276, 333, 375, 597
Florsheim, W. H., 210, 357
Flurscheim, B., 426
Fodor, G., 293, 294
Fones, W. S., 217
Fonken, G. S., 219
Fookson, A., 248
Ford, W. G., 650
Formin, W., 305
Foster, T. T., 310
Fourneau, E., 113
Fowden, L., 541
Fox, C. J., 609
Fox, J. J., 520
Fraenkel, G. K., 368, 514
France, H., 488
Frank, E., 322
Franke, A., 375
Frankenburg, P. E., 238
Frankland, P. F., 316
Franklin, J. L., 85, 451
Franzen, H., 90, 190
Fraser, G. L., 244
Frazer, W., 138, 354
Freedman, L. D., 572
Freeman, J. P., 144
Freeman, K., 51
Freeman, N. K., 39, 227
French, H. E., 397
Frenkiel, L., 42, 353
Freudenberg, K., 66, 375

Freundlich, H., 115
Freure, B. T., 109
Fried, J. P., 120
Fried, S., 158, 216
Friedel, R. A., 488
Friedlander, P., 174
Friedlander, W. S., 198
Friedman, L. J., 78
Friehmelt, E., 251
Friess, S. I., 238, 575
Frost, A. A., 69, 563, 585, 609, 647, 662
Frush, H. L., 295
Fuchs, R., 109
Fugate, W. O., 402
Fulhart, L., 109
Fuller, R. K., 109
Furst, A., 51, 130, 131
Fuson, R. C., 74, 91, 104, 115, 198, 217, 240, 248, 402, 403, 408, 409, 410, 424, 505

Gaddum, L. W., 397
Gallagher, T. F., 130
Gallaway, W. S., 485, 506
Gallop, G. A., 572
Gardner, J. D., 175, 361
Gardner, P. D., 104
Garfield, E., 653
Garner, C. S., 154
Garrett, A. B., 203, 217, 218, 668
Gassmann, A. G., 211, 589
Gasson, E. J., 152
Geissman, T. A., 372, 373, 451
Geffrey, G. H, 428
Gelles, E., 609
Gent, W. L. G., 616
George, R. S., 418
Gerard, L., 255
Gercke, A., 322
Gerhardt, L. S., 84
Gerichten, E. V., 170
German, W. L., 428
Gerrard, W., 78, 81
Gershevich, A. T., 102
Gerstein, M., 121, 278, 455, 600, 633
Gettler, J. D., 585, 652
Giacomo, A. D., 20
Giauque, W. F., 564
Gilbert, B., 474
Gilbert, E. C., 26
Gilbert, F. L., 436
Gildenhorn, H. L., 232
Gilkerson, W. R., 572
Gillespie, R. J., 63
Gilman, H., 65, 103, 105, 109, 140, 152, 215, 397, 404, 409, 439, 440, 475, 538

Ginsberg, E., 391, 392
Gintes, D., 644
Gist, W. J., 410
Gittins, J. M., 212
Gladding, E. K., 381
Glasstone, S., 562
Glick, C. F., 531
Glickman, S. A., 109
Glusker, D. L., 227
Goepp, R. M., Jr., 462
Goering, H. L., 20, 96, 98, 99, 224, 243, 258, 575, 580
Gold, V., 66, 171
Goll, O., 64
Gol'mov, V.P., 101, 115, 119
Gomberg, M., 387
Gordon, A. B., 280
Gordon, J. J., 589, 610, 671
Gordon, L. B., 84
Gordon, M., 622
Gordy, W., 87
Govaert, F., 118
Grabenstetter, R. I., 516
Graefe, A. F., 68
Granger, R., 20, 129
Graybill, B. M., 156
Grayson, M., 158, 459
Green, C., 519
Greene, C., 512
Greene, F. D., 142, 149, 272, 343, 415
Greenlee, K. W., 117, 155, 246
Greenwood, F. L., 418
Greer, F., 241
Gregory, T. M., 505
Grignard, V., 213
Grigsby, W. E., 111
Groocock, C. M., 594, 610
Grosse, A. V., 354, 356
Groth, M., 485, 491
Grovenstein, E., Jr., 364
Grubb, J., 48
Grubb, W. J., 128
Grubb, W. T., 513
Grunwald, E., 65, 69, 123, 259, 262, 292, 324, 327, 570, 572
Gudgeon, H., 116
Gunthard, H. H., 51
Guss, C. O., 109, 113, 243
Gustafson, C., 442
Gutberlet, C., 109
Gutbezahl, B., 572
Guter, G., 447
Gutowsky, H. S., 627
Gutt, J., 128, 129
Gwinn, W. D., 53, 57

Häfliger, O., 42
Halben, H. V., 436
Hale, W. F., 148
Hall, D. M., 476, 482
Hall, G. A., Jr., 370
Hall, G. V., 609
Haller, A., 236
Halmann, M., 83, 268
Hamann, S. D., 77, 85
Hamilton, C. E., 167, 200
Hamlin, W. E., 161
Hammel, O., 255
Hammett, L. P., 204, 218, 426, 443, 454, 563, 566, 571, 572, 584, 586, 589, 597, 652, 653, 657, 660, 663, 669
Hammond, G. S., 62, 87, 128, 148, 156, 166, 167, 178, 182, 192, 200, 205, 242, 329, 427, 440, 446, 447, 451, 577, 626
Hampson, G. C., 176, 508
Hanai, S., 145
Hancock, K., 211
Hanford, W. E., 552
Hanhart, W., 317
Hansch, C., 169
Hansley, V. L., 42
Hanson, C., 292
Happe, W., 282
Haresnape, J. N., 36
Harfenist, M., 644
Harford, M. B., 80
Harkness, A. L., 531
Harris, E. E., 154, 155, 273
Hart, H., 80, 298
Hartel, H. V., 610
Hartman, P., 128
Hartman, R. J., 211, 215, 589
Hartung, W. H., 657
Hartwell, E. J., 507
Harvey, S. H., 68
Haskell, V. C., 589, 653
Hass, H. B., 147
Hassel, O., 14, 17, 18, 23, 35, 119, 120, 326
Haszeldine, R. N., 103
Hatch, L. F., 84, 86, 96
Hauptschein, M., 354, 356
Hause, N. L., 319, 321
Hauser, C. R., 280, 282, 321, 347, 370, 403, 404, 412, 650
Haworth, R. D., 104
Hawthorne, M. F., 66, 156, 193, 195, 487, 575
Hayashi, M., 229
Hayes, F. N., 109
Head, A. J., 309
Hearne, G., 84

Heath, D. F., 505
Heathcoat, F., 116
Heck, R., 292
Hedden, G. O., 485
Hedges, R. M., 178
Heidt, L. J., 381
Heins, B., 280
Heinz, W. E., 367
Heisler, R. Y., 109
Helden, Van R., 151
Helmcamp, G., 169
Helmreich, R. F., 109
Henbest, H. B., 377
Henderson, G. G., 135
Henderson, R. B., 106, 111
Heneck, A. H., 161
Henne, A. L., 370, 609, 610
Hennion, G. F., 87, 247
Henri, V., 488
Herbert, J., 148
Herbrandson, H. F., 81
Herbstein, F. H., 477
Heritage, G., 412
Herling, F., 40, 51
Herz, W., 114, 287
Herzberg, G., 502, 526, 536
Herzenstein, A., 391
Herzog, H. L., 489
Hess, H. V., 291
Hester, W. F., 372
Heuberger, O., 126
Heusser, H., 130, 131
Hey, D. F., 199
Hey, D. H., 228, 387, 426
Heyes, J. K., 203
Heyl, G., 228
Heymann, H., 413
Heyningen, E. van, 119
Hickinbottom, W. J., 245
Higginson, W. C. E., 609
Hilbert, G. E., 385, 424
Hill, M. E., 631
Hill, R. L., 585
Hill, T. L., 542, 551, 555
Hilton, J., 66
Himel, C. M., 392
Hind, J., 111
Hine, J., 99, 100, 101, 102, 259, 609
Hine, M., 609
Hinkley, D. F., 319
Hinshelwood, C. N., 71, 75, 86, 586, 589, 610, 661, 671
Hiron, F., 83
Hirschberg, Y., 488, 515
Hirsh, E. L., 295
Hock, M. J., 485

Hockett, R. C., 382
Hoerger, E., 28, 51, 128
Hofer, L. J. E., 516
Hoff, M. C., 155, 246
Hoffman, F. W., 354
Hoffmann, A. K., 101
Hofmann, A. W., 329
Hogg, C. J. A., 161
Hogle, D. H., 205, 427
Hollander, M. A. J. D., 188
Holleman, A. F., 171, 178, 186, 188, 190, 652
Hollenberg, J. L., 55
Holly, H. W., 120
Holmes, H. L., 96
Holness, N. J., 52, 127
Homer, R. F., 132
Hoogsteen, H. M., 589
Hope, E., 126
Horeczy, J., 211
Hornhardt, H., 297
Horning, E. C., 217
Hornyak, F. M., 163
Horowitz, R. H., 644, 674
Horrex, C., 661
Horton, W. J., 104
Houben, J., 240
Houston, A. H. J., 281
Howard, F. L., 248
Huber, G., 295
Hubert-Habart, J., 160
Hückel, E., 390
Hückel, W., 23, 30, 37, 38, 128, 270, 306, 317, 322, 326, 431, 445
Hudson, C. S., 133, 384
Hudson, R. F., 66, 91
Huffman, H. M., 4, 35
Hughes, E. D., 15, 64, 65, 66, 67, 68, 69, 71, 72, 73, 74, 76, 77, 80, 83, 86, 103, 171, 262, 277, 314, 317, 319, 334, 538, 539, 541
Huisgen, R., 88, 235
Hull, R. L., Jr., 354, 356
Hulstkamp, J., 42
Humphlett, W. J., 403
Humphrey, G. L., 119
Humphreys, H. M., 669
Humphries, P., 51
Hunsdieker, C., 354
Hunsdieker, H., 354
Hunt, C. K., 437
Huntress, E. H., 217, 230
Hurd, C. D., 295, 296, 307
Hurley, R. B., 589, 671
Hurwitz, M. J., 283
Hussey, A. S., 78, 476

Hussey, R. E., 74, 84
Huston, R. C., 399
Hutchison, C. A., 388

Ibbotson, K., 186
Ichishima, I., 53
Iffland, D. C., 78, 153, 161
Ingham, C. E., 176, 508
Ingham, R. K., 354
Ingold, C., 15, 65, 66, 67, 68, 69, 71, 72,
    73, 74, 75, 77, 80, 83, 86, 101, 119,
    166, 171, 177, 180, 237, 242, 250, 262,
    280, 314, 317, 319, 324, 334, 346, 429,
    431, 463, 468, 538, 541, 568, 587, 589,
    594, 610, 636
Ingold, E. H., 177
Ingraham, L., 72, 262, 498
Isbell, H. S., 295
Ito, K., 8
Ivash, E. V., 55

Jackson, A., 594
Jackson, E. C., 381
Jackson, E. L., 384
Jackson, J., 509
Jacobs, J., 483, 494
Jacobs, J. K., 87
Jacobs, T. L., 77, 210, 357
Jacquier, R., 110, 129
Jaffe, H. H., 63, 571, 572, 581, 627,
    662
Jannakopoulus, T., 140
Jaruzelski, J. J., 577
Jefferson, E. G., 66
Jeffrey, G. H., 466
Jeger, O., 13, 359
Jenkins, D. I., 661
Jiu, J., 38
Johannesen, R. B., 121, 237, 239, 439,
    454, 459, 597, 635
Johnson, H. W., Jr., 155, 301
Johnson, J. R., 95, 414
Johnson, R. G., 354
Johnson, W. S., 31, 219, 224, 233, 292,
    367
Jolibois, P., 397
Jones, B., 88, 90, 365
Jones, E. R. H., 484, 499
Jones, H. W., 65, 123, 259, 262, 327
Jones, J. A. G., 89
Jones, L. W., 251
Jones, M. M., 572
Jones, R., 103
Jones, R. G., 440
Jones, R. N., 40, 51, 481, 488, 489, 490,
    501

Jones, W. A., 352
Jones, W. W., 168
Jordan, R. H., 319
Josien, M. L., 505
Jules, L. H., 109
Julian, P. L., 410
Juliusburger, F., 66, 539
Jungers, J. C., 145
Juvala, A., 139

Kaarsemaker, J. J., 4, 533
Kadesch, R. G., 109, 216, 509
Kaelin, A., 109
Kagarise, R. E., 53
Kaiser, L. E., 157
Kaiser, T. E., 73
Kaizerman, S., 109
Kalischev, A., 375
Kalm, M. J., 355
Kantor, S. W., 280, 282
Kaplan, J. F., 392
Karabinos, J. V., 322
Karagunis, G., 140, 141
Karpitschka, N., 110
Karve, D. D., 657
Kasper, R., 575
Kaufmann, H. P., 155
Kaufmann, S., 98
Kauranen, P., 69
Kehrmann, F., 213
Kelkar, B. W., 657
Kellom, D. B., 313
Kelso, R. G., 117
Kemp, J. D., 6
Kenner, J., 186
Kenyon, J., 66, 80, 251, 252, 281, 355,
    539
Keown, R. W., 161
Kepner, R. E., 84, 95
Kerr, C. A., 135
Keuning, K. J., 118
Key, A., 609
Khan, N. A., 248
Kharasch, M. S., 141, 142, 145, 146,
    149, 283, 411, 590
Kibbler, C. J., 406
Kice, J. L., 575
Kierstead, R. W., 96
Kiesow, J., 145
Kilpatrick, J. E., 35, 57, 518, 533, 535
Kilpatrick, M., 20, 609, 610
Kimball, G. E., 204
Kindler, K., 589
Kindler, L. P., 586
King, C., 313
King, L. C., 104, 109

King, W. H., 604, 670
Kirkwood, J. G., 426, 568
Kirner, W. R., 84, 139
Kirpal, A., 226
Kiss, J., 293
Kistiakowsky, G. B., 340, 513, 552, 555
Kitchens, G. C., 373
Klages, A., 362
Kland-English, M. J., 96
Kleene, R. D., 163, 181
Kleinberg, J., 354
Klevens, H. B., 484, 486
Kline, M. W., 281
Klotz, I. M., 519
Kluiber, R. W., 297
Klyne, W., 39, 66
Knell, M., 77, 381
Knight, H. B., 109
Knight, J. D., 261
Knott, E. B., 516
Knox, L. H., 71, 135, 253, 353, 538
Kobe, K. A., 181
Kobelt, M., 42, 238
Koch, H. P., 484
Kochi, J. K., 87, 577
Koelsch, C. F., 451, 515
Koezka, K., 293
Kofod, H., 509
Kohlenberg, A. I., 487
Kohler, E. P., 342, 365, 372, 396, 408, 412, 416
Kohlrausch, K. W. F., 14, 16, 52, 507
Kohn, M., 118
Komont, W., 466
Komppa, G., 307, 352
Kon, G. A. R., 445, 467
Kooyman, E. C., 148, 149, 151
Kornblum, N., 78, 153, 161
Kornblum, R. B., 70
Korolev, A. I., 147
Kortun, G., 436
Kost, V. N., 126
Kötz, A., 464
Kovaca, C., 293
Kovacs, O., 294
Kowalsky, A., 388
Kozima, K., 20
Kraft, L., 379
Krämer, K., 144
Kreevoy, M. M., 609, 636
Krestornikov, A., 115
Kroepelin, H., 115
Kroll, H., 381
Kromann, P. B., 109
Kruys, P., 87

Krysiak, H R., 596
Küchler, K., 155
Kuderna, J., 142
Kuhn, H. H., 51
Kuhn, L. P., 386
Kuhn, M., 64
Kuhn, R., 153, 431, 433, 553
Kuivila, H. G., 217, 218
Kulkarni, A. B., 130
Kümmerle, K., 128, 326
Kung, F. E., 81
Kung, W., 289
Kunze, H., 226
Kuratani, K., 53
Kurbatow, A., 188
Kurtz, P., 126

Labaton, V. Y., 132
La Combe, E., 421, 422
LaForge, F. B., 237
Laidler, K. J., 75, 86, 228, 562, 661
Laird, W. E., 130
La Manná, A., 369
Landauer, S. R., 78
Landor, E. B., 406
Lane, J. F., 251, 252
Lanfear, E. W., 463
Langemann, A., 153
Langer, S. H., 103
Langsdorf, W. P., Jr., 65, 259, 575, 621
Langseth, A., 52, 53
Lapkin, I. I., 91
Lapkina, O. M., 91
Lapworth, A., 177, 568, 657
Larsen, D. W., 243
Lasheen, M. A., 39
Latourette, H. K., 175, 361, 485
Lauer, W. M., 296
Laxton, F. C., 436
Lazzell, C. L., 220
Leak, J. C., 93
Leary, R. E., 389
Lebas, J. M., 505
Lecomte, J., 507
Lecoq, J., 151
Lednicer, D., 474, 477
Lee, C. C., 83, 257
Lee, D. E., 100, 364
LeFevre, R. J. W., 170, 185
Leffler, J. E., 142, 575, 612, 663
Legard, A. R., 586
Legutke, G., 128, 306, 317, 326
Leimu, R., 622
Le Maistre, J. W., 650
Lemieux, R. U., 295
Lennard-Jones, J. E., 530

Leonard, F., 126
Leonard, N. J., 489, 499
Le Roux, L. J., 67, 73, 74
Lesslie, M. S., 482
Lester, C. T., 236, 371, 372, 419
Letang, N. J., 172
Letsinger, R. L., 153, 348, 396
Lettré, H., 307
Levene, P. A., 80
Levenson, H. S., 210, 586, 589, 668, 671
Levin, H., 181
Levine, P., 247
Levitz, M., 137
Levy, J. B., 652
Levy, L. K., 163, 441
Levy, R., 91
Lewis, C. E., 403, 417
Lewis, F. S., 81, 442, 497, 596
Lewis, G. N., 491, 500, 561, 568
Lewis, R. H., 428
Lewis, T. A., 226
Liao, H. P., 78
Lichtin, N. N., 153, 226
Lickroth, G., 362
Lifshits, B. V., 126
Lilker, J., 148
Lincoln, D. C., 578
Lindegren, C. R., 72, 262
Lindsey, A. S., 135
Linnett, J. W., 505, 520
Linsk, J., 240
Linstead, R., 32, 96, 247, 359, 462
Lipp, P., 237
Lipschitz, A., 229
Liskear, M., 194
Livingston, R., 614, 625
Llewellyn, D. R., 226
Lloyd, H. A., 217
Lloyd, L. L., 589
Lochte, H. L., 211
Lock, G., 242
Loening, K. L., 203, 668
Loevenich, J., 123
Loewenthal, F., 515
Loewus, F. A., 67
Lohman, L., 282
London, A., 484
Long, F. A., 539, 610
Long, G., 665
Long, W. P., 130
Longuet-Higgins, H. C., 493
Louden, J. D., 451
Luberoff, B., 341
Lu, C. S., 74
Lucas, H. J., 316, 341, 568, 636

Lumbroso, H., 511
Lumpkin, H. E., 85
Lüttringhaus, A., 117, 396
Lutz, R. E., 109, 319, 406, 469, 490
Lutz, W. B., 474

Mabbott, E. E., 145
Macbeth, A. K., 227
Maccoll, A., 517
MacDonald, C. G., 37
MacDonald, K. A., 144
Mackie, J., 541
Mackie, J. H. D., 73, 74
MacLean, R. L., 78
MacNicol, M., 280
Mader, P. M., 499
Madoff, M., 254
Magel, T. T., 491
Magerlein, B. J., 109
Mailhe, A., 129
Maloney, D. E., 87
Mangold, R., 280
Mann, F. H., 160
Mannerskanz, C., 28, 83, 128
Mannich, C., 113
Manske, R. H. F., 96, 657
Marchand, B., 379
Margenan, H., 532
Markarian, M., 144, 145
Marker, R. E., 590
Markowitz, J. M., 610
Maron, S. H., 441
Marple, K. E., 84
Marrian, S. F., 118
Marsden, R. J. B., 509
Marshall, F. C. B., 228
Marshall, H., 72, 85, 123, 262, 327
Marshall, T. R., 465
Martin, A. E., 520
Martin, J. C., 577
Martin, R. J. L., 67
Martinez, H., 98
Mason, C. T., 101
Mason, E. A., 531
Masterman, S., 80, 539
Marvel, C. S., 215, 391, 392
Matheson, N. K., 126
Matlow, S. L., 514
Matsen, F. A., 491, 508, 517, 519
Maudour, A. M., 314
Mautner, H. G., 109
Maw, G. A., 314
Maxwell, W. R., 435
Mayer, H., 232
Mayer, J. E., 15, 531, 543
Mayer, W. W., 252

Mayo, F. R., 151
Mazur, R. H., 124, 279
McBay, H. C., 146, 147
McBee, E. T., 103
McCaffery, E. L., 73
McCarty, J., 310
McCasland, G. E., 49, 292
McCleary, C. D., 218, 230
McClement, C. S., 196
McCubbin, R. J., 236
McCullough, J. P., 9, 53
McElhill, E. A., 151, 596
McElvain, S. M., 160
McEwen, W. E., 109
McFarnum, J., 622
McGuire, W. J., 103
McIntosh, A. D., 477
McKay, F. C., 189
McKay, H. A. C., 74
McKay, W. B., 267
McKee, R. L., 103
McKenzie, A., 266, 267, 272
McMaster, L., 233
McNivan, N. L., 309, 318
McRae, J. A., 109
McReynolds, J. P., 207
Mears, T. W., 248
Meek, E. G., 454
Meek, J. S., 109, 319
Meer, N., 64, 610
Meerwein, H., 254, 466
Mehltretter, C. L., 385
Neigh, D. F., 67
Meisenheimer, J., 253, 401
Meislich, E. K., 273
Melander, L., 165, 652
Meloche, I., 228, 661
Menschutkin, N., 69
Mergenthaler, E., 88
Metcalf, R. P., 581, 604
Meyer, K. H., 444
Meyer, V., 119, 175, 213, 214, 228, 586
Michael, A., 155, 316
Milburn, R. M., 247
Milhorat, A. T., 51
Miller, E., 9
Miller, E. B., 596
Miller, J. G., 622
Miller, P. C., 78
Millidge, A. F., 152
Milligan, A., 147
Mills, J. A., 28, 44, 51, 125, 128, 227, 272
Mills, R. H., 355
Mills, W. H., 153

Mirjollet, M., 374
Mislow, K., 252, 267
Mitter, P. C., 230
Miyazawa, T., 53
Mizushima, S., 9, 52, 53, 272, 517
Mock, G. V., 155
Modic, F. J., 178
Moede, J. A., 589
Moersch, G. W., 248
Moffitt, W. E., 518, 535, 613
Mohr, E., 3
Mohrhenn, H. G. G., 431
Moldenhauer, O., 96
Moldrickx, P., 123
Morath, R. J., 193
Moreau, H., 449
Moreland, W. T., Jr., 138, 354, 578, 594, 609, 629
Morgan, C. R., 636
Morino, Y., 9, 272
Morita, H., 151
Moritani, I., 71, 157, 333, 338
Morris, H., 389
Morris, L., 373
Morris, P. J., 91
Morris, R. J., 488
Morschel, H., 466
Morse, B. K., 89, 123, 262, 324, 327
Morse, H. N., 170
Morse, J. G., 20, 609
Morton, J., 439
Moseley, R. B., 66, 157
Moser, C. M., 487
Mosher, H. S., 421, 422
Mosher, W. A., 287
Mosses, A. N., 116
Mousseron, M., 20, 110, 129
Mousseron-Canet, M., 110
Mudrak, A., 49, 308
Mueller, C. R., 616
Mueller, M. B., 391, 392
Mukherjee, S., 133
Müller, E., 388, 391, 516
Müller-Rodloff, I., 388, 391
Mulligan, M. J., 307
Mulliken, R. S., 493, 494, 496, 514, 613, 618
Mumm, O., 297
Munday, D. A., 88
Mur, V. I., 147
Murat, A., 129
Murray, M. J., 139, 485, 506
Music, J. F., 519
Muth, C. W., 214, 230, 470
Myers, R. R., 589, 668
Myers, R. T., 220

Naab, H., 30
Nace, H. R., 48, 309, 584, 610
Nador, K., 294
Nagakawa, M., 70, 333, 338
Nagel, R. J., 20
Nagel, S. C., 251
Nakagawa, I., 53
Nakamura, F. I., 104, 240
Nathan, W. S., 90, 157, 589
Nauta, W. T., 90
Nazzewski, M., 144, 145
Nechvatal, A., 81
Nef, J. U., 101
Nelson, K. L., 158, 168, 459
Nerdel, F., 37
Nesbitt, S. S., 84
Nesmeyanov, A. N., 154, 406
Neuhoff, H., 516
Neumann, W., 115
Neunhoeffer, O., 322
Nevell, T. P., 66, 256
Nevitt, T. D., 99, 128, 242, 329
Newling, W. B. S., 589, 671
Newman, A. C. D., 475
Newman, M. S., 109, 203, 206, 209, 214,
    217, 218, 220, 222, 224, 228, 230, 232,
    233, 240, 248, 286, 362, 406, 418, 470,
    472, 473, 474, 476, 477, 491, 501, 580,
    586, 587, 609, 644, 649, 668
Newth, F. H., 130, 132, 399
Nicholls, R. V. V., 123
Nichols, J., 242
Nicolaides, N., 151, 283, 313
Nielsen, A. T., 162
Nielsen, W. G., 514
Nilsson, H., 117
Nixon, A. C., 225, 657, 661
Noller, C. R., 233, 397
Nordmann, J. B., 153, 254
Norris, J. F., 89, 225, 226, 622
Norris, W. P., 364
Norton, H. M., 209
Noyce, D. S., 20, 47
Noyes, R., 143
Nozaki, K., 258
Nudenberg, W., 142
Nutland, J. H., 445
Nygaard, E. M., 408
Nyman, G. A., 307
Nyquist, F. L., 275
Nystrom, R. F., 93, 109

Oae, S., 84, 139
O'Connor, G. L., 309, 584, 610
O'Connor, P. R., 296
Odioso, R., 512

Ogg, R., 143
O'Gorman, J. M., 120, 636
Ohegyi, G., 293
Okamoto, Y., 70, 333, 338
Okasaki, H., 53
Oldham, J. W. H., 354
Oliver, W. H., 247
Olivier, S. C. H., 90, 572
Ollis, W. D., 474
Olson, A. C., 575
Olson, A. R., 539
Olson, F. W., 519
Olsson, H., 220
Opotsky, V., 99
Opstall, H. J. Van, 196
Orchin, M., 472, 488
Orgel, L. E., 432
Orloff, H. D., 13
Osborne, G. O., 89
O'Shaughnessy, M. T., 485
Ostwald, W., 428
Ott, C. J., 84
Ott, E., 80, 104, 144
Ottar, B., 130, 326
Ourisson, G., 73
Ourisson, P. P., 72
Overbaugh, S. C., 409
Overberger, C. G., 148
Overend, W. G., 132
Ovist, E. B. W., 162
Owen, L. N., 126, 322, 326
Oxford, D. W. E., 53

Palmer, K. Y., 9
Palomaa, M. H., 586
Papa, D., 228
Parasol, M., 431
Parker, R. E., 182
Parker, S. H., 596
Parkin, M., 186
Parks, L. R., 166
Partington, J. R., 435
Pasternack, R., 319
Pasternak, R. A., 39
Pasternak, V. Z., 361
Pastor, R. C., 388
Patel, C. S., 64
Patton, J. T., 153
Pauling, L., 87, 121, 390, 519, 532, 563,
    594, 613
Pausaker, K. H., 386
Pavelich, W. A., 609, 644, 648
Pavia, G., 175
Pearlman, H., 531
Pearson, D. E., 241, 267, 577
Pearson, R. G., 69, 103, 397, 563, 569,

580, 584, 585, 596, 609, 612, 625, 647, 662
Peat, S., 295
Pechet, M., 488
Peckham, P., 96
Pedersen, K. J., 351
Peirce, G., 518
Pelley, R. L., 610
Pennington, F. C., 225
Penny, G. F., 292
Percival, E., 134
Perkin, W. H., 126
Perkin, W. H., Jr., 465
Perrin, M. W., 161
Perry, R. H., 84
Person, W. B., 53
Peterson, W. D., 342, 365
Petrenko-Kritschenko, P., 99
Petri, H., 396
Pfeiffer, P., 233, 316, 342, 401
Pfister, C., 292
Pfister, K. H. T., 230
Pfluger, R., 96
Phillips, A. H., 80
Phillips, D. D., 96
Phillips, G. O., 130
Phillips, H., 66, 539
Piantanida, M., 217
Pickett, L. W., 485, 488, 491
Pieck, R., 145
Pietrzok, H., 128
Pigman, W. W., 462
Pike, R. A., 246, 310
Pimentel, G. C., 53
Pinck, L. A., 424
Pinkus, A. G., 143
Pinner, A., 233
Pitkethly, R. C., 245
Pitt, B. N., 77
Pittman, V., 539
Pitzer, K. S., 6, 8, 14, 16, 17, 35, 39, 53, 55, 57, 269, 326, 458, 533, 635
Platon, B., 117
Platt, J. R., 484, 486, 493
Plattner, Pl. A., 42, 130, 131, 234
Poddubnaya, S. S., 154
Polanyi, C. M., 74
Polanyi, M., 64, 143, 148, 562, 610
Pollak, M. A., 296
Pollak, P. I., 271, 273
Pomerantz, P., 248
Ponomarey, F. G., 109
Porter, H. D., 424
Pouncy, H. W., Jr., 101
Powell, H. M., 474, 475
Powell, S. G., 162

Powell, W. J., 101
Pratesi, P., 369
Pratt, R. J., 155
Prelog, V., 13, 17, 42, 44, 75, 115, 116, 153, 217, 238, 239, 246, 289, 353, 354, 356
Pressman, D., 10, 271, 316
Prévost, C., 92, 94, 415
Price, C. C., 143, 151, 269, 314, 322, 355, 381, 484
Price, F. P., Jr., 566, 597, 652, 654, 657
Prideaux, E. B. R., 436
Primavesi, G. R., 152
Pritchard, H. O., 143
Pritchard, J. G., 610
Prochaska, R. J., 356
Pudovik, A. N., 87
Pullman, A., 495, 517
Pullman, B., 517
Pullman, M. B., 495
Purlee, E. L., 652
Purves, C. B., 381

Quayle, O. R., 209, 237
Qudrat-I-Khuda, A. M., 466
Quinn, M. J., 182, 187

Rabjohn, N., 91, 146, 229
Raether, L. O., 451
Rainsford, A. E., 650
Ramart-Lucas, P., 233, 485, 487
Ramsey, D. A., 40
Randall, D. I., 237, 419
Randall, M., 561
Rank, B., 379
Rank, D. H., 53
Rao, P. A. D., 83
Rapala, R. T., 489
Raphael, R. A., 501
Rapp, W., 88
Rasmussen, R. S., 14
Rassack, R. C., 91
Raulins, R., 298
Read, J., 48, 68, 128, 309, 318
Reagan, H., 485
Reber, T., 237
Reed, R. I., 144
Reeve, W., 73, 109
Reeves, R. E., 383, 384
Regan, C. M., 268, 580
Reggel, L., 488
Reichstein, T., 95
Reitz, A. W., 16
Relyea, D. I., 243
Remsen, I., 170
Remick, A. E., 475, 568, 652

Remington, W. R., 485
Renfrew, W. B., 404
Renoll, M., 109
Reutov, O. A., 154
Reynolds, R. D., 297
Rhoads, S. J., 297
Rice, O. K., 530
Richard, G., 374
Richards, G. N., 399, 400
Richards, M. B., 115
Richards, R. E., 507
Richardson, A. C., 272
Richardson, R. W., 484
Richmond, J. H., 307
Richter, J., 486
Richtmeyer, N. K., 133, 372
Ried, E. E., 169, 644, 650
Rieger, M., 543
Riesz, P., 653
Ringler, B. I., 370
Rinker, J. W., 469
Ritchie, M., 586
Ritter, H., 129
Rivett, A. C. D., 119
Riviere, C., 421
Ro, R. S., 126
Roberts, C. W., 103
Roberts, G., 130
Roberts, I., 204
Roberts, J. D., 83, 123, 124, 134, 138, 209, 257, 268, 276, 278, 279, 335, 354, 415, 423, 519, 521, 535, 536, 578, 580, 594, 595, 596, 609, 629
Roberts, J. S., 147
Roberts, R., 148
Robertson, G. J., 128, 135
Robertson, J. M., 477
Robertson, P. W., 171, 203, 243, 247
Robertson, W. G. P., 227
Robertson, W. W., 491, 519
Robinson, C. A., 292
Robinson, C. C., 610
Robinson, C. H., 156
Robinson, G. C., 127, 259
Robinson, R., 177, 370
Robison, M. M., 225
Rodebush, W. H., 485, 489, 490, 491
Roe, E. M. F., 487
Roger, R., 266, 267
Rogers, J. W., 224
Rogers, M. T., 213, 519, 521
Romero, M. A., 97
Romo, J., 98
Rondestvedt, E., 362
Rongone, R., 512
Roothaan, C. C. J., 494, 514

Rosanoff, M. A., 214
Rose, J. B., 317
Rosen, L. J., 76, 538
Rosenberg, I., 90
Rosenfelder, W. J., 48, 309
Rosenkrantz, H., 51
Rosenkranz, G., 98
Rosenmund, K. W., 362
Rosenthal, R., 113
Ross, A., 31
Ross, F., 96
Ross, S. D., 109, 144, 145, 485, 506
Ross, W. E., 403
Rossini, F. D., 567, 655
Rossow, A. G., 610
Rothen, A., 80
Rothrock, H. S., 81
Rothstein, E., 95
Rothstein, R., 109
Rowland, S. P., 248
Royer, R., 160
Rubin, T., 224, 580
Ruhoff, J. R., 340, 555
Rule, J. M., 96
Rumpf, P., 511
Runde, M. M., 95
Rundle, R. E., 431
Rupp, E., 214
Russ, J. J., 84
Russel, G. A., 146, 148
Russell, M., 168
Russell, R. R., 109
Ruzicka, L., 42, 235, 238, 353, 359
Ryan, J. P., 296
Ryan, M. J., 149
Rydon, H. N., 78
Rydone, H. H., 462
Rylander, P. N., 594, 610, 613, 645

Sabatier, P., 129
Sachs, M., 37
Sachse, H., 3
Sadle, A., 109
Salas, E. de, 256
Sallay, I., 293
Salmon-Legagneur, F., 233
Salomon, G., 114, 115
Samelson, H., 653
Sandin, R. B., 176, 194
Saperstein, P. O., 412
Sarel, S., 220, 222, 228, 644
Saunders, B. C., 241
Saunders, W. H., Jr., 257
Savard, K., 51
Savel'eva, I. S., 77
Sawyer, D. W., 437

Saxton, B., 428
Sayigh, A., 137
Saylor, J. H., 87
Saytzeff, A., 330
Sazonova, V. A., 407
Schaaf, E., 151
Schaefer, E., 123
Schaefgen, J. R., 594, 610, 645
Schäfer, W., 424
Schaub, R. E., 295
Schenck, F., 307
Schenck, R. Ten Eyck, 109
Schenkel, H., 367
Schenkel-Rudin, M., 367
Schenker, K., 44, 246, 289
Scheurer, P., 229
Schiefle, A. J., 199
Schlenk, W., 391, 397
Schlenk, W., Jr., 475
Schlesinger, A. H., 262
Schlichenmaier, W., 401
Schmerling, L., 295
Schmid, H., 296
Schmid, K., 296
Schmidt, G. M. J., 477
Schmidt, M. T., 404
Schmitt, F., 113
Schneider, A., 219, 613
Schneider, R. F., 120
Schnurr, W., 362
Schoenewaldt, E. F., 137
Schomaker, V., 9, 119, 533
Schonne, A., 162
Schorigin, P., 348
Schramm, J., 145, 339
Schreck, R., 448
Schreiber, J., 152
Schreiber, K., 258, 262, 324
Schriescheim, A., 577
Schubert, E. N., 292
Schubert, W. M., 175, 361, 364, 485
Schuerch, C., Jr., 217
Schulthess, O., 155
Schumacher, M., 147
Schumann, S. C., 35, 122
Schumann, W., 151
Schwab, G. M., 388
Schwarz, M., 103, 143
Schwarzenbach, G., 444, 449, 453
Schwartzman, L. H., 485
Schwenk, E., 228
Scotini, R., 51, 131
Scott, A., 539
Scott, A. D., 66, 80
Scott, A. I., 501
Scott, C. B., 157, 575

Scott, D. W., 53
Scott, E. W., 95
Scott, P. T., 267
Searles, S., 415, 460
Seeler, F., 316
Seeles, H., 237
Seelig, E., 188
Seiwerth, R., 356
Selwood, P. W., 387, 389
Sen, J. N., 167, 200
Serini, A., 255
Serres, C., Jr., 20
Setter, H., 160
Seubold, F. H., 283, 285
Sexton, A. R., 109
Seymour, D., 271, 292
Shabica, A. C., 292
Shapiro, U. G., 73
Sharpe, A. G., 103
Shechter, H., 232, 234, 239, 359, 440, 445
Sheehan, J., 226
Sheppard, N., 53
Sherwood, D. W., 485
Shih, Chin-Hua, 96
Shimanouchi, T., 272
Shine, H. J., 411
Shiner, V. J., Jr., 71, 313, 334
Shive, B., 211
Shivers, J. C., 347, 412
Shoemaker, G. L., 161
Shoemaker, V., 120
Shoesmith, J. B., 88
Shoolery, J. N., 614
Shoppee, C. W., 39, 128, 130
Shorter, J., 71
Shriner, R. L., 66, 140, 153, 215
Shryne, T. M., 80
Sidgwick, N. V., 119
Siegel, M., 267
Siegel, S., 68, 279, 414
Silversmith, E. F., 99
Simonetta, M., 102, 570
Simonsen, J. L., 322, 326
Simpson, T. P., 341
Singh, Y., 162
Singleton, E., 650
Sixma, F. L. J., 627
Skell, P. S., 321, 347
Skinner, H. A., 147
Skita, A., 20, 129
Sklar, A. L., 483
Skrabal, A., 610, 636
Skrabal, R., 507
Slater, R. H., 88
Slator, A., 102, 106

Smiles, S., 197
Smiley, R. A., 161
Smith, A. S., 406
Smith, D. J., 609, 629
Smith, F. D., 230
Smith, G. G., 309
Smith, H. A., 20, 70, 207, 208, 210, 217, 218, 340, 555, 586, 589, 604, 667, 668, 670, 671
Smith, J. F., 72, 262
Smith, J. G., 128
Smith, J. W., 509
Smith, L., 117, 220
Smith, L. I., 242
Smith, M. S., 171
Smith, P. A., 292
Smith, P. A. S., 31
Smith, R. D., 228
Smith, R. J., 217
Smith, R. P., 568, 624, 627
Smith, W. R., 552
Smith, W. T., Jr., 354, 356
Smyth, C. P., 20
Smyth, I. F. B., 355
Sneddon, W. W., 280
Snyder, H. R., 68, 95, 161, 240
Sobel, B., 512
Sobotka, H., 237
Sochanski, N., 305
Soffer, H., 596
Solomon, A. L., 124
Sommer, L. H., 78, 609, 647, 654
Sommers, A. H., 160
Sondheimer, F., 98, 484, 499
Southwick, P. L., 248
Späth, A., 151
Speck, S. B., 409
Speight, E. A., 445
Spencer, C. F., 44, 245, 246, 288, 310
Sperber, N., 228
Spiegel, L., 233
Spielman, M. A., 404
Spinks, J. W. T., 83
Spinner, E., 86
Spinrad, B. I., 521
Spitzer, R., 4, 14, 16, 35, 326, 458, 518, 533, 535, 635
Spitzer, W. C., 185
Sprague, R. H., 481, 494
Sprankling, C. H. G., 120
Sprecher, M., 137
Srivastava, H. C., 133
Stand, C. J., 226
Starks, F. W., 157
Staudinger, H., 237
Steacie, E. W. R., 148

Stearns, H. A., 473
Steinberg, H., 498, 501
Steinberger, H. R., 264
Steinberger, R., 360
Steiner, E. G., 155
Steinmetz, W. E., 272
Stempel, G. H., Jr., 512
Stephenson, R. J., 130
Stern, A., 73, 375
Stevens, P. G., 307, 411
Stevens, T. S., 280, 281
Stevenson, A., 467
Stevenson, D. P., 9, 614
Stewart, F. H. C., 160
Stiles, M., 72
Stiller, E. T., 280
Stillson, G. H., 437
Stitt, F., 501
Stockmair, W., 14, 16
Stokes, C. S., 354, 356
Stoll, M., 42
Stone, F. W., 143
Stone, H., 473
Stork, G., 78, 96
Storms, L. B., 211
Stoven, O., 109
Strang, A., 149, 151
Straus, F., 395
Streitwieser, A., Jr., 66, 67, **610**
Strickland, T., 404
Stubbs, F. J., 610
Sudborough, J. J., 207, 209, 210, 211, 212, 214, 215, 586, 589
Sugden, S., 67, 74
Sujishi, S., 456, 610, 635
Sumrell, G., 227
Surmatis, J. D., 244
Sutton, L. E., 119, 142, 509, 510, 511, 512, 513
Swain, C. G., 65, 66, 70, 71, 157, 396, 400, 575, 621
Swain, C. S., 259
Swamer, F. W., 370
Swart, E. R., 73
Sweeney, W. A., 485
Swern, D., 109
Synerholm, M. E., 354
Szasz, G. J., 53, 493
Szwarc, M., 147, 387

Taft, R. W., Jr., 587, 589, 599, 606, 609, 612, 620, 629, 633, 636, 643, 644, 648, 649, 652, 654, 656, 665, 669, 670, 672
Taher, N. A., 86
Takeda, M., 9

Takemura, K. H., 472
Tamele, M., 84
Tamres, M., 460
Tang, C. S., 625
Tappe, W., 128, 306, 317, 326
Tarbell, D. S., 104, 295, 594, 610, 613, 645
Taylor, H. T., 88
Taylor, J. E., 381
Taylor, M. D., 440, 454, 456, 610, 635
Tchelinzeff, W., 396
Teach, E. G., 87
Terent'ev, A. P., 398
TerWeel, M. J., 190
Theilacker, W., 390 476
Thomas, C. A., 241
Thomas, C. H., 101
Thomas, E. R., 211
Thomas, H. C., 124
Thomas, J. R., 53
Thompson, A. F., 446
Thompson, G., 70, 512, 513
Thompson, H. W., 507
Thompson, R. H. K., 74
Thompson, T., 280
Thorpe, J. F., 119, 463, 467
Thurston, J. T., 153
Tiemann, P., 151
Tiffenean, M., 266
Timm, E. W., 86, 661
Tishler, M., 292
Todd, R. W., 148
Tolcher, P., 78
Tomasewski, A. J., 78
Tommila, E., 69, 590, 668, 671
Toogood, J. B., 484, 499
Topley, B., 66, 539
Towle, P. H., 310
Trachtenberg, E. N., 103
Trautmann, G., 96
Traylor, T. G., 154
Treffers, H. P., 218
Trevoy, L. W., 109
Triebs, W., 416
Trifan, D., 123, 257, 262, 327
Tronov, V. V., 102
Trotman-Dickenson, A. F., 143, 147, 148, 458
Trouse, F. W., 665
Tsai, L., 228
Tsatsas, G., 128, 412
Tsou, Kwang-Chung, 110
Tsuruoka, S., 229
Tsutsui, M., 614
Tuck, J. L., 74
Tucker, O., 147

Tulagin, V., 372
Tulinskie, A., 20
Tull, R., 410
Tunnicliff, D. D., 473
Turnbull, D., 441
Turnbull, J. H., 454
Turner, E. E., 66, 145, 476, 482, 484
Turner, E. G., 116
Turner, M. K., 214, 215, 589
Turner, R. B., 15, 251
Tutwiler, F. B., 103
Tweit, R. C., 28, 78, 83, 128
Twiss, D. F., 106

Ugi, I., 88
Ullyot, G. E., 402
Underwood, G., 109
Urey, H. C., 503
Urry, W. H., 142, 146, 149, 283
Utsch, H., 123

Valette, A., 94
Valette, J., 129
Vand, V., 477
Vanderhorst, P. J., 519
VanderWerf, C. A., 84, 109, 112, 139
Van Duin, C. F., 316
van Gulick, N. M., 117
Van Heldin, R., 484, 486
van Loon, J., 214
Van Straten, S. F., 123
van Tamelen, E. E., 78, 113, 293
Van Zandt, G., 481, 494
Van Zyl, G., 109, 113
Vaughan, W. E., 340, 555
Vaughn, G., 132
Vavon, G., 91, 152, 169, 207, 213, 221, 222, 322, 421
Vennesland, B., 67
Verhoek, F. H., 370, 587, 649
Verkade, P. E., 119, 484, 486, 650
Vermeulen, M. H., 188
Vernon, C. A., 84, 87, 96, 98
Verschelden, P., 123
Vidal, F., 153
Viervoll, H., 14, 35, 120
Vodoz, C. A., 104
Vogel, A. I., 428, 465
Vogel, K. H., 610, 613
Voitle, D. M., 484
von Auwers, K., 20
Vörster, J., 255

Waddington, G., 53
Wade, C. W. R., 101
Wagner-Jauregg, T., 66, 126

Walborsky, H. M., **78**, 103, 124, 125, 163
Walker, H. G., 511
Walker, I. S., 501
Walker, J., 68
Walker, J. T., 240
Walker, W., 134
Wallach, O., 128, 134, 359, 445
Walling, C., 151
Wallingford, H. P., 408
Wallis, E. S., 141, 153, 250, 251, 252
Walsh, A. D., 120, 493, 520, 590
Walter, G. F., 488
Walther, W., 380
Walz, H., 88
Wankel, R. A., 519
Wannowius, H., 379
Warhurst, E., 147
Waring, D. H., 476, 488
Warner, J. C., 610, 613
Warner, R., 258
Wash, G., 211
Wasserman, A., 431, 433
Wasserman, H. H., 134
Watanabe, I., 9
Waterer, J. A., 91
Waters, G. W., 428
Waters, W. A., 152, 199, 568, 590
Watson, A. T., 517
Watson, H. B., 280, 589, 650, 671
Watson, M. B., 83
Weale, K. E., 160
Webb, I. D., 96
Webb, R. L., 596
Weber, A. P., 90
Webers, V. J., 159, 484, 486
Webster, W., 152
Wed, H., 42
Wedekind, E. von, 352
Weedon, B. C. L., 96
Wegscheider, R., 229
Weikel, T., 391
Weinhouse, S., 411
Weinstock, J., 96
Weiss, J., 66, 539
Weller, S. W., 509
Welsh, L. H., 293
Wenzel, A., 484
Wepster, B. M., **75**, 484, 485, 486, 650
Werner, A., 120
Westheimer, F. H., 15, 48, 67, 111, 151, 235, 313, 352, 360, 462, 543, 568, 581, 604
Wheatley, W. B., 109, 473, 476
Wheeler, N. G., 272
Wheeler, O. H., 238, 338, 359

Whelan, W. P., 137
Wheland, G. W., 142, 163, 179, 185, 199, 250, 264, 387, 388, 390, 475, 568, 580, 603, 625, 656, 672
Whetstone, R., 247
White, E. H., 80
White, F. L., 481, 494
White, W. N., 96
Whitmore, F. C., 10, 76, 81, 235, 236, 237, 244, 250, 253, 371, 372, 403, 417, 418, 419
Wiberg, K. B., 80, 233
Wichterle, O., 418
Widiger, A. H., 172
Wieland, P., 153
Wiggins, L. F., 132, 399, 400
Wiig, E. O., 516
Wilder, P., Jr., 354
Wilip, E., 128
Wilke, G., 375
Wilken, P. H., 80, 141
Williams, F. V., 103, 439
Williams, G. H., 199
Williams, H. R., 109
Williams, J. R. L., 176
Williams, R., 650
Williams, R. B., 340
Williams, R. J., 309
Williamson, B., 489, 491
Williamson, K. D., 53
Wilms, H., 312
Wilson, B. M., 81
Wilson, C. D., 244
Wilson, C. L., 66, 96, 256
Wilson, E., 64
Wilson, H. F., 104
Wilson, K. W., 415
Wilson, T. P., 533
Wilson, W., 454
Winckler, C. A., 123
Windaus, A., 307
Winkelmann, E., 151
Winstein, S., 52, 65, 69, 72, 85, 89, 95, 98, 105, 106, 111, 123, 127, 154, 257, 258, 259, 262, 271, 283, 291, 292, 316, 324, 327, 329, 373, 570
Winston, A., 354
Wise, R. M., 477
Wislicenus, J., 64, 316
Wittek, H., 14
Wittig, G., 153, 280, 282, 396
Wittwer, C., 444, 449
Witzens, P. H., 650
Wohlgemuth, K., 117
Wolf, G., 380
Wolf, H. P., 288

Wolf, M., 501
Wolfhagen, H., 207
Wolfhagen, H. J., 227
Wolleman, J., 445
Wood, A. P., 272
Woodward, R. B., 244
Woolf, L. I., 314
Woolley, H. W., 493
Wordie, J. D., 228
Wren, H., 266
Wright, G. F., 128, 155, 395, 396, 397, 398, 404, 405
Wyman, G. M., 487

Yancey, J. A., 83, 268, 335, 580
Yantschulewitsch, J., 37
Yoshima, T., 20
Young, D. P., 152, 251
Young, H. H., 225, 226

Young, J. H., 153
Young, W. G., 10, 83, 84, 92, 95, 96, 98, 99, 316, 414, 415, 423
Yuan, H. C., 543
Yuang, W., 40

Zack, J. F., 109
Zagdoun, R., 110
Zahler, R. E., 166, 196, 361
Zaremba, C., 152, 221
Zderic, J. A., 143
Zeiss, H. H., 67, 259, 614
Zelinski, N. D., 126, 129
Ziegler, C., 312
Ziegler, K., 117, 151, 424
Zimmerman, H. E., 357, 376
Zimmerman, M., 353
Zook, H. D., 236
Zuidema, G. D., 109, 113

Subject Index

Acetoacetic ester, acidity of, 453
  enolization of, 446
Acetomesitylene, acylation of in Friedel-Crafts reaction, 241
  enolization of in Reformatsky reaction, 240
  failure of haloform reaction with, 240
Acetone, enolization of, 444
Acetylacetone, acidity of, 453
  enolization of, 446, 449
1-Acetyl-1,4-cyclohexadiene, spectrum of, 499
2-Acetylcyclohexanone, acidity of, 453
  enolization of, 449
2-Acetylcyclopentanone, acidity of, 453
  enolization of, 449
Acetylenes, di-*t*-butyl, 247
  dimesityl, 248
  mesityl, 248
Acid chlorides, reactivity of, 225
Acidity of C—H bonds, 439
Acids, aliphatic, highly hindered, 211, 213
Activated complex, energy of racemization of optically active biphenyls, 550
  for displacement reaction, 538
  for interconversion of conformational isomers, 535
  for racemization of optically active biphenyls, 549
  minimizing energy of, 542–548
Activation energy, for displacements, 538
  for interconverting conformational isomers, 535
  for racemization of optically active biphenyls, 549, 550
Acylation, intramolecular, 233–235
Acyl-oxygen fission in esters, 218, 219
Adamantane-1,3-dicarboxylic acid, decarboxylation of silver salt, 355
Adam's rule, 554
Aldehydes, decarbonylation, 363

Alkylbenzenes, o/p ratios in the nitration of, 169
Alkyl chlorosulfites, use of in esterification, 217
Alkyl halides, 538
Alkyl-oxygen fission in esters, 219, 224
Allyl halides, 84–86
  allylic rearrangements of, 92
  relative reactivity of, 84
  S_N1 reactions of, 85
  S_N2 reactions of, 86
  S_N2' reactions of, 95
Allylic rearrangement (S_N1' reaction), 92–98
  stereochemistry of, 94
  steric effects in, 93
Alternation effects in nucleophilic displacement, 138–140
Amides, hydrolysis of highly hindered, 228
4-Amino-4'-nitrobiphenyl, absorption intensity of, 485
Ammonia, basicity toward protons, 457
  trimethylboron adduct, 456
Anchimeric assistance, 262, 570, 641, 642
  in ring compounds, 124
  in solvolysis of highly branched halides, 72
Angle deformation, 277
Anhydrides, unsymmetrical, reactions of, 228, 229, 231
Aniline, ionization of, 438
Aniline derivatives, electronic spectra of, 485
  molecular refraction of, 513
Anilines, ionization of, 438
Anilinium ions, 437
  ionization constants of, 438
Anions and bases, nucleophilic substitution constants of, 156
  stereochemistry in displacement on, 153–156
  steric effects involving, 156–163

697

Anions and bases, steric requirements of, 75, 76, 112, 113, 157–161
Anisole, absorption intensity of derivatives, 485
Apocamphyl cation, strain in, 538
Argon, van der Waals potential of, 530
Aromatic ketones, sterically hindered, acid-catalyzed cleavage of, 175
    nuclear substituents in, 198
    nucleophilic displacement of, 198
Aromatic substitution, transition-state model, 165–167
    electrophilic, coulombic interaction between substituents and entering groups, 177
    effect of steric interaction among resident groups, 172
    o/p ratio as measure of steric hindrance to, 168
    primary kinetic isotope effect in sulfonation, 165
    sensitivity of "ortho effect" in solvent, 180
    types of steric effects in, 167
β-Aroyl-α- and β-methacrylic acids, cyclization of, 469
Aroyl nitrates, nitration by, 171
Asymmetric induction, 29
    conformational analysis of, 12
    rule of, 239
Axial bonds, definition of, 16

Baeyer strain theory, 3
Baeyer-Villiger rearrangement, 251, 283
Balbiano's acid, 467
Beckmann rearrangement, 253, 254
Bending, see Valence angles, deformation of
Benzaldehyde, dipole moment of, 509
Benzene polycarboxylic acids, 435
Benzene ring, deformations, 549
Benzenes, substituted, o/p ratios in nitration of, 178
Benzil, spectrum of, 499
Benzils, absorption spectra of, 489
Benzoic acid derivatives, absorption spectra of, 487
Benzoic acids, ortho effects on ionization, 428
    rates of esterification of, 215
Benzo[c]phenanthrene, crystal structure of, 477
Benzophenone, reaction with phenylmagnesium bromide, 401

Benzoyl alcohol, dipole moment of, 509
o-Benzoylbenzoic acid, cyclization of, 470
    esterification of, 217
o-Benzoylbenzoic acids, tautomerism of, 469
Benzyl halides, 88–92
    S_N1 reaction of, 88
    S_N2 reaction of, 90, 91
    steric inhibition of resonance in, 88, 89
Benzyl nitrite, stretching frequency of nitrite group in, 506
Biphenyl, electronic spectrum, 484
    resonance energy and twist, 482
Biphenyls, 543–554
Bond angles, see Valence angles
Bonds, $2p\pi$, 496
    $2p\sigma$, 496
    $2p\sigma$-$2p\pi$ hybrid, 497
Bredt's rule in decarboxylation of β-keto acids, 353
Bridgehead compounds, anion formation in, 163
    in free-radical reactions, 149
    in nucleophilic displacement, 81, 134–138
    in $S_N i$ reaction, 81, 135
    in S_N1 reaction, 82, 135–138
Bromine-hydrogen van der Waals interaction, 544
3-Bromoacetylacetone, acidity of, 453
Bromocyclohexanone, conformation, 40
α-Bromo-β,β-dimethylglutaric acid, cyclypropane formation from, 59
α-Bromoglutaric acid, cyclopropane formation from, 463
α-Bromo-β-methylglutaric acid, cyclopropane formation from, 463
cis-4-Bromo-4'-nitrostilbene, dipole moment of, 510
    molecular refraction of, 513
Brönsted catalysis law, 584
Brunings-Corwin effect, 494
B strain, 25, 27, 28, 32, 276, 286, 333, 334, 336
    in free-radical reactions, 147, 148
    in geminal dihalides, 100
    in ring closure, 62, 119
    in S_N1 reaction, 72, 73
Butane, conformations, 7
    potential barrier in, 7
    restricted rotation in, 7
Butene-2, cis-, 554
    trans-, 554
Buttressing effect, 552
    on absorption intensity, 486

t-Butylamine, trimethylboron adduct, 456
t-Butyl benzoate, hydrolysis of, 219
2-Butyl bromide, resolution of with tri-o-thymotide, 474
t-Butylethylene, bromination of, 243
t-Butyl methyl ether, formation of, 219

Carbanions, configuration and basicity of, 440
Carbohydrates, tautomerism of, 464
Carbon dioxide, normal vibrations of, 526, 527
Carbonium ions, distortion of, 538
    planar, 538
Carbonyl compounds, enol content, 444
    enolization and acidity, 442, 444
Carboxylic acids, acidity of cis and trans isomers, 431, 433
    ionization of dibasic, 431
    ionization of hindered benzoic, 428
    ionization of unsaturated, 428
Catalytic reduction, stereochemistry of, 143, 144
Catechol, ionization of, 436
2-Chloroöctane, resolution of with urea, 475
3-Chlorophthalic anhydride, reactions of, 230
ω-Chlorotoluenes, o/p ratios in nitration of, 178
cis effect, 271
Claisen condensation, Grignard reagents in, 404
Claisen rearrangement, 295–303
Clathrate compounds, 474
Cleavage, of β-diketones by Grignard reagents, 372
    of 1,3-diol monotosylates, 377
    of 1,3-diols, 375
    of α-epoxy ketones by Grignard reagents, 372
    of 1,2-glycols, 378
    of β-haloketones by Grignard reagents, 372
    of hindered β-diketones, 371
    of meso vs. racemic diols, 381
Compressibility, 530
Concerted mechanism (or "push-pull" mechanism), in epoxides, 112
    in nucleophilic displacement reaction, 65
Conformation, biphenyls, 550
    boat, for dichlorocyclooctadiene, 535
    bromocyclohexanone, 40
    butane, 7

Conformation, butene, 58
    chair, for dichlorocyclooctadiene, 535
    cyclohexane, 13
    cyclohexanone, 39
    cyclohexene, 38
    cyclopentane, 35
    cyclopentene, 39
    decalin, 23
    decalol, 27
    dimethylcyclohexanes, 18
    dimethylcyclopentane, 36
    dipolar effects on, 20
    effect on chromatography, 51
    effect on deamination reactions, 50
    effect on equilibrium, 30
    effect on 1,2-glycol cleavage in six ring, 383
    effect on infrared spectra, 51
    effect on ionic elimination, 48
    effect on pyrolytic elimination, 49
    effect on rate of reaction, 28
    effect on reactivity, 9, 44
    effect on rearrangement, 49
    effect on stability, 47
    energy differences, 51
    ethane, 5
    gauche, 8
    hydrindane, 37
    hydrindanol, 37
    large rings, 42
    medium rings, 42
    methylcyclohexane, 17
    9-methyldecalin, 30
    multiple internal rotations, 57
    perhydroanthracenes, 34
    perhydroaromatic systems, 31–34
    perhydrophenanthrenes, 32
    quantitative energy values, 51
    skew, 8
    skew for dichlorocyclooctadiene, 535
    staggered, 6
Conformational analysis in cleavage of acyclic 1,2-glycols, 382
Conformational effects, in displacement reactions in rings, 125–133
    in epoxide ring opening, 130–133
    in nucleophilic displacement reactions, 92
    in oxidation reactions, 151, 152
    in radical dimerization, 146, 147
    in ring closure, 120
    on strain in common rings, 121, 122
Cope elimination reaction, 310
Corrosion, formation of organometallics by, 395
Crystal violet, isomerism in, 491

p-Cyanobromobenzenes, rates of reaction with piperidine, 185
Cyclic ethers, basicity of, 460
Cyclic intermediates, in cleavage of β-diketones by Grignard reagents, 373
  in cleavage of 1,2-glycols, 379
  in cleavage of 1,3-glycols, 377
  in decarboxylation of β-ketoacids, 352
  in decarboxylation of metal chelates, 360
  in decarboxylation of unsaturated acids, 358
  in Grignard reactions, 411
  in reduction with Grignard reagents, 421
Cycloalkanecarboxylic acids, esterification rates of, 210
Cycloalkanedicarboxylic acids, 431, 433
Cyclobutane, 533
Cyclobutanone, carbonyl stretching frequency in, 507
Cyclohexane, conformations, 13
Cyclohexanedicarboxylic acids, conformational analysis of, 434
  ionization constants of, 433, 435
1,3-Cyclohexanedione, acidity of, 453
1,2-Cyclohexanedione, enolization of, 449
Cyclohexanone, conformation, 39
  enolization, 444
Cyclohexene, conformation, 38
Cyclopentadienones, 451
1,2-Cyclopentanedione, enolization of, 449
Cyclopentanone, enolization of, 444
Cyclopentene, conformation of, 39
Cyclopentyl chloride, dipole moment of, 521
Cyclopropane, bond orbitals in, 519
  ring opening of, 464
  strain in, 534
Cyclopropanes, from α-bromoacids, 463
  ring opening with hydrogen bromide, 464
Cyclopropanols, in ring-chain tautomerism, 463, 464
Cyclopropyl chloride, dipole moment of, 521

Deacylation, 364
Decalin conformation, 23
  stability, 23
Decalol, conformation, 27
  stability, 27

Decarbonylation of aldehydes, 363
Decarboxylation, attempted, of camphenoic and ketopinic acids, 352
  catalysis by organic bases, 369
  in 5,3,1-bicyclic systems, 353
  in treatment of silver salts with bromine, 354
  of adamantane-1,3-dicarboxylic acid, 355
  of alkylbenzoic acids, 362
  of arylidenemalonic acid derivatives, 368
  of α,α-dimethylacetoacetic acids, 351
  of 2,2-dimethylbutene-3-oic acid, 360
  of 2,5-dimethylcyclopentanedicarboxylic acid, 357
  of 4,4-dimethyl-2-pentenoic acid, 359
  of β-halocinnamic acids, 364
  of hindered aromatic acids, 361
  of β-keto acids, 351, 353
  of mesitoic acid, 363
  of methylpicolinic acids, 364
  of optically active acids, 369
  of oxaloacetic acids, 360
  of *erythro*- and *threo*-α-phenyl-β-benzoyl-β-bromopropionic acid, 365
  of β-phenyl-β-bromo-α-phenylpropionic acids, 365
  of β-phenylcinnamic acid, 367
  of α-pyridylacetic acid analogs, 361
  of trialkylbenzoic acids, 363
  of trihaloacetic acids, 370
  of β,γ-unsaturated acids, 357
  resistance to, 352
Deformation of bond angles, *see* Valence angles, deformation of
Deuterium exchange, nuclear, steric inhibition of resonance in aromatic amines, 173
Diazo coupling of *t*-aromatic amines, steric inhibition of resonance in, 174
1,4-Dibenzoylbutane, failure to cyclize, 465
Dibenzoylmethane, enolization of, 446
Dibiphenylene-butadiene, molecular orbital treatment of, 494
Dibiphenylene-ethylene, electronic spectrum of, 494
  half-wave potential of, 517
Dibiphenylene-hexatriene, molecular orbital treatment of, 494
Dibromo acid, *see* 2,2'-Dibromo-4,4'-dicarboxybiphenyl
2,2'-Dibromo-4-amino-4'-nitrobiphenyl, 551

2,2′-Dibromo-4,4′-diaminobiphenyl, 551
2,2′-Dibromo-4,4′-dicarboxybiphenyl, 542–552
Di-t-butyl carbonate, inertness to ammonolysis, 224
2,6-Di-t-butylphenol, dipole moment of, 511
2,6-Di-t-butylpyridine, 439
    ionization of, 439
β-Dicarbonyl compounds, acidity, 453
    cyclic, 448
    enolization, 446
    sterically hindered, 447
2,2′-Dicarboxybiphenyl, absorption spectrum of, 489
3,3′-Dichlorobenzidine, angle of twist in, 511
Dichlorobenzoic acids, carbonyl stretching frequency of, 506
2,2′-Dichlorobiphenyl, angle of twist in, 511
Dichlorocyclooctadiene, 535
Dichloronitrobenzenes, molecular refraction of, 512
Diethylamine, trimethylboron adduct, 457
Diethyl isopropylidenemalonate, esterification of, 218
9,10-Dihydro-3,4,5,6-dibenzophenanthrene, [α]D 1496°, 476
5,7-Dihydrodibenz[c,e]oxepin, spectrum of, 491
Diiodo acid, see 2,2′-Diiodo-5,5′-dicarboxybiphenyl
2,2′-Diiodo-5,5′-dicarboxybiphenyl, 549, 553
Diisobutyrylmethane enolization, 447
α-Diketones, enolization, 449, 450, 451
β-Diketones, see β-Dicarbonyl compounds
    cleavage of, 370, 372
1,6-Diketones, 465
Dimedone, acidity of, 453
    enolization of, 449
1,5-Dimethoxyanthracene, angle of twist in, 512
2,2′-Dimethoxybiphenyl, absorption spectrum of, 492
1,4-Dimethoxynaphthalene, angle of twist in, 512
1,5-Dimethoxynaphthalene, angle of twist in, 512
2,6-Dimethylacetanilide, steric effects in nitration of, 176
α,α-Dimethylacetoacetic acid, decarboxylation of, 350

Dimethylamine, basicity toward protons, 457
    trimethyl boron adduct, 456
N,N-Dimethylaniline, ionization of, 438
Dimethylaniline and derivatives, absorption spectra of, 486
1,12-Dimethylbenzo[c]phenanthrene, spectrum of, 501
1,12-Dimethylbenzo[c]phenanthrene-5-acetic acid, [α]D ±360°, 478
3,6-Dimethyl-2-benzoylbenzoic acid, cyclization of, 470
4,4′-Dimethyl-2-benzoylbenzoic acid, cyclization of, 470
Dimethylcyclohexanes, conformation, 18
    stabilities, 19
    stereochemistry, 19, 21
Dimethylcyclopentane, conformation, 36
    stereochemistry, 36
2,5-Dimethylcyclopentanecarboxylic acids, rates of esterification of, 210
1,1-Dimethylcyclopropane, ring opening of, 464
4,5-Dimethylphenanthrene, spectrum of, 501
N,N-Dimethyltoluidines, ionization of, 438
N,N-Dimethylxylidines, ionization of, 438
Dineopentylacetic acid, esterification of, 205
    formation of, 244
1,1-Dineopentylethylene, oxidation of, 244
    reactions of, 244
Dinitrophenols, ionization of, 436
4,4′-Dinitrobiphenyl, absorption intensity of, 485
2,2′-Dinitrobiphenyl, absorption spectrum of, 489
1,3-Diol monotosylates, cleavage of, 377
1,3-Diols, cleavage of, 375
1,2-Diols, resistance to cleavage by periodic acid, 385
1,2-Diphenyl-3,4-diketocyclopentene, enolization, 451
Dipivaloylmethane, enolization, 447
Dipole-dipole interactions, 551
N,N-Di-n-propylaniline, ionization of, 438
Diradicals, paramagnetism in, 516

Displacement coordinates, 544
    magnitudes, for racemization of opti-
        cally active biphenyls, 549
Displacement reaction, 538
Dissociation, of diphenyldibiphenylene,
        389
    of dibiphenyltetraphenylethanes, 392
    of hexaarylethanes, 387
    of hexa-*m*-biphenylethane, 391
    of hexa-*p*-biphenylethane, 391
    of hexaphenylethane, 389
    of hexa-*o*-tolylditin, 389
    of hexa-*o*-tolylethane, 393
Di-*p*-xylylene, spectrum of, 498, 501
Durenol, 509

Eclipsing effects, 266, 270, 273, 275, 336,
        339, 343, 344
Elasticity, of polyethylene, 517
    of polyisobutylene, 517
Electrical effect, definitions of, 569
Electronegativity and electron-with-
        drawing power, 613–618
Electronic spectrum intensity, 483
Elimination, bimolecular Hofmann, 318
    Chugaev, 305–307, 309
    conformational analysis of, 9, 48
    Cope, 310
    in *cis*-2-alkylcyclohexanols, 322
    in alkyl methyl sulfites, 314
    in amine oxides, 312
    in α-benzenehexachloride, 337
    in β-benzenehexachloride, 317, 319
    in 2-deutero-1,2-diphenyl-1-ethyl sys-
        tem, 313, 319, 346
    in 11,12-dichloro-9,10-dihydro-9,10-
        ethanoanthracene, 321
    in diethyl-*t*-butylcarbinyl chloride,
        329
    in dimethyl-*t*-butylcarbinyl chloride,
        335
    in 1,2-dimethylcyclohexyl bromides,
        328, 329
    in 1,2-diphenyl-1-propyl halides, 319,
        343
    in 1,2-diphenyl-1-propyl xanthate,
        308
    in menthyl and neomenthyl chlorides,
        327
    in menthyl and neomenthyl *p*-toluene-
        sulfonates, 327
    in menthyl chloride, 317
    in methyl 2-phenylcyclohexyl ether,
        348
    in neomenthyl chloride, 317
    in neomenthyl xanthate, 306

Elimination, in neopentylcarbinyl chlo-
        ride, 336
    in 3-phenyl-2-butyl *p*-toluenesulfo-
        nate, 319, 323, 335
    in 3-phenyl-2-butyl xanthate, 308
    in 2-phenylethyl benzoate, with po-
        tassium amide, 347
    of methyl xanthate, 306, 307
cis elimination, 306–310, 314, 318
Elimination reaction, 1,2 intramolecu-
        lar, 305
Enolization, 442
Enthalpy of activation, 566
Entropy of activation, 566
    in racemization of optically active bi-
        phenyls, 549
Epoxides, 106–114
    concerted mechanism in nucleophilic
        displacement of, 112
    conformational effects in opening of,
        130–134
    ring opening in, 107–108
Epoxyketones, 114
    cleavage by Grignard reagents, 372
Equatorial bonds, definition, 16
Ester hydrolysis, conformational effects
        on, 222
Esters, structure vs. reactivity with
        Grignard reagents, 417
Essential double bond, effect of twist-
        ing of, 493
Ethane, conformations of, 5
    potential barrier in, 6, 7
Ethers, basicity by hydrogen bonding
        to, 460
Ethyl acetoacetate, acidity, 413
    enolization, 446
3-Ethylacetylacetone, enolization, 446
Ethylamine, trimethylboron adduct of,
        457
N-Ethylaniline, ionization of, 438
Ethyl cyclohexanone-2-carboxylate,
        enolization, 449
Ethyl cyclopentanone-2-carboxylate,
        enolization, 449
2-Ethyl-4-dimethylaminostilbene, di-
        pole moment of, 509
Ethyl-7,7-dimethyl-2,2,1-bicyclohepta-
        none-3-carboxylate, enolization
        of, 448
Ethylene, energy-level diagram of,
        494
Ethyleneimine, trimethylboron adduct
        of, 460
Ethylene oxides, absorption spectra of,
        519

Ethylenesulfide, C—H stretching force constant in, 520
Ethyl-2-ethylacetoacetate, enolization, 446
Ethyl-1-indanone-2-carboxylate, enolization, 448
Ethylisopropylacetoacetate, enolization, 446
Ethyl-2-methylacetoacetate, enolization of, 446
Ethyl-2-n-propylacetoacetate, enolization, 446
Exocyclic double bond, enols containing, 445
Exocyclic positions, steric effects at, 134

Fine structure effect, 500
Fluorescence in cyanine dyes, 516
Force constants, 525, 545
   bending, 529
   bending C—C—Br angle, 548, 549
   bending C—C—C angle, 529, 549
   bending C—C—H angle, 529, 549
   calculation of, 527, 528
   equations for, 525
   stretching, 529
   stretching C—Br bond in activated complex, 549
   table, 529
   uncertainties in, 550
2-Formylcyclohexanone, acidity of, 453
   enolization of, 449
2-Formylcyclopentanone, acidity of, 453
   enolization of, 449
Free energy of activation, 566
   for racemization of optically active biphenyls, 549
Free-energy–polar-energy relationship, 605–613, 620–623, 632
Free-radical aromatic substitution, 199
   lack of apparent "ortho effect," 199
   orientation of substituents, 199
   role of complex formation in, 200
Free-radical substitution, 64, 140–151
   at bridge heads, 149
   inductive effects in, 151
   mechanism types in, 142
   retention of configuration in, 141
   steric effects in, 146–150
   steric inhibition of resonance in, 150
Frequency, see Vibration frequency
Friedel-Crafts acetylation, steric effects in activation of, 175
Friedel-Crafts reaction, cyclization of ω-phenylalkanoyl chlorides by high-dilution technique, 234

F strain, in free radical reaction, 146
   in substitution by amines, 75, 157–160
Furanose rings, 462

Gauche conformation, definition, 8
Gem dimethyl effect, 462, 464, 468
Glutaraldehydes, cyclization of, 465, 466
1,2-Glycols, cleavage of, 378
   cleavage of by non-cyclic intermediate, 386
   conformation analysis in cleavage of acyclic, 382
   reaction with cuprammonium, 383
Grignard reactions, enolate formation in, 419
Grignard reagents, 1,4 addition of, 396, 407, 409
   1,6 addition of, 408, 410
   allylic systems, 414
   asymmetric syntheses with, 405, 422
   cleavage of β-diketones by, 372
   cleavage of α-epoxyketones by, 372
   cleavage of β-haloketones by, 372
   derived (enolates), 402, 413, 420
   electrolysis of, 398
   optically active, 421
   reaction, with acid chlorides, 419
      with aldehydes, 411, 414
      with alkenes, 424
      with aminoketones, 417
      with anhydrides, 406
      with 1,3-diketones, 416
      with dimethyl sulfate, 397
      with epoxides, 399
      with esters, 412, 415, 417
      with magnesium halides, 399, 400
      with nitriles, 396, 403
      with zinc chloride, 399
   reaction media, 395, 397
   reduction with, 420
   structure of, 398, 402, 406
Ground state, stabilization and destabilization, 62

Halobenzene, o/p ratios in nitration of, 176
β-Halocinnamic acids, decarboxylation of, 364
α-Haloethers, nucleophilic displacement in, 101
β-Haloethers, S_N2 reaction in, 103
Haloform reaction, failure with hindered methyl ketones, 237, 240
Halogen-metal interconversion, 440
Halohydrins, 103

α-Haloketones, in nucleophilic displacement reactions, 75, 103–106
S_N2 reaction in, 103–106
β-Haloketones, cleavage by Grignard reagents, 372
α-Halo nitro compounds, 103
α-Halosulfones, 103
Hammett equation, discussion of, 570–584, 622, 660–663
    resonance and the, 576–583, 594–597
Harmonic vibrations, 525, 527
Heat of activation, see Activation energy
Heats of hydrogenation, 555
Helium, van der Waals potential, 531
Hexaarylethanes, dissociation of, 387
    effect of o-, m-, and p-substituents on dissociation, 392
2,2',4,4',6,6'-Hexachlorobiphenyl, absorption spectrum of, 488
Hexahelicene, $[\alpha]_D$ −3640°, 478
Hexaphenylethane, heats of combustion, oxidation, and hydrogenation, 389
Hindered aromatic acids, decarboxylation of, 361
Hofmann rearrangement, 253
Hofmann rule, 329, 336, 338
Homomorphs, 459
Hooke's law, 525, 527
Hydrindane, conformation, 37
    stability, 37
Hydrindanol, conformation of, 37
    stereochemistry of, 37
Hydrogen, steric requirements of, 439
Hydrogen as migrating group, 267, 268, 269, 270, 287–290
Hydrogen atoms, eclipsed, 534, 542
Hydrogen bonding, as measure of bacity of cyclic ethers, 460
    in bimaleate ion, 432
    in β-dicarbonyl compounds, 446
    in o-nitrophenols, 437
Hydrogen-bridged ion, 326
Hydrogen participation in ionization, 324, 325, 327
Hydroquinone, ionization of, 436
Hydroxymethylenecyclohexanone, see 2-Formylcyclohexanone
Hydroxymethylenecyclopentanone, see 2-Formylcyclopentanone
Hyperconjugation, 444
    effects, 636–641, 672
Hyperconjugative effects, in elimination reaction, 331, 332, 334, 335

Iminoether formation, hindrance to, 233
Inductive effects, in elimination reaction, 330
Infrared spectra, 526, 527
Ingold-Taft equation, 587–590
Interaction terms in vibrational spectra, 502
Interannular bond, 544, 546
Internal return, 257
Iodination, retro-, of substituted anilines, steric effects in, 176
Ionization constants, of anilines, 438
    of hindered aliphatic acids, 205
    of ortho-substituted benzoic acids, 428
    of phenols, 436, 437
Ion pairs, bridged, 258, 282
    open, 259, 299
Ions, bridged, 258, 262, 275, 279, 290, 292
    open, 259, 263
I strain, 278
    in carbanions, 162
    in free-radical reactions, 148, 149
    in nucleophilic displacement, 121–125
Isomerization of trans to cis olefins by chemical means, 246

δ-Ketoacids, cyclization of, 466
2-Ketobutyrolactone, enolization, 449
α-Keto-β,β-diethylglutaric acid, cyclization of, 464
α-Keto-β,β-dimethylglutaric acid, cyclization of, 464
α-Keto-β-ethyl-β-methylglutaric acid, cyclization of, 464
α-Ketoglutaric acids, cyclization of, 464, 467
    cyclization to hydroxycyclopropanes, 464
δ-Ketomalonic acids, cyclic forms, 465
Ketones, see also Carbonyl compounds
    aromatic, hindrance in, 240
    cyclic, formation of, 234
    highly hindered aliphatic, 236
    ring, reactivity of, 238
α-Keto-β,β-pentamethyleneglutaric acid, cyclization of, 464
Ketopinic acid, resistance to decarboxylation, 352
Kinetic acceleration, 277
Kinetic energy, 564–570
Kinetic energy steric effects, 597, 652–655, 665–670, 674
Kurt Meyer titration, 444

Lacto-enoic tautomerism, 461, 462
α-Lactones, 464

Lead tetraacetate, as oxidant for 1,2-glycol cleavage, 378
Lennard-Jones potential, 503
Lennard-Jones potential function, 530
Lewis acids and bases, 454
Limits of error, for calculated energy of activation, 550
Linear free-energy–polar-energy relationship, 605–613, 620–623, 632
Linear free-energy relationships, 585, 611, 646, 647, 658, 659
Linear polar-energy relationships, 622, 623, 632, 633, 658, 659
Linear steric energy relationships, 642–648, 674, 675
Linear strain energy relationships, 672–675
Lithium alkyls and aryls, 396, 405, 423

Magnesium dialkyls, 397
Malonic acid derivatives, decarboxylation of, 360
Mannich bases, steric assistance in alkylations with, 161
Melting point, effect of steric hindrance on, 518
Menthyl system, 270
Mesitil, spectrum of, 499
Mesitoic acid, decarboxylation of, 363
Mesitoyl chloride, hydrolysis of, 225, 226
  inertness to diazomethane, 227
  non-ionization of in SO₂, 226
Mesitylene, condensation with unsymmetrical anhydrides, 231
Mesityl oxide, reductive cyclization of, 465
Mesitylphenyldiketone, spectrum of, 499
Mesomeric moment, effect of twisting on, 508
Metalation reactions, 440
Methyl acetoacetate, enolization of, 446
3-Methylacetylacetone, acidity, 453
  enolization, 446
2-Methyl-1-acetyl-1-cyclohexene, S-cis and S-trans isomers of, 493
Methylamine, basicity toward protons, 457
  trimethylboron adduct, 456
Methylamines, basicity, 457
N-Methylaniline, ionization of, 438
Methyl-1,2-benzanthracenes, complexes of, 472
Methylbenzo[c]phenanthrenes, complexes of, 472

6-Methyl-2-benzoylbenzoic acid, cyclization of, 470
3-Methyl-2-benzoylbenzoic acid, cyclization of, 470
Methyl cyclohexane, conformation, 17
3-Methyl-1,2-cyclohexanedione, enolization, 449
Methyl cyclopropyl ketone, dipole moment of, 521
  electronic spectrum, 520
9-Methyldecalin, conformation, 30
  stability, 30
2-Methyl-4-dimethylaminostilbene, dipole moment of, 509
Methyl groups, interference, 554
o-Methylisopropenylbenzene, double-bond deformation frequency in, 506
p-Methylisopropenylbenzene, double-bond deformation frequency in, 506
Methyl isopropyl ketone, 520
  absorption spectrum of, 520
Methylolation of t-aromatic amines, steric effects in, 174
3-Methylphthalic anhydride, reactions of, 230
1-Methylpyrrole, dipole moment of, 509
2-Methylstyrene, refractive index of, 512
4-Methyl-2,5,7-trithiabicyclo-(2.2.2)-octane-2,2,6,6,7,7-hexaoxide, 441
Methyl vinyl ketone, absorption spectrum of, 520
Molecular beam, 531
Molecular complex formation, 472
  steric inhibition of, 473
Migrating group, 251
Migration, origin, 251
  terminus, 251
Migratory aptitude, 264–270

Neighboring group, acetoxyl, 291, 292
  benzamido, 292
  complex, 292
  participation, 262, 263, 264, 268, 277
Neomenthyl system, 270
Neon, van der Waals potential, 531
  van der Waals radius, 548
Neopentyl bromide, 538
Neopentylethylene, bromination of, 243
Neopentyl halides, in nucleophilic displacement, 76–78, 81
Nitroalkanes, acidity and tautomerism of, 441

p-Nitroaniline and derivatives, absorption intensity of, 485

Nitrobenzene, stretching frequency of nitro group in, 506

p-Nitrobromobenzenes, rates of reaction with piperidine, 185

2-Nitro-6-carboxy-2'-methoxybiphenyl and substituted derivatives, 552

3-Nitrocatechol, ionization of, 436

Nitrocumenes, absorption intensity of, 485

Nitroethane, ionization and tautomerism of, 441

Nitrohydroquinone, ionization of, 436

Nitromesitylene, 506
   stretching frequency of nitro group in, 506

Nitromethane, ionization and tautomerism of, 441

Nitrophenols, ionization of, 436

2-Nitropropane, ionization and tautomerism of, 441

Nitroresorcinols, ionization of, 436

Nitrotoluenes, absorption intensity of, 485
   stretching frequency for nitro group in, 506

Non-bonded atom interaction, bromocyclohexanone, 40
   butane, 7
   cyclohexane, 13
   cyclohexanone, 39
   cyclohexene, 38
   cyclopentane, 35
   cyclopentene, 39
   decalin, 23
   decalol, 27
   dimethylcyclohexanes, 18
   ethane, 5
   hydrindane, 37
   hydrindanol, 37
   in medium and large rings, 42
   methylcyclohexane, 17
   9-methyldecalin, 30
   perhydroanthracenes, 34
   perhydroaromatic systems, 31
   perhydrophenanthrenes, 32

Normal vibrations, 526

Nortricyclonium ion, 257

Nucleophilic aromatic substitution, displacement of the most hindered leaving group in, 186–188
   effect of transition state configuration on halogen reactivity, 166

Nucleophilic aromatic substitution, effect of transition state configuration on relative reactivities of *o*- and *p*-nitrohalobenzenes with amines and alkoxides in, 190–192
   mechanism of, 182
   relative reactivity of *o*- and *p*-halonitrobenzenes and benzonitriles in, 189
   steric compression at the reaction, effect of, 193
     (*a*) *ortho* substituents, 194, 195
     (*b*) bulky amines, 196
   steric inhibition of activation in, 184
   transition state model of, 183
   types of, 182

2,7-Octanedione, failure to cyclize, 465

Optical activity due to intramolecular overcrowding, 476

Optical stability, of anions, 152–156
   of free radicals, 140–142

p-Orbital overlap, 496

"*Ortho* effect," 586, 587, 648–652
   in thermal decomposition of *o-t*-butyl-N-nitrosoacetanilide, 200

Overlap integral, 496

Oxaloacetic acids, decarboxylation of, 360

Oxidation, conformational effects in, 152
   steric effects in, 151
   steric hindrance to, 241, 244
   steric inhibition of resonance in, 152
   transannular effects in, 245

Paramagnetism, in diradicals, 516

Partition function, 564, 566, 660–663

Pentamethylene imine, trimethylboron adduct, 459, 460

2,4,4,5,5-Pentamethyl-2-hydroxy-1-acetylcyclopentanone, ring opening to acyclic diketone, 465

2,5,2',4',6'-Pentamethyl-1-phenylpyrrole, dipole moment of, 509

Pentaphenylcyclopentadienyl radical, stability of, 391

Perhydroanthracenes, conformation, 34
   stabilities, 34

Perhydroaromatic systems, conformation in, 31
   stability of, 32

Perhydrophenanthrenes, conformation of, 32
   stability of, 32

Periodic acid in cleavage of 1,2-glycols, 378

Phenols, ionization of 2,6-di-t-alkyl, 437
    ionization of nitro-substituted, 436
Phenonium ion, 256, 258, 275
Phenylacetic acids, 430
Phenylacetone, carbonyl stretching frequency of, 506
cis-α-Phenylchalcone, absorption spectrum of, 490
Phenylcyclopropane, dipole moment, 521
    electronic spectrum, 520
1-Phenylpyrrole, dipole moment of, 509
Physical properties and polar effects, 613–615
Picolines, basicity towards protons, 455
    trimethylboron adducts, 456
Picric acid, complexes of, 472
Pinacol rearrangement, 253, 254, 265, 267, 274
Polar bonds, see Axial bonds
Polar effects, additive nature of, 575, 592, 623–625
    and structure, 590–597, 603, 605, 606, 613–625, 627, 647–649, 660–663
    definitions of, 569
Polar entropy effects, 569, 570, 660–663
Polar interactions, definition of, 568
Polarographic reduction potential, calculation of, 517
Polar substituent constants, table of, 571, 591, 595, 619
Polyethylene, elasticity of, 517
Polyhalides, geminal, S_N1 reaction in, 99
    geminal, S_N2 reaction in, 100
    vicinal, S_N1 reaction in, 102
    vicinal, S_N2 reaction in, 102
Polyisobutylene, elasticity of, 517
Polymethyleneimines, stability of compounds with trimethylboron, 460
Polynitrobiphenyls, 473
Potential barriers, quantitative values, 54
Potential energy, 525, 544, 545, 564–570, 660–675
Price and Hammett rule, 652–655, 669
Primary alkyl acetates, relative rates of hydrolysis of, 220
Propargyl halides, 86, 87
    S_N1 reaction of, 86
    S_N2 reaction of, 87
    tertiary, 87
N-n-Propylaniline, ionization of, 438
Protonium ion, 290
Pseudo esters, formation of, 214
Pyranose rings, 462
Pyridine, trimethylboron adduct, 456

Pyrolysis, of esters, 307
    of tetramethylammonium salts, 217
    xanthate, 305–307

Quinuclidine, basicity, 456
    trimethyl boron adduct, 456

Racemization of optically active biphenyls, 543–554
Raman spectra, 526, 527
Rate of reaction, conformational effects on, 44, 47
Reaction, E_1, 315, 331, 332, 333
    E_2, 315, 331, 333, 337, 339, 341
    S_Ni, 79–83
        at bridgehead positions, 135
        in ring compounds, 128–130
    S_Ni' (internal return), 98
    S_N1, 63, 65
        allylic halides, 84, 85
        anchimeric assistance in, 72
        at bridge heads, 137, 138
        benzylic halides, 88–90
        geminal dihalides, 99, 100
        in ring compounds, 122–125
        in vicinal dihalides, 102
        polar and solvent effects in, 69–70
        propargylic halides, 86, 87
        steric assistance in, 71
        steric effects in, 70–73
    S_N2, allylic halides, 84, 86
        at bridgehead positions, 135
        benzylic halides, 90, 91
        geminal dihalides, 100–101
        β-haloesters, 103
        α-haloketones, 103–106
        in ring compounds, 122–124
        neopentyl halides, 76–78
        polar and steric effects in, 73
        propargylic halides, 87
        vicinal dihalides, 102
    S_N2', 93, 95–98
        stereochemistry of, 96–98
    von Richter, steric inhibition of, 189
Reactivity, conformational effects, 9, 44
    effect of structure on, 563–566, 626–632
Rearrangement, acyl, 290, 294, 295
    effect of conformation on, 49
    electrophilic, 251, 279
    homolytic, 251, 283, 289
    N $\rightarrow$ O, 293–295
    nucleophilic, 251, 252, 264, 270
    of $trans$-2-acetoxycyclohexyl system, 292
    of asymmetrical molecules, 252

Rearrangement, of camphene, 255
  of camphenilylamine, 288
  of cyclodecene oxide, 289
  of cycloöctene oxide, 288
  of cyclopropylcarbinylamine, 279
  of α,α-dimethylallyl chloride, 258
  of 4,4-dimethyl-2-ethyl-2-pentanol, 287
  of 2,5-dimethyl-4-phenyl-3-hexyl system, 275
  of 3,4-dimethyl-4-phenyl-3-hexyl system, 261, 268
  of 1,1-diphenyl-2-propyl system, 261, 275
  of ephedrine derivatives, 293
  of β-fenchol, 288
  of norbornyl system, 255, 257, 261, 288
  of nortropine derivatives, 294
  of 3-phenyl-2-butyl system, 256–260, 263, 274
  of α-phenylethyl aryl ethers, 299
  of 2-phenyl-3-pentanol system, 257, 258, 260
  of 3-phenyl-2-pentanol system, 257, 258, 260
  of pinene, 255
  transannular, 287, 288
Rearrangements, Baeyer-Villiger, 251, 283
  Beckmann, 253, 254
  Claisen, 295–303
  Hofmann, 253
  pinacol, 253, 254, 265, 267, 274
  Smiles, steric assistance in, 197
  Stevens, 279–281
  Wagner-Meerwein, 253–257, 261, 268, 283, 287
  Wittig, 279, 282
  Wolff, 251, 283, 286
Reduced mass, 525, 527
Repulsion terms, 503
Resolving agent α-(2,4,5,7-tetranitro-fluorenidylaminoöxy)-propionic acid, 474
  tri-o-thymotide, 474
  urea, clathrate compound, 475
Resonance effects, 548, 550
  definitions of, 569
  in dissociation of hexaarylethanes, 390
  of α,β-unsaturated substituent, 603–605, 636–641, 655–657, 670–672
Resonance energies, 581–583, 631, 632, 640, 641, 656, 670–672
Resonance interactions, definition of, 568

Resonance polar effect, 570, 578–580, 594–597
Restricted rotation, in butane, 7
  in ethane, 5
Reverse Fries rearrangement, 364
Rho values, relation to mechanism, 574, 611, 612
  table of, 607–610, 614, 649
Ring-chain tautomerism, 460
Ring-closure reactions, conformation effects in, 120
  steric effects in, 115–120
Ring conformations, large, 42
  medium, 42
Ring ketones, carbonyl stretching frequencies in, 507
Rule of six, 206
  in amides, 227
  in Grignard reactions, 418
  in ketones, 236
  in olefins, 243
  in saturated aliphatic acids, 206

Saturated cyclic acids, hindrance in, 210
Saytzeff rule, 330, 336, 339
Schlenk equilibrium, 397
S-cis and S-trans isomerization, 492
Secondary acids, 439
Secondary alkyl acetates, conformational effects in hydrolysis of, 222
  relative rates of hydrolysis of, 221
Semipinacolic deamination, conformational analysis in, 10
Silver salts of acids, brominative decarboxylation of, 354
Six-number, definition, 206
  use of, in estimation of steric hindrance, 207
Skew conformation, definition of, 8
Smiles rearrangement, 197
Solvation, steric hindrance to, 70, 89, 427, 428, 437, 439, 459
  Y values (power of solvents for), 69
Spectroscopic moment, 484
Spiropyrans, thermochromism of, 515
Stability, conformational effect, 47
  relative thermodynamic, of stereoisomers, 272
Staggered conformation, definition of, 6
Standard enthalpy of reaction, 565
Standard entropy of reaction, 565
Standard free energy of reaction, 564
Stereochemistry, of allylic rearrangements, 94
  of bimolecular elimination reaction, 315, 316
  of catalytic reduction, 143, 144

Stereochemistry, of Cope reaction, 310
of displacement on anions, 153–156
of free-radical reactions, 141, 142
of intramolecular elimination reaction, 305
of migrating group, 251
of migration origin, 254
of migration terminus, 253, 255, 284
of monomolecular elimination reaction, 322, 324–326
of nucleophilic substitution, 66–68
of S_N2' reaction, 96–98
Steric assistance, 630, 642, 651
in alkylation with Mannich bases, 161
in hydrolysis of mesitoyl chloride, 225
in Smiles rearrangement, 197
in S_N1 reaction, 71, 73
in 2,4,6-trimethylbenzyl halides, 91
Steric compression, 266, 270, 276, 286, 333
Steric effects, and structure, 599–603, 629–631, 633–636, 642–655, 665–670, 672–674
definitions of, 569
in dissociation of hexaarylethanes, 388, 389
Steric hindrance, in benzylic halides, 90, 91
in chlorination, 144–146
in cleavage of β-diketones, 371
in hexasubstituted ethanes, 388
in S_N1 reaction, 70
in S_N2 reaction, 73–77
in solvation, 70, 89
Steric inhibition of resonance, 344, 426, 429, 437, 442, 446
in benzylic carbanions, 162
in coupling with aromatic amines, 174
in deuterium exchange of aromatic amines, 173
in free-radical substitution, 150
in nucleophilic displacement reactions of benzyl halides, 88, 89
in oxidation reactions, 152
Steric interactions, definitions of, 568
Steric strain energies, 568, 597, 633–636, 665–670, 672–675
Steric substituent constants, 598, 601, 602, 645, 650, 668
Steroids, trimethylene oxide formation in, 377
Stevens rearrangement, 279–281
Stilbene, absorption spectrum of, 494
trans-Stilbene, absorption spectrum of, 489, 490
Stilbene and derivatives, changes in oscillator strength of, 487

Stobbe condensation, use of t-butyl succinate in, 224
Strain energy, in cyclobutane, 533
in cyclopropane, 534
in transition state for dichlorocyclooctadienes, 535
in transition state for displacement reactions, 541
in transition state for racemization of optically active biphenyl, 549
minimizing, 543
Substituents, para, effect of, on racemization of optically active biphenyls, 552
Substitution, electrophilic, F strain in, 157–160
I strain in, 162
on anions and bases, 63
pressure effects in, 160
steric assistance in, 161
steric effects in, 156–163
steric inhibition, 162
Substitution, nucleophilic, see also Reactions, S_N1 and S_N2
alternation effects in, 138–140
at bridgeheads, 134–138
in epoxides, 110–114
in α-haloethers, 101
in ring compounds, 121–134
nucleophilic substitution constants, 156

Tetraiodo acid, see 2,2',3,3'-Tetraiodo-5,5'-dicarboxybiphenyl
2,2',3,3'-Tetraiodo-5,5'-dicarboxybiphenyl, 549, 553
2',3,4',6-Tetramethyl-2-benzoylbenzoic acid, cyclization of, 470
Tetramethylcyclobutane-1,3-dione, reaction with Grignard reagents, 373
Tetramethyleneimine trimethylboron adduct, 460
4,4,5,5-Tetramethyl-2,7-octanedione, cyclization of, 465
α-(2,4,5,7-Tetranitrofluorenidylaminooxy)-propionic acid as resolving agent, 474
Tetraphenylethylene, absorption spectrum of, 489
Thermochromism, 513
Thioctic acid, spectrum of, 500
Three-membered rings, strain in, 518
Toluidines, ionization of, 438
Transannular reactions, of olefins, 245
trans elimination, 315–319

Transition state, 62, 63; *see also* Activated complex
  in nucleophilic displacement on α-haloketones, 105, 106
  in S_N2 reactions, 63, 68, 79, 92
  theory, 562
Triacetylmethane, acidity of, 453
2,4,6-Trialkylbenzoic acids, esterification of, 217
2,4,6-Tribromobenzoic acid, esterification of, 214, 217
Tri-*t*-butylboron, amine adducts, 456
Tri-*p*-chlorophenylcarbonium ion, spectrum of, in sulfuric acid, 491
Triethylamine trimethylboron adduct, 457
Trimesitylvinylalcohol, effects of unsymmetrical twists on absorption spectrum of, 490
2,4,6-Trimethylacetophenone, carbonyl stretching frequency, 506
  dipole moment, 509
  electronic spectrum, 485
  heat of combustion, 509
Trimethylamine, basicity toward protons, 457
  trimethylboron adduct, 456
Trimethylamine-borane compounds, 456
2,4,6-Trimethylbenzaldehyde, dipole moment of, 509
2′,3,4′-Trimethyl-2-benzoylbenzoic acid, cyclization of, 470
2′,4′,6-Trimethyl-2-benzoylbenzoic acid, cyclization of, 470
2,4,6-Trimethylbenzyl halides, in S_N1 reactions, 89, 90
  in S_N2 reactions, 90, 91
Trimethylboron amine adducts, 456
trans-2,2,6-Trimethylcyclohexanecarboxylic acid, non-esterification of, 210
Trimethyleneimine trimethylboron adduct, 460
Trimethylene oxide ring, as intermediate in 1,3-diol cleavage, 375
2,4,6-Trinitroanisoles, relative rates of reaction with piperidine, 185
2,4,6-Trinitrobenzoyl chloride, hydrolysis of, 226
2,4,7-Trinitrofluorenone (TNF), complexes of, 472
Triphenylethylene, effects of unsymmetrical twists on absorption spectrum of, 490
Triphenylmethide ion, 442
Triplet state, 514
Triptycene, acidity of, 442

Tropolone, 451
Twist, angle of, in substituted biphenyls, 511
  in cyclobutane, 534
  in transition state for dichlorocyclooctadienes, 537
Twisting a double bond, effect on spectrum, 493
Twisting a single bond, effect, on conjugated system, 505
  on electronic spectra, 484
  on mesomeric moment, 508
  on resonance energy, 482
  on vibrational spectra, 505

α,β-Unsaturated acids, decarboxylation of, 359, 366
β,γ-Unsaturated acids, decarboxylation of, 357
Unsaturated acids, esterification rates of, 212
Unsymmetrical anhydrides, reactions of, 228
Unsymmetrical twists, effect on absorption spectra, 489

Valence angles, C—C—C angle, 534
  C—C—H angle, 534
  deformation of, 524, 533, 549
  for racemization of optically active biphenyls, 549
  H—C—H angle, 534
  in cyclobutane, 533, 534
  in dichlorocyclooctadiene, 536
Valence bonds, for racemization of optically active biphenyls, 549
  stretching (and compression), 533, 541
van der Waals potential function, 525, 529–532, 540, 545
  approximation to, 544
  directional properties, 532, 540
  for halogen-methyl interaction, 540
  uncertainties in, 525, 550
van der Waals radii, 532, 540, 548, 554
Vibration frequency, 527
von Richter reaction, steric inhibition of, 189

Wagner-Meerwein rearrangement, 253–257, 261, 268, 283, 287
Walden inversion, 66–68
Wittig rearrangement, 279, 282
Wolff rearrangement, 251, 283, 286

Xylidines, ionization of, 438

Y values, table of, 69

Zero-point energy, 551